CFA Institute®
CFA Program

ETHICAL AND PROFESSIONAL STANDARDS AND QUANTITATIVE METHODS

CFA® Program Curriculum
2020 • LEVEL I • VOLUME 1

WILEY

ISBN 978-1-946442-76-5 (paper)
ISBN 978-1-950157-00-6 (ebk)

SKY8331E3F4-1F71-47F7-A722-46B5D30F191F_091620

Please visit our website at
www.WileyGlobalFinance.com.

WILEY

FSC
www.fsc.org
MIX
Paper from
responsible sources
FSC® C084269

CONTENTS

◘ indicates an optional segment

◘ indicates an optional segment

▣ indicates an optional segment

■ indicates an optional segment

How to Use the CFA Program Curriculum

Congratulations on your decision to enter the Chartered Financial Analyst (CFA®) Program. This exciting and rewarding program of study reflects your desire to become a serious investment professional. You are embarking on a program noted for its high ethical standards and the breadth of knowledge, skills, and abilities (competencies) it develops. Your commitment to the CFA Program should be educationally and professionally rewarding.

The credential you seek is respected around the world as a mark of accomplishment and dedication. Each level of the program represents a distinct achievement in professional development. Successful completion of the program is rewarded with membership in a prestigious global community of investment professionals. CFA charterholders are dedicated to life-long learning and maintaining currency with the ever-changing dynamics of a challenging profession. The CFA Program represents the first step toward a career-long commitment to professional education.

The CFA examination measures your mastery of the core knowledge, skills, and abilities required to succeed as an investment professional. These core competencies are the basis for the Candidate Body of Knowledge (CBOK™). The CBOK consists of four components:

- A broad outline that lists the major topic areas covered in the CFA Program (https://www.cfainstitute.org/programs/cfa/curriculum/cbok);
- Topic area weights that indicate the relative exam weightings of the top-level topic areas (https://www.cfainstitute.org/programs/cfa/curriculum/overview);
- Learning outcome statements (LOS) that advise candidates about the specific knowledge, skills, and abilities they should acquire from readings covering a topic area (LOS are provided in candidate study sessions and at the beginning of each reading); and
- The CFA Program curriculum that candidates receive upon examination registration.

Therefore, the key to your success on the CFA examinations is studying and understanding the CBOK. The following sections provide background on the CBOK, the organization of the curriculum, features of the curriculum, and tips for designing an effective personal study program.

BACKGROUND ON THE CBOK

The CFA Program is grounded in the practice of the investment profession. Beginning with the Global Body of Investment Knowledge (GBIK), CFA Institute performs a continuous practice analysis with investment professionals around the world to determine the competencies that are relevant to the profession. Regional expert panels and targeted surveys are conducted annually to verify and reinforce the continuous feedback about the GBIK. The practice analysis process ultimately defines the CBOK. The

CBOK reflects the competencies that are generally accepted and applied by investment professionals. These competencies are used in practice in a generalist context and are expected to be demonstrated by a recently qualified CFA charterholder.

The CFA Institute staff, in conjunction with the Education Advisory Committee and Curriculum Level Advisors, who consist of practicing CFA charterholders, designs the CFA Program curriculum in order to deliver the CBOK to candidates. The examinations, also written by CFA charterholders, are designed to allow you to demonstrate your mastery of the CBOK as set forth in the CFA Program curriculum. As you structure your personal study program, you should emphasize mastery of the CBOK and the practical application of that knowledge. For more information on the practice analysis, CBOK, and development of the CFA Program curriculum, please visit www.cfainstitute.org.

ORGANIZATION OF THE CURRICULUM

The Level I CFA Program curriculum is organized into 10 topic areas. Each topic area begins with a brief statement of the material and the depth of knowledge expected. It is then divided into one or more study sessions. These study sessions—19 sessions in the Level I curriculum—should form the basic structure of your reading and preparation. Each study session includes a statement of its structure and objective and is further divided into assigned readings. An outline illustrating the organization of these 19 study sessions can be found at the front of each volume of the curriculum.

The readings are commissioned by CFA Institute and written by content experts, including investment professionals and university professors. Each reading includes LOS and the core material to be studied, often a combination of text, exhibits, and in-text examples and questions. A reading typically ends with practice problems followed by solutions to these problems to help you understand and master the material. The LOS indicate what you should be able to accomplish after studying the material. The LOS, the core material, and the practice problems are dependent on each other, with the core material and the practice problems providing context for understanding the scope of the LOS and enabling you to apply a principle or concept in a variety of scenarios.

The entire readings, including the practice problems at the end of the readings, are the basis for all examination questions and are selected or developed specifically to teach the knowledge, skills, and abilities reflected in the CBOK.

You should use the LOS to guide and focus your study because each examination question is based on one or more LOS and the core material and practice problems associated with the LOS. As a candidate, you are responsible for the entirety of the required material in a study session.

We encourage you to review the information about the LOS on our website (www.cfainstitute.org/programs/cfa/curriculum/study-sessions), including the descriptions of LOS "command words" on the candidate resources page at www.cfainstitute.org.

FEATURES OF THE CURRICULUM

OPTIONAL SEGMENT

Required vs. Optional Segments You should read all of an assigned reading. In some cases, though, we have reprinted an entire publication and marked certain parts of the reading as "optional." The CFA examination is based only on the required segments, and the optional segments are included only when it is determined that they might help you to better understand the required segments (by seeing the required material in its full context). When an optional segment begins, you will see an icon and a dashed vertical bar in the outside margin that will continue until the optional segment ends, accompanied by another icon. *Unless the material is specifically marked as optional, you should assume it is required.* You should rely on the required segments and the reading-specific LOS in preparing for the examination.

END OPTIONAL SEGMENT

Practice Problems/Solutions *All practice problems at the end of the readings as well as their solutions are part of the curriculum and are required material for the examination.* In addition to the in-text examples and questions, these practice problems should help demonstrate practical applications and reinforce your understanding of the concepts presented. Some of these practice problems are adapted from past CFA examinations and/or may serve as a basis for examination questions.

Glossary For your convenience, each volume includes a comprehensive glossary. Throughout the curriculum, a **bolded** word in a reading denotes a term defined in the glossary.

Note that the digital curriculum that is included in your examination registration fee is searchable for key words, including glossary terms.

LOS Self-Check We have inserted checkboxes next to each LOS that you can use to track your progress in mastering the concepts in each reading.

Source Material The CFA Institute curriculum cites textbooks, journal articles, and other publications that provide additional context or information about topics covered in the readings. As a candidate, you are not responsible for familiarity with the original source materials cited in the curriculum.

Note that some readings may contain a web address or URL. The referenced sites were live at the time the reading was written or updated but may have been deactivated since then.

Some readings in the curriculum cite articles published in the *Financial Analysts Journal®*, which is the flagship publication of CFA Institute. Since its launch in 1945, the *Financial Analysts Journal* has established itself as the leading practitioner-oriented journal in the investment management community. Over the years, it has advanced the knowledge and understanding of the practice of investment management through the publication of peer-reviewed practitioner-relevant research from leading academics and practitioners. It has also featured thought-provoking opinion pieces that advance the common level of discourse within the investment management profession. Some of the most influential research in the area of investment management has appeared in the pages of the *Financial Analysts Journal*, and several Nobel laureates have contributed articles.

Candidates are not responsible for familiarity with *Financial Analysts Journal* articles that are cited in the curriculum. But, as your time and studies allow, we strongly encourage you to begin supplementing your understanding of key investment management issues by reading this practice-oriented publication. Candidates have full online access to the *Financial Analysts Journal* and associated resources. All you need is to log in on www.cfapubs.org using your candidate credentials.

Errata The curriculum development process is rigorous and includes multiple rounds of reviews by content experts. Despite our efforts to produce a curriculum that is free of errors, there are times when we must make corrections. Curriculum errata are periodically updated and posted on the candidate resources page at www.cfainstitute.org.

DESIGNING YOUR PERSONAL STUDY PROGRAM

Create a Schedule An orderly, systematic approach to examination preparation is critical. You should dedicate a consistent block of time every week to reading and studying. Complete all assigned readings and the associated problems and solutions in each study session. Review the LOS both before and after you study each reading to ensure that you have mastered the applicable content and can demonstrate the knowledge, skills, and abilities described by the LOS and the assigned reading. Use the LOS self-check to track your progress and highlight areas of weakness for later review.

Successful candidates report an average of more than 300 hours preparing for each examination. Your preparation time will vary based on your prior education and experience, and you will probably spend more time on some study sessions than on others. As the Level I curriculum includes 19 study sessions, a good plan is to devote 15–20 hours per week for 19 weeks to studying the material and use the final four to six weeks before the examination to review what you have learned and practice with practice questions and mock examinations. This recommendation, however, may underestimate the hours needed for appropriate examination preparation depending on your individual circumstances, relevant experience, and academic background. You will undoubtedly adjust your study time to conform to your own strengths and weaknesses and to your educational and professional background.

You should allow ample time for both in-depth study of all topic areas and additional concentration on those topic areas for which you feel the least prepared.

As part of the supplemental study tools that are included in your examination registration fee, you have access to a study planner to help you plan your study time. The study planner calculates your study progress and pace based on the time remaining until examination. For more information on the study planner and other supplemental study tools, please visit www.cfainstitute.org.

As you prepare for your examination, we will e-mail you important examination updates, testing policies, and study tips. Be sure to read these carefully.

CFA Institute Practice Questions Your examination registration fee includes digital access to hundreds of practice questions that are additional to the practice problems at the end of the readings. These practice questions are intended to help you assess your mastery of individual topic areas as you progress through your studies. After each practice question, you will be able to receive immediate feedback noting the correct responses and indicating the relevant assigned reading so you can identify areas of weakness for further study. For more information on the practice questions, please visit www.cfainstitute.org.

CFA Institute Mock Examinations Your examination registration fee also includes digital access to three-hour mock examinations that simulate the morning and afternoon sessions of the actual CFA examination. These mock examinations are intended to be taken after you complete your study of the full curriculum and take practice questions so you can test your understanding of the curriculum and your readiness for the examination. You will receive feedback at the end of the mock examination, noting the correct responses and indicating the relevant assigned readings so you can assess areas of weakness for further study during your review period. We recommend that you take mock examinations during the final stages of your preparation for the actual CFA examination. For more information on the mock examinations, please visit www.cfainstitute.org.

Preparatory Providers After you enroll in the CFA Program, you may receive numerous solicitations for preparatory courses and review materials. When considering a preparatory course, make sure the provider belongs to the CFA Institute Approved Prep Provider Program. Approved Prep Providers have committed to follow CFA Institute guidelines and high standards in their offerings and communications with candidates. For more information on the Approved Prep Providers, please visit www.cfainstitute.org/programs/cfa/exam/prep-providers.

Remember, however, that there are no shortcuts to success on the CFA examinations; reading and studying the CFA curriculum *is* the key to success on the examination. The CFA examinations reference only the CFA Institute assigned curriculum—no preparatory course or review course materials are consulted or referenced.

SUMMARY

Every question on the CFA examination is based on the content contained in the required readings and on one or more LOS. Frequently, an examination question is based on a specific example highlighted within a reading or on a specific practice problem and its solution. To make effective use of the CFA Program curriculum, please remember these key points:

1 All pages of the curriculum are required reading for the examination except for occasional sections marked as optional. You may read optional pages as background, but you will not be tested on them.

2 All questions, problems, and their solutions—found at the end of readings—are part of the curriculum and are required study material for the examination.

3 You should make appropriate use of the practice questions and mock examinations as well as other supplemental study tools and candidate resources available at www.cfainstitute.org.

4 Create a schedule and commit sufficient study time to cover the 19 study sessions, using the study planner. You should also plan to review the materials and take practice questions and mock examinations.

5 Some of the concepts in the study sessions may be superseded by updated rulings and/or pronouncements issued after a reading was published. Candidates are expected to be familiar with the overall analytical framework contained in the assigned readings. Candidates are not responsible for changes that occur after the material was written.

FEEDBACK

At CFA Institute, we are committed to delivering a comprehensive and rigorous curriculum for the development of competent, ethically grounded investment professionals. We rely on candidate and investment professional comments and feedback as we work to improve the curriculum, supplemental study tools, and candidate resources.

Please send any comments or feedback to info@cfainstitute.org. You can be assured that we will review your suggestions carefully. Ongoing improvements in the curriculum will help you prepare for success on the upcoming examinations and for a lifetime of learning as a serious investment professional.

Ethical and Professional Standards

STUDY SESSION

Study Session 1	Ethical and Professional Standards

TOPIC LEVEL LEARNING OUTCOME

The candidate should be able to explain the need for high ethical standards in the investment industry and the ethical responsibilities required by the CFA Institute Code of Ethics and Standards of Professional Conduct and to demonstrate the application of the Code and Standards. The candidate should also be able to demonstrate an understanding of the Global Investment Performance Standards.

Trust in the investment profession is achieved only if those practicing within the industry adhere to the highest levels of ethical conduct and behavior. The CFA Institute Code of Ethics and Standards of Professional Conduct (Code and Standards) serve as the ethical foundation for the CFA Institute self-regulatory program.

The Standards of Practice Handbook provides practical application of the Code and Standards by explaining the purpose and scope of each standard, presenting recommended procedures for compliance, and providing examples of each standard in practice.

The Global Investment Performance Standards (GIPS®) establish global standards for performance reporting by investment managers. By providing a consistent set of standards and methodology, GIPS facilitate the fair and accurate comparison of managers around the world, while minimizing the potential for ambiguous or misleading performance reporting practices.

ETHICAL AND PROFESSIONAL STANDARDS

STUDY SESSION 1

Ethical and Professional Standards

This study session introduces ethics, related challenges to ethical behavior, and the role played by ethics and professionalism in the investment industry. A framework to support ethical decision-making is provided to help guide behavior. The CFA Institute Code of Ethics and Standards of Professional Conduct (Code and Standards) are examined, with attention given to each standard and its application. The session concludes with coverage of the Global Investment Performance Standards.

READING ASSIGNMENTS

Reading 1	Ethics and Trust in the Investment Profession by Bidhan L. Parmar, PhD, Dorothy C. Kelly, CFA, and David B. Stevens, CIMC, CFA
Reading 2	Code of Ethics and Standards of Professional Conduct *Standards of Practice Handbook*, Eleventh Edition
Reading 3	Guidance for Standards I–VII *Standards of Practice Handbook*, Eleventh Edition
Reading 4	Introduction to the Global Investment Performance Standards (GIPS)
Reading 5	Global Investment Performance Standards (GIPS)

READING

1

Ethics and Trust in the Investment Profession

by Bidhan L. Parmar, PhD, Dorothy C. Kelly, CFA, and David B. Stevens, CIMC, CFA

Bidhan L. Parmar, PhD, is at the University of Virginia (USA). Dorothy C. Kelly, CFA, is at McIntire School of Commerce, University of Virginia (USA). David B. Stevens, CIMC, CFA, is at Wells Fargo Private Bank (USA).

LEARNING OUTCOMES

Mastery	The candidate should be able to:
☐	a. explain ethics;
☐	b. describe the role of a code of ethics in defining a profession;
☐	c. describe professions and how they establish trust;
☐	d. describe the need for high ethical standards in investment management;
☐	e. explain professionalism in investment management;
☐	f. identify challenges to ethical behavior;
☐	g. distinguish between ethical and legal standards;
☐	h. describe a framework for ethical decision making.

INTRODUCTION

1

As a candidate in the CFA Program, you are both expected and required to meet high ethical standards. This reading introduces ideas and concepts that will help you understand the importance of ethical behavior in the investment industry. You will be introduced to various types of ethical issues within the investment profession and learn about the CFA Institute Code of Ethics.

The readings covering ethics and professional standards demonstrate that ethical behavior is central to creating trust. Professional behavior is equally important. Professions help maintain trust in an industry by establishing codes and setting standards that put a framework around ethical behavior and technical competence. Professions also set the wider goal of gaining and maintaining the trust of society as a whole. In this regard, professions have a sense of purpose that society values.

Imagine that you are employed in the research department of a large financial services firm. You and your colleagues spend your days researching, analyzing, and valuing the shares of publicly traded companies and sharing your investment recommendations with clients. You love your work and take great satisfaction in knowing that your recommendations can help the firm's investing clients make informed investment decisions that will help them meet their financial goals and improve their lives.

Several months after starting at the firm, you learn that an analyst at the firm has been terminated for writing and publishing research reports that misrepresented the fundamental risks of some companies to investors. You learn that the analyst wrote the reports with the goal of pleasing the management of the companies that were the subjects of the research reports. He hoped that these companies would hire your firm's investment banking division for its services and he would be rewarded with large bonuses for helping the firm increase its investment banking fees. Some clients bought shares based on the analyst's reports and suffered losses. They posted stories on the internet about their losses and the misleading nature of the reports. When the media investigated and published the story, the firm's reputation for investment research suffered. Investors began to question the firm's motives and the objectivity of its research recommendations. The firm's investment clients started to look elsewhere for investment advice, and company clients begin to transfer their business to firms with untarnished reputations. With business declining, management is forced to trim staff. Along with many other hard-working colleagues, you lose your job—through no fault of your own.

Imagine how you would feel in this situation. Most people would feel upset and resentful that their hard and honest work was derailed by someone else's unethical behavior. Yet, this type of scenario is not uncommon. Around the world, unsuspecting employees at such companies as SAC Capital, Stanford Financial Group, Everbright Securities, Enron, Satyam Computer Services, Arthur Andersen, and other large companies have experienced such career setbacks when someone else's actions destroyed trust in their companies and industries.

Businesses and financial markets thrive on trust—defined as a strong belief in the reliability of a person or institution. In a 2016 study on trust, investors indicated that to earn their trust, the top two attributes of an investment manager should be that it (1) has transparent and open business practices, and (2) has ethical business practices.[1] Although these attributes are valued by customers and clients in any industry, this reading will explore why they are of particular importance to the investment industry.

People may think that ethical behavior is simply about following laws, regulations, and other rules, but throughout our lives and careers we will encounter situations in which there is no definitive rule that specifies how to act, or the rules that exist may be unclear or even in conflict with each other. Responsible people, including investment professionals, must be willing and able to identify potential ethical issues and create solutions to them even in the absence of clearly stated rules.

1 CFA Institute From Trust to Loyalty: A Global Survey of What Investors Want (2013): http://www.cfapubs.org/doi/pdf/10.2469/ccb.v2013.n14.1.(2016): https://www.cfainstitute.org/research/survey-reports/from-trust-to-loyalty

ETHICS

2

Through our individual actions, each of us can affect the lives of others. Our decisions and behavior can harm or benefit a variety of **stakeholders**—individuals or groups of individuals who could be affected either directly or indirectly by a decision and thus have an interest, or stake, in the decision. Examples of stakeholders in decisions made by investment industry professionals include our colleagues, our clients, our employers, the communities in which we live and work, the investment profession, trade associations, regulators, and other financial market participants. In some cases, our actions may benefit all of these stakeholder groups; in other cases, our actions may benefit only some stakeholder groups; and in still other cases, our actions may benefit some stakeholder groups and harm others. For example, recall the research analyst in the introduction who wrote misleading research reports with the aim of increasing the financial benefit to himself and his employer. In the very short term, his conduct seemed to directly benefit some stakeholders (certain clients, himself, and his employer) and to harm other stakeholders (clients who invested based on his reports). Over a longer time period, his conduct resulted in harm to himself and many other stakeholders—his employer, his employer's clients, his colleagues, investors, and through loss of trust when the story was published, the larger financial market.

Ethics encompasses a set of moral principles and rules of conduct that provide guidance for our behavior. The word "ethics" comes from the Greek word "ethos," meaning character, used to describe the guiding beliefs or ideals characterizing a society or societal group. Beliefs are assumptions or thoughts we hold to be true. A principle is defined as a belief or fundamental truth that serves as the foundation for a system of belief or behavior or a chain of reasoning. Our beliefs form our values—those things we deem to have worth or merit.

Moral principles or **ethical principles** are beliefs regarding what is good, acceptable, or obligatory behavior and what is bad, unacceptable, or forbidden behavior. Ethical principles may refer to beliefs regarding behavior that an individual expects of himself or herself, as well as shared beliefs regarding standards of behavior expected or required by a community or societal group.

The study of ethics examines the role of consequences and personal character in defining what is considered good, or ethical, conduct.

Ethical conduct is behavior that follows moral principles and balances self-interest with both the direct and the indirect consequences of the behavior on others. Ethical actions are those actions that are perceived as beneficial and conforming to the ethical expectations of society. An action may be considered beneficial if it improves the outcomes or consequences for stakeholders affected by the action. Telling the truth about the risks or costs associated with a recommended investment, for example, is an ethical action—that is, one that conforms to the ethical expectations of society in general and clients in particular. Telling the truth is also beneficial; telling the truth builds trust with customers and clients and enables them to make more informed decisions, which should lead to better outcomes for them and higher levels of client/customer satisfaction for you and your employer.

Widely acknowledged ethical principles include honesty, transparency, fairness or justice, diligence, and respect for the rights of others. Most societal groups share these fundamental ethical principles and build on them, establishing a shared set of rules regarding how members should behave in certain situations. The principles or rules may take different forms depending on the community establishing them.

Governments and related entities, for example, may establish laws and/or regulations to reflect widely shared beliefs about obligatory and forbidden conduct. Laws and regulations are rules of conduct specified by a governing body, such as a legislature or a regulator, identifying how individuals and entities under its jurisdiction should behave in certain situations. Most countries have laws and regulations governing the investment industry and the conduct of its participants. Differences in laws may reflect differences in beliefs and values.

In some countries, for example, the law requires that an investment adviser act in the best interests of his or her clients. Other countries require that investment professionals recommend investments that are suitable for their clients. These differing requirements can also hold true within one country where some advisers are held to a suitability standard and others to the fiduciary standard of the client's best interests. Investment advisers and portfolio managers who are required by law to act in their clients' best interests must always put their clients' interests ahead of their own or their employers' interests. An investment adviser who is required by law to act in a client's best interest must understand the client's financial objectives and risk tolerance, research and investigate multiple investment opportunities, and recommend the investment or investment portfolio that is *most* suitable for the client in terms of meeting his or her long-term financial objectives. In addition, the investment adviser would be expected to monitor the client's financial situation and investments to ensure that the investments recommended remain the *best* overall option for meeting the client's long-term financial objectives. In countries with only a suitability requirement, it is legal for investment professionals to recommend a suitable investment to a client even if other, similar suitable investments with lower fees are available. These differences in laws reflect differences in beliefs and values.

Specific communities or societal groups in which we live and work sometimes codify their beliefs about obligatory and forbidden conduct in a written set of principles, often called a **code of ethics**. Universities, employers, and professional associations often adopt a code of ethics to communicate the organization's values and overall expectations regarding member behavior. The code of ethics serves as a general guide for how community members should act. Some communities will also expand on their codes of ethics and adopt explicit rules or standards that identify specific behaviors required of community members. These **standards of conduct** serve as benchmarks for the minimally acceptable behavior of community members and can help clarify the code of ethics. Members can choose behaviors that demonstrate even higher standards. By joining the community, members are agreeing to adhere to the community's code of ethics and standards of conduct. To promote their code of ethics and reduce the incidence of violations, communities frequently display their codes in prominent locations and in written materials. In addition, most communities require that members commit to their codes in writing on an annual or more frequent basis.

Violations of a community's established code of ethics and/or standards of conduct can harm the community in a variety of ways. Violations have the potential to damage the community's reputation among external stakeholders and the general public. Violations can also damage the community's reputation internally and lead to reduced trust among community members and can cause the organization to fracture or splinter from within. To protect the reputation of its membership and limit potential harm to innocent members, the community may take corrective actions to investigate possible violations, repair any damages, and attempt to discipline the violator or, in severe cases, revoke the violator's membership in the community.

EXAMPLE 1

Ethics

1 Which of the following statements is *most* accurate? Ethics can be described as:

A a commitment to upholding the law.

B an individual's personal opinion about right and wrong.

C a set of moral principles that provide guidance for our behavior.

2 Which of the following statements is *most* accurate? Standards of conduct:

A are a necessary component of any code of ethics.

B serve as a general guide regarding proper conduct by members of a group.

C serve as benchmarks for the minimally acceptable behavior required of members of a group.

Solution to 1:

C is correct. Ethics can be described as a set of moral principles that provide guidance for our behavior; these may be moral principles shared by a community or societal group.

Solution to 2:

C is correct. Standards of conduct serve as benchmarks for the minimally acceptable behavior required of members of a group. Some organizations will adopt only a code of ethics, which communicates the organization's values and overall expectations regarding member behavior. Others may adopt both a code of ethics and standards of conduct. Standards of conduct identify specific behavior required of community members and serve as benchmarks for the minimally acceptable behavior of community members.

ETHICS AND PROFESSIONALISM

3

A **profession** is an occupational community that has specific education, expert knowledge, and a framework of practice and behavior that underpins community trust, respect, and recognition. Most professions emphasize an ethical approach, the importance of good service, and empathy with the client.

Professions have grown in size and number over the last century: the rise of new specialist areas of expertise has created new professions. Driving forces of a new profession include governments and regulators, which encourage the formation of an ethical relationship between professionals and society at large. There is also demand for professions from individuals who see an advantage in working as a professional and from clients who desire to work with professionals.

Professions have not developed in every country. But in most countries, those who work in specialized areas—such as doctors, lawyers, actuaries, accountants, architects, and engineers—are subject to some combination of licensed status and technical standards. These standards distinguish professions from the craft guilds and trade bodies that were established in many countries. In particular, the requirement for members of professions to uphold high ethical standards is one clear difference. Another difference is that trade bodies do not normally have a mission to serve society or to set and enforce professional conduct rules for practitioners.

3.1 How Professions Establish Trust

For a profession to be credible, a primary goal is to establish trust among clients and among society in general. In doing so, professions have a number of common characteristics that, when combined, greatly increase confidence and credibility in professionals and their organizations.

Professions normalize practitioner behavior. Professionalism is underpinned by codes and standards developed by professional bodies. Regulators typically support professional ethics and recognize the framework for ethics that professions can provide. Many regulators around the world have engaged closely with professional bodies to understand their codes and standards, as well as how they are enforced. Codes and standards developed by practitioners can be complementary to regulations, codifying many more individual practices than the high-level principles set by regulation.

Many governments have recognized that a profession can develop a more sophisticated system of standards than a regulator can, via continuous practitioner input and a strong mutual interest within the profession to maintain good standards and adopt best practices. Government support of professions is attributable to the role of professions in helping the public and ensuring expert and principled performance of complex services.

Professions provide a service to society. There is an obligation for professionals to go beyond codes and standards. Professionals should advocate for higher educational and ethical standards in the industry, individually and through their companies. Professions can widen access to services and support economic activity by encouraging trust in the industries they serve. Professions have realized that earning community trust not only creates professional pride and acceptance but also delivers commercial benefits. A profession that earns trust may ultimately have greater flexibility and independence from government regulators to manage its own affairs, which allows members of the profession to develop service models that are both useful to clients and beneficial to members.

Professions are client focused. An integral part of a profession's mission is to develop and administer codes, best practice guidelines, and standards that guide an industry. These codes, standards, and guidelines help ensure that all professionals place the integrity of their profession and the interests of clients above their own personal interests. At a minimum, professionals must act in the best interest of the client, exercising a reasonable level of care, skill, and diligence. The obligation to deliver a high standard of care when acting for the benefit of another party is called *fiduciary duty*. Other entities, including employers, regulators, trade associations, and not-for-profit organizations, may also support an industry but are not the same as professional bodies. Unlike professions, these other entities generally do not exist to set and maintain professional standards. Most employers encourage employees to be members of relevant professions, and many give financial support for this membership to ideally improve the quality of client service and reinforce ethical awareness.

Professions have high entry standards. Membership in a profession is a signal to the market that the professional will deliver high-quality service of a promised standard, going beyond simply academic credentials. Professions develop curricula that equip future professionals with competence, including technical skills, knowledge, and ethics.

Professions possess a body of expert knowledge. A repository of knowledge, developed by experienced and skilled practitioners, is made available to all members of a profession. This knowledge helps members work effectively and ethically and is based on best practice.

Professions encourage and facilitate continuing education. Entry into a profession does not, on its own, guarantee that an individual will maintain competency and continue to uphold professional standards. After qualification and throughout the working life of a professional, there will be changes in knowledge and technical skills to perform certain jobs, in technology and standards of ethical behavior, in services that can be offered, and in the legal and business environment in which professional services are delivered. These all require the development of competence and ethical awareness. Most professional bodies make it a condition of membership that a specific amount of new learning is undertaken each year. Typically, such conditions specify a time commitment, which may be separated into different competencies and types of learning activity. This is often referred to as *continuing professional development* and is seen as an important part of maintaining professional standards. The training and education that professionals undertake increase the value of human capital, which can contribute to economic growth and social mobility.

Professions monitor professional conduct. Members of a profession must be held accountable for their conduct to maintain the integrity and reputation of an industry. Doing so often involves self-regulation by professional bodies through monitoring and imposition of sanctions on members.

Professions are collegial. Professionals should be respectful to each other, even when they are competing. At the very least, they must respect the rights, dignity, and autonomy of others.

Professions are recognized oversight bodies. Many professional bodies are not-for-profit organizations with a mission emphasizing excellence, integrity, and public service. Although it is the responsibility of individual professionals to remain competent, an oversight body typically monitors this responsibility. Such bodies provide individuals with ongoing educational resources and access to information about changes in standards and imposes a framework of discipline. Continuing membership indicates sustained competence in (and updating of) practical skills while maintaining ongoing compliance with an ethical code of conduct.

Professions encourage the engagement of members. Participation by members as volunteers is part of the essence of a profession. Professionals are more likely to refer to, use, and adhere to values that they have helped develop, and they typically have the power as members to revise these values. A good professional will want to mentor and inspire others who recently entered or wish to enter the profession. Professionals should be willing to volunteer to advance the profession and engage with peers to develop expertise and ethics. Professionals should volunteer to help educate new generations in ethical knowledge and ethical decision making and to foster a productive debate about new areas of ethics. Most professionals find that the experience of volunteering within the profession enhances their skills and widens their contacts within the industry. Membership in a professional body allows the necessary engagement with other professionals.

3.2 Professions Are Evolving

No profession stands still. Such trends as greater transparency and public accountability force professions to adapt to change. Meanwhile, technology opens up possibilities for new services and different ways of working. In addition, key processes of a profession's responsibilities may need to be reviewed by a government agency or independent public body. In general, professions often engage with non-member individuals. This can help a profession evaluate the viewpoints of the public, clients, or other stakeholders when determining policy and practice and can encourage public trust for a profession's conduct and disciplinary process.

Effective professions continue to develop their role to account for changing best practices. Some medical professional bodies, for instance, have been established for more than 500 years but may now have the same need to adapt as the much younger investment management profession. This means that at any point in time, society may recognize an area of work as a profession even if it has not fully or universally implemented all the expectations. As the requirements for a profession evolve, gaps open up that may take time to remedy. Effective professions also actively learn from other professions, particularly in the area of ethics. New standards of conduct in the accounting profession might be an influence on standards considered in investment management, for example.

4 PROFESSIONALISM IN INVESTMENT MANAGEMENT

> Successful investing professionals are disciplined and consistent and they think a great deal about what they do and how they do it.
>
> —Benjamin Graham, *The Intelligent Investor* (1949)

Investment management is a relatively young profession, which means that public understanding of its practice and codes is still developing. Recognition by regulators and employers also lags established professions. Not everyone engaged in investment management is a professional; some practitioners have not undertaken specific investment training or are not members of a professional body. That creates a challenge for the investment management profession to gain trust, because not all practitioners need to be committed to high ethical standards. However, key elements of the profession have been steadily established over several decades. For example, the publication of Graham and Dodd's *Security Analysis* in 1934 was an important step in establishing a body of knowledge for investment.

The investment management profession meets most, but currently not all, of the expectations of a profession. In most countries, some form of certification or licensing is needed to practice, but there may not be a requirement to join a professional body. Globally, the trend is to require examined entry to practice investment management and to maintain competence. But few professions have perfect implementation of all the expected attributes. The investment management profession, similar to other professions, is on a journey to improve implementation and keep up with changing demands.

The investment management profession has become increasingly global as capital markets have opened up around the world. Investment management professionals may seek cross-border opportunities or may need to relocate between offices within multinational asset management firms. Regulatory coordination across borders and the emergence of technology are contributing factors to this globalization of investment management. Various investment management professional bodies have developed in individual countries, and several of these bodies have expanded internationally. In addition, several other professional bodies, including those focused on actuarial and accountancy services, have investment management professionals as members.

4.1 Trust in Investment Management

The investment management professional today has similarities with professionals in longer-established professions, such as medicine and law. Like doctors and lawyers, investment management professionals are trusted to draw on a body of formal knowledge and apply that knowledge with care and judgement. In comparison to clients, investment professionals are also expected to have superior financial expertise, technical knowledge, and knowledge of the applicable laws and regulations. There is a risk that clients may not be fully aware of the conflicts, risks, and fees involved, so investment management professionals must always handle and fully disclose these issues in a way that serves the best interests of clients. Compliance with codes of ethics and professional standards is essential, and practice must be guided by care, transparency, and integrity.

The investment management profession and investment firms must be interdependent to maintain trust. Employers and regulators have their own standards and practices that may differ from regulations and standards set by professional bodies. The investment management professional bodies typically direct professionals in how to resolve these differences.

In many developed economies, the investment management profession affects many key aspects of the economy, including savings, retirement planning, and the pricing and allocation of capital. In most countries, skilled evaluation of securities leads to more efficient capital allocation and, combined with ethical corporate governance, can assist in attracting investment from international investors. The investment management profession can deliver more value to society when higher levels of trust and better capital allocation reduce transaction costs and help meet client objectives. These reasons explain why practitioners, clients, regulators, and governments have supported the development of an investment management profession.

4.2 CFA Institute as an Investment Management Professional Body

CFA Institute is the largest body for investment management professionals.[2] Reflecting the globalization of investment management, CFA Institute moved beyond North America in the 1980s. CFA Institute initiated a number of other changes in line with the growth of investment management. One significant change occurred in 2015, when CFA Institute decided to implement the highest standards of governance in the US not-for-profit sector. The Board of Governors resolved "to implement US Public Company Standards and US not-for-profit leading practices, unless the Board determines that it is not in the best interest of the membership or organization to do so."

The mission of CFA Institute is "to lead the investment profession globally, by promoting the highest standards of ethics, education, and professional excellence for the ultimate benefit of society." The CFA Institute Code of Ethics and Standards of Professional Conduct (Code and Standards) promote the integrity of charterholders and establish a model for ethical behavior. CFA Institute candidates and charterholders must meet the highest standards among those established by CFA Institute, regulators, or the employer. If candidates and charterholders do not meet these standards, there are negative consequences. Where client interests and market interests conflict, the Code and Standards set an investment management professional's duty to market integrity as the overriding obligation. The advocacy efforts of CFA Institute aim to build market integrity by calling for regulations that align the interests of firms and clients.

As a professional body, CFA Institute gathers knowledge from practicing investment professionals, conducts rigorous examinations, and ensures practitioner involvement in developing its codes and values. The CFA Institute Global Body of Investment Knowledge (GBIK) and Candidate Body of Knowledge (CBOK) are updated on an ongoing basis through a process known as *practice analysis*. Through interactions with practicing investment management professionals, practice analysis helps ensure that the body of knowledge for the investment management profession remains current and globally relevant. The CFA Program ensures that candidates have sufficiently mastered the core knowledge, skills, and abilities (competencies) necessary that are generally accepted and applied by investment professionals. CFA Institute also contributes to

2 Eligibility and requirements for becoming a member of CFA Institute vary by jurisdiction. Please consult www.cfainstitute.org for further details.

the dissemination of new research and ideas in finance with the publication of the *Financial Analysts Journal*; CFA Institute Research Foundation books, research briefs, and reviews; and *CFA Institute Magazine*.

CFA Institute encourages charterholders to engage in their professional communities and involves charterholders in its initiatives. CFA Institute local societies keep charterholders connected and engaged in their communities. CFA Institute assists local societies with providing continuing education programs and events that facilitate charterholders engagement. For CFA charterholders, a local CFA society is an important route to maintaining professionalism, particularly for continuing professional development.

CFA charterholders and CFA Program candidates are required to adhere to the Code and Standards and to sign annually a statement attesting to that continued adherence. Charterholders and candidates must maintain and improve their professional competence and strive to maintain and improve the competence of other investment professionals.

EXAMPLE 2

Ethics and Professionalism

1 Which of the following statements is *most* accurate? Investment professionals have a special responsibility to act ethically because:

A the industry is heavily regulated.

B they are entrusted to protect clients' assets.

C the profession requires compliance with its code of ethics.

2 Which of the following statements *best* completes the following sentence? Professionals use their specialized knowledge and skills:

A in service to others.

B to advance their career.

C for the exclusive benefit of their employers.

3 Which of the following statements is *most* accurate? A profession's code of ethics:

A includes standards of conduct or specific benchmarks for behavior.

B ensures that all members of a profession will act ethically at all times.

C publicly communicates the shared principles and expected behaviors of a profession's members.

Solution to 1:

B is correct. Investment professionals have a special responsibility because clients entrust them to protect the clients' assets.

Solution to 2:

A is correct. Professionals use specialized knowledge and skills in service to others. Their career and employer may benefit, but those results are not the primary focus of a professional's use of his or her specialized knowledge and skills.

Solution to 3:

C is correct. A profession's code of ethics publicly communicates the shared principles and expected behaviors of a profession's members. The existence of a code of ethics does not ensure that all members will behave in a manner consistent with the code and act ethically at all times. A profession will often establish a disciplinary process to address alleged violations of the code of ethics. A profession may adopt standards of conduct to enhance and clarify the code of ethics.

CHALLENGES TO ETHICAL CONDUCT

5

Professionals generally aim to be responsible and to adhere to high moral standards, so what is the benefit of studying ethics? Throughout our careers, we may find ourselves in difficult or at least unfamiliar situations in which an appropriate course of action is not immediately clear and/or there may be more than one seemingly acceptable choice; studying ethics helps us prepare for such situations. This section addresses challenges to engaging in ethical conduct. Failure to acknowledge, understand, or consider these challenges can lead to poor decision making, resulting in unintentional consequences, such as unethical conduct and potential violations of the Code and Standards.

Several challenges can make adherence to ethical conduct difficult. First, people tend to believe that they are ethical people and that their ethical standards are higher than average. Of course, everyone cannot be above average. However, surveys show this belief in above averageness remains.

These survey results illustrate overconfidence, a common behavioral bias that can lead to faulty decision making. Studies have shown that our beliefs and emotions frequently interfere with our cognitive reasoning and result in behavioral bias, a tendency to behave in a way that is not strictly rational. As a result of the overconfidence bias, we are more likely to overestimate the morality of our own behavior, particularly in situations that we have not faced before. The overconfidence bias can result in a failure to consider, explicitly or implicitly, important inputs and variables needed to form the best decision from an ethical perspective. In general, the overconfidence bias leads us to place too much importance on internal traits and intrinsic motivations, such as "I'm honest and would not lie," even though studies have shown that internal traits are generally not the main determinant of whether or not someone will behave ethically in a given situation.

A second challenge is that decision makers often fail to recognize and/or significantly underestimate the effect of situational influences, such as what other people around them are doing. **Situational influences** are external factors, such as environmental or cultural elements, that shape our thinking, decision making, and behavior. Social psychologists have studied how much situational influences affect our behavior and have found that even good people with honorable motives can and often will be influenced to do unethical things when put into difficult situations. Experiments have shown that even people who consider themselves strong, independent, free thinkers will conform to social pressures in many situations. The bystander effect, for example, demonstrates that people are less likely to intervene in an emergency when others are present. Fortunately, experiments have also shown that situational influences can induce people to act more ethically. For example, people tend to behave more ethically when they think someone else is watching or when there is a mirror placed close to them. The important concept to understand is that situational influences have a very powerful and often unrecognized effect on our thinking and behavior. Thus, learning to recognize situational influences is critical to making good decisions.

Common situational influences in the investment industry that can shape thinking and behavior include money and prestige. One experiment found that simply mentioning money can reduce ethical behavior. In the experiment, participants were less likely to cooperate when playing a game if the game was called the Wall Street Game, rather than the Community Game. In the investment industry, large financial rewards—including individual salaries, bonuses, and/or investment gains—can induce honest and well-intentioned individuals to act in ways that others might not consider ethical. Large financial rewards and/or prestige can motivate individuals to act in their own short-term self-interests, ignoring possible short-term risks or consequences to themselves and others as well as long-term risks or consequences for both themselves and others. Another extremely powerful situational influence is loyalty. Loyalty to supervisors or organizations, fellow employees, and other colleagues can tempt individuals to make compromises and take actions that they would reject under different situational influences or judge harshly when taken by others.

Situational influences often blind people to other important considerations. Bonuses, promotions, prestige, and loyalty to employer and colleagues are examples of situational influences that frequently have a disproportionate weight in our decision making. Our brains more easily and quickly identify, recognize, and consider these short-term situational influences than longer-term considerations, such as a commitment to maintaining our integrity and contributing to the integrity of the financial markets. Although absolutely important, these long-term considerations often have less immediate consequences than situational influences, making them less obvious as factors to consider in a decision and, therefore, less likely to influence our overall decision making. Situational influences shift our brain's focus from the long term to the short or immediate term. When our decision making is too narrowly focused on short-term factors and/or self-interest, we tend to ignore and/or minimize the longer-term risks and/or costs and consequences to ourselves and others, and the likelihood of suffering ethical lapses and making poor decisions increases.

Loyalty to employer and/or colleagues is an extremely powerful situational influence. Our colleagues can influence our thinking and behavior in both positive and negative ways. For example, colleagues may have encouraged you to signal your commitment to your career and high ethical standards by enrolling in the CFA Program. If you work for or with people who are not bound by the Code and Standards, they might encourage you to take actions that are consistent with local law, unaware that the recommended conduct falls short of the Code and Standards.

Well-intentioned firms may adopt or develop strong compliance programs to encourage adherence to rules, regulations, and policies. A strong compliance policy is a good start to developing an ethical culture, but a focus on adherence to rules may not be sufficient. A compliance approach may not encourage decision makers to consider the larger picture and can oversimplify decision making. Taken to the extreme, a strong compliance culture can become another situational influence that blinds employees to other important considerations. In a firm focused primarily on compliance, employees may adopt a "check the box" mentality rather than an ethical decision-making approach. Employees may ask the question "What *can* I do?" rather than "What *should* I do?"

EXAMPLE 3

Challenges to Ethical Conduct

1 Which of the following will *most likely* determine whether an individual will behave unethically?
   - **A** The person's character
   - **B** The person's internal traits and intrinsic motivation
   - **C** External factors, such as environmental or cultural elements

2 Which of the following statements is *most* accurate?

A Large financial rewards, such as bonuses, are the most powerful situational influences.

B When decision making focuses on short-term factors, the likelihood of ethical conduct increases.

C Situational influences can motivate individuals to act in their short-term self-interests without recognizing the long-term risks or consequences for themselves and others.

Solution to 1:

C is correct. Social psychologists have shown that even good people may behave unethically in difficult situations. Situational influences, which are external factors (e.g., environmental or cultural elements), can shape our thinking, decision making, and behavior and are more likely to lead to unethical behavior than internal traits or character.

Solution to 2:

C is correct. Situational influences can motivate individuals to act in their short-term self-interests without recognizing the long-term risks or consequences for themselves and others. Large financial rewards are powerful situational influences, but in some situations, other situational influences, such as loyalty to colleagues, may be even more powerful.

6 ETHICAL VS. LEGAL STANDARDS

Many times, stakeholders have common ethical expectations. Other times, different stakeholders will have different perceptions and perspectives and use different criteria to decide whether something is beneficial and/or ethical.

Laws and regulations often codify ethical actions that lead to better outcomes for society or specific groups of stakeholders. For example, some laws and regulations require businesses and their representatives to tell the truth. They require specific written disclosures in marketing and other materials. Complying with such rules is considered an ethical action; it creates a more satisfactory outcome that conforms to stakeholders' ethical expectations. As an example, consider disclosure requirements mandated by securities regulators regarding the risks of investing. Complying with such rules creates better outcomes for you, your clients, and your employer. First, compliance with the rule reduces the risk that clients will invest in securities without understanding the risks involved, which, in turn, reduces the risk that clients will file complaints and/or take legal action if their investments decline in value. Complying with the rules also reduces the risk that regulators will initiate an investigation, file charges, or/and discipline or sanction you and/or your employer. Any of these actions could jeopardize the reputation and future prospects of you and your employer. Conduct that reduces these risks (e.g., following disclosure rules) would be considered ethical; it leads to better outcomes for you, your clients, and your employer and conforms to the ethical expectations of various stakeholders.

Although laws frequently codify ethical actions, legal and ethical conduct are not always the same. Think about the diagram in Exhibit 1. Many types of conduct are both legal and ethical, but some conduct may be one and not the other. Some legal behaviors or activities may be considered unethical, and some behaviors or activities considered ethical may be deemed illegal in certain jurisdictions. Acts of civil disobedience, such as peaceful protests, may be in response to laws that individuals consider unethical. The act of civil disobedience may itself be considered ethical, and yet it violates existing local laws.

The investment industry has examples of conduct that may be legal but considered by some to be unethical. Some countries, for example, do not have laws prohibiting trading while in possession of material nonpublic information, but many investment professionals and CFA Institute consider such trading unethical.

Another area in which ethics and laws may conflict is the area of "whistleblowing." Whistleblowing refers to the disclosure by an individual of dishonest, corrupt, or illegal activity by an organization or government. Depending on the circumstances, a whistleblower may violate organizational policies and even local laws with the disclosure; thus, a whistleblower's actions may be deemed illegal and yet considered by some to be ethical.

Exhibit 1 Types of Conduct

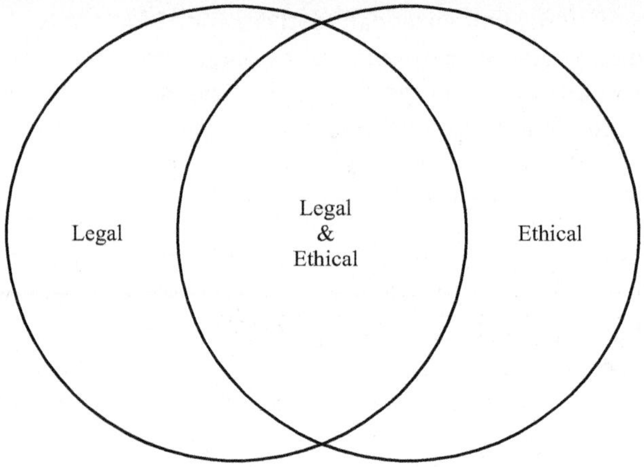

Some people advocate that increased regulation and monitoring of the behavior of participants in the investment industry will increase trust in the financial markets. Although this approach may work in some circumstances, the law is not always the best mechanism to reduce unethical behavior for several reasons. First, laws typically follow market practices; regulators may proactively design laws and regulations to address existing or anticipated practices that may adversely affect the fairness and efficiency of markets or reactively design laws and regulations in response to a crisis or an event that resulted in significant monetary losses and loss of confidence/trust in the financial system. Regulators' responses typically take significant time, during which the problematic practice may continue or even grow. Once enacted, a new law may be vague, conflicting, and/or too narrow in scope. A new law may reduce or even eliminate the existing activity while simultaneously creating an opportunity for a different, but similarly problematic, activity. Additionally, laws vary across countries or jurisdictions, allowing questionable practices to move to places that lack laws relevant to the questionable practice. Laws are also subject to interpretation and compliance by market participants, who may choose to interpret the law in the most advantageous way possible or delay compliance until a later date. For these reasons, laws and regulations are insufficient to ensure the ethical behavior of investment professionals and market participants.

Ethical conduct goes beyond what is legally required and encompasses what different societal groups or communities, including professional associations, consider to be ethically correct behavior. To act ethically, individuals need to be able to think through the facts of the situation and make good choices even in the absence of clear laws or rules. In many cases, there is no simple algorithm or formula that will always lead to an ethical course of action. Ethics requires judgment—the ability to make considered decisions and reach sensible conclusions. Good ethical judgment requires actively considering the interests of stakeholders and trying to benefit multiple stakeholders—clients, family, colleagues, employers, market participants, and so forth—and minimize risks, including reputational risk.

EXAMPLE 4

Ethical vs. Legal Standards

1 Which of the following statements is *most* accurate?

- A All legal behavior is ethical behavior.
- B Some ethical behavior may be illegal.
- C Legal standards represent the highest standard.

2 Which of the following statements is *most* accurate?

- A Increased regulations are the most useful means to reduce unethical behavior by market participants.
- B Regulators quickly design and implement laws and regulations to address practices that adversely affect the fairness and efficiency of markets.
- C New laws designed to reduce or eliminate conduct that adversely affects the markets can create opportunities for different, but similarly problematic, conduct.

Solution to 1:

B is correct. Some ethical behavior may be illegal. Civil disobedience is an example of what may be illegal behavior that some consider to be ethical. Legal and ethical behavior often coincide but not always. Standards of conduct based on ethical principles may represent a higher standard of behavior than the behavior required by law.

Solution to 2:

C is correct. New laws designed to reduce or eliminate conduct that adversely affects the markets can create opportunities for different, but similarly problematic, conduct.

ETHICAL DECISION-MAKING FRAMEWORKS 7

Laws, regulations, professional standards, and codes of ethics can guide ethical behavior, but individual judgment is a critical ingredient in making principled choices and engaging in appropriate conduct. One strategy to increase trust in the investment industry is to increase the ability and motivation of market participants to act ethically and help them minimize the likelihood of unethical actions. By integrating ethics into the decision-making activities of employees, firms can enhance the ability and the motivation of employees to act ethically, thereby reducing the likelihood of unethical actions. The ability to relate an ethical decision-making framework to a firm's or profession's code of ethics allows investment professionals to bring the principles of the code of ethics to life. An investment professional's natural desire to "do the right thing" can be reinforced by building a culture of integrity and accountability in the workplace. Development, maintenance, and demonstration of a strong culture of integrity within the firm by senior management may be the single most important factor in promoting ethical behavior among the firm's employees.

Adopting a code that clearly lays out the ethical principles that guide the thought processes and conduct the firm expects from its employees is a critical first step. But a code of ethics, although necessary, is insufficient. Simply nurturing an inclination to do right is no match for the multitude of daily decisions that investment professionals make. We need to exercise ethical decision-making skills to develop the muscle memory necessary for fundamentally ethical people to make good decisions despite the reality of conflicts and our natural instinct for self-preservation. Just as coaching and practice transform our natural ability to run across a field into the technique and endurance required to run a race, teaching, reinforcing, and practicing ethical decision-making skills prepare us to confront the hard issues effectively. It is good for business, individuals, firms, the industry, and the markets, as well as society as a whole, to engage in the investment management profession in a highly ethical manner. A strong ethical culture, built on a defined set of principles, that helps honest, ethical people engage in ethical behavior will foster the trust of investors, lead to robust global financial markets, and ultimately benefit society. That is why ethics matter.

7.1 The Framework for Ethical Decision-Making

When faced with decisions that can affect multiple stakeholders, investment professionals must have a well-developed set of principles; otherwise, their thought processes can lead to, at best, indecision and, at worst, fraudulent conduct and destruction of the public trust. Establishing an ethical framework to guide your internal thought process regarding how to act is a crucial step to engaging in ethical conduct. Investment professionals are generally comfortable analyzing and making decisions from an economic (profit/loss) perspective. Given the importance of ethical behavior in carrying out professional responsibilities, it is also important to analyze decisions and their potential consequences from an ethical perspective. Using a framework for ethical decision making will help investment professionals to effectively examine their choices in the context of conflicting interests common to their professional obligations (e.g., researching and gathering information, developing investment recommendations, and managing money for others). Such a framework will allow investment professionals to analyze and choose options in a way that allows them to meet high standards of ethical behavior. An ethical decision-making framework provides investment professionals with a tool to help them adhere to a code of ethics. By applying the framework and analyzing the particular circumstances of each available alternative, investment professionals are able to determine the best course of action to fulfill their responsibilities in an ethical manner.

An ethical decision-making framework will help a decision maker see the situation from multiple perspectives and pay attention to aspects of the situation that may be less evident with a short-term, self-focused perspective. The goal of getting a broader picture of a situation is to be able to create a plan of action that is less likely to harm stakeholders and more likely to benefit them. If a decision maker does not know or understand the effects of his or her actions on stakeholders, the likelihood of making a decision and taking action that harms stakeholders is more likely to occur, even if unintentionally. Finally, an ethical decision-making framework helps decision makers explain and justify their actions to a broader audience of stakeholders.

Ethical decision-making frameworks are designed to facilitate the decision-making process for all decisions. They help people look at and evaluate a decision from multiple perspectives, enabling them to identify important issues they might not otherwise consider. Using an ethical decision-making framework consistently will help you develop sound judgment and decision-making skills and avoid making decisions that have unanticipated ethical consequences. Ethical decision-making frameworks come in many forms with varying degrees of detail. A general ethical decision-making framework is shown in Exhibit 2.

Exhibit 2 Ethical Decision-Making Framework

- Identify: Relevant facts, stakeholders and duties owed, ethical principles, conflicts of interest
- Consider: Situational influences, additional guidance, alternative actions
- Decide and act
- Reflect: Was the outcome as anticipated? Why or why not?

The ethical decision-making process includes multiple phases, each of which has multiple components. The process is often iterative, and you, the decision maker, may move between phases in an order different from what is presented. For simplicity, we will discuss the phases sequentially. In the initial phase, you will want to identify the important facts that you have available to you, as well as information that you may not have but would like to have to give yourself a more complete understanding of the situation. It is helpful to distinguish between facts and personal opinion, judgements, and biases. You will also want to identify the stakeholders—clients, family, colleagues, your employer, market participants, and so forth—and the duties you have to each of them. You will then want to identify relevant ethical principles and/or legal requirements that might apply to the situation. You should also identify any potential conflicts of interest inherent in the situation or conflicts in the duties you hold to others. For example, your duty to your client may conflict with your duty to your employer.

In the second phase of ethical decision making, you will take time to consider the situational influences as well as personal behavioral biases that could affect your thinking and thus decision making. These situational influences and biases could include a desire to please your boss, to be seen as successful by your peers and family, to gain acceptance, to earn a large bonus, and so on. During this phase, you may seek additional guidance from trusted sources—perhaps a family member, colleague, or mentor who can help you think through the situation and help you identify and evaluate alternative actions. You may turn to your compliance department for assistance or you may even consult outside legal counsel. Seeking additional guidance is a critical step in viewing the situation from different perspectives. You should seek guidance from someone, possibly external to the firm, who is not affected by the same situational influences and behavioral biases as you are and can, therefore, provide a fresh perspective. You should also seek guidance from your firm's policies and procedures and the CFA Institute Code and Standards. A helpful technique might be to imagine how an ethical peer or role model might act in the situation.

The next phase of the framework is to make a decision and act. After you have acted on your decision, you should take the time to reflect on and assess your decision and its outcome. Was the outcome what you anticipated? Why or why not? Had you properly identified all the important facts, stakeholders, duties to stakeholders, conflicts of interest, and relevant ethical principles? Had you considered the situational influences? Did you identify personal behavioral biases that might affect your thinking? Had you sought sufficient guidance? Had you considered and properly evaluated a variety of alternative actions? You may want to reflect on the decision multiple times as the immediate and longer-term consequences of your decision and actions become apparent.

The process is often iterative. After identifying the relevant facts and considering situational influences, you may, for example, decide that you cannot make a decision without more information. You may seek additional guidance on how to obtain the information you need. You may also begin considering alternative actions regarding how to proceed based on expectations of what the additional information will reveal, or you may wait until you have more information, reflect on what you have done and learned so far, and start the process over again. Sometimes cases can be complicated and multiple iterations may reveal that no totally acceptable solution can be created. Applying an ethical decision-making framework can help you evaluate the situation so you can make the best possible decision. The next section shows applications of the framework shown in Exhibit 2.

7.2 Applying the Framework

To illustrate how the framework could be applied in your career, consider the scenario in Example 5.

EXAMPLE 5

Applying an Ethical Decision-Making Framework I

You have been hired as a junior analyst with a major investment bank. When you join the bank, you receive a copy of the firm's policies as well as training on the policies. Your supervisor is the senior technology analyst for the investment bank. As part of your duties, you gather information, draft documents, conduct analysis, and perform other support functions for the senior analyst.

Your employer is one of several investment banks working on the initial public offering (IPO) of a well-known technology company. The IPO is expected to generate significant revenues for the investment banks participating in the offering. The IPO has been highly anticipated and is in the news every day.

You are thrilled when your supervisor asks you to work on several research projects related to analyzing and valuing the upcoming IPO for investors. You eagerly compile information and draft a one-page outline. You stop to consider what other information you could add to improve the report before proceeding. You realize that you have two excellent contacts in the technology industry who could review your work and provide some additional and potentially valuable perspectives. You draft an email to your contacts reading:

> I am working on an analysis and valuation of Big Tech Company for investors. My employer is one of the banks participating in the IPO, and I want to make sure I have considered everything. I was hoping you could give me feedback on the prospects and risks facing Big Tech. Please treat all the attached material as confidential.

Before hitting the send button, you stop and think about the ethical decision-making framework you have studied. You decide to apply the framework and jot down some notes as you work through the process: On the first page, you work through the identification phase and make a list of the relevant facts, stakeholders to whom you owe a duty, potential conflicts of interest, and ethical principles. This list is shown is Exhibit 3.

Exhibit 3 Identification Phase

1 Relevant facts:
- *Working on the deal/IPO of the decade*
- *Employer is one of several investment banks working on IPO*
- *The IPO is highly anticipated*
- *A successful IPO could lead to additional investment banking deals and revenues for the firm*
- *Supervisor is relying on me*
- *Employer has documented policies and procedures*
- *Industry is regulated, with many rules and regulations in place*

2 Stakeholders and duties owed. I have a duty to the following:
- *Supervisor*
- *Employer*
- *Employer's corporate client, the technology company*
- *Employer's asset management and other investing clients*
- *Employer's partners in the IPO*
- *Investors and market participants interested in the IPO*
- *All capital market participants*
- *Profession*
- *Society as a whole*

3 Conflicts or potential conflicts of interest include the following:
- *Gathering additional research from external sources versus maintaining confidentiality*
- *Duty to supervisor versus desire to impress*
- *Duty to corporate client versus duty to other clients of the firm*
- *The firm's corporate client benefits from a high IPO price whereas the firm's asset management clients would benefit from a low IPO price*
- *Making the IPO look attractive to the market (sell-side marketing) versus objective analysis of the investment potential of this deal (buy-side analysis)*
- *My bonus, compensation, and career prospects are tied to my supervisor's and the IPO's success; duty to employer, employer's investing clients, profession*

4 Ethical principles that are relevant to this situation include the following:
- *Duty of loyalty to employer*
- *Client interests come first*
- *Maintain confidences and confidentiality of information*
- *Objectivity of analysis*
- *Fairness to market participants*

On the next page, you write notes relating to the second phase of the framework, considering the various situational factors and the guidance available to you before considering alternative actions. These notes are shown in Exhibit 4.

Exhibit 4 Consideration Phase

1 Situational influences:
- *The firm's written policies*
- *The bank will earn big fees from the IPO*
- *I want to impress my boss—and potential future bosses*
- *My bonus, compensation, and career prospects will be influenced by my contribution to the success of this deal and other deals*
- *I am one of very few people working on this deal; it is a real honor, and others would be impressed that I am working on this deal*
- *My employer is filled with successful and wealthy people who are go-getters; I want to be successful and wealthy like them*

2 Additional guidance. I could seek guidance from the following:
- *The firm's code of ethics*
- *The firm's written policies*
- *A peer in my firm*
- *My supervisor, the senior analyst*
- *The compliance department*
- *A mentor either at the firm or perhaps from university or industry*
- *The CFA Institute Code and Standards*
- *Outside legal counsel*

3 Alternative actions. I could consider the following:
- *Asking contacts what they have heard*
- *Submitting the report as a draft and suggesting that contacts in the industry might be able to provide more perspective*
- *Sending a survey to various technology industry veterans soliciting their viewpoints on developments*

After completing these steps, you decide to check the firm's policies. Under a section entitled "Research Analyst Role in Securities Offerings," the manual states, "You may not distribute any written (which include email, fax, electronic, and other means) material related to companies and/or their offerings . . . during the course of any offering and the related quiet period."

You read further and note a section entitled "Wall Crossing Policy and Procedures" that states that "employees with confidential information may not communicate the information to anyone who does not have a valid need to know" without first obtaining clearance from the legal and compliance department.

You decide that your contacts do not have a "valid need to know" and that it is unlikely the firm's legal and compliance professionals would approve sharing the information. You then decide to mention your contacts to the senior research analyst. He suggests that they may have some useful perspective and that you might talk to them to hear their perspective and cautions you not to disclose any information about any of the firm's clients, pending deals, or research. You return to your desk, delete the email, and following the senior research analyst's advice, call your contacts on the telephone to discuss the technology sector, its prospects, and its challenges. During the calls, you take care not to reveal any details about Big Tech Company or its offering.

Whatever action you take, you should take time afterward to reflect on the decision and the outcome. Was the outcome as anticipated? Why or why not?

The initial facts presented in the example are based on the real-life experience of a young junior analyst working on a highly anticipated IPO. The junior analyst may or may not have used an ethical decision-making framework to evaluate his situation. Without seeking additional guidance, the junior analyst sent an email similar to the one in the example with an attachment that included confidential, proprietary information, including the senior analyst's analysis and forecasts. Months later, long after the IPO offering, the junior analyst's email was discovered by his employer. When questioned, he admitted that he had received training regarding the firm's policies and that he did not discuss or seek approval from anyone before sending the email. Two days later, the firm terminated the junior analyst's employment and reported to regulatory authorities that he had been terminated for distributing written materials, by email, during a securities offering in violation of firm policies that prohibit the dissemination of any written materials during the course of a securities offering and related periods. The junior analyst's supervisor also lost his job for failing to properly supervise the analyst. Multiple regulators investigated the matter, and the firm was fined millions of dollars for failing to supervise its employees properly. The information regarding the junior analyst's termination was posted and remains available on the regulator's website for all to see. Future employers conducting routine background checks will know that the analyst was terminated for violating firm policies relating to a securities offering.

The example presented is similar to situations faced by many analysts. Using an ethical decision-making framework will help you evaluate situations from multiple perspectives, avoid poor decision making, and avoid the consequences that can result from taking an ill-conceived course of action. Using an ethical decision-making framework is no guarantee of a positive outcome but may help you avoid making unethical decisions.

EXAMPLE 6

Applying an Ethical Decision-Making Framework II

A financial adviser has been saving a portion of his salary to purchase a new vehicle. He is on track to have enough saved within the next three months. His employer has offered a special bonus for this quarter, which will go to the team that attracts the most new investors into the firm's investment funds. In addition to the potential bonus, the firm pays a 5% commission to employees who sell shares in the firm's investment funds. Several of the funds are highly rated, including one designed to provide steady income to investors.

The financial adviser has added only a few new investors to the firm's funds, but his teammates have been very successful in their efforts. The end of the quarter is one week away, and his team is competing closely with another team for the bonus. One of his teammates informs the financial adviser that he really needs the bonus so his elderly mother can receive medical treatment.

Later that day, the financial adviser meets with an elderly client on a limited income who is seeking more income from his investment portfolio. The client is 89 years old and in poor health. According to the client's will, the client's investment portfolio will go to his favorite charity upon his death.

1 Which of the following situational influences is likely to have the *most* effect on the financial adviser's efforts to get new clients to invest in the funds? His relationship with his:

A client.

B employer.

C teammates.

2 Which of the following statements is *most* accurate? An ethical decision-making framework:

A is only beneficial when a firm lacks a code of ethics.

B is used to improve compliance with laws and regulations.

C is a tool for analyzing the potential alternative actions and consequences of a decision.

3 Which of the following is *most* accurate? Ethical decision-making frameworks:

A raise awareness of different perspectives.

B focus attention on short-term consequences.

C allocate more weight to those who will directly benefit from the decision.

4 Which of the following is *most* accurate? Ethical decision-making frameworks:

A are not needed if behavior is legal.

B identify who gains the most from a decision.

C can help reduce unanticipated ethical lapses and unexpected consequences.

5 Using an ethical decision-making framework, which of the following duties would *most likely* take precedence in the scenario described? The financial adviser's duty to his:

A client.

B employer.

C colleagues.

6 Using an ethical decision-making framework, the financial adviser would *most likely*:

A recommend that the elderly client invest at least some of his assets in the highly rated fund.

B research other investments that can provide steady income before making a recommendation to his elderly client.

C disclose the commission he would earn before recommending that the elderly client invest at least some of his assets in the highly rated fund.

Solution to 1:

C is correct. The financial adviser's relationship with his teammates is likely to have the most effect on the financial adviser's efforts. The teammates share in earning the bonus from the employer. In addition, the team works with each other on a regular basis where there is a likelihood that social influences of working together play a role in decision making and effort.

Solution to 2:

C is correct. An ethical decision-making framework is a tool for analyzing the potential alternative actions and consequences of a decision.

Solution to 3:

A is correct. Ethical decision-making frameworks raise awareness of different perspectives. The framework should consider short-term consequences, but they are not the focus of the framework. Similarly, the framework may allocate more weight to those who directly benefit from decisions, but this is not the primary goal of an ethical decision-making framework.

Solution to 4:

C is correct. Ethical decision-making frameworks can help avoid unanticipated ethical consequences. As it relates to A, ethics standards are often higher than legal standards so an ethical decision-making framework would be needed. Although C is accurate, identifying who gains most from the decision is a small component of the framework.

Solution to 5:

A is correct. Using an ethical decision-making framework, the financial adviser's relationship with his client would most likely take precedence in this scenario. The adviser should put his client's interests first. The exception to client interests taking precedence occurs when market integrity effects take precedence.

Solution to 6:

B is correct. Using an ethical decision-making framework, the financial adviser would identify the relevant facts, stakeholders, duties owed, and potential conflicts. In this scenario, the financial adviser owes a duty to his client as well as his employer. His client's interests take precedence over all other interests. The bonus and his colleague's desire to help his mother are situational influences. To navigate this situation, the financial adviser should seek additional information; he should research the risk and return parameters and fee structures of other investments that can provide steady income before making a recommendation to his client.

CONCLUSION

8

This reading introduced ideas and concepts that will help you understand the importance of ethical behavior in the investment industry as well as the challenges to adhering to high ethical standards. A code of ethics will communicate an organization's values and the expected behavior of its members as well as provide guidance for decision making. A code of ethics may be further enhanced and clarified by the adoption of standards of conduct. Professions and professional organizations, such as the CFA Institute, can help to establish codes and standards that provide a framework and technical competence for practitioners. An ethical decision-making framework combined with a code of ethics may help investment professionals analyze their decisions in a way that identifies potential conflicts and negative consequences.

Knowing the rules to apply in a particular situation, although important, may not be sufficient to ensure ethical conduct if used alone. Responsible professionals in the investment industry must be able both to recognize areas that are prone to ethical pitfalls and to identify and process those circumstances and influences that can impair judgment and lead to ethical lapses.

SUMMARY

- Ethics refers to the study of making good choices. Ethics encompasses a set of moral principles and rules of conduct that provide guidance for our behavior.
- Situational influences are external factors that may shape our behavior.
- Challenges to ethical behavior include being overconfident in our own morality, underestimating the effect of situational influences, and focusing on the immediate rather than long-term outcomes or consequences of a decision.
- In any given profession, the code of ethics publicly communicates the established principles and expected behavior of its members.
- Members of a profession use specialized knowledge and skills to serve others; they share and agree to adhere to a common code of ethics to serve others and advance the profession.
- A code of ethics helps foster public confidence that members of the profession will use their specialized skills and knowledge to serve their clients and others.
- A profession is an occupational group that has specific education, expert knowledge, and a framework of practice and behavior that underpins community trust, respect, and recognition.
- The requirement to uphold high ethical standards is one clear difference between professions and craft guilds or trade bodies.
- A primary goal of professions is to establish trust among clients and among society in general.
- Common characteristics of professions include normalization of practitioner behavior, service to society, client focus, high entry standards, a body of expert knowledge, encouragement and facilitation of continuing education, monitoring of professional conduct, collegiality, recognized overseeing bodies, and encouragement of member engagement.
- The investment management profession has become increasingly global, driven by the opening of capital markets, coordination of regulation across borders, and the emergence of technology.
- Investment management professionals are trusted to draw on a body of formal knowledge and apply that knowledge with care and judgement. In comparison to clients, investment professionals are also expected to have superior financial expertise, technical knowledge, and knowledge of the applicable laws and regulations.
- As a professional body, CFA Institute gathers knowledge from practicing investment professionals, conducts rigorous examinations, and ensures practitioner involvement in developing its codes and values.

- Investment management professionals are likely to encounter dilemmas, including those with ethical implications. Professionals should consider carefully how to determine the facts of the issue and assess the implications.
- High ethical standards always matter and are of particular importance in the investment management profession, which is based almost entirely on trust. Clients trust investment professionals to use their specialized skills and knowledge to serve clients and protect client assets. All stakeholders gain long-term benefits when investment professionals adhere to high ethical standards.
- Legal standards are often rule based. Ethical conduct goes beyond legal standards, balancing self-interest with the direct and indirect consequences of behavior on others.
- A framework for ethical decision making can help people look at and evaluate a decision from different perspectives, enabling them to identify important issues, make wise decisions, and limit unintended consequences.

REFERENCES

Beaton, George Ramsay. 2010. *Why Professionalism is Still Relevant.* University of Melbourne Legal Studies Research Paper No. 445. Available at SSRN: https://ssrn.com/abstract=1545509 or .

Bellis, C. S. 2000. "Professions in Society." *British Actuarial Journal* 6 (2): 317–64.

Bogle, John C. 2017. "Balancing Professional Values and Business Values." *Financial Analysts Journal* 73 (2): 14–23.

CFA Institute. 2017. *Future State of the Investment Profession.* www.cfainstitute.org/learning/future/Documents/future_state_of_investment_profession.pdf

CFA Society UK.April 2016. The Value of the Investment Profession: A Report on Stakeholders' Views. www.cfauk.org/-/media/files/pdf/professionalism/value-of-the-investment-profession-report.pdf

Graham, Benjamin. 1949. *The Intelligent Investor.* New York: HarperCollins.

Graham, Benjamin, and David Dodd. 1934. *Security Analysis.* New York: McGraw-Hill.

Intelligence, Edelman. 2017. *"2017 Edelman Trust Barometer"* (17 January). https://www.edelman.com/trust2017/.

Sanders, Deen, and Alex Roberts. 2015. *Professionalisation of Financial Services.* White Paper. https://www.psc.gov.au/sites/default/files/NEW-PSC%20Whitepaper_final.pdf.

PRACTICE PROBLEMS

1 Benchmarks for minimally acceptable behaviors of community members are:
   A a code of ethics.
   B laws and regulations.
   C standards of conduct.

2 Specialized knowledge and skills, a commitment to serve others, and a shared code of ethics *best* characterize a(n):
   A vocation.
   B profession.
   C occupation.

3 Which of the following *best* identifies an internal trait that may lead to poor ethical decision making?
   A Overconfidence
   B Loyalty to employer
   C Promise of money or prestige

4 Situational influences in decision making will *most likely* be minimized if:
   A strong compliance programs are in place.
   B longer-term consequences are considered.
   C individuals believe they are truthful and honest.

5 Decision makers who use a compliance approach are *most likely* to:
   A avoid situational influences.
   B oversimplify decision making.
   C consider more factors than when using an ethical decision-making approach.

6 When unethical behavior erodes trust in an investment firm, that firm is *more likely* to experience:
   A lower revenues only.
   B higher expenses only.
   C lower revenues and higher expenses.

7 Which is an example of an activity that may be legal but that CFA Institute considers unethical?
   A Making legally required disclosures in marketing materials
   B Trading while in possession of material nonpublic information
   C Disclosure by an employee of his or her own company's dishonest activity

8 An ethical decision-making framework will *most likely*:
   A include a pre-determined, uniform sequence.
   B focus exclusively on confirmable facts and relationships.
   C help avoid a decision that has unanticipated ethical consequences.

9 High ethical standards are distinguishing features of which of the following bodies?
   A Craft guilds

B Trade bodies

C Professional bodies

10 Fiduciary duty is a standard *most likely* to be upheld by members of a(n):

A employer.

B profession.

C not-for-profit body.

11 To maintain trust, the investment management profession must be interdependent with:

A regulators.

B employers.

C investment firms.

12 When an ethical dilemma occurs, an investment professional should *most likely* first raise the issue with a:

A mentor outside the firm.

B professional body's hotline.

C senior individual in the firm.

SOLUTIONS

1 C is correct. Standards of conduct are applied to specific communities or societal groups and identify specific behaviors required of community members. These standards of conduct serve as benchmarks for the minimally acceptable behavior of community members. Codes of ethics serve as a general guide for how community members should act; they communicate the organization's values and overall expectations regarding member behavior, but they do not identify specific behaviors required of community members. Laws and regulations are rules of conduct defined by governments and related entities about obligatory and forbidden conduct broadly applicable for individuals and entities under their jurisdiction.

2 B is correct. A profession has several characteristics that distinguish it from an occupation or vocation, such as specialized knowledge and skills, service to others, and a code of ethics shared by its members. A profession is the ultimate evolution of an occupation, resulting from excellence in practice, a mastery mindest, and expected adherence to a code of ethics and standards of practice.

3 A is correct. An overconfidence bias can lead individuals to put too much importance on internal traits and intrinsic motivations, such as their own perceptions of personal honesty, that can lead to faulty decision making. Loyalty to an employer and promise of money or prestige are situational influences that can lead to faulty decision making.

4 B is correct. Consciously considering long-term consequences will help offset situational influences. We more easily recognize and consider short-term situational influences than longer-term considerations because longer-term considerations have fewer immediate consequences than situational influences do. When decision making is too narrowly focused on short-term factors, we tend to ignore longer-term risks and consequences, and the likelihood of poor ethical decision making increases. A strong compliance policy is a good first step toward developing an ethical culture; a focus on rules adherence may not be sufficient. Emphasis on compliance may not encourage decision makers to consider the larger picture and can oversimplify decision making. Taken to the extreme, a strong compliance culture can become another situational influence that blinds employees to other important considerations. An overconfidence bias can place too much importance on internal traits and intrinsic motivations, such as "I'm honest and would not lie," even though studies have shown that internal traits are generally not the main determinant of whether or not someone will behave ethically in a given situation.

5 B is correct. A compliance approach can oversimplify decision making and may not encourage decision makers to consider the larger picture. A strong compliance culture may be a good start in developing an ethical culture but can become another situational influence that may result in employees failing to consider other important factors.

6 C is correct. Unethical behavior ultimately harms investment firms. Clients are not attracted if they suspect unethical behavior, leading to less business and lower revenues. Investment firms may also experience higher relative costs because regulators are more likely to have cause to initiate costly investigations.

7 B is correct. The investment industry has examples of conduct that may be legal but that CFA Institute considers unethical. Trading while in possession of material nonpublic information is not prohibited by law worldwide and can, therefore, be legal, but CFA Institute considers such trading unethical.

8 C is correct. Using an ethical decision-making framework consistently will help you develop sound judgment and decision-making skills and avoid making decisions that have unanticipated ethical consequences. The decision-making process is often iterative, and the decision maker may move between phases of the framework. A decision maker should consider more than confirmable facts and relationships; for example, the decision maker should consider situational influences and personal biases.

9 C is correct. High ethical standards distinguish professions from the craft guilds or trade bodies. Unlike trade bodies, professional bodies also typically have a mission to serve society and enforce professional conduct rules for practitioners.

10 B is correct. Fiduciary duty is an obligation to deliver a high standard of care when acting for the benefit of another party. Professionals must act in the best interest of the client, exercising a reasonable level of care, skill, and diligence. Other entities—including employers, regulators, trade associations, and not-for-profit bodies—may also support an industry but are not the same as professional bodies. Unlike professions, these other entities generally do not exist to set and maintain professional standards.

11 C is correct. The investment management profession and investment firms must be interdependent to maintain trust. Employers and regulators have their own standards and practices, which may differ from regulations and standards set by professional bodies.

12 C is correct. When a dilemma occurs, raising an issue internally with a senior employee is often a good starting place and creates an opportunity for an independent internal review. Protecting the client and the firm may take priority over the position of an individual professional raising a concern.

READING

2

Code of Ethics and Standards of Professional Conduct

LEARNING OUTCOMES

Mastery	The candidate should be able to:
☐	a. describe the structure of the CFA Institute Professional Conduct Program and the process for the enforcement of the Code and Standards;
☐	b. state the six components of the Code of Ethics and the seven Standards of Professional Conduct;
☐	c. explain the ethical responsibilities required by the Code and Standards, including the sub-sections of each Standard.

PREFACE

The *Standards of Practice Handbook* (*Handbook*) provides guidance to the people who grapple with real ethical dilemmas in the investment profession on a daily basis; the *Handbook* addresses the professional intersection where theory meets practice and where the concept of ethical behavior crosses from the abstract to the concrete. The *Handbook* is intended for a diverse and global audience: CFA Institute members navigating ambiguous ethical situations; supervisors and direct/indirect reports determining the nature of their responsibilities to each other, to existing and potential clients, and to the broader financial markets; and candidates preparing for the Chartered Financial Analyst (CFA) examinations.

Recent events in the global financial markets have tested the ethical mettle of financial market participants, including CFA Institute members. The standards taught in the CFA Program and by which CFA Institute members and candidates must abide represent timeless ethical principles and professional conduct for all market conditions. Through adherence to these standards, which continue to serve as the model for ethical behavior in the investment professional globally, each market participant does his or her part to improve the integrity and efficient operations of the financial markets.

The *Handbook* provides guidance in understanding the interconnectedness of the aspirational and practical principles and provisions of the Code of Ethics and Standards of Professional Conduct (Code and Standards). The Code contains high-level

This reading is a verbatim reprint of *Standards of Practice Handbook*, Eleventh Edition, updated March 2018, p. i to 12 included (www.cfainstitute.org/en/ethics/codes/standards-practice-handbook).

aspirational ethical principles that drive members and candidates to create a positive and reputable investment profession. The Standards contain practical ethical principles of conduct that members and candidates must follow to achieve the broader industry expectations. However, applying the principles individually may not capture the complexity of ethical requirements related to the investment industry. The Code and Standards should be viewed and interpreted as an interwoven tapestry of ethical requirements. Through members' and candidates' adherence to these principles as a whole, the integrity of and trust in the capital markets are improved.

Evolution of the CFA Institute Code of Ethics and Standards of Professional Conduct

Generally, changes to the Code and Standards over the years have been minor. CFA Institute has revised the language of the Code and Standards and occasionally added a new standard to address a prominent issue of the day. For instance, in 1992, CFA Institute added the standard addressing performance presentation to the existing list of standards.

Major changes came in 2005 with the ninth edition of the *Handbook*. CFA Institute adopted new standards, revised some existing standards, and reorganized the standards. The revisions were intended to clarify the requirements of the Code and Standards and effectively convey to its global membership what constitutes "best practice" in a number of areas relating to the investment profession.

The Code and Standards must be regularly reviewed and updated if they are to remain effective and continue to represent the highest ethical standards in the global investment industry. CFA Institute strongly believes that revisions of the Code and Standards are not undertaken for cosmetic purposes but to add value by addressing legitimate concerns and improving comprehension.

Changes to the Code and Standards have far-reaching implications for the CFA Institute membership, the CFA Program, and the investment industry as a whole. CFA Institute members and candidates are *required* to adhere to the Code and Standards. In addition, the Code and Standards are increasingly being adopted, in whole or in part, by firms and regulatory authorities. Their relevance goes well beyond CFA Institute members and candidates.

Standards of Practice Handbook

The periodic revisions of the Code and Standards have come in conjunction with updates of the *Standards of Practice Handbook*. The *Handbook* is the fundamental element of the ethics education effort of CFA Institute and the primary resource for guidance in interpreting and implementing the Code and Standards. The *Handbook* seeks to educate members and candidates on how to apply the Code and Standards to their professional lives and thereby benefit their clients, employers, and the investing public in general. The *Handbook* explains the purpose of the Code and Standards and how they apply in a variety of situations. The sections discuss and amplify each standard and suggest procedures to prevent violations.

Examples in the "Application of the Standard" sections are meant to illustrate how the standard applies to hypothetical but factual situations. The names contained in the examples are fictional and are not meant to refer to any actual person or entity. Unless otherwise stated (e.g., one or more people specifically identified), individuals in each example are CFA Institute members and holders of the CFA designation. Because factual circumstances vary so widely and often involve gray areas, the explanatory material and examples are not intended to be all inclusive. Many examples set forth in the application sections involve standards that have legal counterparts; ***members***

are strongly urged to discuss with their supervisors and legal and compliance departments the content of the Code and Standards and the members' general obligations under the Code and Standards.

CFA Institute recognizes that the presence of any set of ethical standards may create a false sense of security unless the documents are fully understood, enforced, and made a meaningful part of everyday professional activities. The *Handbook* is intended to provide a useful frame of reference that suggests ethical professional behavior in the investment decision-making process. This book cannot cover every contingency or circumstance, however, and it does not attempt to do so. The development and interpretation of the Code and Standards are evolving processes; the Code and Standards will be subject to continuing refinement.

Summary of Changes in the Eleventh Edition

The comprehensive review of the Code and Standards in 2005 resulted in principle requirements that remain applicable today. The review carried out for the eleventh edition focused on market practices that have evolved since the tenth edition. Along with updates to the guidance and examples within the *Handbook*, the eleventh edition includes an update to the Code of Ethics that embraces the members' role of maintaining the social contract between the industry and investors. Additionally, there are three changes to the Standards of Professional Conduct, which recognize the importance of proper supervision, clear communications with clients, and the expanding educational programs of CFA Institute.

Inclusion of Updated CFA Institute Mission

The CFA Institute Board of Governors approved an updated mission for the organization that is included in the Preamble to the Code and Standards. The new mission conveys the organization's conviction in the investment industry's role in the betterment of society at large.

> ***Mission:***
>
> To lead the investment profession globally by promoting the highest standards of ethics, education, and professional excellence for the ultimate benefit of society.

Updated Code of Ethics Principle

One of the bullets in the Code of Ethics was updated to reflect the role that the capital markets have in the greater society. As members work to promote and maintain the integrity of the markets, their actions should also help maintain the social contract with investors.

> ***Old:***
>
> Promote the integrity of and uphold the rules governing capital markets.
>
> ***New:***
>
> Promote the integrity and viability of the global capital markets for the ultimate benefit of society.

New Standard Regarding Responsibilities of Supervisors [IV(C)]

The standard for members and candidates with supervision or authority over others within their firms was updated to bring about improvements in preventing illegal and unethical actions from occurring. The prior version of Standard IV(C) focused on the detection and prevention of violations. The updated version stresses broader compliance expectations, which include the detection and prevention aspects of the original version.

> ***Old:***
>
> Members and Candidates must make reasonable efforts to detect and prevent violations of applicable laws, rules, regulations, and the Code and Standards by anyone subject to their supervision or authority.
>
> ***New:***
>
> Members and Candidates must make reasonable efforts to ensure that anyone subject to their supervision or authority complies with applicable laws, rules, regulations, and the Code and Standards.

Additional Requirement under the Standard for Communication with Clients and Prospective Clients [V(B)]

Given the constant development of new and exotic financial instruments and strategies, the standard regarding communicating with clients now includes an implicit requirement to discuss the risks and limitations of recommendations being made to clients. The new principle and related guidance take into account the fact that levels of disclosure will differ between products and services. Members and candidates, along with their firms, must determine the specific disclosures their clients should receive while ensuring appropriate transparency of the individual firms' investment processes.

> ***Addition:***
>
> Disclose to clients and prospective clients significant limitations and risks associated with the investment process.

Modification to Standard VII(A)

Since this standard was developed, CFA Institute has launched additional educational programs. The updated standard not only maintains the integrity of the CFA Program but also expands the same ethical considerations when members or candidates participate in such programs as the CIPM Program and the CFA Institute Investment Foundations certificate program. Whether participating as a member assisting with the curriculum or an examination or as a sitting candidate within a program, we expect them to engage in these programs as they would participate in the CFA Program.

> ***Old:***
>
> Conduct as Members and Candidates in the CFA Program
>
> Members and Candidates must not engage in any conduct that compromises the reputation or integrity of CFA Institute or the CFA designation or the integrity, validity, or security of the CFA examinations.

New:

Conduct as Participants in CFA Institute Programs

Members and Candidates must not engage in any conduct that compromises the reputation or integrity of CFA Institute or the CFA designation or the integrity, validity, or security of CFA Institute programs.

General Guidance and Example Revision

The guidance and examples were updated to reflect practices and scenarios applicable to today's investment industry. Two concepts that appear frequently in the updates in this edition relate to the increased use of social media for business communications and the use of and reliance on the output of quantitative models. The use of social media platforms has increased significantly since the publication of the tenth edition. And although financial modeling is not new to the industry, this update reflects upon actions that are viewed as possible contributing factors to the financial crises of the past decade.

CFA Institute Professional Conduct Program

All CFA Institute members and candidates enrolled in the CFA Program are required to comply with the Code and Standards. The CFA Institute Board of Governors maintains oversight and responsibility for the Professional Conduct Program (PCP), which, in conjunction with the Disciplinary Review Committee (DRC), is responsible for enforcement of the Code and Standards. The DRC is a volunteer committee of CFA charterholders who serve on panels to review conduct and partner with Professional Conduct staff to establish and review professional conduct policies. The CFA Institute Bylaws and Rules of Procedure for Professional Conduct (Rules of Procedure) form the basic structure for enforcing the Code and Standards. The Professional Conduct division is also responsible for enforcing testing policies of other CFA Institute education programs as well as the professional conduct of Certificate in Investment Performance Measurement (CIPM) certificants.

Professional Conduct inquiries come from a number of sources. First, members and candidates must self-disclose on the annual Professional Conduct Statement all matters that question their professional conduct, such as involvement in civil litigation or a criminal investigation or being the subject of a written complaint. Second, written complaints received by Professional Conduct staff can bring about an investigation. Third, CFA Institute staff may become aware of questionable conduct by a member or candidate through the media, regulatory notices, or another public source. Fourth, candidate conduct is monitored by proctors who complete reports on candidates suspected to have violated testing rules on exam day. Lastly, CFA Institute may also conduct analyses of scores and exam materials after the exam, as well as monitor online and social media to detect disclosure of confidential exam information.

When an inquiry is initiated, the Professional Conduct staff conducts an investigation that may include requesting a written explanation from the member or candidate; interviewing the member or candidate, complaining parties, and third parties; and collecting documents and records relevant to the investigation. Upon reviewing the material obtained during the investigation, the Professional Conduct staff may conclude the inquiry with no disciplinary sanction, issue a cautionary letter, or continue proceedings to discipline the member or candidate. If the Professional Conduct staff believes a violation of the Code and Standards or testing policies has occurred, the member or candidate has the opportunity to reject or accept any charges and the proposed sanctions.

If the member or candidate does not accept the charges and proposed sanction, the matter is referred to a panel composed of DRC members. Panels review materials and presentations from Professional Conduct staff and from the member or candidate. The panel's task is to determine whether a violation of the Code and Standards or testing policies occurred and, if so, what sanction should be imposed.

Sanctions imposed by CFA Institute may have significant consequences; they include public censure, suspension of membership and use of the CFA designation, and revocation of the CFA charter. Candidates enrolled in the CFA Program who have violated the Code and Standards or testing policies may be suspended or prohibited from further participation in the CFA Program.

Adoption of the Code and Standards

The Code and Standards apply to individual members of CFA Institute and candidates in the CFA Program. CFA Institute does encourage firms to adopt the Code and Standards, however, as part of their code of ethics. Those who claim compliance should fully understand the requirements of each of the principles of the Code and Standards.

Once a party—nonmember or firm—ensures its code of ethics meets the principles of the Code and Standards, that party should make the following statement whenever claiming compliance:

> "[Insert name of party] claims compliance with the CFA Institute Code of Ethics and Standards of Professional Conduct. This claim has not been verified by CFA Institute."

CFA Institute welcomes public acknowledgement, when appropriate, that firms are complying with the CFA Institute Code of Ethics and Standards of Professional Conduct and encourages firms to notify us of the adoption plans. For firms that would like to distribute the Code and Standards to clients and potential clients, attractive one-page copies of the Code and Standards, including translations, are available on the CFA Institute website (www.cfainstitute.org).

CFA Institute has also published the Asset Manager Code of Professional Conduct, which is designed, in part, to help asset managers comply with the regulations mandating codes of ethics for investment advisers. Whereas the Code and Standards are aimed at individual investment professionals who are members of CFA Institute or candidates in the CFA Program, the Asset Manager Code was drafted specifically for firms. The Asset Manager Code provides specific, practical guidelines for asset managers in six areas: loyalty to clients, the investment process, trading, compliance, performance evaluation, and disclosure. The Asset Manager Code and the appropriate steps to acknowledge adoption or compliance can be found on the CFA Institute website (www.cfainstitute.org).

Acknowledgments

CFA Institute is a not-for-profit organization that is heavily dependent on the expertise and intellectual contributions of member volunteers. Members devote their time because they share a mutual interest in the organization's mission to promote and achieve ethical practice in the investment profession. CFA Institute owes much to the volunteers' abundant generosity and energy in extending ethical integrity.

The CFA Institute Standards of Practice Council (SPC), a group consisting of CFA charterholder volunteers from many different countries, is charged with maintaining and interpreting the Code and Standards and ensuring that they are effective. The SPC draws its membership from a broad spectrum of organizations in the securities field, including brokers, investment advisers, banks, and insurance companies. In most instances, the SPC members have important supervisory responsibilities within their firms.

The SPC continually evaluates the Code and Standards, as well as the guidance in the *Handbook*, to ensure that they are

- representative of high standards of professional conduct,
- relevant to the changing nature of the investment profession,
- globally applicable,
- sufficiently comprehensive, practical, and specific,
- enforceable, and
- testable for the CFA Program.

The SPC has spent countless hours reviewing and discussing revisions to the Code and Standards and updates to the guidance that make up the eleventh edition of the *Handbook*. Following is a list of the current and former members of the SPC who generously donated their time and energy to this effort.

James E. Hollis III, CFA, Chair
Rik Albrecht, CFA
Terence E. Burns, CFA
Laura Dagan, CFA
Samuel B. Jones, Jr., CFA
Ulrike Kaiser-Boeing, CFA
Jinliang (Jack) Li, CFA
Christopher C. Loop, CFA,
James M. Meeth, CFA
Guy G. Rutherfurd, Jr., CFA
Edouard Senechal, CFA
Wenliang (Richard) Wang, CFA
Peng Lian Wee, CFA

ETHICS AND THE INVESTMENT INDUSTRY

Society ultimately benefits from efficient markets where capital can freely flow to the most productive or innovative destination. Well-functioning capital markets efficiently match those needing capital with those seeking to invest their assets in revenue-generating ventures. In order for capital markets to be efficient, investors must be able to trust that the markets are fair and transparent and offer them the opportunity to be rewarded for the risk they choose to take. Laws, regulations, and enforcement play a vital role but are insufficient alone to guarantee fair and transparent markets. The markets depend on an ethical foundation to guide participants' judgment and behavior. CFA Institute maintains and promotes the Code of Ethics and Standards of Professional Conduct in order to create a culture of ethics for the ultimate benefit of society.

Why Ethics Matters

Ethics can be defined as a set of moral principles or rules of conduct that provide guidance for our behavior when it affects others. Widely acknowledged fundamental ethical principles include honesty, fairness, diligence, and care and respect for others. Ethical conduct follows those principles and balances self-interest with both the direct and the indirect consequences of that behavior for other people.

Not only does unethical behavior by individuals have serious personal consequences—ranging from job loss and reputational damage to fines and even jail—but unethical conduct from market participants, investment professionals, and those who service investors can damage investor trust and thereby impair the sustainability of the global capital markets as a whole. Unfortunately, there seems to be an unending parade of stories bringing to light accounting frauds and manipulations, Ponzi schemes, insider-trading scandals, and other misdeeds. Not surprisingly, this has led to erosion in public confidence in investment professionals. Empirical evidence from numerous surveys documents the low standing in the eyes of the investing public of banks and financial services firms—the very institutions that are entrusted with the economic well-being and retirement security of society.

Governments and regulators have historically tried to combat misconduct in the industry through regulatory reform, with various levels of success. Global capital markets are highly regulated to protect investors and other market participants. However, compliance with regulation alone is insufficient to fully earn investor trust. Individuals and firms must develop a "culture of integrity" that permeates all levels of operations and promotes the ethical principles of stewardship of investor assets and working in the best interests of clients, above and beyond strict compliance with the law. A strong ethical culture that helps honest, ethical people engage in ethical behavior will foster the trust of investors, lead to robust global capital markets, and ultimately benefit society. That is why ethics matters.

Ethics, Society, and the Capital Markets

CFA Institute recently added the concept "for the ultimate benefit of society" to its mission. The premise is that we want to live in a socially, politically, and financially stable society that fosters individual well-being and welfare of the public. A key ingredient for this goal is global capital markets that facilitate the efficient allocation of resources so that the available capital finds its way to places where it most benefits that society. These investments are then used to produce goods and services, to fund innovation and jobs, and to promote improvements in standards of living. Indeed, such a function serves the interests of the society. Efficient capital markets, in turn, provide a host of benefits to those providing the investment capital. Investors are provided the opportunity to transfer and transform risk because the capital markets serve as an information exchange, create investment products, provide liquidity, and limit transaction costs.

However, a well-functioning and efficient capital market system is dependent on trust of the participants. If investors believe that capital market participants—investment professionals and firms—cannot be trusted with their financial assets or that the capital markets are unfair such that only insiders can be successful, they will be unlikely to invest or, at the very least, will require a higher risk premium. Decreased investment capital can reduce innovation and job creation and hurt the economy and society as a whole. Reduced trust in capital markets can also result in a less vibrant, if not smaller, investment industry.

Ethics for a global investment industry should be universal and ultimately support trust and integrity above acceptable local or regional customs and culture. Universal ethics for a global industry strongly supports the efficiency, values, and mission of the industry as a whole. Different countries may be at different stages of development in establishing standards of practice, but the end goal must be to achieve rules, regulations, and standards that support and promote fundamental ethical principles on a global basis.

Capital Market Sustainability and the Actions of One

Individuals and firms also have to look at the indirect impacts of their actions on the broader investment community. The increasingly interconnected nature of global finance brings to the fore an added consideration of market sustainability that was, perhaps, less appreciated in years past. In addition to committing to the highest levels of ethical behavior, today's investment professionals and their employers should consider the long-term health of the market as a whole.

As recent events have demonstrated, apparently isolated and unrelated decisions, however innocuous when considered on an individual basis, in aggregate can precipitate a market crisis. In an interconnected global economy and marketplace, each participant should strive to be aware of how his or her actions or the products he or she distributes may have an impact on capital market participants in other regions or countries.

Investment professionals should consider how their investment decision-making processes affect the global financial markets in the broader context of how they apply their ethical and professional obligations. Those in positions of authority have a special responsibility to consider the broader context of market sustainability in their development and approval of corporate policies, particularly those involving risk management and product development. In addition, corporate compensation strategies should not encourage otherwise ethically sound individuals to engage in unethical or questionable conduct for financial gain. Ethics, sustainability, and properly functioning capital markets are components of the same concept of protecting the best interests of all. To always place the interests of clients ahead of both investment professionals' own interests and those of their employer remains a key ethos.

The Relationship between Ethics and Regulations

Some equate ethical behavior with legal behavior: If you are following the law, you must be acting appropriately. Ethical principles, like laws and regulations, prescribe appropriate constraints on our natural tendency to pursue self-interest that could harm the interests of others. Laws and regulations often attempt to guide people toward ethical behavior, but they do not cover all unethical behavior. Ethical behavior is often distinguished from legal conduct by describing legal behavior as what is required and ethical behavior as conduct that is morally correct. Ethical principles go beyond that which is legally sufficient and encompass what is the right thing to do.

Given many regulators' lack of sufficient resources to enforce well-conceived rules and regulations, relying on a regulatory framework to lead the charge in establishing ethical behavior has its challenges. Therefore, reliance on compliance with laws and regulation alone is insufficient to ensure ethical behavior of investment professionals or to create a truly ethical culture in the industry.

The recent past has shown us that some individuals will succeed at circumventing the regulatory rules for their personal gain. Only the application of strong ethical principles, at both the individual level and the firm level, will limit abuses. Knowing the rules or regulations to apply in a particular situation, although important, may not be sufficient to ensure ethical conduct. Individuals must be able both to recognize areas that are prone to ethical pitfalls and to identify and process those circumstances and influences that can impair ethical judgment.

Applying an Ethical Framework

Laws, regulations, professional standards, and codes of ethics can guide ethical behavior, but individual judgment is a critical ingredient in making principled choices and engaging in appropriate conduct. When faced with an ethical dilemma, individuals must have a well-developed set of principles; otherwise, their thought processes can lead to, at best, equivocation and indecision and, at worst, fraudulent conduct and destruction of the public trust. Establishing an ethical framework for an internal thought process prior to deciding to act is a crucial step in engaging in ethical conduct.

Most investment professionals are used to making decisions from a business (profit/loss) outlook. But given the importance of ethical behavior in carrying out professional responsibilities, it is critical to also analyze decisions and potential conduct from an ethical perspective. Utilizing a framework for ethical decision making will help investment professionals effectively examine their conduct in the context of conflicting interests common to their professional obligations (e.g., researching and gathering information, developing investment recommendations, and managing money for others). Such a framework will allow investment professionals to analyze their conduct in a way that meets high standards of ethical behavior.

An ethical decision-making framework can come in many forms but should provide investment professionals with a tool for following the principles of the firm's code of ethics. Through analyzing the particular circumstances of each decision, investment professionals are able to determine the best course of action to fulfill their responsibilities in an ethical manner.

Commitment to Ethics by Firms

A firm's code of ethics risks becoming a largely ignored, dusty compilation if it is not truly integrated into the fabric of the business. The ability to relate an ethical decision-making framework to a firm's code of ethics allows investment professionals to bring the aspirations and principles of the code of ethics to life—transforming it from a compliance exercise to something that is at the heart of a firm's culture.

An investment professional's natural desire to "do the right thing" must be reinforced by building a culture of integrity in the workplace. Development, maintenance, and demonstration of a strong culture of integrity within the firm by senior management may be the single most important factor in promoting ethical behavior among the firm's employees. Adopting a code that clearly lays out the ethical principles that guide the thought processes and conduct the firm expects from its employees is a critical first step. But a code of ethics, while necessary, is insufficient.

Simply nurturing an inclination to do right is no match for the multitude of daily decisions that investment managers make. We need to exercise ethical decision-making skills to develop the muscle memory necessary for fundamentally ethical people to make good decisions despite the reality of agent conflicts. Just as coaching and practice transform our natural ability to run across a field into the technique and endurance required to run a race, teaching, reinforcing, and practicing ethical decision-making skills prepare us to confront the hard issues effectively. It is good for business, individuals, firms, the industry, and the markets, as well as society as a whole, to engage in the investment management profession in a highly ethical manner.

Ethical Commitment of CFA Institute

An important goal of CFA Institute is to ensure that the organization and its members and candidates develop, promote, and follow the highest ethical standards in the investment industry. The CFA Institute Code of Ethics (Code) and Standards of Professional Conduct (Standards) are the foundation supporting the organization's quest to uphold the industry's highest standards of individual and corporate practice and to help serve the greater good. The Code is a set of principles that define the overarching conduct CFA Institute expects from its members and CFA Program candidates. The Code works in tandem with the Standards, which outline professional conduct that constitutes fair and ethical business practices.

For more than 50 years, CFA Institute members and candidates have been required to abide by the organization's Code and Standards. Periodically, CFA Institute has revised and updated its Code and Standards to ensure that they remain relevant to the changing nature of the investment profession and representative of the highest standard of professional conduct. Within this *Handbook*, CFA Institute addresses ethical principles for the profession, including individual professionalism; responsibilities to capital markets, clients, and employers; ethics involved in investment analysis, recommendations, and actions; and possible conflicts of interest. Although the investment world has become a far more complex place since the first publication of the *Standard of Practice Handbook*, distinguishing right from wrong remains the paramount principle of the Code and Standards.

New challenges will continually arise for members and candidates in applying the Code and Standards because many decisions are not unambiguously right or wrong. The dilemma exists because the choice between right and wrong is not always clear. Even well-intentioned investment professionals can find themselves in circumstances that may tempt them to cut corners. Situational influences can overpower the best of intentions.

CFA Institute has made a significant commitment to providing members and candidates with the resources to extend and deepen their understanding of how to appropriately apply the principles of the Code and Standards. The product offerings from CFA Institute offer a wealth of material. Through publications, conferences, webcasts, and podcasts, the ethical challenges of investment professionals are brought to light. Archived issues of these items are available on the CFA Institute website (www.cfainstitute.org).

By reviewing these resources and discussing with their peers, market participants can further enhance their abilities to apply an effective ethical decision-making framework. In time, this should help restore some of the trust recently lost by investors.

Markets function to an important extent on trust. Recent events have shown the fragility of this foundation and the devastating consequences that can ensue when it is fundamentally questioned. Investment professionals should remain mindful of the long-term health of financial markets and incorporate this concern for the market's sustainability in their investment decision making. CFA Institute and the Standards of Practice Council hope this edition of the *Handbook* will assist and guide investment professionals in meeting the ethical demands of the highly interconnected global capital markets for the ultimate benefit of society.

CFA INSTITUTE CODE OF ETHICS AND STANDARDS OF PROFESSIONAL CONDUCT

Preamble

The CFA Institute Code of Ethics and Standards of Professional Conduct are fundamental to the values of CFA Institute and essential to achieving its mission to lead the investment profession globally by promoting the highest standards of ethics, education, and professional excellence for the ultimate benefit of society. High ethical standards are critical to maintaining the public's trust in financial markets and in the investment profession. Since their creation in the 1960s, the Code and Standards have promoted the integrity of CFA Institute members and served as a model for measuring the ethics of investment professionals globally, regardless of job function, cultural differences, or local laws and regulations. All CFA Institute members (including holders of the Chartered Financial Analyst [CFA] designation) and CFA candidates have the personal responsibility to embrace and uphold the provisions of the Code and Standards and are encouraged to notify their employer of this responsibility. Violations may result in disciplinary sanctions by CFA Institute. Sanctions can include revocation of membership, revocation of candidacy in the CFA Program, and revocation of the right to use the CFA designation.

The Code of Ethics

Members of CFA Institute (including CFA charterholders) and candidates for the CFA designation ("Members and Candidates") must:

- Act with integrity, competence, diligence, and respect and in an ethical manner with the public, clients, prospective clients, employers, employees, colleagues in the investment profession, and other participants in the global capital markets.
- Place the integrity of the investment profession and the interests of clients above their own personal interests.
- Use reasonable care and exercise independent professional judgment when conducting investment analysis, making investment recommendations, taking investment actions, and engaging in other professional activities.
- Practice and encourage others to practice in a professional and ethical manner that will reflect credit on themselves and the profession.
- Promote the integrity and viability of the global capital markets for the ultimate benefit of society.
- Maintain and improve their professional competence and strive to maintain and improve the competence of other investment professionals.

Standards of Professional Conduct

I. PROFESSIONALISM

A Knowledge of the Law

Members and Candidates must understand and comply with all applicable laws, rules, and regulations (including the CFA Institute Code of Ethics and Standards of Professional Conduct) of any government, regulatory organization, licensing agency, or professional association governing their professional activities. In the event of conflict, Members and Candidates must comply with the more strict law, rule, or regulation. Members and Candidates must not knowingly participate or assist in and must dissociate from any violation of such laws, rules, or regulations.

B Independence and Objectivity

Members and Candidates must use reasonable care and judgment to achieve and maintain independence and objectivity in their professional activities. Members and Candidates must not offer, solicit, or accept any gift, benefit, compensation, or consideration that reasonably could be expected to compromise their own or another's independence and objectivity.

C Misrepresentation

Members and Candidates must not knowingly make any misrepresentations relating to investment analysis, recommendations, actions, or other professional activities.

D Misconduct

Members and Candidates must not engage in any professional conduct involving dishonesty, fraud, or deceit or commit any act that reflects adversely on their professional reputation, integrity, or competence.

II. INTEGRITY OF CAPITAL MARKETS

A Material Nonpublic Information

Members and Candidates who possess material nonpublic information that could affect the value of an investment must not act or cause others to act on the information.

B Market Manipulation

Members and Candidates must not engage in practices that distort prices or artificially inflate trading volume with the intent to mislead market participants.

III. DUTIES TO CLIENTS

A Loyalty, Prudence, and Care

Members and Candidates have a duty of loyalty to their clients and must act with reasonable care and exercise prudent judgment. Members and Candidates must act for the benefit of their clients and place their clients' interests before their employer's or their own interests.

B Fair Dealing

Members and Candidates must deal fairly and objectively with all clients when providing investment analysis, making investment recommendations, taking investment action, or engaging in other professional activities.

C Suitability

1 When Members and Candidates are in an advisory relationship with a client, they must:

a Make a reasonable inquiry into a client's or prospective client's investment experience, risk and return objectives, and financial constraints prior to making any investment recommendation or taking investment action and must reassess and update this information regularly.

b Determine that an investment is suitable to the client's financial situation and consistent with the client's written objectives, mandates, and constraints before making an investment recommendation or taking investment action.

c Judge the suitability of investments in the context of the client's total portfolio.

2 When Members and Candidates are responsible for managing a portfolio to a specific mandate, strategy, or style, they must make only investment recommendations or take only investment actions that are consistent with the stated objectives and constraints of the portfolio.

D Performance Presentation

When communicating investment performance information, Members and Candidates must make reasonable efforts to ensure that it is fair, accurate, and complete.

E Preservation of Confidentiality

Members and Candidates must keep information about current, former, and prospective clients confidential unless:

1 The information concerns illegal activities on the part of the client or prospective client,

2 Disclosure is required by law, or

3 The client or prospective client permits disclosure of the information.

IV. DUTIES TO EMPLOYERS

A Loyalty

In matters related to their employment, Members and Candidates must act for the benefit of their employer and not deprive their employer of the advantage of their skills and abilities, divulge confidential information, or otherwise cause harm to their employer.

B Additional Compensation Arrangements

Members and Candidates must not accept gifts, benefits, compensation, or consideration that competes with or might reasonably be expected to create a conflict of interest with their employer's interest unless they obtain written consent from all parties involved.

C Responsibilities of Supervisors

Members and Candidates must make reasonable efforts to ensure that anyone subject to their supervision or authority complies with applicable laws, rules, regulations, and the Code and Standards.

V. INVESTMENT ANALYSIS, RECOMMENDATIONS, AND ACTIONS

A Diligence and Reasonable Basis

Members and Candidates must:

1. Exercise diligence, independence, and thoroughness in analyzing investments, making investment recommendations, and taking investment actions.
2. Have a reasonable and adequate basis, supported by appropriate research and investigation, for any investment analysis, recommendation, or action.

B Communication with Clients and Prospective Clients

Members and Candidates must:

1. Disclose to clients and prospective clients the basic format and general principles of the investment processes they use to analyze investments, select securities, and construct portfolios and must promptly disclose any changes that might materially affect those processes.
2. Disclose to clients and prospective clients significant limitations and risks associated with the investment process.
3. Use reasonable judgment in identifying which factors are important to their investment analyses, recommendations, or actions and include those factors in communications with clients and prospective clients.
4. Distinguish between fact and opinion in the presentation of investment analysis and recommendations.

C Record Retention

Members and Candidates must develop and maintain appropriate records to support their investment analyses, recommendations, actions, and other investment-related communications with clients and prospective clients.

VI. CONFLICTS OF INTEREST

A Disclosure of Conflicts

Members and Candidates must make full and fair disclosure of all matters that could reasonably be expected to impair their independence and objectivity or interfere with respective duties to their clients, prospective clients, and employer. Members and Candidates must ensure that such disclosures are prominent, are delivered in plain language, and communicate the relevant information effectively.

B Priority of Transactions

Investment transactions for clients and employers must have priority over investment transactions in which a Member or Candidate is the beneficial owner.

C Referral Fees

Members and Candidates must disclose to their employer, clients, and prospective clients, as appropriate, any compensation, consideration, or benefit received from or paid to others for the recommendation of products or services.

VII. RESPONSIBILITIES AS A CFA INSTITUTE MEMBER OR CFA CANDIDATE

A Conduct as Participants in CFA Institute Programs

Members and Candidates must not engage in any conduct that compromises the reputation or integrity of CFA Institute or the CFA designation or the integrity, validity, or security of CFA Institute programs.

B Reference to CFA Institute, the CFA Designation, and the CFA Program

When referring to CFA Institute, CFA Institute membership, the CFA designation, or candidacy in the CFA Program, Members and Candidates must not misrepresent or exaggerate the meaning or implications of membership in CFA Institute, holding the CFA designation, or candidacy in the CFA Program.

PRACTICE PROBLEMS

1 The Standards of Practice Handbook provides guidance:

A regarding the penalties incurred as a result of ethical violations.

B to which all CFA Institute members and candidates must adhere.

C through explanatory material and examples intended to be all inclusive.

2 Which of the following statements *best* describes an aspect of the Professional Conduct Program process?

A Inquiries are not initiated in response to information provided by the media.

B Investigations result in Disciplinary Review Committee panels for each case.

C Investigations may include requesting a written explanation from the member or candidate.

3 A current Code of Ethics principle reads in full, "Promote the integrity:

A and viability of the global capital markets."

B of and uphold the rules governing capital markets."

C and viability of the global capital markets for the ultimate benefit of society."

4 As stated in the revised 11th edition, the Standards of Professional Conduct:

A require supervisors to focus on the detection and prevention of violations.

B adopt separate ethical considerations for programs such as CIPM and Investment Foundations.

C address the risks and limitations of recommendations being made to clients.

5 According to the Code of Ethics, members of CFA Institute and candidates for the CFA designation must:

A maintain their professional competence to exercise independent professional judgment.

B place the integrity of the investment profession and the interests of clients above their own personal interests.

C practice in a professional and ethical manner with the public, clients, and others in the global capital markets.

6 Which of the following statements *best* describes an aspect of the Standards of Professional Conduct? Members and candidates are required to:

A ensure any portfolio mandate followed is fair, accurate, and complete.

B promptly disclose changes that might materially affect investment processes.

C have a reasonable and adequate basis for decisions about client confidentiality.

7 Which of the following categories completely represents an ethical principle of CFA Institute as outlined in the *Standards of Practice Handbook*?

A Individual professionalism

B Responsibilities to clients and employers

C Ethics involved in investment analysis and recommendations

8 A CFA Institute member would violate the standard for material nonpublic information by:

A conducting price distortion practices.

B inappropriately causing others to act.

C inadequately maintaining investment records.

9 According to the Duties to Clients standard, suitability requires members and candidates in an advisory relationship with a client to:

A place their clients' interests before their own interests.

B consider investments in the context of the client's total portfolio.

C not knowingly make misrepresentations relating to recommendations.

10 As part of the Duties to Clients standard, members and candidates must:

A document client financial constraints after an initial investment action.

B maintain an equal balance of interests owed to their clients and employers.

C deal fairly and objectively with all clients when engaging in professional activities.

11 The Duties to Employers standard states that members and candidates must not:

A accept any gifts that might compromise their independence and objectivity.

B deprive their employer of their skills and abilities as related to their employment.

C accept compensation competing with their employer's interest and with the written consent of all parties involved.

12 The Investment Analysis, Recommendations, and Actions standard states that members and candidates must:

A find an investment suitable for their client before making a recommendation.

B make reasonable efforts to ensure that performance presentation is fair, accurate, and complete.

C distinguish between fact and opinion in the presentation of investment analysis and recommendations.

13 Based on the Conflicts of Interest standard, members and candidates must:

A disclose, as required by law, those conflicts interfering with their professional duties.

B disclose, as appropriate, any benefit paid to others for the recommendation of products.

C seek employer approval before prioritizing their investment transactions over those clients.

14 The Responsibilities as a CFA Institute Member or CFA Candidate Standard explicitly states a requirement regarding:

A loyalty.

B responsibility of supervisors.

C reference to the CFA Program.

SOLUTIONS

1 B is correct. The *Standards of Practice Handbook* provides guidance to which CFA Institute members and candidates are required to adhere.

A is incorrect because the *Handbook* provides guidance in understanding the interconnectedness of the aspirational and practical principles (not regarding penalties for violations) of the Code of Ethics and Standards of Conduct.

C is incorrect because although the *Standards of Practice Handbook* provides hypothetical but factual situations, the explanatory material and examples are not intended to be all inclusive.

2 C is correct. When an inquiry is initiated, the Professional Conduct staff conducts an investigation that may include requesting a written explanation from the member or candidate.

A is incorrect because Professional Conduct inquiries can be initiated in response to information provided by the media. CFA Institute staff may become aware of questionable conduct by a member or candidate through the media, regulatory notices, or another public source.

B is incorrect because although the Disciplinary Review Committee (DRC) is responsible for enforcement of the Code and Standards in conjunction with the Professional Conduct Program (PCP), only in the event that a member or candidate does not accept the charges and proposed sanction is the matter referred to a panel composed of DRC members.

3 C is correct. One of the principles in the Code of Ethics was updated to reflect the role that the capital markets have in society as a whole.

A is incorrect because it is incomplete, missing the additional language to reflect the role that the capital markets have in society as a whole.

B is incorrect because this is the old principle as written in the Code of Ethics, which was recently updated to reflect the role of the capital markets in society as a whole.

4 C is correct. Given the constant development of new and exotic financial instruments and strategies, the standard regarding communicating with clients now includes an implicit requirement to discuss the risks and limitations of recommendations being made to clients.

A is incorrect because the updated standard for members and candidates with supervision or authority over others within their firms stresses broader compliance expectations, which include the detection and prevention aspects of the original version that was the prior focus.

B is incorrect because the updated standard not only maintains the integrity of the CFA Program but also expands the same (not separate) ethical considerations when members or candidates participate in such programs as the CIPM Program and the Investment Foundations Certificate.

5 B is correct. Members of CFA Institute and candidates for the CFA designation must place the integrity of the investment profession and the interests of clients above their own personal interests.

A is incorrect because members of CFA Institute and candidates for the CFA designation must maintain and improve their professional competence and strive to maintain and improve the competence of other investment professionals. The exercise of independent professional judgment is associated with using reasonable care.

C is incorrect because members of CFA Institute and candidates for the CFA designation must practice and encourage others to practice in a professional and ethical manner that will reflect credibly on themselves and the profession. Members are supposed to act with integrity, competence, diligence, and respect and in an ethical manner with the public, clients, and other market participants.

6 B is correct. The current Standards of Professional Conduct requires members and candidates to promptly disclose any changes that might materially affect investment processes.

A is incorrect because under Standard III.C.2 Suitability, when members and candidates are responsible for managing a portfolio according to a specific mandate, they must take only investment actions that are consistent with the stated objectives of the portfolio. The "fair, accurate, and complete" criterion relates to the Standard III D Performance Presentation.

C is incorrect because under Standard III.E.1, 2, 3 Preservation of Confidentiality, members and candidates must keep information about current clients confidential unless the information concerns illegal activities on the part of the client, disclosure is required by law, or the client permits disclosure. No decisions on confidentiality are required, with the "reasonable and adequate basis" criterion related to Standard V.A.2 Diligence and Reasonable Basis.

7 A is correct. Within the *Standards of Practice Handbook*, CFA Institute addresses ethical principles for the profession, including individual professionalism; responsibilities to capital markets, clients, and employers; ethics involved in investment analysis; recommendations, and actions; and possible conflicts of interest.

B is incorrect because it does not include responsibilities to capital markets.

C is incorrect because the ethical principles not only address ethics involved in investment analysis and recommendations but also address actions.

8 B is correct. Under Standard II.A Material Nonpublic Information, members having material nonpublic information that could affect the value of an investment must not cause others to act on the information.

A is incorrect because price distortion is mentioned in the Standard II.B Market Manipulation, not Standard II.A Material Nonpublic Information.

C is incorrect because the maintenance of appropriate records to support investment analyses is noted in Standard V.C Record Retention, not Standard II.A Material Nonpublic Information.

9 B is correct. Standard III.C.1c Suitability states that when members and candidates are in an advisory relationship with a client, they must judge the suitability of investments in the context of the client's total portfolio.

A is incorrect because this is a requirement addressed under Standard III.A Loyalty, Prudence, and Care, not Standard III.C.1c Suitability.

C is incorrect because this is a requirement addressed under Standard I.C Misrepresentation, not Standard III.C.1c Suitability.

10 C is correct. Under the III.B Fair Dealing section of the Duty to Clients standard, members and candidates must deal fairly and objectively with all clients when providing investment analysis, making investment recommendations, taking investment action, or engaging in other professional activities.

A is incorrect because under Standard III.C.1a Suitability, a section of Duties to Clients, members and candidates in an advisory relationship must make a reasonable inquiry into a client's financial constraints prior to (not after) taking investment action and must reassess and update this regularly.

B is incorrect because under Standard III.A Loyalty, Prudence, and Care, members and candidates must act for the benefit of their clients and place their clients' interests before (not maintain an equal balance with) their employer's or their own interests.

11 B is correct. The IV.A Loyalty section of the Duties to Employers standard states that members and candidates cannot deprive their employer of the advantage of their skills and abilities in matters related to their employment.

A is incorrect because accepting gifts that might compromise a member or candidate's independence and objectivity is addressed by Standard I.B Independence and Objectivity, a section of Professionalism, not under Standard IV Duties to Employers.

C is incorrect because IV.B Additional Compensation Arrangements, part of the Duties to Employers standard, permits members and candidates to accept compensation that competes with their employer's interest if they obtain written consent from all parties involved.

12 C is correct. The V.B.4 Communications with Clients and Prospective Clients section of the Investment Analysis, Recommendations, and Actions standard states that members and candidates must distinguish between fact and opinion in the presentation of investment analysis and recommendations.

A is incorrect because this standard is discussed in the III.C.1b Suitability section of the Duties to Clients standard.

B is incorrect because performance presentation is discussed in the III.D Performance Presentation section of the Duties to Clients standard.

13 B is correct. The VI.C Referral Fees section of the Conflicts of Interest standard requires members and candidates to disclose to their employer, clients, and prospective clients, as appropriate, any compensation, consideration, or benefit received from or paid to others for the recommendation of products or services.

A is incorrect because the VI.A Disclosure of Conflicts section of the Conflicts of Interest standard requires members and candidates to make full and fair disclosure of all matters (not limited to legal requirements) that could reasonably be expected to impair their independence and objectivity or interfere with respective duties to their clients, prospective clients, and employer.

C is incorrect because the VI.B Priority of Transactions section of the Conflicts of Interest standard requires members and candidates to give priority to investment transactions for clients and employers versus those in which a member or candidate is the beneficial owner. This requirement is not waived by an employer's approval.

14 C is correct. The VII.B Reference to CFA Institute, the CFA Designation, and the CFA Program section of the Responsibilities as a CFA Institute Member or CFA Candidate standard explicitly states the appropriate manner to make reference to CFA Institute, CFA Institute membership, the CFA designation, or candidacy in the CFA Program.

A is incorrect because Standard VII Responsibilities as a CFA Institute Member or CFA Candidate standard does not refer to loyalty. Loyalty is addressed in two other standards, Standard III.A Loyalty, Prudence, and Care and Standard IV.A Loyalty.

B is incorrect because Standard VII Responsibilities as a CFA Institute Member or CFA Candidate standard does not refer to the responsibility of supervisors. The responsibility of supervisors is addressed in Standard IV.C Responsibility of Supervisors.

READING

3

Guidance for Standards I–VII

LEARNING OUTCOMES

Mastery	*The candidate should be able to:*
☐	**a.** demonstrate the application of the Code of Ethics and Standards of Professional Conduct to situations involving issues of professional integrity;
☐	**b.** distinguish between conduct that conforms to the Code and Standards and conduct that violates the Code and Standards;
☐	**c.** recommend practices and procedures designed to prevent violations of the Code of Ethics and Standards of Professional Conduct.

STANDARD I: PROFESSIONALISM

Standard I(A) Knowledge of the Law

Members and Candidates must understand and comply with all applicable laws, rules, and regulations (including the CFA Institute Code of Ethics and Standards of Professional Conduct) of any government, regulatory organization, licensing agency, or professional association governing their professional activities. In the event of conflict, Members and Candidates must comply with the more strict law, rule, or regulation. Members and Candidates must not knowingly participate or assist in and must dissociate from any violation of such laws, rules, or regulations.

Guidance

Highlights:

- *Relationship between the Code and Standards and Applicable Law*

This reading is a verbatim reprint of *Standards of Practice Handbook*, Eleventh Edition, updated March 2018, p. 13 to 174 included (www.cfainstitute.org/en/ethics/codes/standards-practice-handbook).

- *Participation in or Association with Violations by Others*
- *Investment Products and Applicable Laws*

Members and candidates must understand the applicable laws and regulations of the countries and jurisdictions where they engage in professional activities. These activities may include, but are not limited to, trading of securities or other financial instruments, providing investment advice, conducting research, or performing other investment services. On the basis of their reasonable and good faith understanding, members and candidates must comply with the laws and regulations that directly govern their professional activities and resulting outcomes and that protect the interests of the clients.

When questions arise, members and candidates should know their firm's policies and procedures for accessing compliance guidance. This standard does not require members and candidates to become experts, however, in compliance. Additionally, members and candidates are not required to have detailed knowledge of or be experts on all the laws that could potentially govern their activities.

During times of changing regulations, members and candidates must remain vigilant in maintaining their knowledge of the requirements for their professional activities. New financial products and processes, along with uncovered ethical missteps, create an environment for recurring and potentially wide-ranging regulatory changes. Members and candidates are also continually provided improved and enhanced methods of communicating with both clients and potential clients, such as mobile applications and web-based social networking platforms. As new local, regional, and global requirements are updated to address these and other changes, members, candidates, and their firms must adjust their procedures and practices to remain in compliance.

Relationship between the Code and Standards and Applicable Law

Some members or candidates may live, work, or provide investment services to clients living in a country that has no law or regulation governing a particular action or that has laws or regulations that differ from the requirements of the Code and Standards. When applicable law and the Code and Standards require different conduct, members and candidates must follow the more strict of the applicable law or the Code and Standards.

"Applicable law" is the law that governs the member's or candidate's conduct. Which law applies will depend on the particular facts and circumstances of each case. The "more strict" law or regulation is the law or regulation that imposes greater restrictions on the action of the member or candidate or calls for the member or candidate to exert a greater degree of action that protects the interests of investors. For example, applicable law or regulation may not require members and candidates to disclose referral fees received from or paid to others for the recommendation of investment products or services. Because the Code and Standards impose this obligation, however, members and candidates must disclose the existence of such fees.

Members and candidates must adhere to the following principles:

- Members and candidates must comply with applicable laws or regulations related to their professional activities.
- Members and candidates must not engage in conduct that constitutes a violation of the Code and Standards, even though it may otherwise be legal.
- In the absence of any applicable law or regulation or when the Code and Standards impose a higher degree of responsibility than applicable laws and regulations, members and candidates must adhere to the Code and Standards. Applications of these principles are outlined in Exhibit 1.

The applicable laws governing the responsibilities of a member or candidate should be viewed as the minimal threshold of acceptable actions. When members and candidates take actions that exceed the minimal requirements, they further support the conduct required of Standard I(A).

CFA Institute members are obligated to abide by the CFA Institute Articles of Incorporation, Bylaws, Code of Ethics, Standards of Professional Conduct, Rules of Procedure, Membership Agreement, and other applicable rules promulgated by CFA Institute, all as amended periodically. CFA candidates who are not members must also abide by these documents (except for the Membership Agreement) as well as rules and regulations related to the administration of the CFA examination, the Candidate Responsibility Statement, and the Candidate Pledge.

Participation in or Association with Violations by Others

Members and candidates are responsible for violations in which they *knowingly* participate or assist. Although members and candidates are presumed to have knowledge of all applicable laws, rules, and regulations, CFA Institute acknowledges that members may not recognize violations if they are not aware of all the facts giving rise to the violations. Standard I(A) applies when members and candidates know or should know that their conduct may contribute to a violation of applicable laws, rules, or regulations or the Code and Standards.

If a member or candidate has reasonable grounds to believe that imminent or ongoing client or employer activities are illegal or unethical, the member or candidate must dissociate, or separate, from the activity. In extreme cases, dissociation may require a member or candidate to leave his or her employment. Members and candidates may take the following intermediate steps to dissociate from ethical violations of others when direct discussions with the person or persons committing the violation are unsuccessful. The first step should be to attempt to stop the behavior by bringing it to the attention of the employer through a supervisor or the firm's compliance department. If this attempt is unsuccessful, then members and candidates have a responsibility to step away and dissociate from the activity. Dissociation practices will differ on the basis of the member's or candidate's role in the investment industry. It may include removing one's name from written reports or recommendations, asking for a different assignment, or refusing to accept a new client or continue to advise a current client. Inaction combined with continuing association with those involved in illegal or unethical conduct may be construed as participation or assistance in the illegal or unethical conduct.

CFA Institute strongly encourages members and candidates to report potential violations of the Code and Standards committed by fellow members and candidates. Although a failure to report is less likely to be construed as a violation than a failure to dissociate from unethical conduct, the impact of inactivity on the integrity of capital markets can be significant. Although the Code and Standards do not compel members and candidates to report violations to their governmental or regulatory organizations unless such disclosure is mandatory under applicable law (voluntary reporting is often referred to as whistleblowing), such disclosure may be prudent under certain circumstances. Members and candidates should consult their legal and compliance advisers for guidance.

Additionally, CFA Institute encourages members, nonmembers, clients, and the investing public to report violations of the Code and Standards by CFA Institute members or CFA candidates by submitting a complaint in writing to the CFA Institute Professional Conduct Program via e-mail (pcprogram@cfainstitute.org) or the CFA Institute website (www.cfainstitute.org).

Investment Products and Applicable Laws

Members and candidates involved in creating or maintaining investment services or investment products or packages of securities and/or derivatives should be mindful of where these products or packages will be sold as well as their places of origination. The applicable laws and regulations of the countries or regions of origination and expected sale should be understood by those responsible for the supervision of the services or creation and maintenance of the products or packages. Members or candidates should make reasonable efforts to review whether associated firms that are distributing products or services developed by their employing firm also abide by the laws and regulations of the countries and regions of distribution. Members and candidates should undertake the necessary due diligence when transacting cross-border business to understand the multiple applicable laws and regulations in order to protect the reputation of their firm and themselves.

Given the complexity that can arise with business transactions in today's market, there may be some uncertainty surrounding which laws or regulations are considered applicable when activities are being conducted in multiple jurisdictions. Members and candidates should seek the appropriate guidance, potentially including the firm's compliance or legal departments and legal counsel outside the organization, to gain a reasonable understanding of their responsibilities and how to implement them appropriately.

Exhibit 1 Global Application of the Code and Standards

Members and candidates who practice in multiple jurisdictions may be subject to varied securities laws and regulations. If applicable law is stricter than the requirements of the Code and Standards, members and candidates must adhere to applicable law; otherwise, they must adhere to the Code and Standards. The following chart provides illustrations involving a member who may be subject to the securities laws and regulations of three different types of countries:

NS: country with no securities laws or regulations

LS: country with ***less*** strict securities laws and regulations than the Code and Standards

MS: country with ***more*** strict securities laws and regulations than the Code and Standards

Applicable Law	Duties	Explanation
Member resides in NS country, does business in LS country; LS law applies.	Member must adhere to the Code and Standards.	Because applicable law is less strict than the Code and Standards, the member must adhere to the Code and Standards.
Member resides in NS country, does business in MS country; MS law applies.	Member must adhere to the law of MS country.	Because applicable law is stricter than the Code and Standards, member must adhere to the more strict applicable law.
Member resides in LS country, does business in NS country; LS law applies.	Member must adhere to the Code and Standards.	Because applicable law is less strict than the Code and Standards, member must adhere to the Code and Standards.

Exhibit 1 (Continued)

Applicable Law	Duties	Explanation
Member resides in LS country, does business in MS country; MS law applies.	Member must adhere to the law of MS country.	Because applicable law is stricter than the Code and Standards, member must adhere to the more strict applicable law.
Member resides in LS country, does business in NS country; LS law applies, but it states that law of locality where business is conducted governs.	Member must adhere to the Code and Standards.	Because applicable law states that the law of the locality where the business is conducted governs and there is no local law, the member must adhere to the Code and Standards.
Member resides in LS country, does business in MS country; LS law applies, but it states that law of locality where business is conducted governs.	Member must adhere to the law of MS country.	Because applicable law of the locality where the business is conducted governs and local law is stricter than the Code and Standards, member must adhere to the more strict applicable law.
Member resides in MS country, does business in LS country; MS law applies.	Member must adhere to the law of MS country.	Because applicable law is stricter than the Code and Standards, member must adhere to the more strict applicable law.
Member resides in MS country, does business in LS country; MS law applies, but it states that law of locality where business is conducted governs.	Member must adhere to the Code and Standards.	Because applicable law states that the law of the locality where the business is conducted governs and local law is less strict than the Code and Standards, member must adhere to the Code and Standards.
Member resides in MS country, does business in LS country with a client who is a citizen of LS country; MS law applies, but it states that the law of the client's home country governs.	Member must adhere to the Code and Standards.	Because applicable law states that the law of the client's home country governs (which is less strict than the Code and Standards), member must adhere to the Code and Standards.
Member resides in MS country, does business in LS country with a client who is a citizen of MS country; MS law applies, but it states that the law of the client's home country governs.	Member must adhere to the law of MS country.	Because applicable law states that the law of the client's home country governs and the law of the client's home country is stricter than the Code and Standards, the member must adhere to the more strict applicable law.

Recommended Procedures for Compliance

Members and Candidates

Suggested methods by which members and candidates can acquire and maintain understanding of applicable laws, rules, and regulations include the following:

- *Stay informed*: Members and candidates should establish or encourage their employers to establish a procedure by which employees are regularly informed about changes in applicable laws, rules, regulations, and case law. In many instances, the employer's compliance department or legal counsel can provide such information in the form of memorandums distributed to employees in the organization. Also, participation in an internal or external continuing education program is a practical method of staying current.
- *Review procedures*: Members and candidates should review, or encourage their employers to review, the firm's written compliance procedures on a regular basis to ensure that the procedures reflect current law and provide adequate guidance to employees about what is permissible conduct under the law and/or the Code and Standards. Recommended compliance procedures for specific items of the Code and Standards are discussed in this *Handbook* in the "Guidance" sections associated with each standard.
- *Maintain current files*: Members and candidates should maintain or encourage their employers to maintain readily accessible current reference copies of applicable statutes, rules, regulations, and important cases.

Distribution Area Laws

Members and candidates should make reasonable efforts to understand the applicable laws—both country and regional—for the countries and regions where their investment products are developed and are most likely to be distributed to clients.

Legal Counsel

When in doubt about the appropriate action to undertake, it is recommended that a member or candidate seek the advice of compliance personnel or legal counsel concerning legal requirements. If a potential violation is being committed by a fellow employee, it may also be prudent for the member or candidate to seek the advice of the firm's compliance department or legal counsel.

Dissociation

When dissociating from an activity that violates the Code and Standards, members and candidates should document the violation and urge their firms to attempt to persuade the perpetrator(s) to cease such conduct. To dissociate from the conduct, a member or candidate may have to resign his or her employment.

Firms

The formality and complexity of compliance procedures for firms depend on the nature and size of the organization and the nature of its investment operations. Members and candidates should encourage their firms to consider the following policies and procedures to support the principles of Standard I(A):

- *Develop and/or adopt a code of ethics*: The ethical culture of an organization starts at the top. Members and candidates should encourage their supervisors or managers to adopt a code of ethics. Adhering to a code of ethics facilitates solutions when people face ethical dilemmas and can prevent the need for employees to resort to a "whistleblowing" solution publicly alleging concealed misconduct. CFA Institute has published the *Asset Manager Code of Professional Conduct*, which firms may adopt or use as the basis for their codes (visit www.cfainstitute.org).

- *Provide information on applicable laws*: Pertinent information that highlights applicable laws and regulations might be distributed to employees or made available in a central location. Information sources might include primary information developed by the relevant government, governmental agencies, regulatory organizations, licensing agencies, and professional associations (e.g., from their websites); law firm memorandums or newsletters; and association memorandums or publications (e.g., *CFA Institute Magazine*).
- *Establish procedures for reporting violations*: Firms might provide written protocols for reporting suspected violations of laws, regulations, or company policies.

Application of the Standard

Example 1 (Notification of Known Violations):

Michael Allen works for a brokerage firm and is responsible for an underwriting of securities. A company official gives Allen information indicating that the financial statements Allen filed with the regulator overstate the issuer's earnings. Allen seeks the advice of the brokerage firm's general counsel, who states that it would be difficult for the regulator to prove that Allen has been involved in any wrongdoing.

> *Comment*: Although it is recommended that members and candidates seek the advice of legal counsel, the reliance on such advice does not absolve a member or candidate from the requirement to comply with the law or regulation. Allen should report this situation to his supervisor, seek an independent legal opinion, and determine whether the regulator should be notified of the error.

Example 2 (Dissociating from a Violation):

Lawrence Brown's employer, an investment banking firm, is the principal underwriter for an issue of convertible debentures by the Courtney Company. Brown discovers that the Courtney Company has concealed severe third-quarter losses in its foreign operations. The preliminary prospectus has already been distributed.

> *Comment*: Knowing that the preliminary prospectus is misleading, Brown should report his findings to the appropriate supervisory persons in his firm. If the matter is not remedied and Brown's employer does not dissociate from the underwriting, Brown should sever all his connections with the underwriting. Brown should also seek legal advice to determine whether additional reporting or other action should be taken.

Example 3 (Dissociating from a Violation):

Kamisha Washington's firm advertises its past performance record by showing the 10-year return of a composite of its client accounts. Washington discovers, however, that the composite omits the performance of accounts that have left the firm during the 10-year period, whereas the description of the composite indicates the inclusion of all firm accounts. This omission has led to an inflated performance figure. Washington is asked to use promotional material that includes the erroneous performance number when soliciting business for the firm.

> *Comment*: Misrepresenting performance is a violation of the Code and Standards. Although she did not calculate the performance herself, Washington would be assisting in violating Standard I(A) if she were to use the inflated performance number when soliciting clients. She must dissociate herself from the activity. If discussing the misleading number with the person responsible is not an option for correcting the problem, she can bring the situation to the attention of her supervisor or the compliance department at her firm. If her firm is unwilling to recalculate performance, she must refrain from using the misleading promotional material and should notify the firm of her reasons. If the firm insists that she use the material, she should consider whether her obligation to dissociate from the activity requires her to seek other employment.

Example 4 (Following the Highest Requirements):

James Collins is an investment analyst for a major Wall Street brokerage firm. He works in a developing country with a rapidly modernizing economy and a growing capital market. Local securities laws are minimal—in form and content—and include no punitive prohibitions against insider trading.

> *Comment*: Collins must abide by the requirements of the Code and Standards, which might be more strict than the rules of the developing country. He should be aware of the risks that a small market and the absence of a fairly regulated flow of information to the market represent to his ability to obtain information and make timely judgments. He should include this factor in formulating his advice to clients. In handling material nonpublic information that accidentally comes into his possession, he must follow Standard II(A)–Material Nonpublic Information.

Example 5 (Following the Highest Requirements):

Laura Jameson works for a multinational investment adviser based in the United States. Jameson lives and works as a registered investment adviser in the tiny, but wealthy, island nation of Karramba. Karramba's securities laws state that no investment adviser registered and working in that country can participate in initial public offerings (IPOs) for the adviser's personal account. Jameson, believing that, as a US citizen working for a US-based company, she should comply only with US law, has ignored this Karrambian law. In addition, Jameson believes that as a charterholder, as long as she adheres to the Code and Standards requirement that she disclose her participation in any IPO to her employer and clients when such ownership creates a conflict of interest, she is meeting the highest ethical requirements.

> *Comment*: Jameson is in violation of Standard I(A). As a registered investment adviser in Karramba, Jameson is prevented by Karrambian securities law from participating in IPOs regardless of the law of her home country. In addition, because the law of the country where she is working is stricter than the Code and Standards, she must follow the stricter requirements of the local law rather than the requirements of the Code and Standards.

Example 6 (Laws and Regulations Based on Religious Tenets):

Amanda Janney is employed as a fixed-income portfolio manager for a large international firm. She is on a team within her firm that is responsible for creating and managing a fixed-income hedge fund to be sold throughout the firm's distribution centers to high-net-worth clients. Her firm receives expressions of interest from potential clients from the Middle East who are seeking investments that comply with Islamic law. The marketing and promotional materials for the fixed-income hedge fund do not specify whether or not the fund is a suitable investment for an investor seeking compliance with Islamic law. Because the fund is being distributed globally, Janney is concerned about the reputation of the fund and the firm and believes disclosure of whether or not the fund complies with Islamic law could help minimize potential mistakes with placing this investment.

> *Comment*: As the financial market continues to become globalized, members and candidates will need to be aware of the differences between cultural and religious laws and requirements as well as the different governmental laws and regulations. Janney and the firm could be proactive in their efforts to acknowledge areas where the new fund may not be suitable for clients.

Example 7 (Reporting Potential Unethical Actions):

Krista Blume is a junior portfolio manager for high-net-worth portfolios at a large global investment manager. She observes a number of new portfolios and relationships coming from a country in Europe where the firm did not have previous business and is told that a broker in that country is responsible for this new business. At a meeting on allocation of research resources to third-party research firms, Blume notes that this broker has been added to the list and is allocated payments for research. However, she knows the portfolios do not invest in securities in the broker's country, and she has not seen any research come from this broker. Blume asks her supervisor about the name being on the list and is told that someone in marketing is receiving the research and that the name being on the list is OK. She believes that what may be going on is that the broker is being paid for new business through the inappropriate research payments, and she wishes to dissociate from the misconduct.

> *Comment*: Blume should follow the firm's policies and procedures for reporting potential unethical activity, which may include discussions with her supervisor or someone in a designated compliance department. She should communicate her concerns appropriately while advocating for disclosure between the new broker relationship and the research payments.

Example 8 (Failure to Maintain Knowledge of the Law):

Colleen White is excited to use new technology to communicate with clients and potential clients. She recently began posting investment information, including performance reports and investment opinions and recommendations, to her Facebook page. In addition, she sends out brief announcements, opinions, and thoughts via her Twitter account (for example, "Prospects for future growth of XYZ company look good! #makingmoney4U"). Prior to White's use of these social media platforms, the local regulator had issued new requirements and guidance governing online electronic communication. White's communications appear to conflict with the recent regulatory announcements.

> *Comment*: White is in violation of Standard I(A) because her communications do not comply with the existing guidance and regulation governing use of social media. White must be aware of the evolving legal requirements pertaining to new and dynamic areas of the financial services industry that are applicable to her. She should seek guidance from appropriate, knowledgeable, and reliable sources, such as her firm's compliance department, external service providers, or outside counsel, unless she diligently follows legal and regulatory trends affecting her professional responsibilities.

Standard I(B) Independence and Objectivity

Members and Candidates must use reasonable care and judgment to achieve and maintain independence and objectivity in their professional activities. Members and Candidates must not offer, solicit, or accept any gift, benefit, compensation, or consideration that reasonably could be expected to compromise their own or another's independence and objectivity.

Guidance

Highlights:

- *Buy-Side Clients*
- *Fund Manager and Custodial Relationships*
- *Investment Banking Relationships*
- *Performance Measurement and Attribution*
- *Public Companies*
- *Credit Rating Agency Opinions*
- *Influence during the Manager Selection/Procurement Process*
- *Issuer-Paid Research*
- *Travel Funding*

Standard I(B) states the responsibility of CFA Institute members and candidates in the CFA Program to maintain independence and objectivity so that their clients will have the benefit of their work and opinions unaffected by any potential conflict of interest or other circumstance adversely affecting their judgment. Every member and candidate should endeavor to avoid situations that could cause or be perceived to cause a loss of independence or objectivity in recommending investments or taking investment action.

External sources may try to influence the investment process by offering analysts and portfolio managers a variety of benefits. Corporations may seek expanded research coverage, issuers and underwriters may wish to promote new securities offerings, brokers may want to increase commission business, and independent rating agencies may be influenced by the company requesting the rating. Benefits may include gifts, invitations to lavish functions, tickets, favors, or job referrals. One type of benefit is the allocation of shares in oversubscribed IPOs to investment managers for their personal accounts. This practice affords managers the opportunity to make quick profits that may not be available to their clients. Such a practice is prohibited under Standard I(B). Modest gifts and entertainment are acceptable, but special care must be taken by members and candidates to resist subtle and not-so-subtle pressures to act in conflict with the interests of their clients. Best practice dictates that members and candidates reject any offer of gift or entertainment that could be expected to threaten their independence and objectivity.

Receiving a gift, benefit, or consideration from a *client* can be distinguished from gifts given by entities seeking to influence a member or candidate to the detriment of other clients. In a client relationship, the client has already entered some type of compensation arrangement with the member, candidate, or his or her firm. A gift from a client could be considered supplementary compensation. The potential for obtaining influence to the detriment of other clients, although present, is not as great as in situations where no compensation arrangement exists. When possible, prior to accepting "bonuses" or gifts from clients, members and candidates should disclose to their employers such benefits offered by clients. If notification is not possible prior to acceptance, members and candidates must disclose to their employer benefits previously accepted from clients. Disclosure allows the employer of a member or candidate to make an independent determination about the extent to which the gift may affect the member's or candidate's independence and objectivity.

Members and candidates may also come under pressure from their own firms to, for example, issue favorable research reports or recommendations for certain companies with potential or continuing business relationships with the firm. The situation may be aggravated if an executive of the company sits on the bank or investment firm's board and attempts to interfere in investment decision making. Members and candidates acting in a sales or marketing capacity must be especially mindful of their objectivity in promoting appropriate investments for their clients.

Left unmanaged, pressures that threaten independence place research analysts in a difficult position and may jeopardize their ability to act independently and objectively. One of the ways that research analysts have coped with these pressures in the past is to use subtle and ambiguous language in their recommendations or to temper the tone of their research reports. Such subtleties are lost on some investors, however, who reasonably expect research reports and recommendations to be straightforward and transparent and to communicate clearly an analyst's views based on unbiased analysis and independent judgment.

Members and candidates are personally responsible for maintaining independence and objectivity when preparing research reports, making investment recommendations, and taking investment action on behalf of clients. Recommendations must convey the member's or candidate's true opinions, free of bias from internal or external pressures, and be stated in clear and unambiguous language.

Members and candidates also should be aware that some of their professional or social activities within CFA Institute or its member societies may subtly threaten their independence or objectivity. When seeking corporate financial support for conventions, seminars, or even weekly society luncheons, the members or candidates responsible for the activities should evaluate both the actual effect of such solicitations on their independence and whether their objectivity might be perceived to be compromised in the eyes of their clients.

Buy-Side Clients

One source of pressure on sell-side analysts is buy-side clients. Institutional clients are traditionally the primary users of sell-side research, either directly or with soft dollar brokerage. Portfolio managers may have significant positions in the security of a company under review. A rating downgrade may adversely affect the portfolio's performance, particularly in the short term, because the sensitivity of stock prices to ratings changes has increased in recent years. A downgrade may also affect the manager's compensation, which is usually tied to portfolio performance. Moreover, portfolio performance is subject to media and public scrutiny, which may affect the manager's professional reputation. Consequently, some portfolio managers implicitly or explicitly support sell-side ratings inflation.

Portfolio managers have a responsibility to respect and foster the intellectual honesty of sell-side research. Therefore, it is improper for portfolio managers to threaten or engage in retaliatory practices, such as reporting sell-side analysts to the covered company in order to instigate negative corporate reactions. Although most portfolio managers do not engage in such practices, the perception by the research analyst that a reprisal is possible may cause concern and make it difficult for the analyst to maintain independence and objectivity.

Fund Manager and Custodial Relationships

Research analysts are not the only people who must be concerned with maintaining their independence. Members and candidates who are responsible for hiring and retaining outside managers and third-party custodians should not accepts gifts, entertainment, or travel funding that may be perceived as impairing their decisions. The use of secondary fund managers has evolved into a common practice to manage specific asset allocations. The use of third-party custodians is common practice for independent investment advisory firms and helps them with trading capabilities and reporting requirements. Primary and secondary fund managers, as well as third-party custodians, often arrange educational and marketing events to inform others about their business strategies, investment process, or custodial services. Members and candidates must review the merits of each offer individually in determining whether they may attend yet maintain their independence.

Investment Banking Relationships

Some sell-side firms may exert pressure on their analysts to issue favorable research reports on current or prospective investment banking clients. For many of these firms, income from investment banking has become increasingly important to overall firm profitability because brokerage income has declined as a result of price competition. Consequently, firms offering investment banking services work hard to develop and maintain relationships with investment banking clients and prospects. These companies are often covered by the firm's research analysts because companies often select their investment banks on the basis of the reputation of their research analysts, the quality of their work, and their standing in the industry.

In some countries, research analysts frequently work closely with their investment banking colleagues to help evaluate prospective investment banking clients. In other countries, because of past abuses in managing the obvious conflicts of interest, regulators have established clear rules prohibiting the interaction of these groups. Although collaboration between research analysts and investment banking colleagues may benefit the firm and enhance market efficiency (e.g., by allowing firms to assess risks more accurately and make better pricing assumptions), it requires firms to carefully balance the conflicts of interest inherent in the collaboration. Having analysts work with investment bankers is appropriate only when the conflicts are adequately and effectively managed and disclosed. Firm managers have a responsibility to provide an environment in which analysts are neither coerced nor enticed into issuing research that does not reflect their true opinions. Firms should require public disclosure of actual conflicts of interest to investors.

Members, candidates, and their firms must adopt and follow perceived best practices in maintaining independence and objectivity in the corporate culture and protecting analysts from undue pressure by their investment banking colleagues. The "firewalls" traditionally built between these two functions must be managed to minimize conflicts of interest; indeed, enhanced firewall policies may go as far as prohibiting all communications between these groups. A key element of an enhanced firewall is separate reporting structures for personnel on the research side and personnel on the investment banking side. For example, investment banking personnel should not have any authority to approve, disapprove, or make changes to research reports or recommendations. Another element should be a compensation arrangement that minimizes the pressures on research analysts and rewards objectivity and accuracy. Compensation arrangements should not link analyst remuneration directly to investment banking assignments in which the analyst may participate as a team member. Firms should also regularly review their policies and procedures to determine whether analysts are adequately safeguarded and to improve the transparency of disclosures relating to conflicts of interest. The highest level of transparency is achieved when disclosures are prominent and specific rather than marginalized and generic.

Performance Measurement and Attribution

Members and candidates working within a firm's investment performance measurement department may also be presented with situations that challenge their independence and objectivity. As performance analysts, their analyses may reveal instances where managers may appear to have strayed from their mandate. Additionally, the performance analyst may receive requests to alter the construction of composite indexes owing to negative results for a selected account or fund. The member or candidate must not allow internal or external influences to affect their independence and objectivity as they faithfully complete their performance calculation and analysis-related responsibilities.

Public Companies

Analysts may be pressured to issue favorable reports and recommendations by the companies they follow. Not every stock is a "buy," and not every research report is favorable—for many reasons, including the cyclical nature of many business activities and market fluctuations. For instance, a "good company" does not always translate into a "good stock" rating if the current stock price is fully valued. In making an investment recommendation, the analyst is responsible for anticipating, interpreting, and assessing a company's prospects and stock price performance in a factual manner. Many company managers, however, believe that their company's stock is undervalued, and these managers may find it difficult to accept critical research reports or ratings downgrades. Company managers' compensation may also be dependent on stock performance.

Due diligence in financial research and analysis involves gathering information from a wide variety of sources, including public disclosure documents (such as proxy statements, annual reports, and other regulatory filings) and also company management and investor-relations personnel, suppliers, customers, competitors, and other relevant sources. Research analysts may justifiably fear that companies will limit their ability to conduct thorough research by denying analysts who have "negative" views direct access to company managers and/or barring them from conference calls and other communication venues. Retaliatory practices include companies bringing legal action against analysts personally and/or their firms to seek monetary damages for the economic effects of negative reports and recommendations. Although few companies engage in such behavior, the perception that a reprisal is possible is a reasonable concern for analysts. This concern may make it difficult for them to conduct the comprehensive research needed to make objective recommendations. For further information and guidance, members and candidates should refer to the CFA Institute publication *Best Practice Guidelines Governing Analyst/Corporate Issuer Relations* (www.cfainstitute.org).

Credit Rating Agency Opinions

Credit rating agencies provide a service by grading the fixed-income products offered by companies. Analysts face challenges related to incentives and compensation schemes that may be tied to the final rating and successful placement of the product. Members and candidates employed at rating agencies should ensure that procedures and processes at the agencies prevent undue influences from a sponsoring company during the analysis. Members and candidates should abide by their agencies' and the industry's standards of conduct regarding the analytical process and the distribution of their reports.

The work of credit rating agencies also raises concerns similar to those inherent in investment banking relationships. Analysts may face pressure to issue ratings at a specific level because of other services the agency offers companies—namely, advising on the development of structured products. The rating agencies need to develop the necessary firewalls and protections to allow the independent operations of their different business lines.

When using information provided by credit rating agencies, members and candidates should be mindful of the potential conflicts of interest. And because of the potential conflicts, members and candidates may need to independently validate the rating granted.

Influence during the Manager Selection/Procurement Process

Members and candidates may find themselves on either side of the manager selection process. An individual may be on the hiring side as a representative of a pension organization or an investment committee member of an endowment or a charitable organization. Additionally, other members may be representing their organizations in attempts to earn new investment allocation mandates. The responsibility of members and candidates to maintain their independence and objectivity extends to the hiring or firing of those who provide business services beyond investment management.

When serving in a hiring capacity, members and candidates should not solicit gifts, contributions, or other compensation that may affect their independence and objectivity. Solicitations do not have to benefit members and candidates personally to conflict with Standard I(B). Requesting contributions to a favorite charity or political organization may also be perceived as an attempt to influence the decision-making process. Additionally, members and candidates serving in a hiring capacity should refuse gifts, donations, and other offered compensation that may be perceived to influence their decision-making process.

When working to earn a new investment allocation, members and candidates should not offer gifts, contributions, or other compensation to influence the decision of the hiring representative. The offering of these items with the intent to impair the independence and objectivity of another person would not comply with Standard I(B). Such prohibited actions may include offering donations to a charitable organization or political candidate referred by the hiring representative.

A clear example of improperly influencing hiring representatives was displayed in the "pay-to-play" scandal involving government-sponsored pension funds in the United States. Managers looking to gain lucrative allocations from the large funds made requested donations to the political campaigns of individuals directly responsible for the hiring decisions. This scandal and other similar events have led to new laws requiring additional reporting concerning political contributions and bans on hiring—or hiring delays for—managers that made campaign contributions to representatives associated with the decision-making process.

Issuer-Paid Research

In light of the recent reduction of sell-side research coverage, many companies, seeking to increase visibility both in the financial markets and with potential investors, have hired analysts to produce research reports analyzing their companies. These reports bridge the gap created by the lack of coverage and can be an effective method of communicating with investors.

Issuer-paid research conducted by independent analysts, however, is fraught with potential conflicts. Depending on how the research is written and distributed, investors may be misled into believing that the research is from an independent source when, in reality, it has been paid for by the subject company.

Members and candidates must adhere to strict standards of conduct that govern how the research is to be conducted and what disclosures must be made in the report. Analysts must engage in thorough, independent, and unbiased analysis and must fully disclose potential conflicts of interest, including the nature of their compensation. Otherwise, analysts risk misleading investors.

Investors need clear, credible, and thorough information about companies, and they need research based on independent thought. At a minimum, issuer-paid research should include a thorough analysis of the company's financial statements based on publicly disclosed information, benchmarking within a peer group, and industry analysis. Analysts must exercise diligence, independence, and thoroughness in conducting their research in an objective manner. Analysts must distinguish between fact and opinion in their reports. Conclusions must have a reasonable and adequate basis and must be supported by appropriate research.

Independent analysts must also strictly limit the type of compensation that they accept for conducting issuer-paid research. Otherwise, the content and conclusions of the reports could reasonably be expected to be determined or affected by compensation from the sponsoring companies. Compensation that might influence the research report could be direct, such as payment based on the conclusions of the report, or indirect, such as stock warrants or other equity instruments that could increase in value on the basis of positive coverage in the report. In such instances, the independent analyst has an incentive to avoid including negative information or making negative conclusions. Best practice is for independent analysts, prior to writing their reports, to negotiate only a flat fee for their work that is not linked to their conclusions or recommendations.

Travel Funding

The benefits related to accepting paid travel extend beyond the cost savings to the member or candidate and his firm, such as the chance to talk exclusively with the executives of a company or learning more about the investment options provided by an investment organization. Acceptance also comes with potential concerns; for example, members and candidates may be influenced by these discussions when flying on a corporate or chartered jet or attending sponsored conferences where many expenses, including airfare and lodging, are covered. To avoid the appearance of compromising their independence and objectivity, best practice dictates that members and candidates always use commercial transportation at their expense or at the expense of their firm rather than accept paid travel arrangements from an outside company. Should commercial transportation be unavailable, members and candidates may accept modestly arranged travel to participate in appropriate information-gathering events, such as a property tour.

Recommended Procedures for Compliance

Members and candidates should adhere to the following practices and should encourage their firms to establish procedures to avoid violations of Standard I(B):

- *Protect the integrity of opinions*: Members, candidates, and their firms should establish policies stating that every research report concerning the securities of a corporate client should reflect the unbiased opinion of the analyst. Firms should also design compensation systems that protect the integrity of the investment decision process by maintaining the independence and objectivity of analysts.

- *Create a restricted list*: If the firm is unwilling to permit dissemination of adverse opinions about a corporate client, members and candidates should encourage the firm to remove the controversial company from the research universe and put it on a restricted list so that the firm disseminates only factual information about the company.
- *Restrict special cost arrangements*: When attending meetings at an issuer's headquarters, members and candidates should pay for commercial transportation and hotel charges. No corporate issuer should reimburse members or candidates for air transportation. Members and candidates should encourage issuers to limit the use of corporate aircraft to situations in which commercial transportation is not available or in which efficient movement could not otherwise be arranged. Members and candidates should take particular care that when frequent meetings are held between an individual issuer and an individual member or candidate, the issuer should not always host the member or candidate.
- *Limit gifts*: Members and candidates must limit the acceptance of gratuities and/or gifts to token items. Standard I(B) does not preclude customary, ordinary business-related entertainment as long as its purpose is not to influence or reward members or candidates. Firms should consider a strict value limit for acceptable gifts that is based on the local or regional customs and should address whether the limit is per gift or an aggregate annual value.
- *Restrict investments*: Members and candidates should encourage their investment firms to develop formal policies related to employee purchases of equity or equity-related IPOs. Firms should require prior approval for employee participation in IPOs, with prompt disclosure of investment actions taken following the offering. Strict limits should be imposed on investment personnel acquiring securities in private placements.
- *Review procedures*: Members and candidates should encourage their firms to implement effective supervisory and review procedures to ensure that analysts and portfolio managers comply with policies relating to their personal investment activities.
- *Independence policy*: Members, candidates, and their firms should establish a formal written policy on the independence and objectivity of research and implement reporting structures and review procedures to ensure that research analysts do not report to and are not supervised or controlled by any department of the firm that could compromise the independence of the analyst. More detailed recommendations related to a firm's policies regarding research objectivity are set forth in the CFA Institute statement *Research Objectivity Standards* (www.cfainstitute.org).
- *Appointed officer*: Firms should appoint a senior officer with oversight responsibilities for compliance with the firm's code of ethics and all regulations concerning its business. Firms should provide every employee with the procedures and policies for reporting potentially unethical behavior, violations of regulations, or other activities that may harm the firm's reputation.

Application of the Standard

Example 1 (Travel Expenses):

Steven Taylor, a mining analyst with Bronson Brokers, is invited by Precision Metals to join a group of his peers in a tour of mining facilities in several western US states. The company arranges for chartered group flights from site to site and for accommodations in Spartan Motels, the only chain with accommodations near the mines, for three nights. Taylor allows Precision Metals to pick up his tab, as do the other analysts, with one exception—John Adams, an employee of a large trust company who insists on following his company's policy and paying for his hotel room himself.

> *Comment*: The policy of the company where Adams works complies closely with Standard I(B) by avoiding even the appearance of a conflict of interest, but Taylor and the other analysts were not necessarily violating Standard I(B). In general, when allowing companies to pay for travel and/or accommodations in these circumstances, members and candidates must use their judgment. They must be on guard that such arrangements not impinge on a member's or candidate's independence and objectivity. In this example, the trip was strictly for business and Taylor was not accepting irrelevant or lavish hospitality. The itinerary required chartered flights, for which analysts were not expected to pay. The accommodations were modest. These arrangements are not unusual and did not violate Standard I(B) as long as Taylor's independence and objectivity were not compromised. In the final analysis, members and candidates should consider both whether they can remain objective and whether their integrity might be perceived by their clients to have been compromised.

Example 2 (Research Independence):

Susan Dillon, an analyst in the corporate finance department of an investment services firm, is making a presentation to a potential new business client that includes the promise that her firm will provide full research coverage of the potential client.

> *Comment*: Dillon may agree to provide research coverage, but she must not commit her firm's research department to providing a favorable recommendation. The firm's recommendation (favorable, neutral, or unfavorable) must be based on an independent and objective investigation and analysis of the company and its securities.

Example 3 (Research Independence and Intrafirm Pressure):

Walter Fritz is an equity analyst with Hilton Brokerage who covers the mining industry. He has concluded that the stock of Metals & Mining is overpriced at its current level, but he is concerned that a negative research report will hurt the good relationship between Metals & Mining and the investment banking division of his firm. In fact, a senior manager of Hilton Brokerage has just sent him a copy of a proposal his firm has made to Metals & Mining to underwrite a debt offering. Fritz needs to produce a report right away and is concerned about issuing a less-than-favorable rating.

> *Comment*: Fritz's analysis of Metals & Mining must be objective and based solely on consideration of company fundamentals. Any pressure from other divisions of his firm is inappropriate. This conflict could have been eliminated if, in anticipation of the offering, Hilton Brokerage had placed Metals & Mining on a restricted list for its sales force.

Example 4 (Research Independence and Issuer Relationship Pressure):

As in Example 3, Walter Fritz has concluded that Metals & Mining stock is overvalued at its current level, but he is concerned that a negative research report might jeopardize a close rapport that he has nurtured over the years with Metals & Mining's CEO, chief finance officer, and investment relations officer. Fritz is concerned that a negative report might result also in management retaliation—for instance, cutting him off from participating in conference calls when a quarterly earnings release is made, denying him the ability to ask questions on such calls, and/or denying him access to top management for arranging group meetings between Hilton Brokerage clients and top Metals & Mining managers.

> *Comment*: As in Example 3, Fritz's analysis must be objective and based solely on consideration of company fundamentals. Any pressure from Metals & Mining is inappropriate. Fritz should reinforce the integrity of his conclusions by stressing that his investment recommendation is based on relative valuation, which may include qualitative issues with respect to Metals & Mining's management.

Example 5 (Research Independence and Sales Pressure):

As support for the sales effort of her corporate bond department, Lindsey Warner offers credit guidance to purchasers of fixed-income securities. Her compensation is closely linked to the performance of the corporate bond department. Near the quarter's end, Warner's firm has a large inventory position in the bonds of Milton, Ltd., and has been unable to sell the bonds because of Milton's recent announcement of an operating problem. Salespeople have asked her to contact large clients to push the bonds.

> *Comment*: Unethical sales practices create significant potential violations of the Code and Standards. Warner's opinion of the Milton bonds must not be affected by internal pressure or compensation. In this case, Warner must refuse to push the Milton bonds unless she is able to justify that the market price has already adjusted for the operating problem.

Example 6 (Research Independence and Prior Coverage):

Jill Jorund is a securities analyst following airline stocks and a rising star at her firm. Her boss has been carrying a "buy" recommendation on International Airlines and asks Jorund to take over coverage of that airline. He tells Jorund that under no circumstances should the prevailing buy recommendation be changed.

> *Comment*: Jorund must be independent and objective in her analysis of International Airlines. If she believes that her boss's instructions have compromised her, she has two options: She can tell her boss that she cannot cover the company under these constraints, or she can take over coverage of the company, reach her own independent conclusions, and if they conflict with her boss's opinion, share the conclusions with her boss or other supervisors in the firm so that they can make appropriate recommendations. Jorund must issue only recommendations that reflect her independent and objective opinion.

Example 7 (Gifts and Entertainment from Related Party):

Edward Grant directs a large amount of his commission business to a New York–based brokerage house. In appreciation for all the business, the brokerage house gives Grant two tickets to the World Cup in South Africa, two nights at a nearby resort, several meals, and transportation via limousine to the game. Grant fails to disclose receiving this package to his supervisor.

> *Comment*: Grant has violated Standard I(B) because accepting these substantial gifts may impede his independence and objectivity. Every member and candidate should endeavor to avoid situations that might cause or be perceived to cause a loss of independence or objectivity in recommending

investments or taking investment action. By accepting the trip, Grant has opened himself up to the accusation that he may give the broker favored treatment in return.

Example 8 (Gifts and Entertainment from Client):

Theresa Green manages the portfolio of Ian Knowlden, a client of Tisbury Investments. Green achieves an annual return for Knowlden that is consistently better than that of the benchmark she and the client previously agreed to. As a reward, Knowlden offers Green two tickets to Wimbledon and the use of Knowlden's flat in London for a week. Green discloses this gift to her supervisor at Tisbury.

Comment: Green is in compliance with Standard I(B) because she disclosed the gift from one of her clients in accordance with the firm's policies. Members and candidates may accept bonuses or gifts from clients as long as they disclose them to their employer because gifts in a client relationship are deemed less likely to affect a member's or candidate's objectivity and independence than gifts in other situations. Disclosure is required, however, so that supervisors can monitor such situations to guard against employees favoring a gift-giving client to the detriment of other fee-paying clients (such as by allocating a greater proportion of IPO stock to the gift-giving client's portfolio).

Best practices for monitoring include comparing the transaction costs of the Knowlden account with the costs of other accounts managed by Green and other similar accounts within Tisbury. The supervisor could also compare the performance returns with the returns of other clients with the same mandate. This comparison will assist in determining whether a pattern of favoritism by Green is disadvantaging other Tisbury clients or the possibility that this favoritism could affect her future behavior.

Example 9 (Travel Expenses from External Manager):

Tom Wayne is the investment manager of the Franklin City Employees Pension Plan. He recently completed a successful search for a firm to manage the foreign equity allocation of the plan's diversified portfolio. He followed the plan's standard procedure of seeking presentations from a number of qualified firms and recommended that his board select Penguin Advisors because of its experience, well-defined investment strategy, and performance record. The firm claims compliance with the Global Investment Performance Standards (GIPS) and has been verified. Following the selection of Penguin, a reporter from the *Franklin City Record* calls to ask if there was any connection between this action and the fact that Penguin was one of the sponsors of an "investment fact-finding trip to Asia" that Wayne made earlier in the year. The trip was one of several conducted by the Pension Investment Academy, which had arranged the itinerary of meetings with economic, government, and corporate officials in major cities in several Asian countries. The Pension Investment Academy obtains support for the cost of these trips from a number of investment managers, including Penguin Advisors; the Academy then pays the travel expenses of the various pension plan managers on the trip and provides all meals and accommodations. The president of Penguin Advisors was also one of the travelers on the trip.

Comment: Although Wayne can probably put to good use the knowledge he gained from the trip in selecting portfolio managers and in other areas of managing the pension plan, his recommendation of Penguin Advisors may be tainted by the possible conflict incurred when he participated in a trip partly paid for by Penguin Advisors and when he was in the daily company of the president of Penguin Advisors. To avoid violating Standard I(B),

Wayne's basic expenses for travel and accommodations should have been paid by his employer or the pension plan; contact with the president of Penguin Advisors should have been limited to informational or educational events only; and the trip, the organizer, and the sponsor should have been made a matter of public record. Even if his actions were not in violation of Standard I(B), Wayne should have been sensitive to the public perception of the trip when reported in the newspaper and the extent to which the subjective elements of his decision might have been affected by the familiarity that the daily contact of such a trip would encourage. This advantage would probably not be shared by firms competing with Penguin Advisors.

Example 10 (Research Independence and Compensation Arrangements):

Javier Herrero recently left his job as a research analyst for a large investment adviser. While looking for a new position, he was hired by an investor-relations firm to write a research report on one of its clients, a small educational software company. The investor-relations firm hopes to generate investor interest in the technology company. The firm will pay Herrero a flat fee plus a bonus if any new investors buy stock in the company as a result of Herrero's report.

Comment: If Herrero accepts this payment arrangement, he will be in violation of Standard I(B) because the compensation arrangement can reasonably be expected to compromise his independence and objectivity. Herrero will receive a bonus for attracting investors, which provides an incentive to draft a positive report regardless of the facts and to ignore or play down any negative information about the company. Herrero should accept only a flat fee that is not tied to the conclusions or recommendations of the report. Issuer-paid research that is objective and unbiased can be done under the right circumstances as long as the analyst takes steps to maintain his or her objectivity and includes in the report proper disclosures regarding potential conflicts of interest.

Example 11 (Recommendation Objectivity and Service Fees):

Two years ago, Bob Wade, trust manager for Central Midas Bank, was approached by Western Funds about promoting its family of funds, with special interest in the service-fee class of funds. To entice Central to promote this class, Western Funds offered to pay the bank a service fee of 0.25%. Without disclosing the fee being offered to the bank, Wade asked one of the investment managers to review Western's funds to determine whether they were suitable for clients of Central Midas Bank. The manager completed the normal due diligence review and determined that the new funds were fairly valued in the market with fee structures on a par with competitors. Wade decided to accept Western's offer and instructed the team of portfolio managers to exclusively promote these funds and the service-fee class to clients seeking to invest new funds or transfer from their current investments.

Now, two years later, the funds managed by Western begin to underperform their peers. Wade is counting on the fees to reach his profitability targets and continues to push these funds as acceptable investments for Central's clients.

Comment: Wade is violating Standard I(B) because the fee arrangement has affected the objectivity of his recommendations. Wade is relying on the fee as a component of the department's profitability and is unwilling to offer other products that may affect the fees received.

See also Standard VI(A)–Disclosure of Conflicts.

Example 12 (Recommendation Objectivity):

Bob Thompson has been doing research for the portfolio manager of the fixed-income department. His assignment is to do sensitivity analysis on securitized subprime mortgages. He has discussed with the manager possible scenarios to use to calculate expected returns. A key assumption in such calculations is housing price appreciation (HPA) because it drives "prepays" (prepayments of mortgages) and losses. Thompson is concerned with the significant appreciation experienced over the previous five years as a result of the increased availability of funds from subprime mortgages. Thompson insists that the analysis should include a scenario run with −10% for Year 1, −5% for Year 2, and then (to project a worst-case scenario) 0% for Years 3 through 5. The manager replies that these assumptions are too dire because there has never been a time in their available database when HPA was negative.

Thompson conducts his research to better understand the risks inherent in these securities and evaluates these securities in the worst-case scenario, an unlikely but possible environment. Based on the results of the enhanced scenarios, Thompson does not recommend the purchase of the securitization. Against the general market trends, the manager follows Thompson's recommendation and does not invest. The following year, the housing market collapses. In avoiding the subprime investments, the manager's portfolio outperforms its peer group that year.

> *Comment*: Thompson's actions in running the worst-case scenario against the protests of the portfolio manager are in alignment with the principles of Standard I(B). Thompson did not allow his research to be pressured by the general trends of the market or the manager's desire to limit the research to historical norms.
>
> See also Standard V(A)–Diligence and Reasonable Basis.

Example 13 (Influencing Manager Selection Decisions):

Adrian Mandel, CFA, is a senior portfolio manager for ZZYY Capital Management who oversees a team of investment professionals who manage labor union pension funds. A few years ago, ZZYY sought to win a competitive asset manager search to manage a significant allocation of the pension fund of the United Doughnut and Pretzel Bakers Union (UDPBU). UDPBU's investment board is chaired by a recognized key decision maker and long-time leader of the union, Ernesto Gomez. To improve ZZYY's chances of winning the competition, Mandel made significant monetary contributions to Gomez's union reelection campaign fund. Even after ZZYY was hired as a primary manager of the pension, Mandel believed that his firm's position was not secure. Mandel continued to contribute to Gomez's reelection campaign chest as well as to entertain lavishly the union leader and his family at top restaurants on a regular basis. All of Mandel's outlays were routinely handled as marketing expenses reimbursed by ZZYY's expense accounts and were disclosed to his senior management as being instrumental in maintaining a strong close relationship with an important client.

> *Comment*: Mandel not only offered but actually gave monetary gifts, benefits, and other considerations that reasonably could be expected to compromise Gomez's objectivity. Therefore, Mandel was in violation of Standard I(B).

Example 14 (Influencing Manager Selection Decisions):

Adrian Mandel, CFA, had heard about the manager search competition for the UDPBU Pension Fund through a broker/dealer contact. The contact told him that a well-known retired professional golfer, Bobby "The Bear" Finlay, who had become a licensed broker/dealer serving as a pension consultant, was orchestrating the UDPBU manager search. Finlay had gained celebrity status with several labor union pension fund boards by entertaining their respective board members and regaling them with colorful stories of fellow pro golfers' antics in clubhouses around the world. Mandel decided to improve ZZYY's chances of being invited to participate in the search competition by befriending Finlay to curry his favor. Knowing Finlay's love of entertainment, Mandel wined and dined Finlay at high-profile bistros where Finlay could glow in the fan recognition lavished on him by all the other patrons. Mandel's endeavors paid off handsomely when Finlay recommended to the UDPBU board that ZZYY be entered as one of three finalist asset management firms in its search.

> *Comment*: Similar to Example 13, Mandel lavished gifts, benefits, and other considerations in the form of expensive entertainment that could reasonably be expected to influence the consultant to recommend the hiring of his firm. Therefore, Mandel was in violation of Standard I(B).

Example 15 (Fund Manager Relationships):

Amie Scott is a performance analyst within her firm with responsibilities for analyzing the performance of external managers. While completing her quarterly analysis, Scott notices a change in one manager's reported composite construction. The change concealed the bad performance of a particularly large account by placing that account into a new residual composite. This change allowed the manager to remain at the top of the list of manager performance. Scott knows her firm has a large allocation to this manager, and the fund's manager is a close personal friend of the CEO. She needs to deliver her final report but is concerned with pointing out the composite change.

> *Comment*: Scott would be in violation of Standard I(B) if she did not disclose the change in her final report. The analysis of managers' performance should not be influenced by personal relationships or the size of the allocation to the outside managers. By not including the change, Scott would not be providing an independent analysis of the performance metrics for her firm.

Example 16 (Intrafirm Pressure):

Jill Stein is head of performance measurement for her firm. During the last quarter, many members of the organization's research department were removed because of the poor quality of their recommendations. The subpar research caused one larger account holder to experience significant underperformance, which resulted in the client withdrawing his money after the end of the quarter. The head of sales requests that Stein remove this account from the firm's performance composite because the performance decline can be attributed to the departed research team and not the client's adviser.

> *Comment*: Pressure from other internal departments can create situations that cause a member or candidate to violate the Code and Standards. Stein must maintain her independence and objectivity and refuse to exclude specific accounts from the firm's performance composites to which they belong. As long as the client invested under a strategy similar to that of the defined composite, it cannot be excluded because of the poor stock selections that led to the underperformance and asset withdrawal.

Standard I(C) Misrepresentation

Members and Candidates must not knowingly make any misrepresentations relating to investment analysis, recommendations, actions, or other professional activities.

Guidance

Highlights:

- *Impact on Investment Practice*
- *Performance Reporting*
- *Social Media*
- *Omissions*
- *Plagiarism*
- *Work Completed for Employer*

Trust is the foundation of the investment profession. Investors must be able to rely on the statements and information provided to them by those with whom the investors have trusted their financial well-being. Investment professionals who make false or misleading statements not only harm investors but also reduce the level of investor confidence in the investment profession and threaten the integrity of capital markets as a whole.

A misrepresentation is any untrue statement or omission of a fact or any statement that is otherwise false or misleading. A member or candidate must not knowingly omit or misrepresent information or give a false impression of a firm, organization, or security in the member's or candidate's oral representations, advertising (whether in the press or through brochures), electronic communications, or written materials (whether publicly disseminated or not). In this context, "knowingly" means that the member or candidate either knows or should have known that the misrepresentation was being made or that omitted information could alter the investment decision-making process.

Written materials include, but are not limited to, research reports, underwriting documents, company financial reports, market letters, newspaper columns, and books. Electronic communications include, but are not limited to, internet communications, webpages, mobile applications, and e-mails. Members and candidates who use webpages should regularly monitor materials posted on these sites to ensure that they contain current information. Members and candidates should also ensure that all reasonable precautions have been taken to protect the site's integrity and security and that the site does not misrepresent any information and does provide full disclosure.

Standard I(C) prohibits members and candidates from guaranteeing clients any specific return on volatile investments. Most investments contain some element of risk that makes their return inherently unpredictable. For such investments, guaranteeing either a particular rate of return or a guaranteed preservation of investment capital (e.g., "I can guarantee that you will earn 8% on equities this year" or "I can guarantee that you will not lose money on this investment") is misleading to investors. Standard I(C) does not prohibit members and candidates from providing clients with information on investment products that have guarantees built into the structure of the products themselves or for which an institution has agreed to cover any losses.

Impact on Investment Practice

Members and candidates must not misrepresent any aspect of their practice, including (but not limited to) their qualifications or credentials, the qualifications or services provided by their firm, their performance record and the record of their firm, and the characteristics of an investment. Any misrepresentation made by a member or candidate relating to the member's or candidate's professional activities is a breach of this standard.

Members and candidates should exercise care and diligence when incorporating third-party information. Misrepresentations resulting from the use of the credit ratings, research, testimonials, or marketing materials of outside parties become the responsibility of the investment professional when it affects that professional's business practices.

Investing through outside managers continues to expand as an acceptable method of investing in areas outside a firm's core competencies. Members and candidates must disclose their intended use of external managers and must not represent those managers' investment practices as their own. Although the level of involvement of outside managers may change over time, appropriate disclosures by members and candidates are important in avoiding misrepresentations, especially if the primary activity is to invest directly with a single external manager. Standard V(B)–Communication with Clients and Prospective Clients discusses in further detail communicating the firm's investment practices.

Performance Reporting

The performance benchmark selection process is another area where misrepresentations may occur. Members and candidates may misrepresent the success of their performance record through presenting benchmarks that are not comparable to their strategies. Further, clients can be misled if the benchmark's results are not reported on a basis comparable to that of the fund's or client's results. Best practice is selecting the most appropriate available benchmark from a universe of available options. The transparent presentation of appropriate performance benchmarks is an important aspect in providing clients with information that is useful in making investment decisions.

However, Standard I(C) does not require that a benchmark always be provided in order to comply. Some investment strategies may not lend themselves to displaying an appropriate benchmark because of the complexity or diversity of the investments included. Furthermore, some investment strategies may use reference indexes that do not reflect the opportunity set of the invested assets—for example, a hedge fund comparing its performance with a "cash plus" basis. When such a benchmark is used, members and candidates should make reasonable efforts to ensure that they disclose the reasons behind the use of this reference index to avoid misrepresentations of their performance. Members and candidates should discuss with clients on a continuous basis the appropriate benchmark to be used for performance evaluations and related fee calculations.

Reporting misrepresentations may also occur when valuations for illiquid or non-traded securities are available from more than one source. When different options are available, members and candidates may be tempted to switch providers to obtain higher security valuations. The process of shopping for values may misrepresent a security's worth, lead to misinformed decisions to sell or hold an investment, and result in overcharging clients advisory fees.

Members and candidates should take reasonable steps to provide accurate and reliable security pricing information to clients on a consistent basis. Changing pricing providers should not be based solely on the justification that the new provider reports a higher current value of a security. Consistency in the reported information will improve the perception of the valuation process for illiquid securities. Clients will likely have additional confidence that they were able to make an informed decision about continuing to hold these securities in their portfolios.

Social Media

The advancement of online discussion forums and communication platforms, commonly referred to as "social media," is placing additional responsibilities on members and candidates. When communicating through social media channels, members and candidates should provide only the same information they are allowed to distribute to clients and potential clients through other traditional forms of communication. The online or interactive aspects of social media do not remove the need to be open and honest about the information being distributed.

Along with understanding and following existing and newly developing rules and regulations regarding the allowed use of social media, members and candidates should also ensure that all communications in this format adhere to the requirements of the Code and Standards. The perceived anonymity granted through these platforms may entice individuals to misrepresent their qualifications or abilities or those of their employer. Actions undertaken through social media that knowingly misrepresent investment recommendations or professional activities are considered a violation of Standard I(C).

Omissions

The omission of a fact or outcome can be misleading, especially given the growing use of models and technical analysis processes. Many members and candidates rely on such models and processes to scan for new investment opportunities, to develop investment vehicles, and to produce investment recommendations and ratings. When inputs are knowingly omitted, the resulting outcomes may provide misleading information to those who rely on it for making investment decisions. Additionally, the outcomes from models shall not be presented as fact because they represent the expected results based on the inputs and analysis process incorporated.

Omissions in the performance measurement and attribution process can also misrepresent a manager's performance and skill. Members and candidates should encourage their firms to develop strict policies for composite development to prevent cherry picking—situations in which selected accounts are presented as representative of the firm's abilities. The omission of any accounts appropriate for the defined composite may misrepresent to clients the success of the manager's implementation of its strategy.

Plagiarism

Standard I(C) also prohibits plagiarism in the preparation of material for distribution to employers, associates, clients, prospects, or the general public. Plagiarism is defined as copying or using in substantially the same form materials prepared by others without acknowledging the source of the material or identifying the author and publisher of such material. Members and candidates must not copy (or represent as their own) original ideas or material without permission and must acknowledge and identify the source of ideas or material that is not their own.

The investment profession uses a myriad of financial, economic, and statistical data in the investment decision-making process. Through various publications and presentations, the investment professional is constantly exposed to the work of others and to the temptation to use that work without proper acknowledgment.

Misrepresentation through plagiarism in investment management can take various forms. The simplest and most flagrant example is to take a research report or study done by another firm or person, change the names, and release the material as one's own original analysis. This action is a clear violation of Standard I(C). Other practices include (1) using excerpts from articles or reports prepared by others either verbatim or with only slight changes in wording without acknowledgment, (2) citing specific quotations as attributable to "leading analysts" and "investment experts" without naming the specific references, (3) presenting statistical estimates of forecasts prepared by others and identifying the sources but without including the qualifying statements or caveats that may have been used, (4) using charts and graphs without stating their sources, and (5) copying proprietary computerized spreadsheets or algorithms without seeking the cooperation or authorization of their creators.

In the case of distributing third-party, outsourced research, members and candidates may use and distribute such reports as long as they do not represent themselves as the report's authors. Indeed, the member or candidate may add value for the client by sifting through research and repackaging it for clients. In such cases, clients should be fully informed that they are paying for the ability of the member or candidate to find the best research from a wide variety of sources. Members and candidates must not misrepresent their abilities, the extent of their expertise, or the extent of their work in a way that would mislead their clients or prospective clients. Members and candidates should disclose whether the research being presented to clients comes from another source—from either within or outside the member's or candidate's firm. This allows clients to understand who has the expertise behind the report or whether the work is being done by the analyst, other members of the firm, or an outside party.

Standard I(C) also applies to plagiarism in oral communications, such as through group meetings; visits with associates, clients, and customers; use of audio/video media (which is rapidly increasing); and telecommunications, including electronic data transfer and the outright copying of electronic media.

One of the most egregious practices in violation of this standard is the preparation of research reports based on multiple sources of information without acknowledging the sources. Examples of information from such sources include ideas, statistical compilations, and forecasts combined to give the appearance of original work. Although there is no monopoly on ideas, members and candidates must give credit where it is clearly due. Analysts should not use undocumented forecasts, earnings projections, asset values, and so on. Sources must be revealed to bring the responsibility directly back to the author of the report or the firm involved.

Work Completed for Employer

The preceding paragraphs address actions that would constitute a violation of Standard I(C). In some situations, however, members or candidates may use research conducted or models developed by others within the same firm without committing a violation. The most common example relates to the situation in which one (or more) of the original analysts is no longer with the firm. Research and models developed while employed by a firm are the property of the firm. The firm retains the right to continue using the work completed after a member or candidate has left the organization. The firm may issue future reports without providing attribution to the prior analysts. A member or candidate cannot, however, reissue a previously released report solely under his or her name.

Recommended Procedures for Compliance

Factual Presentations

Members and candidates can prevent unintentional misrepresentations of their qualifications or the services they or their firms provide if each member and candidate understands the limit of the firm's or individual's capabilities and the need to be accurate and complete in presentations. Firms can provide guidance for employees who make written or oral presentations to clients or potential clients by providing a written list of the firm's available services and a description of the firm's qualifications. This list should suggest ways of describing the firm's services, qualifications, and compensation that are both accurate and suitable for client or customer presentations. Firms can also help prevent misrepresentation by specifically designating which employees are authorized to speak on behalf of the firm. Regardless of whether the firm provides guidance, members and candidates should make certain that they understand the services the firm can perform and its qualifications.

Qualification Summary

In addition, to ensure accurate presentations to clients, each member and candidate should prepare a summary of his or her own qualifications and experience and a list of the services the member or candidate is capable of performing. Firms can assist member and candidate compliance by periodically reviewing employee correspondence and documents that contain representations of individual or firm qualifications.

Verify Outside Information

When providing information to clients from a third party, members and candidates share a responsibility for the accuracy of the marketing and distribution materials that pertain to the third party's capabilities, services, and products. Misrepresentation by third parties can damage the member's or candidate's reputation, the reputation of the firm, and the integrity of the capital markets. Members and candidates should encourage their employers to develop procedures for verifying information of third-party firms.

Maintain Webpages

Members and candidates who publish a webpage should regularly monitor materials posted on the site to ensure that the site contains current information. Members and candidates should also ensure that all reasonable precautions have been taken to protect the site's integrity, confidentiality, and security and that the site does not misrepresent any information and provides full disclosure.

Plagiarism Policy

To avoid plagiarism in preparing research reports or conclusions of analysis, members and candidates should take the following steps:

- *Maintain copies*: Keep copies of all research reports, articles containing research ideas, material with new statistical methodologies, and other materials that were relied on in preparing the research report.
- *Attribute quotations*: Attribute to their sources any direct quotations, including projections, tables, statistics, model/product ideas, and new methodologies prepared by persons other than recognized financial and statistical reporting services or similar sources.
- *Attribute summaries*: Attribute to their sources any paraphrases or summaries of material prepared by others. For example, to support his analysis of Brown Company's competitive position, the author of a research report on Brown might summarize another analyst's report on Brown's chief competitor, but the author of the Brown report must acknowledge in his own report the reliance on the other analyst's report.

Application of the Standard

Example 1 (Disclosure of Issuer-Paid Research):

Anthony McGuire is an issuer-paid analyst hired by publicly traded companies to electronically promote their stocks. McGuire creates a website that promotes his research efforts as a seemingly independent analyst. McGuire posts a profile and a strong buy recommendation for each company on the website indicating that the stock is expected to increase in value. He does not disclose the contractual relationships with the companies he covers on his website, in the research reports he issues, or in the statements he makes about the companies in internet chat rooms.

> *Comment*: McGuire has violated Standard I(C) because the website is misleading to potential investors. Even if the recommendations are valid and supported with thorough research, his omissions regarding the true relationship between himself and the companies he covers constitute a misrepresentation. McGuire has also violated Standard VI(A)–Disclosure of Conflicts by not disclosing the existence of an arrangement with the companies through which he receives compensation in exchange for his services.

Example 2 (Correction of Unintentional Errors):

Hijan Yao is responsible for the creation and distribution of the marketing materials for his firm, which claims compliance with the GIPS standards. Yao creates and distributes a presentation of performance by the firm's Asian equity composite that states the composite has ¥350 billion in assets. In fact, the composite has only ¥35 billion in assets, and the higher figure on the presentation is a result of a typographical error. Nevertheless, the erroneous material is distributed to a number of clients before Yao catches the mistake.

> *Comment*: Once the error is discovered, Yao must take steps to cease distribution of the incorrect material and correct the error by informing those who have received the erroneous information. Because Yao did not knowingly make the misrepresentation, however, he did not violate Standard I(C). Because his firm claims compliance with the GIPS standards, it must also comply with the GIPS Guidance Statement on Error Correction in relation to the error.

Example 3 (Noncorrection of Known Errors):

Syed Muhammad is the president of an investment management firm. The promotional material for the firm, created by the firm's marketing department, incorrectly claims that Muhammad has an advanced degree in finance from a prestigious business school in addition to the CFA designation. Although Muhammad attended the school for a short period of time, he did not receive a degree. Over the years, Muhammad and others in the firm have distributed this material to numerous prospective clients and consultants.

> *Comment*: Even though Muhammad may not have been directly responsible for the misrepresentation of his credentials in the firm's promotional material, he used this material numerous times over an extended period and should have known of the misrepresentation. Thus, Muhammad has violated Standard I(C).

Example 4 (Plagiarism):

Cindy Grant, a research analyst for a Canadian brokerage firm, has specialized in the Canadian mining industry for the past 10 years. She recently read an extensive research report on Jefferson Mining, Ltd., by Jeremy Barton, another analyst. Barton provided extensive statistics on the mineral reserves, production capacity, selling rates, and marketing factors affecting Jefferson's operations. He also noted that initial drilling results on a new ore body, which had not been made public, might show the existence of mineral zones that could increase the life of Jefferson's main mines, but Barton cited no specific data as to the initial drilling results. Grant called an officer of Jefferson, who gave her the initial drilling results over the telephone. The data indicated that the expected life of the main mines would be tripled. Grant added these statistics to Barton's report and circulated it within her firm as her own report.

> *Comment*: Grant plagiarized Barton's report by reproducing large parts of it in her own report without acknowledgment.

Example 5 (Misrepresentation of Information):

When Ricki Marks sells mortgage-backed derivatives called "interest-only strips" (IOs) to public pension plan clients, she describes them as "guaranteed by the US government." Purchasers of the IOs are entitled only to the interest stream generated by the mortgages, however, not the notional principal itself. One particular municipality's investment policies and local law require that securities purchased by its public pension plans be guaranteed by the US government. Although the underlying mortgages are guaranteed, neither the investor's investment nor the interest stream on the IOs is guaranteed. When interest rates decline, causing an increase in prepayment of mortgages, interest payments to the IOs' investors decline, and these investors lose a portion of their investment.

> *Comment*: Marks violated Standard I(C) by misrepresenting the terms and character of the investment.

Example 6 (Potential Information Misrepresentation):

Khalouck Abdrabbo manages the investments of several high-net-worth individuals in the United States who are approaching retirement. Abdrabbo advises these individuals that a portion of their investments be moved from equity to bank-sponsored certificates of deposit and money market accounts so that the principal will be "guaranteed" up to a certain amount. The interest is not guaranteed.

> *Comment*: Although there is risk that the institution offering the certificates of deposits and money market accounts could go bankrupt, in the United States, these accounts are insured by the US government through the Federal Deposit Insurance Corporation. Therefore, using the term "guaranteed" in this context is not inappropriate as long as the amount is within the government-insured limit. Abdrabbo should explain these facts to the clients.

Example 7 (Plagiarism):

Steve Swanson is a senior analyst in the investment research department of Ballard and Company. Apex Corporation has asked Ballard to assist in acquiring the majority ownership of stock in the Campbell Company, a financial consulting firm, and to prepare a report recommending that stockholders of Campbell agree to the acquisition. Another investment firm, Davis and Company, had already prepared a report for Apex analyzing both Apex and Campbell and recommending an exchange ratio. Apex has given the Davis report to Ballard officers, who have passed it on to Swanson. Swanson reviews the Davis report and other available material on Apex and Campbell. From his analysis, he concludes that the common stocks of Campbell and Apex represent good value at their current prices; he believes, however, that the Davis report does not consider all the factors a Campbell stockholder would need to know to make a decision. Swanson reports his conclusions to the partner in charge, who tells him to "use the Davis report, change a few words, sign your name, and get it out."

> *Comment*: If Swanson does as requested, he will violate Standard I(C). He could refer to those portions of the Davis report that he agrees with if he identifies Davis as the source; he could then add his own analysis and conclusions to the report before signing and distributing it.

Example 8 (Plagiarism):

Claude Browning, a quantitative analyst for Double Alpha, Inc., returns from a seminar in great excitement. At that seminar, Jack Jorrely, a well-known quantitative analyst at a national brokerage firm, discussed one of his new models in great detail, and Browning is intrigued by the new concepts. He proceeds to test the model, making some minor mechanical changes but retaining the concepts, until he produces some very positive results. Browning quickly announces to his supervisors at Double Alpha that he has discovered a new model and that clients and prospective clients should be informed of this positive finding as ongoing proof of Double Alpha's continuing innovation and ability to add value.

> *Comment*: Although Browning tested Jorrely's model on his own and even slightly modified it, he must still acknowledge the original source of the idea. Browning can certainly take credit for the final, practical results; he can also support his conclusions with his own test. The credit for the innovative thinking, however, must be awarded to Jorrely.

Example 9 (Plagiarism):

Fernando Zubia would like to include in his firm's marketing materials some "plain-language" descriptions of various concepts, such as the price-to-earnings (P/E) multiple and why standard deviation is used as a measure of risk. The descriptions come from other sources, but Zubia wishes to use them without reference to the original authors. Would this use of material be a violation of Standard I(C)?

> *Comment*: Copying verbatim any material without acknowledgement, including plain-language descriptions of the P/E multiple and standard deviation, violates Standard I(C). Even though these concepts are general, best practice would be for Zubia to describe them in his own words or cite the sources from which the descriptions are quoted. Members and candidates would be violating Standard I(C) if they either were responsible for creating marketing materials without attribution or knowingly use plagiarized materials.

Example 10 (Plagiarism):

Through a mainstream media outlet, Erika Schneider learns about a study that she would like to cite in her research. Should she cite both the mainstream intermediary source as well as the author of the study itself when using that information?

> *Comment*: In all instances, a member or candidate must cite the actual source of the information. Best practice for Schneider would be to obtain the information directly from the author and review it before citing it in

a report. In that case, Schneider would not need to report how she found out about the information. For example, suppose Schneider read in the *Financial Times* about a study issued by CFA Institute; best practice for Schneider would be to obtain a copy of the study from CFA Institute, review it, and then cite it in her report. If she does not use any interpretation of the report from the *Financial Times* and the newspaper does not add value to the report itself, the newspaper is merely a conduit of the original information and does not need to be cited. If she does not obtain the report and review the information, Schneider runs the risk of relying on second-hand information that may misstate facts. If, for example, the *Financial Times* erroneously reported some information from the original CFA Institute study and Schneider copied that erroneous information without acknowledging CFA Institute, she could be the object of complaints. Best practice would be either to obtain the complete study from its original author and cite only that author or to use the information provided by the intermediary and cite both sources.

Example 11 (Misrepresentation of Information):

Paul Ostrowski runs a two-person investment management firm. Ostrowski's firm subscribes to a service from a large investment research firm that provides research reports that can be repackaged by smaller firms for those firms' clients. Ostrowski's firm distributes these reports to clients as its own work.

Comment: Ostrowski can rely on third-party research that has a reasonable and adequate basis, but he cannot imply that he is the author of such research. If he does, Ostrowski is misrepresenting the extent of his work in a way that misleads the firm's clients or prospective clients.

Example 12 (Misrepresentation of Information):

Tom Stafford is part of a team within Appleton Investment Management responsible for managing a pool of assets for Open Air Bank, which distributes structured securities to offshore clients. He becomes aware that Open Air is promoting the structured securities as a much less risky investment than the investment management policy followed by him and the team to manage the original pool of assets. Also, Open Air has procured an independent rating for the pool that significantly overstates the quality of the investments. Stafford communicates his concerns to his supervisor, who responds that Open Air owns the product and is responsible for all marketing and distribution. Stafford's supervisor goes on to say that the product is outside of the US regulatory regime that Appleton follows and that all risks of the product are disclosed at the bottom of page 184 of the prospectus.

Comment: As a member of the investment team, Stafford is qualified to recognize the degree of accuracy of the materials that characterize the portfolio, and he is correct to be worried about Appleton's responsibility for a misrepresentation of the risks. Thus, he should continue to pursue the issue of Open Air's inaccurate promotion of the portfolio according to the firm's policies and procedures.

The Code and Standards stress protecting the reputation of the firm and the sustainability and integrity of the capital markets. Misrepresenting the quality and risks associated with the investment pool may lead to negative consequences for others well beyond the direct investors.

Example 13 (Avoiding a Misrepresentation):

Trina Smith is a fixed-income portfolio manager at a pension fund. She has observed that the market for highly structured mortgages is the focus of salespeople she meets and that these products represent a significant number of trading opportunities. In discussions about this topic with her team, Smith learns that calculating yields on changing cash flows within the deal structure requires very specialized vendor software. After more research, they find out that each deal is unique and that deals can have more than a dozen layers and changing cash flow priorities. Smith comes to the conclusion that, because of the complexity of these securities, the team cannot effectively distinguish between potentially good and bad investment options. To avoid misrepresenting their understanding, the team decides that the highly structured mortgage segment of the securitized market should not become part of the core of the fund's portfolio; they will allow some of the less complex securities to be part of the core.

> *Comment*: Smith is in compliance with Standard I(C) by not investing in securities that she and her team cannot effectively understand. Because she is not able to describe the risk and return profile of the securities to the pension fund beneficiaries and trustees, she appropriately limits the fund's exposure to this sector.

Example 14 (Misrepresenting Composite Construction):

Robert Palmer is head of performance for a fund manager. When asked to provide performance numbers to fund rating agencies, he avoids mentioning that the fund manager is quite liberal in composite construction. The reason accounts are included/excluded is not fully explained. The performance values reported to the rating agencies for the composites, although accurate for the accounts shown each period, may not present a true representation of the fund manager's ability.

> *Comment*: "Cherry picking" accounts to include in either published reports or information provided to rating agencies conflicts with Standard I(C). Moving accounts into or out of a composite to influence the overall performance results materially misrepresents the reported values over time. Palmer should work with his firm to strengthen its reporting practices concerning composite construction to avoid misrepresenting the firm's track record or the quality of the information being provided.

Example 15 (Presenting Out-of-Date Information):

David Finch is a sales director at a commercial bank, where he directs the bank's client advisers in the sale of third-party mutual funds. Each quarter, he holds a division-wide training session where he provides fact sheets on investment funds the bank is allowed to offer to clients. These fact sheets, which can be redistributed to potential clients, are created by the fund firms and contain information about the funds, including investment strategy and target distribution rates.

Finch knows that some of the fact sheets are out of date; for example, one long-only fund approved the use of significant leverage last quarter as a method to enhance returns. He continues to provide the sheets to the sales team without updates because the bank has no control over the marketing material released by the mutual fund firms.

> *Comment*: Finch is violating Standard I(C) by providing information that misrepresents aspects of the funds. By not providing the sales team and, ultimately, the clients with the updated information, he is misrepresenting the potential risks associated with the funds with outdated fact sheets. Finch

can instruct the sales team to clarify the deficiencies in the fact sheets with clients and ensure they have the most recent fund prospectus document before accepting orders for investing in any fund.

Example 16 (Overemphasis of Firm Results):

Bob Anderson is chief compliance officer for Optima Asset Management Company, a firm currently offering eight funds to clients. Seven of the eight had 10-year returns below the median for their respective sectors. Anderson approves a recent advertisement, which includes this statement: "Optima Asset Management is achieving excellent returns for its investors. The Optima Emerging Markets Equity fund, for example, has 10-year returns that exceed the sector median by more than 10%."

> *Comment*: From the information provided it is difficult to determine whether a violation has occurred as long as the sector outperformance is correct. Anderson may be attempting to mislead potential clients by citing the performance of the sole fund that achieved such results. Past performance is often used to demonstrate a firm's skill and abilities in comparison to funds in the same sectors.
>
> However, if all the funds outperformed their respective benchmarks, then Anderson's assertion that the company "is achieving excellent returns" may be factual. Funds may exhibit positive returns for investors, exceed benchmarks, and yet have returns below the median in their sectors.
>
> Members and candidates need to ensure that their marketing efforts do not include statements that misrepresent their skills and abilities to remain compliant with Standard I(C). Unless the returns of a single fund reflect the performance of a firm as a whole, the use of a singular fund for performance comparisons should be avoided.

Standard I(D) Misconduct

Members and Candidates must not engage in any professional conduct involving dishonesty, fraud, or deceit or commit any act that reflects adversely on their professional reputation, integrity, or competence.

Guidance

Whereas Standard I(A) addresses the obligation of members and candidates to comply with applicable law that governs their professional activities, Standard I(D) addresses *all* conduct that reflects poorly on the professional integrity, good reputation, or competence of members and candidates. Any act that involves lying, cheating, stealing, or other dishonest conduct is a violation of this standard if the offense reflects adversely on a member's or candidate's professional activities. Although CFA Institute discourages any sort of unethical behavior by members and candidates, the Code and Standards are primarily aimed at conduct and actions related to a member's or candidate's professional life.

Conduct that damages trustworthiness or competence may include behavior that, although not illegal, nevertheless negatively affects a member's or candidate's ability to perform his or her responsibilities. For example, abusing alcohol during business hours might constitute a violation of this standard because it could have a detrimental effect on the member's or candidate's ability to fulfill his or her professional responsibilities. Personal bankruptcy may not reflect on the integrity or trustworthiness of the person declaring bankruptcy, but if the circumstances of the bankruptcy involve fraudulent or deceitful business conduct, the bankruptcy may be a violation of this standard.

In some cases, the absence of appropriate conduct or the lack of sufficient effort may be a violation of Standard I(D). The integrity of the investment profession is built on trust. A member or candidate—whether an investment banker, rating or research analyst, or portfolio manager—is expected to conduct the necessary due diligence to properly understand the nature and risks of an investment before making an investment recommendation. By not taking these steps and, instead, relying on someone else in the process to perform them, members or candidates may violate the trust their clients have placed in them. This loss of trust may have a significant impact on the reputation of the member or candidate and the operations of the financial market as a whole.

Individuals may attempt to abuse the CFA Institute Professional Conduct Program by actively seeking CFA Institute enforcement of the Code and Standards, and Standard I(D) in particular, as a method of settling personal, political, or other disputes unrelated to professional ethics. CFA Institute is aware of this issue, and appropriate disciplinary policies, procedures, and enforcement mechanisms are in place to address misuse of the Code and Standards and the Professional Conduct Program in this way.

Recommended Procedures for Compliance

In addition to ensuring that their own behavior is consistent with Standard I(D), to prevent general misconduct, members and candidates should encourage their firms to adopt the following policies and procedures to support the principles of Standard I(D):

- *Code of ethics*: Develop and/or adopt a code of ethics to which every employee must subscribe, and make clear that any personal behavior that reflects poorly on the individual involved, the institution as a whole, or the investment industry will not be tolerated.
- *List of violations*: Disseminate to all employees a list of potential violations and associated disciplinary sanctions, up to and including dismissal from the firm.
- *Employee references*: Check references of potential employees to ensure that they are of good character and not ineligible to work in the investment industry because of past infractions of the law.

Application of the Standard

Example 1 (Professionalism and Competence):

Simon Sasserman is a trust investment officer at a bank in a small affluent town. He enjoys lunching every day with friends at the country club, where his clients have observed him having numerous drinks. Back at work after lunch, he clearly is intoxicated while making investment decisions. His colleagues make a point of handling any business with Sasserman in the morning because they distrust his judgment after lunch.

> *Comment*: Sasserman's excessive drinking at lunch and subsequent intoxication at work constitute a violation of Standard I(D) because this conduct has raised questions about his professionalism and competence. His behavior reflects poorly on him, his employer, and the investment industry.

Example 2 (Fraud and Deceit):

Howard Hoffman, a security analyst at ATZ Brothers, Inc., a large brokerage house, submits reimbursement forms over a two-year period to ATZ's self-funded health insurance program for more than two dozen bills, most of which have been altered to increase the amount due. An investigation by the firm's director of employee benefits uncovers the inappropriate conduct. ATZ subsequently terminates Hoffman's employment and notifies CFA Institute.

> *Comment*: Hoffman violated Standard I(D) because he engaged in intentional conduct involving fraud and deceit in the workplace that adversely reflected on his integrity.

Example 3 (Fraud and Deceit):

Jody Brink, an analyst covering the automotive industry, volunteers much of her spare time to local charities. The board of one of the charitable institutions decides to buy five new vans to deliver hot lunches to low-income elderly people. Brink offers to donate her time to handle purchasing agreements. To pay a long-standing debt to a friend who operates an automobile dealership—and to compensate herself for her trouble—she agrees to a price 20% higher than normal and splits the surcharge with her friend. The director of the charity ultimately discovers the scheme and tells Brink that her services, donated or otherwise, are no longer required.

> *Comment*: Brink engaged in conduct involving dishonesty, fraud, and misrepresentation and has violated Standard I(D).

Example 4 (Personal Actions and Integrity):

Carmen Garcia manages a mutual fund dedicated to socially responsible investing. She is also an environmental activist. As the result of her participation in nonviolent protests, Garcia has been arrested on numerous occasions for trespassing on the property of a large petrochemical plant that is accused of damaging the environment.

> *Comment*: Generally, Standard I(D) is not meant to cover legal transgressions resulting from acts of civil disobedience in support of personal beliefs because such conduct does not reflect poorly on the member's or candidate's professional reputation, integrity, or competence.

Example 5 (Professional Misconduct):

Meredith Rasmussen works on a buy-side trading desk of an investment management firm and concentrates on in-house trades for a hedge fund subsidiary managed by a team at the investment management firm. The hedge fund has been very successful and is marketed globally by the firm. From her experience as the trader for much of the activity of the fund, Rasmussen has become quite knowledgeable about the hedge fund's strategy, tactics, and performance. When a distinct break in the market occurs and many of the securities involved in the hedge fund's strategy decline markedly in value, Rasmussen observes that the reported performance of the hedge fund does not reflect this decline. In her experience, the lack of effect is a very unlikely occurrence. She approaches the head of trading about her concern and is told that she should not ask any questions and that the fund is big and successful and is not her concern. She is fairly sure something is not right, so she contacts the compliance officer, who also tells her to stay away from the issue of the hedge fund's reporting.

> *Comment*: Rasmussen has clearly come across an error in policies, procedures, and compliance practices within the firm's operations. According to the firm's procedures for reporting potentially unethical activity, she

should pursue the issue by gathering some proof of her reason for doubt. Should all internal communications within the firm not satisfy her concerns, Rasmussen should consider reporting the potential unethical activity to the appropriate regulator.

See also Standard IV(A) for guidance on whistleblowing and Standard IV(C) for the duties of a supervisor.

STANDARD II: INTEGRITY OF CAPITAL MARKETS

Standard II(A) Material Nonpublic Information

Members and Candidates who possess material nonpublic information that could affect the value of an investment must not act or cause others to act on the information.

Guidance

Highlights:

- *What Is "Material" Information?*
- *What Constitutes "Nonpublic" Information?*
- *Mosaic Theory*
- *Social Media*
- *Using Industry Experts*
- *Investment Research Reports*

Trading or inducing others to trade on material nonpublic information erodes confidence in capital markets, institutions, and investment professionals by supporting the idea that those with inside information and special access can take unfair advantage of the general investing public. Although trading on inside information may lead to short-term profits, in the long run, individuals and the profession as a whole suffer from such trading. These actions have caused and will continue to cause investors to avoid capital markets because the markets are perceived to be "rigged" in favor of the knowledgeable insider. When the investing public avoids capital markets, the markets and capital allocation become less efficient and less supportive of strong and vibrant economies. Standard II(A) promotes and maintains a high level of confidence in market integrity, which is one of the foundations of the investment profession.

The prohibition on using this information goes beyond the direct buying and selling of individual securities or bonds. Members and candidates must not use material nonpublic information to influence their investment actions related to derivatives (e.g., swaps or option contracts), mutual funds, or other alternative investments. *Any* trading based on material nonpublic information constitutes a violation of Standard II(A). The expansion of financial products and the increasing interconnectivity of financial markets globally have resulted in new potential opportunities for trading on material nonpublic information.

What Is "Material" Information?

Information is "material" if its disclosure would probably have an impact on the price of a security or if reasonable investors would want to know the information before making an investment decision. In other words, information is material if it would significantly alter the total mix of information currently available about a security in such a way that the price of the security would be affected.

The specificity of the information, the extent of its difference from public information, its nature, and its reliability are key factors in determining whether a particular piece of information fits the definition of material. For example, material information may include, but is not limited to, information on the following:

- earnings;
- mergers, acquisitions, tender offers, or joint ventures;
- changes in assets or asset quality;
- innovative products, processes, or discoveries (e.g., new product trials or research efforts);
- new licenses, patents, registered trademarks, or regulatory approval/rejection of a product;
- developments regarding customers or suppliers (e.g., the acquisition or loss of a contract);
- changes in management;
- change in auditor notification or the fact that the issuer may no longer rely on an auditor's report or qualified opinion;
- events regarding the issuer's securities (e.g., defaults on senior securities, calls of securities for redemption, repurchase plans, stock splits, changes in dividends, changes to the rights of security holders, and public or private sales of additional securities);
- bankruptcies;
- significant legal disputes;
- government reports of economic trends (employment, housing starts, currency information, etc.);
- orders for large trades before they are executed; and
- new or changing equity or debt ratings issued by a third party (e.g., sell-side recommendations and credit ratings).

In addition to the substance and specificity of the information, the source or relative reliability of the information also determines materiality. The less reliable a source, the less likely the information provided would be considered material. For example, factual information from a corporate insider regarding a significant new contract for a company is likely to be material, whereas an assumption based on speculation by a competitor about the same contract is likely to be less reliable and, therefore, not material. Additionally, information about trials of a new drug, product, or service under development from qualified personnel involved in the trials is likely to be material, whereas educated conjecture by subject experts not connected to the trials is unlikely to be material.

Also, the more ambiguous the effect of the information on price, the less material that information is considered. If it is unclear whether and to what extent the information will affect the price of a security, the information may not be considered material. The passage of time may also render information that was once important immaterial.

What Constitutes "Nonpublic" Information?

Information is "nonpublic" until it has been disseminated or is available to the marketplace in general (as opposed to a select group of investors). "Disseminated" can be defined as "made known." For example, a company report of profits that is posted on the internet and distributed widely through a press release or accompanied by a filing has been effectively disseminated to the marketplace. Members and candidates must have a reasonable expectation that people have received the information before it can be considered public. It is not necessary, however, to wait for the slowest method of delivery. Once the information is disseminated to the market, it is public information that is no longer covered by this standard.

Members and candidates must be particularly aware of information that is selectively disclosed by corporations to a small group of investors, analysts, or other market participants. Information that is made available to analysts remains nonpublic until it is made available to investors in general. Corporations that disclose information on a limited basis create the potential for insider-trading violations.

Issues of selective disclosure often arise when a corporate insider provides material information to analysts in a briefing or conference call before that information is released to the public. Analysts must be aware that a disclosure made to a room full of analysts does not necessarily make the disclosed information "public." Analysts should also be alert to the possibility that they are selectively receiving material nonpublic information when a company provides them with guidance or interpretation of such publicly available information as financial statements or regulatory filings.

A member or candidate may use insider information provided legitimately by the source company for the specific purpose of conducting due diligence according to the business agreement between the parties for such activities as mergers, loan underwriting, credit ratings, and offering engagements. In such instances, the investment professional would not be considered in violation of Standard II(A) by using the material information. However, the use of insider information provided by the source company for other purposes, especially to trade or entice others to trade the securities of the firm, conflicts with this standard.

Mosaic Theory

A financial analyst gathers and interprets large quantities of information from many sources. The analyst may use significant conclusions derived from the analysis of public and nonmaterial nonpublic information as the basis for investment recommendations and decisions even if those conclusions would have been material inside information had they been communicated directly to the analyst by a company. Under the "mosaic theory," financial analysts are free to act on this collection, or mosaic, of information without risking violation.

The practice of financial analysis depends on the free flow of information. For the fair and efficient operation of the capital markets, analysts and investors must have the greatest amount of information possible to facilitate making well-informed investment decisions about how and where to invest capital. Accurate, timely, and intelligible communication is essential if analysts and investors are to obtain the data needed to make informed decisions about how and where to invest capital. These disclosures must go beyond the information mandated by the reporting requirements of the securities laws and should include specific business information about items used to guide a company's future growth, such as new products, capital projects, and the competitive environment. Analysts seek and use such information to compare and contrast investment alternatives.

Much of the information used by analysts comes directly from companies. Analysts often receive such information through contacts with corporate insiders, especially investor-relations staff and financial officers. Information may be disseminated in the form of press releases, through oral presentations by company executives in analysts' meetings or conference calls, or during analysts' visits to company premises. In seeking to develop the most accurate and complete picture of a company, analysts should also reach beyond contacts with companies themselves and collect information from other sources, such as customers, contractors, suppliers, and the companies' competitors.

Analysts are in the business of formulating opinions and insights that are not obvious to the general investing public about the attractiveness of particular securities. In the course of their work, analysts actively seek out corporate information not generally known to the market for the express purpose of analyzing that information, forming an opinion on its significance, and informing their clients, who can be expected to trade on the basis of the recommendation. Analysts' initiatives to discover and analyze information and communicate their findings to their clients significantly enhance market efficiency, thus benefiting all investors (see *Dirks v. Securities and Exchange Commission*). Accordingly, violations of Standard II(A) will *not* result when a perceptive analyst reaches a conclusion about a corporate action or event through an analysis of public information and items of nonmaterial nonpublic information.

Investment professionals should note, however, that although analysts are free to use mosaic information in their research reports, they should save and document all their research [see Standard V(C)–Record Retention]. Evidence of the analyst's knowledge of public and nonmaterial nonpublic information about a corporation strengthens the assertion that the analyst reached his or her conclusions solely through appropriate methods rather than through the use of material nonpublic information.

Social Media

The continuing advancement in technology allows members, candidates, and the industry at large to exchange information at rates not previously available. It is important for investment professionals to understand the implications of using information from the internet and social media platforms because all such information may not actually be considered public.

Some social media platforms require membership in specific groups in order to access the published content. Members and candidates participating in groups with membership limitations should verify that material information obtained from these sources can also be accessed from a source that would be considered available to the public (e.g., company filings, webpages, and press releases).

Members and candidates may use social media platforms to communicate with clients or investors without conflicting with this standard. As long as the information reaches all clients or is open to the investing public, the use of these platforms would be comparable with other traditional forms of communications, such as e-mails and press releases. Members and candidates, as required by Standard I(A), should also complete all appropriate regulatory filings related to information distributed through social media platforms.

Using Industry Experts

The increased demand for insights for understanding the complexities of some industries has led to an expansion of engagement with outside experts. As the level of engagement increased, new businesses formed to connect analysts and investors with individuals who have specialized knowledge of their industry (e.g., technology or pharmaceuticals). These networks offer investors the opportunity to reach beyond their usual business circles to speak with experts regarding economic conditions, industry trends, and technical issues relating to specific products and services.

Members and candidates may provide compensation to individuals for their insights without violating this standard. However, members and candidates are ultimately responsible for ensuring that they are not requesting or acting on confidential information received from external experts, which is in violation of security regulations and laws or duties to others. As the recent string of insider-trading cases displayed, some experts are willing to provide confidential and protected information for the right incentive.

Firms connecting experts with members or candidates often require both parties to sign agreements concerning the disclosure of material nonpublic information. Even with the protections from such compliance practices, if an expert provides material nonpublic information, members and candidates would be prohibited from taking investment actions on the associated firm until the information became publicly known to the market.

Investment Research Reports

When a particularly well-known or respected analyst issues a report or makes changes to his or her recommendation, that information alone may have an effect on the market and thus may be considered material. Theoretically, under Standard II(A), such a report would have to be made public at the time it was distributed to clients. The analyst is not a company insider, however, and does not have access to inside information. Presumably, the analyst created the report from information available to the public (mosaic theory) and by using his or her expertise to interpret the information. The analyst's hard work, paid for by the client, generated the conclusions.

Simply because the public in general would find the conclusions material does not require that the analyst make his or her work public. Investors who are not clients of the analyst can either do the work themselves or become clients of the analyst to gain access to the analyst's expertise.

Recommended Procedures for Compliance

Achieve Public Dissemination

If a member or candidate determines that information is material, the member or candidate should make reasonable efforts to achieve public dissemination of the information. These efforts usually entail encouraging the issuing company to make the information public. If public dissemination is not possible, the member or candidate must communicate the information only to the designated supervisory and compliance personnel within the member's or candidate's firm and must not take investment action or alter current investment recommendations on the basis of the information. Moreover, members and candidates must not knowingly engage in any conduct that may induce company insiders to privately disclose material nonpublic information.

Adopt Compliance Procedures

Members and candidates should encourage their firms to adopt compliance procedures to prevent the misuse of material nonpublic information. Particularly important is improving compliance in such areas as the review of employee and proprietary trading, the review of investment recommendations, documentation of firm procedures, and the supervision of interdepartmental communications in multiservice firms. Compliance procedures should suit the particular characteristics of a firm, including its size and the nature of its business.

Members and candidates are encouraged to inform their supervisor and compliance personnel of suspected inappropriate use of material nonpublic information as the basis for security trading activities or recommendations being made within their firm.

Adopt Disclosure Procedures

Members and candidates should encourage their firms to develop and follow disclosure policies designed to ensure that information is disseminated to the marketplace in an equitable manner. For example, analysts from small firms should receive the same information and attention from a company as analysts from large firms receive. Similarly, companies should not provide certain information to buy-side analysts but not to sell-side analysts, or vice versa. Furthermore, a company should not discriminate among analysts in the provision of information or "blackball" particular analysts who have given negative reports on the company in the past.

Within investment and research firms, members and candidates should encourage the development of and compliance with procedures for distributing new and updated investment opinions to clients. Recommendations of this nature may represent material market-moving information that needs to be communicated to all clients fairly.

Issue Press Releases

Companies should consider issuing press releases prior to analyst meetings and conference calls and scripting those meetings and calls to decrease the chance that further information will be disclosed. If material nonpublic information is disclosed for the first time in an analyst meeting or call, the company should promptly issue a press release or otherwise make the information publicly available.

Firewall Elements

An information barrier commonly referred to as a "firewall" is the most widely used approach for preventing the communication of material nonpublic information within firms. It restricts the flow of confidential information to those who need to know the information to perform their jobs effectively. The minimum elements of such a system include, but are not limited to, the following:

- substantial control of relevant interdepartmental communications, preferably through a clearance area within the firm in either the compliance or legal department;
- review of employee trading through the maintenance of "watch," "restricted," and "rumor" lists;
- documentation of the procedures designed to limit the flow of information between departments and of the actions taken to enforce those procedures; and
- heightened review or restriction of proprietary trading while a firm is in possession of material nonpublic information.

Appropriate Interdepartmental Communications

Although documentation requirements must, for practical reasons, take into account the differences between the activities of small firms and those of large, multiservice firms, firms of all sizes and types benefit by improving the documentation of their internal enforcement of firewall procedures. Therefore, even at small firms, procedures concerning interdepartmental communication, the review of trading activity, and the investigation of possible violations should be compiled and formalized.

Physical Separation of Departments

As a practical matter, to the greatest extent possible, firms should consider the physical separation of departments and files to prevent the communication of sensitive information that should not be shared. For example, the investment banking and corporate finance areas of a brokerage firm should be separated from the sales and research departments, and a bank's commercial lending department should be segregated from its trust and research departments.

Prevention of Personnel Overlap

There should be no overlap of personnel between the investment banking and corporate finance areas of a brokerage firm and the sales and research departments or between a bank's commercial lending department and its trust and research departments. For a firewall to be effective in a multiservice firm, an employee should be on only one side of the firewall at any time. Inside knowledge may not be limited to information about a specific offering or the current financial condition of a company. Analysts may be exposed to much information about the company, including new product developments or future budget projections that clearly constitute inside knowledge and thus preclude the analyst from returning to his or her research function. For example, an analyst who follows a particular company may provide limited assistance to the investment bankers under carefully controlled circumstances when the firm's investment banking department is involved in a deal with the company. That analyst must then be treated as though he or she were an investment banker; the analyst must remain on the investment banking side of the wall until any information he or she learns is publicly disclosed. In short, the analyst cannot use any information learned in the course of the project for research purposes and cannot share that information with colleagues in the research department.

A Reporting System

A primary objective of an effective firewall procedure is to establish a reporting system in which authorized people review and approve communications between departments. If an employee behind a firewall believes that he or she needs to share confidential information with someone on the other side of the wall, the employee should consult a designated compliance officer to determine whether sharing the information is necessary and how much information should be shared. If the sharing is necessary, the compliance officer should coordinate the process of "looking over the wall" so that the necessary information will be shared and the integrity of the procedure will be maintained.

A single supervisor or compliance officer should have the specific authority and responsibility of deciding whether information is material and whether it is sufficiently public to be used as the basis for investment decisions. Ideally, the supervisor or compliance officer responsible for communicating information to a firm's research or brokerage area would not be a member of that area.

Personal Trading Limitations

Firms should consider restrictions or prohibitions on personal trading by employees and should carefully monitor both proprietary trading and personal trading by employees. Firms should require employees to make periodic reports (to the extent that such reporting is not already required by securities laws) of their own transactions and transactions made for the benefit of family members. Securities should be placed on a restricted list when a firm has or may have material nonpublic information. The broad distribution of a restricted list often triggers the sort of trading the list was developed to avoid. Therefore, a watch list shown to only the few people responsible for compliance should be used to monitor transactions in specified securities. The use of a watch list in combination with a restricted list is an increasingly common means of ensuring effective control of personal trading.

Record Maintenance

Multiservice firms should maintain written records of the communications between various departments. Firms should place a high priority on training and should consider instituting comprehensive training programs, particularly for employees in sensitive areas.

Proprietary Trading Procedures

Procedures concerning the restriction or review of a firm's proprietary trading while the firm possesses material nonpublic information will necessarily depend on the types of proprietary trading in which the firm may engage. A prohibition on all types of proprietary activity when a firm comes into possession of material nonpublic information is *not* appropriate. For example, when a firm acts as a market maker, a prohibition on proprietary trading may be counterproductive to the goals of maintaining the confidentiality of information and market liquidity. This concern is particularly important in the relationships between small, regional broker/dealers and small issuers. In many situations, a firm will take a small issuer public with the understanding that the firm will continue to be a market maker in the stock. In such instances, a withdrawal by the firm from market-making activities would be a clear tip to outsiders. Firms that continue market-making activity while in the possession of material nonpublic information should, however, instruct their market makers to remain passive with respect to the market—that is, to take only the contra side of unsolicited customer trades.

In risk-arbitrage trading, the case for a trading prohibition is more compelling than it is in the case of market making. The impetus for arbitrage trading is neither passive nor reactive, and the potential for illegal profits is greater than in market making. The most prudent course for firms is to suspend arbitrage activity when a security is placed on the watch list. Those firms that continue arbitrage activity face a high hurdle in proving the adequacy of their internal procedures for preventing trading on material nonpublic information and must demonstrate a stringent review and documentation of firm trades.

Communication to All Employees

Members and candidates should encourage their employers to circulate written compliance policies and guidelines to all employees. Policies and guidelines should be used in conjunction with training programs aimed at enabling employees to recognize material nonpublic information. Such information is not always clearly identifiable.

Employees must be given sufficient training to either make an informed decision or to realize they need to consult a supervisor or compliance officer before engaging in questionable transactions. Appropriate policies reinforce that using material nonpublic information is illegal in many countries. Such trading activities based on material nonpublic information undermine the integrity of the individual, the firm, and the capital markets.

Application of the Standard

Example 1 (Acting on Nonpublic Information):

Frank Barnes, the president and controlling shareholder of the SmartTown clothing chain, decides to accept a tender offer and sell the family business at a price almost double the market price of its shares. He describes this decision to his sister (SmartTown's treasurer), who conveys it to her daughter (who owns no stock in the family company at present), who tells her husband, Staple. Staple, however, tells his stockbroker, Alex Halsey, who immediately buys SmartTown stock for himself.

> *Comment*: The information regarding the pending sale is both material and nonpublic. Staple has violated Standard II(A) by communicating the inside information to his broker. Halsey also has violated the standard by buying the shares on the basis of material nonpublic information.

Example 2 (Controlling Nonpublic Information):

Samuel Peter, an analyst with Scotland and Pierce Incorporated, is assisting his firm with a secondary offering for Bright Ideas Lamp Company. Peter participates, via telephone conference call, in a meeting with Scotland and Pierce investment banking employees and Bright Ideas' CEO. Peter is advised that the company's earnings projections for the next year have significantly dropped. Throughout the telephone conference call, several Scotland and Pierce salespeople and portfolio managers walk in and out of Peter's office, where the telephone call is taking place. As a result, they are aware of the drop in projected earnings for Bright Ideas. Before the conference call is concluded, the salespeople trade the stock of the company on behalf of the firm's clients and other firm personnel trade the stock in a firm proprietary account and in employees' personal accounts.

> *Comment*: Peter has violated Standard II(A) because he failed to prevent the transfer and misuse of material nonpublic information to others in his firm. Peter's firm should have adopted information barriers to prevent the communication of nonpublic information between departments of the firm. The salespeople and portfolio managers who traded on the information have also violated Standard II(A) by trading on inside information.

Example 3 (Selective Disclosure of Material Information):

Elizabeth Levenson is based in Hanoi and covers the Vietnamese market for her firm, which is based in Singapore. She is invited, together with the other 10 largest shareholders of a manufacturing company, to meet the finance director of that company. During the meeting, the finance director states that the company expects its workforce to strike next Friday, which will cripple productivity and distribution. Can Levenson use this information as a basis to change her rating on the company from "buy" to "sell"?

> *Comment*: Levenson must first determine whether the material information is public. According to Standard II(A), if the company has not made this information public (a small group forum does not qualify as a method of public dissemination), she cannot use the information.

Example 4 (Determining Materiality):

Leah Fechtman is trying to decide whether to hold or sell shares of an oil-and-gas exploration company that she owns in several of the funds she manages. Although the company has underperformed the index for some time already, the trends in the industry sector signal that companies of this type might become takeover targets. While she is considering her decision, her doctor, who casually follows the markets, mentions that she thinks that the company in question will soon be bought out by a large multinational conglomerate and that it would be a good idea to buy the stock right now. After talking to various investment professionals and checking their opinions on the company as well as checking industry trends, Fechtman decides the next day to accumulate more stock in the oil-and-gas exploration company.

> *Comment*: Although information on an expected takeover bid may be of the type that is generally material and nonpublic, in this case, the source of information is unreliable, so the information cannot be considered material. Therefore, Fechtman is not prohibited from trading the stock on the basis of this information.

Example 5 (Applying the Mosaic Theory):

Jagdish Teja is a buy-side analyst covering the furniture industry. Looking for an attractive company to recommend as a buy, he analyzes several furniture makers by studying their financial reports and visiting their operations. He also talks to some designers and retailers to find out which furniture styles are trendy and popular. Although none of the companies that he analyzes are a clear buy, he discovers that one of them, Swan Furniture Company (SFC), may be in financial trouble. SFC's extravagant new designs have been introduced at substantial cost. Even though these designs initially attracted attention, the public is now buying more conservative furniture from other makers. Based on this information and on a profit-and-loss analysis, Teja believes that SFC's next quarter earnings will drop substantially. He issues a sell recommendation for SFC. Immediately after receiving that recommendation, investment managers start reducing the SFC stock in their portfolios.

> *Comment*: Information on quarterly earnings data is material and nonpublic. Teja arrived at his conclusion about the earnings drop on the basis of public information and on pieces of nonmaterial nonpublic information (such as opinions of designers and retailers). Therefore, trading based on Teja's correct conclusion is not prohibited by Standard II(A).

Example 6 (Applying the Mosaic Theory):

Roger Clement is a senior financial analyst who specializes in the European automobile sector at Rivoli Capital. Because he has been repeatedly nominated by many leading industry magazines and newsletters as a "best analyst" for the automobile industry, he is widely regarded as an authority on the sector. After speaking with representatives of Turgot Chariots—a European auto manufacturer with sales primarily in South Korea—and after conducting interviews with salespeople, labor leaders, his firm's Korean currency analysts, and banking officials, Clement analyzed Turgot Chariots and concluded that (1) its newly introduced model will probably not meet sales expectations, (2) its corporate restructuring strategy may well face serious opposition from unions, (3) the depreciation of the Korean won should lead to pressure on margins for the industry in general and Turgot's market segment in particular, and (4) banks could take a tougher-than-expected stance in the upcoming round of credit renegotiations with the company. For these reasons, he changes his conclusion about the company from "market outperform" to "market underperform." Clement retains the support material used to reach his conclusion in case questions later arise.

> *Comment*: To reach a conclusion about the value of the company, Clement has pieced together a number of nonmaterial or public bits of information that affect Turgot Chariots. Therefore, under the mosaic theory, Clement has not violated Standard II(A) in drafting the report.

Example 7 (Analyst Recommendations as Material Nonpublic Information):

The next day, Clement is preparing to be interviewed on a global financial news television program where he will discuss his changed recommendation on Turgot Chariots for the first time in public. While preparing for the program, he mentions to the show's producers and Mary Zito, the journalist who will be interviewing him, the information he will be discussing. Just prior to going on the air, Zito sells her holdings in Turgot Chariots. She also phones her father with the information because she knows that he and other family members have investments in Turgot Chariots.

> *Comment*: When Zito receives advance notice of Clement's change of opinion, she knows it will have a material impact on the stock price, even if she is not totally aware of Clement's underlying reasoning. She is not a client

of Clement but obtains early access to the material nonpublic information prior to publication. Her trades are thus based on material nonpublic information and violate Standard II(A).

Zito further violates the Standard by relaying the information to her father. It would not matter if he or any other family member traded; the act of providing the information violates Standard II(A). The fact that the information is provided to a family member does not absolve someone of the prohibition of using or communicating material nonpublic information.

Example 8 (Acting on Nonpublic Information):

Ashton Kellogg is a retired investment professional who manages his own portfolio. He owns shares in National Savings, a large local bank. A close friend and golfing buddy, John Mayfield, is a senior executive at National. National has seen its stock price drop considerably, and the news and outlook are not good. In a conversation about the economy and the banking industry on the golf course, Mayfield relays the information that National will surprise the investment community in a few days when it announces excellent earnings for the quarter. Kellogg is pleasantly surprised by this information, and thinking that Mayfield, as a senior executive, knows the law and would not disclose inside information, he doubles his position in the bank. Subsequently, National announces that it had good operating earnings but had to set aside reserves for anticipated significant losses on its loan portfolio. The combined news causes the stock to go down 60%.

Comment: Even though Kellogg believes that Mayfield would not break the law by disclosing inside information and money was lost on the purchase, Kellogg should not have purchased additional shares of National. It is the member's or candidate's responsibility to make sure, before executing investment actions, that comments about earnings are not material nonpublic information. Kellogg has violated Standard II(A).

Example 9 (Mosaic Theory):

John Doll is a research analyst for a hedge fund that also sells its research to a select group of paying client investment firms. Doll's focus is medical technology companies and products, and he has been in the business long enough and has been successful enough to build up a very credible network of friends and experts in the business. Doll has been working on a major research report recommending Boyce Health, a medical device manufacturer. He recently ran into an old acquaintance at a wedding who is a senior executive at Boyce, and Doll asked about the business. Doll was drawn to a statement that the executive, who has responsibilities in the new products area, made about a product: "I would not get too excited about the medium-term prospects; we have a lot of work to do first." Doll incorporated this and other information about the new Boyce product in his long-term recommendation of Boyce.

Comment: Doll's conversation with the senior executive is part of the mosaic of information used in recommending Boyce. When holding discussions with a firm executive, Doll would need to guard against soliciting or obtaining material nonpublic information. Before issuing the report, the executive's statement about the continuing development of the product would need to be weighed against the other known public facts to determine whether it would be considered material.

Example 10 (Materiality Determination):

Larry Nadler, a trader for a mutual fund, gets a text message from another firm's trader, whom he has known for years. The message indicates a software company is going to report strong earnings when the firm publicly announces in two days. Nadler has a buy order from a portfolio manager within his firm to purchase several hundred thousand shares of the stock. Nadler is aggressive in placing the portfolio manager's order and completes the purchases by the following morning, a day ahead of the firm's planned earnings announcement.

> *Comment*: There are often rumors and whisper numbers before a release of any kind. The text message from the other trader would most likely be considered market noise. Unless Nadler knew that the trader had an ongoing business relationship with the public firm, he had no reason to suspect he was receiving material nonpublic information that would prevent him from completing the trading request of the portfolio manager.

Example 11 (Using an Expert Network):

Mary McCoy is the senior drug analyst at a mutual fund. Her firm hires a service that connects her to experts in the treatment of cancer. Through various phone conversations, McCoy enhances her understanding of the latest therapies for successful treatment. This information is critical to Mary making informed recommendations of the companies producing these drugs.

> *Comment*: McCoy is appropriately using the expert networks to enhance her evaluation process. She has neither asked for nor received information that may be considered material and nonpublic, such as preliminary trial results. McCoy is allowed to seek advice from professionals within the industry that she follows.

Example 12 (Using an Expert Network):

Tom Watson is a research analyst working for a hedge fund. To stay informed, Watson relies on outside experts for information on such industries as technology and pharmaceuticals, where new advancements occur frequently. The meetings with the industry experts often are arranged through networks or placement agents that have specific policies and procedures in place to deter the exchange of material nonpublic information.

Watson arranges a call to discuss future prospects for one of the fund's existing technology company holdings, a company that was testing a new semiconductor product. The scientist leading the tests indicates his disappointment with the performance of the new semiconductor. Following the call, Watson relays the insights he received to others at the fund. The fund sells its current position in the company and buys many put options because the market is anticipating the success of the new semiconductor and the share price reflects the market's optimism.

> *Comment*: Watson has violated Standard II(A) by passing along material nonpublic information concerning the ongoing product tests, which the fund used to trade in the securities and options of the related company. Watson cannot simply rely on the agreements signed by individuals who participate in expert networks that state that he has not received information that would prohibit his trading activity. He must make his own determination whether information he received through these arrangements reaches a materiality threshold that would affect his trading abilities.

Standard II(B) Market Manipulation

Members and Candidates must not engage in practices that distort prices or artificially inflate trading volume with the intent to mislead market participants.

Guidance

Highlights:

- *Information-Based Manipulation*
- *Transaction-Based Manipulation*

Standard II(B) requires that members and candidates uphold market integrity by prohibiting market manipulation. Market manipulation includes practices that distort security prices or trading volume with the intent to deceive people or entities that rely on information in the market. Market manipulation damages the interests of all investors by disrupting the smooth functioning of financial markets and lowering investor confidence.

Market manipulation may lead to a lack of trust in the fairness of the capital markets, resulting in higher risk premiums and reduced investor participation. A reduction in the efficiency of a local capital market may negatively affect the growth and economic health of the country and may also influence the operations of the globally interconnected capital markets. Although market manipulation may be less likely to occur in mature financial markets than in emerging markets, cross-border investing increasingly exposes all global investors to the potential for such practices.

Market manipulation includes (1) the dissemination of false or misleading information and (2) transactions that deceive or would be likely to mislead market participants by distorting the price-setting mechanism of financial instruments. The development of new products and technologies increases the incentives, means, and opportunities for market manipulation. Additionally, the increasing complexity and sophistication of the technologies used for communicating with market participants have created new avenues for manipulation.

Information-Based Manipulation

Information-based manipulation includes, but is not limited to, spreading false rumors to induce trading by others. For example, members and candidates must refrain from "pumping up" the price of an investment by issuing misleading positive information or overly optimistic projections of a security's worth only to later "dump" the investment (i.e., sell it) once the price, fueled by the misleading information's effect on other market participants, reaches an artificially high level.

Transaction-Based Manipulation

Transaction-based manipulation involves instances where a member or candidate knew or should have known that his or her actions could affect the pricing of a security. This type of manipulation includes, but is not limited to, the following:

- transactions that artificially affect prices or volume to give the impression of activity or price movement in a financial instrument, which represent a diversion from the expectations of a fair and efficient market, and
- securing a controlling, dominant position in a financial instrument to exploit and manipulate the price of a related derivative and/or the underlying asset.

Standard II(B) is not intended to preclude transactions undertaken on legitimate trading strategies based on perceived market inefficiencies. The intent of the action is critical to determining whether it is a violation of this standard.

Application of the Standard

Example 1 (Independent Analysis and Company Promotion):

The principal owner of Financial Information Services (FIS) entered into an agreement with two microcap companies to promote the companies' stock in exchange for stock and cash compensation. The principal owner caused FIS to disseminate e-mails, design and maintain several websites, and distribute an online investment newsletter—all of which recommended investment in the two companies. The systematic publication of purportedly independent analyses and recommendations containing inaccurate and highly promotional and speculative statements increased public investment in the companies and led to dramatically higher stock prices.

> *Comment*: The principal owner of FIS violated Standard II(B) by using inaccurate reporting and misleading information under the guise of independent analysis to artificially increase the stock price of the companies. Furthermore, the principal owner violated Standard V(A)–Diligence and Reasonable Basis by not having a reasonable and adequate basis for recommending the two companies and violated Standard VI(A)–Disclosure of Conflicts by not disclosing to investors the compensation agreements (which constituted a conflict of interest).

Example 2 (Personal Trading Practices and Price):

John Gray is a private investor in Belgium who bought a large position several years ago in Fame Pharmaceuticals, a German small-cap security with limited average trading volume. He has now decided to significantly reduce his holdings owing to the poor price performance. Gray is worried that the low trading volume for the stock may cause the price to decline further as he attempts to sell his large position.

Gray devises a plan to divide his holdings into multiple accounts in different brokerage firms and private banks in the names of family members, friends, and even a private religious institution. He then creates a rumor campaign on various blogs and social media outlets promoting the company.

Gray begins to buy and sell the stock using the accounts in hopes of raising the trading volume and the price. He conducts the trades through multiple brokers, selling slightly larger positions than he bought on a tactical schedule, and over time, he is able to reduce his holding as desired without negatively affecting the sale price.

> *Comment*: John violated Standard II(B) by fraudulently creating the appearance that there was a greater investor interest in the stock through the online rumors. Additionally, through his trading strategy, he created the

appearance that there was greater liquidity in the stock than actually existed. He was able to manipulate the price through both misinformation and trading practices.

Example 3 (Creating Artificial Price Volatility):

Matthew Murphy is an analyst at Divisadero Securities & Co., which has a significant number of hedge funds among its most important brokerage clients. Some of the hedge funds hold short positions on Wirewolf Semiconductor. Two trading days before the publication of a quarter-end report, Murphy alerts his sales force that he is about to issue a research report on Wirewolf that will include the following opinions:

- quarterly revenues are likely to fall short of management's guidance,
- earnings will be as much as 5 cents per share (or more than 10%) below consensus, and
- Wirewolf's highly respected chief financial officer may be about to join another company.

Knowing that Wirewolf has already entered its declared quarter-end "quiet period" before reporting earnings (and thus would be reluctant to respond to rumors), Murphy times the release of his research report specifically to sensationalize the negative aspects of the message in order to create significant downward pressure on Wirewolf's stock—to the distinct advantage of Divisadero's hedge fund clients. The report's conclusions are based on speculation, not on fact. The next day, the research report is broadcast to all of Divisadero's clients and to the usual newswire services.

Before Wirewolf's investor-relations department can assess the damage on the final trading day of the quarter and refute Murphy's report, its stock opens trading sharply lower, allowing Divisadero's clients to cover their short positions at substantial gains.

> *Comment*: Murphy violated Standard II(B) by aiming to create artificial price volatility designed to have a material impact on the price of an issuer's stock. Moreover, by lacking an adequate basis for the recommendation, Murphy also violated Standard V(A)–Diligence and Reasonable Basis.

Example 4 (Personal Trading and Volume):

Rajesh Sekar manages two funds—an equity fund and a balanced fund—whose equity components are supposed to be managed in accordance with the same model. According to that model, the funds' holdings in stock of Digital Design Inc. (DD) are excessive. Reduction of the DD holdings would not be easy, however, because the stock has low liquidity in the stock market. Sekar decides to start trading larger portions of DD stock back and forth between his two funds to slowly increase the price; he believes market participants will see growing volume and increasing price and become interested in the stock. If other investors are willing to buy the DD stock because of such interest, then Sekar will be able to get rid of at least some of his overweight position without inducing price decreases. In this way, the whole transaction will be for the benefit of fund participants, even if additional brokers' commissions are incurred.

> *Comment*: Sekar's plan would be beneficial for his funds' participants but is based on artificial distortion of both trading volume and the price of the DD stock and thus constitutes a violation of Standard II(B).

Example 5 ("Pump-Priming" Strategy):

ACME Futures Exchange is launching a new bond futures contract. To convince investors, traders, arbitrageurs, hedgers, and so on, to use its contract, the exchange attempts to demonstrate that it has the best liquidity. To do so, it enters into agreements with members in which they commit to a substantial minimum trading volume on the new contract over a specific period in exchange for substantial reductions of their regular commissions.

> *Comment*: The formal liquidity of a market is determined by the obligations set on market makers, but the actual liquidity of a market is better estimated by the actual trading volume and bid–ask spreads. Attempts to mislead participants about the actual liquidity of the market constitute a violation of Standard II(B). In this example, investors have been intentionally misled to believe they chose the most liquid instrument for some specific purpose, but they could eventually see the actual liquidity of the contract significantly reduced after the term of the agreement expires. If the ACME Futures Exchange fully discloses its agreement with members to boost transactions over some initial launch period, it will not violate Standard II(B). ACME's intent is not to harm investors but, on the contrary, to give them a better service. For that purpose, it may engage in a liquidity-pumping strategy, but the strategy must be disclosed.

Example 6 (Creating Artificial Price Volatility):

Emily Gordon, an analyst of household products companies, is employed by a research boutique, Picador & Co. Based on information that she has gathered during a trip through Latin America, she believes that Hygene, Inc., a major marketer of personal care products, has generated better-than-expected sales from its new product initiatives in South America. After modestly boosting her projections for revenue and for gross profit margin in her worksheet models for Hygene, Gordon estimates that her earnings projection of US$2.00 per diluted share for the current year may be as much as 5% too low. She contacts the chief financial officer (CFO) of Hygene to try to gain confirmation of her findings from her trip and to get some feedback regarding her revised models. The CFO declines to comment and reiterates management's most recent guidance of US$1.95–US$2.05 for the year.

Gordon decides to try to force a comment from the company by telling Picador & Co. clients who follow a momentum investment style that consensus earnings projections for Hygene are much too low; she explains that she is considering raising her published estimate by an ambitious US$0.15 to US$2.15 per share. She believes that when word of an unrealistically high earnings projection filters back to Hygene's investor-relations department, the company will feel compelled to update its earnings guidance. Meanwhile, Gordon hopes that she is at least correct with respect to the earnings direction and that she will help clients who act on her insights to profit from a quick gain by trading on her advice.

> *Comment*: By exaggerating her earnings projections in order to try to fuel a quick gain in Hygene's stock price, Gordon is in violation of Standard II(B). Furthermore, by virtue of previewing her intentions of revising upward her earnings projections to only a select group of clients, she is in violation of Standard III(B)–Fair Dealing. However, it would have been acceptable for Gordon to write a report that
>
> - framed her earnings projection in a range of possible outcomes,

- outlined clearly the assumptions used in her Hygene models that took into consideration the findings from her trip through Latin America, and
- was distributed to all Picador & Co. clients in an equitable manner.

Example 7 (Pump and Dump Strategy):

In an effort to pump up the price of his holdings in Moosehead & Belfast Railroad Company, Steve Weinberg logs on to several investor chat rooms on the internet to start rumors that the company is about to expand its rail network in anticipation of receiving a large contract for shipping lumber.

> *Comment*: Weinberg has violated Standard II(B) by disseminating false information about Moosehead & Belfast with the intent to mislead market participants.

Example 8 (Manipulating Model Inputs):

Bill Mandeville supervises a structured financing team for Superior Investment Bank. His responsibilities include packaging new structured investment products and managing Superior's relationship with relevant rating agencies. To achieve the best rating possible, Mandeville uses mostly positive scenarios as model inputs—scenarios that reflect minimal downside risk in the assets underlying the structured products. The resulting output statistics in the rating request and underwriting prospectus support the idea that the new structured products have minimal potential downside risk. Additionally, Mandeville's compensation from Superior is partially based on both the level of the rating assigned and the successful sale of new structured investment products but does not have a link to the long-term performance of the instruments.

Mandeville is extremely successful and leads Superior as the top originator of structured investment products for the next two years. In the third year, the economy experiences difficulties and the values of the assets underlying structured products significantly decline. The subsequent defaults lead to major turmoil in the capital markets, the demise of Superior Investment Bank, and the loss of Mandeville's employment.

> *Comment*: Mandeville manipulates the inputs of a model to minimize associated risk to achieve higher ratings. His understanding of structured products allows him to skillfully decide which inputs to include in support of the desired rating and price. This information manipulation for short-term gain, which is in violation of Standard II(B), ultimately causes significant damage to many parties and the capital markets as a whole. Mandeville should have realized that promoting a rating and price with inaccurate information could cause not only a loss of price confidence in the particular structured product but also a loss of investor trust in the system. Such loss of confidence affects the ability of the capital markets to operate efficiently.

Example 9 (Information Manipulation):

Allen King is a performance analyst for Torrey Investment Funds. King believes that the portfolio manager for the firm's small- and microcap equity fund dislikes him because the manager never offers him tickets to the local baseball team's games but does offer tickets to other employees. To incite a potential regulatory review of the manager, King creates user profiles on several online forums under the portfolio manager's name and starts rumors about potential mergers for several of the smaller companies in the portfolio. As the prices of these companies' stocks increase, the portfolio manager sells the position, which leads to an investigation by the regulator as King desired.

> *Comment*: King has violated Standard II(B) even though he did not personally profit from the market's reaction to the rumor. In posting the false information, King misleads others into believing the companies were likely to be acquired. Although his intent was to create trouble for the portfolio manager, his actions clearly manipulated the factual information that was available to the market.

STANDARD III: DUTIES TO CLIENTS

Standard III(A) Loyalty, Prudence, and Care

Members and Candidates have a duty of loyalty to their clients and must act with reasonable care and exercise prudent judgment. Members and Candidates must act for the benefit of their clients and place their clients' interests before their employer's or their own interests.

Guidance

Highlights:

- *Understanding the Application of Loyalty, Prudence, and Care*
- *Identifying the Actual Investment Client*
- *Developing the Client's Portfolio*
- *Soft Commission Policies*
- *Proxy Voting Policies*

Standard III(A) clarifies that client interests are paramount. A member's or candidate's responsibility to a client includes a duty of loyalty and a duty to exercise reasonable care. Investment actions must be carried out for the sole benefit of the client and in a manner the member or candidate believes, given the known facts and circumstances, to be in the best interest of the client. Members and candidates must exercise the same level of prudence, judgment, and care that they would apply in the management and disposition of their own interests in similar circumstances.

Prudence requires caution and discretion. The exercise of prudence by investment professionals requires that they act with the care, skill, and diligence that a reasonable person acting in a like capacity and familiar with such matters would use. In the context of managing a client's portfolio, prudence requires following the investment parameters set forth by the client and balancing risk and return. Acting with care requires members and candidates to act in a prudent and judicious manner in avoiding harm to clients.

Standard III(A) sets minimum expectations for members and candidates when fulfilling their responsibilities to their clients. Regulatory and legal requirements for such duties can vary across the investment industry depending on a variety of factors, including job function of the investment professional, the existence of an adviser/client relationship, and the nature of the recommendations being offered. From the perspective of the end user of financial services, these different standards can be arcane and confusing, leaving investors unsure of what level of service to expect from investment professionals they employ. The single standard of conduct described in Standard III(A) benefits investors by establishing a benchmark for the duties of loyalty, prudence, and care and clarifies that all CFA Institute members and candidates, regardless of job title, local laws, or cultural differences, are required to comply with these fundamental responsibilities. Investors hiring members or candidates who must adhere to the duty of loyalty, prudence, and care set forth in this standard can be confident that these responsibilities are a requirement regardless of any legally imposed fiduciary duties.

Standard III(A), however, is not a substitute for a member's or candidate's legal or regulatory obligations. As stated in Standard I(A), members and candidates must abide by the most strict requirements imposed on them by regulators or the Code and Standards, including any legally imposed fiduciary duty. Members and candidates must also be aware of whether they have "custody" or effective control of client assets. If so, a heightened level of responsibility arises. Members and candidates are considered to have custody if they have any direct or indirect access to client funds. Members and candidates must manage any pool of assets in their control in accordance with the terms of the governing documents (such as trust documents and investment management agreements), which are the primary determinant of the manager's powers and duties. Whenever their actions are contrary to provisions of those instruments or applicable law, members and candidates are at risk of violating Standard III(A).

Understanding the Application of Loyalty, Prudence, and Care

Standard III(A) establishes a minimum benchmark for the duties of loyalty, prudence, and care that are required of all members and candidates regardless of whether a legal fiduciary duty applies. Although fiduciary duty often encompasses the principles of loyalty, prudence, and care, Standard III(A) does not render all members and candidates fiduciaries. The responsibilities of members and candidates for fulfilling their obligations under this standard depend greatly on the nature of their professional responsibilities and the relationships they have with clients. The conduct of members and candidates may or may not rise to the level of being a fiduciary, depending on the type of client, whether the member or candidate is giving investment advice, and the many facts and circumstances surrounding a particular transaction or client relationship.

Fiduciary duties are often imposed by law or regulation when an individual or institution is charged with the duty of acting for the benefit of another party, such as managing investment assets. The duty required in fiduciary relationships exceeds what is acceptable in many other business relationships because a fiduciary is in an enhanced position of trust. Although members and candidates must comply with any legally imposed fiduciary duty, the Code and Standards neither impose such a legal responsibility nor require all members or candidates to act as fiduciaries. However, Standard III(A) requires members and candidates to work in the client's best interest no matter what the job function.

A member or candidate who does not provide advisory services to a client but who acts only as a trade execution professional must prudently work in the client's interest when completing requested trades. Acting in the client's best interest requires these professionals to use their skills and diligence to execute trades in the most favorable terms that can be achieved. Members and candidates operating in such positions must use care to operate within the parameters set by the client's trading instructions.

Members and candidates may also operate in a blended environment where they execute client trades and offer advice on a limited set of investment options. The extent of the advisory arrangement and limitations should be outlined in the agreement with the client at the outset of the relationship. For instance, members and candidates should inform clients that the advice provided will be limited to the propriety products of the firm and not include other products available on the market. Clients who want access to a wider range of investment products would have the information necessary to decide not to engage with members or candidates working under these restrictions.

Members and candidates operating in this blended context would comply with their obligations by recommending the allowable products that are consistent with the client's objectives and risk tolerance. They would exercise care through diligently aligning the client's needs with the attributes of the products being recommended. Members and candidates should place the client's interests first by disregarding any firm or personal interest in motivating a recommended transaction.

There is a large variety of professional relationships that members and candidates have with their clients. Standard III(A) requires them to fulfill the obligations outlined explicitly or implicitly in the client agreements to the best of their abilities and with loyalty, prudence, and care. Whether a member or candidate is structuring a new securitization transaction, completing a credit rating analysis, or leading a public company, he or she must work with prudence and care in delivering the agreed-on services.

Identifying the Actual Investment Client

The first step for members and candidates in fulfilling their duty of loyalty to clients is to determine the identity of the "client" to whom the duty of loyalty is owed. In the context of an investment manager managing the personal assets of an individual, the client is easily identified. When the manager is responsible for the portfolios of pension plans or trusts, however, the client is not the person or entity who hires the manager but, rather, the beneficiaries of the plan or trust. The duty of loyalty is owed to the ultimate beneficiaries.

In some situations, an actual client or group of beneficiaries may not exist. Members and candidates managing a fund to an index or an expected mandate owe the duty of loyalty, prudence, and care to invest in a manner consistent with the stated mandate. The decisions of a fund's manager, although benefiting all fund investors, do not have to be based on an individual investor's requirements and risk profile. Client loyalty and care for those investing in the fund are the responsibility of members and candidates who have an advisory relationship with those individuals.

Situations involving potential conflicts of interest with respect to responsibilities to clients may be extremely complex because they may involve a number of competing interests. The duty of loyalty, prudence, and care applies to a large number of persons in varying capacities, but the exact duties may differ in many respects in accord with the relationship with each client or each type of account in which the assets are managed. Members and candidates must not only put their obligations to clients first in all dealings but also endeavor to avoid all real or potential conflicts of interest.

Members and candidates with positions whose responsibilities do not include direct investment management also have "clients" that must be considered. Just as there are various types of advisory relationships, members and candidates must look at their roles and responsibilities when making a determination of who their clients are. Sometimes the client is easily identifiable; such is the case in the relationship between a company executive and the firm's public shareholders. At other times, the client may be the investing public as a whole, in which case the goals of independence and objectivity of research surpass the goal of loyalty to a single organization.

Developing the Client's Portfolio

The duty of loyalty, prudence, and care owed to the individual client is especially important because the professional investment manager typically possesses greater knowledge in the investment arena than the client does. This disparity places the individual client in a vulnerable position; the client must trust the manager. The manager in these situations should ensure that the client's objectives and expectations for the performance of the account are realistic and suitable to the client's circumstances and that the risks involved are appropriate. In most circumstances, recommended investment strategies should relate to the long-term objectives and circumstances of the client.

Particular care must be taken to detect whether the goals of the investment manager or the firm in conducting business, selling products, and executing security transactions potentially conflict with the best interests and objectives of the client. When members and candidates cannot avoid potential conflicts between their firm and clients' interests, they must provide clear and factual disclosures of the circumstances to the clients.

Members and candidates must follow any guidelines set by their clients for the management of their assets. Some clients, such as charitable organizations and pension plans, have strict investment policies that limit investment options to certain types or classes of investment or prohibit investment in certain securities. Other organizations have aggressive policies that do not prohibit investments by type but, instead, set criteria on the basis of the portfolio's total risk and return.

Investment decisions must be judged in the context of the total portfolio rather than by individual investment within the portfolio. The member's or candidate's duty is satisfied with respect to a particular investment if the individual has thoroughly considered the investment's place in the overall portfolio, the risk of loss and opportunity for gains, tax implications, and the diversification, liquidity, cash flow, and overall return requirements of the assets or the portion of the assets for which the manager is responsible.

Soft Commission Policies

An investment manager often has discretion over the selection of brokers executing transactions. Conflicts may arise when an investment manager uses client brokerage to purchase research services, a practice commonly called "soft dollars" or "soft commissions." A member or candidate who pays a higher brokerage commission than he or she would normally pay to allow for the purchase of goods or services, without corresponding benefit to the client, violates the duty of loyalty to the client.

From time to time, a client will direct a manager to use the client's brokerage to purchase goods or services for the client, a practice that is commonly called "directed brokerage." Because brokerage commission is an asset of the client and is used to benefit that client, not the manager, such a practice does not violate any duty of loyalty. However, a member or candidate is obligated to seek "best price" and "best execution" and be assured by the client that the goods or services purchased from the brokerage will benefit the account beneficiaries. "Best execution" refers to a trading process that seeks to maximize the value of the client's portfolio within the client's stated investment objectives and constraints. In addition, the member or candidate should disclose to the client that the client may not be getting best execution from the directed brokerage.

Proxy Voting Policies

The duty of loyalty, prudence, and care may apply in a number of situations facing the investment professional besides those related directly to investing assets.

Part of a member's or candidate's duty of loyalty includes voting proxies in an informed and responsible manner. Proxies have economic value to a client, and members and candidates must ensure that they properly safeguard and maximize this value. An investment manager who fails to vote, casts a vote without considering the impact of the question, or votes blindly with management on nonroutine governance issues (e.g., a change in company capitalization) may violate this standard. Voting of proxies is an integral part of the management of investments.

A cost–benefit analysis may show that voting all proxies may not benefit the client, so voting proxies may not be necessary in all instances. Members and candidates should disclose to clients their proxy voting policies.

Recommended Procedures for Compliance

Regular Account Information

Members and candidates with control of client assets (1) should submit to each client, at least quarterly, an itemized statement showing the funds and securities in the custody or possession of the member or candidate plus all debits, credits, and transactions that occurred during the period, (2) should disclose to the client where the assets are to be maintained, as well as where or when they are moved, and (3) should separate the client's assets from any other party's assets, including the member's or candidate's own assets.

Client Approval

If a member or candidate is uncertain about the appropriate course of action with respect to a client, the member or candidate should consider what he or she would expect or demand if the member or candidate were the client. If in doubt, a member or candidate should disclose the questionable matter in writing to the client and obtain client approval.

Firm Policies

Members and candidates should address and encourage their firms to address the following topics when drafting the statements or manuals containing their policies and procedures regarding responsibilities to clients:

- *Follow all applicable rules and laws*: Members and candidates must follow all legal requirements and applicable provisions of the Code and Standards.
- *Establish the investment objectives of the client*: Make a reasonable inquiry into a client's investment experience, risk and return objectives, and financial constraints prior to making investment recommendations or taking investment actions.
- *Consider all the information when taking actions*: When taking investment actions, members and candidates must consider the appropriateness and suitability of the investment relative to (1) the client's needs and circumstances, (2) the investment's basic characteristics, and (3) the basic characteristics of the total portfolio.
- *Diversify*: Members and candidates should diversify investments to reduce the risk of loss, unless diversification is not consistent with plan guidelines or is contrary to the account objectives.
- *Carry out regular reviews*: Members and candidates should establish regular review schedules to ensure that the investments held in the account adhere to the terms of the governing documents.
- *Deal fairly with all clients with respect to investment actions*: Members and candidates must not favor some clients over others and should establish policies for allocating trades and disseminating investment recommendations.
- *Disclose conflicts of interest*: Members and candidates must disclose all actual and potential conflicts of interest so that clients can evaluate those conflicts.
- *Disclose compensation arrangements*: Members and candidates should make their clients aware of all forms of manager compensation.

- *Vote proxies*: In most cases, members and candidates should determine who is authorized to vote shares and vote proxies in the best interests of the clients and ultimate beneficiaries.
- *Maintain confidentiality*: Members and candidates must preserve the confidentiality of client information.
- *Seek best execution*: Unless directed by the client as ultimate beneficiary, members and candidates must seek best execution for their clients. (Best execution is defined in the preceding text.)
- *Place client interests first*: Members and candidates must serve the best interests of clients.

Application of the Standard

Example 1 (Identifying the Client—Plan Participants):

First Country Bank serves as trustee for the Miller Company's pension plan. Miller is the target of a hostile takeover attempt by Newton, Inc. In attempting to ward off Newton, Miller's managers persuade Julian Wiley, an investment manager at First Country Bank, to purchase Miller common stock in the open market for the employee pension plan. Miller's officials indicate that such action would be favorably received and would probably result in other accounts being placed with the bank. Although Wiley believes the stock is overvalued and would not ordinarily buy it, he purchases the stock to support Miller's managers, to maintain Miller's good favor toward the bank, and to realize additional new business. The heavy stock purchases cause Miller's market price to rise to such a level that Newton retracts its takeover bid.

> *Comment*: Standard III(A) requires that a member or candidate, in evaluating a takeover bid, act prudently and solely in the interests of plan participants and beneficiaries. To meet this requirement, a member or candidate must carefully evaluate the long-term prospects of the company against the short-term prospects presented by the takeover offer and by the ability to invest elsewhere. In this instance, Wiley, acting on behalf of his employer, which was the trustee for a pension plan, clearly violated Standard III(A). He used the pension plan to perpetuate existing management, perhaps to the detriment of plan participants and the company's shareholders, and to benefit himself. Wiley's responsibilities to the plan participants and beneficiaries should have taken precedence over any ties of his bank to corporate managers and over his self-interest. Wiley had a duty to examine the takeover offer on its own merits and to make an independent decision. The guiding principle is the appropriateness of the investment decision to the pension plan, not whether the decision benefited Wiley or the company that hired him.

Example 2 (Client Commission Practices):

JNI, a successful investment counseling firm, serves as investment manager for the pension plans of several large regionally based companies. Its trading activities generate a significant amount of commission-related business. JNI uses the brokerage and research services of many firms, but most of its trading activity is handled through a large brokerage company, Thompson, Inc., because the executives of the two firms have a close friendship. Thompson's commission structure is high in comparison with charges for similar brokerage services from other firms. JNI considers Thompson's research services and execution capabilities average. In exchange for JNI directing its brokerage to Thompson, Thompson absorbs a number of JNI overhead expenses, including those for rent.

> *Comment*: JNI executives are breaching their responsibilities by using client brokerage for services that do not benefit JNI clients and by not obtaining best price and best execution for their clients. Because JNI executives are not upholding their duty of loyalty, they are violating Standard III(A).

Example 3 (Brokerage Arrangements):

Charlotte Everett, a struggling independent investment adviser, serves as investment manager for the pension plans of several companies. One of her brokers, Scott Company, is close to consummating management agreements with prospective new clients whereby Everett would manage the new client accounts and trade the accounts exclusively through Scott. One of Everett's existing clients, Crayton Corporation, has directed Everett to place securities transactions for Crayton's account exclusively through Scott. But to induce Scott to exert efforts to send more new accounts to her, Everett also directs transactions to Scott from other clients without their knowledge.

> *Comment*: Everett has an obligation at all times to seek best price and best execution on all trades. Everett may direct new client trades exclusively through Scott Company as long as Everett receives best price and execution on the trades or receives a written statement from new clients that she is *not* to seek best price and execution and that they are aware of the consequence for their accounts. Everett may trade other accounts through Scott as a reward for directing clients to Everett only if the accounts receive best price and execution and the practice is disclosed to the accounts. Because Everett does not disclose the directed trading, Everett has violated Standard III(A).

Example 4 (Brokerage Arrangements):

Emilie Rome is a trust officer for Paget Trust Company. Rome's supervisor is responsible for reviewing Rome's trust account transactions and her monthly reports of personal stock transactions. Rome has been using Nathan Gray, a broker, almost exclusively for trust account brokerage transactions. When Gray makes a market in stocks, he has been giving Rome a lower price for personal purchases and a higher price for sales than he gives to Rome's trust accounts and other investors.

> *Comment*: Rome is violating her duty of loyalty to the bank's trust accounts by using Gray for brokerage transactions simply because Gray trades Rome's personal account on favorable terms. Rome is placing her own interests before those of her clients.

Example 5 (Client Commission Practices):

Lauren Parker, an analyst with Provo Advisors, covers South American equities for her firm. She likes to travel to the markets for which she is responsible and decides to go on a trip to Chile, Argentina, and Brazil. The trip is sponsored by SouthAM, Inc., a research firm with a small broker/dealer affiliate that uses the clearing facilities of a larger New York brokerage house. SouthAM specializes in arranging South American trips for analysts during which they can meet with central bank officials, government ministers, local economists, and senior executives of corporations. SouthAM accepts commission dollars at a ratio of 2 to 1 against the hard-dollar costs of the research fee for the trip. Parker is not sure that SouthAM's execution is competitive, but without informing her supervisor, she directs the trading desk at Provo to start giving commission business to SouthAM so she can take the trip. SouthAM has conveniently timed the briefing trip to coincide with the beginning of Carnival season, so Parker also decides to spend five days of vacation in Rio de Janeiro at the end of the trip. Parker uses commission dollars to pay for the five days of hotel expenses.

> *Comment*: Parker is violating Standard III(A) by not exercising her duty of loyalty to her clients. She should have determined whether the commissions charged by SouthAM are reasonable in relation to the benefit of the research provided by the trip. She also should have determined whether best execution and prices could be received from SouthAM. In addition, the five extra days are not part of the research effort because they do not assist in the investment decision making. Thus, the hotel expenses for the five days should not be paid for with client assets.

Example 6 (Excessive Trading):

Vida Knauss manages the portfolios of a number of high-net-worth individuals. A major part of her investment management fee is based on trading commissions. Knauss engages in extensive trading for each of her clients to ensure that she attains the minimum commission level set by her firm. Although the securities purchased and sold for the clients are appropriate and fall within the acceptable asset classes for the clients, the amount of trading for each account exceeds what is necessary to accomplish the client's investment objectives.

> *Comment*: Knauss has violated Standard III(A) because she is using the assets of her clients to benefit her firm and herself.

Example 7 (Managing Family Accounts):

Adam Dill recently joined New Investments Asset Managers. To assist Dill in building a book of clients, both his father and brother opened new fee-paying accounts. Dill followed all the firm's procedures in noting his relationships with these clients and in developing their investment policy statements.

After several years, the number of Dill's clients has grown, but he still manages the original accounts of his family members. An IPO is coming to market that is a suitable investment for many of his clients, including his brother. Dill does not receive the amount of stock he requested, so to avoid any appearance of a conflict of interest, he does not allocate any shares to his brother's account.

> *Comment*: Dill has violated Standard III(A) because he is not acting for the benefit of his brother's account as well as his other accounts. The brother's account is a regular fee-paying account comparable to the accounts of his other clients. By not allocating the shares proportionately across *all* accounts for which he thought the IPO was suitable, Dill is disadvantaging specific clients.
>
> Dill would have been correct in not allocating shares to his brother's account if that account was being managed outside the normal fee structure of the firm.

Example 8 (Identifying the Client):

Donna Hensley has been hired by a law firm to testify as an expert witness. Although the testimony is intended to represent impartial advice, she is concerned that her work may have negative consequences for the law firm. If the law firm is Hensley's client, how does she ensure that her testimony will not violate the required duty of loyalty, prudence, and care to one's client?

Comment: In this situation, the law firm represents Hensley's employer and the aspect of "who is the client" is not well defined. When acting as an expert witness, Hensley is bound by the standard of independence and objectivity in the same manner as an independent research analyst would be bound. Hensley must not let the law firm influence the testimony she provides in the legal proceedings.

Example 9 (Identifying the Client):

Jon Miller is a mutual fund portfolio manager. The fund is focused on the global financial services sector. Wanda Spears is a private wealth manager in the same city as Miller and is a friend of Miller. At a local CFA Institute society meeting, Spears mentions to Miller that her new client is an investor in Miller's fund. She states that the two of them now share a responsibility to this client.

Comment: Spears' statement is not totally correct. Because she provides the advisory services to her new client, she alone is bound by the duty of loyalty to this client. Miller's responsibility is to manage the fund according to the investment policy statement of the fund. His actions should not be influenced by the needs of any particular fund investor.

Example 10 (Client Loyalty):

After providing client account investment performance to the external-facing departments but prior to it being finalized for release to clients, Teresa Nguyen, an investment performance analyst, notices the reporting system missed a trade. Correcting the omission resulted in a large loss for a client that had previously placed the firm on "watch" for potential termination owing to underperformance in prior periods. Nguyen knows this news is unpleasant but informs the appropriate individuals that the report needs to be updated before releasing it to the client.

Comment: Nguyen's actions align with the requirements of Standard III(A). Even though the correction may lead to the firm's termination by the client, withholding information on errors would not be in the best interest of the client.

Example 11 (Execution-Only Responsibilities):

Baftija Sulejman recently became a candidate in the CFA Program. He is a broker who executes client-directed trades for several high-net-worth individuals. Sulejman does not provide any investment advice and only executes the trading decisions made by clients. He is concerned that the Code and Standards impose a fiduciary duty on him in his dealing with clients and sends an e-mail to the CFA Ethics Helpdesk (ethics@cfainstitute.org) to seek guidance on this issue.

Comment: In this instance, Sulejman serves in an execution-only capacity and his duty of loyalty, prudence, and care is centered on the skill and diligence used when executing trades—namely, by seeking best execution and making trades within the parameters set by the clients (instructions on quantity, price, timing, etc.). Acting in the best interests of the client dictates that trades are executed on the most favorable terms that can be achieved for the client. Given this job function, the requirements of the Code and Standards for loyalty, prudence, and care clearly do not impose a fiduciary duty.

Standard III(B) Fair Dealing

Members and Candidates must deal fairly and objectively with all clients when providing investment analysis, making investment recommendations, taking investment action, or engaging in other professional activities.

Guidance

Highlights:

- *Investment Recommendations*
- *Investment Action*

Standard III(B) requires members and candidates to treat all clients fairly when disseminating investment recommendations or making material changes to prior investment recommendations or when taking investment action with regard to general purchases, new issues, or secondary offerings. Only through the fair treatment of all parties can the investment management profession maintain the confidence of the investing public.

When an investment adviser has multiple clients, the potential exists for the adviser to favor one client over another. This favoritism may take various forms—from the quality and timing of services provided to the allocation of investment opportunities.

The term "fairly" implies that the member or candidate must take care not to discriminate against any clients when disseminating investment recommendations or taking investment action. Standard III(B) does not state "equally" because members and candidates could not possibly reach all clients at exactly the same time—whether by printed mail, telephone (including text messaging), computer (including internet updates and e-mail distribution), facsimile (fax), or wire. Each client has unique needs, investment criteria, and investment objectives, so not all investment opportunities are suitable for all clients. In addition, members and candidates may provide more personal, specialized, or in-depth service to clients who are willing to pay for premium services through higher management fees or higher levels of brokerage. Members and candidates may differentiate their services to clients, but different levels of service must not disadvantage or negatively affect clients. In addition, the different service levels should be disclosed to clients and prospective clients and should be available to everyone (i.e., different service levels should not be offered selectively).

Standard III(B) covers conduct in two broadly defined categories—investment recommendations and investment action.

Investment Recommendations

The first category of conduct involves members and candidates whose primary function is the preparation of investment recommendations to be disseminated either to the public or within a firm for the use of others in making investment decisions. This group includes members and candidates employed by investment counseling, advisory, or consulting firms as well as banks, brokerage firms, and insurance companies. The criterion is that the member's or candidate's primary responsibility is the preparation of recommendations to be acted on by others, including those in the member's or candidate's organization.

An investment recommendation is any opinion expressed by a member or candidate in regard to purchasing, selling, or holding a given security or other investment. The opinion may be disseminated to customers or clients through an initial detailed research report, through a brief update report, by addition to or deletion from a list of recommended securities, or simply by oral communication. A recommendation that is distributed to anyone outside the organization is considered a communication for general distribution under Standard III(B).

Standard III(B) addresses the manner in which investment recommendations or changes in prior recommendations are disseminated to clients. Each member or candidate is obligated to ensure that information is disseminated in such a manner that all clients have a fair opportunity to act on every recommendation. Communicating with all clients on a uniform basis presents practical problems for members and candidates because of differences in timing and methods of communication with various types of customers and clients. Members and candidates should encourage their firms to design an equitable system to prevent selective or discriminatory disclosure and should inform clients about what kind of communications they will receive.

The duty to clients imposed by Standard III(B) may be more critical when members or candidates change their recommendations than when they make initial recommendations. Material changes in a member's or candidate's prior investment recommendations because of subsequent research should be communicated to all current clients; particular care should be taken that the information reaches those clients who the member or candidate knows have acted on or been affected by the earlier advice. Clients who do not know that the member or candidate has changed a recommendation and who, therefore, place orders contrary to a current recommendation should be advised of the changed recommendation before the order is accepted.

Investment Action

The second category of conduct includes those members and candidates whose primary function is taking investment action (portfolio management) on the basis of recommendations prepared internally or received from external sources. Investment action, like investment recommendations, can affect market value. Consequently, Standard III(B) requires that members or candidates treat all clients fairly in light of their investment objectives and circumstances. For example, when making investments in new offerings or in secondary financings, members and candidates should distribute the issues to all customers for whom the investments are appropriate in a manner consistent with the policies of the firm for allocating blocks of stock. If the issue is oversubscribed, then the issue should be prorated to all subscribers. This action should be taken on a round-lot basis to avoid odd-lot distributions. In addition, if the issue is oversubscribed, members and candidates should forgo any sales to themselves or their immediate families in order to free up additional shares for clients. If the investment professional's family-member accounts are managed similarly to the accounts of other clients of the firm, however, the family-member accounts should not be excluded from buying such shares.

Members and candidates must make every effort to treat all individual and institutional clients in a fair and impartial manner. A member or candidate may have multiple relationships with an institution; for example, the member or candidate may be a corporate trustee, pension fund manager, manager of funds for individuals employed by the customer, loan originator, or creditor. A member or candidate must exercise care to treat all clients fairly.

Members and candidates should disclose to clients and prospective clients the documented allocation procedures they or their firms have in place and how the procedures would affect the client or prospect. The disclosure should be clear and complete so that the client can make an informed investment decision. Even when complete disclosure is made, however, members and candidates must put client interests ahead of their own. A member's or candidate's duty of fairness and loyalty to clients can never be overridden by client consent to patently unfair allocation procedures.

Treating clients fairly also means that members and candidates should not take advantage of their position in the industry to the detriment of clients. For instance, in the context of IPOs, members and candidates must make bona fide public distributions of "hot issue" securities (defined as securities of a public offering that are trading at a premium in the secondary market whenever such trading commences because of the great demand for the securities). Members and candidates are prohibited from withholding such securities for their own benefit and must not use such securities as a reward or incentive to gain benefit.

Recommended Procedures for Compliance

Develop Firm Policies

Although Standard III(B) refers to a member's or candidate's responsibility to deal fairly and objectively with clients, members and candidates should also encourage their firms to establish compliance procedures requiring all employees who disseminate investment recommendations or take investment actions to treat customers and clients fairly. At the very least, a member or candidate should recommend appropriate procedures to management if none are in place. And the member or candidate should make management aware of possible violations of fair-dealing practices within the firm when they come to the attention of the member or candidate.

The extent of the formality and complexity of such compliance procedures depends on the nature and size of the organization and the type of securities involved. An investment adviser who is a sole proprietor and handles only discretionary accounts might not disseminate recommendations to the public, but that adviser should have formal written procedures to ensure that all clients receive fair investment action.

Good business practice dictates that initial recommendations be made available to all customers who indicate an interest. Although a member or candidate need not communicate a recommendation to all customers, the selection process by which customers receive information should be based on suitability and known interest, not on any preferred or favored status. A common practice to assure fair dealing is to communicate recommendations simultaneously within the firm and to customers.

Members and candidates should consider the following points when establishing fair-dealing compliance procedures:

- *Limit the number of people involved*: Members and candidates should make reasonable efforts to limit the number of people who are privy to the fact that a recommendation is going to be disseminated.
- *Shorten the time frame between decision and dissemination*: Members and candidates should make reasonable efforts to limit the amount of time that elapses between the decision to make an investment recommendation and the time the actual recommendation is disseminated. If a detailed institutional recommendation that might take two or three weeks to publish is in preparation, a short summary report including the conclusion might be published in advance. In an organization where both a research committee and an investment policy committee must approve a recommendation, the meetings should be held on the same day if possible. The process of reviewing reports and printing and mailing them, faxing them, or distributing them by e-mail necessarily involves the passage of time, sometimes long periods of time. In large firms with extensive review processes, the time factor is usually not within the control of the analyst who prepares the report. Thus, many firms and their analysts communicate

to customers and firm personnel the new or changed recommendations by an update or "flash" report. The communication technique might be fax, e-mail, wire, or short written report.

- *Publish guidelines for pre-dissemination behavior*: Members and candidates should encourage firms to develop guidelines that prohibit personnel who have prior knowledge of an investment recommendation from discussing or taking any action on the pending recommendation.
- *Simultaneous dissemination*: Members and candidates should establish procedures for the timing of dissemination of investment recommendations so that all clients are treated fairly—that is, are informed at approximately the same time. For example, if a firm is going to announce a new recommendation, supervisory personnel should time the announcement to avoid placing any client or group of clients at an unfair advantage relative to other clients. A communication to all branch offices should be sent at the time of the general announcement. (When appropriate, the firm should accompany the announcement of a new recommendation with a statement that trading restrictions for the firm's employees are now in effect. The trading restrictions should stay in effect until the recommendation is widely distributed to all relevant clients.) Once this distribution has occurred, the member or candidate may follow up separately with individual clients, but members and candidates should not give favored clients advance information when such advance notification may disadvantage other clients.
- *Maintain a list of clients and their holdings*: Members and candidates should maintain a list of all clients and the securities or other investments each client holds in order to facilitate notification of customers or clients of a change in an investment recommendation. If a particular security or other investment is to be sold, such a list can be used to ensure that all holders are treated fairly in the liquidation of that particular investment.
- *Develop and document trade allocation procedures*: When formulating procedures for allocating trades, members and candidates should develop a set of guiding principles that ensure
  - fairness to advisory clients, both in priority of execution of orders and in the allocation of the price obtained in execution of block orders or trades,
  - timeliness and efficiency in the execution of orders, and
  - accuracy of the member's or candidate's records as to trade orders and client account positions.

With these principles in mind, members and candidates should develop or encourage their firm to develop written allocation procedures, with particular attention to procedures for block trades and new issues. Procedures to consider are as follows:

- requiring orders and modifications or cancellations of orders to be documented and time stamped;
- processing and executing orders on a first-in, first-out basis with consideration of bundling orders for efficiency as appropriate for the asset class or the security;
- developing a policy to address such issues as calculating execution prices and "partial fills" when trades are grouped, or in a block, for efficiency;
- giving all client accounts participating in a block trade the same execution price and charging the same commission;

- when the full amount of the block order is not executed, allocating partially executed orders among the participating client accounts pro rata on the basis of order size while not going below an established minimum lot size for some securities (e.g., bonds); and
- when allocating trades for new issues, obtaining advance indications of interest, allocating securities by client (rather than portfolio manager), and providing a method for calculating allocations.

Disclose Trade Allocation Procedures

Members and candidates should disclose to clients and prospective clients how they select accounts to participate in an order and how they determine the amount of securities each account will buy or sell. Trade allocation procedures must be fair and equitable, and disclosure of inequitable allocation methods does not relieve the member or candidate of this obligation.

Establish Systematic Account Review

Member and candidate supervisors should review each account on a regular basis to ensure that no client or customer is being given preferential treatment and that the investment actions taken for each account are suitable for each account's objectives. Because investments should be based on individual needs and circumstances, an investment manager may have good reasons for placing a given security or other investment in one account while selling it from another account and should fully document the reasons behind both sides of the transaction. Members and candidates should encourage firms to establish review procedures, however, to detect whether trading in one account is being used to benefit a favored client.

Disclose Levels of Service

Members and candidates should disclose to all clients whether the organization offers different levels of service to clients for the same fee or different fees. Different levels of service should not be offered to clients selectively.

Application of the Standard

Example 1 (Selective Disclosure):

Bradley Ames, a well-known and respected analyst, follows the computer industry. In the course of his research, he finds that a small, relatively unknown company whose shares are traded over the counter has just signed significant contracts with some of the companies he follows. After a considerable amount of investigation, Ames decides to write a research report on the small company and recommend purchase of its shares. While the report is being reviewed by the company for factual accuracy, Ames schedules a luncheon with several of his best clients to discuss the company. At the luncheon, he mentions the purchase recommendation scheduled to be sent early the following week to all the firm's clients.

> *Comment*: Ames has violated Standard III(B) by disseminating the purchase recommendation to the clients with whom he has lunch a week before the recommendation is sent to all clients.

Example 2 (Fair Dealing between Funds):

Spencer Rivers, president of XYZ Corporation, moves his company's growth-oriented pension fund to a particular bank primarily because of the excellent investment performance achieved by the bank's commingled fund for the prior five-year period.

Later, Rivers compares the results of his pension fund with those of the bank's commingled fund. He is startled to learn that, even though the two accounts have the same investment objectives and similar portfolios, his company's pension fund has significantly underperformed the bank's commingled fund. Questioning this result at his next meeting with the pension fund's manager, Rivers is told that, as a matter of policy, when a new security is placed on the recommended list, Morgan Jackson, the pension fund manager, first purchases the security for the commingled account and then purchases it on a pro rata basis for all other pension fund accounts. Similarly, when a sale is recommended, the security is sold first from the commingled account and then sold on a pro rata basis from all other accounts. Rivers also learns that if the bank cannot get enough shares (especially of hot issues) to be meaningful to all the accounts, its policy is to place the new issues only in the commingled account.

Seeing that Rivers is neither satisfied nor pleased by the explanation, Jackson quickly adds that nondiscretionary pension accounts and personal trust accounts have a lower priority on purchase and sale recommendations than discretionary pension fund accounts. Furthermore, Jackson states, the company's pension fund had the opportunity to invest up to 5% in the commingled fund.

> *Comment*: The bank's policy does not treat all customers fairly, and Jackson has violated her duty to her clients by giving priority to the growth-oriented commingled fund over all other funds and to discretionary accounts over nondiscretionary accounts. Jackson must execute orders on a systematic basis that is fair to all clients. In addition, trade allocation procedures should be disclosed to all clients when they become clients. Of course, in this case, disclosure of the bank's policy would not change the fact that the policy is unfair.

Example 3 (Fair Dealing and IPO Distribution):

Dominic Morris works for a small regional securities firm. His work consists of corporate finance activities and investing for institutional clients. Arena, Ltd., is planning to go public. The partners have secured rights to buy an arena football league franchise and are planning to use the funds from the issue to complete the purchase. Because arena football is the current rage, Morris believes he has a hot issue on his hands. He has quietly negotiated some options for himself for helping convince Arena to do the financing through his securities firm. When he seeks expressions of interest, the institutional buyers oversubscribe the issue. Morris, assuming that the institutions have the financial clout to drive the stock up, then fills all orders (including his own) and decreases the institutional blocks.

> *Comment*: Morris has violated Standard III(B) by not treating all customers fairly. He should not have taken any shares himself and should have prorated the shares offered among all clients. In addition, he should have disclosed to his firm and to his clients that he received options as part of the deal [see Standard VI(A)–Disclosure of Conflicts].

Example 4 (Fair Dealing and Transaction Allocation):

Eleanor Preston, the chief investment officer of Porter Williams Investments (PWI), a medium-size money management firm, has been trying to retain a client, Colby Company. Management at Colby, which accounts for almost half of PWI's revenues, recently told Preston that if the performance of its account did not improve, it would find a new money manager. Shortly after this threat, Preston purchases mortgage-backed securities (MBSs) for several accounts, including Colby's. Preston is busy with a number of transactions that day, so she fails to allocate the trades immediately or write up the trade tickets. A few days later, when Preston is allocating trades, she notes that some of the MBSs have significantly increased in price and some have dropped. Preston decides to allocate the profitable trades to Colby and spread the losing trades among several other PWI accounts.

> *Comment*: Preston has violated Standard III(B) by failing to deal fairly with her clients in taking these investment actions. Preston should have allocated the trades prior to executing the orders, or she should have had a systematic approach to allocating the trades, such as pro rata, as soon as practical after they were executed. Among other things, Preston must disclose to the client that the adviser may act as broker for, receive commissions from, and have a potential conflict of interest regarding both parties in agency cross-transactions. After the disclosure, she should obtain from the client consent authorizing such transactions in advance.

Example 5 (Selective Disclosure):

Saunders Industrial Waste Management (SIWM) publicly indicates to analysts that it is comfortable with the somewhat disappointing earnings-per-share projection of US$1.16 for the quarter. Bernard Roberts, an analyst at Coffey Investments, is confident that SIWM management has understated the forecasted earnings so that the real announcement will cause an "upside surprise" and boost the price of SIWM stock. The "whisper number" (rumored) estimate based on extensive research and discussed among knowledgeable analysts is higher than US$1.16. Roberts repeats the US$1.16 figure in his research report to all Coffey clients but informally tells his large clients that he expects the earnings per share to be higher, making SIWM a good buy.

> *Comment*: By not sharing his opinion regarding the potential for a significant upside earnings surprise with all clients, Roberts is not treating all clients fairly and has violated Standard III(B).

Example 6 (Additional Services for Select Clients):

Jenpin Weng uses e-mail to issue a new recommendation to all his clients. He then calls his three largest institutional clients to discuss the recommendation in detail.

> *Comment*: Weng has not violated Standard III(B) because he widely disseminated the recommendation and provided the information to all his clients prior to discussing it with a select few. Weng's largest clients received additional personal service because they presumably pay higher fees or because they have a large amount of assets under Weng's management. If Weng had discussed the report with a select group of clients prior to distributing it to all his clients, he would have violated Standard III(B).

Example 7 (Minimum Lot Allocations):

Lynn Hampton is a well-respected private wealth manager in her community with a diversified client base. She determines that a new 10-year bond being offered by Healthy Pharmaceuticals is appropriate for five of her clients. Three clients request to purchase US$10,000 each, and the other two request US$50,000 each. The minimum lot size is established at US$5,000, and the issue is oversubscribed at the time of placement. Her firm's policy is that odd-lot allocations, especially those below the minimum, should be avoided because they may affect the liquidity of the security at the time of sale.

Hampton is informed she will receive only US$55,000 of the offering for all accounts. Hampton distributes the bond investments as follows: The three accounts that requested US$10,000 are allocated US$5,000 each, and the two accounts that requested US$50,000 are allocated US$20,000 each.

> *Comment*: Hampton has not violated Standard III(B), even though the distribution is not on a completely pro rata basis because of the required minimum lot size. With the total allocation being significantly below the amount requested, Hampton ensured that each client received at least the minimum lot size of the issue. This approach allowed the clients to efficiently sell the bond later if necessary.

Example 8 (Excessive Trading):

Ling Chan manages the accounts for many pension plans, including the plan of his father's employer. Chan developed similar but not identical investment policies for each client, so the investment portfolios are rarely the same. To minimize the cost to his father's pension plan, he intentionally trades more frequently in the accounts of other clients to ensure the required brokerage is incurred to continue receiving free research for use by all the pensions.

> *Comment*: Chan is violating Standard III(B) because his trading actions are disadvantaging his clients to enhance a relationship with a preferred client. All clients are benefiting from the research being provided and should incur their fair portion of the costs. This does not mean that additional trading should occur if a client has not paid an equal portion of the commission; trading should occur only as required by the strategy.

Example 9 (Limited Social Media Disclosures):

Mary Burdette was recently hired by Fundamental Investment Management (FIM) as a junior auto industry analyst. Burdette is expected to expand the social media presence of the firm because she is active with various networks, including Facebook, LinkedIn, and Twitter. Although Burdette's supervisor, Joe Graf, has never used social media, he encourages Burdette to explore opportunities to increase FIM's online presence and ability to share content, communicate, and broadcast information to clients. In response to Graf's encouragement, Burdette is working on a proposal detailing the advantages of getting FIM onto Twitter in addition to launching a company Facebook page.

As part of her auto industry research for FIM, Burdette is completing a report on the financial impact of Sun Drive Auto Ltd.'s new solar technology for compact automobiles. This research report will be her first for FIM, and she believes Sun Drive's technology could revolutionize the auto industry. In her excitement, Burdette sends a quick tweet to FIM Twitter followers summarizing her "buy" recommendation for Sun Drive Auto stock.

> *Comment*: Burdette has violated Standard III(B) by sending an investment recommendation to a select group of contacts prior to distributing it to all clients. Burdette must make sure she has received the appropriate training about FIM's policies and procedures, including the appropriate business use of personal social media networks before engaging in such activities.
>
> See Standard IV(C) for guidance related to the duties of the supervisor.

Example 10 (Fair Dealing between Clients):

Paul Rove, performance analyst for Alpha-Beta Investment Management, is describing to the firm's chief investment officer (CIO) two new reports he would like to develop to assist the firm in meeting its obligations to treat clients fairly. Because many of the firm's clients have similar investment objectives and portfolios, Rove suggests a report detailing securities owned across several clients and the percentage of the portfolio the security represents. The second report would compare the monthly performance of portfolios with similar strategies. The outliers within each report would be submitted to the CIO for review.

> *Comment*: As a performance analyst, Rove likely has little direct contact with clients and thus has limited opportunity to treat clients differently. The recommended reports comply with Standard III(B) while helping the firm conduct after-the-fact reviews of how effectively the firm's advisers are dealing with their clients' portfolios. Reports that monitor the fair treatment of clients are an important oversight tool to ensure that clients are treated fairly.

Standard III(C) Suitability

1. When Members and Candidates are in an advisory relationship with a client, they must:
   - a. Make a reasonable inquiry into a client's or prospective client's investment experience, risk and return objectives, and financial constraints prior to making any investment recommendation or taking investment action and must reassess and update this information regularly.
   - b. Determine that an investment is suitable to the client's financial situation and consistent with the client's written objectives, mandates, and constraints before making an investment recommendation or taking investment action.
   - c. Judge the suitability of investments in the context of the client's total portfolio.
2. When Members and Candidates are responsible for managing a portfolio to a specific mandate, strategy, or style, they must make only investment recommendations or take only investment actions that are consistent with the stated objectives and constraints of the portfolio.

Guidance

Highlights:

- *Developing an Investment Policy*
- *Understanding the Client's Risk Profile*
- *Updating an Investment Policy*
- *The Need for Diversification*
- *Addressing Unsolicited Trading Requests*
- *Managing to an Index or Mandate*

Standard III(C) requires that members and candidates who are in an investment advisory relationship with clients consider carefully the needs, circumstances, and objectives of the clients when determining the appropriateness and suitability of a given investment or course of investment action. An appropriate suitability determination will not, however, prevent some investments or investment actions from losing value.

In judging the suitability of a potential investment, the member or candidate should review many aspects of the client's knowledge, experience related to investing, and financial situation. These aspects include, but are not limited to, the risk profile of the investment as compared with the constraints of the client, the impact of the investment on the diversity of the portfolio, and whether the client has the means or net worth to assume the associated risk. The investment professional's determination of suitability should reflect only the investment recommendations or actions that a prudent person would be willing to undertake. Not every investment opportunity will be suitable for every portfolio, regardless of the potential return being offered.

The responsibilities of members and candidates to gather information and make a suitability analysis prior to making a recommendation or taking investment action fall on those members and candidates who provide investment advice in the course of an advisory relationship with a client. Other members and candidates may be simply executing specific instructions for retail clients when buying or selling securities, such as shares in mutual funds. These members and candidates and some others, such as sell-side analysts, may not have the opportunity to judge the suitability of a particular investment for the ultimate client.

Developing an Investment Policy

When an advisory relationship exists, members and candidates must gather client information at the inception of the relationship. Such information includes the client's financial circumstances, personal data (such as age and occupation) that are relevant to investment decisions, attitudes toward risk, and objectives in investing. This information should be incorporated into a written investment policy statement (IPS) that addresses the client's risk tolerance, return requirements, and all investment constraints (including time horizon, liquidity needs, tax concerns, legal and regulatory factors, and unique circumstances). Without identifying such client factors, members and candidates cannot judge whether a particular investment or strategy is suitable for a particular client. The IPS also should identify and describe the roles and responsibilities of the parties to the advisory relationship and investment process, as well as schedules for review and evaluation of the IPS. After formulating long-term capital market expectations, members and candidates can assist in developing an appropriate strategic asset allocation and investment program for the client, whether these are presented in separate documents or incorporated in the IPS or in appendices to the IPS.

Understanding the Client's Risk Profile

One of the most important factors to be considered in matching appropriateness and suitability of an investment with a client's needs and circumstances is measuring that client's tolerance for risk. The investment professional must consider the possibilities of rapidly changing investment environments and their likely impact on a client's holdings, both individual securities and the collective portfolio. The risk of many investment strategies can and should be analyzed and quantified in advance.

The use of synthetic investment vehicles and derivative investment products has introduced particular issues of risk. Members and candidates should pay careful attention to the leverage inherent in many of these vehicles or products when considering them for use in a client's investment program. Such leverage and limited liquidity, depending on the degree to which they are hedged, bear directly on the issue of suitability for the client.

Updating an Investment Policy

Updating the IPS should be repeated at least annually and also prior to material changes to any specific investment recommendations or decisions on behalf of the client. The effort to determine the needs and circumstances of each client is not a one-time occurrence. Investment recommendations or decisions are usually part of an ongoing process that takes into account the diversity and changing nature of portfolio and client characteristics. The passage of time is bound to produce changes that are important with respect to investment objectives.

For an individual client, important changes might include the number of dependents, personal tax status, health, liquidity needs, risk tolerance, amount of wealth beyond that represented in the portfolio, and extent to which compensation and other income provide for current income needs. With respect to an institutional client, such changes might relate to the magnitude of unfunded liabilities in a pension fund, the withdrawal privileges in an employee savings plan, or the distribution requirements of a charitable foundation. Without efforts to update information concerning client factors, one or more factors could change without the investment manager's knowledge.

Suitability review can be done most effectively when the client fully discloses his or her complete financial portfolio, including those portions not managed by the member or candidate. If clients withhold information about their financial portfolios, the suitability analysis conducted by members and candidates cannot be expected to be complete; it must be based on the information provided.

The Need for Diversification

The investment profession has long recognized that combining several different investments is likely to provide a more acceptable level of risk exposure than having all assets in a single investment. The unique characteristics (or risks) of an individual investment may become partially or entirely neutralized when it is combined with other individual investments within a portfolio. Some reasonable amount of diversification is thus the norm for many portfolios, especially those managed by individuals or institutions that have some degree of legal fiduciary responsibility.

An investment with high relative risk on its own may be a suitable investment in the context of the entire portfolio or when the client's stated objectives contemplate speculative or risky investments. The manager may be responsible for only a portion of the client's total portfolio, or the client may not have provided a full financial picture. Members and candidates can be responsible for assessing the suitability of an investment only on the basis of the information and criteria actually provided by the client.

Addressing Unsolicited Trading Requests

Members and candidates may receive requests from a client for trades that do not properly align with the risk and return objectives outlined in the client's investment policy statement. These transaction requests may be based on the client's individual biases or professional experience. Members and candidates will need to make reasonable efforts to balance their clients' trading requests with their responsibilities to follow the agreed-on investment policy statement.

In cases of unsolicited trade requests that a member or candidate knows are unsuitable for a client, the member or candidate should refrain from making the trade until he or she discusses the concerns with the client. The discussions and resulting actions may encompass a variety of scenarios depending on how the requested unsuitable investment relates to the client's full portfolio.

Many times, an unsolicited request may be expected to have only a minimum impact on the entire portfolio because the size of the requested trade is small or the trade would result in a limited change to the portfolio's risk profile. In discussing the trade, the member or candidate should focus on educating the investor on how the request deviates from the current policy statement. Following the discussion, the member or candidate may follow his or her firm's policies regarding the necessary client approval for executing unsuitable trades. At a minimum, the client should acknowledge the discussion and accept the conditions that make the recommendation unsuitable.

Should the unsolicited request be expected to have a material impact on the portfolio, the member or candidate should use this opportunity to update the investment policy statement. Doing so would allow the client to fully understand the potential effect of the requested trade on his or her current goals or risk levels.

Members and candidates may have some clients who decline to modify their policy statements while insisting an unsolicited trade be made. In such instances, members or candidates will need to evaluate the effectiveness of their services to the client. The options available to the members or candidates will depend on the services provided by their employer. Some firms may allow for the trade to be executed in a new unmanaged account. If alternative options are not available, members and candidates ultimately will need to determine whether they should continue the advisory arrangement with the client.

Managing to an Index or Mandate

Some members and candidates do not manage money for individuals but are responsible for managing a fund to an index or an expected mandate. The responsibility of these members and candidates is to invest in a manner consistent with the stated mandate. For example, a member or candidate who serves as the fund manager for a large-cap income fund would not be following the fund mandate by investing heavily in small-cap or start-up companies whose stock is speculative in nature. Members and candidates who manage pooled assets to a specific mandate are not responsible for determining the suitability of the *fund* as an investment for investors who may be purchasing shares in the fund. The responsibility for determining the suitability of an investment for clients can be conferred only on members and candidates who have an advisory relationship with clients.

Recommended Procedures for Compliance

Investment Policy Statement

To fulfill the basic provisions of Standard III(C), a member or candidate should put the needs and circumstances of each client and the client's investment objectives into a written investment policy statement. In formulating an investment policy for the client, the member or candidate should take the following into consideration:

- client identification—(1) type and nature of client, (2) the existence of separate beneficiaries, and (3) approximate portion of total client assets that the member or candidate is managing;
- investor objectives—(1) return objectives (income, growth in principal, maintenance of purchasing power) and (2) risk tolerance (suitability, stability of values);
- investor constraints—(1) liquidity needs, (2) expected cash flows (patterns of additions and/or withdrawals), (3) investable funds (assets and liabilities or other commitments), (4) time horizon, (5) tax considerations, (6) regulatory and legal circumstances, (7) investor preferences, prohibitions, circumstances, and unique needs, and (8) proxy voting responsibilities and guidance; and
- performance measurement benchmarks.

Regular Updates

The investor's objectives and constraints should be maintained and reviewed periodically to reflect any changes in the client's circumstances. Members and candidates should regularly compare client constraints with capital market expectations to arrive at an appropriate asset allocation. Changes in either factor may result in a fundamental change in asset allocation. Annual review is reasonable unless business or other reasons, such as a major change in market conditions, dictate more frequent review. Members and candidates should document attempts to carry out such a review if circumstances prevent it.

Suitability Test Policies

With the increase in regulatory required suitability tests, members and candidates should encourage their firms to develop related policies and procedures. The procedures will differ according to the size of the firm and the scope of the services offered to its clients.

The test procedures should require the investment professional to look beyond the potential return of the investment and include the following:

- an analysis of the impact on the portfolio's diversification,
- a comparison of the investment risks with the client's assessed risk tolerance, and
- the fit of the investment with the required investment strategy.

Application of the Standard

Example 1 (Investment Suitability—Risk Profile):

Caleb Smith, an investment adviser, has two clients: Larry Robertson, 60 years old, and Gabriel Lanai, 40 years old. Both clients earn roughly the same salary, but Robertson has a much higher risk tolerance because he has a large asset base. Robertson is willing to invest part of his assets very aggressively; Lanai wants only to achieve a steady rate of return with low volatility to pay for his children's education. Smith recommends investing 20% of both portfolios in zero-yield, small-cap, high-technology equity issues.

> *Comment*: In Robertson's case, the investment may be appropriate because of his financial circumstances and aggressive investment position, but this investment is not suitable for Lanai. Smith is violating Standard III(C) by applying Robertson's investment strategy to Lanai because the two clients' financial circumstances and objectives differ.

Example 2 (Investment Suitability—Entire Portfolio):

Jessica McDowell, an investment adviser, suggests to Brian Crosby, a risk-averse client, that covered call options be used in his equity portfolio. The purpose would be to enhance Crosby's income and partially offset any untimely depreciation in the portfolio's value should the stock market or other circumstances affect his holdings unfavorably. McDowell educates Crosby about all possible outcomes, including the risk of incurring an added tax liability if a stock rises in price and is called away and, conversely, the risk of his holdings losing protection on the downside if prices drop sharply.

> *Comment*: When determining suitability of an investment, the primary focus should be the characteristics of the client's entire portfolio, not the characteristics of single securities on an issue-by-issue basis. The basic characteristics of the entire portfolio will largely determine whether investment

recommendations are taking client factors into account. Therefore, the most important aspects of a particular investment are those that will affect the characteristics of the total portfolio. In this case, McDowell properly considers the investment in the context of the entire portfolio and thoroughly explains the investment to the client.

Example 3 (IPS Updating):

In a regular meeting with client Seth Jones, the portfolio managers at Blue Chip Investment Advisors are careful to allow some time to review his current needs and circumstances. In doing so, they learn that some significant changes have recently taken place in his life. A wealthy uncle left Jones an inheritance that increased his net worth fourfold, to US$1 million.

> *Comment*: The inheritance has significantly increased Jones's ability (and possibly his willingness) to assume risk and has diminished the average yield required to meet his current income needs. Jones's financial circumstances have definitely changed, so Blue Chip managers must update Jones's investment policy statement to reflect how his investment objectives have changed. Accordingly, the Blue Chip portfolio managers should consider a somewhat higher equity ratio for his portfolio than was called for by the previous circumstances, and the managers' specific common stock recommendations might be heavily tilted toward low-yield, growth-oriented issues.

Example 4 (Following an Investment Mandate):

Louis Perkowski manages a high-income mutual fund. He purchases zero-dividend stock in a financial services company because he believes the stock is undervalued and is in a potential growth industry, which makes it an attractive investment.

> *Comment*: A zero-dividend stock does not seem to fit the mandate of the fund that Perkowski is managing. Unless Perkowski's investment fits within the mandate or is within the realm of allowable investments the fund has made clear in its disclosures, Perkowski has violated Standard III(C).

Example 5 (IPS Requirements and Limitations):

Max Gubler, chief investment officer of a property/casualty insurance subsidiary of a large financial conglomerate, wants to improve the diversification of the subsidiary's investment portfolio and increase its returns. The subsidiary's investment policy statement provides for highly liquid investments, such as large-cap equities and government, supranational, and corporate bonds with a minimum credit rating of AA and maturity of no more than five years. In a recent presentation, a venture capital group offered very attractive prospective returns on some of its private equity funds that provide seed capital to ventures. An exit strategy was already contemplated, but investors would have to observe a minimum three-year lockup period and a subsequent laddered exit option for a maximum of one-third of their shares per year. Gubler does not want to miss this opportunity. After extensive analysis, with the intent to optimize the return on the equity assets within the subsidiary's current portfolio, he invests 4% in this seed fund, leaving the portfolio's total equity exposure still well below its upper limit.

> *Comment*: Gubler is violating Standard III(A)–Loyalty, Prudence, and Care as well as Standard III(C). His new investment locks up part of the subsidiary's assets for at least three years and up to as many as five years and possibly beyond. The IPS requires investments in highly liquid investments and describes accepted asset classes; private equity investments with

a lockup period certainly do not qualify. Even without a lockup period, an asset class with only an occasional, and thus implicitly illiquid, market may not be suitable for the portfolio. Although an IPS typically describes objectives and constraints in great detail, the manager must also make every effort to understand the client's business and circumstances. Doing so should enable the manager to recognize, understand, and discuss with the client other factors that may be or may become material in the investment management process.

Example 6 (Submanager and IPS Reviews):

Paul Ostrowski's investment management business has grown significantly over the past couple of years, and some clients want to diversify internationally. Ostrowski decides to find a submanager to handle the expected international investments. Because this will be his first subadviser, Ostrowski uses the CFA Institute model "request for proposal" to design a questionnaire for his search. By his deadline, he receives seven completed questionnaires from a variety of domestic and international firms trying to gain his business. Ostrowski reviews all the applications in detail and decides to select the firm that charges the lowest fees because doing so will have the least impact on his firm's bottom line.

Comment: When selecting an external manager or subadviser, Ostrowski needs to ensure that the new manager's services are appropriate for his clients. This due diligence includes comparing the risk profile of the clients with the investment strategy of the manager. In basing the decision on the fee structure alone, Ostrowski may be violating Standard III(C).

When clients ask to diversify into international products, it is an appropriate time to review and update the clients' IPSs. Ostrowski's review may determine that the risk of international investments modifies the risk profiles of the clients or does not represent an appropriate investment.

See also Standard V(A)–Diligence and Reasonable Basis for further discussion of the review process needed in selecting appropriate submanagers.

Example 7 (Investment Suitability—Risk Profile):

Samantha Snead, a portfolio manager for Thomas Investment Counsel, Inc., specializes in managing public retirement funds and defined benefit pension plan accounts, all of which have long-term investment objectives. A year ago, Snead's employer, in an attempt to motivate and retain key investment professionals, introduced a bonus compensation system that rewards portfolio managers on the basis of quarterly performance relative to their peers and to certain benchmark indexes. In an attempt to improve the short-term performance of her accounts, Snead changes her investment strategy and purchases several high-beta stocks for client portfolios. These purchases are seemingly contrary to the clients' investment policy statements. Following their purchase, an officer of Griffin Corporation, one of Snead's pension fund clients, asks why Griffin Corporation's portfolio seems to be dominated by high-beta stocks of companies that often appear among the most actively traded issues. No change in objective or strategy has been recommended by Snead during the year.

Comment: Snead violated Standard III(C) by investing the clients' assets in high-beta stocks. These high-risk investments are contrary to the long-term risk profile established in the clients' IPSs. Snead has changed the investment strategy of the clients in an attempt to reap short-term rewards offered by her firm's new compensation arrangement, not in response to changes in clients' investment policy statements.

See also Standard VI(A)–Disclosure of Conflicts.

Example 8 (Investment Suitability):

Andre Shrub owns and operates Conduit, an investment advisory firm. Prior to opening Conduit, Shrub was an account manager with Elite Investment, a hedge fund managed by his good friend Adam Reed. To attract clients to a new Conduit fund, Shrub offers lower-than-normal management fees. He can do so because the fund consists of two top-performing funds managed by Reed. Given his personal friendship with Reed and the prior performance record of these two funds, Shrub believes this new fund is a winning combination for all parties. Clients quickly invest with Conduit to gain access to the Elite funds. No one is turned away because Conduit is seeking to expand its assets under management.

Comment: Shrub has violated Standard III(C) because the risk profile of the new fund may not be suitable for every client. As an investment adviser, Shrub needs to establish an investment policy statement for each client and recommend only investments that match each client's risk and return profile in the IPS. Shrub is required to act as more than a simple sales agent for Elite.

Although Shrub cannot disobey the direct request of a client to purchase a specific security, he should fully discuss the risks of a planned purchase and provide reasons why it might not be suitable for a client. This requirement may lead members and candidates to decline new customers if those customers' requested investment decisions are significantly out of line with their stated requirements.

See also Standard V(A)–Diligence and Reasonable Basis.

Standard III(D) Performance Presentation

When communicating investment performance information, Members and Candidates must make reasonable efforts to ensure that it is fair, accurate, and complete.

Guidance

Standard III(D) requires members and candidates to provide credible performance information to clients and prospective clients and to avoid misstating performance or misleading clients and prospective clients about the investment performance of members or candidates or their firms. This standard encourages full disclosure of investment performance data to clients and prospective clients.

Standard III(D) covers any practice that would lead to misrepresentation of a member's or candidate's performance record, whether the practice involves performance presentation or performance measurement. This standard prohibits misrepresentations of past performance or reasonably expected performance. A member or candidate must give a fair and complete presentation of performance information whenever communicating data with respect to the performance history of individual accounts, composites or groups of accounts, or composites of an analyst's or firm's performance results. Furthermore, members and candidates should not state or imply that clients will obtain or benefit from a rate of return that was generated in the past.

The requirements of this standard are not limited to members and candidates managing separate accounts. Whenever a member or candidate provides performance information for which the manager is claiming responsibility, such as for pooled funds, the history must be accurate. Research analysts promoting the success or accuracy of their recommendations must ensure that their claims are fair, accurate, and complete.

If the presentation is brief, the member or candidate must make available to clients and prospects, on request, the detailed information supporting that communication. Best practice dictates that brief presentations include a reference to the limited nature of the information provided.

Recommended Procedures for Compliance

Apply the GIPS Standards

For members and candidates who are showing the performance history of the assets they manage, compliance with the GIPS standards is the best method to meet their obligations under Standard III(D). Members and candidates should encourage their firms to comply with the GIPS standards.

Compliance without Applying GIPS Standards

Members and candidates can also meet their obligations under Standard III(D) by

- considering the knowledge and sophistication of the audience to whom a performance presentation is addressed,
- presenting the performance of the weighted composite of similar portfolios rather than using a single representative account,
- including terminated accounts as part of performance history with a clear indication of when the accounts were terminated,
- including disclosures that fully explain the performance results being reported (for example, stating, when appropriate, that results are simulated when model results are used, clearly indicating when the performance record is that of a prior entity, or disclosing whether the performance is gross of fees, net of fees, or after tax), and
- maintaining the data and records used to calculate the performance being presented.

Application of the Standard

Example 1 (Performance Calculation and Length of Time):

Kyle Taylor of Taylor Trust Company, noting the performance of Taylor's common trust fund for the past two years, states in a brochure sent to his potential clients, "You can expect steady 25% annual compound growth of the value of your investments over the year." Taylor Trust's common trust fund did increase at the rate of 25% per year for the past year, which mirrored the increase of the entire market. The fund has never averaged that growth for more than one year, however, and the average rate of growth of all of its trust accounts for five years is 5% per year.

> *Comment*: Taylor's brochure is in violation of Standard III(D). Taylor should have disclosed that the 25% growth occurred only in one year. Additionally, Taylor did not include client accounts other than those in the firm's common trust fund. A general claim of firm performance should take into account the performance of all categories of accounts. Finally, by

stating that clients can expect a steady 25% annual compound growth rate, Taylor is also violating Standard I(C)–Misrepresentation, which prohibits assurances or guarantees regarding an investment.

Example 2 (Performance Calculation and Asset Weighting):

Anna Judd, a senior partner of Alexander Capital Management, circulates a performance report for the capital appreciation accounts for the years 1988 through 2004. The firm claims compliance with the GIPS standards. Returns are not calculated in accordance with the requirements of the GIPS standards, however, because the composites are not asset weighted.

> *Comment*: Judd is in violation of Standard III(D). When claiming compliance with the GIPS standards, firms must meet *all* of the requirements, make mandatory disclosures, and meet any other requirements that apply to that firm's specific situation. Judd's violation is not from any misuse of the data but from a false claim of GIPS compliance.

Example 3 (Performance Presentation and Prior Fund/Employer):

Aaron McCoy is vice president and managing partner of the equity investment group of Mastermind Financial Advisors, a new business. Mastermind recruited McCoy because he had a proven six-year track record with G&P Financial. In developing Mastermind's advertising and marketing campaign, McCoy prepares an advertisement that includes the equity investment performance he achieved at G&P Financial. The advertisement for Mastermind does not identify the equity performance as being earned while at G&P. The advertisement is distributed to existing clients and prospective clients of Mastermind.

> *Comment*: McCoy has violated Standard III(D) by distributing an advertisement that contains material misrepresentations about the historical performance of Mastermind. Standard III(D) requires that members and candidates make every reasonable effort to ensure that performance information is a fair, accurate, and complete representation of an individual's or firm's performance. As a general matter, this standard does not prohibit showing past performance of funds managed at a prior firm as part of a performance track record as long as showing that record is accompanied by appropriate disclosures about where the performance took place and the person's specific role in achieving that performance. If McCoy chooses to use his past performance from G&P in Mastermind's advertising, he should make full disclosure of the source of the historical performance.

Example 4 (Performance Presentation and Simulated Results):

Jed Davis has developed a mutual fund selection product based on historical information from the 1990–95 period. Davis tested his methodology by applying it retroactively to data from the 1996–2003 period, thus producing simulated performance results for those years. In January 2004, Davis's employer decided to offer the product and Davis began promoting it through trade journal advertisements and direct dissemination to clients. The advertisements included the performance results for the 1996–2003 period but did not indicate that the results were simulated.

> *Comment*: Davis violated Standard III(D) by failing to clearly identify simulated performance results. Standard III(D) prohibits members and candidates from making any statements that misrepresent the performance achieved by them or their firms and requires members and candidates

to make every reasonable effort to ensure that performance information presented to clients is fair, accurate, and complete. Use of simulated results should be accompanied by full disclosure as to the source of the performance data, including the fact that the results from 1995 through 2003 were the result of applying the model retroactively to that time period.

Example 5 (Performance Calculation and Selected Accounts Only):

In a presentation prepared for prospective clients, William Kilmer shows the rates of return realized over a five-year period by a "composite" of his firm's discretionary accounts that have a "balanced" objective. This composite, however, consisted of only a few of the accounts that met the balanced criterion set by the firm, excluded accounts under a certain asset level without disclosing the fact of their exclusion, and included accounts that did not have the balanced mandate because those accounts would boost the investment results. In addition, to achieve better results, Kilmer manipulated the narrow range of accounts included in the composite by changing the accounts that made up the composite over time.

Comment: Kilmer violated Standard III(D) by misrepresenting the facts in the promotional material sent to prospective clients, distorting his firm's performance record, and failing to include disclosures that would have clarified the presentation.

Example 6 (Performance Attribution Changes):

Art Purell is reviewing the quarterly performance attribution reports for distribution to clients. Purell works for an investment management firm with a bottom-up, fundamentals-driven investment process that seeks to add value through stock selection. The attribution methodology currently compares each stock with its sector. The attribution report indicates that the value added this quarter came from asset allocation and that stock selection contributed negatively to the calculated return.

Through running several different scenarios, Purell discovers that calculating attribution by comparing each stock with its industry and then rolling the effect to the sector level improves the appearance of the manager's stock selection activities. Because the firm defines the attribution terms and the results better reflect the stated strategy, Purell recommends that the client reports should use the revised methodology.

Comment: Modifying the attribution methodology without proper notifications to clients would fail to meet the requirements of Standard III(D). Purrell's recommendation is being done solely for the interest of the firm to improve its perceived ability to meet the stated investment strategy. Such changes are unfair to clients and obscure the facts regarding the firm's abilities.

Had Purell believed the new methodology offered improvements to the original model, then he would have needed to report the results of both calculations to the client. The report should also include the reasons why the new methodology is preferred, which would allow the client to make a meaningful comparison to prior results and provide a basis for comparing future attributions.

Example 7 (Performance Calculation Methodology Disclosure):

While developing a new reporting package for existing clients, Alisha Singh, a performance analyst, discovers that her company's new system automatically calculates both time-weighted and money-weighted returns. She asks the head of client services and retention which value would be preferred given that the firm has various investment strategies that include bonds, equities, securities without leverage, and alternatives. Singh is told not to label the return value so that the firm may show whichever value is greatest for the period.

> *Comment*: Following these instructions would lead to Singh violating Standard III(D). In reporting inconsistent return values, Singh would not be providing complete information to the firm's clients. Full information is provided when clients have sufficient information to judge the performance generated by the firm.

Example 8 (Performance Calculation Methodology Disclosure):

Richmond Equity Investors manages a long–short equity fund in which clients can trade once a week (on Fridays). For transparency reasons, a daily net asset value of the fund is calculated by Richmond. The monthly fact sheets of the fund report month-to-date and year-to-date performance. Richmond publishes the performance based on the higher of the last trading day of the month (typically, not the last business day) or the last business day of the month as determined by Richmond. The fact sheet mentions only that the data are as of the end of the month, without giving the exact date. Maggie Clark, the investment performance analyst in charge of the calculations, is concerned about the frequent changes and asks her supervisor whether they are appropriate.

> *Comment*: Clark's actions in questioning the changing performance metric comply with Standard III(D). She has shown concern that these changes are not presenting an accurate and complete picture of the performance generated.

Standard III(E) Preservation of Confidentiality

Members and Candidates must keep information about current, former, and prospective clients confidential unless:

1. The information concerns illegal activities on the part of the client;
2. Disclosure is required by law; or
3. The client or prospective client permits disclosure of the information.

Guidance

Highlights:

- *Status of Client*
- *Compliance with Laws*
- *Electronic Information and Security*
- *Professional Conduct Investigations by CFA Institute*

Standard III(E) requires that members and candidates preserve the confidentiality of information communicated to them by their clients, prospective clients, and former clients. This standard is applicable when (1) the member or candidate receives information because of his or her special ability to conduct a portion of the client's business or personal affairs and (2) the member or candidate receives information that arises from or is relevant to that portion of the client's business that is the subject of the special or confidential relationship. If disclosure of the information is required by law or the information concerns illegal activities by the client, however, the member or candidate may have an obligation to report the activities to the appropriate authorities.

Status of Client

This standard protects the confidentiality of client information even if the person or entity is no longer a client of the member or candidate. Therefore, members and candidates must continue to maintain the confidentiality of client records even after the client relationship has ended. If a client or former client expressly authorizes the member or candidate to disclose information, however, the member or candidate may follow the terms of the authorization and provide the information.

Compliance with Laws

As a general matter, members and candidates must comply with applicable law. If applicable law requires disclosure of client information in certain circumstances, members and candidates must comply with the law. Similarly, if applicable law requires members and candidates to maintain confidentiality, even if the information concerns illegal activities on the part of the client, members and candidates should not disclose such information. Additionally, applicable laws, such as inter-departmental communication restrictions within financial institutions, can impose limitations on information flow about a client within an entity that may lead to a violation of confidentiality. When in doubt, members and candidates should consult with their employer's compliance personnel or legal counsel before disclosing confidential information about clients.

Electronic Information and Security

Because of the ever-increasing volume of electronically stored information, members and candidates need to be particularly aware of possible accidental disclosures. Many employers have strict policies about how to electronically communicate sensitive client information and store client information on personal laptops, mobile devices, or portable disk/flash drives. In recent years, regulatory authorities have imposed stricter data security laws applying to the use of mobile remote digital communication, including the use of social media, that must be considered. Standard III(E) does not require members or candidates to become experts in information security technology, but they should have a thorough understanding of the policies of their employer. The size and operations of the firm will lead to differing policies for ensuring the security of confidential information maintained within the firm. Members and candidates should encourage their firm to conduct regular periodic training on confidentiality procedures for all firm personnel, including portfolio associates, receptionists, and other non-investment staff who have routine direct contact with clients and their records.

Professional Conduct Investigations by CFA Institute

The requirements of Standard III(E) are not intended to prevent members and candidates from cooperating with an investigation by the CFA Institute Professional Conduct Program (PCP). When permissible under applicable law, members and candidates shall consider the PCP an extension of themselves when requested to provide information about a client in support of a PCP investigation into their own conduct. Members and candidates are encouraged to cooperate with investigations into the conduct of others. Any information turned over to the PCP is kept in the strictest confidence. Members and candidates will not be considered in violation of this standard by forwarding confidential information to the PCP.

Recommended Procedures for Compliance

The simplest, most conservative, and most effective way to comply with Standard III(E) is to avoid disclosing any information received from a client except to authorized fellow employees who are also working for the client. In some instances, however, a member or candidate may want to disclose information received from clients that is outside the scope of the confidential relationship and does not involve illegal activities. Before making such a disclosure, a member or candidate should ask the following:

- In what context was the information disclosed? If disclosed in a discussion of work being performed for the client, is the information relevant to the work?
- Is the information background material that, if disclosed, will enable the member or candidate to improve service to the client?

Members and candidates need to understand and follow their firm's electronic information communication and storage procedures. If the firm does not have procedures in place, members and candidates should encourage the development of procedures that appropriately reflect the firm's size and business operations.

Communicating with Clients

Technological changes are constantly enhancing the methods that are used to communicate with clients and prospective clients. Members and candidates should make reasonable efforts to ensure that firm-supported communication methods and compliance procedures follow practices designed for preventing accidental distribution of confidential information. Given the rate at which technology changes, a regular review of privacy protection measures is encouraged.

Members and candidates should be diligent in discussing with clients the appropriate methods for providing confidential information. It is important to convey to clients that not all firm-sponsored resources may be appropriate for such communications.

Application of the Standard

Example 1 (Possessing Confidential Information):

Sarah Connor, a financial analyst employed by Johnson Investment Counselors, Inc., provides investment advice to the trustees of City Medical Center. The trustees have given her a number of internal reports concerning City Medical's needs for physical plant renovation and expansion. They have asked Connor to recommend investments that would generate capital appreciation in endowment funds to meet projected capital expenditures. Connor is approached by a local businessman, Thomas Kasey, who is considering a substantial contribution either to City Medical Center or to another local hospital. Kasey wants to find out the building plans of both institutions before making a decision, but he does not want to speak to the trustees.

> *Comment*: The trustees gave Connor the internal reports so she could advise them on how to manage their endowment funds. Because the information in the reports is clearly both confidential and within the scope of the confidential relationship, Standard III(E) requires that Connor refuse to divulge information to Kasey.

Example 2 (Disclosing Confidential Information):

Lynn Moody is an investment officer at the Lester Trust Company. She has an advisory customer who has talked to her about giving approximately US$50,000 to charity to reduce her income taxes. Moody is also treasurer of the Home for Indigent Widows (HIW), which is planning its annual giving campaign. HIW hopes to expand its list of prospects, particularly those capable of substantial gifts. Moody recommends that HIW's vice president for corporate gifts call on her customer and ask for a donation in the US$50,000 range.

> *Comment*: Even though the attempt to help the Home for Indigent Widows was well intended, Moody violated Standard III(E) by revealing confidential information about her client.

Example 3 (Disclosing Possible Illegal Activity):

Government officials approach Casey Samuel, the portfolio manager for Garcia Company's pension plan, to examine pension fund records. They tell her that Garcia's corporate tax returns are being audited and the pension fund is being reviewed. Two days earlier, Samuel had learned in a regular investment review with Garcia officers that potentially excessive and improper charges were being made to the pension plan by Garcia. Samuel consults her employer's general counsel and is advised that Garcia has probably violated tax and fiduciary regulations and laws.

> *Comment*: Samuel should inform her supervisor of these activities, and her employer should take steps, with Garcia, to remedy the violations. If that approach is not successful, Samuel and her employer should seek advice of legal counsel to determine the appropriate steps to be taken. Samuel may well have a duty to disclose the evidence she has of the continuing legal violations and to resign as asset manager for Garcia.

Example 4 (Disclosing Possible Illegal Activity):

David Bradford manages money for a family-owned real estate development corporation. He also manages the individual portfolios of several of the family members and officers of the corporation, including the chief financial officer (CFO). Based on the financial records of the corporation and some questionable practices of the CFO that Bradford has observed, Bradford believes that the CFO is embezzling money from the corporation and putting it into his personal investment account.

> *Comment*: Bradford should check with his firm's compliance department or appropriate legal counsel to determine whether applicable securities regulations require reporting the CFO's financial records.

Example 5 (Accidental Disclosure of Confidential Information):

Lynn Moody is an investment officer at the Lester Trust Company (LTC). She has stewardship of a significant number of individually managed taxable accounts. In addition to receiving quarterly written reports, about a dozen high-net-worth individuals have indicated to Moody a willingness to receive communications about overall economic and financial market outlooks directly from her by way of a social media platform. Under the direction of her firm's technology and compliance departments, she established a new group page on an existing social media platform specifically for her clients. In the instructions provided to clients, Moody asked them to "join" the group so they may be granted access to the posted content. The instructions also advised clients that all comments posted would be available to the public and thus the platform was not an appropriate method for communicating personal or confidential information.

Six months later, in early January, Moody posted LTC's year-end "Market Outlook." The report outlined a new asset allocation strategy that the firm is adding to its recommendations in the new year. Moody introduced the publication with a note informing her clients that she would be discussing the changes with them individually in their upcoming meetings.

One of Moody's clients responded directly on the group page that his family recently experienced a major change in their financial profile. The client described highly personal and confidential details of the event. Unfortunately, all clients that were part of the group were also able to read the detailed posting until Moody was able to have the comment removed.

> *Comment*: Moody has taken reasonable steps for protecting the confidentiality of client information while using the social media platform. She provided instructions clarifying that all information posted to the site would be publically viewable to all group members and warned against using this method for communicating confidential information. The accidental disclosure of confidential information by a client is not under Moody's control. Her actions to remove the information promptly once she became aware further align with Standard III(E).
>
> In understanding the potential sensitivity clients express surrounding the confidentiality of personal information, this event highlights a need for further training. Moody might advocate for additional warnings or controls for clients when they consider using social media platforms for two-way communications.

STANDARD IV: DUTIES TO EMPLOYERS

Standard IV(A) Loyalty

> In matters related to their employment, Members and Candidates must act for the benefit of their employer and not deprive their employer of the advantage of their skills and abilities, divulge confidential information, or otherwise cause harm to their employer.

Guidance

Highlights:

- *Employer Responsibilities*
- *Independent Practice*
- *Leaving an Employer*
- *Use of Social Media*
- *Whistleblowing*
- *Nature of Employment*

Standard IV(A) requires members and candidates to protect the interests of their firm by refraining from any conduct that would injure the firm, deprive it of profit, or deprive it of the member's or candidate's skills and ability. Members and candidates must always place the interests of clients above the interests of their employer but should also consider the effects of their conduct on the sustainability and integrity of the employer firm. In matters related to their employment, members and candidates must not engage in conduct that harms the interests of their employer. Implicit in this standard is the obligation of members and candidates to comply with the policies and procedures established by their employers that govern the employer–employee relationship—to the extent that such policies and procedures do not conflict with applicable laws, rules, or regulations or the Code and Standards.

This standard is not meant to be a blanket requirement to place employer interests ahead of personal interests in all matters. The standard does not require members and candidates to subordinate important personal and family obligations to their work. Members and candidates should enter into a dialogue with their employer about balancing personal and employment obligations when personal matters may interfere with their work on a regular or significant basis.

Employer Responsibilities

The employer–employee relationship imposes duties and responsibilities on both parties. Employers must recognize the duties and responsibilities that they owe to their employees if they expect to have content and productive employees.

Members and candidates are encouraged to provide their employer with a copy of the Code and Standards. These materials will inform the employer of the responsibilities of a CFA Institute member or a candidate in the CFA Program. The Code and Standards also serve as a basis for questioning employer policies and practices that conflict with these responsibilities.

Employers are not obligated to adhere to the Code and Standards. In expecting to retain competent employees who are members and candidates, however, they should not develop conflicting policies and procedures. The employer is responsible for a positive working environment, which includes an ethical workplace. Senior management has the additional responsibility to devise compensation structures and incentive arrangements that do not encourage unethical behavior.

Independent Practice

Included in Standard IV(A) is the requirement that members and candidates abstain from independent competitive activity that could conflict with the interests of their employer. Although Standard IV(A) does not preclude members or candidates from entering into an independent business while still employed, members and candidates who plan to engage in independent practice for compensation must notify their employer and describe the types of services they will render to prospective independent clients, the expected duration of the services, and the compensation for the services. Members and candidates should not render services until they receive consent from their employer to all of the terms of the arrangement. "Practice" means any service that the employer currently makes available for remuneration. "Undertaking independent practice" means engaging in competitive business, as opposed to making preparations to begin such practice.

Leaving an Employer

When members and candidates are planning to leave their current employer, they must continue to act in the employer's best interest. They must not engage in any activities that would conflict with this duty until their resignation becomes effective. It is difficult to define specific guidelines for those members and candidates who are planning to compete with their employer as part of a new venture. The circumstances of each situation must be reviewed to distinguish permissible preparations from violations of duty. Activities that might constitute a violation, especially in combination, include the following:

- misappropriation of trade secrets,
- misuse of confidential information,
- solicitation of the employer's clients prior to cessation of employment,
- self-dealing (appropriating for one's own property a business opportunity or information belonging to one's employer), and
- misappropriation of clients or client lists.

A departing employee is generally free to make arrangements or preparations to go into a competitive business before terminating the relationship with his or her employer as long as such preparations do not breach the employee's duty of loyalty. A member or candidate who is contemplating seeking other employment must not contact existing clients or potential clients prior to leaving his or her employer for purposes of soliciting their business for the new employer. Once notice is provided to the employer of the intent to resign, the member or candidate must follow the employer's policies and procedures related to notifying clients of his or her planned departure. In addition, the member or candidate must not take records or files to a new employer without the written permission of the previous employer.

Once an employee has left the firm, the skills and experience that an employee obtained while employed are not "confidential" or "privileged" information. Similarly, simple knowledge of the names and existence of former clients is generally not confidential information unless deemed such by an agreement or by law. Standard IV(A) does not prohibit experience or knowledge gained at one employer from being used at another employer. Firm records or work performed on behalf of the firm that is stored in paper copy or electronically for the member's or candidate's convenience while employed, however, should be erased or returned to the employer unless the firm gives permission to keep those records after employment ends.

The standard does not prohibit former employees from contacting clients of their previous firm as long as the contact information does not come from the records of the former employer or violate an applicable "noncompete agreement." Members and candidates are free to use public information after departing to contact former clients without violating Standard IV(A) as long as there is no specific agreement not to do so.

Employers often require employees to sign noncompete agreements that preclude a departing employee from engaging in certain conduct. Members and candidates should take care to review the terms of any such agreement when leaving their employer to determine what, if any, conduct those agreements may prohibit.

In some markets, there are agreements between employers within an industry that outline information that departing employees are permitted to take upon resignation, such as the "Protocol for Broker Recruiting" in the United States. These agreements ease individuals' transition between firms that have agreed to follow the outlined procedures. Members and candidates who move between firms that sign such agreements may rely on the protections provided as long as they faithfully adhere to all the procedures outlined.

For example, under the agreement between many US brokers, individuals are allowed to take some general client contact information when departing. To be protected, a copy of the information the individual is taking must be provided to the local management team for review. Additionally, the specific client information may only be used by the departing employee and not others employed by the new firm.

Use of Social Media

The growth in various online networking platforms, such as LinkedIn, Twitter, and Facebook (commonly referred to as social media platforms), is providing new opportunities and challenges for businesses. Members and candidates should understand and abide by all applicable firm policies and regulations as to the acceptable use of social media platforms to interact with clients and prospective clients. This is especially important when a member or candidate is planning to leave an employer.

Social media use makes determining how and when departure notification is delivered to clients more complex. Members and candidates may have developed profiles on these platforms that include connections with individuals who are clients of the firm, as well as individuals unrelated to their employer. Communications through social media platforms that potentially reach current clients should adhere to the employer's policies and procedures regarding notification of departing employees.

Social media connections with clients are also raising questions concerning the differences between public information and firm property. Specific accounts and user profiles of members and candidates may be created for solely professional reasons, including firm-approved accounts for client engagements. Such firm-approved business-related accounts would be considered part of the firm's assets, thus requiring members and candidates to transfer or delete the accounts as directed by their firm's policies and procedures. Best practice for members and candidates is to maintain separate accounts for their personal and professional social media activities. Members and candidates should discuss with their employers how profiles should be treated when a single account includes personal connections and also is used to conduct aspects of their professional activities.

Whistleblowing

A member's or candidate's personal interests, as well as the interests of his or her employer, are secondary to protecting the integrity of capital markets and the interests of clients. Therefore, circumstances may arise (e.g., when an employer is engaged in illegal or unethical activity) in which members and candidates must act contrary to their employer's interests in order to comply with their duties to the market and clients. In such instances, activities that would normally violate a member's or candidate's duty to his or her employer (such as contradicting employer instructions, violating certain policies and procedures, or preserving a record by copying employer records) may be justified. Such action would be permitted only if the intent is clearly aimed at protecting clients or the integrity of the market, not for personal gain.

Nature of Employment

A wide variety of business relationships exists within the investment industry. For instance, a member or candidate may be an employee or an independent contractor. Members and candidates must determine whether they are employees or independent contractors in order to determine the applicability of Standard IV(A). This issue will be decided largely by the degree of control exercised by the employing entity over the member or candidate. Factors determining control include whether the member's or candidate's hours, work location, and other parameters of the job are set; whether facilities are provided to the member or candidate; whether the member's or candidate's expenses are reimbursed; whether the member or candidate seeks work from other employers; and the number of clients or employers the member or candidate works for.

A member's or candidate's duties within an independent contractor relationship are governed by the oral or written agreement between the member and the client. Members and candidates should take care to define clearly the scope of their responsibilities and the expectations of each client within the context of each relationship. Once a member or candidate establishes a relationship with a client, the member or candidate has a duty to abide by the terms of the agreement.

Recommended Procedures for Compliance

Employers may establish codes of conduct and operating procedures for their employees to follow. Members and candidates should fully understand the policies to ensure that they are not in conflict with the Code and Standards. The following topics identify policies that members and candidates should encourage their firms to adopt if the policies are not currently in place.

Competition Policy

A member or candidate must understand any restrictions placed by the employer on offering similar services outside the firm while employed by the firm. The policy may outline the procedures for requesting approval to undertake the outside service or may be a strict prohibition of such service. If a member's or candidate's employer elects to have its employees sign a noncompete agreement as part of the employment agreement, the member or candidate should ensure that the details are clear and fully explained prior to signing the agreement.

Termination Policy

Members and candidates should clearly understand the termination policies of their employer. Termination policies should establish clear procedures regarding the resignation process, including addressing how the termination will be disclosed to clients and staff and whether updates posted through social media platforms will be allowed. The firm's policy may also outline the procedures for transferring ongoing research and account management responsibilities. Finally, the procedures should address agreements that allow departing employees to remove specific client-related information upon resignation.

Incident-Reporting Procedures

Members and candidates should be aware of their firm's policies related to whistleblowing and encourage their firm to adopt industry best practices in this area. Many firms are required by regulatory mandates to establish confidential and anonymous reporting procedures that allow employees to report potentially unethical and illegal activities in the firm.

Employee Classification

Members and candidates should understand their status within their employer firm. Firms are encouraged to adopt a standardized classification structure (e.g., part time, full time, outside contractor) for their employees and indicate how each of the firm's policies applies to each employee class.

Application of the Standard

Example 1 (Soliciting Former Clients):

Samuel Magee manages pension accounts for Trust Assets, Inc., but has become frustrated with the working environment and has been offered a position with Fiduciary Management. Before resigning from Trust Assets, Magee asks four big accounts to leave that firm and open accounts with Fiduciary. Magee also persuades several prospective clients to sign agreements with Fiduciary Management. Magee had previously made presentations to these prospects on behalf of Trust Assets.

> *Comment*: Magee violated the employee–employer principle requiring him to act solely for his employer's benefit. Magee's duty is to Trust Assets as long as he is employed there. The solicitation of Trust Assets' current clients and prospective clients is unethical and violates Standard IV(A).

Example 2 (Former Employer's Documents and Files):

James Hightower has been employed by Jason Investment Management Corporation for 15 years. He began as an analyst but assumed increasing responsibilities and is now a senior portfolio manager and a member of the firm's investment policy committee. Hightower has decided to leave Jason Investment and start his own investment management business. He has been careful not to tell any of Jason's clients that he is leaving; he does not want to be accused of breaching his duty to Jason by soliciting Jason's clients before his departure. Hightower is planning to copy and take with him the following documents and information he developed or worked on while at Jason: (1) the client list, with addresses, telephone numbers, and other pertinent client information; (2) client account statements; (3) sample marketing presentations to prospective clients containing Jason's performance record; (4) Jason's recommended list of securities; (5) computer models to determine asset allocations for accounts with various objectives; (6) computer models for stock selection; and (7) personal computer spreadsheets for Hightower's major corporate recommendations, which he developed when he was an analyst.

> *Comment*: Except with the consent of their employer, departing members and candidates may not take employer property, which includes books, records, reports, and other materials, because taking such materials may interfere with their employer's business opportunities. Taking any employer records, even those the member or candidate prepared, violates Standard IV(A). Employer records include items stored in hard copy or any other medium (e.g., home computers, portable storage devices, cell phones).

Example 3 (Addressing Rumors):

Reuben Winston manages all-equity portfolios at Target Asset Management (TAM), a large, established investment counselor. Ten years previously, Philpott & Company, which manages a family of global bond mutual funds, acquired TAM in a diversification move. After the merger, the combined operations prospered in the fixed-income business but the equity management business at TAM languished. Lately, a few of the equity pension accounts that had been with TAM before the merger have terminated their relationships with TAM. One day, Winston finds on his voice mail the following message from a concerned client: "Hey! I just heard that Philpott is close to announcing the sale of your firm's equity management business to Rugged Life. What is going on?" Not being aware of any such deal, Winston and his associates are stunned. Their internal inquiries are met with denials from Philpott management, but the rumors persist. Feeling left in the dark, Winston contemplates leading an employee buyout of TAM's equity management business.

> *Comment*: An employee-led buyout of TAM's equity asset management business would be consistent with Standard IV(A) because it would rest on the permission of the employer and, ultimately, the clients. In this case,

however, in which employees suspect the senior managers or principals are not truthful or forthcoming, Winston should consult legal counsel to determine appropriate action.

Example 4 (Ownership of Completed Prior Work):

Laura Clay, who is unemployed, wants part-time consulting work while seeking a full-time analyst position. During an interview at Bradley Associates, a large institutional asset manager, Clay is told that the firm has no immediate research openings but would be willing to pay her a flat fee to complete a study of the wireless communications industry within a given period of time. Clay would be allowed unlimited access to Bradley's research files and would be welcome to come to the offices and use whatever support facilities are available during normal working hours. Bradley's research director does not seek any exclusivity for Clay's output, and the two agree to the arrangement on a handshake. As Clay nears completion of the study, she is offered an analyst job in the research department of Winston & Company, a brokerage firm, and she is pondering submitting the draft of her wireless study for publication by Winston.

> *Comment*: Although she is under no written contractual obligation to Bradley, Clay has an obligation to let Bradley act on the output of her study before Winston & Company or Clay uses the information to their advantage. That is, unless Bradley gives permission to Clay and waives its rights to her wireless report, Clay would be in violation of Standard IV(A) if she were to immediately recommend to Winston the same transactions recommended in the report to Bradley. Furthermore, Clay must not take from Bradley any research file material or other property that she may have used.

Example 5 (Ownership of Completed Prior Work):

Emma Madeline, a recent college graduate and a candidate in the CFA Program, spends her summer as an unpaid intern at Murdoch and Lowell. The senior managers at Murdoch are attempting to bring the firm into compliance with the GIPS standards, and Madeline is assigned to assist in its efforts. Two months into her internship, Madeline applies for a job at McMillan & Company, which has plans to become GIPS compliant. Madeline accepts the job with McMillan. Before leaving Murdoch, she copies the firm's software that she helped develop because she believes this software will assist her in her new position.

> *Comment*: Even though Madeline does not receive monetary compensation for her services at Murdoch, she has used firm resources in creating the software and is considered an employee because she receives compensation and benefits in the form of work experience and knowledge. By copying the software, Madeline violated Standard IV(A) because she misappropriated Murdoch's property without permission.

Example 6 (Soliciting Former Clients):

Dennis Elliot has hired Sam Chisolm, who previously worked for a competing firm. Chisolm left his former firm after 18 years of employment. When Chisolm begins working for Elliot, he wants to contact his former clients because he knows them well and is certain that many will follow him to his new employer. Is Chisolm in violation of Standard IV(A) if he contacts his former clients?

> *Comment*: Because client records are the property of the firm, contacting former clients for any reason through the use of client lists or other information taken from a former employer without permission would be a

violation of Standard IV(A). In addition, the nature and extent of the contact with former clients may be governed by the terms of any noncompete agreement signed by the employee and the former employer that covers contact with former clients after employment.

Simple knowledge of the names and existence of former clients is not confidential information, just as skills or experience that an employee obtains while employed are not "confidential" or "privileged" information. The Code and Standards do not impose a prohibition on the use of experience or knowledge gained at one employer from being used at another employer. The Code and Standards also do not prohibit former employees from contacting clients of their previous firm, in the absence of a noncompete agreement. Members and candidates are free to use public information about their former firm after departing to contact former clients without violating Standard IV(A).

In the absence of a noncompete agreement, as long as Chisolm maintains his duty of loyalty to his employer before joining Elliot's firm, does not take steps to solicit clients until he has left his former firm, and does not use material from his former employer without its permission after he has left, he is not in violation of the Code and Standards.

Example 7 (Starting a New Firm):

Geraldine Allen currently works at a registered investment company as an equity analyst. Without notice to her employer, she registers with government authorities to start an investment company that will compete with her employer, but she does not actively seek clients. Does registration of this competing company with the appropriate regulatory authorities constitute a violation of Standard IV(A)?

Comment: Allen's preparation for the new business by registering with the regulatory authorities does not conflict with the work for her employer if the preparations have been done on Allen's own time outside the office and if Allen will not be soliciting clients for the business or otherwise operating the new company until she has left her current employer.

Example 8 (Competing with Current Employer):

Several employees are planning to depart their current employer within a few weeks and have been careful to not engage in any activities that would conflict with their duty to their current employer. They have just learned that one of their employer's clients has undertaken a request for proposal (RFP) to review and possibly hire a new investment consultant. The RFP has been sent to the employer and all of its competitors. The group believes that the new entity to be formed would be qualified to respond to the RFP and be eligible for the business. The RFP submission period is likely to conclude before the employees' resignations are effective. Is it permissible for the group of departing employees to respond to the RFP for their anticipated new firm?

Comment: A group of employees responding to an RFP that their employer is also responding to would lead to direct competition between the employees and the employer. Such conduct violates Standard IV(A) unless the group of employees receives permission from their employer as well as the entity sending out the RFP.

Example 9 (Externally Compensated Assignments):

Alfonso Mota is a research analyst with Tyson Investments. He works part time as a mayor for his hometown, a position for which he receives compensation. Must Mota seek permission from Tyson to serve as mayor?

> *Comment*: If Mota's mayoral duties are so extensive and time-consuming that they might detract from his ability to fulfill his responsibilities at Tyson, he should discuss his outside activities with his employer and come to a mutual agreement regarding how to manage his personal commitments with his responsibilities to his employer.

Example 10 (Soliciting Former Clients):

After leaving her employer, Shawna McQuillen establishes her own money management business. While with her former employer, she did not sign a noncompete agreement that would have prevented her from soliciting former clients. Upon her departure, she does not take any of her client lists or contact information and she clears her personal computer of any employer records, including client contact information. She obtains the phone numbers of her former clients through public records and contacts them to solicit their business.

> *Comment*: McQuillen is not in violation of Standard IV(A) because she has not used information or records from her former employer and is not prevented by an agreement with her former employer from soliciting her former clients.

Example 11 (Whistleblowing Actions):

Meredith Rasmussen works on a buy-side trading desk and concentrates on in-house trades for a hedge fund subsidiary managed by a team at the investment management firm. The hedge fund has been very successful and is marketed globally by the firm. From her experience as the trader for much of the activity of the fund, Rasmussen has become quite knowledgeable about the hedge fund's strategy, tactics, and performance. When a distinct break in the market occurs, however, and many of the securities involved in the hedge fund's strategy decline markedly in value, Rasmussen observes that the reported performance of the hedge fund does not reflect this decline. In her experience, the lack of any effect is a very unlikely occurrence. She approaches the head of trading about her concern and is told that she should not ask any questions and that the fund is big and successful and is not her concern. She is fairly sure something is not right, so she contacts the compliance officer, who also tells her to stay away from the issue of this hedge fund's reporting.

> *Comment*: Rasmussen has clearly come upon an error in policies, procedures, and compliance practices in the firm's operations. Having been unsuccessful in finding a resolution with her supervisor and the compliance officer, Rasmussen should consult the firm's whistleblowing policy to determine the appropriate next step toward informing management of her concerns. The potentially unethical actions of the investment management division are appropriate grounds for further disclosure, so Rasmussen's whistleblowing would not represent a violation of Standard IV(A).
>
> See also Standard I(D)–Misconduct and Standard IV(C)–Responsibilities of Supervisors.

Example 12 (Soliciting Former Clients):

Angel Crome has been a private banker for YBSafe Bank for the past eight years. She has been very successful and built a considerable client portfolio during that time but is extremely frustrated by the recent loss of reputation by her current employer and subsequent client insecurity. A locally renowned headhunter contacted Crome a few days ago and offered her an interesting job with a competing private bank. This bank offers a substantial signing bonus for advisers with their own client portfolios. Crome figures that she can solicit at least 70% of her clients to follow her and gladly enters into the new employment contract.

> *Comment*: Crome may contact former clients upon termination of her employment with YBSafe Bank, but she is prohibited from using client records built by and kept with her in her capacity as an employee of YBSafe Bank. Client lists are proprietary information of her former employer and must not be used for her or her new employer's benefit. The use of written, electronic, or any other form of records other than publicly available information to contact her former clients at YBSafe Bank will be a violation of Standard IV(A).

Example 13 (Notification of Code and Standards):

Krista Smith is a relatively new assistant trader for the fixed-income desk of a major investment bank. She is on a team responsible for structuring collateralized debt obligations (CDOs) made up of securities in the inventory of the trading desk. At a meeting of the team, senior executives explain the opportunity to eventually separate the CDO into various risk-rated tranches to be sold to the clients of the firm. After the senior executives leave the meeting, the head trader announces various responsibilities of each member of the team and then says, "This is a good time to unload some of the junk we have been stuck with for a while and disguise it with ratings and a thick, unreadable prospectus, so don't be shy in putting this CDO together. Just kidding." Smith is worried by this remark and asks some of her colleagues what the head trader meant. They all respond that he was just kidding but that there is some truth in the remark because the CDO is seen by management as an opportunity to improve the quality of the securities in the firm's inventory.

Concerned about the ethical environment of the workplace, Smith decides to talk to her supervisor about her concerns and provides the head trader with a copy of the Code and Standards. Smith discusses the principle of placing the client above the interest of the firm and the possibility that the development of the new CDO will not adhere to this responsibility. The head trader assures Smith that the appropriate analysis will be conducted when determining the appropriate securities for collateral. Furthermore, the ratings are assigned by an independent firm and the prospectus will include full and factual disclosures. Smith is reassured by the meeting, but she also reviews the company's procedures and requirements for reporting potential violations of company policy and securities laws.

> *Comment*: Smith's review of the company policies and procedures for reporting violations allows her to be prepared to report through the appropriate whistleblower process if she decides that the CDO development process involves unethical actions by others. Smith's actions comply with the Code and Standards principles of placing the client's interests first and being loyal to her employer. In providing her supervisor with a copy of the Code and Standards, Smith is highlighting the high level of ethical conduct she is required to adhere to in her professional activities.

Example 14 (Leaving an Employer):

Laura Webb just left her position as portfolio analyst at Research Systems, Inc. (RSI). Her employment contract included a non-solicitation agreement that requires her to wait two years before soliciting RSI clients for any investment-related services. Upon leaving, Webb was informed that RSI would contact clients immediately about her departure and introduce her replacement.

While working at RSI, Webb connected with clients, other industry associates, and friends through her LinkedIn network. Her business and personal relationships were intermingled because she considered many of her clients to be personal friends. Realizing that her LinkedIn network would be a valuable resource for new employment opportunities, she updated her profile several days following her departure from RSI. LinkedIn automatically sent a notification to Webb's entire network that her employment status had been changed in her profile.

> *Comment*: Prior to her departure, Webb should have discussed any client information contained in her social media networks. By updating her LinkedIn profile after RSI notified clients and after her employment ended, she has appropriately placed her employer's interests ahead of her own personal interests. In addition, she has not violated the non-solicitation agreement with RSI, unless it prohibited any contact with clients during the two-year period.

Example 15 (Confidential Firm Information):

Sanjay Gupta is a research analyst at Naram Investment Management (NIM). NIM uses a team-based research process to develop recommendations on investment opportunities covered by the team members. Gupta, like others, provides commentary for NIM's clients through the company blog, which is posted weekly on the NIM password-protected website. According to NIM's policy, every contribution to the website must be approved by the company's compliance department before posting. Any opinions expressed on the website are disclosed as representing the perspective of NIM.

Gupta also writes a personal blog to share his experiences with friends and family. As with most blogs, Gupta's personal blog is widely available to interested readers through various internet search engines. Occasionally, when he disagrees with the team-based research opinions of NIM, Gupta uses his personal blog to express his own opinions as a counterpoint to the commentary posted on the NIM website. Gupta believes this provides his readers with a more complete perspective on these investment opportunities.

> *Comment*: Gupta is in violation of Standard IV(A) for disclosing confidential firm information through his personal blog. The recommendations on the firm's blog to clients are not freely available across the internet, but his personal blog post indirectly provides the firm's recommendations.
>
> Additionally, by posting research commentary on his personal blog, Gupta is using firm resources for his personal advantage. To comply with Standard IV(A), members and candidates must receive consent from their employer prior to using company resources.

Standard IV(B) Additional Compensation Arrangements

Members and Candidates must not accept gifts, benefits, compensation, or consideration that competes with or might reasonably be expected to create a conflict of interest with their employer's interest unless they obtain written consent from all parties involved.

Guidance

Standard IV(B) requires members and candidates to obtain permission from their employer before accepting compensation or other benefits from third parties for the services rendered to the employer or for any services that might create a conflict with their employer's interest. Compensation and benefits include direct compensation by the client and any indirect compensation or other benefits received from third parties. "Written consent" includes any form of communication that can be documented (for example, communication via e-mail that can be retrieved and documented).

Members and candidates must obtain permission for additional compensation/benefits because such arrangements may affect loyalties and objectivity and create potential conflicts of interest. Disclosure allows an employer to consider the outside arrangements when evaluating the actions and motivations of members and candidates. Moreover, the employer is entitled to have full knowledge of all compensation/benefit arrangements so as to be able to assess the true cost of the services members or candidates are providing.

There may be instances in which a member or candidate is hired by an employer on a "part-time" basis. "Part-time" status applies to employees who do not commit the full number of hours required for a normal work week. Members and candidates should discuss possible limitations to their abilities to provide services that may be competitive with their employer during the negotiation and hiring process. The requirements of Standard IV(B) would be applicable to limitations identified at that time.

Recommended Procedures for Compliance

Members and candidates should make an immediate written report to their supervisor and compliance officer specifying any compensation they propose to receive for services in addition to the compensation or benefits received from their employer. The details of the report should be confirmed by the party offering the additional compensation, including performance incentives offered by clients. This written report should state the terms of any agreement under which a member or candidate will receive additional compensation; "terms" include the nature of the compensation, the approximate amount of compensation, and the duration of the agreement.

Application of the Standard

Example 1 (Notification of Client Bonus Compensation):

Geoff Whitman, a portfolio analyst for Adams Trust Company, manages the account of Carol Cochran, a client. Whitman is paid a salary by his employer, and Cochran pays the trust company a standard fee based on the market value of assets in her portfolio. Cochran proposes to Whitman that "any year that my portfolio achieves at least a 15% return before taxes, you and your wife can fly to Monaco at my expense and use my condominium during the third week of January." Whitman does not inform his employer of the arrangement and vacations in Monaco the following January as Cochran's guest.

> *Comment*: Whitman violated Standard IV(B) by failing to inform his employer in writing of this supplemental, contingent compensation arrangement. The nature of the arrangement could have resulted in partiality to Cochran's account, which could have detracted from Whitman's performance with respect to other accounts he handles for Adams Trust. Whitman must obtain the consent of his employer to accept such a supplemental benefit.

Example 2 (Notification of Outside Compensation):

Terry Jones sits on the board of directors of Exercise Unlimited, Inc. In return for his services on the board, Jones receives unlimited membership privileges for his family at all Exercise Unlimited facilities. Jones purchases Exercise Unlimited stock for the client accounts for which it is appropriate. Jones does not disclose this arrangement to his employer because he does not receive monetary compensation for his services to the board.

> *Comment*: Jones has violated Standard IV(B) by failing to disclose to his employer benefits received in exchange for his services on the board of directors. The nonmonetary compensation may create a conflict of interest in the same manner as being paid to serve as a director.

Example 3 (Prior Approval for Outside Compensation):

Jonathan Hollis is an analyst of oil-and-gas companies for Specialty Investment Management. He is currently recommending the purchase of ABC Oil Company shares and has published a long, well-thought-out research report to substantiate his recommendation. Several weeks after publishing the report, Hollis receives a call from the investor-relations office of ABC Oil saying that Thomas Andrews, CEO of the company, saw the report and really liked the analyst's grasp of the business and his company. The investor-relations officer invites Hollis to visit ABC Oil to discuss the industry further. ABC Oil offers to send a company plane to pick Hollis up and arrange for his accommodations while visiting. Hollis, after gaining the appropriate approvals, accepts the meeting with the CEO but declines the offered travel arrangements.

Several weeks later, Andrews and Hollis meet to discuss the oil business and Hollis's report. Following the meeting, Hollis joins Andrews and the investment relations officer for dinner at an upscale restaurant near ABC Oil's headquarters.

Upon returning to Specialty Investment Management, Hollis provides a full review of the meeting to the director of research, including a disclosure of the dinner attended.

> *Comment*: Hollis's actions did not violate Standard IV(B). Through gaining approval before accepting the meeting and declining the offered travel arrangements, Hollis sought to avoid any potential conflicts of interest between his company and ABC Oil. Because the location of the dinner was not available prior to arrival and Hollis notified his company of the dinner upon his return, accepting the dinner should not impair his objectivity. By disclosing the dinner, Hollis has enabled Specialty Investment Management to assess whether it has any impact on future reports and recommendations by Hollis related to ABC Oil.

Standard IV(C) Responsibilities of Supervisors

Members and Candidates must make reasonable efforts to ensure that anyone subject to their supervision or authority complies with applicable laws, rules, regulations, and the Code and Standards.

Guidance

Highlights:

- *System for Supervision*
- *Supervision Includes Detection*

Standard IV(C) states that members and candidates must promote actions by all employees under their supervision and authority to comply with applicable laws, rules, regulations, and firm policies and the Code and Standards.

Any investment professional who has employees subject to her or his control or influence—whether or not the employees are CFA Institute members, CFA charterholders, or candidates in the CFA Program—exercises supervisory responsibility. Members and candidates acting as supervisors must also have in-depth knowledge of the Code and Standards so that they can apply this knowledge in discharging their supervisory responsibilities.

The conduct that constitutes reasonable supervision in a particular case depends on the number of employees supervised and the work performed by those employees. Members and candidates with oversight responsibilities for large numbers of employees may not be able to personally evaluate the conduct of these employees on a continuing basis. These members and candidates may delegate supervisory duties to subordinates who directly oversee the other employees. A member's or candidate's responsibilities under Standard IV(C) include instructing those subordinates to whom supervision is delegated about methods to promote compliance, including preventing and detecting violations of laws, rules, regulations, firm policies, and the Code and Standards.

At a minimum, Standard IV(C) requires that members and candidates with supervisory responsibility make reasonable efforts to prevent and detect violations by ensuring the establishment of effective compliance systems. However, an effective compliance system goes beyond enacting a code of ethics, establishing policies and procedures to achieve compliance with the code and applicable law, and reviewing employee actions to determine whether they are following the rules.

To be effective supervisors, members and candidates should implement education and training programs on a recurring or regular basis for employees under their supervision. Such programs will assist the employees with meeting their professional obligations to practice in an ethical manner within the applicable legal system. Further, establishing incentives—monetary or otherwise—for employees not only to meet business goals but also to reward ethical behavior offers supervisors another way to assist employees in complying with their legal and ethical obligations.

Often, especially in large organizations, members and candidates may have supervisory responsibility but not the authority to establish or modify firm-wide compliance policies and procedures or incentive structures. Such limitations should not prevent a member or candidate from working with his or her own superiors and within the firm structure to develop and implement effective compliance tools, including but not limited to:

- a code of ethics,
- compliance policies and procedures,
- education and training programs,
- an incentive structure that rewards ethical conduct, and
- adoption of firm-wide best practice standards (e.g., the GIPS standards, the CFA Institute Asset Manager Code of Professional Conduct).

A member or candidate with supervisory responsibility should bring an inadequate compliance system to the attention of the firm's senior managers and recommend corrective action. If the member or candidate clearly cannot discharge supervisory responsibilities because of the absence of a compliance system or because of an inadequate compliance system, the member or candidate should decline in writing to accept supervisory responsibility until the firm adopts reasonable procedures to allow adequate exercise of supervisory responsibility.

System for Supervision

Members and candidates with supervisory responsibility must understand what constitutes an adequate compliance system for their firms and make reasonable efforts to see that appropriate compliance procedures are established, documented, communicated to covered personnel, and followed. "Adequate" procedures are those designed to meet industry standards, regulatory requirements, the requirements of the Code and Standards, and the circumstances of the firm. Once compliance procedures are established, the supervisor must also make reasonable efforts to ensure that the procedures are monitored and enforced.

To be effective, compliance procedures must be in place prior to the occurrence of a violation of the law or the Code and Standards. Although compliance procedures cannot be designed to anticipate every potential violation, they should be designed to anticipate the activities most likely to result in misconduct. Compliance programs must be appropriate for the size and nature of the organization. The member or candidate should review model compliance procedures or other industry programs to ensure that the firm's procedures meet the minimum industry standards.

Once a supervisor learns that an employee has violated or may have violated the law or the Code and Standards, the supervisor must promptly initiate an assessment to determine the extent of the wrongdoing. Relying on an employee's statements about the extent of the violation or assurances that the wrongdoing will not reoccur is not enough. Reporting the misconduct up the chain of command and warning the employee to cease the activity are also not enough. Pending the outcome of the investigation, a supervisor should take steps to ensure that the violation will not be repeated, such as placing limits on the employee's activities or increasing the monitoring of the employee's activities.

Supervision Includes Detection

Members and candidates with supervisory responsibility must also make reasonable efforts to detect violations of laws, rules, regulations, firm policies, and the Code and Standards. The supervisors exercise reasonable supervision by establishing and implementing written compliance procedures and ensuring that those procedures are followed through periodic review. If a member or candidate has adopted reasonable procedures and taken steps to institute an effective compliance program, then the member or candidate may not be in violation of Standard IV(C) if he or she does not detect violations that occur despite these efforts. The fact that violations do occur may indicate, however, that the compliance procedures are inadequate. In addition, in some cases, merely enacting such procedures may not be sufficient to fulfill the duty required by Standard IV(C). A member or candidate may be in violation of Standard IV(C) if he or she knows or should know that the procedures designed to promote compliance, including detecting and preventing violations, are not being followed.

Recommended Procedures for Compliance

Codes of Ethics or Compliance Procedures

Members and candidates are encouraged to recommend that their employers adopt a code of ethics. Adoption of a code of ethics is critical to establishing a strong ethical foundation for investment advisory firms and their employees. Codes of ethics formally emphasize and reinforce the client loyalty responsibilities of investment firm personnel, protect investing clients by deterring misconduct, and protect the firm's reputation for integrity.

There is a distinction, however, between codes of ethics and the specific policies and procedures needed to ensure compliance with the codes and with securities laws and regulations. Although both are important, codes of ethics should consist of fundamental, principle-based ethical and fiduciary concepts that are applicable to all of the firm's employees. In this way, firms can best convey to employees and clients the ethical ideals that investment advisers strive to achieve. These concepts need to be implemented, however, by detailed, firm-wide compliance policies and procedures. Compliance procedures assist the firm's personnel in fulfilling the responsibilities enumerated in the code of ethics and make probable that the ideals expressed in the code of ethics will be adhered to in the day-to-day operation of the firm.

Stand-alone codes of ethics should be written in plain language and should address general fiduciary concepts. They should be unencumbered by numerous detailed procedures. Codes presented in this way are the most effective in stressing to employees that they are in positions of trust and must act with integrity at all times. Mingling compliance procedures in the firm's code of ethics goes against the goal of reinforcing the ethical obligations of employees.

Separating the code of ethics from compliance procedures will also reduce, if not eliminate, the legal terminology and "boilerplate" language that can make the underlying ethical principles incomprehensible to the average person. Above all, to ensure the creation of a culture of ethics and integrity rather than one that merely focuses on following the rules, the principles in the code of ethics must be stated in a way that is accessible and understandable to everyone in the firm.

Members and candidates should encourage their employers to provide their codes of ethics to clients. In this case also, a simple, straightforward code of ethics will be best understood by clients. Unencumbered by the compliance procedures, the code of ethics will be effective in conveying that the firm is committed to conducting business in an ethical manner and in the best interests of the clients.

Adequate Compliance Procedures

A supervisor complies with Standard IV(C) by identifying situations in which legal violations or violations of the Code and Standards are likely to occur and by establishing and enforcing compliance procedures to prevent such violations. Adequate compliance procedures should

- be contained in a clearly written and accessible manual that is tailored to the firm's operations,
- be drafted so that the procedures are easy to understand,

- designate a compliance officer whose authority and responsibility are clearly defined and who has the necessary resources and authority to implement the firm's compliance procedures,
- describe the hierarchy of supervision and assign duties among supervisors,
- implement a system of checks and balances,
- outline the scope of the procedures,
- outline procedures to document the monitoring and testing of compliance procedures,
- outline permissible conduct, and
- delineate procedures for reporting violations and sanctions.

Once a compliance program is in place, a supervisor should

- disseminate the contents of the program to appropriate personnel,
- periodically update procedures to ensure that the measures are adequate under the law,
- continually educate personnel regarding the compliance procedures,
- issue periodic reminders of the procedures to appropriate personnel,
- incorporate a professional conduct evaluation as part of an employee's performance review,
- review the actions of employees to ensure compliance and identify violators, and
- take the necessary steps to enforce the procedures once a violation has occurred.

Once a violation is discovered, a supervisor should

- respond promptly,
- conduct a thorough investigation of the activities to determine the scope of the wrongdoing,
- increase supervision or place appropriate limitations on the wrongdoer pending the outcome of the investigation, and
- review procedures for potential changes necessary to prevent future violations from occurring.

Implementation of Compliance Education and Training

No amount of ethics education and awareness will deter someone determined to commit fraud for personal enrichment. But the vast majority of investment professionals strive to achieve personal success with dedicated service to their clients and employers.

Regular ethics and compliance training, in conjunction with adoption of a code of ethics, is critical to investment firms seeking to establish a strong culture of integrity and to provide an environment in which employees routinely engage in ethical conduct in compliance with the law. Training and education assist individuals in both recognizing areas that are prone to ethical and legal pitfalls and identifying those circumstances and influences that can impair ethical judgment.

By implementing educational programs, supervisors can train their subordinates to put into practice what the firm's code of ethics requires. Education helps employees make the link between legal and ethical conduct and the long-term success of the business; a strong culture of compliance signals to clients and potential clients that the firm has truly embraced ethical conduct as fundamental to the firm's mission to serve its clients.

Establish an Appropriate Incentive Structure

Even if individuals want to make the right choices and follow an ethical course of conduct and are aware of the obstacles that may trip them up, they can still be influenced to act improperly by a corporate culture that embraces a "succeed at all costs" mentality, stresses results regardless of the methods used to achieve those results, and does not reward ethical behavior. Supervisors can reinforce an individual's natural desire to "do the right thing" by building a culture of integrity in the workplace.

Supervisors and firms must look closely at their incentive structure to determine whether the structure encourages profits and returns at the expense of ethically appropriate conduct. Reward structures may turn a blind eye to how desired outcomes are achieved and encourage dysfunctional or counterproductive behavior. Only when compensation and incentives are firmly tied to client interests and *how* outcomes are achieved, rather than *how much* is generated for the firm, will employees work to achieve a culture of integrity.

Application of the Standard

Example 1 (Supervising Research Activities):

Jane Mattock, senior vice president and head of the research department of H&V, Inc., a regional brokerage firm, has decided to change her recommendation for Timber Products from buy to sell. In line with H&V's procedures, she orally advises certain other H&V executives of her proposed actions before the report is prepared for publication. As a result of Mattock's conversation with Dieter Frampton, one of the H&V executives accountable to Mattock, Frampton immediately sells Timber's stock from his own account and from certain discretionary client accounts. In addition, other personnel inform certain institutional customers of the changed recommendation before it is printed and disseminated to all H&V customers who have received previous Timber reports.

> *Comment*: Mattock has violated Standard IV(C) by failing to reasonably and adequately supervise the actions of those accountable to her. She did not prevent or establish reasonable procedures designed to prevent dissemination of or trading on the information by those who knew of her changed recommendation. She must ensure that her firm has procedures for reviewing or recording any trading in the stock of a corporation that has been the subject of an unpublished change in recommendation. Adequate procedures would have informed the subordinates of their duties and detected sales by Frampton and selected customers.

Example 2 (Supervising Research Activities):

Deion Miller is the research director for Jamestown Investment Programs. The portfolio managers have become critical of Miller and his staff because the Jamestown portfolios do not include any stock that has been the subject of a merger or tender offer. Georgia Ginn, a member of Miller's staff, tells Miller that she has been studying a local company, Excelsior, Inc., and recommends its purchase. Ginn adds that the company has been widely rumored to be the subject of a merger study by a well-known conglomerate and discussions between them are under way. At Miller's request, Ginn prepares a memo recommending the stock. Miller passes along Ginn's memo to the portfolio managers prior to leaving for vacation, and he notes that he has not reviewed the memo. As a result of the memo, the portfolio managers buy Excelsior stock immediately. The day Miller returns to the office, he learns that Ginn's only sources for the report were her brother, who is an acquisitions analyst with Acme Industries, the "well-known conglomerate," and that the merger discussions were planned but not held.

Comment: Miller violated Standard IV(C) by not exercising reasonable supervision when he disseminated the memo without checking to ensure that Ginn had a reasonable and adequate basis for her recommendations and that Ginn was not relying on material nonpublic information.

Example 3 (Supervising Trading Activities):

David Edwards, a trainee trader at Wheeler & Company, a major national brokerage firm, assists a customer in paying for the securities of Highland, Inc., by using anticipated profits from the immediate sale of the same securities. Despite the fact that Highland is not on Wheeler's recommended list, a large volume of its stock is traded through Wheeler in this manner. Roberta Ann Mason is a Wheeler vice president responsible for supervising compliance with the securities laws in the trading department. Part of her compensation from Wheeler is based on commission revenues from the trading department. Although she notices the increased trading activity, she does nothing to investigate or halt it.

Comment: Mason's failure to adequately review and investigate purchase orders in Highland stock executed by Edwards and her failure to supervise the trainee's activities violate Standard IV(C). Supervisors should be especially sensitive to actual or potential conflicts between their own self-interests and their supervisory responsibilities.

Example 4 (Supervising Trading Activities and Record Keeping):

Samantha Tabbing is senior vice president and portfolio manager for Crozet, Inc., a registered investment advisory and registered broker/dealer firm. She reports to Charles Henry, the president of Crozet. Crozet serves as the investment adviser and principal underwriter for ABC and XYZ public mutual funds. The two funds' prospectuses allow Crozet to trade financial futures for the funds for the limited purpose of hedging against market risks. Henry, extremely impressed by Tabbing's performance in the past two years, directs Tabbing to act as portfolio manager for the funds. For the benefit of its employees, Crozet has also organized the Crozet Employee Profit-Sharing Plan (CEPSP), a defined contribution retirement plan. Henry assigns Tabbing to manage 20% of the assets of CEPSP. Tabbing's investment objective for her portion of CEPSP's assets is aggressive growth. Unbeknownst to Henry, Tabbing frequently places S&P 500 Index purchase and sale orders for the funds and the CEPSP without providing the futures commission merchants (FCMs) who take the orders with any prior or simultaneous designation of the account for which the trade has been placed. Frequently, neither Tabbing nor anyone else at Crozet completes an internal trade ticket to record the time an order was placed or the specific account for which the order was intended. FCMs often designate a specific account only after the trade, when Tabbing provides such designation. Crozet has no written operating procedures or compliance manual concerning its futures trading, and its compliance department does not review such trading. After observing the market's movement, Tabbing assigns to CEPSP the S&P 500 positions with more favorable execution prices and assigns positions with less favorable execution prices to the funds.

Comment: Henry violated Standard IV(C) by failing to adequately supervise Tabbing with respect to her S&P 500 trading. Henry further violated Standard IV(C) by failing to establish record-keeping and reporting procedures to prevent or detect Tabbing's violations. Henry must make a reasonable effort to determine that adequate compliance procedures covering all employee trading activity are established, documented, communicated, and followed.

Example 5 (Accepting Responsibility):

Meredith Rasmussen works on a buy-side trading desk and concentrates on in-house trades for a hedge fund subsidiary managed by a team at the investment management firm. The hedge fund has been very successful and is marketed globally by the firm. From her experience as the trader for much of the activity of the fund, Rasmussen has become quite knowledgeable about the hedge fund's strategy, tactics, and performance. When a distinct break in the market occurs and many of the securities involved in the hedge fund's strategy decline markedly in value, however, Rasmussen observes that the reported performance of the hedge fund does not at all reflect this decline. From her experience, this lack of an effect is a very unlikely occurrence. She approaches the head of trading about her concern and is told that she should not ask any questions and that the fund is too big and successful and is not her concern. She is fairly sure something is not right, so she contacts the compliance officer and is again told to stay away from the hedge fund reporting issue.

> *Comment*: Rasmussen has clearly come upon an error in policies, procedures, and compliance practices within the firm's operations. According to Standard IV(C), the supervisor and the compliance officer have the responsibility to review the concerns brought forth by Rasmussen. Supervisors have the responsibility of establishing and encouraging an ethical culture in the firm. The dismissal of Rasmussen's question violates Standard IV(C) and undermines the firm's ethical operations.
>
> See also Standard I(D)–Misconduct and, for guidance on whistleblowing, Standard IV(A)–Loyalty.

Example 6 (Inadequate Procedures):

Brendan Witt, a former junior sell-side technology analyst, decided to return to school to earn an MBA. To keep his research skills and industry knowledge sharp, Witt accepted a position with On-line and Informed, an independent internet-based research company. The position requires the publication of a recommendation and report on a different company every month. Initially, Witt is a regular contributor of new research and a participant in the associated discussion boards that generally have positive comments on the technology sector. Over time, his ability to manage his educational requirements and his work requirements begin to conflict with one another. Knowing a recommendation is due the next day for On-line, Witt creates a report based on a few news articles and what the conventional wisdom of the markets has deemed the "hot" security of the day.

> *Comment*: Allowing the report submitted by Witt to be posted highlights a lack of compliance procedures by the research firm. Witt's supervisor needs to work with the management of On-line to develop an appropriate review process to ensure that all contracted analysts comply with the requirements.
>
> See also Standard V(A)–Diligence and Reasonable Basis because it relates to Witt's responsibility for substantiating a recommendation.

Example 7 (Inadequate Supervision):

Michael Papis is the chief investment officer of his state's retirement fund. The fund has always used outside advisers for the real estate allocation, and this information is clearly presented in all fund communications. Thomas Nagle, a recognized sell-side research analyst and Papis's business school classmate, recently left the investment bank he worked for to start his own asset management firm, Accessible Real Estate. Nagle is trying to build his assets under management and contacts Papis about gaining some of the retirement fund's allocation. In the previous few years, the performance of the retirement fund's real estate investments was in line with the fund's benchmark but was not extraordinary. Papis decides to help out his old friend and also to seek better returns by moving the real estate allocation to Accessible. The only notice of the change in adviser appears in the next annual report in the listing of associated advisers.

> *Comment*: Papis's actions highlight the need for supervision and review at all levels in an organization. His responsibilities may include the selection of external advisers, but the decision to change advisers appears arbitrary. Members and candidates should ensure that their firm has appropriate policies and procedures in place to detect inappropriate actions, such as the action taken by Papis.
>
> See also Standard V(A)–Diligence and Reasonable Basis, Standard V(B)–Communication with Clients and Prospective Clients, and Standard VI(A)–Disclosure of Conflicts.

Example 8 (Supervising Research Activities):

Mary Burdette was recently hired by Fundamental Investment Management (FIM) as a junior auto industry analyst. Burdette is expected to expand the social media presence of the firm because she is active with various networks, including Facebook, LinkedIn, and Twitter. Although Burdette's supervisor, Joe Graf, has never used social media, he encourages Burdette to explore opportunities to increase FIM's online presence and ability to share content, communicate, and broadcast information to clients. In response to Graf's encouragement, Burdette is working on a proposal detailing the advantages of getting FIM onto Twitter in addition to launching a company Facebook page.

As part of her auto industry research for FIM, Burdette is completing a report on the financial impact of Sun Drive Auto Ltd.'s new solar technology for compact automobiles. This research report will be her first for FIM, and she believes Sun Drive's technology could revolutionize the auto industry. In her excitement, Burdette sends a quick tweet to FIM Twitter followers summarizing her "buy" recommendation for Sun Drive Auto stock.

> *Comment*: Graf has violated Standard IV(C) by failing to reasonably supervise Burdette with respect to the contents of her tweet. He did not establish reasonable procedures to prevent the unauthorized dissemination of company research through social media networks. Graf must make sure all employees receive regular training about FIM's policies and procedures, including the appropriate business use of personal social media networks.
>
> See Standard III(B) for additional guidance.

Example 9 (Supervising Research Activities):

Chen Wang leads the research department at YYRA Retirement Planning Specialists. Chen supervises a team of 10 analysts in a fast-paced and understaffed organization. He is responsible for coordinating the firm's approved process to review all reports before they are provided to the portfolio management team for use in rebalancing client portfolios.

One of Chen's direct reports, Huang Mei, covers the banking industry. Chen must submit the latest updates to the portfolio management team tomorrow morning. Huang has yet to submit her research report on ZYX Bank because she is uncomfortable providing a "buy" or "sell" opinion of ZYX on the basis of the completed analysis. Pressed for time and concerned that Chen will reject a "hold" recommendation, she researches various websites and blogs on the banking sector for whatever she can find on ZYX. One independent blogger provides a new interpretation of the recently reported data Huang has analyzed and concludes with a strong "sell" recommendation for ZYX. She is impressed by the originality and resourcefulness of this blogger's report.

Very late in the evening, Huang submits her report and "sell" recommendation to Chen without any reference to the independent blogger's report. Given the late time of the submission and the competence of Huang's prior work, Chen compiles this report with the recommendations from each of the other analysts and meets with the portfolio managers to discuss implementation.

> *Comment*: Chen has violated Standard IV(C) by neglecting to reasonably and adequately follow the firm's approved review process for Huang's research report. The delayed submission and the quality of prior work do not remove Chen's requirement to uphold the designated review process. A member or candidate with supervisory responsibility must make reasonable efforts to see that appropriate procedures are established, documented, communicated to covered personnel, and followed.

STANDARD V: INVESTMENT ANALYSIS, RECOMMENDATIONS, AND ACTIONS

Standard V(A) Diligence and Reasonable Basis

Members and Candidates must:

1 Exercise diligence, independence, and thoroughness in analyzing investments, making investment recommendations, and taking investment actions.

2 Have a reasonable and adequate basis, supported by appropriate research and investigation, for any investment analysis, recommendation, or action.

Guidance

Highlights:

- *Defining Diligence and Reasonable Basis*
- *Using Secondary or Third-Party Research*
- *Using Quantitatively Oriented Research*
- *Developing Quantitatively Oriented Techniques*
- *Selecting External Advisers and Subadvisers*
- *Group Research and Decision Making*

The application of Standard V(A) depends on the investment philosophy the member, candidate, or firm is following, the role of the member or candidate in the investment decision-making process, and the support and resources provided by the member's or candidate's employer. These factors will dictate the nature of the diligence and thoroughness of the research and the level of investigation required by Standard V(A).

The requirements for issuing conclusions based on research will vary in relation to the member's or candidate's role in the investment decision-making process, but the member or candidate must make reasonable efforts to cover all pertinent issues when arriving at a recommendation. Members and candidates enhance transparency by providing or offering to provide supporting information to clients when recommending a purchase or sale or when changing a recommendation.

Defining Diligence and Reasonable Basis

Every investment decision is based on a set of facts known and understood at the time. Clients turn to members and candidates for advice and expect these advisers to have more information and knowledge than they do. This information and knowledge is the basis from which members and candidates apply their professional judgment in taking investment actions and making recommendations.

At a basic level, clients want assurance that members and candidates are putting forth the necessary effort to support the recommendations they are making. Communicating the level and thoroughness of the information reviewed before the member or candidate makes a judgment allows clients to understand the reasonableness of the recommended investment actions.

As with determining the suitability of an investment for the client, the necessary level of research and analysis will differ with the product, security, or service being offered. In providing an investment service, members and candidates typically use a variety of resources, including company reports, third-party research, and results from quantitative models. A reasonable basis is formed through a balance of these resources appropriate for the security or decision being analyzed.

The following list provides some, but definitely not all, examples of attributes to consider while forming the basis for a recommendation:

- global, regional, and country macroeconomic conditions,
- a company's operating and financial history,
- the industry's and sector's current conditions and the stage of the business cycle,
- a mutual fund's fee structure and management history,
- the output and potential limitations of quantitative models,
- the quality of the assets included in a securitization, and
- the appropriateness of selected peer-group comparisons.

Even though an investment recommendation may be well informed, downside risk remains for any investment. Members and candidates can base their decisions only on the information available at the time decisions are made. The steps taken in developing a diligent and reasonable recommendation should minimize unexpected downside events.

Using Secondary or Third-Party Research

If members and candidates rely on secondary or third-party research, they must make reasonable and diligent efforts to determine whether such research is sound. Secondary research is defined as research conducted by someone else in the member's or candidate's firm. Third-party research is research conducted by entities outside the member's or candidate's firm, such as a brokerage firm, bank, or research firm. If a member or candidate has reason to suspect that either secondary or third-party research or information comes from a source that lacks a sound basis, the member or candidate must not rely on that information.

Members and candidates should make reasonable enquiries into the source and accuracy of all data used in completing their investment analysis and recommendations. The sources of the information and data will influence the level of the review a member or candidate must undertake. Information and data taken from internet sources, such as personal blogs, independent research aggregation websites, or social media websites, likely require a greater level of review than information from more established research organizations.

Criteria that a member or candidate can use in forming an opinion on whether research is sound include the following:

- assumptions used,
- rigor of the analysis performed,
- date/timeliness of the research, and
- evaluation of the objectivity and independence of the recommendations.

A member or candidate may rely on others in his or her firm to determine whether secondary or third-party research is sound and use the information in good faith unless the member or candidate has reason to question its validity or the processes and procedures used by those responsible for the research. For example, a portfolio manager may not have a choice of a data source because the firm's senior managers conducted due diligence to determine which vendor would provide services; the member or candidate can use the information in good faith assuming the due diligence process was deemed adequate.

A member or candidate should verify that the firm has a policy about the timely and consistent review of approved research providers to ensure that the quality of the research continues to meet the necessary standards. If such a policy is not in place at the firm, the member or candidate should encourage the development and adoption of a formal review practice.

Using Quantitatively Oriented Research

Standard V(A) applies to the rapidly expanding use of quantitatively oriented research models and processes, such as computer-generated modeling, screening, and ranking of investment securities; the creation or valuation of derivative instruments; and quantitative portfolio construction techniques. These models and processes are being used for much more than the back testing of investment strategies, especially with continually advancing technology and techniques. The continued broad development of quantitative methods and models is an important part of capital market developments.

Members and candidates need to have an understanding of the parameters used in models and quantitative research that are incorporated into their investment recommendations. Although they are not required to become experts in every technical aspect of the models, they must understand the assumptions and limitations inherent in any model and how the results were used in the decision-making process.

The reliance on and potential limitations of financial models became clear through the investment crisis that unfolded in 2007 and 2008. In some cases, the financial models used to value specific securities and related derivative products did not adequately demonstrate the level of associated risks. Members and candidates should make reasonable efforts to test the output of investment models and other pre-programed analytical tools they use. Such validation should occur before incorporating the process into their methods, models, or analyses.

Although not every model can test for every factor or outcome, members and candidates should ensure that their analyses incorporate a broad range of assumptions sufficient to capture the underlying characteristics of investments. The omission from the analysis of potentially negative outcomes or of levels of risk outside the norm may misrepresent the true economic value of an investment. The possible scenarios for analysis should include factors that are likely to have a substantial influence on the investment value and may include extremely positive and negative scenarios.

Developing Quantitatively Oriented Techniques

Individuals who create new quantitative models and services must exhibit a higher level of diligence in reviewing new products than the individuals who ultimately use the analytical output. Members and candidates involved in the development and oversight of quantitatively oriented models, methods, and algorithms must understand the technical aspects of the products they provide to clients. A thorough testing of the model and resulting analysis should be completed prior to product distribution.

Members and candidates need to consider the source and time horizon of the data used as inputs in financial models. The information from many commercially available databases may not effectively incorporate both positive and negative market cycles. In the development of a recommendation, the member or candidate may need to test the models by using volatility and performance expectations that represent scenarios outside the observable databases. In reviewing the computer models or the resulting output, members and candidates need to pay particular attention to the assumptions used in the analysis and the rigor of the analysis to ensure that the model incorporates a wide range of possible input expectations, including negative market events.

Selecting External Advisers and Subadvisers

Financial instruments and asset allocation techniques continue to develop and evolve. This progression has led to the use of specialized managers to invest in specific asset classes or diversification strategies that complement a firm's in-house expertise. Standard V(A) applies to the level of review necessary in selecting an external adviser or subadviser to manage a specifically mandated allocation. Members and candidates must review managers as diligently as they review individual funds and securities.

Members and candidates who are directly involved with the use of external advisers need to ensure that their firms have standardized criteria for reviewing these selected external advisers and managers. Such criteria would include, but would not be limited to, the following:

- reviewing the adviser's established code of ethics,
- understanding the adviser's compliance and internal control procedures,
- assessing the quality of the published return information, and
- reviewing the adviser's investment process and adherence to its stated strategy.

Codes, standards, and guides to best practice published by CFA Institute provide members and candidates with examples of acceptable practices for external advisers and advice in selecting a new adviser. The following guides are available at the CFA Institute website (www.cfainstitute.org): Asset Manager Code of Professional Conduct, Global Investment Performance Standards, and Model Request for Proposal (for equity, credit, or real estate managers).

Group Research and Decision Making

Commonly, members and candidates are part of a group or team that is collectively responsible for producing investment analysis or research. The conclusions or recommendations of the group report represent the consensus of the group and are not necessarily the views of the member or candidate, even though the name of the member or candidate is included on the report. In some instances, a member or candidate will not agree with the view of the group. If, however, the member or candidate believes that the consensus opinion has a reasonable and adequate basis and is independent and objective, the member or candidate need not decline to be identified with the report. If the member or candidate is confident in the process, the member or candidate does not need to dissociate from the report even if it does not reflect his or her opinion.

Recommended Procedures for Compliance

Members and candidates should encourage their firms to consider the following policies and procedures to support the principles of Standard V(A):

- Establish a policy requiring that research reports, credit ratings, and investment recommendations have a basis that can be substantiated as reasonable and adequate. An individual employee (a supervisory analyst) or a group of employees (a review committee) should be appointed to review and approve such items prior to external circulation to determine whether the criteria established in the policy have been met.
- Develop detailed, written guidance for analysts (research, investment, or credit), supervisory analysts, and review committees that establishes the due diligence procedures for judging whether a particular recommendation has a reasonable and adequate basis.
- Develop measurable criteria for assessing the quality of research, the reasonableness and adequacy of the basis for any recommendation or rating, and the accuracy of recommendations over time. In some cases, firms may consider implementing compensation arrangements that depend on these measurable criteria and that are applied consistently to all related analysts.
- Develop detailed, written guidance that establishes minimum levels of scenario testing of all computer-based models used in developing, rating, and evaluating financial instruments. The policy should contain criteria related to the breadth of the scenarios tested, the accuracy of the output over time, and the analysis of cash flow sensitivity to inputs.
- Develop measurable criteria for assessing outside providers, including the quality of information being provided, the reasonableness and adequacy of the provider's collection practices, and the accuracy of the information over time. The established policy should outline how often the provider's products are reviewed.
- Adopt a standardized set of criteria for evaluating the adequacy of external advisers. The policy should include how often and on what basis the allocation of funds to the adviser will be reviewed.

Application of the Standard

Example 1 (Sufficient Due Diligence):

Helen Hawke manages the corporate finance department of Sarkozi Securities, Ltd. The firm is anticipating that the government will soon close a tax loophole that currently allows oil-and-gas exploration companies to pass on drilling expenses to holders of a certain class of shares. Because market demand for this tax-advantaged class of stock is currently high, Sarkozi convinces several companies to undertake new equity financings at once, before the loophole closes. Time is of the essence, but Sarkozi lacks sufficient resources to conduct adequate research on all the prospective issuing companies. Hawke decides to estimate the IPO prices on the basis of the relative size of each company and to justify the pricing later when her staff has time.

> *Comment*: Sarkozi should have taken on only the work that it could adequately handle. By categorizing the issuers by general size, Hawke has bypassed researching all the other relevant aspects that should be considered when pricing new issues and thus has not performed sufficient due diligence. Such an omission can result in investors purchasing shares at prices that have no actual basis. Hawke has violated Standard V(A).

Example 2 (Sufficient Scenario Testing):

Babu Dhaliwal works for Heinrich Brokerage in the corporate finance group. He has just persuaded Feggans Resources, Ltd., to allow his firm to do a secondary equity financing at Feggans Resources' current stock price. Because the stock has been trading at higher multiples than similar companies with equivalent production, Dhaliwal presses the Feggans Resources managers to project what would be the maximum production they could achieve in an optimal scenario. Based on these numbers, he is able to justify the price his firm will be asking for the secondary issue. During a sales pitch to the brokers, Dhaliwal then uses these numbers as the base-case production levels that Feggans Resources will achieve.

> *Comment*: When presenting information to the brokers, Dhaliwal should have given a range of production scenarios and the probability of Feggans Resources achieving each level. By giving the maximum production level as the likely level of production, he has misrepresented the chances of achieving that production level and seriously misled the brokers. Dhaliwal has violated Standard V(A).

Example 3 (Developing a Reasonable Basis):

Brendan Witt, a former junior sell-side technology analyst, decided to return to school to earn an MBA. To keep his research skills and industry knowledge sharp, Witt accepted a position with On-line and Informed, an independent internet-based research company. The position requires the publication of a recommendation and report on a different company every month. Initially, Witt is a regular contributor of new research and a participant in the associated discussion boards that generally have positive comments on the technology sector. Over time, his ability to manage his educational requirements and his work requirements begin to conflict with one another. Knowing a recommendation is due the next day for On-line, Witt creates a report based on a few news articles and what the conventional wisdom of the markets has deemed the "hot" security of the day.

> *Comment*: Witt's knowledge of and exuberance for technology stocks, a few news articles, and the conventional wisdom of the markets do not constitute, without more information, a reasonable and adequate basis for a stock recommendation that is supported by appropriate research and investigation. Therefore, Witt has violated Standard V(A).
>
> See also Standard IV(C)–Responsibilities of Supervisors because it relates to the firm's inadequate procedures.

Example 4 (Timely Client Updates):

Kristen Chandler is an investment consultant in the London office of Dalton Securities, a major global investment consultant firm. One of her UK pension funds has decided to appoint a specialist US equity manager. Dalton's global manager of research relies on local consultants to cover managers within their regions and, after conducting thorough due diligence, puts their views and ratings in Dalton's manager database. Chandler accesses Dalton's global manager research database and conducts a screen of all US equity managers on the basis of a match with the client's desired philosophy/style, performance, and tracking-error targets. She selects the five managers that meet these criteria and puts them in a briefing report that is delivered to the client 10 days later. Between the time of Chandler's database search and the delivery of the report to the client, Chandler is told that Dalton has updated the database with the information that one of the firms that Chandler has recommended for consideration lost its chief investment officer, the head of its US equity research, and the majority of its portfolio managers on the US equity product—all of whom have left to establish their own firm. Chandler does not revise her report with this updated information.

> *Comment*: Chandler has failed to satisfy the requirement of Standard V(A). Although Dalton updated the manager ratings to reflect the personnel turnover at one of the firms, Chandler did not update her report to reflect the new information.

Example 5 (Group Research Opinions):

Evelyn Mastakis is a junior analyst who has been asked by her firm to write a research report predicting the expected interest rate for residential mortgages over the next six months. Mastakis submits her report to the fixed-income investment committee of her firm for review, as required by firm procedures. Although some committee members support Mastakis's conclusion, the majority of the committee disagrees with her conclusion, and the report is significantly changed to indicate that interest rates are likely to increase more than originally predicted by Mastakis. Should Mastakis ask that her name be taken off the report when it is disseminated?

> *Comment*: The results of research are not always clear, and different people may have different opinions based on the same factual evidence. In this case, the committee may have valid reasons for issuing a report that differs from the analyst's original research. The firm can issue a report that is different from the original report of an analyst as long as there is a reasonable and adequate basis for its conclusions.
>
> Generally, analysts must write research reports that reflect their own opinion and can ask the firm not to put their name on reports that ultimately differ from that opinion. When the work is a group effort, however, not all members of the team may agree with all aspects of the report. Ultimately, members and candidates can ask to have their names removed from the report, but if they are satisfied that the process has produced results or conclusions that have a reasonable and adequate basis, members and candidates do not have to dissociate from the report even when they do not agree with its contents. If Mastakis is confident in the process, she does not need to dissociate from the report even if it does not reflect her opinion.

Example 6 (Reliance on Third-Party Research):

Gary McDermott runs a two-person investment management firm. McDermott's firm subscribes to a service from a large investment research firm that provides research reports. McDermott's firm makes investment recommendations on the basis of these reports.

> *Comment*: Members and candidates can rely on third-party research but must make reasonable and diligent efforts to determine that such research is sound. If McDermott undertakes due diligence efforts on a regular basis to ensure that the research produced by the large firm is objective and reasonably based, McDermott can rely on that research when making investment recommendations to clients.

Example 7 (Due Diligence in Submanager Selection):

Paul Ostrowski's business has grown significantly over the past couple of years, and some clients want to diversify internationally. Ostrowski decides to find a submanager to handle the expected international investments. Because this will be his first subadviser, Ostrowski uses the CFA Institute model "request for proposal" to design a questionnaire for his search. By his deadline, he receives seven completed questionnaires from a variety of domestic and international firms trying to gain his business. Ostrowski reviews all the applications in detail and decides to select the firm that charges the lowest fees because doing so will have the least impact on his firm's bottom line.

> *Comment*: The selection of an external adviser or subadviser should be based on a full and complete review of the adviser's services, performance history, and cost structure. In basing the decision on the fee structure alone, Ostrowski may be violating Standard V(A).
>
> See also Standard III(C)–Suitability because it relates to the ability of the selected adviser to meet the needs of the clients.

Example 8 (Sufficient Due Diligence):

Michael Papis is the chief investment officer of his state's retirement fund. The fund has always used outside advisers for the real estate allocation, and this information is clearly presented in all fund communications. Thomas Nagle, a recognized sell-side research analyst and Papis's business school classmate, recently left the investment bank he worked for to start his own asset management firm, Accessible Real Estate. Nagle is trying to build his assets under management and contacts Papis about gaining some of the retirement fund's allocation. In the previous few years, the performance of the retirement fund's real estate investments was in line with the fund's benchmark but was not extraordinary. Papis decides to help out his old friend and also to seek better returns by moving the real estate allocation to Accessible. The only notice of the change in adviser appears in the next annual report in the listing of associated advisers.

> *Comment*: Papis violated Standard V(A). His responsibilities may include the selection of the external advisers, but the decision to change advisers appears to have been arbitrary. If Papis was dissatisfied with the current real estate adviser, he should have conducted a proper solicitation to select the most appropriate adviser.
>
> See also Standard IV(C)–Responsibilities of Supervisors, Standard V(B)–Communication with Clients and Prospective Clients, and Standard VI(A)–Disclosure of Conflicts.

Example 9 (Sufficient Due Diligence):

Andre Shrub owns and operates Conduit, an investment advisory firm. Prior to opening Conduit, Shrub was an account manager with Elite Investment, a hedge fund managed by his good friend Adam Reed. To attract clients to a new Conduit fund, Shrub offers lower-than-normal management fees. He can do so because the fund consists of two top-performing funds managed by Reed. Given his personal friendship with Reed and the prior performance record of these two funds, Shrub believes this new fund is a winning combination for all parties. Clients quickly invest with Conduit to gain access to the Elite funds. No one is turned away because Conduit is seeking to expand its assets under management.

> *Comment*: Shrub violated Standard V(A) by not conducting a thorough analysis of the funds managed by Reed before developing the new Conduit fund. Shrub's reliance on his personal relationship with Reed and his prior knowledge of Elite are insufficient justification for the investments. The funds may be appropriately considered, but a full review of their operating procedures, reporting practices, and transparency are some elements of the necessary due diligence.

See also Standard III(C)–Suitability.

Example 10 (Sufficient Due Diligence):

Bob Thompson has been doing research for the portfolio manager of the fixed-income department. His assignment is to do sensitivity analysis on securitized subprime mortgages. He has discussed with the manager possible scenarios to use to calculate expected returns. A key assumption in such calculations is housing price appreciation (HPA) because it drives "prepays" (prepayments of mortgages) and losses. Thompson is concerned with the significant appreciation experienced over the previous five years as a result of the increased availability of funds from subprime mortgages. Thompson insists that the analysis should include a scenario run with −10% for Year 1, −5% for Year 2, and then (to project a worst-case scenario) 0% for Years 3 through 5. The manager replies that these assumptions are too dire because there has never been a time in their available database when HPA was negative.

Thompson conducts his research to better understand the risks inherent in these securities and evaluates these securities in the worst-case scenario, a less likely but possible environment. Based on the results of the enhanced scenarios, Thompson does not recommend the purchase of the securitization. Against the general market trends, the manager follows Thompson's recommendation and does not invest. The following year, the housing market collapses. In avoiding the subprime investments, the manager's portfolio outperforms its peer group that year.

Comment: Thompson's actions in running the scenario test with inputs beyond the historical trends available in the firm's databases adhere to the principles of Standard V(A). His concerns over recent trends provide a sound basis for further analysis. Thompson understands the limitations of his model, when combined with the limited available historical information, to accurately predict the performance of the funds if market conditions change negatively.

See also Standard I(B)–Independence and Objectivity.

Example 11 (Use of Quantitatively Oriented Models):

Espacia Liakos works in sales for Hellenica Securities, a firm specializing in developing intricate derivative strategies to profit from particular views on market expectations. One of her clients is Eugenie Carapalis, who has become convinced that commodity prices will become more volatile over the coming months. Carapalis asks Liakos to quickly engineer a strategy that will benefit from this expectation. Liakos turns to Hellenica's modeling group to fulfill this request. Because of the tight deadline, the modeling group outsources parts of the work to several trusted third parties. Liakos implements the disparate components of the strategy as the firms complete them.

Within a month, Carapalis is proven correct: Volatility across a range of commodities increases sharply. But her derivatives position with Hellenica returns huge losses, and the losses increase daily. Liakos investigates and realizes that although each of the various components of the strategy had been validated, they had never been evaluated as an integrated whole. In extreme conditions, portions of the model worked at cross-purposes with other portions, causing the overall strategy to fail dramatically.

Comment: Liakos violated Standard V(A). Members and candidates must understand the statistical significance of the results of the models they recommend and must be able to explain them to clients. Liakos did not take adequate care to ensure a thorough review of the whole model; its components were evaluated only individually. Because Carapalis clearly intended to implement the strategy as a whole rather than as separate parts, Liakos should have tested how the components of the strategy interacted as well as how they performed individually.

Example 12 (Successful Due Diligence/Failed Investment):

Alton Newbury is an investment adviser to high-net-worth clients. A client with an aggressive risk profile in his investment policy statement asks about investing in the Top Shelf hedge fund. This fund, based in Calgary, Alberta, Canada, has reported 20% returns for the first three years. The fund prospectus states that its strategy involves long and short positions in the energy sector and extensive leverage. Based on his analysis of the fund's track record, the principals involved in managing the fund, the fees charged, and the fund's risk profile, Newbury recommends the fund to the client and secures a position in it. The next week, the fund announces that it has suffered a loss of 60% of its value and is suspending operations and redemptions until after a regulatory review. Newbury's client calls him in a panic and asks for an explanation.

Comment: Newbury's actions were consistent with Standard V(A). Analysis of an investment that results in a reasonable basis for recommendation does not guarantee that the investment has no downside risk. Newbury should discuss the analysis process with the client while reminding him or her that past performance does not lead to guaranteed future gains and that losses in an aggressive investment portfolio should be expected.

Example 13 (Quantitative Model Diligence):

Barry Cannon is the lead quantitative analyst at CityCenter Hedge Fund. He is responsible for the development, maintenance, and enhancement of the proprietary models the fund uses to manage its investors' assets. Cannon reads several high-level mathematical publications and blogs to stay informed of current developments. One blog, run by Expert CFA, presents some intriguing research that may benefit one of CityCenter's current models. Cannon is under pressure from firm executives to improve the model's predictive abilities, and he incorporates the factors discussed in the online research. The updated output recommends several new investments to the fund's portfolio managers.

Comment: Cannon has violated Standard V(A) by failing to have a reasonable basis for the new recommendations made to the portfolio managers. He needed to diligently research the effect of incorporating the new factors before offering the output recommendations. Cannon may use the blog for ideas, but it is his responsibility to determine the effect on the firm's proprietary models.

See Standard VII(B) regarding the violation by "Expert CFA" in the use of the CFA designation.

Example 14 (Selecting a Service Provider):

Ellen Smith is a performance analyst at Artic Global Advisors, a firm that manages global equity mandates for institutional clients. She was asked by her supervisor to review five new performance attribution systems and recommend one that would more appropriately explain the firm's investment strategy to clients. On the list was a system she recalled learning about when visiting an exhibitor booth at a recent conference. The system is highly quantitative and something of a "black box" in how it calculates the attribution values. Smith recommended this option without researching the others because the sheer complexity of the process was sure to impress the clients.

Comment: Smith's actions do not demonstrate a sufficient level of diligence in reviewing this product to make a recommendation for selecting the service. Besides not reviewing or considering the other four potential systems, she did not determine whether the "black box" attribution process aligns with the investment practices of the firm, including its investments in different countries and currencies. Smith must review and understand the process of any software or system before recommending its use as the firm's attribution system.

Example 15 (Subadviser Selection):

Craig Jackson is working for Adams Partners, Inc., and has been assigned to select a hedge fund subadviser to improve the diversification of the firm's large fund-of-funds product. The allocation must be in place before the start of the next quarter. Jackson uses a consultant database to find a list of suitable firms that claim compliance with the GIPS standards. He calls more than 20 firms on the list to confirm their potential interest and to determine their most recent quarterly and annual total return values. Because of the short turnaround, Jackson recommends the firm with the greatest total return values for selection.

Comment: By considering only performance and GIPS compliance, Jackson has not conducted sufficient review of potential firms to satisfy the requirements of Standard V(A). A thorough investigation of the firms and their operations should be conducted to ensure that their addition would increase the diversity of clients' portfolios and that they are suitable for the fund-of-funds product.

Example 16 (Manager Selection):

Timothy Green works for Peach Asset Management, where he creates proprietary models that analyze data from the firm request for proposal questionnaires to identify managers for possible inclusion in the firm's fund-of-funds investment platform. Various criteria must be met to be accepted to the platform. Because of the number of respondents to the questionnaires, Green uses only the data submitted to make a recommendation for adding a new manager.

Comment: By failing to conduct any additional outside review of the information to verify what was submitted through the request for proposal, Green has likely not satisfied the requirements of Standard V(A). The amount of information requested from outside managers varies among firms. Although the requested information may be comprehensive, Green should ensure sufficient effort is undertaken to verify the submitted information before recommending a firm for inclusion. This requires that he go beyond the information provided by the manager on the request for proposal questionnaire and may include interviews with interested managers, reviews of regulatory filings, and discussions with the managers' custodian or auditor.

Example 17 (Technical Model Requirements):

Jérôme Dupont works for the credit research group of XYZ Asset Management, where he is in charge of developing and updating credit risk models. In order to perform accurately, his models need to be regularly updated with the latest market data.

Dupont does not interact with or manage money for any of the firm's clients. He is in contact with the firm's US corporate bond fund manager, John Smith, who has only very superficial knowledge of the model and who from time to time asks very basic questions regarding the output recommendations. Smith does not consult Dupont with respect to finalizing his clients' investment strategies.

Dupont's recently assigned objective is to develop a new emerging market corporate credit risk model. The firm is planning to expand into emerging credit, and the development of such a model is a critical step in this process. Because Smith seems to follow the model's recommendations without much concern for its quality as he develops his clients' investment strategies, Dupont decides to focus his time on the development of the new emerging market model and neglects to update the US model.

After several months without regular updates, Dupont's diagnostic statistics start to show alarming signs with respect to the quality of the US credit model. Instead of conducting the long and complicated data update, Dupont introduces new codes into his model with some limited new data as a quick "fix." He thinks this change will address the issue without needing to complete the full data update, so he continues working on the new emerging market model.

Several months following the quick "fix," another set of diagnostic statistics reveals nonsensical results and Dupont realizes that his earlier change contained an error. He quickly corrects the error and alerts Smith. Smith realizes that some of the prior trades he performed were due to erroneous model results. Smith rebalances the portfolio to remove the securities purchased on the basis of the questionable results without reporting the issue to anyone else.

> *Comment*: Smith violated standard V(A) because exercising "diligence, independence, and thoroughness in analyzing investments, making investment recommendations, and taking investment actions" means that members and candidates must understand the technical aspects of the products they provide to clients. Smith does not understand the model he is relying on to manage money. Members and candidates should also make reasonable enquiries into the source and accuracy of all data used in completing their investment analysis and recommendations.
>
> Dupont violated V(A) even if he does not trade securities or make investment decisions. Dupont's models give investment recommendations, and Dupont is accountable for the quality of those recommendations. Members and candidates should make reasonable efforts to test the output of pre-programed analytical tools they use. Such validation should occur before incorporating the tools into their decision-making process.
>
> See also Standard V(B)–Communication with Clients and Prospective Clients.

Standard V(B) Communication with Clients and Prospective Clients

Members and Candidates must:

1 Disclose to clients and prospective clients the basic format and general principles of the investment processes they use to analyze investments, select securities, and construct portfolios and must promptly disclose any changes that might materially affect those processes.

2 Disclose to clients and prospective clients significant limitations and risks associated with the investment process.
3 Use reasonable judgment in identifying which factors are important to their investment analyses, recommendations, or actions and include those factors in communications with clients and prospective clients.
4 Distinguish between fact and opinion in the presentation of investment analyses and recommendations.

Guidance

Highlights:

- *Informing Clients of the Investment Process*
- *Different Forms of Communication*
- *Identifying Risk and Limitations*
- *Report Presentation*
- *Distinction between Facts and Opinions in Reports*

Standard V(B) addresses member and candidate conduct with respect to communicating with clients. Developing and maintaining clear, frequent, and thorough communication practices is critical to providing high-quality financial services to clients. When clients understand the information communicated to them, they also can understand exactly how members and candidates are acting on their behalf, which gives clients the opportunity to make well-informed decisions about their investments. Such understanding can be accomplished only through clear communication.

Standard V(B) states that members and candidates should communicate in a recommendation the factors that were instrumental in making the investment recommendation. A critical part of this requirement is to distinguish clearly between opinions and facts. In preparing a research report, the member or candidate must present the basic characteristics of the security(ies) being analyzed, which will allow the reader to evaluate the report and incorporate information the reader deems relevant to his or her investment decision-making process.

Similarly, in preparing a recommendation about, for example, an asset allocation strategy, alternative investment vehicle, or structured investment product, the member or candidate should include factors that are relevant to the asset classes that are being discussed. Follow-up communication of significant changes in the risk characteristics of a security or asset strategy is required. Providing regular updates to any changes in the risk characteristics is recommended.

Informing Clients of the Investment Process

Members and candidates must adequately describe to clients and prospective clients the manner in which they conduct the investment decision-making process. Such disclosure should address factors that have positive and negative influences on the recommendations, including significant risks and limitations of the investment process used. The member or candidate must keep clients and other interested parties informed on an ongoing basis about changes to the investment process, especially newly identified significant risks and limitations. Only by thoroughly understanding the nature of the investment product or service can a client determine whether changes to that product or service could materially affect his or her investment objectives.

Understanding the basic characteristics of an investment is of great importance in judging the suitability of that investment on a standalone basis, but it is especially important in determining the impact each investment will have on the characteristics of a portfolio. Although the risk and return characteristics of a common stock might seem to be essentially the same for any investor when the stock is viewed in isolation, the effects of those characteristics greatly depend on the other investments held. For instance, if the particular stock will represent 90% of an individual's investments, the stock's importance in the portfolio is vastly different from what it would be to an investor with a highly diversified portfolio for whom the stock will represent only 2% of the holdings.

A firm's investment policy may include the use of outside advisers to manage various portions of clients' assets under management. Members and candidates should inform the clients about the specialization or diversification expertise provided by the external adviser(s). This information allows clients to understand the full mix of products and strategies being applied that may affect their investment objectives.

Different Forms of Communication

For purposes of Standard V(B), communication is not confined to a written report of the type traditionally generated by an analyst researching a security, company, or industry. A presentation of information can be made via any means of communication, including in-person recommendation or description, telephone conversation, media broadcast, or transmission by computer (e.g., on the internet).

Computer and mobile device communications have rapidly evolved over the past few years. Members and candidates using any social media service to communicate business information must be diligent in their efforts to avoid unintended problems because these services may not be available to all clients. When providing information to clients through new technologies, members and candidates should take reasonable steps to ensure that such delivery would treat all clients fairly and, if necessary, be considered publicly disseminated.

The nature of client communications is highly diverse—from one word ("buy" or "sell") to in-depth reports of more than 100 pages. A communication may contain a general recommendation about the market, asset allocations, or classes of investments (e.g., stocks, bonds, real estate) or may relate to a specific security. If recommendations are contained in capsule form (such as a recommended stock list), members and candidates should notify clients that additional information and analyses are available from the producer of the report.

Identifying Risks and Limitations

Members and candidates must outline to clients and prospective clients significant risks and limitations of the analysis contained in their investment products or recommendations. The type and nature of significant risks will depend on the investment process that members and candidates are following and on the personal circumstances of the client. In general, the use of leverage constitutes a significant risk and should be disclosed.

Members and candidates must adequately disclose the general market-related risks and the risks associated with the use of complex financial instruments that are deemed significant. Other types of risks that members and candidates may consider disclosing include, but are not limited to, counterparty risk, country risk, sector or industry risk, security-specific risk, and credit risk.

Investment securities and vehicles may have limiting factors that influence a client's or potential client's investment decision. Members and candidates must report to clients and prospective clients the existence of limitations significant to the decision-making process. Examples of such factors and attributes include, but are not limited to, investment liquidity and capacity. Liquidity is the ability to liquidate an investment on a timely basis at a reasonable cost. Capacity is the investment amount beyond which returns will be negatively affected by new investments.

The appropriateness of risk disclosure should be assessed on the basis of what was known at the time the investment action was taken (often called an *ex ante* basis). Members and candidates must disclose significant risks known to them at the time of the disclosure. Members and candidates cannot be expected to disclose risks they are unaware of at the time recommendations or investment actions are made. In assessing compliance with Standard V(B), it is important to establish knowledge of a purported significant risk or limitation. A one-time investment loss that occurs after the disclosure does not constitute a pertinent factor in assessing whether significant risks and limitations were properly disclosed. Having no knowledge of a risk or limitation that subsequently triggers a loss may reveal a deficiency in the diligence and reasonable basis of the research of the member or candidate but may not reveal a breach of Standard V(B).

Report Presentation

Once the analytical process has been completed, the member or candidate who prepares the report must include those elements that are important to the analysis and conclusions of the report so that the reader can follow and challenge the report's reasoning. A report writer who has done adequate investigation may emphasize certain areas, touch briefly on others, and omit certain aspects deemed unimportant. For instance, a report may dwell on a quarterly earnings release or new-product introduction and omit other matters as long as the analyst clearly stipulates the limits to the scope of the report.

Investment advice based on quantitative research and analysis must be supported by readily available reference material and should be applied in a manner consistent with previously applied methodology. If changes in methodology are made, they should be highlighted.

Distinction between Facts and Opinions in Reports

Standard V(B) requires that opinion be separated from fact. Violations often occur when reports fail to separate the past from the future by not indicating that earnings estimates, changes in the outlook for dividends, or future market price information are *opinions* subject to future circumstances.

In the case of complex quantitative analyses, members and candidates must clearly separate fact from statistical conjecture and should identify the known limitations of an analysis. Members and candidates may violate Standard V(B) by failing to identify the limits of statistically developed projections because such omission leaves readers unaware of the limits of the published projections.

Members and candidates should explicitly discuss with clients and prospective clients the assumptions used in the investment models and processes to generate the analysis. Caution should be used in promoting the perceived accuracy of any model or process to clients because the ultimate output is merely an estimate of future results and not a certainty.

Recommended Procedures for Compliance

Because the selection of relevant factors is an analytical skill, determination of whether a member or candidate has used reasonable judgment in excluding and including information in research reports depends heavily on case-by-case review rather than a specific checklist.

Members and candidates should encourage their firms to have a rigorous methodology for reviewing research that is created for publication and dissemination to clients.

To assist in the after-the-fact review of a report, the member or candidate must maintain records indicating the nature of the research and should, if asked, be able to supply additional information to the client (or any user of the report) covering factors not included in the report.

Application of the Standard

Example 1 (Sufficient Disclosure of Investment System):

Sarah Williamson, director of marketing for Country Technicians, Inc., is convinced that she has found the perfect formula for increasing Country Technicians' income and diversifying its product base. Williamson plans to build on Country Technicians' reputation as a leading money manager by marketing an exclusive and expensive investment advice letter to high-net-worth individuals. One hitch in the plan is the complexity of Country Technicians' investment system—a combination of technical trading rules (based on historical price and volume fluctuations) and portfolio construction rules designed to minimize risk. To simplify the newsletter, she decides to include only each week's top five "buy" and "sell" recommendations and to leave out details of the valuation models and the portfolio structuring scheme.

> *Comment*: Williamson's plans for the newsletter violate Standard V(B). Williamson need not describe the investment system in detail in order to implement the advice effectively, but she must inform clients of Country Technicians' basic process and logic. Without understanding the basis for a recommendation, clients cannot possibly understand its limitations or its inherent risks.

Example 2 (Providing Opinions as Facts):

Richard Dox is a mining analyst for East Bank Securities. He has just finished his report on Boisy Bay Minerals. Included in his report is his own assessment of the geological extent of mineral reserves likely to be found on the company's land. Dox completed this calculation on the basis of the core samples from the company's latest drilling. According to Dox's calculations, the company has more than 500,000 ounces of gold on the property. Dox concludes his research report as follows: "Based on the fact that the company has 500,000 ounces of gold to be mined, I recommend a strong BUY."

> *Comment*: If Dox issues the report as written, he will violate Standard V(B). His calculation of the total gold reserves for the property based on the company's recent sample drilling is a quantitative opinion, not a fact. Opinion must be distinguished from fact in research reports.

Example 3 (Proper Description of a Security):

Olivia Thomas, an analyst at Government Brokers, Inc., which is a brokerage firm specializing in government bond trading, has produced a report that describes an investment strategy designed to benefit from an expected decline in US interest rates. The firm's derivative products group has designed a structured product that will allow the firm's clients to benefit from this strategy. Thomas's report describing the strategy indicates that high returns are possible if various scenarios for declining interest rates are assumed. Citing the proprietary nature of the structured product underlying the strategy, the report does not describe in detail how the firm is able to offer such returns or the related risks in the scenarios, nor does the report address the likely returns of the strategy if, contrary to expectations, interest rates rise.

Comment: Thomas has violated Standard V(B) because her report fails to describe properly the basic characteristics of the actual and implied risks of the investment strategy, including how the structure was created and the degree to which leverage was embedded in the structure. The report should include a balanced discussion of how the strategy would perform in the case of rising as well as falling interest rates, preferably illustrating how the strategies might be expected to perform in the event of a reasonable variety of interest rate and credit risk–spread scenarios. If liquidity issues are relevant with regard to the valuation of either the derivatives or the underlying securities, provisions the firm has made to address those risks should also be disclosed.

Example 4 (Notification of Fund Mandate Change):

May & Associates is an aggressive growth manager that has represented itself since its inception as a specialist at investing in small-cap US stocks. One of May's selection criteria is a maximum capitalization of US$250 million for any given company. After a string of successful years of superior performance relative to its peers, May has expanded its client base significantly, to the point at which assets under management now exceed US$3 billion. For liquidity purposes, May's chief investment officer (CIO) decides to lift the maximum permissible market-cap ceiling to US$500 million and change the firm's sales and marketing literature accordingly to inform prospective clients and third-party consultants.

Comment: Although May's CIO is correct about informing potentially interested parties as to the change in investment process, he must also notify May's existing clients. Among the latter group might be a number of clients who not only retained May as a small-cap manager but also retained mid-cap and large-cap specialists in a multiple-manager approach. Such clients could regard May's change of criteria as a style change that distorts their overall asset allocations.

Example 5 (Notification of Fund Mandate Change):

Rather than lifting the ceiling for its universe from US$250 million to US$500 million, May & Associates extends its small-cap universe to include a number of non-US companies.

Comment: Standard V(B) requires that May's CIO advise May's clients of this change because the firm may have been retained by some clients specifically for its prowess at investing in US small-cap stocks. Other changes that require client notification are introducing derivatives to emulate a certain market sector or relaxing various other constraints, such as portfolio beta. In all such cases, members and candidates must disclose changes to all interested parties.

Example 6 (Notification of Changes to the Investment Process):

RJZ Capital Management is an active value-style equity manager that selects stocks by using a combination of four multifactor models. The firm has found favorable results when back testing the most recent 10 years of available market data in a new dividend discount model (DDM) designed by the firm. This model is based on projected inflation rates, earnings growth rates, and interest rates. The president of RJZ decides to replace its simple model that uses price to trailing 12-month earnings with the new DDM.

Comment: Because the introduction of a new and different valuation model represents a material change in the investment process, RJZ's president must communicate the change to the firm's clients. RJZ is moving away from a model based on hard data toward a new model that is at least partly dependent on the firm's forecasting skills. Clients would likely view such a model as a significant change rather than a mere refinement of RJZ's process.

Example 7 (Notification of Changes to the Investment Process):

RJZ Capital Management loses the chief architect of its multifactor valuation system. Without informing its clients, the president of RJZ decides to redirect the firm's talents and resources toward developing a product for passive equity management—a product that will emulate the performance of a major market index.

Comment: By failing to disclose to clients a substantial change to its investment process, the president of RJZ has violated Standard V(B).

Example 8 (Notification of Changes to the Investment Process):

At Fundamental Asset Management, Inc., the responsibility for selecting stocks for addition to the firm's "approved" list has just shifted from individual security analysts to a committee consisting of the research director and three senior portfolio managers. Eleanor Morales, a portfolio manager with Fundamental Asset Management, thinks this change is not important enough to communicate to her clients.

Comment: Morales must disclose the process change to all her clients. Some of Fundamental's clients might be concerned about the morale and motivation among the firm's best research analysts after such a change. Moreover, clients might challenge the stock-picking track record of the portfolio managers and might even want to monitor the situation closely.

Example 9 (Sufficient Disclosure of Investment System):

Amanda Chinn is the investment director for Diversified Asset Management, which manages the endowment of a charitable organization. Because of recent staff departures, Diversified has decided to limit its direct investment focus to large-cap securities and supplement the needs for small-cap and mid-cap management by hiring outside fund managers. In describing the planned strategy change to the charity, Chinn's update letter states, "As investment director, I will directly oversee the investment team managing the endowment's large-capitalization allocation. I will coordinate the selection and ongoing review of external managers responsible for allocations to other classes." The letter also describes the reasons for the change and the characteristics external managers must have to be considered.

Comment: Standard V(B) requires the disclosure of the investment process used to construct the portfolio of the fund. Changing the investment process from managing all classes of investments within the firm to the use of external managers is one example of information that needs to be communicated to clients. Chinn and her firm have embraced the principles of Standard V(B) by providing their client with relevant information. The charity can now make a reasonable decision about whether Diversified Asset Management remains the appropriate manager for its fund.

Example 10 (Notification of Changes to the Investment Process):

Michael Papis is the chief investment officer of his state's retirement fund. The fund has always used outside advisers for the real estate allocation, and this information is clearly presented in all fund communications. Thomas Nagle, a recognized sell-side research analyst and Papis's business school classmate, recently left the investment bank he worked for to start his own asset management firm, Accessible Real Estate. Nagle is trying to build his assets under management and contacts Papis about gaining some of the retirement fund's allocation. In the previous few years, the performance of the retirement fund's real estate investments was in line with the fund's benchmark but was not extraordinary. Papis decides to help out his old friend and also to seek better returns by moving the real estate allocation to Accessible. The only notice of the change in adviser appears in the next annual report in the listing of associated advisers.

Comment: Papis has violated Standard V(B). He attempted to hide the nature of his decision to change external managers by making only a limited disclosure. The plan recipients and the fund's trustees need to be aware when changes are made to ensure that operational procedures are being followed.

See also Standard IV(C)–Responsibilities of Supervisors, Standard V(A)–Diligence and Reasonable Basis, and Standard VI(A)–Disclosure of Conflicts.

Example 11 (Notification of Errors):

Jérôme Dupont works for the credit research group of XYZ Asset Management, where he is in charge of developing and updating credit risk models. In order to perform accurately, his models need to be regularly updated with the latest market data.

Dupont does not interact with or manage money for any of the firm's clients. He is in contact with the firm's US corporate bond fund manager, John Smith, who has only very superficial knowledge of the model and who from time to time asks very basic questions regarding the output recommendations. Smith does not consult Dupont with respect to finalizing his clients' investment strategies.

Dupont's recently assigned objective is to develop a new emerging market corporate credit risk model. The firm is planning to expand into emerging credit, and the development of such a model is a critical step in this process. Because Smith seems to follow the model's recommendations without much concern for its quality as he develops his clients' investment strategies, Dupont decides to focus his time on the development of the new emerging market model and neglects to update the US model.

After several months without regular updates, Dupont's diagnostic statistics start to show alarming signs with respect to the quality of the US credit model. Instead of conducting the long and complicated data update, Dupont introduces new codes into his model with some limited new data as a quick "fix." He thinks this change will address the issue without needing to complete the full data update, so he continues working on the new emerging market model.

Several months following the quick "fix," another set of diagnostic statistics reveals nonsensical results and Dupont realizes that his earlier change contained an error. He quickly corrects the error and alerts Smith. Smith realizes that some of the prior trades he performed were due to erroneous model results. Smith rebalances the portfolio to remove the securities purchased on the basis of the questionable results without reporting the issue to anyone else.

Comment: Smith violated V(B) by not disclosing a material error in the investment process. Clients should have been informed about the error and the corrective actions the firm was undertaking on their behalf.

See also Standard V(A)–Diligence and Reasonable Basis.

Example 12 (Notification of Risks and Limitations):

Quantitative analyst Yuri Yakovlev has developed an investment strategy that selects small-cap stocks on the basis of quantitative signals. Yakovlev's strategy typically identifies only a small number of stocks (10–20) that tend to be illiquid, but according to his backtests, the strategy generates significant risk-adjusted returns. The partners at Yakovlev's firm, QSC Capital, are impressed by these results. After a thorough examination of the strategy's risks, stress testing, historical back testing, and scenario analysis, QSC decides to seed the strategy with US$10 million of internal capital in order for Yakovlev to create a track record for the strategy.

After two years, the strategy has generated performance returns greater than the appropriate benchmark and the Sharpe ratio of the fund is close to 1.0. On the basis of these results, QSC decides to actively market the fund to large institutional investors. While creating the offering materials, Yakovlev informs the marketing team that the capacity of the strategy is limited. The extent of the limitation is difficult to ascertain with precision; it depends on market liquidity and other factors in his model that can evolve over time. Yakovlev indicates that given the current market conditions, investments in the fund beyond US$100 million of capital could become more difficult and negatively affect expected fund returns.

Alan Wellard, the manager of the marketing team, is a partner with 30 years of marketing experience and explains to Yakovlev that these are complex technical issues that will muddy the marketing message. According to Wellard, the offering material should focus solely on the great track record of the fund. Yakovlev does not object because the fund has only US$12 million of capital, very far from the US$100 million threshold.

> *Comment*: Yakovlev and Wellard have not appropriately disclosed a significant limitation associated with the investment product. Yakovlev believes this limitation, once reached, will materially affect the returns of the fund. Although the fund is currently far from the US$100 million mark, current and prospective investors must be made aware of this capacity issue. If significant limitations are complicated to grasp and clients do not have the technical background required to understand them, Yakovlev and Wellard should either educate the clients or ascertain whether the fund is suitable for each client.

Example 13 (Notification of Risks and Limitations):

Brickell Advisers offers investment advisory services mainly to South American clients. Julietta Ramon, a risk analyst at Brickell, describes to clients how the firm uses value at risk (VaR) analysis to track the risk of its strategies. Ramon assures clients that calculating a VaR at a 99% confidence level, using a 20-day holding period, and applying a methodology based on an *ex ante* Monte Carlo simulation is extremely effective. The firm has never had losses greater than those predicted by this VaR analysis.

> *Comment*: Ramon has not sufficiently communicated the risks associated with the investment process to satisfy the requirements of Standard V(B). The losses predicted by a VaR analysis depend greatly on the inputs used in the model. The size and probability of losses can differ significantly from what an individual model predicts. Ramon must disclose how the inputs were selected and the potential limitations and risks associated with the investment strategy.

Example 14 (Notification of Risks and Limitations):

Lily Smith attended an industry conference and noticed that John Baker, an investment manager with Baker Associates, attracted a great deal of attention from the conference participants. On the basis of her knowledge of Baker's reputation and the interest he received at the conference, Smith recommends adding Baker Associates to the approved manager platform. Her recommendation to the approval committee included the statement "John Baker is well respected in the industry, and his insights are consistently sought after by investors. Our clients are sure to benefit from investing with Baker Associates."

> *Comment*: Smith is not appropriately separating facts from opinions in her recommendation to include the manager within the platform. Her actions conflict with the requirements of Standard V(B). Smith is relying on her opinions about Baker's reputation and the fact that many attendees were talking with him at the conference. Smith should also review the requirements of Standard V(A) regarding reasonable basis to determine the level of review necessary to recommend Baker Associates.

Standard V(C) Record Retention

> Members and Candidates must develop and maintain appropriate records to support their investment analyses, recommendations, actions, and other investment-related communications with clients and prospective clients.

Guidance

Highlights:

- *New Media Records*
- *Records Are Property of the Firm*
- *Local Requirements*

Members and candidates must retain records that substantiate the scope of their research and reasons for their actions or conclusions. The retention requirement applies to decisions to buy or sell a security as well as reviews undertaken that do not lead to a change in position. Which records are required to support recommendations or investment actions depends on the role of the member or candidate in the investment decision-making process. Records may be maintained either in hard copy or electronic form.

Some examples of supporting documentation that assists the member or candidate in meeting the requirements for retention are as follows:

- personal notes from meetings with the covered company,
- press releases or presentations issued by the covered company,
- computer-based model outputs and analyses,
- computer-based model input parameters,
- risk analyses of securities' impacts on a portfolio,
- selection criteria for external advisers,

- notes from clients from meetings to review investment policy statements, and
- outside research reports.

New Media Records

The increased use of new and evolving technological formats (e.g., social media) for gathering and sharing information creates new challenges in maintaining the appropriate records and files. The nature or format of the information does not remove a member's or candidate's responsibility to maintain a record of information used in his or her analysis or communicated to clients.

Members and candidates should understand that although employers and local regulators are developing digital media retention policies, these policies may lag behind the advent of new communication channels. Such lag places greater responsibility on the individual for ensuring that all relevant information is retained. Examples of non-print media formats that should be retained include, but are not limited to,

- e-mails,
- text messages,
- blog posts, and
- Twitter posts.

Records Are Property of the Firm

As a general matter, records created as part of a member's or candidate's professional activity on behalf of his or her employer are the property of the firm. When a member or candidate leaves a firm to seek other employment, the member or candidate cannot take the property of the firm, including original forms or copies of supporting records of the member's or candidate's work, to the new employer without the express consent of the previous employer. The member or candidate cannot use historical recommendations or research reports created at the previous firm because the supporting documentation is unavailable. For future use, the member or candidate must re-create the supporting records at the new firm with information gathered through public sources or directly from the covered company and not from memory or sources obtained at the previous employer.

Local Requirements

Local regulators often impose requirements on members, candidates, and their firms related to record retention that must be followed. Firms may also implement policies detailing the applicable time frame for retaining research and client communication records. Fulfilling such regulatory and firm requirements satisfies the requirements of Standard V(C). In the absence of regulatory guidance or firm policies, CFA Institute recommends maintaining records for at least seven years.

Recommended Procedures for Compliance

The responsibility to maintain records that support investment action generally falls with the firm rather than individuals. Members and candidates must, however, archive research notes and other documents, either electronically or in hard copy, that support their current investment-related communications. Doing so will assist their firms in complying with requirements for preservation of internal or external records.

Application of the Standard

Example 1 (Record Retention and IPS Objectives and Recommendations):

One of Nikolas Lindstrom's clients is upset by the negative investment returns of his equity portfolio. The investment policy statement for the client requires that the portfolio manager follow a benchmark-oriented approach. The benchmark for the client includes a 35% investment allocation in the technology sector. The client acknowledges that this allocation was appropriate, but over the past three years, technology stocks have suffered severe losses. The client complains to the investment manager for allocating so much money to this sector.

> *Comment*: For Lindstrom, having appropriate records is important to show that over the past three years, the portion of technology stocks in the benchmark index was 35%, as called for in the IPS. Lindstrom should also have the client's IPS stating that the benchmark was appropriate for the client's investment objectives. He should also have records indicating that the investment has been explained appropriately to the client and that the IPS was updated on a regular basis. Taking these actions, Lindstrom would be in compliance with Standard V(C).

Example 2 (Record Retention and Research Process):

Malcolm Young is a research analyst who writes numerous reports rating companies in the luxury retail industry. His reports are based on a variety of sources, including interviews with company managers, manufacturers, and economists; on-site company visits; customer surveys; and secondary research from analysts covering related industries.

> *Comment*: Young must carefully document and keep copies of all the information that goes into his reports, including the secondary or third-party research of other analysts. Failure to maintain such files would violate Standard V(C).

Example 3 (Records as Firm, Not Employee, Property):

Martin Blank develops an analytical model while he is employed by Green Partners Investment Management, LLP (GPIM). While at the firm, he systematically documents the assumptions that make up the model as well as his reasoning behind the assumptions. As a result of the success of his model, Blank is hired to be the head of the research department of one of GPIM's competitors. Blank takes copies of the records supporting his model to his new firm.

> *Comment*: The records created by Blank supporting the research model he developed at GPIM are the records of GPIM. Taking the documents with him to his new employer without GPIM's permission violates Standard V(C). To use the model in the future, Blank must re-create the records supporting his model at the new firm.

STANDARD VI: CONFLICTS OF INTEREST

Standard VI(A) Disclosure of Conflicts

> Members and Candidates must make full and fair disclosure of all matters that could reasonably be expected to impair their independence and objectivity or interfere with respective duties to their clients, prospective clients, and employer. Members and Candidates must ensure that such disclosures are prominent, are delivered in plain language, and communicate the relevant information effectively.

Guidance

Highlights:

- *Disclosure of Conflicts to Employers*
- *Disclosure to Clients*
- *Cross-Departmental Conflicts*
- *Conflicts with Stock Ownership*
- *Conflicts as a Director*

Best practice is to avoid actual conflicts or the appearance of conflicts of interest when possible. Conflicts of interest often arise in the investment profession. Conflicts can occur between the interests of clients, the interests of employers, and the member's or candidate's own personal interests. Common sources for conflict are compensation structures, especially incentive and bonus structures that provide immediate returns for members and candidates with little or no consideration of long-term value creation.

Identifying and managing these conflicts is a critical part of working in the investment industry and can take many forms. When conflicts cannot be reasonably avoided, clear and complete disclosure of their existence is necessary.

Standard VI(A) protects investors and employers by requiring members and candidates to fully disclose to clients, potential clients, and employers all actual and potential conflicts of interest. Once a member or candidate has made full disclosure, the member's or candidate's employer, clients, and prospective clients will have the information needed to evaluate the objectivity of the investment advice or action taken on their behalf.

To be effective, disclosures must be prominent and must be made in plain language and in a manner designed to effectively communicate the information. Members and candidates have the responsibility of determining how often, in what manner, and in what particular circumstances the disclosure of conflicts must be made. Best practices dictate updating disclosures when the nature of a conflict of interest changes materially—for example, if the nature of a conflict of interest worsens through the introduction of bonuses based on each quarter's profits as to opposed annual profits. In making and updating disclosures of conflicts of interest, members and candidates should err on the side of caution to ensure that conflicts are effectively communicated.

Disclosure of Conflicts to Employers

Disclosure of conflicts to employers may be appropriate in many instances. When reporting conflicts of interest to employers, members and candidates must give their employers enough information to assess the impact of the conflict. By complying with employer guidelines, members and candidates allow their employers to avoid potentially embarrassing and costly ethical or regulatory violations.

Reportable situations include conflicts that would interfere with rendering unbiased investment advice and conflicts that would cause a member or candidate to act not in the employer's best interest. The same circumstances that generate conflicts to be reported to clients and prospective clients also would dictate reporting to employers. Ownership of stocks analyzed or recommended, participation on outside boards, and financial or other pressures that could influence a decision are to be promptly reported to the employer so that their impact can be assessed and a decision on how to resolve the conflict can be made.

The mere appearance of a conflict of interest may create problems for members, candidates, and their employers. Therefore, many of the conflicts previously mentioned could be explicitly prohibited by an employer. For example, many employers restrict personal trading, outside board membership, and related activities to prevent situations that might not normally be considered problematic from a conflict-of-interest point of view but that could give the appearance of a conflict of interest. Members and candidates must comply with these restrictions. Members and candidates must take reasonable steps to avoid conflicts and, if they occur inadvertently, must report them promptly so that the employer and the member or candidate can resolve them as quickly and effectively as possible.

Standard VI(A) also deals with a member's or candidate's conflicts of interest that might be detrimental to the employer's business. Any potential conflict situation that could prevent clear judgment about or full commitment to the execution of a member's or candidate's duties to the employer should be reported to the member's or candidate's employer and promptly resolved.

Disclosure to Clients

Members and candidates must maintain their objectivity when rendering investment advice or taking investment action. Investment advice or actions may be perceived to be tainted in numerous situations. Can a member or candidate remain objective if, on behalf of the firm, the member or candidate obtains or assists in obtaining fees for services? Can a member or candidate give objective advice if he or she owns stock in the company that is the subject of an investment recommendation or if the member or candidate has a close personal relationship with the company managers? Requiring members and candidates to disclose all matters that reasonably could be expected to impair the member's or candidate's objectivity allows clients and prospective clients to judge motives and possible biases for themselves.

Often in the investment industry, a conflict, or the perception of a conflict, cannot be avoided. The most obvious conflicts of interest, which should always be disclosed, are relationships between an issuer and the member, the candidate, or his or her firm (such as a directorship or consultancy by a member; investment banking, underwriting, and financial relationships; broker/dealer market-making activities; and material beneficial ownership of stock). For the purposes of Standard VI(A), members and candidates beneficially own securities or other investments if they have a direct or indirect pecuniary interest in the securities, have the power to vote or direct the voting of the shares of the securities or investments, or have the power to dispose or direct the disposition of the security or investment.

A member or candidate must take reasonable steps to determine whether a conflict of interest exists and disclose to clients any known conflicts of the member's or candidate's firm. Disclosure of broker/dealer market-making activities alerts clients that a purchase or sale might be made from or to the firm's principal account and that the firm has a special interest in the price of the stock.

Additionally, disclosures should be made to clients regarding fee arrangements, subadvisory agreements, or other situations involving nonstandard fee structures. Equally important is the disclosure of arrangements in which the firm benefits directly from investment recommendations. An obvious conflict of interest is the rebate of a portion of the service fee some classes of mutual funds charge to investors. Members and candidates should ensure that their firms disclose such relationships so clients can fully understand the costs of their investments and the benefits received by their investment manager's employer.

Cross-Departmental Conflicts

Other circumstances can give rise to actual or potential conflicts of interest. For instance, a sell-side analyst working for a broker/dealer may be encouraged, not only by members of her or his own firm but by corporate issuers themselves, to write research reports about particular companies. The buy-side analyst is likely to be faced with similar conflicts as banks exercise their underwriting and security-dealing powers. The marketing division may ask an analyst to recommend the stock of a certain company in order to obtain business from that company.

The potential for conflicts of interest also exists with broker-sponsored limited partnerships formed to invest venture capital. Increasingly, members and candidates are expected not only to follow issues from these partnerships once they are offered to the public but also to promote the issues in the secondary market after public offerings. Members, candidates, and their firms should attempt to resolve situations presenting potential conflicts of interest or disclose them in accordance with the principles set forth in Standard VI(A).

Conflicts with Stock Ownership

The most prevalent conflict requiring disclosure under Standard VI(A) is a member's or candidate's ownership of stock in companies that he or she recommends to clients or that clients hold. Clearly, the easiest method for preventing a conflict is to prohibit members and candidates from owning any such securities, but this approach is overly burdensome and discriminates against members and candidates.

Therefore, sell-side members and candidates should disclose any materially beneficial ownership interest in a security or other investment that the member or candidate is recommending. Buy-side members and candidates should disclose their procedures for reporting requirements for personal transactions. Conflicts arising from personal investing are discussed more fully in the guidance for Standard VI(B).

Conflicts as a Director

Service as a director poses three basic conflicts of interest. First, a conflict may exist between the duties owed to clients and the duties owed to shareholders of the company. Second, investment personnel who serve as directors may receive the securities or options to purchase securities of the company as compensation for serving on the board, which could raise questions about trading actions that might increase the value of those securities. Third, board service creates the opportunity to receive material nonpublic information involving the company. Even though the information is confidential, the perception could be that information not available to the public is being communicated to a director's firm—whether a broker, investment adviser, or other type of organization. When members or candidates providing investment services also serve as directors, they should be isolated from those making investment decisions by the use of firewalls or similar restrictions.

Recommended Procedures for Compliance

Members or candidates should disclose special compensation arrangements with the employer that might conflict with client interests, such as bonuses based on short-term performance criteria, commissions, incentive fees, performance fees, and referral fees. If the member's or candidate's firm does not permit such disclosure, the member or candidate should document the request and may consider dissociating from the activity.

Members' and candidates' firms are encouraged to include information on compensation packages in firms' promotional literature. If a member or candidate manages a portfolio for which the fee is based on capital gains or capital appreciation (a performance fee), this information should be disclosed to clients. If a member, a candidate, or a member's or candidate's firm has outstanding agent options to buy stock as part of the compensation package for corporate financing activities, the amount and expiration date of these options should be disclosed as a footnote to any research report published by the member's or candidate's firm.

Application of the Standard

Example 1 (Conflict of Interest and Business Relationships):

Hunter Weiss is a research analyst with Farmington Company, a broker and investment banking firm. Farmington's merger and acquisition department has represented Vimco, a conglomerate, in all of Vimco's acquisitions for 20 years. From time to time, Farmington officers sit on the boards of directors of various Vimco subsidiaries. Weiss is writing a research report on Vimco.

> *Comment*: Weiss must disclose in his research report Farmington's special relationship with Vimco. Broker/dealer management of and participation in public offerings must be disclosed in research reports. Because the position of underwriter to a company entails a special past and potential future relationship with a company that is the subject of investment advice, it threatens the independence and objectivity of the report writer and must be disclosed.

Example 2 (Conflict of Interest and Business Stock Ownership):

The investment management firm of Dover & Roe sells a 25% interest in its partnership to a multinational bank holding company, First of New York. Immediately after the sale, Margaret Hobbs, president of Dover & Roe, changes her recommendation for First of New York's common stock from "sell" to "buy" and adds First of New York's commercial paper to Dover & Roe's approved list for purchase.

> *Comment*: Hobbs must disclose the new relationship with First of New York to all Dover & Roe clients. This relationship must also be disclosed to clients by the firm's portfolio managers when they make specific investment recommendations or take investment actions with respect to First of New York's securities.

Example 3 (Conflict of Interest and Personal Stock Ownership):

Carl Fargmon, a research analyst who follows firms producing office equipment, has been recommending purchase of Kincaid Printing because of its innovative new line of copiers. After his initial report on the company, Fargmon's wife inherits from a distant relative US$3 million of Kincaid stock. He has been asked to write a follow-up report on Kincaid.

> *Comment*: Fargmon must disclose his wife's ownership of the Kincaid stock to his employer and in his follow-up report. Best practice would be to avoid the conflict by asking his employer to assign another analyst to draft the follow-up report.

Example 4 (Conflict of Interest and Personal Stock Ownership):

Betty Roberts is speculating in penny stocks for her own account and purchases 100,000 shares of Drew Mining, Inc., for US$0.30 a share. She intends to sell these shares at the sign of any substantial upward price movement of the stock. A week later, her employer asks her to write a report on penny stocks in the mining industry to be published in two weeks. Even without owning the Drew stock, Roberts would recommend it in her report as a "buy." A surge in the price of the stock to the US$2 range is likely to result once the report is issued.

> *Comment*: Although this holding may not be material, Roberts must disclose it in the report and to her employer before writing the report because the gain for her will be substantial if the market responds strongly to her recommendation. The fact that she has only recently purchased the stock adds to the appearance that she is not entirely objective.

Example 5 (Conflict of Interest and Compensation Arrangements):

Samantha Snead, a portfolio manager for Thomas Investment Counsel, Inc., specializes in managing public retirement funds and defined benefit pension plan accounts, all of which have long-term investment objectives. A year ago, Snead's employer, in an attempt to motivate and retain key investment professionals, introduced a bonus compensation system that rewards portfolio managers on the basis of quarterly performance relative to their peers and to certain benchmark indexes. In an attempt to improve the short-term performance of her accounts, Snead changes her investment strategy and purchases several high-beta stocks for client portfolios. These purchases are seemingly contrary to the clients' investment policy statements. Following their purchase, an officer of Griffin Corporation, one of Snead's pension fund clients, asks why Griffin Corporation's portfolio seems to be dominated by high-beta stocks of companies that often appear among the most actively traded issues. No change in objective or strategy has been recommended by Snead during the year.

> *Comment*: Snead has violated Standard VI(A) by failing to inform her clients of the changes in her compensation arrangement with her employer, which created a conflict of interest between her compensation and her clients' IPSs. Firms may pay employees on the basis of performance, but pressure by Thomas Investment Counsel to achieve short-term performance goals is in basic conflict with the objectives of Snead's accounts.
>
> See also Standard III(C)–Suitability.

Example 6 (Conflict of Interest, Options, and Compensation Arrangements):

Wayland Securities works with small companies doing IPOs or secondary offerings. Typically, these deals are in the US$10 million to US$50 million range, and as a result, the corporate finance fees are quite small. To compensate for the small fees, Wayland Securities usually takes "agent options"—that is, rights (exercisable within a two-year time frame) to acquire up to an additional 10% of the current offering. Following an IPO performed by Wayland for Falk Resources, Ltd., Darcy Hunter, the head of corporate finance at Wayland, is concerned about receiving value for her Falk Resources options. The options are due to expire in one month, and the stock is not doing well. She contacts John Fitzpatrick in the research department of Wayland Securities, reminds him that he is eligible for 30% of these options, and indicates that now would be a good time to give some additional coverage to Falk Resources. Fitzpatrick agrees and immediately issues a favorable report.

> *Comment*: For Fitzpatrick to avoid being in violation of Standard VI(A), he must indicate in the report the volume and expiration date of agent options outstanding. Furthermore, because he is personally eligible for some of the options, Fitzpatrick must disclose the extent of this compensation. He also must be careful to not violate his duty of independence and objectivity under Standard I(B).

Example 7 (Conflict of Interest and Compensation Arrangements):

Gary Carter is a representative with Bengal International, a registered broker/dealer. Carter is approached by a stock promoter for Badger Company, who offers to pay Carter additional compensation for sales of Badger Company's stock to Carter's clients. Carter accepts the stock promoter's offer but does not disclose the arrangements to his clients or to his employer. Carter sells shares of the stock to his clients.

> *Comment*: Carter has violated Standard VI(A) by failing to disclose to clients that he is receiving additional compensation for recommending and selling Badger stock. Because he did not disclose the arrangement with Badger to his clients, the clients were unable to evaluate whether Carter's recommendations to buy Badger were affected by this arrangement. Carter's conduct also violated Standard VI(A) by failing to disclose to his employer monetary compensation received in addition to the compensation and benefits conferred by his employer. Carter was required by Standard VI(A) to disclose the arrangement with Badger to his employer so that his employer could evaluate whether the arrangement affected Carter's objectivity and loyalty.

Example 8 (Conflict of Interest and Directorship):

Carol Corky, a senior portfolio manager for Universal Management, recently became involved as a trustee with the Chelsea Foundation, a large not-for-profit foundation in her hometown. Universal is a small money manager (with assets under management of approximately US$100 million) that caters to individual investors. Chelsea has assets in excess of US$2 billion. Corky does not believe informing Universal of her involvement with Chelsea is necessary.

> *Comment*: By failing to inform Universal of her involvement with Chelsea, Corky violated Standard VI(A). Given the large size of the endowment at Chelsea, Corky's new role as a trustee can reasonably be expected to be time consuming, to the possible detriment of Corky's portfolio responsibilities with Universal. Also, as a trustee, Corky may become involved in the investment decisions at Chelsea. Therefore, Standard VI(A) obligates Corky to discuss becoming a trustee at Chelsea with her compliance officer

or supervisor at Universal before accepting the position, and she should have disclosed the degree to which she would be involved in investment decisions at Chelsea.

Example 9 (Conflict of Interest and Personal Trading):

Bruce Smith covers eastern European equities for Marlborough Investments, an investment management firm with a strong presence in emerging markets. While on a business trip to Russia, Smith learns that investing in Russian equities directly is difficult but that equity-linked notes that replicate the performance of underlying Russian equities can be purchased from a New York–based investment bank. Believing that his firm would not be interested in such a security, Smith purchases a note linked to a Russian telecommunications company for his own account without informing Marlborough. A month later, Smith decides that the firm should consider investing in Russian equities by way of the equity-linked notes. He prepares a write-up on the market that concludes with a recommendation to purchase several of the notes. One note he recommends is linked to the same Russian telecom company that Smith holds in his personal account.

> *Comment*: Smith has violated Standard VI(A) by failing to disclose his purchase and ownership of the note linked to the Russian telecom company. Smith is required by the standard to disclose the investment opportunity to his employer and look to his company's policies on personal trading to determine whether it was proper for him to purchase the note for his own account. By purchasing the note, Smith may or may not have impaired his ability to make an unbiased and objective assessment of the appropriateness of the derivative instrument for his firm, but Smith's failure to disclose the purchase to his employer impaired his employer's ability to decide whether his ownership of the security is a conflict of interest that might affect Smith's future recommendations. Then, when he recommended the particular telecom notes to his firm, Smith compounded his problems by not disclosing that he owned the notes in his personal account—a clear conflict of interest.

Example 10 (Conflict of Interest and Requested Favors):

Michael Papis is the chief investment officer of his state's retirement fund. The fund has always used outside advisers for the real estate allocation, and this information is clearly presented in all fund communications. Thomas Nagle, a recognized sell-side research analyst and Papis's business school classmate, recently left the investment bank he worked for to start his own asset management firm, Accessible Real Estate. Nagle is trying to build his assets under management and contacts Papis about gaining some of the retirement fund's allocation. In the previous few years, the performance of the retirement fund's real estate investments was in line with the fund's benchmark but was not extraordinary. Papis decides to help out his old friend and also to seek better returns by moving the real estate allocation to Accessible. The only notice of the change in adviser appears in the next annual report in the listing of associated advisers.

> *Comment*: Papis has violated Standard VI(A) by not disclosing to his employer his personal relationship with Nagle. Disclosure of his past history with Nagle would allow his firm to determine whether the conflict may have impaired Papis's independence in deciding to change managers.
>
> See also Standard IV(C)–Responsibilities of Supervisors, Standard V(A)–Diligence and Reasonable Basis, and Standard V(B)–Communication with Clients and Prospective Clients.

Example 11 (Conflict of Interest and Business Relationships):

Bob Wade, trust manager for Central Midas Bank, was approached by Western Funds about promoting its family of funds, with special interest in the service-fee class. To entice Central to promote this class, Western Funds offered to pay the bank a service fee of 0.25%. Without disclosing the fee being offered to the bank, Wade asked one of the investment managers to review the Western Funds family of funds to determine whether they were suitable for clients of Central. The manager completed the normal due diligence review and determined that the funds were fairly valued in the market with fee structures on a par with their competitors. Wade decided to accept Western's offer and instructed the team of portfolio managers to exclusively promote these funds and the service-fee class to clients seeking to invest new funds or transfer from their current investments. So as to not influence the investment managers, Wade did not disclose the fee offer and allowed that income to flow directly to the bank.

> *Comment*: Wade is violating Standard VI(A) by not disclosing the portion of the service fee being paid to Central. Although the investment managers may not be influenced by the fee, neither they nor the client have the proper information about Wade's decision to exclusively market this fund family and class of investments. Central may come to rely on the new fee as a component of the firm's profitability and may be unwilling to offer other products in the future that could affect the fees received.
>
> See also Standard I(B)–Independence and Objectivity.

Example 12 (Disclosure of Conflicts to Employers):

Yehudit Dagan is a portfolio manager for Risk Management Bank (RMB), whose clients include retirement plans and corporations. RMB provides a defined contribution retirement plan for its employees that offers 20 large diversified mutual fund investment options, including a mutual fund managed by Dagan's RMB colleagues. After being employed for six months, Dagan became eligible to participate in the retirement plan, and she intends to allocate her retirement plan assets in six of the investment options, including the fund managed by her RMB colleagues. Dagan is concerned that joining the plan will lead to a potentially significant amount of paperwork for her (e.g., disclosure of her retirement account holdings and needing preclearance for her transactions), especially with her investing in the in-house fund.

> *Comment*: Standard VI(A) would not require Dagan to disclose her personal or retirement investments in large diversified mutual funds, unless specifically required by her employer. For practical reasons, the standard does not require Dagan to gain preclearance for ongoing payroll deduction contributions to retirement plan account investment options.
>
> Dagan should ensure that her firm does not have a specific policy regarding investment—whether personal or in the retirement account—for funds managed by the company's employees. These mutual funds may be subject to the company's disclosure, preclearance, and trading restriction procedures to identify possible conflicts prior to the execution of trades.

Standard VI(B) Priority of Transactions

Investment transactions for clients and employers must have priority over investment transactions in which a Member or Candidate is the beneficial owner.

Guidance

Highlights:

- *Avoiding Potential Conflicts*
- *Personal Trading Secondary to Trading for Clients*
- *Standards for Nonpublic Information*
- *Impact on All Accounts with Beneficial Ownership*

Standard VI(B) reinforces the responsibility of members and candidates to give the interests of their clients and employers priority over their personal financial interests. This standard is designed to prevent any potential conflict of interest or the appearance of a conflict of interest with respect to personal transactions. Client interests have priority. Client transactions must take precedence over transactions made on behalf of the member's or candidate's firm or personal transactions.

Avoiding Potential Conflicts

Conflicts between the client's interest and an investment professional's personal interest may occur. Although conflicts of interest exist, nothing is inherently unethical about individual managers, advisers, or mutual fund employees making money from personal investments as long as (1) the client is not disadvantaged by the trade, (2) the investment professional does not benefit personally from trades undertaken for clients, and (3) the investment professional complies with applicable regulatory requirements.

Some situations occur where a member or candidate may need to enter a personal transaction that runs counter to current recommendations or what the portfolio manager is doing for client portfolios. For example, a member or candidate may be required at some point to sell an asset to make a college tuition payment or a down payment on a home, to meet a margin call, or so on. The sale may be contrary to the long-term advice the member or candidate is currently providing to clients. In these situations, the same three criteria given in the preceding paragraph should be applied in the transaction so as to not violate Standard VI(B).

Personal Trading Secondary to Trading for Clients

Standard VI(B) states that transactions for clients and employers must have priority over transactions in securities or other investments for which a member or candidate is the beneficial owner. The objective of the standard is to prevent personal transactions from adversely affecting the interests of clients or employers. A member or candidate having the same investment positions or being co-invested with clients does not always create a conflict. Some clients in certain investment situations require members or candidates to have aligned interests. Personal investment positions or transactions of members or candidates or their firm should never, however, adversely affect client investments.

Standards for Nonpublic Information

Standard VI(B) covers the activities of members and candidates who have knowledge of pending transactions that may be made on behalf of their clients or employers, who have access to nonpublic information during the normal preparation of research recommendations, or who take investment actions. Members and candidates are prohibited from conveying nonpublic information to any person whose relationship to the member or candidate makes the member or candidate a beneficial owner of the person's securities. Members and candidates must not convey this information to any other person if the nonpublic information can be deemed material.

Impact on All Accounts with Beneficial Ownership

Members or candidates may undertake transactions in accounts for which they are a beneficial owner only after their clients and employers have had adequate opportunity to act on a recommendation. Personal transactions include those made for the member's or candidate's own account, for family (including spouse, children, and other immediate family members) accounts, and for accounts in which the member or candidate has a direct or indirect pecuniary interest, such as a trust or retirement account. Family accounts that are client accounts should be treated like any other firm account and should neither be given special treatment nor be disadvantaged because of the family relationship. If a member or candidate has a beneficial ownership in the account, however, the member or candidate may be subject to preclearance or reporting requirements of the employer or applicable law.

Recommended Procedures for Compliance

Policies and procedures designed to prevent potential conflicts of interest, and even the appearance of a conflict of interest, with respect to personal transactions are critical to establishing investor confidence in the securities industry. Therefore, members and candidates should urge their firms to establish such policies and procedures. Because investment firms vary greatly in assets under management, types of clients, number of employees, and so on, each firm should have policies regarding personal investing that are best suited to the firm. Members and candidates should then prominently disclose these policies to clients and prospective clients.

The specific provisions of each firm's standards will vary, but all firms should adopt certain basic procedures to address the conflict areas created by personal investing. These procedures include the following:

- *Limited participation in equity IPOs*: Some eagerly awaited IPOs rise significantly in value shortly after the issue is brought to market. Because the new issue may be highly attractive and sought after, the opportunity to participate in the IPO may be limited. Therefore, purchases of IPOs by investment personnel create conflicts of interest in two principal ways. First, participation in an IPO may have the appearance of taking away an attractive investment opportunity from clients for personal gain—a clear breach of the duty of loyalty to clients. Second, personal purchases in IPOs may have the appearance that the investment opportunity is being bestowed as an incentive to make future investment decisions for the benefit of the party providing the opportunity. Members and candidates can avoid these conflicts or appearances of conflicts of interest by not participating in IPOs.

  Reliable and systematic review procedures should be established to ensure that conflicts relating to IPOs are identified and appropriately dealt with by supervisors. Members and candidates should preclear their participation in IPOs, even in situations without any conflict of interest between a member's or candidate's participation in an IPO and the client's interests. Members and candidates should not benefit from the position that their clients occupy in the marketplace—through preferred trading, the allocation of limited offerings, or oversubscription.

- *Restrictions on private placements*: Strict limits should be placed on investment personnel acquiring securities in private placements, and appropriate supervisory and review procedures should be established to prevent noncompliance.

  Firms do not routinely use private placements for clients (e.g., venture capital deals) because of the high risk associated with them. Conflicts related to private placements are more significant to members and candidates who manage large pools of assets or act as plan sponsors because these managers may be offered special opportunities, such as private placements, as a reward or an enticement for continuing to do business with a particular broker.

  Participation in private placements raises conflict-of-interest issues that are similar to issues surrounding IPOs. Investment personnel should not be involved in transactions, including (but not limited to) private placements, that could be perceived as favors or gifts that seem designed to influence future judgment or to reward past business deals.

  Whether the venture eventually proves to be good or bad, managers have an immediate conflict concerning private placement opportunities. If and when the investments go public, participants in private placements have an incentive to recommend the investments to clients regardless of the suitability of the investments for their clients. Doing so increases the value of the participants' personal portfolios.

- *Establish blackout/restricted periods*: Investment personnel involved in the investment decision-making process should establish blackout periods prior to trades for clients so that managers cannot take advantage of their knowledge of client activity by "front-running" client trades (trading for one's personal account before trading for client accounts).

  Individual firms must decide who within the firm should be required to comply with the trading restrictions. At a minimum, all individuals who are involved in the investment decision-making process should be subject to the same restricted period. Each firm must determine specific requirements related to blackout and restricted periods that are most relevant to the firm while ensuring that the procedures are governed by the guiding principles set forth in the Code and Standards. Size of firm and type of securities purchased are relevant factors. For example, in a large firm, a blackout requirement is, in effect, a total trading ban because the firm is continually trading in most securities. In a small firm, the blackout period is more likely to prevent the investment manager from front-running.

- *Reporting requirements*: Supervisors should establish reporting procedures for investment personnel, including disclosure of personal holdings/beneficial ownerships, confirmations of trades to the firm and the employee, and preclearance procedures. Once trading restrictions are in place, they must be enforced. The best method for monitoring and enforcing procedures to eliminate conflicts of interest in personal trading is through reporting requirements, including the following:

  - **Disclosure of holdings in which the employee has a beneficial interest.** Disclosure by investment personnel to the firm should be made upon commencement of the employment relationship and at least annually thereafter. To address privacy considerations, disclosure of personal holdings should be handled in a confidential manner by the firm.

- **Providing duplicate confirmations of transactions**. Investment personnel should be required to direct their brokers to supply to firms duplicate copies or confirmations of all their personal securities transactions and copies of periodic statements for all securities accounts. The duplicate confirmation requirement has two purposes: (1) The requirement sends a message that there is independent verification, which reduces the likelihood of unethical behavior, and (2) it enables verification of the accounting of the flow of personal investments that cannot be determined from merely looking at holdings.
- **Preclearance procedures**. Investment personnel should examine all planned personal trades to identify possible conflicts prior to the execution of the trades. Preclearance procedures are designed to identify possible conflicts before a problem arises.

■ *Disclosure of policies*: Members and candidates should fully disclose to investors their firm's policies regarding personal investing. The information about employees' personal investment activities and policies will foster an atmosphere of full and complete disclosure and calm the public's legitimate concerns about the conflicts of interest posed by investment personnel's personal trading. The disclosure must provide helpful information to investors; it should not be simply boilerplate language, such as "investment personnel are subject to policies and procedures regarding their personal trading."

Application of the Standard

Example 1 (Personal Trading):

Research analyst Marlon Long does not recommend purchase of a common stock for his employer's account because he wants to purchase the stock personally and does not want to wait until the recommendation is approved and the stock is purchased by his employer.

> *Comment*: Long has violated Standard VI(B) by taking advantage of his knowledge of the stock's value before allowing his employer to benefit from that information.

Example 2 (Trading for Family Member Account):

Carol Baker, the portfolio manager of an aggressive growth mutual fund, maintains an account in her husband's name at several brokerage firms with which the fund and a number of Baker's other individual clients do a substantial amount of business. Whenever a hot issue becomes available, she instructs the brokers to buy it for her husband's account. Because such issues normally are scarce, Baker often acquires shares in hot issues but her clients are not able to participate in them.

> *Comment*: To avoid violating Standard VI(B), Baker must acquire shares for her mutual fund first and acquire them for her husband's account only after doing so, even though she might miss out on participating in new issues via her husband's account. She also must disclose the trading for her husband's account to her employer because this activity creates a conflict between her personal interests and her employer's interests.

Example 3 (Family Accounts as Equals):

Erin Toffler, a portfolio manager at Esposito Investments, manages the retirement account established with the firm by her parents. Whenever IPOs become available, she first allocates shares to all her other clients for whom the investment is appropriate; only then does she place any remaining portion in her parents' account, if the issue is appropriate for them. She has adopted this procedure so that no one can accuse her of favoring her parents.

> *Comment*: Toffler has violated Standard VI(B) by breaching her duty to her parents by treating them differently from her other accounts simply because of the family relationship. As fee-paying clients of Esposito Investments, Toffler's parents are entitled to the same treatment as any other client of the firm. If Toffler has beneficial ownership in the account, however, and Esposito Investments has preclearance and reporting requirements for personal transactions, she may have to preclear the trades and report the transactions to Esposito.

Example 4 (Personal Trading and Disclosure):

Gary Michaels is an entry-level employee who holds a low-paying job serving both the research department and the investment management department of an active investment management firm. He purchases a sports car and begins to wear expensive clothes after only a year of employment with the firm. The director of the investment management department, who has responsibility for monitoring the personal stock transactions of all employees, investigates and discovers that Michaels has made substantial investment gains by purchasing stocks just before they were put on the firm's recommended "buy" list. Michaels was regularly given the firm's quarterly personal transaction form but declined to complete it.

> *Comment*: Michaels violated Standard VI(B) by placing personal transactions ahead of client transactions. In addition, his supervisor violated Standard IV(C)–Responsibilities of Supervisors by permitting Michaels to continue to perform his assigned tasks without having signed the quarterly personal transaction form. Note also that if Michaels had communicated information about the firm's recommendations to a person who traded the security, that action would be a misappropriation of the information and a violation of Standard II(A)–Material Nonpublic Information.

Example 5 (Trading Prior to Report Dissemination):

A brokerage's insurance analyst, Denise Wilson, makes a closed-circuit TV report to her firm's branches around the country. During the broadcast, she includes negative comments about a major company in the insurance industry. The following day, Wilson's report is printed and distributed to the sales force and public customers. The report recommends that both short-term traders and intermediate investors take profits by selling that insurance company's stock. Seven minutes after the broadcast, however, Ellen Riley, head of the firm's trading department, had closed out a long "call" position in the stock. Shortly thereafter, Riley established a sizable "put" position in the stock. When asked about her activities, Riley claimed she took the actions to facilitate anticipated sales by institutional clients.

> *Comment*: Riley did not give customers an opportunity to buy or sell in the options market before the firm itself did. By taking action before the report was disseminated, Riley's firm may have depressed the price of the calls and increased the price of the puts. The firm could have avoided a conflict

of interest if it had waited to trade for its own account until its clients had an opportunity to receive and assimilate Wilson's recommendations. As it is, Riley's actions violated Standard VI(B).

Standard VI(C) Referral Fees

Members and Candidates must disclose to their employer, clients, and prospective clients, as appropriate, any compensation, consideration, or benefit received from or paid to others for the recommendation of products or services.

Guidance

Standard VI(C) states the responsibility of members and candidates to inform their employer, clients, and prospective clients of any benefit received for referrals of customers and clients. Such disclosures allow clients or employers to evaluate (1) any partiality shown in any recommendation of services and (2) the full cost of the services. Members and candidates must disclose when they pay a fee or provide compensation to others who have referred prospective clients to the member or candidate.

Appropriate disclosure means that members and candidates must advise the client or prospective client, before entry into any formal agreement for services, of any benefit given or received for the recommendation of any services provided by the member or candidate. In addition, the member or candidate must disclose the nature of the consideration or benefit—for example, flat fee or percentage basis, one-time or continuing benefit, based on performance, benefit in the form of provision of research or other noncash benefit—together with the estimated dollar value. Consideration includes all fees, whether paid in cash, in soft dollars, or in kind.

Recommended Procedures for Compliance

Members and candidates should encourage their employers to develop procedures related to referral fees. The firm may completely restrict such fees. If the firm does not adopt a strict prohibition of such fees, the procedures should indicate the appropriate steps for requesting approval.

Employers should have investment professionals provide to the clients notification of approved referral fee programs and provide the employer regular (at least quarterly) updates on the amount and nature of compensation received.

Application of the Standard

Example 1 (Disclosure of Referral Arrangements and Outside Parties):

Brady Securities, Inc., a broker/dealer, has established a referral arrangement with Lewis Brothers, Ltd., an investment counseling firm. In this arrangement, Brady Securities refers all prospective tax-exempt accounts, including pension, profit-sharing, and endowment accounts, to Lewis Brothers. In return, Lewis Brothers makes available to Brady Securities on a regular basis the security recommendations and reports of its research staff, which registered representatives of Brady Securities use in serving customers. In addition, Lewis Brothers conducts monthly economic and market reviews for Brady Securities personnel and directs all stock commission business generated by referral accounts to Brady Securities.

Willard White, a partner in Lewis Brothers, calculates that the incremental costs involved in functioning as the research department of Brady Securities are US$20,000 annually.

Referrals from Brady Securities last year resulted in fee income of US$200,000 for Lewis Brothers, and directing all stock trades through Brady Securities resulted in additional costs to Lewis Brothers' clients of US$10,000.

Diane Branch, the chief financial officer of Maxwell Inc., contacts White and says that she is seeking an investment manager for Maxwell's profit-sharing plan. She adds, "My friend Harold Hill at Brady Securities recommended your firm without qualification, and that's good enough for me. Do we have a deal?" White accepts the new account but does not disclose his firm's referral arrangement with Brady Securities.

> *Comment*: White has violated Standard VI(C) by failing to inform the prospective customer of the referral fee payable in services and commissions for an indefinite period to Brady Securities. Such disclosure could have caused Branch to reassess Hill's recommendation and make a more critical evaluation of Lewis Brothers' services.

Example 2 (Disclosure of Interdepartmental Referral Arrangements):

James Handley works for the trust department of Central Trust Bank. He receives compensation for each referral he makes to Central Trust's brokerage department and personal financial management department that results in a sale. He refers several of his clients to the personal financial management department but does not disclose the arrangement within Central Trust to his clients.

> *Comment*: Handley has violated Standard VI(C) by not disclosing the referral arrangement at Central Trust Bank to his clients. Standard VI(C) does not distinguish between referral payments paid by a third party for referring clients to the third party and internal payments paid within the firm to attract new business to a subsidiary. Members and candidates must disclose all such referral fees. Therefore, Handley is required to disclose, at the time of referral, any referral fee agreement in place among Central Trust Bank's departments. The disclosure should include the nature and the value of the benefit and should be made in writing.

Example 3 (Disclosure of Referral Arrangements and Informing Firm):

Katherine Roberts is a portfolio manager at Katama Investments, an advisory firm specializing in managing assets for high-net-worth individuals. Katama's trading desk uses a variety of brokerage houses to execute trades on behalf of its clients. Roberts asks the trading desk to direct a large portion of its commissions to Naushon, Inc., a small broker/dealer run by one of Roberts' business school classmates. Katama's traders have found that Naushon is not very competitive on pricing, and although Naushon generates some research for its trading clients, Katama's other analysts have found most of Naushon's research to be not especially useful. Nevertheless, the traders do as Roberts asks, and in return for receiving a large portion of Katama's business, Naushon recommends the investment services of Roberts and Katama to its wealthiest clients. This arrangement is not disclosed to either Katama or the clients referred by Naushon.

> *Comment*: Roberts is violating Standard VI(C) by failing to inform her employer of the referral arrangement.

Example 4 (Disclosure of Referral Arrangements and Outside Organizations):

Alex Burl is a portfolio manager at Helpful Investments, a local investment advisory firm. Burl is on the advisory board of his child's school, which is looking for ways to raise money to purchase new playground equipment for the school. Burl discusses a plan with his supervisor in which he will donate to the school a portion of his service fee from new clients referred by the parents of students at the school. Upon getting the approval from Helpful, Burl presents the idea to the school's advisory board and directors. The school agrees to announce the program at the next parent event and asks Burl to provide the appropriate written materials to be distributed. A week following the distribution of the flyers, Burl receives the first school-related referral. In establishing the client's investment policy statement, Burl clearly discusses the school's referral and outlines the plans for distributing the donation back to the school.

> *Comment*: Burl has not violated Standard VI(C) because he secured the permission of his employer, Helpful Investments, and the school prior to beginning the program and because he discussed the arrangement with the client at the time the investment policy statement was designed.

Example 5 (Disclosure of Referral Arrangements and Outside Parties):

The sponsor of a state employee pension is seeking to hire a firm to manage the pension plan's emerging market allocation. To assist in the review process, the sponsor has hired Thomas Arrow as a consultant to solicit proposals from various advisers. Arrow is contracted by the sponsor to represent its best interest in selecting the most appropriate new manager. The process runs smoothly, and Overseas Investments is selected as the new manager.

The following year, news breaks that Arrow is under investigation by the local regulator for accepting kickbacks from investment managers after they are awarded new pension allocations. Overseas Investments is included in the list of firms allegedly making these payments. Although the sponsor is happy with the performance of Overseas since it has been managing the pension plan's emerging market funds, the sponsor still decides to have an independent review of the proposals and the selection process to ensure that Overseas was the appropriate firm for its needs. This review confirms that, even though Arrow was being paid by both parties, the recommendation of Overseas appeared to be objective and appropriate.

> *Comment*: Arrow has violated Standard VI(C) because he did not disclose the fee being paid by Overseas. Withholding this information raises the question of a potential lack of objectivity in the recommendation of Overseas by Arrow; this aspect is in addition to questions about the legality of having firms pay to be considered for an allocation.
>
> Regulators and governmental agencies may adopt requirements concerning allowable consultant activities. Local regulations sometimes include having a consultant register with the regulatory agency's ethics board. Regulator policies may include a prohibition on acceptance of payments from investment managers receiving allocations and require regular reporting of contributions made to political organizations and candidates. Arrow would have to adhere to these requirements as well as the Code and Standards.

STANDARD VII: RESPONSIBILITIES AS A CFA INSTITUTE MEMBER OR CFA CANDIDATE

Standard VII(A) Conduct as Participants in CFA Institute Programs

Members and Candidates must not engage in any conduct that compromises the reputation or integrity of CFA Institute or the CFA designation or the integrity, validity, or security of CFA Institute programs.

Guidance

Highlights:

- *Confidential Program Information*
- *Additional CFA Program Restrictions*
- *Expressing an Opinion*

Standard VII(A) covers the conduct of CFA Institute members and candidates involved with the CFA Program and prohibits any conduct that undermines the public's confidence that the CFA charter represents a level of achievement based on merit and ethical conduct. There is an array of CFA Institute programs beyond the CFA Program that provide additional educational and credentialing opportunities, including the Certificate in Investment Performance Measurement (CIPM) Program and the CFA Institute Investment Foundations™ Program. The standard's function is to hold members and candidates to a high ethical criterion while they are participating in or involved with any CFA Institute program. Conduct covered includes but is not limited to

- giving or receiving assistance (cheating) on any CFA Institute examinations;
- violating the rules, regulations, and testing policies of CFA Institute programs;
- providing confidential program or exam information to candidates or the public;
- disregarding or attempting to circumvent security measures established for any CFA Institute examinations;
- improperly using an association with CFA Institute to further personal or professional goals; and
- misrepresenting information on the Professional Conduct Statement or in the CFA Institute Continuing Education Program.

Confidential Program Information

CFA Institute is vigilant about protecting the integrity of CFA Institute programs' content and examination processes. CFA Institute program rules, regulations, and policies prohibit candidates from disclosing confidential material gained during the exam process.

Examples of information that cannot be disclosed by candidates sitting for an exam include but are not limited to

- specific details of questions appearing on the exam and
- broad topical areas and formulas tested or not tested on the exam.

All aspects of the exam, including questions, broad topical areas, and formulas, tested or not tested, are considered confidential until such time as CFA Institute elects to release them publicly. This confidentiality requirement allows CFA Institute to maintain the integrity and rigor of exams for future candidates. Standard VII(A) does not prohibit candidates from discussing nonconfidential information or curriculum material with others or in study groups in preparation for the exam.

Candidates increasingly use online forums and new technology as part of their exam preparations. CFA Institute actively polices blogs, forums, and related social networking groups for information considered confidential. The organization works with both individual candidates and the sponsors of online or offline services to promptly remove any and all violations. As noted in the discussion of Standard I(A)–Knowledge of the Law, candidates, members, and the public are encouraged to report suspected violations to CFA Institute.

Additional CFA Program Restrictions

The CFA Program rules, regulations, and policies define additional allowed and disallowed actions concerning the exams. Violating any of the testing policies, such as the calculator policy, personal belongings policy, or the Candidate Pledge, constitutes a violation of Standard VII(A). Candidates will find all of these policies on the CFA Program portion of the CFA Institute website (www.cfainstitute.org). Exhibit 2 provides the Candidate Pledge, which highlights the respect candidates must have for the integrity, validity, and security of the CFA exam.

Members may participate as volunteers in various aspects of the CFA Program. Standard VII(A) prohibits members from disclosing and/or soliciting confidential material gained prior to or during the exam and grading processes with those outside the CFA exam development process.

Examples of information that cannot be shared by members involved in developing, administering, or grading the exams include but are not limited to

- questions appearing on the exam or under consideration,
- deliberation related to the exam process, and
- information related to the scoring of questions.

Members may also be asked to offer assistance with other CFA Institute programs, including but not limited to the CIPM and Investment Foundations programs. Members participating in any CFA Institute program should do so with the same level of integrity and confidentiality as is required of participation in the CFA Program.

Expressing an Opinion

Standard VII(A) does *not* cover expressing opinions regarding CFA Institute, the CFA Program, or other CFA Institute programs. Members and candidates are free to disagree and express their disagreement with CFA Institute on its policies, its procedures, or any advocacy positions taken by the organization. When expressing a personal opinion, a candidate is prohibited from disclosing content-specific information, including any actual exam question and the information as to subject matter covered or not covered in the exam.

Exhibit 2 Sample of CFA Program Testing Policies

Candidate Pledge	As a candidate in the CFA Program, I am obligated to follow Standard VII(A) of the CFA Institute Standards of Professional Conduct, which states that members and candidates must not engage in any conduct that compromises the reputation or integrity of CFA Institute or the CFA designation or the integrity, validity, or security of the CFA exam. ■ Prior to this exam, I have not given or received information regarding the content of this exam. During this exam, I will not give or receive any information regarding the content of this exam. ■ After this exam, I will not disclose **ANY** portion of this exam and I will not remove **ANY** exam materials from the testing room in original or copied form. I understand that all exam materials, including my answers, are the property of CFA Institute and will not be returned to me in any form. ■ I will follow **ALL** rules of the CFA Program as stated on the CFA Institute website and the back cover of the exam book. My violation of any rules of the CFA Program will result in CFA Institute voiding my exam results and may lead to suspension or termination of my candidacy in the CFA Program.

Application of the Standard

Example 1 (Sharing Exam Questions):

Travis Nero serves as a proctor for the administration of the CFA examination in his city. In the course of his service, he reviews a copy of the Level II exam on the evening prior to the exam's administration and provides information concerning the exam questions to two candidates who use it to prepare for the exam.

> *Comment*: Nero and the two candidates have violated Standard VII(A). By giving information about the exam questions to two candidates, Nero provided an unfair advantage to the two candidates and undermined the integrity and validity of the Level II exam as an accurate measure of the knowledge, skills, and abilities necessary to earn the right to use the CFA designation. By accepting the information, the candidates also compromised the integrity and validity of the Level II exam and undermined the ethical framework that is a key part of the designation.

Example 2 (Bringing Written Material into Exam Room):

Loren Sullivan is enrolled to take the Level II CFA examination. He has been having difficulty remembering a particular formula, so prior to entering the exam room, he writes the formula on the palm of his hand. During the afternoon section of the exam, a proctor notices Sullivan looking at the palm of his hand. She asks to see his hand and finds the formula.

> *Comment*: Because Sullivan wrote down information from the Candidate Body of Knowledge (CBOK) and took that written information into the exam room, his conduct compromised the validity of his exam performance and violated Standard VII(A). Sullivan's conduct was also in direct contradiction with the rules and regulations of the CFA Program, the Candidate Pledge, and the CFA Institute Code and Standards.

Example 3 (Writing after Exam Period End):

At the conclusion of the morning section of the Level I CFA examination, the proctors announce, "Stop writing now." John Davis has not completed the exam, so he continues to randomly fill in ovals on his answer sheet. A proctor approaches Davis's desk and reminds him that he should stop writing immediately. Davis, however, continues to complete the answer sheet. After the proctor asks him to stop writing two additional times, Davis finally puts down his pencil.

> *Comment*: By continuing to complete his exam after time was called, Davis has violated Standard VII(A). By continuing to write, Davis took an unfair advantage over other candidates, and his conduct compromised the validity of his exam performance. Additionally, by not heeding the proctor's repeated instructions, Davis violated the rules and regulations of the CFA Program.

Example 4 (Sharing Exam Content):

After completing Level II of the CFA exam, Annabelle Rossi posts on her blog about her experience. She posts the following: "Level II is complete! I think I did fairly well on the exam. It was really difficult, but fair. I think I did especially well on the derivatives questions. And there were tons of them! I think I counted 18! The ethics questions were really hard. I'm glad I spent so much time on the Code and Standards. I was surprised to see there were no questions at all about IPO allocations. I expected there to be a couple. Well, off to celebrate getting through it. See you tonight?"

> *Comment*: Rossi did not violate Standard VII(A) when she wrote about how difficult she found the exam or how well she thinks she may have done. By revealing portions of the CBOK covered on the exam and areas not covered, however, she did violate Standard VII(A) and the Candidate Pledge. Depending on the time frame in which the comments were posted, Rossi not only may have assisted future candidates but also may have provided an unfair advantage to candidates yet to sit for the same exam, thereby undermining the integrity and validity of the Level II exam.

Example 5 (Sharing Exam Content):

Level I candidate Etienne Gagne has been a frequent visitor to an internet forum designed specifically for CFA Program candidates. The week after completing the Level I examination, Gagne and several others begin a discussion thread on the forum about the most challenging questions and attempt to determine the correct answers.

> *Comment*: Gagne has violated Standard VII(A) by providing and soliciting confidential exam information, which compromises the integrity of the exam process and violates the Candidate Pledge. In trying to determine correct answers to specific questions, the group's discussion included question-specific details considered to be confidential to the CFA Program.

Example 6 (Sharing Exam Content):

CFA4Sure is a company that produces test-preparation materials for CFA Program candidates. Many candidates register for and use the company's products. The day after the CFA examination, CFA4Sure sends an e-mail to all its customers asking them to share with the company the hardest questions from the exam so that CFA4Sure can better prepare its customers for the next exam administration. Marisol Pena e-mails a summary of the questions she found most difficult on the exam.

Comment: Pena has violated Standard VII(A) by disclosing a portion of the exam questions. The information provided is considered confidential until publicly released by CFA Institute. CFA4Sure is likely to use such feedback to refine its review materials for future candidates. Pena's sharing of the specific questions undermines the integrity of the exam while potentially making the exam easier for future candidates.

If the CFA4Sure employees who participated in the solicitation of confidential CFA Program information are CFA Institute members or candidates, they also have violated Standard VII(A).

Example 7 (Discussion of Exam Grading Guidelines and Results):

Prior to participating in grading CFA examinations, Wesley Whitcomb is required to sign a CFA Institute Grader Agreement. As part of the Grader Agreement, Whitcomb agrees not to reveal or discuss the exam materials with anyone except CFA Institute staff or other graders. Several weeks after the conclusion of the CFA exam grading, Whitcomb tells several colleagues who are candidates in the CFA Program which question he graded. He also discusses the guideline answer and adds that few candidates scored well on the question.

Comment: Whitcomb violated Standard VII(A) by breaking the Grader Agreement and disclosing information related to a specific question on the exam, which compromised the integrity of the exam process.

Example 8 (Compromising CFA Institute Integrity as a Volunteer):

Jose Ramirez is an investor-relations consultant for several small companies that are seeking greater exposure to investors. He is also the program chair for the CFA Institute society in the city where he works. Ramirez schedules only companies that are his clients to make presentations to the society and excludes other companies.

Comment: Ramirez, by using his volunteer position at CFA Institute to benefit himself and his clients, compromises the reputation and integrity of CFA Institute and thus violates Standard VII(A).

Example 9 (Compromising CFA Institute Integrity as a Volunteer):

Marguerite Warrenski is a member of the CFA Institute GIPS Executive Committee, which oversees the creation, implementation, and revision of the GIPS standards. As a member of the Executive Committee, she has advance knowledge of confidential information regarding the GIPS standards, including any new or revised standards the committee is considering. She tells her clients that her Executive Committee membership will allow her to better assist her clients in keeping up with changes to the Standards and facilitating their compliance with the changes.

Comment: Warrenski is using her association with the GIPS Executive Committee to promote her firm's services to clients and potential clients. In defining her volunteer position at CFA Institute as a strategic business advantage over competing firms and implying to clients that she would use confidential information to further their interests, Warrenski is compromising the reputation and integrity of CFA Institute and thus violating Standard VII(A). She may factually state her involvement with the Executive Committee but cannot infer any special advantage to her clients from such participation.

Standard VII(B) Reference to CFA Institute, the CFA Designation, and the CFA Program

When referring to CFA Institute, CFA Institute membership, the CFA designation, or candidacy in the CFA Program, Members and Candidates must not misrepresent or exaggerate the meaning or implications of membership in CFA Institute, holding the CFA designation, or candidacy in the CFA Program.

Guidance

Highlights:

- *CFA Institute Membership*
- *Using the CFA Designation*
- *Referring to Candidacy in the CFA Program*

Standard VII(B) is intended to prevent promotional efforts that make promises or guarantees that are tied to the CFA designation. Individuals must not exaggerate the meaning or implications of membership in CFA Institute, holding the CFA designation, or candidacy in the CFA Program.

Standard VII(B) is not intended to prohibit factual statements related to the positive benefit of earning the CFA designation. However, statements referring to CFA Institute, the CFA designation, or the CFA Program that overstate the competency of an individual or imply, either directly or indirectly, that superior performance can be expected from someone with the CFA designation are not allowed under the standard.

Statements that highlight or emphasize the commitment of CFA Institute members, CFA charterholders, and CFA candidates to ethical and professional conduct or mention the thoroughness and rigor of the CFA Program are appropriate. Members and candidates may make claims about the relative merits of CFA Institute, the CFA Program, or the Code and Standards as long as those statements are implicitly or explicitly stated as the opinion of the speaker. Statements that do not express opinions have to be supported by facts.

Standard VII(B) applies to any form of communication, including but not limited to communications made in electronic or written form (such as on firm letterhead, business cards, professional biographies, directory listings, printed advertising, firm brochures, or personal resumes) and oral statements made to the public, clients, or prospects.

CFA Institute Membership

The term "CFA Institute member" refers to "regular" and "affiliate" members of CFA Institute who have met the membership requirements as defined in the CFA Institute Bylaws. Once accepted as a CFA Institute member, the member must satisfy the following requirements to maintain his or her status:

- remit annually to CFA Institute a completed Professional Conduct Statement, which renews the commitment to abide by the requirements of the Code and Standards and the CFA Institute Professional Conduct Program, and
- pay applicable CFA Institute membership dues on an annual basis.

If a CFA Institute member fails to meet any of these requirements, the individual is no longer considered an active member. Until membership is reactivated, individuals must not present themselves to others as active members. They may state, however, that they were CFA Institute members in the past or refer to the years when their membership was active.

Using the CFA Designation

Those who have earned the right to use the Chartered Financial Analyst designation are encouraged to do so but only in a manner that does not misrepresent or exaggerate the meaning or implications of the designation. The use of the designation may be accompanied by an accurate explanation of the requirements that have been met to earn the right to use the designation.

"CFA charterholders" are those individuals who have earned the right to use the CFA designation granted by CFA Institute. These people have satisfied certain requirements, including completion of the CFA Program and required years of acceptable work experience. Once granted the right to use the designation, individuals must also satisfy the CFA Institute membership requirements (see above) to maintain their right to use the designation.

If a CFA charterholder fails to meet any of the membership requirements, he or she forfeits the right to use the CFA designation. Until membership is reactivated, individuals must not present themselves to others as CFA charterholders. They may state, however, that they were charterholders in the past.

Given the growing popularity of social media, where individuals may anonymously express their opinions, pseudonyms or online profile names created to hide a member's identity should not be tagged with the CFA designation.

Use of the CFA designation by a CFA charterholder is governed by the terms and conditions of the annual Professional Conduct Statement Agreement, entered into between CFA Institute and its membership prior to commencement of use of the CFA designation and reaffirmed annually.

Referring to Candidacy in the CFA Program

Candidates in the CFA Program may refer to their participation in the CFA Program, but such references must clearly state that an individual is a *candidate* in the CFA Program and must not imply that the candidate has achieved any type of partial designation. A person is a candidate in the CFA Program if

- the person's application for registration in the CFA Program has been accepted by CFA Institute, as evidenced by issuance of a notice of acceptance, and the person is enrolled to sit for a specified examination or
- the registered person has sat for a specified examination but exam results have not yet been received.

If an individual is registered for the CFA Program but declines to sit for an exam or otherwise does not meet the definition of a candidate as described in the CFA Institute Bylaws, then that individual is no longer considered an active candidate. Once the person is enrolled to sit for a future examination, his or her CFA Program candidacy resumes.

CFA Program candidates must never state or imply that they have a partial designation as a result of passing one or more levels or cite an expected completion date of any level of the CFA Program. Final award of the charter is subject to meeting the CFA Program requirements and approval by the CFA Institute Board of Governors.

If a candidate passes each level of the exam in consecutive years and wants to state that he or she did so, that is not a violation of Standard VII(B) because it is a statement of fact. If the candidate then goes on to claim or imply superior ability by obtaining the designation in only three years, however, he or she is in violation of Standard VII(B).

Exhibit 3 provides examples of proper and improper references to the CFA designation.

Exhibit 3 Proper and Improper References to the CFA Designation

Proper References	Improper References
"Completion of the CFA Program has enhanced my portfolio management skills."	"CFA charterholders achieve better performance results."
"John Smith passed all three CFA Program examinations in three consecutive years."	"John Smith is among the elite, having passed all three CFA examinations in three consecutive attempts."
"The CFA designation is globally recognized and attests to a charterholder's success in a rigorous and comprehensive study program in the field of investment management and research analysis."	"As a CFA charterholder, I am the most qualified to manage client investments."
"The credibility that the CFA designation affords and the skills the CFA Program cultivates are key assets for my future career development."	"As a CFA charterholder, Jane White provides the best value in trade execution."
"I enrolled in the CFA Program to obtain the highest set of credentials in the global investment management industry."	"Enrolling as a candidate in the CFA Program ensures one of becoming better at valuing debt securities."
"I passed Level I of the CFA Program."	"CFA, Level II"
"I am a 2010 Level III candidate in the CFA Program."	"CFA, Expected 2011"
"I passed all three levels of the CFA Program and may be eligible for the CFA charter upon completion of the required work experience."	"CFA, Expected 2011" "John Smith, Charter Pending"

Recommended Procedures for Compliance

Misuse of a member's CFA designation or CFA candidacy or improper reference to it is common by those in a member's or candidate's firm who do not possess knowledge of the requirements of Standard VII(B). As an appropriate step to reduce this risk, members and candidates should disseminate written information about Standard VII(B) and the accompanying guidance to their firm's legal, compliance, public relations, and marketing departments (see www.cfainstitute.org).

For materials that refer to employees' affiliation with CFA Institute, members and candidates should encourage their firms to create templates that are approved by a central authority (such as the compliance department) as being consistent with Standard VII(B). This practice promotes consistency and accuracy in the firm of references to CFA Institute membership, the CFA designation, and CFA candidacy.

Application of the Standard

Example 1 (Passing Exams in Consecutive Years):

An advertisement for AZ Investment Advisors states that all the firm's principals are CFA charterholders and all passed the three examinations on their first attempt. The advertisement prominently links this fact to the notion that AZ's mutual funds have achieved superior performance.

> *Comment*: AZ may state that all principals passed the three examinations on the first try as long as this statement is true, but it must not be linked to performance or imply superior ability. Implying that (1) CFA charterholders achieve better investment results and (2) those who pass the exams on the first try may be more successful than those who do not violates Standard VII(B).

Example 2 (Right to Use CFA Designation):

Five years after receiving his CFA charter, Louis Vasseur resigns his position as an investment analyst and spends the next two years traveling abroad. Because he is not actively engaged in the investment profession, he does not file a completed Professional Conduct Statement with CFA Institute and does not pay his CFA Institute membership dues. At the conclusion of his travels, Vasseur becomes a self-employed analyst accepting assignments as an independent contractor. Without reinstating his CFA Institute membership by filing his Professional Conduct Statement and paying his dues, he prints business cards that display "CFA" after his name.

> *Comment*: Vasseur has violated Standard VII(B) because his right to use the CFA designation was suspended when he failed to file his Professional Conduct Statement and stopped paying dues. Therefore, he no longer is able to state or imply that he is an active CFA charterholder. When Vasseur files his Professional Conduct Statement, resumes paying CFA Institute dues to activate his membership, and completes the CFA Institute reinstatement procedures, he will be eligible to use the CFA designation.

Example 3 ("Retired" CFA Institute Membership Status):

After a 25-year career, James Simpson retires from his firm. Because he is not actively engaged in the investment profession, he does not file a completed Professional Conduct Statement with CFA Institute and does not pay his CFA Institute membership dues. Simpson designs a plain business card (without a corporate logo) to hand out to friends with his new contact details, and he continues to put "CFA" after his name.

> *Comment*: Simpson has violated Standard VII(B). Because he failed to file his Professional Conduct Statement and ceased paying dues, his membership has been suspended and he has given up the right to use the CFA designation. CFA Institute has procedures, however, for reclassifying a member and charterholder as "retired" and reducing the annual dues. If he wants to obtain retired status, he needs to file the appropriate paperwork with CFA Institute. When Simpson receives his notification from CFA Institute that his membership has been reclassified as retired and he resumes paying reduced dues, his membership will be reactivated and his right to use the CFA designation will be reinstated.

Example 4 (Stating Facts about CFA Designation and Program):

Rhonda Reese has been a CFA charterholder since 2000. In a conversation with a friend who is considering enrolling in the CFA Program, she states that she has learned a great deal from the CFA Program and that many firms require their employees to be CFA charterholders. She would recommend the CFA Program to anyone pursuing a career in investment management.

> *Comment*: Reese's comments comply with Standard VII(B). Her statements refer to facts: The CFA Program enhanced her knowledge, and many firms require the CFA designation for their investment professionals.

Example 5 (Order of Professional and Academic Designations):

Tatiana Prittima has earned both her CFA designation and a PhD in finance. She would like to cite both her accomplishments on her business card but is unsure of the proper method for doing so.

> *Comment*: The order of designations cited on such items as resumes and business cards is a matter of personal preference. Prittima is free to cite the CFA designation either before or after citing her PhD. Multiple designations must be separated by a comma.

Example 6 (Use of Fictitious Name):

Barry Glass is the lead quantitative analyst at CityCenter Hedge Fund. Glass is responsible for the development, maintenance, and enhancement of the proprietary models the fund uses to manage its investors' assets. Glass reads several high-level mathematical publications and blogs to stay informed on current developments. One blog, run by Expert CFA, presents some intriguing research that may benefit one of CityCenter's current models. Glass is under pressure from firm executives to improve the model's predictive abilities, and he incorporates the factors discussed in the online research. The updated output recommends several new investments to the fund's portfolio managers.

> *Comment*: "Expert CFA" has violated Standard VII(B) by using the CFA designation inappropriately. As with any research report, authorship of online comments must include the charterholder's full name along with any reference to the CFA designation.
>
> See also Standard V(A), which Glass has violated for guidance on diligence and reasonable basis.

PRACTICE PROBLEMS

Unless otherwise stated in the question, all individuals in the following questions are CFA Institute members or candidates in the CFA Program and, therefore, are subject to the CFA Institute Code of Ethics and Standards of Professional Conduct.

1 Smith, a research analyst with a brokerage firm, decides to change his recommendation for the common stock of Green Company, Inc., from a "buy" to a "sell." He mails this change in investment advice to all the firm's clients on Wednesday. The day after the mailing, a client calls with a buy order for 500 shares of Green Company. In this circumstance, Smith should:

A Accept the order.

B Advise the customer of the change in recommendation before accepting the order.

C Not accept the order because it is contrary to the firm's recommendation.

2 Which statement about a manager's use of client brokerage commissions violates the Code and Standards?

A A client may direct a manager to use that client's brokerage commissions to purchase goods and services for that client.

B Client brokerage commissions should be used to benefit the client and should be commensurate with the value of the brokerage and research services received.

C Client brokerage commissions may be directed to pay for the investment manager's operating expenses.

3 Jamison is a junior research analyst with Howard & Howard, a brokerage and investment banking firm. Howard & Howard's mergers and acquisitions department has represented the Britland Company in all of its acquisitions for the past 20 years. Two of Howard & Howard's senior officers are directors of various Britland subsidiaries. Jamison has been asked to write a research report on Britland. What is the best course of action for her to follow?

A Jamison may write the report but must refrain from expressing any opinions because of the special relationships between the two companies.

B Jamison should not write the report because the two Howard & Howard officers serve as directors for subsidiaries of Britland.

C Jamison may write the report if she discloses the special relationships with the company in the report.

4 Which of the following statements clearly *conflicts* with the recommended procedures for compliance presented in the CFA Institute *Standards of Practice Handbook*?

A Firms should disclose to clients the personal investing policies and procedures established for their employees.

B Prior approval must be obtained for the personal investment transactions of all employees.

C For confidentiality reasons, personal transactions and holdings should not be reported to employers unless mandated by regulatory organizations.

5 Bronson provides investment advice to the board of trustees of a private university endowment fund. The trustees have provided Bronson with the fund's financial information, including planned expenditures. Bronson receives a

phone call on Friday afternoon from Murdock, a prominent alumnus, requesting that Bronson fax him comprehensive financial information about the fund. According to Murdock, he has a potential contributor but needs the information that day to close the deal and cannot contact any of the trustees. Based on the CFA Institute Standards, Bronson should:

A Send Murdock the information because disclosure would benefit the client.

B Not send Murdock the information to preserve confidentiality.

C Send Murdock the information, provided Bronson promptly notifies the trustees.

6 Willier is the research analyst responsible for following Company X. All the information he has accumulated and documented suggests that the outlook for the company's new products is poor, so the stock should be rated a weak "hold." During lunch, however, Willier overhears a financial analyst from another firm whom he respects offer opinions that conflict with Willier's forecasts and expectations. Upon returning to his office, Willier releases a strong "buy" recommendation to the public. Willier:

A Violated the Standards by failing to distinguish between facts and opinions in his recommendation.

B Violated the Standards because he did not have a reasonable and adequate basis for his recommendation.

C Was in full compliance with the Standards.

7 An investment management firm has been hired by ETV Corporation to work on an additional public offering for the company. The firm's brokerage unit now has a "sell" recommendation on ETV, but the head of the investment banking department has asked the head of the brokerage unit to change the recommendation from "sell" to "buy." According to the Standards, the head of the brokerage unit would be permitted to:

A Increase the recommendation by no more than one increment (in this case, to a "hold" recommendation).

B Place the company on a restricted list and give only factual information about the company.

C Assign a new analyst to decide if the stock deserves a higher rating.

8 Albert and Tye, who recently started their own investment advisory business, have registered to take the Level III CFA examination. Albert's business card reads, "Judy Albert, CFA Level II." Tye has not put anything about the CFA designation on his business card, but promotional material that he designed for the business describes the CFA requirements and indicates that Tye participates in the CFA Program and has completed Levels I and II. According to the Standards:

A Albert has violated the Standards, but Tye has not.

B Tye has violated the Standards, but Albert has not.

C Both Albert and Tye have violated the Standards.

9 Scott works for a regional brokerage firm. He estimates that Walkton Industries will increase its dividend by US$1.50 a share during the next year. He realizes that this increase is contingent on pending legislation that would, if enacted, give Walkton a substantial tax break. The US representative for Walkton's home district has told Scott that, although she is lobbying hard for the bill and prospects for its passage are favorable, concern of the US Congress over the federal deficit could cause the tax bill to be voted down. Walkton Industries has not made any statements about a change in dividend policy. Scott writes in his research report, "We expect Walkton's stock price to rise by at least US$8.00 a share by the end of the year because the dividend will increase by US$1.50 a share. Investors buying the stock at the current time should expect to realize a total return of at least 15% on the stock." According to the Standards:

A Scott violated the Standards because he used material inside information.

B Scott violated the Standards because he failed to separate opinion from fact.

C Scott violated the Standards by basing his research on uncertain predictions of future government action.

10 Which one of the following actions will help to ensure the fair treatment of brokerage firm clients when a new investment recommendation is made?

A Informing all people in the firm in advance that a recommendation is to be disseminated.

B Distributing recommendations to institutional clients prior to individual accounts.

C Minimizing the time between the decision and the dissemination of a recommendation.

11 The mosaic theory holds that an analyst:

A Violates the Code and Standards if the analyst fails to have knowledge of and comply with applicable laws.

B Can use material public information and nonmaterial nonpublic information in the analyst's analysis.

C Should use all available and relevant information in support of an investment recommendation.

12 Jurgen is a portfolio manager. One of her firm's clients has told Jurgen that he will compensate her beyond the compensation provided by her firm on the basis of the capital appreciation of his portfolio each year. Jurgen should:

A Turn down the additional compensation because it will result in conflicts with the interests of other clients' accounts.

B Turn down the additional compensation because it will create undue pressure on her to achieve strong short-term performance.

C Obtain permission from her employer prior to accepting the compensation arrangement.

13 One of the discretionary accounts managed by Farnsworth is the Jones Corporation employee profit-sharing plan. Jones, the company president, recently asked Farnsworth to vote the shares in the profit-sharing plan in favor of the slate of directors nominated by Jones Corporation and against the directors sponsored by a dissident stockholder group. Farnsworth does not want to lose this account because he directs all the account's trades to a brokerage firm that provides Farnsworth with useful information about tax-free investments. Although this information is not of value in managing the Jones Corporation account, it does help in managing several other accounts. The brokerage firm providing this information also offers the lowest commissions for trades and provides best execution. Farnsworth investigates the director issue, concludes that the management-nominated slate is better for the long-run performance of the company than the dissident group's slate, and votes accordingly. Farnsworth:

A Violated the Standards in voting the shares in the manner requested by Jones but not in directing trades to the brokerage firm.

B Did not violate the Standards in voting the shares in the manner requested by Jones or in directing trades to the brokerage firm.

C Violated the Standards in directing trades to the brokerage firm but not in voting the shares as requested by Jones.

14 Brown works for an investment counseling firm. Green, a new client of the firm, is meeting with Brown for the first time. Green used another counseling firm for financial advice for years, but she has switched her account to Brown's firm. After spending a few minutes getting acquainted, Brown explains to Green that she has discovered a highly undervalued stock that offers large potential gains. She recommends that Green purchase the stock. Brown has committed a violation of the Standards. What should she have done differently?

A Brown should have determined Green's needs, objectives, and tolerance for risk before making a recommendation of any type of security.

B Brown should have thoroughly explained the characteristics of the company to Green, including the characteristics of the industry in which the company operates.

C Brown should have explained her qualifications, including her education, training, and experience and the meaning of the CFA designation.

15 Grey recommends the purchase of a mutual fund that invests solely in long-term US Treasury bonds. He makes the following statements to his clients:

I. "The payment of the bonds is guaranteed by the US government; therefore, the default risk of the bonds is virtually zero."

II. "If you invest in the mutual fund, you will earn a 10% rate of return each year for the next several years based on historical performance of the market."

Did Grey's statements violate the CFA Institute Code and Standards?

A Neither statement violated the Code and Standards.

B Only statement I violated the Code and Standards.

C Only statement II violated the Code and Standards.

16 Anderb, a portfolio manager for XYZ Investment Management Company—a registered investment organization that advises investment firms and private accounts—was promoted to that position three years ago. Bates, her supervisor, is responsible for reviewing Anderb's portfolio account transactions and her required monthly reports of personal stock transactions. Anderb has been using Jonelli, a broker, almost exclusively for brokerage transactions for the portfolio account. For securities in which Jonelli's firm makes a market, Jonelli has been giving Anderb lower prices for personal purchases and higher prices for personal sales than Jonelli gives to Anderb's portfolio accounts and other investors. Anderb has been filing monthly reports with Bates only for those months in which she has no personal transactions, which is about every fourth month. Which of the following is *most likely* to be a violation of the Code and Standards?

A Anderb failed to disclose to her employer her personal transactions.

B Anderb owned the same securities as those of her clients.

C Bates allowed Anderb to use Jonelli as her broker for personal trades.

17 Which of the following is a correct statement of a member's or candidate's duty under the Code and Standards?

A In the absence of specific applicable law or other regulatory requirements, the Code and Standards govern the member's or candidate's actions.

B A member or candidate is required to comply only with applicable local laws, rules, regulations, or customs, even though the Code and Standards may impose a higher degree of responsibility or a higher duty on the member or candidate.

C A member or candidate who trades securities in a securities market where no applicable local laws or stock exchange rules regulate the use of material nonpublic information may take investment action based on material nonpublic information.

18 Ward is scheduled to visit the corporate headquarters of Evans Industries. Ward expects to use the information he obtains there to complete his research report on Evans stock. Ward learns that Evans plans to pay all of Ward's expenses for the trip, including costs of meals, hotel room, and air transportation. Which of the following actions would be the *best* course for Ward to take under the Code and Standards?

A Accept the expense-paid trip and write an objective report.

B Pay for all travel expenses, including costs of meals and incidental items.

C Accept the expense-paid trip but disclose the value of the services accepted in the report.

19 Which of the following statements is *correct* under the Code and Standards?

A CFA Institute members and candidates are prohibited from undertaking independent practice in competition with their employer.

B Written consent from the employer is necessary to permit independent practice that could result in compensation or other benefits in competition with a member's or candidate's employer.

C Members and candidates are prohibited from making arrangements or preparations to go into a competitive business before terminating their relationship with their employer.

20 Smith is a financial analyst with XYZ Brokerage Firm. She is preparing a purchase recommendation on JNI Corporation. Which of the following situations is *most likely* to represent a conflict of interest for Smith that would have to be disclosed?

A Smith frequently purchases items produced by JNI.

B XYZ holds for its own account a substantial common stock position in JNI.

C Smith's brother-in-law is a supplier to JNI.

21 Michelieu tells a prospective client, "I may not have a long-term track record yet, but I'm sure that you'll be very pleased with my recommendations and service. In the three years that I've been in the business, my equity-oriented clients have averaged a total return of more than 26% a year." The statement is true, but Michelieu only has a few clients, and one of his clients took a large position in a penny stock (against Michelieu's advice) and realized a huge gain. This large return caused the average of all of Michelieu's clients to exceed 26% a year. Without this one investment, the average gain would have been 8% a year. Has Michelieu violated the Standards?

A No, because Michelieu is not promising that he can earn a 26% return in the future.

B No, because the statement is a true and accurate description of Michelieu's track record.

C Yes, because the statement misrepresents Michelieu's track record.

22 An investment banking department of a brokerage firm often receives material nonpublic information that could have considerable value if used in advising the firm's brokerage clients. In order to conform to the Code and Standards, which one of the following is the best policy for the brokerage firm?

A Permanently prohibit both "buy" and "sell" recommendations of the stocks of clients of the investment banking department.

B Establish physical and informational barriers within the firm to prevent the exchange of information between the investment banking and brokerage operations.

C Monitor the exchange of information between the investment banking department and the brokerage operation.

23 Stewart has been hired by Goodner Industries, Inc., to manage its pension fund. Stewart's duty of loyalty, prudence, and care is owed to:

A The management of Goodner.

B The participants and beneficiaries of Goodner's pension plan.

C The shareholders of Goodner.

24 Which of the following statements is a stated purpose of disclosure in Standard VI(C)–Referral Fees?

A Disclosure will allow the client to request discounted service fees.

B Disclosure will help the client evaluate any possible partiality shown in the recommendation of services.

C Disclosure means advising a prospective client about the referral arrangement once a formal client relationship has been established.

25 Rose, a portfolio manager for a local investment advisory firm, is planning to sell a portion of his personal investment portfolio to cover the costs of his child's academic tuition. Rose wants to sell a portion of his holdings in Household Products, but his firm recently upgraded the stock to "strong buy." Which of the following describes Rose's options under the Code and Standards?

A Based on his firm's "buy" recommendation, Rose cannot sell the shares because he would be improperly prospering from the inflated recommendation.

B Rose is free to sell his personal holdings once his firm is properly informed of his intentions.

C Rose can sell his personal holdings but only when a client of the firm places an order to buy shares of Household.

26 A former hedge fund manager, Jackman, has decided to launch a new private wealth management firm. From his prior experiences, he believes the new firm needs to achieve US$1 million in assets under management in the first year. Jackman offers a $10,000 incentive to any adviser who joins his firm with the minimum of $200,000 in committed investments. Jackman places notice of the opening on several industry web portals and career search sites. Which of the following is *correct* according to the Code and Standards?

A A member or candidate is eligible for the new position and incentive if he or she can arrange for enough current clients to switch to the new firm and if the member or candidate discloses the incentive fee.

B A member or candidate may not accept employment with the new firm because Jackman's incentive offer violates the Code and Standards.

C A member or candidate is not eligible for the new position unless he or she is currently unemployed because soliciting the clients of the member's or candidate's current employer is prohibited.

27 Carter works for Invest Today, a local asset management firm. A broker that provides Carter with proprietary research through client brokerage arrangements is offering a new trading service. The broker is offering low-fee, execution-only trades to complement its traditional full-service, execution-and-research trades. To entice Carter and other asset managers to send additional business its way, the broker will apply the commissions paid on the new service toward satisfying the brokerage commitment of the prior full-service arrangements. Carter has always been satisfied with the execution provided on the full-service trades, and the new low-fee trades are comparable to the fees of other brokers currently used for the accounts that prohibit soft dollar arrangements.

A Carter can trade for his accounts that prohibit soft dollar arrangements under the new low-fee trading scheme.

B Carter cannot use the new trading scheme because the commissions are prohibited by the soft dollar restrictions of the accounts.

C Carter should trade only through the new low-fee scheme and should increase his trading volume to meet his required commission commitment.

28 Rule has worked as a portfolio manager for a large investment management firm for the past 10 years. Rule earned his CFA charter last year and has decided to open his own investment management firm. After leaving his current employer, Rule creates some marketing material for his new firm. He states in the material, "In earning the CFA charter, a highly regarded credential in the investment management industry, I further enhanced the portfolio management skills learned during my professional career. While completing the examination process in three consecutive years, I consistently received the highest possible scores on the topics of Ethics, Alternative Investments, and Portfolio Management." Has Rule violated Standard VII(B)–Reference to CFA Institute, the CFA Designation, and the CFA Program in his marketing material?

A Rule violated Standard VII(B) in stating that he completed the exams in three consecutive years.

B Rule violated Standard VII(B) in stating that he received the highest scores in the topics of Ethics, Alternative Investments, and Portfolio Management.

C Rule did not violate Standard VII(B).

29 Stafford is a portfolio manager for a specialized real estate mutual fund. Her firm clearly describes in the fund's prospectus its soft dollar policies. Stafford decides that entering the CFA Program will enhance her investment decision-making skill and decides to use the fund's soft dollar account to pay the registration and exam fees for the CFA Program. Which of the following statements is *most likely* correct?

A Stafford did not violate the Code and Standards because the prospectus informed investors of the fund's soft dollar policies.

B Stafford violated the Code and Standards because improving her investment skills is not a reasonable use of the soft dollar account.

C Stafford violated the Code and Standards because the CFA Program does not meet the definition of research allowed to be purchased with brokerage commissions.

30 Long has been asked to be the keynote speaker at an upcoming investment conference. The event is being hosted by one of the third-party investment managers currently used by his pension fund. The manager offers to cover all

conference and travel costs for Long and make the conference registrations free for three additional members of his investment management team. To ensure that the conference obtains the best speakers, the host firm has arranged for an exclusive golf outing for the day following the conference on a local championship-caliber course. Which of the following is *least likely* to violate Standard I(B)?

A Long may accept only the offer to have his conference-related expenses paid by the host firm.

B Long may accept the offer to have his conference-related expenses paid and may attend the exclusive golf outing at the expense of the hosting firm.

C Long may accept the entire package of incentives offered to speak at this conference.

31 Andrews, a private wealth manager, is conducting interviews for a new research analyst for his firm. One of the candidates is Wright, an analyst with a local investment bank. During the interview, while Wright is describing his analytical skills, he mentions a current merger in which his firm is acting as the adviser. Andrews has heard rumors of a possible merger between the two companies, but no releases have been made by the companies concerned. Which of the following actions by Andrews is *least likely* a violation of the Code and Standards?

A Waiting until the next day before trading on the information to allow time for it to become public.

B Notifying all investment managers in his firm of the new information so none of their clients are disadvantaged.

C Placing the securities mentioned as part of the merger on the firm's restricted trading list.

32 Pietro, president of Local Bank, has hired the bank's market maker, Vogt, to seek a merger partner. Local is currently not listed on a stock exchange and has not reported that it is seeking strategic alternatives. Vogt has discussed the possibility of a merger with several firms, but they have all decided to wait until after the next period's financial data are available. The potential buyers believe the results will be worse than the results of prior periods and will allow them to pay less for Local Bank.

Pietro wants to increase the likelihood of structuring a merger deal quickly. Which of the following actions would *most likely* be a violation of the Code and Standards?

A Pietro could instruct Local Bank to issue a press release announcing that it has retained Vogt to find a merger partner.

B Pietro could place a buy order for 2,000 shares (or four times the average weekly volume) through Vogt for his personal account.

C After confirming with Local's chief financial officer, Pietro could instruct Local to issue a press release reaffirming the firm's prior announced earnings guidance for the full fiscal year.

33 ABC Investment Management acquires a new, very large account with two concentrated positions. The firm's current policy is to add new accounts for the purpose of performance calculation after the first full month of management. Cupp is responsible for calculating the firm's performance returns. Before the end of the initial month, Cupp notices that one of the significant holdings of the new accounts is acquired by another company, causing the value of the investment to double. Because of this holding, Cupp decides to account for the new portfolio as of the date of transfer, thereby allowing ABC Investment to reap the positive impact of that month's portfolio return.

A Cupp did not violate the Code and Standards because the GIPS standards allow composites to be updated on the date of large external cash flows.

B Cupp did not violate the Code and Standards because companies are allowed to determine when to incorporate new accounts into their composite calculation.

C Cupp violated the Code and Standards because the inclusion of the new account produces an inaccurate calculation of the monthly results according to the firm's stated policies.

34 Cannan has been working from home on weekends and occasionally saves correspondence with clients and completed work on her home computer. Because of worsening market conditions, Cannan is one of several employees released by her firm. While Cannan is looking for a new job, she uses the files she saved at home to request letters of recommendation from former clients. She also provides to prospective clients some of the reports as examples of her abilities.

A Cannan violated the Code and Standards because she did not receive permission from her former employer to keep or use the files after her employment ended.

B Cannan did not violate the Code and Standards because the files were created and saved on her own time and computer.

C Cannan violated the Code and Standards because she is prohibited from saving files on her home computer.

35 Quinn sat for the Level III CFA exam this past weekend. He updates his resume with the following statement: "In finishing the CFA Program, I improved my skills related to researching investments and managing portfolios. I will be eligible for the CFA charter upon completion of the required work experience."

A Quinn violated the Code and Standards by claiming he improved his skills through the CFA Program.

B Quinn violated the Code and Standards by incorrectly stating that he is eligible for the CFA charter.

C Quinn did not violate the Code and Standards with his resume update.

36 During a round of golf, Rodriguez, chief financial officer of Mega Retail, mentions to Hart, a local investment adviser and long-time personal friend, that Mega is having an exceptional sales quarter. Rodriguez expects the results to be almost 10% above the current estimates. The next day, Hart initiates the purchase of a large stake in the local exchange-traded retail fund for her personal account.

A Hart violated the Code and Standards by investing in the exchange-traded fund that included Mega Retail.

B Hart did not violate the Code and Standards because she did not invest directly in securities of Mega Retail.

C Rodriguez did not violate the Code and Standards because the comments made to Hart were not intended to solicit an investment in Mega Retail.

37 Park is very frustrated after taking her Level II exam. While she was studying for the exam, to supplement the curriculum provided, she ordered and used study material from a third-party provider. Park believes the additional material focused her attention on specific topic areas that were not tested while ignoring other areas. She posts the following statement on the provider's discussion board: "I am very dissatisfied with your firm's CFA Program Level II material. I found the exam extremely difficult and myself unprepared for specific questions after using your product. How could your service provide such limited

instructional resources on the analysis of inventories and taxes when the exam had multiple questions about them? I will not recommend your products to other candidates."

A Park violated the Code and Standards by purchasing third-party review material.

B Park violated the Code and Standards by providing her opinion on the difficulty of the exam.

C Park violated the Code and Standards by providing specific information on topics tested on the exam.

38 Paper was recently terminated as one of a team of five managers of an equity fund. The fund had two value-focused managers and terminated one of them to reduce costs. In a letter sent to prospective employers, Paper presents, with written permission of the firm, the performance history of the fund to demonstrate his past success.

A Paper did not violate the Code and Standards.

B Paper violated the Code and Standards by claiming the performance of the entire fund as his own.

C Paper violated the Code and Standards by including the historical results of his prior employer.

39 Townsend was recently appointed to the board of directors of a youth golf program that is the local chapter of a national not-for-profit organization. The program is beginning a new fund-raising campaign to expand the number of annual scholarships it provides. Townsend believes many of her clients make annual donations to charity. The next week in her regular newsletter to all clients, she includes a small section discussing the fund-raising campaign and her position on the organization's board.

A Townsend did not violate the Code and Standards.

B Townsend violated the Code and Standards by soliciting donations from her clients through the newsletter.

C Townsend violated the Code and Standards by not getting approval of the organization before soliciting her clients.

SOLUTIONS

1 The correct answer is B. This question involves Standard III(B)–Fair Dealing. Smith disseminated a change in the stock recommendation to his clients but then received a request contrary to that recommendation from a client who probably had not yet received the recommendation. Prior to executing the order, Smith should take additional steps to ensure that the customer has received the change of recommendation. Answer A is incorrect because the client placed the order prior to receiving the recommendation and, therefore, does not have the benefit of Smith's most recent recommendation. Answer C is also incorrect; simply because the client request is contrary to the firm's recommendation does not mean a member can override a direct request by a client. After Smith contacts the client to ensure that the client has received the changed recommendation, if the client still wants to place a buy order for the shares, Smith is obligated to comply with the client's directive.

2 The correct answer is C. This question involves Standard III(A)–Loyalty, Prudence, and Care and the specific topic of soft dollars or soft commissions. Answer C is the correct choice because client brokerage commissions may not be directed to pay for the investment manager's operating expenses. Answer B describes how members and candidates should determine how to use brokerage commissions—that is, if the use is in the best interests of clients and is commensurate with the value of the services provided. Answer A describes a practice that is commonly referred to as "directed brokerage." Because brokerage is an asset of the client and is used to benefit the client, not the manager, such practice does not violate a duty of loyalty to the client. Members and candidates are obligated in all situations to disclose to clients their practices in the use of client brokerage commissions.

3 The correct answer is C. This question involves Standard VI(A)–Disclosure of Conflicts. The question establishes a conflict of interest in which an analyst, Jamison, is asked to write a research report on a company that is a client of the analyst's employer. In addition, two directors of the company are senior officers of Jamison's employer. Both facts establish that there are conflicts of interest that must be disclosed by Jamison in her research report. Answer B is incorrect because an analyst is not prevented from writing a report simply because of the special relationship the analyst's employer has with the company as long as that relationship is disclosed. Answer A is incorrect because whether or not Jamison expresses any opinions in the report is irrelevant to her duty to disclose a conflict of interest. Not expressing opinions does not relieve the analyst of the responsibility to disclose the special relationships between the two companies.

4 The correct answer is C. This question asks about compliance procedures relating to personal investments of members and candidates. The statement in answer C clearly conflicts with the recommended procedures in the *Standards of Practice Handbook*. Employers should compare personal transactions of employees with those of clients on a regular basis regardless of the existence of a requirement by any regulatory organization. Such comparisons ensure that employees' personal trades do not conflict with their duty to their clients, and the comparisons can be conducted in a confidential manner. The statement in answer A does not conflict with the procedures in the *Handbook*. Disclosure of such policies will give full information to clients regarding potential conflicts of interest on the part of those entrusted to manage their money. Answer B is incorrect because firms are encouraged to establish policies whereby employees clear their personal holdings and transactions with their employers.

5 The correct answer is B. This question relates to Standard III(A)–Loyalty, Prudence, and Care and Standard III(E)–Preservation of Confidentiality. In this case, the member manages funds of a private endowment. Clients, who are, in this case, the trustees of the fund, must place some trust in members and candidates. Bronson cannot disclose confidential financial information to anyone without the permission of the fund, regardless of whether the disclosure may benefit the fund. Therefore, answer A is incorrect. Answer C is incorrect because Bronson must notify the fund and obtain the fund's permission before publicizing the information.

6 The correct answer is B. This question relates to Standard V(A)–Diligence and Reasonable Basis. The opinion of another financial analyst is not an adequate basis for Willier's action in changing the recommendation. Answer C is thus incorrect. So is answer A because, although it is true that members and candidates must distinguish between facts and opinions in recommendations, the question does not illustrate a violation of that nature. If the opinion overheard by Willier had sparked him to conduct additional research and investigation that justified a change of opinion, then a changed recommendation would be appropriate.

7 The correct answer is B. This question relates to Standard I(B)–Independence and Objectivity. When asked to change a recommendation on a company stock to gain business for the firm, the head of the brokerage unit must refuse in order to maintain his independence and objectivity in making recommendations. He must not yield to pressure by the firm's investment banking department. To avoid the appearance of a conflict of interest, the firm should discontinue issuing recommendations about the company. Answer A is incorrect; changing the recommendation in any manner that is contrary to the analyst's opinion violates the duty to maintain independence and objectivity. Answer C is incorrect because merely assigning a new analyst to decide whether the stock deserves a higher rating will not address the conflict of interest.

8 The correct answer is A. Standard VII(B)–Reference to CFA Institute, the CFA Designation, and the CFA Program is the subject of this question. The reference on Albert's business card implies that there is a "CFA Level II" designation; Tye merely indicates in promotional material that he is participating in the CFA Program and has completed Levels I and II. Candidates may not imply that there is some sort of partial designation earned after passing a level of the CFA exam. Therefore, Albert has violated Standard VII(B). Candidates may communicate that they are participating in the CFA Program, however, and may state the levels that they have completed. Therefore, Tye has not violated Standard VII(B).

9 The correct answer is B. This question relates to Standard V(B)–Communication with Clients and Prospective Clients. Scott has issued a research report stating that he expects the price of Walkton Industries stock to rise by US$8 a share "because the dividend will increase" by US$1.50 per share. He has made this statement knowing that the dividend will increase only if Congress enacts certain legislation, an uncertain prospect. By stating that the dividend will increase, Scott failed to separate fact from opinion.

The information regarding passage of legislation is not material nonpublic information because it is conjecture, and the question does not state whether the US representative gave Scott her opinion on the passage of the legislation in confidence. She could have been offering this opinion to anyone who asked. Therefore, statement A is incorrect. It may be acceptable to base a recommendation, in part, on an expectation of future events, even though they may be uncertain. Therefore, answer C is incorrect.

10 The correct answer is C. This question, which relates to Standard III(B)–Fair Dealing, tests the knowledge of the procedures that will assist members and candidates in treating clients fairly when making investment recommendations. The step listed in C will help ensure the fair treatment of clients. Answer A may have negative effects on the fair treatment of clients. The more people who know about a pending change, the greater the chance that someone will inform some clients before the information's release. The firm should establish policies that limit the number of people who are aware in advance that a recommendation is to be disseminated. Answer B, distributing recommendations to institutional clients before distributing them to individual accounts, discriminates among clients on the basis of size and class of assets and is a violation of Standard III(B).

11 The correct answer is B. This question deals with Standard II(A)–Material Nonpublic Information. The mosaic theory states that an analyst may use material public information and nonmaterial nonpublic information in creating a larger picture than shown by any individual piece of information and the conclusions the analyst reaches become material only after the pieces are assembled. Answers A and C are accurate statements relating to the Code and Standards but do not describe the mosaic theory.

12 The correct answer is C. This question involves Standard IV(B)–Additional Compensation Arrangements. The arrangement described in the question—whereby Jurgen would be compensated beyond the compensation provided by her firm, on the basis of an account's performance—is not a violation of the Standards as long as Jurgen discloses the arrangement in writing to her employer and obtains permission from her employer prior to entering into the arrangement. Answers A and B are incorrect; although the private compensation arrangement could conflict with the interests of other clients and lead to short-term performance pressures, members and candidates may enter into such agreements as long as they have disclosed the arrangements to their employer and obtained permission for the arrangement from their employer.

13 The correct answer is B. This question relates to Standard III(A)–Loyalty, Prudence, and Care—specifically, a member's or candidate's responsibility for voting proxies and the use of client brokerage. According to the facts stated in the question, Farnsworth did not violate Standard III(A). Although the company president asked Farnsworth to vote the shares of the Jones Corporation profit-sharing plan a certain way, Farnsworth investigated the issue and concluded, independently, the best way to vote. Therefore, even though his decision coincided with the wishes of the company president, Farnsworth is not in violation of his responsibility to be loyal and to provide care to his clients. In this case, the participants and the beneficiaries of the profit-sharing plan are the clients, not the company's management. Had Farnsworth not investigated the issue or had he yielded to the president's wishes and voted for a slate of directors that he had determined was not in the best interest of the company, Farnsworth would have violated his responsibilities to the beneficiaries of the plan. In addition, because the brokerage firm provides the lowest commissions and best execution for securities transactions, Farnsworth has met his obligations to the client in using this brokerage firm. It does not matter that the brokerage firm also provides research information that is not useful for the account generating the commission because Farnsworth is not paying extra money of the client's for that information.

14 The correct answer is A. In this question, Brown is providing investment recommendations before making inquiries about the client's financial situation, investment experience, or investment objectives. Brown is thus violating

Standard III(C)–Suitability. Answers B and C provide examples of information members and candidates should discuss with their clients at the outset of the relationship, but these answers do not constitute a complete list of those factors. Answer A is the best answer.

15 The correct answer is C. This question involves Standard I(C)–Misrepresentation. Statement I is a factual statement that discloses to clients and prospects accurate information about the terms of the investment instrument. Statement II, which guarantees a specific rate of return for a mutual fund, is an opinion stated as a fact and, therefore, violates Standard I(C). If statement II were rephrased to include a qualifying statement, such as "in my opinion, investors may earn . . . ," it would not be in violation of the Standards.

16 The correct answer is A. This question involves three of the Standards. Anderb, the portfolio manager, has been obtaining more favorable prices for her personal securities transactions than she gets for her clients, which is a breach of Standard III(A)–Loyalty, Prudence, and Care. In addition, she violated Standard I(D)–Misconduct by failing to adhere to company policy and by hiding her personal transactions from her firm. Anderb's supervisor, Bates, violated Standard IV(C)–Responsibilities of Supervisors; although the company had requirements for reporting personal trading, Bates failed to adequately enforce those requirements. Answer B does not represent a violation because Standard VI(B)–Priority of Transactions requires that personal trading in a security be conducted after the trading in that security of clients and the employer. The Code and Standards do not prohibit owning such investments, although firms may establish policies that limit the investment opportunities of members and candidates. Answer C does not represent a violation because the Code and Standards do not contain a prohibition against employees using the same broker for their personal accounts that they use for their client accounts. This arrangement should be disclosed to the employer so that the employer may determine whether a conflict of interest exists.

17 The correct answer is A because this question relates to Standard I(A)–Knowledge of the Law—specifically, global application of the Code and Standards. Members and candidates who practice in multiple jurisdictions may be subject to various securities laws and regulations. If applicable law is more strict than the requirements of the Code and Standards, members and candidates must adhere to applicable law; otherwise, members and candidates must adhere to the Code and Standards. Therefore, answer A is correct. Answer B is incorrect because members and candidates must adhere to the higher standard set by the Code and Standards if local applicable law is less strict. Answer C is incorrect because when no applicable law exists, members and candidates are required to adhere to the Code and Standards, and the Code and Standards prohibit the use of material nonpublic information.

18 The correct answer is B. The best course of action under Standard I(B)–Independence and Objectivity is to avoid a conflict of interest whenever possible. Therefore, for Ward to pay for all his expenses is the correct answer. Answer C details a course of action in which the conflict would be disclosed, but the solution is not as appropriate as avoiding the conflict of interest. Answer A would not be the best course because it would not remove the appearance of a conflict of interest; even though the report would not be affected by the reimbursement of expenses, it could appear to be.

19 The correct answer is B. Under Standard IV(A)–Loyalty, members and candidates may undertake independent practice that may result in compensation or other benefit in competition with their employer as long as they obtain consent from their employer. Answer C is not consistent with the Standards because

the Standards allow members and candidates to make arrangements or preparations to go into competitive business as long as those arrangements do not interfere with their duty to their current employer. Answer A is not consistent with the Standards because the Standards do not include a complete prohibition against undertaking independent practice.

20 The correct answer is B. This question involves Standard VI(A)–Disclosure of Conflicts—specifically, the holdings of an analyst's employer in company stock. Answers A and C do not describe conflicts of interest that Smith would have to disclose. Answer A describes the use of a firm's products, which would not be a required disclosure. In answer C, the relationship between the analyst and the company through a relative is so tangential that it does not create a conflict of interest necessitating disclosure.

21 The correct answer is C. This question relates to Standard I(C)–Misrepresentation. Although Michelieu's statement about the total return of his clients' accounts on average may be technically true, it is misleading because the majority of the gain resulted from one client's large position taken against Michelieu's advice. Therefore, this statement misrepresents the investment performance the member is responsible for. He has not taken steps to present a fair, accurate, and complete presentation of performance. Answer B is thus incorrect. Answer A is incorrect because although Michelieu is not guaranteeing future results, his words are still a misrepresentation of his performance history.

22 The correct answer is B. The best policy to prevent violation of Standard II(A)–Material Nonpublic Information is the establishment of firewalls in a firm to prevent exchange of insider information. The physical and informational barrier of a firewall between the investment banking department and the brokerage operation prevents the investment banking department from providing information to analysts on the brokerage side who may be writing recommendations on a company stock. Prohibiting recommendations of the stock of companies that are clients of the investment banking department is an alternative, but answer A states that this prohibition would be permanent, which is not the best answer. Once an offering is complete and the material nonpublic information obtained by the investment banking department becomes public, resuming publishing recommendations on the stock is not a violation of the Code and Standards because the information of the investment banking department no longer gives the brokerage operation an advantage in writing the report. Answer C is incorrect because no exchange of information should be occurring between the investment banking department and the brokerage operation, so monitoring of such exchanges is not an effective compliance procedure for preventing the use of material nonpublic information.

23 The correct answer is B. Under Standard III(A)–Loyalty, Prudence, and Care, members and candidates who manage a company's pension fund owe these duties to the participants and beneficiaries of the pension plan, not the management of the company or the company's shareholders.

24 The correct answer is B. Answer B gives one of the two primary reasons listed in the *Handbook* for disclosing referral fees to clients under Standard VI(C)–Referral Fees. (The other is to allow clients and employers to evaluate the full cost of the services.) Answer A is incorrect because Standard VI(C) does not require members or candidates to discount their fees when they receive referral fees. Answer C is inconsistent with Standard VI(C) because disclosure of referral fees, to be effective, should be made to prospective clients before entering into a formal client relationship with them.

25 The correct answer is B. Standard VI(B)–Priority of Transactions does not limit transactions of company employees that differ from current recommendations as long as the sale does not disadvantage current clients. Thus, answer A is incorrect. Answer C is incorrect because the Standard does not require the matching of personal and client trades.

26 Answer C is correct. Standard IV(A)–Loyalty discusses activities permissible to members and candidates when they are leaving their current employer; soliciting clients is strictly prohibited. Thus, answer A is inconsistent with the Code and Standards even with the required disclosure. Answer B is incorrect because the offer does not directly violate the Code and Standards. There may be out-of-work members and candidates who can arrange the necessary commitments without violating the Code and Standards.

27 Answer A is correct. The question relates to Standard III(A)–Loyalty, Prudence, and Care. Carter believes the broker offers effective execution at a fee that is comparable with those of other brokers, so he is free to use the broker for all accounts. Answer B is incorrect because the accounts that prohibit soft dollar arrangements do not want to fund the purchase of research by Carter. The new trading scheme does not incur additional commissions from clients, so it would not go against the prohibitions. Answer C is incorrect because Carter should not incur unnecessary or excessive "churning" of the portfolios (excessive trading) for the purpose of meeting the brokerage commitments of soft dollar arrangements.

28 Answer B is correct according to Standard VII(B)–Reference to CFA Institute, the CFA Designation, and the CFA Program. CFA Program candidates do not receive their actual scores on the exam. Topic and subtopic results are grouped into three broad categories, and the exam is graded only as "pass" or "fail." Although a candidate may have achieved a topical score of "above 70%," she or he cannot factually state that she or he received the highest possible score because that information is not reported. Thus, answer C is incorrect. Answer A is incorrect as long as the member or candidate actually completed the exams consecutively. Standard VII(B) does not prohibit the communication of factual information about completing the CFA Program in three consecutive years.

29 Answer C is correct. According to Standard III(A)–Loyalty, Prudence, and Care, the CFA Program would be considered a personal or firm expense and should not be paid for with the fund's brokerage commissions. Soft dollar accounts should be used only to purchase research services that directly assist the investment manager in the investment decision-making process, not to assist the management of the firm or to further education. Thus, answer A is incorrect. Answer B is incorrect because the reasonableness of how the money is used is not an issue; the issue is that educational expense is not research.

30 Answer A is correct. Standard I(B)–Independence and Objectivity emphasizes the need for members and candidates to maintain their independence and objectivity. Best practices dictate that firms adopt a strict policy not to accept compensation for travel arrangements. At times, however, accepting paid travel would not compromise one's independence and objectivity. Answers B and C are incorrect because the added benefits—free conference admission for additional staff members and an exclusive golf retreat for the speaker—could be viewed as inducements related to the firm's working arrangements and not solely related to the speaking engagement. Should Long wish to bring other team members or participate in the golf outing, he or his firm should be responsible for the associated fees.

31 Answer C is correct. The guidance to Standard II(A)–Material Nonpublic Information recommends adding securities to the firm's restricted list when the firm has or may have material nonpublic information. By adding these securities to this list, Andrews would uphold this standard. Because waiting until the next day will not ensure that news of the merger is made public, answer A is incorrect. Negotiations may take much longer between the two companies, and the merger may never happen. Andrews must wait until the information is disseminated to the market before he trades on that information. Answer B is incorrect because Andrews should not disclose the information to other managers; no trading is allowed on material nonpublic information.

32 Answer B is correct. Through placing a personal purchase order that is significantly greater than the average volume, Pietro is violating Standard IIB–Market Manipulation. He is attempting to manipulate an increase in the share price and thus bring a buyer to the negotiating table. The news of a possible merger and confirmation of the firm's earnings guidance may also have positive effects on the price of Local Bank, but Pietro's actions in instructing the release of the information does not represent a violation through market manipulation. Announcements of this nature are common and practical to keep investors informed. Thus, answers A and C are incorrect.

33 Answer C is correct. Cupp violated Standard III(D)–Performance Presentations when he deviated from the firm's stated policies solely to capture the gain from the holding being acquired. Answer A is incorrect because the firm does not claim GIPS compliance and the GIPS standards require external cash flows to be treated in a consistent manner with the firm's documented policies. Answer B is incorrect because the firm does not state that it is updating its composite policies. If such a change were to occur, all cash flows for the month would have to be reviewed to ensure their consistent treatment under the new policy.

34 Answer A is correct. According to Standard V(C)–Record Retention, Cannan needed the permission of her employer to maintain the files at home after her employment ended. Without that permission, she should have deleted the files. All files created as part of a member's or candidate's professional activity are the property of the firm, even those created outside normal work hours. Thus, answer B is incorrect. Answer C is incorrect because the Code and Standards do not prohibit using one's personal computer to complete work for one's employer.

35 Answer B is correct. According to Standard VII(B)–Reference to CFA Institute, the CFA Designation, and the CFA Program, Quinn cannot claim to have finished the CFA Program or be eligible for the CFA charter until he officially learns that he has passed the Level III exam. Until the results for the most recent exam are released, those who sat for the exam should continue to refer to themselves as "candidates." Thus, answer C is incorrect. Answer A is incorrect because members and candidates may discuss areas of practice in which they believe the CFA Program improved their personal skills.

36 Answer A is correct. Hart's decision to invest in the retail fund appears directly correlated with Rodriguez's statement about the successful quarter of Mega Retail and thus violates Standard II(A)–Material Nonpublic Information. Rodriguez's information would be considered material because it would influence the share price of Mega Retail and probably influence the price of the entire exchange-traded retail fund. Thus, answer B is incorrect. Answer C is also incorrect because Rodriguez shared information that was both material and nonpublic. Company officers regularly have such knowledge about their firms, which is not a violation. The sharing of such information, however, even in a conversation between friends, does violate Standard II(A).

37 Answer C is correct. Standard VII(A)–Conduct as Members and Candidates in the CFA Program prohibits providing information to candidates or the public that is considered confidential to the CFA Program. In revealing that questions related to the analysis of inventories and analysis of taxes were on the exam, Park has violated this standard. Answer B is incorrect because the guidance for the standard explicitly acknowledges that members and candidates are allowed to offer their opinions about the CFA Program. Answer A is incorrect because candidates are not prohibited from using outside resources.

38 Answer B is correct. Paper has violated Standard III(D)–Performance Presentation by not disclosing that he was part of a team of managers that achieved the results shown. If he had also included the return of the portion he directly managed, he would not have violated the standard. Thus, answer A is incorrect. Answer C is incorrect because Paper received written permission from his prior employer to include the results.

39 Answer A is correct. Townsend has not provided any information about her clients to the leaders or managers of the golf program; thus, she has not violated Standard III(E)–Preservation of Confidentiality. Providing contact information about her clients for a direct-mail solicitation would have been a violation. Answer B is incorrect because the notice in the newsletter does not violate Standard III(E). Answer C is incorrect because the golf program's fund-raising campaign had already begun, so discussing the opportunity to donate was appropriate.

READING

4

Introduction to the Global Investment Performance Standards (GIPS)

LEARNING OUTCOMES

Mastery	The candidate should be able to:
☐	a. explain why the GIPS standards were created, what parties the GIPS standards apply to, and who is served by the standards;
☐	b. explain the construction and purpose of composites in performance reporting;
☐	c. explain the requirements for verification.

The objective of this reading is to orient the Level I candidate approaching the assigned sections of the GIPS standards. It explains why the GIPS standards were created, who can claim compliance, and who benefits from compliance. It also introduces the key notion of composites, states the purpose of verification, and previews the structure of the Standards.

WHY WERE THE GIPS STANDARDS CREATED?

1.

Institutions and individuals are constantly scrutinizing past investment performance returns in search of the best manager to achieve their investment objectives.

In the past, the investment community had great difficulty making meaningful comparisons on the basis of accurate investment performance data. Several performance measurement practices hindered the comparability of performance returns from one firm to another, while others called into question the accuracy and credibility of performance reporting overall. Misleading practices included:

- Representative Accounts: Selecting a top-performing portfolio to represent the firm's overall investment results for a specific mandate.

- Survivorship Bias: Presenting an "average" performance history that *excludes* portfolios whose poor performance was weak enough to result in termination of the firm.
- Varying Time Periods: Presenting performance for a selected time period during which the mandate produced excellent returns or out-performed its benchmark—making comparison with other firms' results difficult or impossible.

Making a valid comparison of investment performance among even the most ethical investment management firms was problematic. For example, a pension fund seeking to hire an investment management firm might receive proposals from several firms, all using different methodologies for calculating their results.

The GIPS standards are a practitioner-driven set of ethical principles that establish a standardized, industry-wide approach for investment firms to follow in calculating and presenting their historical investment results to prospective clients. The GIPS standards ensure fair representation and full disclosure of investment performance. In other words, the GIPS standards lead investment management firms to avoid misrepresentations of performance and to communicate all relevant information that prospective clients should know in order to evaluate past results.

II. WHO CAN CLAIM COMPLIANCE?

First, any investment management firm may choose to comply with the GIPS standards. Complying with the GIPS standards is voluntary. Compliance with the GIPS standards is not typically required by legal or regulatory authorities.

Second, only investment management firms that *actually manage* assets can claim compliance with the Standards. Plan sponsors and consultants cannot make a claim of compliance unless they actually manage assets for which they are making a claim of compliance. They can claim to endorse the Standards and/or require that their investment managers comply with the Standards. Similarly, software (and the vendors who supply software) cannot be "compliant." Software can assist firms in achieving compliance with the GIPS standards (e.g., by calculating performance in a manner consistent with the calculation requirements of the Standards) but only an investment management firm can claim compliance once the firm has satisfied all requirements of the Standards.

Third, compliance is a firm-wide process that cannot be achieved on a single product or composite. A firm has only two options with regard to compliance with the GIPS standards: fully comply with *all* requirements of the GIPS standards and claim compliance through the use of the GIPS Compliance Statement; or not comply with all requirements of the GIPS standards and not claim compliance with, or make any reference to, the GIPS standards.

III. WHO BENEFITS FROM COMPLIANCE?

The GIPS standards benefit two main groups: investment management firms and prospective clients.

- By choosing to comply with the GIPS standards, investment management firms assure prospective clients that the historical "track record" they report is both complete and fairly presented. Compliance enables the GIPS-compliant firm to participate in competitive bids against other compliant firms throughout the world. Achieving and maintaining compliance may also strengthen the firm's internal controls over performance-related processes and procedures.

- Investors have a greater level of confidence in the integrity of performance presentations of a GIPS-compliant firm and can more easily compare performance presentations from different investment management firms. While the GIPS standards certainly do not eliminate the need for in-depth due diligence on the part of the investor, compliance with the Standards enhances the credibility of investment management firms that have chosen to undertake this responsibility.

COMPOSITES IV.

One of the key concepts of the Standards is the required use of composites. A composite is an aggregation of one or more portfolios managed according to a similar investment mandate, objective, or strategy. A composite must include all actual, fee-paying, discretionary portfolios managed in accordance with the same investment mandate, objective, or strategy. For example, if a GIPS-compliant firm presents its track record for a Global Equity Composite (the Composite), the Composite must include all portfolios that are managed, or have historically been managed, in the firm's Global Equity strategy. The firm may not subjectively select which Global Equity portfolios will be included in or excluded from the calculation and presentation of the Global Equity Composite. The determination of which portfolios to include in the Composite should be done according to pre-established criteria (i.e., on an ex-ante basis), not after the fact. This prevents a firm from including only their best-performing portfolios in the Composite.

VERIFICATION V.

Firms that claim compliance with the GIPS standards are responsible for their claim of compliance and for maintaining that compliance. That is, firms self-regulate their claim of compliance. Once a firm claims compliance with the Standards, they may voluntarily hire an independent third party to perform a verification in order to increase confidence in the firm's claim of compliance. Verification may also increase the knowledge of the firm's performance measurement team and improve the consistency and quality of the firm's compliant presentations.

Verification is performed with respect to an entire firm, not on specific composites. Verification does not ensure the accuracy of any specific composite presentation. Verification tests:

- whether the investment firm has complied with all the composite construction requirements of the GIPS standards on a firm-wide basis, and
- whether the firm's policies and procedures are designed to calculate and present performance in compliance with the GIPS standards.

Verification must be performed by an independent third party. A firm cannot perform its own verification.

Third-party verification brings additional credibility to a firm's claim of compliance. A verified firm may provide existing and prospective clients with greater assurance about its claim of compliance with the GIPS standards. Verification may also provide improved internal processes and procedures as well as marketing advantages to the firm.

VI. THE STRUCTURE OF THE GIPS STANDARDS

The provisions within the 2010 edition of the GIPS standards are divided into nine sections: Fundamentals of Compliance, Input Data, Calculation Methodology, Composite Construction, Disclosure, Presentation and Reporting, Real Estate, Private Equity, and Wrap Fee/Separately Managed Account (SMA) Portfolios. The provisions are further categorized into requirements and recommendations.

PRACTICE PROBLEMS

1 An investment management firm that does not adopt the GIPS standards could mischaracterize its overall performance by presenting a performance history:

A that includes terminated portfolios.

B composed of a single top-performing portfolio.

C for an investment mandate over all periods since the firm's inception.

2 Which of the following statements regarding GIPS compliance is correct?

A Plan sponsors and consultants that manage assets can claim compliance with GIPS.

B Software that calculates performance in a manner consistent with the GIPS standards can claim compliance with GIPS.

C Investment management firms can comply with GIPS requirements by limiting their compliance claims to the standards they have chosen to follow.

3 Each composite of a GIPS-compliant firm must consist of:

A multiple portfolios.

B portfolios selected on an *ex post* basis.

C portfolios managed according to a similar investment strategy.

4 Verification of a firm's claim of compliance with the GIPS standards is performed:

A by firm personnel.

B on a firm-wide basis.

C to ensure the accuracy of a specific composite presentation.

SOLUTIONS

1 B is correct. Selecting a top-performing portfolio to represent a firm's overall investment results for a specific mandate, also known as using representative accounts, is a misleading practice that is not allowed under the GIPS standards. A is incorrect because including terminated portfolios is consistent with the GIPS standards. If the firm instead presented a performance history that excludes terminated portfolios, however, such a practice would be misleading and not allowed under the GIPS standards. C is incorrect because presenting performance for its mandate covering all periods since the firm's inception is consistent with the GIPS standards. If the firm instead presented performance for a selected period during which it produced excellent returns or outperformed its benchmark, however, such a practice would be misleading and not allowed under the GIPS standards.

2 A is correct. Plan sponsors and consultants can make a claim of compliance if they actually manage assets for which they are making a claim of compliance. B is incorrect because software (and the vendors that supply software) cannot be GIPS compliant. Software can assist firms in achieving compliance with the GIPS standards, but only an investment management firm can claim compliance. C is incorrect because a firm has only two options regarding compliance with the GIPS standards: fully comply with all requirements of the GIPS standards and claim compliance through the use of the GIPS Compliance Statement; or not comply with all requirements of the GIPS standards and not claim compliance with, or make any reference to, the GIPS standards.

3 C is correct. A composite is an aggregation of one or more portfolios managed according to a similar investment mandate, objective, or strategy. For example, if a GIPS-compliant firm presents performance for a global equity composite (the composite), the composite must include portfolios that are managed, or have historically been managed, according to the firm's global equity strategy. A is incorrect because a composite is an aggregation of one or more portfolios managed according to a similar investment mandate, objective, or strategy. A composite may consist of a single portfolio when it is the only portfolio managed according to a particular mandate. B is incorrect because the determination of which portfolio(s) to include in a composite should be done according to pre-established criteria (*ex ante* basis), not after the fact (*ex post* basis).

4 B is correct. Verification is performed with respect to an entire firm, not on specific composites.

READING

5

Global Investment Performance Standards (GIPS)

LEARNING OUTCOMES

Mastery	The candidate should be able to:
☐	**a.** describe the key features of the GIPS standards and the fundamentals of compliance;
☐	**b.** describe the scope of the GIPS standards with respect to an investment firm's definition and historical performance record;
☐	**c.** explain how the GIPS standards are implemented in countries with existing standards for performance reporting and describe the appropriate response when the GIPS standards and local regulations conflict;
☐	**d.** describe the nine major sections of the GIPS standards.

PREFACE

OPTIONAL SEGMENT

CFA Institute is a global not-for-profit association of investment professionals with the mission of leading the investment profession globally by setting the highest standards of ethics, education, and professional excellence. CFA Institute has a long-standing history of and commitment to establishing a broadly accepted ethical standard for calculating and presenting investment performance based on the principles of fair representation and full disclosure. The goals in developing and evolving the Global Investment Performance Standards (GIPS®) are to establish them as the recognized standard for calculating and presenting investment performance around the world and for the GIPS standards to become a firm's "passport" to market investment management services globally. As of January 2010, CFA Institute has partnered with organizations in 32 countries that contribute to the development and promotion of the GIPS standards.

History

In 1995, CFA Institute, formerly known as the Association for Investment Management and Research (AIMR), sponsored and funded the Global Investment Performance Standards Committee to develop global standards for calculating and presenting investment performance, based on the existing AIMR Performance Presentation Standards (AIMR-PPS®).

In 1998, the proposed GIPS standards were posted on the CFA Institute website and circulated for comment to more than 4,000 individuals who had expressed interest. The result was the first Global Investment Performance Standards, published in April 1999.

The initial edition of the GIPS standards was designed to create a minimum global investment performance standard that would:

- Permit and facilitate acceptance and adoption in developing markets;
- Give the global investment management industry one commonly accepted approach for calculating and presenting performance; and
- Address liquid asset classes (equity, fixed income, and cash).

In 1999, the Global Investment Performance Standards Committee was replaced by the Investment Performance Council (IPC) to further develop and promote the GIPS standards. The development of the GIPS standards was a global industry initiative with participation from individuals and organizations from more than 15 countries.

The IPC was charged with developing provisions for other asset classes (e.g., real estate, private equity) and addressing other performance-related issues (e.g., fees, advertising) to broaden the scope and applicability of the GIPS standards. This was accomplished when the second edition of the GIPS standards was published in February 2005.

With the release of the 2005 edition of the GIPS standards and growing adoption and expansion of the GIPS standards, the IPC decided to move to a single global investment performance standard and eliminate the need for local variations of the GIPS standards. All country-specific performance standards converged with the GIPS standards, resulting in 25 countries adopting a single, global standard for the calculation and presentation of investment performance.

In 2005, with the convergence of country-specific versions to the GIPS standards and the need to reorganize the governance structure to facilitate involvement from GIPS sponsors, CFA Institute dissolved the IPC and created the GIPS Executive Committee and the GIPS Council. The GIPS Executive Committee serves as the decision-making authority for the GIPS standards, and the GIPS Council facilitates the involvement of all sponsors in the ongoing development and promotion of the GIPS standards.

To maintain global relevance, and in recognition of the dynamic nature of the investment industry, the GIPS standards must be continually updated through interpretations, guidance, and new provisions. In 2008, the GIPS Executive Committee began its review of the GIPS standards in an effort to further refine the provisions as well as eliminate provisions that are no longer necessary and add new requirements and recommendations that promote best practice. The GIPS Executive Committee worked in close collaboration with its technical subcommittees, specially formed working groups, and GIPS sponsors. These groups reviewed the existing provisions and guidance and conducted surveys and other research as part of the efforts to produce the 2010 edition of the GIPS standards.

END OPTIONAL SEGMENT

INTRODUCTION

Preamble—Why Is a Global Investment Performance Standard Needed?

Standardized Investment Performance

Financial markets and the investment management industry have become increasingly global in nature. The growth in the types and number of financial entities, the globalization of the investment process, and the increased competition among investment management firms demonstrate the need to standardize the calculation and presentation of investment performance.

Global Passport

Asset managers and both existing and prospective clients benefit from an established global standard for calculating and presenting investment performance. Investment practices, regulation, performance measurement, and reporting of performance vary considerably from country to country. By adhering to a global standard, firms in countries with minimal or no investment performance standards will be able to compete for business on an equal footing with firms from countries with more developed standards. Firms from countries with established practices will have more confidence in being fairly compared with local firms when competing for business in countries that have not previously adopted performance standards. Performance standards that are accepted globally enable investment firms to measure and present their investment performance so that investors can readily compare investment performance among firms.

Investor Confidence

Investment managers that adhere to investment performance standards help assure investors that the firm's investment performance is complete and fairly presented. Both prospective and existing clients of investment firms benefit from a global investment performance standard by having a greater degree of confidence in the performance information presented to them.

Objectives

The establishment of a voluntary global investment performance standard leads to an accepted set of best practices for calculating and presenting investment performance that is readily comparable among investment firms, regardless of geographic location. These standards also facilitate a dialogue between investment firms and their existing and prospective clients regarding investment performance.

The goals of the GIPS Executive Committee are:

- To establish investment industry best practices for calculating and presenting investment performance that promote investor interests and instill investor confidence;
- To obtain worldwide acceptance of a single standard for the calculation and presentation of investment performance based on the principles of fair representation and full disclosure;
- To promote the use of accurate and consistent investment performance data;
- To encourage fair, global competition among investment firms without creating barriers to entry; and
- To foster the notion of industry "self-regulation" on a global basis.

Overview

Key features of the GIPS standards include the following:

- The GIPS standards are ethical standards for investment performance presentation to ensure fair representation and full disclosure of investment performance. In order to claim compliance, firms must adhere to the requirements included in the GIPS standards.
- Meeting the objectives of fair representation and full disclosure is likely to require more than simply adhering to the minimum requirements of the GIPS standards. Firms should also adhere to the recommendations to achieve best practice in the calculation and presentation of performance.
- The GIPS standards require firms to include all actual, discretionary, fee-paying portfolios in at least one composite defined by investment mandate, objective, or strategy in order to prevent firms from cherry-picking their best performance.
- The GIPS standards rely on the integrity of input data. The accuracy of input data is critical to the accuracy of the performance presentation. The underlying valuations of portfolio holdings drive the portfolio's performance. It is essential for these and other inputs to be accurate. The GIPS standards require firms to adhere to certain calculation methodologies and to make specific disclosures along with the firm's performance.
- Firms must comply with all requirements of the GIPS standards, including any updates, Guidance Statements, interpretations, Questions & Answers (Q&As), and clarifications published by CFA Institute and the GIPS Executive Committee, which are available on the GIPS website (www.gipsstandards.org) as well as in the *GIPS Handbook*.

The GIPS standards do not address every aspect of performance measurement or cover unique characteristics of each asset class. The GIPS standards will continue to evolve over time to address additional areas of investment performance. Understanding and interpreting investment performance requires consideration of both risk and return. Historically, the GIPS standards focused primarily on returns. In the spirit of fair representation and full disclosure, and in order to provide investors with a more comprehensive view of a firm's performance, the 2010 edition of the GIPS standards includes new provisions related to risk.

Historical Performance Record

- A firm is required to initially present, at a minimum, five years of annual investment performance that is compliant with the GIPS standards. If the firm or the composite has been in existence less than five years, the firm must present performance since the firm's inception or the composite inception date.
- After a firm presents a minimum of five years of GIPS-compliant performance (or for the period since the firm's inception or the composite inception date if the firm or the composite has been in existence less than five years), the firm must present an additional year of performance each year, building up to a minimum of 10 years of GIPS-compliant performance.
- Firms may link non-GIPS-compliant performance to their GIPS-compliant performance provided that only GIPS-compliant performance is presented for periods after 1 January 2000 and the firm discloses the periods of non-compliance. Firms must not link non-GIPS-compliant performance for periods beginning on or after 1 January 2000 to their GIPS-compliant performance.

Firms that manage private equity, real estate, and/or wrap fee/separately managed account (SMA) portfolios must also comply with Sections 6, 7, and 8, respectively, of the Provisions of the GIPS standards that became effective as of 1 January 2006.

Compliance

Firms must take all steps necessary to ensure that they have satisfied all the requirements of the GIPS standards before claiming compliance. Firms are strongly encouraged to perform periodic internal compliance checks. Implementing adequate internal controls during all stages of the investment performance process—from data input to preparing performance presentations—will instill confidence in the validity of performance presented as well as in the claim of compliance.

Firms may choose to have an independent third-party verification that tests the construction of the firm's composites as well as the firm's policies and procedures as they relate to compliance with the GIPS standards. The value of verification is widely recognized, and being verified is considered to be best practice. The GIPS Executive Committee strongly recommends that firms be verified. In addition to verification, firms may also choose to have specifically focused composite testing (performance examination) performed by an independent third-party verifier to provide additional assurance regarding a particular composite.

Effective Date

The effective date for the 2010 edition of the GIPS standards is 1 January 2011. Compliant presentations that include performance for periods that begin on or after 1 January 2011 must be prepared in accordance with the 2010 edition of the GIPS standards. Prior editions of the GIPS standards may be found on the GIPS website (www.gipsstandards.org).

Implementing a Global Standard

The presence of a local sponsoring organization for investment performance standards is essential for effective implementation and ongoing support of the GIPS standards within a jurisdiction. Such sponsors also provide an important link between the GIPS Executive Committee, the governing body for the GIPS standards, and the local markets in which investment managers operate.

The sponsor, by actively supporting the GIPS standards and the work of the GIPS Executive Committee, ensures that the jurisdiction's interests are taken into account as the GIPS standards are developed. Compliance with the GIPS standards is voluntary, and support from the local market sponsor helps to drive the adoption of the GIPS standards.

The GIPS Executive Committee strongly encourages countries without an investment performance standard to promote the GIPS standards as the local standard and translate them into the local language when necessary. Although the GIPS standards may be translated into many languages, if a discrepancy arises, the English version of the GIPS standards is the official governing version.

The GIPS Executive Committee will continue to promote the principles of fair representation and full disclosure and develop the GIPS standards so that they maintain their relevance within the changing investment management industry.

The self-regulatory nature of the GIPS standards necessitates a strong commitment to ethical integrity. Self-regulation also assists regulators in exercising their responsibility for ensuring the fair disclosure of information within financial markets. The GIPS Executive Committee encourages regulators to:

- Recognize the benefit of voluntary compliance with standards that represent global best practices;
- Give consideration to taking enforcement actions against firms that falsely claim compliance with the GIPS standards; and
- Recognize and encourage independent third-party verification.

Where existing laws, regulations, or industry standards already impose requirements related to the calculation and presentation of investment performance, firms are strongly encouraged to comply with the GIPS standards in addition to applicable regulatory requirements. Compliance with applicable law and/or regulation does not necessarily lead to compliance with the GIPS standards. In cases in which laws and/or regulations conflict with the GIPS standards, firms are required to comply with the laws and regulations and make full disclosure of the conflict in the compliant presentation.

OPTIONAL SEGMENT

Sponsors

The presence of a local sponsoring organization for investment performance standards, known as a "sponsor," is essential for effective implementation of the GIPS standards and ongoing support within a local market. Sponsors collectively form the GIPS Council, which provides a formal role in the ongoing development and oversight of the GIPS standards. Sponsors:

- Promote the GIPS standards locally;
- Provide local market support and input for the GIPS standards;
- Present local market–specific issues to the GIPS Executive Committee; and
- Participate in the governance of the GIPS standards via membership in the GIPS Council and Regional Investment Performance Subcommittees.

Each organization undergoes a formal review before being endorsed as a sponsor. Additional information and a current list of sponsors can be found on the GIPS website (www.gipsstandards.org).

Endorsed GIPS Sponsors (as of 1 January 2010)

Australia	Investment and Financial Services Association Limited—Performance Analyst Group
Austria	1) Österreichische Vereinigung für Finanzanalyse und Asset Management and 2) Vereinigung Österreichischer Investmentgesellschaften
Belgium	Belgian Asset Managers Association
Canada	Canadian Investment Performance Committee
Denmark	The Danish Society of Financial Analysts and CFA Denmark
France	1) Société Française des Analystes Financiers and 2) Association Française de la Gestion Financière

Germany	German Asset Management Standards Committee: 1) Bundesverband Investment und Asset Management e.V., 2) Deutsche Vereinigung für Finanzanalyse und Asset Management, and 3) German CFA Society
Greece	Hellenic CFA Society
Hong Kong SAR	Local Sponsor: The Hong Kong Society of Financial Analysts
Hungary	1) CFA Society of Hungary and 2) the Association of Hungarian Investment Fund and Asset Management Companies
Ireland	Irish Association of Investment Managers
Italy	Italian Investment Performance Committee: 1) L'Associazione Bancaria Italiana, 2) L'Associazione Italiana degli Analisti Finanziari, 3) Assogestioni, 4) Sviluppo Mercato Fondi Pensione, 5) Assirevi, and 6) Italian CFA Society
Japan	The Security Analysts Association of Japan
Kazakhstan	Kazakhstan Association of Financial and Investment Analysts
Liechtenstein	Liechtenstein Bankers' Association
Micronesia	Asia Pacific Association for Fiduciary Studies
The Netherlands	The Netherlands Beroepsvereniging van Beleggingsprofessionals
New Zealand	CFA Society of New Zealand
Norway	The Norwegian Society of Financial Analysts
Pakistan	CFA Association of Pakistan
Portugal	Associação Portuguesa de Analista Financeiros
Russia	National League of Management Companies
Singapore	Investment Management Association of Singapore
South Africa	Association for Savings and Investment, South Africa
South Korea	Korea GIPS Committee
Spain	Asociación Española de Presentación de Resultados de Gestión
Sri Lanka	CFA Sri Lanka
Sweden	Swedish Society of Financial Analysts
Switzerland	Swiss Bankers Association
Ukraine	The Ukrainian Association of Investment Business
United Kingdom	UK Investment Performance Committee: 1) Association of British Insurers, 2) Investment Management Association, and 3) National Association of Pension Funds
United States	CFA Institute—US Investment Performance Committee

END OPTIONAL SEGMENT

PROVISIONS OF THE GLOBAL INVESTMENT PERFORMANCE STANDARDS

I.

The provisions within the GIPS standards are divided into the following nine sections: Fundamentals of Compliance, Input Data, Calculation Methodology, Composite Construction, Disclosure, Presentation and Reporting, Real Estate, Private Equity, and Wrap Fee/Separately Managed Account (SMA) Portfolios.

The provisions for each section are categorized into requirements and recommendations. Firms must meet all the requirements to claim compliance with the GIPS standards. Firms are encouraged to implement as many of the recommendations as possible. These recommended provisions are considered to be industry best practice and assist firms in fully adhering to the spirit and intent of the GIPS standards.

0 **Fundamentals of Compliance:** Several core principles create the foundation for the GIPS standards, including properly defining the firm, providing compliant presentations to all prospective clients, adhering to applicable laws and regulations, and ensuring that information presented is not false or misleading. Two important issues that a firm must consider when becoming compliant with the GIPS standards are the definition of the firm and the firm's definition of discretion. The definition of the firm is the foundation for firm-wide compliance and creates defined boundaries whereby total firm assets can be determined. The firm's definition of discretion establishes criteria to judge which portfolios must be included in a composite and is based on the firm's ability to implement its investment strategy.

1 **Input Data:** Consistency of input data used to calculate performance is critical to effective compliance with the GIPS standards and establishes the foundation for full, fair, and comparable investment performance presentations. For periods beginning on or after 1 January 2011, all portfolios must be valued in accordance with the definition of fair value and the GIPS Valuation Principles.

2 **Calculation Methodology:** Achieving comparability among investment management firms' performance presentations requires uniformity in methods used to calculate returns. The GIPS standards mandate the use of certain calculation methodologies to facilitate comparability.

3 **Composite Construction:** A composite is an aggregation of one or more portfolios managed according to a similar investment mandate, objective, or strategy. The composite return is the asset-weighted average of the performance of all portfolios in the composite. Creating meaningful composites is essential to the fair presentation, consistency, and comparability of performance over time and among firms.

4 **Disclosure:** Disclosures allow firms to elaborate on the data provided in the presentation and give the reader the proper context in which to understand the performance. To comply with the GIPS standards, firms must disclose certain information in all compliant presentations regarding their performance and the policies adopted by the firm. Although some disclosures are required for all firms, others are specific to certain circumstances and may not be applicable in all situations. One of the essential disclosures for every firm is the claim of compliance. Once a firm meets all the requirements of the GIPS standards, it must appropriately use the claim of compliance to indicate compliance with the GIPS standards. The 2010 edition of the GIPS standards includes a revised compliance statement that indicates if the firm has or has not been verified.

5 **Presentation and Reporting:** After constructing the composites, gathering the input data, calculating returns, and determining the necessary disclosures, the firm must incorporate this information in presentations based on the requirements in the GIPS standards for presenting investment performance. No finite set of requirements can cover all potential situations or anticipate future developments in investment industry structure, technology, products, or practices. When appropriate, firms have the responsibility to include in GIPS-compliant presentations information not addressed by the GIPS standards.

6 **Real Estate:** Unless otherwise noted, this section supplements all of the required and recommended provisions in Sections 0–5. Real estate provisions were first included in the 2005 edition of the GIPS standards and became effective 1 January 2006. The 2010 edition of the GIPS standards includes new provisions for closed-end real estate funds. Firms should note that certain provisions of Sections 0–5 do not apply to real estate investments or are superseded by provisions within Section 6. The provisions that do not apply have been noted within Section 6.

7 **Private Equity:** Unless otherwise noted, this section supplements all of the required and recommended provisions in Sections 0–5. Private equity provisions were first included in the 2005 edition of the GIPS standards and became effective 1 January 2006. Firms should note that certain provisions in Sections 0–5 do not apply to private equity investments or are superseded by provisions within Section 7. The provisions that do not apply have been noted within Section 7.

8 **Wrap Fee/Separately Managed Account (SMA) Portfolios:** Unless otherwise noted, this section supplements all of the required and recommended provisions in Sections 0–5. Firms should note that certain provisions in Sections 0–5 of the GIPS standards do not apply to wrap fee/SMA portfolios or are superseded by provisions within Section 8. The provisions that do not apply have been noted within Section 8.

Defined Terms: Words appearing in small capital letters in the GIPS standards are defined in the GIPS **Glossary**, which is located at the end of this reading.

0 Fundamentals of Compliance

Fundamentals of Compliance—Requirements

0.A.1 FIRMS MUST comply with all the REQUIREMENTS of the GIPS standards, including any updates, Guidance Statements, interpretations, Questions & Answers (Q&As), and clarifications published by CFA Institute and the GIPS Executive Committee, which are available on the GIPS standards website (www.gipsstandards.org) as well as in the *GIPS Handbook.*

0.A.2 FIRMS MUST comply with all applicable laws and regulations regarding the calculation and presentation of performance.

0.A.3 FIRMS MUST NOT present performance or performance-related information that is false or misleading.

0.A.4 The GIPS standards MUST be applied on a FIRM-wide basis.

0.A.5 FIRMS MUST document their policies and procedures used in establishing and maintaining compliance with the GIPS standards, including ensuring the existence and ownership of client assets, and MUST apply them consistently.

0.A.6 If the FIRM does not meet all the REQUIREMENTS of the GIPS standards, the FIRM MUST NOT represent or state that it is "in compliance with the Global Investment Performance Standards except for . . ." or make any other statements that may indicate partial compliance with the GIPS standards.

0.A.7 Statements referring to the calculation methodology as being "in accordance," "in compliance," or "consistent" with the Global Investment Performance Standards, or similar statements, are prohibited.

0.A.8 Statements referring to the performance of a single, existing client PORTFOLIO as being "calculated in accordance with the Global Investment Performance Standards" are prohibited, except when a GIPS-compliant FIRM reports the performance of an individual client's PORTFOLIO to that client.

0.A.9 FIRMS MUST make every reasonable effort to provide a COMPLIANT PRESENTATION to all PROSPECTIVE CLIENTS. FIRMS MUST NOT choose to whom they present a COMPLIANT PRESENTATION. As long as a PROSPECTIVE CLIENT has received a COMPLIANT PRESENTATION within the previous 12 months, the FIRM has met this REQUIREMENT.

0.A.10 FIRMS MUST provide a complete list of COMPOSITE DESCRIPTIONS to any PROSPECTIVE CLIENT that makes such a request. FIRMS MUST include terminated COMPOSITES on the FIRM's list of COMPOSITE DESCRIPTIONS for at least five years after the COMPOSITE TERMINATION DATE.

0.A.11 FIRMS MUST provide a COMPLIANT PRESENTATION for any COMPOSITE listed on the FIRM's list of COMPOSITE DESCRIPTIONS to any PROSPECTIVE CLIENT that makes such a request.

0.A.12 FIRMS MUST be defined as an investment firm, subsidiary, or division held out to clients or PROSPECTIVE CLIENTS as a DISTINCT BUSINESS ENTITY.

0.A.13 For periods beginning on or after 1 January 2011, TOTAL FIRM ASSETS MUST be the aggregate FAIR VALUE of all discretionary and non-discretionary assets managed by the FIRM. This includes both fee-paying and non-fee-paying PORTFOLIOS.[1]

0.A.14 TOTAL FIRM ASSETS MUST include assets assigned to a SUB-ADVISOR provided the FIRM has discretion over the selection of the SUB-ADVISOR.

0.A.15 Changes in a FIRM's organization MUST NOT lead to alteration of historical COMPOSITE performance.

0.A.16 When the FIRM jointly markets with other firms, the FIRM claiming compliance with the GIPS standards MUST be sure that it is clearly defined and separate relative to other firms being marketed, and that it is clear which FIRM is claiming compliance.

Fundamentals of Compliance—Recommendations

0.B.1 FIRMS SHOULD comply with the RECOMMENDATIONS of the GIPS standards, including RECOMMENDATIONS in any updates, Guidance Statements, interpretations, Questions & Answers (Q&As), and clarifications published by CFA Institute and the GIPS Executive Committee, which will be made available on the GIPS website (www.gipsstandards.org) as well as in the *GIPS Handbook.*

0.B.2 FIRMS SHOULD be verified.

0.B.3 FIRMS SHOULD adopt the broadest, most meaningful definition of the FIRM. The scope of this definition SHOULD include all geographical (country, regional, etc.) offices operating under the same brand name regardless of the actual name of the individual investment management company.

0.B.4 FIRMS SHOULD provide to each existing client, on an annual basis, a COMPLIANT PRESENTATION of the COMPOSITE in which the client's PORTFOLIO is included.

1 For periods prior to 1 January 2011, TOTAL FIRM ASSETS MUST be the aggregate of the MARKET VALUE of all discretionary and non-discretionary assets under management within the defined FIRM.

OPTIONAL SEGMENT

1 Input Data

Input Data—Requirements

1.A.1 All data and information necessary to support all items included in a COMPLIANT PRESENTATION MUST be captured and maintained.

1.A.2 For periods beginning on or after 1 January 2011, PORTFOLIOS MUST be valued in accordance with the definition of FAIR VALUE and the GIPS Valuation Principles.[2]

1.A.3 FIRMS MUST value PORTFOLIOS in accordance with the COMPOSITE-specific valuation policy. PORTFOLIOS MUST be valued:

- **a** For periods beginning on or after 1 January 2001, at least monthly.[3]
- **b** For periods beginning on or after 1 January 2010, on the date of all LARGE CASH FLOWS. FIRMS MUST define LARGE CASH FLOW for each COMPOSITE to determine when PORTFOLIOS in that COMPOSITE MUST be valued.
- **c** No more frequently than required by the valuation policy.

1.A.4 For periods beginning on or after 1 January 2010, FIRMS MUST value PORTFOLIOS as of the calendar month end or the last business day of the month.

1.A.5 For periods beginning on or after 1 January 2005, FIRMS MUST use TRADE DATE ACCOUNTING.

1.A.6 ACCRUAL ACCOUNTING MUST be used for fixed-income securities and all other investments that earn interest income. The value of fixed-income securities MUST include accrued income.

1.A.7 For periods beginning on or after 1 January 2006, COMPOSITES MUST have consistent beginning and ending annual valuation dates. Unless the COMPOSITE is reported on a non-calendar fiscal year, the beginning and ending valuation dates MUST be at calendar year end or on the last business day of the year.

Input Data—Recommendations

1.B.1 FIRMS SHOULD value PORTFOLIOS on the date of all EXTERNAL CASH FLOWS.

1.B.2 Valuations SHOULD be obtained from a qualified independent third party.

1.B.3 ACCRUAL ACCOUNTING SHOULD be used for dividends (as of the ex-dividend date).

1.B.4 FIRMS SHOULD accrue INVESTMENT MANAGEMENT FEES.

2 Calculation Methodology

Calculation Methodology—Requirements

2.A.1 TOTAL RETURNS MUST be used.

2.A.2 FIRMS MUST calculate TIME-WEIGHTED RATES OF RETURN that adjust for EXTERNAL CASH FLOWS. Both periodic and sub-period returns MUST be geometrically LINKED. EXTERNAL CASH FLOWS MUST be treated according to the FIRM'S COMPOSITE-specific policy. At a minimum:

2 For periods prior to 1 January 2011, PORTFOLIO valuations MUST be based on MARKET VALUES (not cost basis or book values).

3 For periods prior to 1 January 2001, PORTFOLIOS MUST be valued at least quarterly.

a For periods beginning on or after 1 January 2001, FIRMS MUST calculate PORTFOLIO returns at least monthly.

b For periods beginning on or after 1 January 2005, FIRMS MUST calculate PORTFOLIO returns that adjust for daily-weighted EXTERNAL CASH FLOWS.

2.A.3 Returns from cash and cash equivalents held in PORTFOLIOS MUST be included in all return calculations.

2.A.4 All returns MUST be calculated after the deduction of the actual TRADING EXPENSES incurred during the period. FIRMS MUST NOT use estimated TRADING EXPENSES.

2.A.5 If the actual TRADING EXPENSES cannot be identified and segregated from a BUNDLED FEE:

a When calculating GROSS-OF-FEES returns, returns MUST be reduced by the entire BUNDLED FEE or the portion of the BUNDLED FEE that includes the TRADING EXPENSES. FIRMS MUST NOT use estimated TRADING EXPENSES.

b When calculating NET-OF-FEES returns, returns MUST be reduced by the entire BUNDLED FEE or the portion of the BUNDLED FEE that includes the TRADING EXPENSES and the INVESTMENT MANAGEMENT FEE. FIRMS MUST NOT use estimated TRADING EXPENSES.

2.A.6 COMPOSITE returns MUST be calculated by asset-weighting the individual PORTFOLIO returns using beginning-of-period values or a method that reflects both beginning-of-period values and EXTERNAL CASH FLOWS.

2.A.7 COMPOSITE returns MUST be calculated:

a For periods beginning on or after 1 January 2006, by asset-weighting the individual PORTFOLIO returns at least quarterly.

b For periods beginning on or after 1 January 2010, by asset-weighting the individual PORTFOLIO returns at least monthly.

Calculation Methodology—Recommendations

2.B.1 Returns SHOULD be calculated net of non-reclaimable withholding taxes on dividends, interest, and capital gains. Reclaimable withholding taxes SHOULD be accrued.

2.B.2 For periods prior to 1 January 2010, FIRMS SHOULD calculate COMPOSITE returns by asset-weighting the individual PORTFOLIO returns at least monthly.

3 Composite Construction

Composite Construction—Requirements

3.A.1 All actual, fee-paying, discretionary PORTFOLIOS MUST be included in at least one COMPOSITE. Although non-fee-paying discretionary PORTFOLIOS may be included in a COMPOSITE (with appropriate disclosure), non-discretionary PORTFOLIOS MUST NOT be included in a FIRM'S COMPOSITES.

3.A.2 COMPOSITES MUST include only actual assets managed by the FIRM.

3.A.3 FIRMS MUST NOT LINK performance of simulated or model PORTFOLIOS with actual performance.

3.A.4 COMPOSITES MUST be defined according to investment mandate, objective, or strategy. COMPOSITES MUST include all PORTFOLIOS that meet the COMPOSITE DEFINITION. Any change to a COMPOSITE DEFINITION MUST NOT be applied retroactively. The COMPOSITE DEFINITION MUST be made available upon request.

3.A.5 COMPOSITES MUST include new PORTFOLIOS on a timely and consistent basis after each PORTFOLIO comes under management.

3.A.6 Terminated PORTFOLIOS MUST be included in the historical performance of the COMPOSITE up to the last full measurement period that each PORTFOLIO was under management.

3.A.7 PORTFOLIOS MUST NOT be switched from one COMPOSITE to another unless documented changes to a PORTFOLIO'S investment mandate, objective, or strategy or the redefinition of the COMPOSITE makes it appropriate. The historical performance of the PORTFOLIO MUST remain with the original COMPOSITE.

3.A.8 For periods beginning on or after 1 January 2010, a CARVE-OUT MUST NOT be included in a COMPOSITE unless the CARVE-OUT is managed separately with its own cash balance.[4]

3.A.9 If the FIRM sets a minimum asset level for PORTFOLIOS to be included in a COMPOSITE, the FIRM MUST NOT include PORTFOLIOS below the minimum asset level in that COMPOSITE. Any changes to a COMPOSITE-specific minimum asset level MUST NOT be applied retroactively.

3.A.10 FIRMS that wish to remove PORTFOLIOS from COMPOSITES in cases of SIGNIFICANT CASH FLOWS MUST define "significant" on an EX-ANTE, COMPOSITE-specific basis and MUST consistently follow the COMPOSITE-specific policy.

Composite Construction—Recommendations

3.B.1 If the FIRM sets a minimum asset level for PORTFOLIOS to be included in a COMPOSITE, the FIRM SHOULD NOT present a COMPLIANT PRESENTATION of the COMPOSITE to a PROSPECTIVE CLIENT known not to meet the COMPOSITE'S minimum asset level.

3.B.2 To remove the effect of a SIGNIFICANT CASH FLOW, the FIRM SHOULD use a TEMPORARY NEW ACCOUNT.

4 Disclosure

Disclosure—Requirements

4.A.1 Once a FIRM has met all the REQUIREMENTS of the GIPS standards, the FIRM MUST disclose its compliance with the GIPS standards using one of the following compliance statements. The claim of compliance MUST only be used in a COMPLIANT PRESENTATION.

For FIRMS that are verified:

> "[Insert name of FIRM] claims compliance with the Global Investment Performance Standards (GIPS®) and has prepared and presented this report in compliance with the GIPS standards.

4 For periods prior to 1 January 2010, if CARVE-OUTS were included in a COMPOSITE, cash MUST have been allocated to the CARVE-OUT in a timely and consistent manner.

[Insert name of FIRM] has been independently verified for the periods [insert dates]. The verification report(s) is/are available upon request.

Verification assesses whether (1) the firm has complied with all the composite construction requirements of the GIPS standards on a firm-wide basis and (2) the firm's policies and procedures are designed to calculate and present performance in compliance with the GIPS standards. Verification does not ensure the accuracy of any specific composite presentation."

For COMPOSITES of a verified FIRM that have also had a PERFORMANCE EXAMINATION:

"[Insert name of FIRM] claims compliance with the Global Investment Performance Standards (GIPS®) and has prepared and presented this report in compliance with the GIPS standards. [Insert name of FIRM] has been independently verified for the periods [insert dates].

Verification assesses whether (1) the firm has complied with all the composite construction requirements of the GIPS standards on a firm-wide basis and (2) the firm's policies and procedures are designed to calculate and present performance in compliance with the GIPS standards. The [insert name of COMPOSITE] composite has been examined for the periods [insert dates]. The verification and performance examination reports are available upon request."

For FIRMS that have not been verified:

"[Insert name of FIRM] claims compliance with the Global Investment Performance Standards (GIPS®) and has prepared and presented this report in compliance with the GIPS standards. [Insert name of FIRM] has not been independently verified."

4.A.2 FIRMS MUST disclose the definition of the FIRM used to determine TOTAL FIRM ASSETS and FIRM-wide compliance.

4.A.3 FIRMS MUST disclose the COMPOSITE DESCRIPTION.

4.A.4 FIRMS MUST disclose the BENCHMARK DESCRIPTION.

4.A.5 When presenting GROSS-OF-FEES returns, FIRMS MUST disclose if any other fees are deducted in addition to the TRADING EXPENSES.

4.A.6 When presenting NET-OF-FEES returns, FIRMS MUST disclose:

a If any other fees are deducted in addition to the INVESTMENT MANAGEMENT FEES and TRADING EXPENSES;

b If model or actual INVESTMENT MANAGEMENT FEES are used; and

c If returns are net of any PERFORMANCE-BASED FEES.

4.A.7 FIRMS MUST disclose the currency used to express performance.

4.A.8 FIRMS MUST disclose which measure of INTERNAL DISPERSION is presented.

4.A.9 FIRMS MUST disclose the FEE SCHEDULE appropriate to the COMPLIANT PRESENTATION.

4.A.10 FIRMS MUST disclose the COMPOSITE CREATION DATE.

4.A.11 FIRMS MUST disclose that the FIRM's list of COMPOSITE DESCRIPTIONS is available upon request.

4.A.12 FIRMS MUST disclose that policies for valuing PORTFOLIOS, calculating performance, and preparing COMPLIANT PRESENTATIONS are available upon request.

4.A.13 FIRMS MUST disclose the presence, use, and extent of leverage, derivatives, and short positions, if material, including a description of the frequency of use and characteristics of the instruments sufficient to identify risks.

4.A.14 FIRMS MUST disclose all significant events that would help a PROSPECTIVE CLIENT interpret the COMPLIANT PRESENTATION.

4.A.15 For any performance presented for periods prior to 1 January 2000 that does not comply with the GIPS standards, FIRMS MUST disclose the periods of non-compliance.

4.A.16 If the FIRM is redefined, the FIRM MUST disclose the date of, description of, and reason for the redefinition.

4.A.17 If a COMPOSITE is redefined, the FIRM MUST disclose the date of, description of, and reason for the redefinition.

4.A.18 FIRMS MUST disclose changes to the name of a COMPOSITE.

4.A.19 FIRMS MUST disclose the minimum asset level, if any, below which PORTFOLIOS are not included in a COMPOSITE. FIRMS MUST also disclose any changes to the minimum asset level.

4.A.20 FIRMS MUST disclose relevant details of the treatment of withholding taxes on dividends, interest income, and capital gains, if material. FIRMS MUST also disclose if BENCHMARK returns are net of withholding taxes if this information is available.

4.A.21 For periods beginning on or after 1 January 2011, FIRMS MUST disclose and describe any known material differences in exchange rates or valuation sources used among the PORTFOLIOS within a COMPOSITE, and between the COMPOSITE and the BENCHMARK.[5]

4.A.22 If the COMPLIANT PRESENTATION conforms with laws and/or regulations that conflict with the REQUIREMENTS of the GIPS standards, FIRMS MUST disclose this fact and disclose the manner in which the laws and/or regulations conflict with the GIPS standards.

4.A.23 For periods prior to 1 January 2010, if CARVE-OUTS are included in a COMPOSITE, FIRMS MUST disclose the policy used to allocate cash to CARVE-OUTS.

4.A.24 If a COMPOSITE contains PORTFOLIOS with BUNDLED FEES, FIRMS MUST disclose the types of fees that are included in the BUNDLED FEE.

4.A.25 For periods beginning on or after 1 January 2006, FIRMS MUST disclose the use of a SUB-ADVISOR and the periods a SUB-ADVISOR was used.

4.A.26 For periods prior to 1 January 2010, FIRMS MUST disclose if any PORTFOLIOS were not valued at calendar month end or on the last business day of the month.

4.A.27 For periods beginning on or after 1 January 2011, FIRMS MUST disclose the use of subjective unobservable inputs for valuing PORTFOLIO investments (as described in the GIPS Valuation Principles) if the PORTFOLIO investments valued using subjective unobservable inputs are material to the COMPOSITE.

4.A.28 For periods beginning on or after 1 January 2011, FIRMS MUST disclose if the COMPOSITE's valuation hierarchy materially differs from the RECOMMENDED hierarchy in the GIPS Valuation Principles.

4.A.29 If the FIRM determines no appropriate BENCHMARK for the COMPOSITE exists, the FIRM MUST disclose why no BENCHMARK is presented.

---

5 For periods prior to 1 January 2011, FIRMS MUST disclose and describe any known inconsistencies in the exchange rates used among the PORTFOLIOS within a COMPOSITE and between the COMPOSITE and the BENCHMARK.

4.A.30 If the FIRM changes the BENCHMARK, the FIRM MUST disclose the date of, description of, and reason for the change.

4.A.31 If a custom BENCHMARK or combination of multiple BENCHMARKS is used, the FIRM MUST disclose the BENCHMARK components, weights, and rebalancing process.

4.A.32 If the FIRM has adopted a SIGNIFICANT CASH FLOW policy for a specific COMPOSITE, the FIRM MUST disclose how the FIRM defines a SIGNIFICANT CASH FLOW for that COMPOSITE and for which periods.

4.A.33 FIRMS MUST disclose if the three-year annualized EX-POST STANDARD DEVIATION of the COMPOSITE and/or BENCHMARK is not presented because 36 monthly returns are not available.

4.A.34 If the FIRM determines that the three-year annualized EX-POST STANDARD DEVIATION is not relevant or appropriate, the FIRM MUST:

- **a** Describe why EX-POST STANDARD DEVIATION is not relevant or appropriate; and
- **b** Describe the additional risk measure presented and why it was selected.

4.A.35 FIRMS MUST disclose if the performance from a past firm or affiliation is LINKED to the performance of the FIRM.

Disclosure—Recommendations

4.B.1 FIRMS SHOULD disclose material changes to valuation policies and/or methodologies.

4.B.2 FIRMS SHOULD disclose material changes to calculation policies and/or methodologies.

4.B.3 FIRMS SHOULD disclose material differences between the BENCHMARK and the COMPOSITE's investment mandate, objective, or strategy.

4.B.4 FIRMS SHOULD disclose the key assumptions used to value PORTFOLIO investments.

4.B.5 If a parent company contains multiple firms, each FIRM within the parent company SHOULD disclose a list of the other firms contained within the parent company.

4.B.6 For periods prior to 1 January 2011, FIRMS SHOULD disclose the use of subjective unobservable inputs for valuing PORTFOLIO investments (as described in the GIPS Valuation Principles) if the PORTFOLIO investments valued using subjective unobservable inputs are material to the COMPOSITE.

4.B.7 For periods prior to 1 January 2006, FIRMS SHOULD disclose the use of a SUB-ADVISOR and the periods a SUB-ADVISOR was used.

4.B.8 FIRMS SHOULD disclose if a COMPOSITE contains PROPRIETARY ASSETS.

5 Presentation and Reporting

Presentation and Reporting—Requirements

5.A.1 The following items MUST be presented in each COMPLIANT PRESENTATION:

- **a** At least five years of performance (or for the period since the FIRM's inception or the COMPOSITE INCEPTION DATE if the FIRM or the COMPOSITE has been in existence less than five years) that meets the REQUIREMENTS of the GIPS standards. After a FIRM presents a minimum of five years of GIPS-compliant performance (or for the period since the FIRM's inception or the COMPOSITE INCEPTION DATE if the FIRM or the COMPOSITE has been in existence less than five years), the FIRM MUST present an additional year of performance each year, building up to a minimum of 10 years of GIPS-compliant performance.

b COMPOSITE returns for each annual period. COMPOSITE returns MUST be clearly identified as GROSS-OF-FEES or NET-OF-FEES.

c For COMPOSITES with a COMPOSITE INCEPTION DATE of 1 January 2011 or later, when the initial period is less than a full year, returns from the COMPOSITE INCEPTION DATE through the initial annual period end.

d For COMPOSITES with a COMPOSITE TERMINATION DATE of 1 January 2011 or later, returns from the last annual period end through the COMPOSITE TERMINATION DATE.

e The TOTAL RETURN for the BENCHMARK for each annual period. The BENCHMARK MUST reflect the investment mandate, objective, or strategy of the COMPOSITE.

f The number of PORTFOLIOS in the COMPOSITE as of each annual period end. If the COMPOSITE contains five or fewer PORTFOLIOS at period end, the number of PORTFOLIOS is not REQUIRED.

g COMPOSITE assets as of each annual period end.

h Either TOTAL FIRM ASSETS or COMPOSITE assets as a percentage of TOTAL FIRM ASSETS, as of each annual period end.

i A measure of INTERNAL DISPERSION of individual PORTFOLIO returns for each annual period. If the COMPOSITE contains five or fewer PORTFOLIOS for the full year, a measure of INTERNAL DISPERSION is not REQUIRED.

5.A.2 For periods ending on or after 1 January 2011, FIRMS MUST present, as of each annual period end:

a The three-year annualized EX-POST STANDARD DEVIATION (using monthly returns) of both the COMPOSITE and the BENCHMARK; and

b An additional three-year EX-POST risk measure for the BENCHMARK (if available and appropriate) and the COMPOSITE, if the FIRM determines that the three-year annualized EX-POST STANDARD DEVIATION is not relevant or appropriate. The PERIODICITY of the COMPOSITE and the BENCHMARK MUST be identical when calculating the EX-POST risk measure.

5.A.3 FIRMS MUST NOT LINK non-GIPS-compliant performance for periods beginning on or after 1 January 2000 to their GIPS-compliant performance. FIRMS may LINK non-GIPS-compliant performance to GIPS-compliant performance provided that only GIPS-compliant performance is presented for periods beginning on or after 1 January 2000.

5.A.4 Returns for periods of less than one year MUST NOT be annualized.

5.A.5 For periods beginning on or after 1 January 2006 and ending prior to 1 January 2011, if a COMPOSITE includes CARVE-OUTS, the FIRM MUST present the percentage of COMPOSITE assets represented by CARVE-OUTS as of each annual period end.

5.A.6 If a COMPOSITE includes non-fee-paying PORTFOLIOS, the FIRM MUST present the percentage of COMPOSITE assets represented by non-fee-paying PORTFOLIOS as of each annual period end.

5.A.7 If a COMPOSITE includes PORTFOLIOS with BUNDLED FEES, the FIRM MUST present the percentage of COMPOSITE assets represented by PORTFOLIOS with BUNDLED FEES as of each annual period end.

5.A.8 **a** Performance of a past firm or affiliation MUST be LINKED to or used to represent the historical performance of a new or acquiring FIRM if, on a COMPOSITE-specific basis:

i. Substantially all of the investment decision makers are employed by the new or acquiring FIRM (e.g., research department staff, portfolio managers, and other relevant staff);

ii. The decision-making process remains substantially intact and independent within the new or acquiring FIRM; and

iii. The new or acquiring FIRM has records that document and support the performance.

b If a FIRM acquires another firm or affiliation, the FIRM has one year to bring any non-compliant assets into compliance.

Presentation and Reporting—Recommendations

5.B.1 FIRMS SHOULD present GROSS-OF-FEES returns.

5.B.2 FIRMS SHOULD present the following items:

a Cumulative returns of the COMPOSITE and the BENCHMARK for all periods;

b Equal-weighted mean and median COMPOSITE returns;

c Quarterly and/or monthly returns; and

d Annualized COMPOSITE and BENCHMARK returns for periods longer than 12 months.

5.B.3 For periods prior to 1 January 2011, FIRMS SHOULD present the three-year annualized EX-POST STANDARD DEVIATION (using monthly returns) of the COMPOSITE and the BENCHMARK as of each annual period end.

5.B.4 For each period for which an annualized EX-POST STANDARD DEVIATION of the COMPOSITE and the BENCHMARK are presented, the corresponding annualized return of the COMPOSITE and the BENCHMARK SHOULD also be presented.

5.B.5 For each period for which an annualized return of the COMPOSITE and the BENCHMARK are presented, the corresponding annualized EX-POST STANDARD DEVIATION (using monthly returns) of the COMPOSITE and the BENCHMARK SHOULD also be presented.

5.B.6 FIRMS SHOULD present additional relevant COMPOSITE-level EX-POST risk measures.

5.B.7 FIRMS SHOULD present more than 10 years of annual performance in the COMPLIANT PRESENTATION.

5.B.8 FIRMS SHOULD comply with the GIPS standards for all historical periods.

5.B.9 FIRMS SHOULD update COMPLIANT PRESENTATIONS quarterly.

6 Real Estate

Unless otherwise noted, the following REAL ESTATE provisions supplement the REQUIRED and RECOMMENDED provisions of the GIPS standards in Sections 0–5.

REAL ESTATE provisions were first included in the GIPS standards in 2005 and became effective 1 January 2006. All COMPLIANT PRESENTATIONS that included REAL ESTATE performance for periods beginning on or after 1 January 2006 were REQUIRED to meet all the REQUIREMENTS of the REAL ESTATE provisions of the 2005 edition of the GIPS standards. The following REAL ESTATE provisions are effective 1

January 2011. All REAL ESTATE COMPOSITES that include performance for periods beginning on or after 1 January 2011 MUST comply with all the REQUIREMENTS and SHOULD adhere to the RECOMMENDATIONS of the following REAL ESTATE provisions.

The following investment types are not considered REAL ESTATE and, therefore, MUST follow Sections 0–5 of the Global Investment Performance Standards:

- Publicly traded REAL ESTATE securities;
- Commercial mortgage-backed securities (CMBS); and
- Private debt investments, including commercial and residential loans where the expected return is solely related to contractual interest rates without any participation in the economic performance of the underlying REAL ESTATE.

Real Estate—Requirements

Input Data—Requirements (the following provisions do not apply: 1.A.3.a, 1.A.3.b, and 1.A.4)

6.A.1 For periods beginning on or after 1 January 2011, REAL ESTATE investments MUST be valued in accordance with the definition of FAIR VALUE and the GIPS Valuation Principles in Chapter II.[6]

6.A.2 For periods beginning on or after 1 January 2008, REAL ESTATE investments MUST be valued at least quarterly.[7]

6.A.3 For periods beginning on or after 1 January 2010, FIRMS MUST value PORTFOLIOS as of each quarter end or the last business day of each quarter.

6.A.4 REAL ESTATE investments MUST have an EXTERNAL VALUATION:

- **a** For periods prior to 1 January 2012, at least once every 36 months.
- **b** For periods beginning on or after 1 January 2012, at least once every 12 months unless client agreements stipulate otherwise, in which case REAL ESTATE investments MUST have an EXTERNAL VALUATION at least once every 36 months or per the client agreement if the client agreement requires EXTERNAL VALUATIONS more frequently than every 36 months.

6.A.5 EXTERNAL VALUATIONS must be performed by an independent external PROFESSIONALLY DESIGNATED, CERTIFIED, OR LICENSED COMMERCIAL PROPERTY VALUER/APPRAISER. In markets where these professionals are not available, the FIRM MUST take the necessary steps to ensure that only well-qualified independent property valuers or appraisers are used.

Calculation Methodology—Requirements (the following provisions do not apply: 2.A.2.a, 2.A.4, and 2.A.7)

6.A.6 FIRMS MUST calculate PORTFOLIO returns at least quarterly.

6.A.7 All returns MUST be calculated after the deduction of actual TRANSACTION EXPENSES incurred during the period.

---

6 For periods prior to 1 January 2011, REAL ESTATE investments MUST be valued at MARKET VALUE (as previously defined for REAL ESTATE in the 2005 edition of the GIPS standards).

7 For periods prior to 1 January 2008, REAL ESTATE investments MUST be valued at least once every 12 months.

6.A.8 For periods beginning on or after 1 January 2011, INCOME RETURNS and CAPITAL RETURNS (component returns) MUST be calculated separately using geometrically LINKED TIME-WEIGHTED RATES OF RETURN.

6.A.9 COMPOSITE TIME-WEIGHTED RATES OF RETURN, including component returns, MUST be calculated by asset-weighting the individual PORTFOLIO returns at least quarterly.

Disclosure—Requirements (the following provisions do not apply: 4.A.5, 4.A.6.a, 4.A.15, 4.A.26, 4.A.33, and 4.A.34)

6.A.10 The following items MUST be disclosed in each COMPLIANT PRESENTATION:

- **a** The FIRM's description of discretion;
- **b** The INTERNAL VALUATION methodologies used to value REAL ESTATE investments for the most recent period;
- **c** For periods beginning on or after 1 January 2011, material changes to valuation policies and/or methodologies;
- **d** For periods beginning on or after 1 January 2011, material differences between an EXTERNAL VALUATION and the valuation used in performance reporting and the reason for the differences;
- **e** The frequency REAL ESTATE investments are valued by an independent external PROFESSIONALLY DESIGNATED, CERTIFIED, OR LICENSED COMMERCIAL PROPERTY VALUER/APPRAISER;
- **f** When component returns are calculated separately using geometrically LINKED TIME-WEIGHTED RATES OF RETURN; and
- **g** For periods prior to 1 January 2011, if component returns are adjusted such that the sum of the INCOME RETURN and the CAPITAL RETURN equals the TOTAL RETURN.

6.A.11 For any performance presented for periods prior to 1 January 2006 that does not comply with the GIPS standards, FIRMS MUST disclose the periods of non-compliance.

6.A.12 When presenting GROSS-OF-FEES returns, FIRMS MUST disclose if any other fees are deducted in addition to the TRANSACTION EXPENSES.

6.A.13 When presenting NET-OF-FEES returns, FIRMS MUST disclose if any other fees are deducted in addition to the INVESTMENT MANAGEMENT FEES and TRANSACTION EXPENSES.

Presentation and Reporting—Requirements (the following provisions do not apply: 5.A.1.i, 5.A.2, and 5.A.3)

6.A.14 FIRMS MUST present component returns in addition to TOTAL RETURNS. COMPOSITE component returns MUST be clearly identified as GROSS-OF-FEES or NET-OF-FEES.

6.A.15 FIRMS MUST NOT LINK non-GIPS-compliant performance for periods beginning on or after 1 January 2006 to their GIPS-compliant performance. FIRMS may LINK non-GIPS-compliant performance to their GIPS-compliant performance provided that only GIPS-compliant performance is presented for periods beginning on or after 1 January 2006.

6.A.16 The following items MUST be presented in each COMPLIANT PRESENTATION:

a As a measure of INTERNAL DISPERSION, high and low annual TIME-WEIGHTED RATES OF RETURN for the individual PORTFOLIOS in the COMPOSITE. If the COMPOSITE contains five or fewer PORTFOLIOS for the full year, a measure of INTERNAL DISPERSION is not REQUIRED.

b As of each annual period end, the percentage of COMPOSITE assets valued using an EXTERNAL VALUATION during the annual period.

The following provisions are additional REQUIREMENTS for REAL ESTATE CLOSED-END FUND COMPOSITES:

Calculation Methodology—Requirements

6.A.17 FIRMS MUST calculate annualized SINCE INCEPTION INTERNAL RATES OF RETURN (SI-IRR).

6.A.18 The SI-IRR MUST be calculated using quarterly cash flows at a minimum.

Composite Construction—Requirements

6.A.19 COMPOSITES MUST be defined by VINTAGE YEAR and investment mandate, objective, or strategy. The COMPOSITE DEFINITION MUST remain consistent throughout the life of the COMPOSITE.

Disclosure—Requirements

6.A.20 FIRMS MUST disclose the FINAL LIQUIDATION DATE for liquidated COMPOSITES.

6.A.21 FIRMS MUST disclose the frequency of cash flows used in the SI-IRR calculation.

6.A.22 FIRMS MUST disclose the VINTAGE YEAR of the COMPOSITE and how the VINTAGE YEAR is defined.

Presentation and Reporting—Requirements

6.A.23 The following items MUST be presented in each COMPLIANT PRESENTATION:

a FIRMS MUST present the NET-OF-FEES SI-IRR of the COMPOSITE through each annual period end. FIRMS MUST initially present at least five years of performance (or for the period since the FIRM's inception or the COMPOSITE INCEPTION DATE if the FIRM or the COMPOSITE has been in existence less than five years) that meets the REQUIREMENTS of the GIPS standards. Each subsequent year, FIRMS MUST present an additional year of performance.

b For periods beginning on or after 1 January 2011, when the initial period is less than a full year, FIRMS MUST present the non-annualized NET-OF-FEES SI-IRR through the initial annual period end.

c For periods ending on or after 1 January 2011, FIRMS MUST present the NET-OF-FEES SI-IRR through the COMPOSITE FINAL LIQUIDATION DATE.

6.A.24 If the GROSS-OF-FEES SI-IRR of the COMPOSITE is presented in the COMPLIANT PRESENTATION, FIRMS MUST present the GROSS-OF-FEES SI-IRR of the COMPOSITE for the same periods as the NET-OF-FEES SI-IRR is presented.

6.A.25 FIRMS MUST present, as of each annual period end:

a COMPOSITE SINCE INCEPTION PAID-IN CAPITAL;

b COMPOSITE SINCE INCEPTION DISTRIBUTIONS;

c COMPOSITE cumulative COMMITTED CAPITAL;

d TOTAL VALUE to SINCE INCEPTION PAID-IN CAPITAL (INVESTMENT MULTIPLE or TVPI);

e SINCE INCEPTION DISTRIBUTIONS to SINCE INCEPTION PAID-IN CAPITAL (REALIZATION MULTIPLE or DPI);

f SINCE INCEPTION PAID-IN CAPITAL to cumulative COMMITTED CAPITAL (PIC MULTIPLE); and

g RESIDUAL VALUE to SINCE INCEPTION PAID-IN CAPITAL (UNREALIZED MULTIPLE or RVPI).

6.A.26 FIRMS MUST present the SI-IRR of the BENCHMARK through each annual period end. The BENCHMARK MUST:

a Reflect the investment mandate, objective, or strategy of the COMPOSITE;

b Be presented for the same time period as presented for the COMPOSITE; and

c Be the same VINTAGE YEAR as the COMPOSITE.

Real Estate—Recommendations

Input Data—Recommendations (the following provision does not apply: 1.B.1)

6.B.1 For periods prior to 1 January 2012, REAL ESTATE investments SHOULD be valued by an independent external PROFESSIONALLY DESIGNATED, CERTIFIED, OR LICENSED COMMERCIAL PROPERTY VALUER/APPRAISER at least once every 12 months.

6.B.2 REAL ESTATE investments SHOULD be valued as of the annual period end by an independent external PROFESSIONALLY DESIGNATED, CERTIFIED, OR LICENSED COMMERCIAL PROPERTY VALUER/APPRAISER.

Disclosure—Recommendations

6.B.3 FIRMS SHOULD disclose the basis of accounting for the PORTFOLIOS in the COMPOSITE (e.g., US GAAP, IFRS).

6.B.4 FIRMS SHOULD explain and disclose material differences between the valuation used in performance reporting and the valuation used in financial reporting as of each annual period end.

6.B.5 For periods prior to 1 January 2011, FIRMS SHOULD disclose material changes to valuation policies and/or methodologies.

Presentation and Reporting—Recommendations (the following provisions do not apply: 5.B.3, 5.B.4, and 5.B.5)

6.B.6 FIRMS SHOULD present both GROSS-OF-FEES and NET-OF-FEES returns.

6.B.7 FIRMS SHOULD present the percentage of the total value of COMPOSITE assets that are not REAL ESTATE as of each annual period end.

6.B.8 FIRMS SHOULD present the component returns of the BENCHMARK, if available.

The following provision is an additional RECOMMENDATION for REAL ESTATE CLOSED-END FUND COMPOSITES:

Calculation Methodology—Recommendations

6.B.9 The SI-IRR SHOULD be calculated using daily cash flows.

7 Private Equity

Unless otherwise noted, the following PRIVATE EQUITY provisions supplement the REQUIRED and RECOMMENDED provisions of the GIPS standards in Sections 0–5.

PRIVATE EQUITY provisions were first included in the GIPS standards in 2005 and became effective 1 January 2006. All COMPLIANT PRESENTATIONS that included PRIVATE EQUITY performance for periods ending on or after 1 January 2006 were REQUIRED to meet all the REQUIREMENTS of the PRIVATE EQUITY provisions of the 2005 edition of the GIPS standards. The following PRIVATE EQUITY provisions are effective 1 January 2011. All PRIVATE EQUITY COMPOSITES that include performance for periods ending on or after 1 January 2011 MUST comply with all the REQUIREMENTS and SHOULD comply with the RECOMMENDATIONS of the following PRIVATE EQUITY provisions.

The following are provisions that apply to the calculation and presentation of PRIVATE EQUITY investments made by fixed life, fixed commitment PRIVATE EQUITY investment vehicles including PRIMARY FUNDS and FUNDS OF FUNDS. These provisions also apply to fixed life, fixed commitment SECONDARY FUNDS, which MUST apply either the provisions applicable to PRIMARY FUNDS or the provisions applicable to FUNDS OF FUNDS, depending on which form the SECONDARY FUND uses to make investments. PRIVATE EQUITY OPEN-END and EVERGREEN FUNDS MUST follow Sections 0–5 in the Provisions of the Global Investment Performance Standards. REAL ESTATE CLOSED-END FUNDS MUST follow Section 6 in the Provisions of the Global Investment Performance Standards.

Private Equity—Requirements

Input Data—Requirements (the following provisions do not apply: 1.A.3.a, 1.A.3.b, and 1.A.4)

7.A.1 For periods ending on or after 1 January 2011, PRIVATE EQUITY investments MUST be valued in accordance with the definition of FAIR VALUE and the GIPS Valuation Principles in Chapter II.[8]

7.A.2 PRIVATE EQUITY investments MUST be valued at least annually.

Calculation Methodology—Requirements (the following provisions do not apply: 2.A.2, 2.A.4, 2.A.6, and 2.A.7)

7.A.3 FIRMS MUST calculate annualized SINCE INCEPTION INTERNAL RATES OF RETURN (SI-IRR).

7.A.4 For periods ending on or after 1 January 2011, the SI-IRR MUST be calculated using daily cash flows. Stock DISTRIBUTIONS MUST be included as cash flows and MUST be valued at the time of DISTRIBUTION.[9]

7.A.5 All returns MUST be calculated after the deduction of actual TRANSACTION EXPENSES incurred during the period.

7.A.6 NET-OF-FEES returns MUST be net of actual INVESTMENT MANAGEMENT FEES (including CARRIED INTEREST).

7.A.7 For FUNDS OF FUNDS, all returns MUST be net of all underlying partnership and/or fund fees and expenses, including CARRIED INTEREST.

---

8 For periods ending prior to 1 January 2011, PRIVATE EQUITY investments MUST be valued according to either the GIPS Private Equity Valuation Principles in Appendix D of the 2005 edition of the GIPS standards or the GIPS Valuation Principles in the 2010 edition of the GIPS standards.

9 For periods ending prior to 1 January 2011, the SI-IRR MUST be calculated using either daily or monthly cash flows.

Composite Construction—Requirements (the following provision does not apply: 3.A.10)

7.A.8 COMPOSITE DEFINITIONS MUST remain consistent throughout the life of the COMPOSITE.

7.A.9 PRIMARY FUNDS MUST be included in at least one COMPOSITE defined by VINTAGE YEAR and investment mandate, objective, or strategy.

7.A.10 FUNDS OF FUNDS MUST be included in at least one COMPOSITE defined by VINTAGE YEAR of the FUND OF FUNDS and/or investment mandate, objective, or strategy.

Disclosure—Requirements (the following provisions do not apply: 4.A.5, 4.A.6.a, 4.A.6.b, 4.A.8, 4.A.15, 4.A.26, 4.A.32, 4.A.33, and 4.A.34)

7.A.11 FIRMS MUST disclose the VINTAGE YEAR of the COMPOSITE and how the VINTAGE YEAR is defined.

7.A.12 FIRMS MUST disclose the FINAL LIQUIDATION DATE for liquidated COMPOSITES.

7.A.13 FIRMS MUST disclose the valuation methodologies used to value PRIVATE EQUITY investments for the most recent period.

7.A.14 For periods ending on or after 1 January 2011, FIRMS MUST disclose material changes to valuation policies and/or methodologies.

7.A.15 If the FIRM adheres to any industry valuation guidelines in addition to the GIPS Valuation Principles, the FIRM MUST disclose which guidelines have been applied.

7.A.16 FIRMS MUST disclose the calculation methodology used for the BENCHMARK. If FIRMS present the PUBLIC MARKET EQUIVALENT of a COMPOSITE as a BENCHMARK, FIRMS MUST disclose the index used to calculate the PUBLIC MARKET EQUIVALENT.

7.A.17 FIRMS MUST disclose the frequency of cash flows used in the SI-IRR calculation if daily cash flows are not used for periods prior to 1 January 2011.

7.A.18 For GROSS-OF-FEES returns, FIRMS MUST disclose if any other fees are deducted in addition to the TRANSACTION EXPENSES.

7.A.19 For NET-OF-FEES returns, FIRMS MUST disclose if any other fees are deducted in addition to the INVESTMENT MANAGEMENT FEES and TRANSACTION EXPENSES.

7.A.20 For any performance presented for periods ending prior to 1 January 2006 that does not comply with the GIPS standards, FIRMS MUST disclose the periods of non-compliance.

Presentation and Reporting—Requirements (the following provisions do not apply: 5.A.1.a, 5.A.1.b, 5.A.1.c, 5.A.1.d, 5.A.1.e, 5.A.1.i, 5.A.2, and 5.A.3)

7.A.21 The following items MUST be presented in each COMPLIANT PRESENTATION:

a FIRMS MUST present both the NET-OF-FEES and GROSS-OF-FEES SI-IRR of the COMPOSITE through each annual period end. FIRMS MUST initially present at least five years of performance (or for the period since the FIRM's inception or the COMPOSITE INCEPTION DATE if the FIRM or the COMPOSITE has been in existence less than five years) that meets the REQUIREMENTS of the GIPS standards. Each subsequent year, FIRMS MUST present an additional year of performance. COMPOSITE returns MUST be clearly identified as GROSS-OF-FEES or NET-OF-FEES.

b For periods beginning on or after 1 January 2011, when the initial period is less than a full year, FIRMS MUST present the non-annualized NET-OF-FEES and GROSS-OF-FEES SI-IRR through the initial annual period end.

c For periods ending on or after 1 January 2011, FIRMS MUST present the NET-OF-FEES and GROSS-OF-FEES SI-IRR through the COMPOSITE FINAL LIQUIDATION DATE.

7.A.22 For periods ending on or after 1 January 2011, for FUND OF FUNDS COMPOSITES, if the COMPOSITE is defined only by investment mandate, objective, or strategy, FIRMS MUST also present the SI-IRR of the underlying investments aggregated by VINTAGE YEAR as well as other measures as REQUIRED in 7.A.23. These measures MUST be presented gross of the FUND OF FUNDS INVESTMENT MANAGEMENT FEES and MUST be presented as of the most recent annual period end.

7.A.23 FIRMS MUST present as of each annual period end:

a COMPOSITE SINCE INCEPTION PAID-IN CAPITAL;

b COMPOSITE SINCE INCEPTION DISTRIBUTIONS;

c COMPOSITE cumulative COMMITTED CAPITAL;

d TOTAL VALUE to SINCE INCEPTION PAID-IN CAPITAL (INVESTMENT MULTIPLE or TVPI);

e SINCE INCEPTION DISTRIBUTIONS to SINCE INCEPTION PAID-IN CAPITAL (REALIZATION MULTIPLE or DPI);

f SINCE INCEPTION PAID-IN CAPITAL to cumulative COMMITTED CAPITAL (PIC MULTIPLE); and

g RESIDUAL VALUE to SINCE INCEPTION PAID-IN CAPITAL (UNREALIZED MULTIPLE or RVPI).

7.A.24 FIRMS MUST present the SI-IRR for the BENCHMARK through each annual period end. The BENCHMARK MUST:

a Reflect the investment mandate, objective, or strategy of the COMPOSITE;

b Be presented for the same time periods as presented for the COMPOSITE; and

c Be the same VINTAGE YEAR as the COMPOSITE.

7.A.25 For FUND OF FUNDS COMPOSITES, if the COMPOSITE is defined only by investment mandate, objective, or strategy and a BENCHMARK is presented for the underlying investments, the BENCHMARK MUST be the same VINTAGE YEAR and investment mandate, objective, or strategy as the underlying investments.

7.A.26 For periods ending on or after 1 January 2011, for FUND OF FUNDS COMPOSITES, FIRMS MUST present the percentage, if any, of COMPOSITE assets that is invested in DIRECT INVESTMENTS (rather than in fund investment vehicles) as of each annual period end.

7.A.27 For periods ending on or after 1 January 2011, for PRIMARY FUND COMPOSITES, FIRMS MUST present the percentage, if any, of COMPOSITE assets that is invested in fund investment vehicles (rather than in DIRECT INVESTMENTS) as of each annual period end.

7.A.28 FIRMS MUST NOT present non-GIPS-compliant performance for periods ending on or after 1 January 2006. For periods ending prior to 1 January 2006, FIRMS may present non-GIPS-compliant performance.

Private Equity—Recommendations

Input Data—Recommendations (the following provision does not apply: 1.B.1)

7.B.1 PRIVATE EQUITY investments SHOULD be valued at least quarterly.

Calculation Methodology—Recommendations (the following provision does not apply: 2.B.2)

7.B.2 For periods ending prior to 1 January 2011, the SI-IRR SHOULD be calculated using daily cash flows.

Composite Construction—Recommendations (the following provision does not apply: 3.B.2)

Disclosure—Recommendations

7.B.3 FIRMS SHOULD explain and disclose material differences between the valuations used in performance reporting and the valuations used in financial reporting as of each annual period end.

7.B.4 For periods prior to 1 January 2011, FIRMS SHOULD disclose material changes to valuation policies and/or methodologies.

Presentation and Reporting—Recommendations (the following provisions do not apply: 5.B.2, 5.B.3, 5.B.4, and 5.B.5)

7.B.5 For periods ending on or after 1 January 2011, for FUND OF FUNDS COMPOSITES, if the COMPOSITE is defined only by VINTAGE YEAR of the FUND OF FUNDS, FIRMS SHOULD also present the SI-IRR of the underlying investments aggregated by investment mandate, objective, or strategy and other measures as listed in 7.A.23. These measures SHOULD be presented gross of the FUND OF FUNDS INVESTMENT MANAGEMENT FEES.

7.B.6 For periods ending prior to 1 January 2011, for FUND OF FUNDS COMPOSITES, FIRMS SHOULD present the percentage, if any, of COMPOSITE assets that is invested in DIRECT INVESTMENTS (rather than in fund investment vehicles) as of each annual period end.

7.B.7 For periods ending prior to 1 January 2011, for PRIMARY FUND COMPOSITES, FIRMS SHOULD present the percentage, if any, of COMPOSITE assets that is invested in fund investment vehicles (rather than in DIRECT INVESTMENTS) as of each annual period end.

8 Wrap Fee/Separately Managed Account (SMA) Portfolios

The following provisions apply to the calculation and presentation of performance when presenting a COMPLIANT PRESENTATION to a WRAP FEE/SMA PROSPECTIVE CLIENT (which includes prospective WRAP FEE/SMA sponsors, prospective WRAP FEE/SMA clients, and existing WRAP FEE/SMA sponsors). Unless otherwise noted, the following WRAP FEE/SMA provisions supplement all the REQUIRED and RECOMMENDED provisions of the GIPS standards in Sections 0–5.

Although there are different types of WRAP FEE/SMA structures, these provisions apply to all WRAP FEE/SMA PORTFOLIOS where there are BUNDLED FEES and the WRAP FEE/SMA sponsor serves as an intermediary between the FIRM and the end user of the investment services. These provisions are not applicable to PORTFOLIOS defined as other types of BUNDLED FEE PORTFOLIOS. These provisions are also not applicable to model PORTFOLIOS that are provided by a FIRM to a WRAP FEE/SMA sponsor if the FIRM does not have discretionary PORTFOLIO management responsibility for the individual WRAP FEE/SMA PORTFOLIOS. Similarly, a FIRM or overlay manager in a Multiple Strategy Portfolio (MSP) or similar program is also excluded from applying these provisions to such PORTFOLIOS if they do not have discretion.

All WRAP FEE/SMA COMPLIANT PRESENTATIONS that include performance results for periods beginning on or after 1 January 2006 MUST meet all the REQUIREMENTS of the following WRAP FEE/SMA provisions.

Wrap Fee/SMA Requirements

Composite Construction—Requirements

8.A.1 FIRMS MUST include the performance record of actual WRAP FEE/SMA PORTFOLIOS in appropriate COMPOSITES in accordance with the FIRM's established PORTFOLIO inclusion policies. Once established, these COMPOSITES (containing actual WRAP FEE/SMA PORTFOLIOS) MUST be used in the FIRM's COMPLIANT PRESENTATIONS presented to WRAP FEE/SMA PROSPECTIVE CLIENTS.

Disclosure—Requirements (the following provision does not apply: 4.A.15)

8.A.2 For all WRAP FEE/SMA COMPLIANT PRESENTATIONS that include periods prior to the inclusion of an actual WRAP FEE/SMA PORTFOLIO in the COMPOSITE, the FIRM MUST disclose, for each period presented, that the COMPOSITE does not contain actual WRAP FEE/SMA PORTFOLIOS.

8.A.3 For any performance presented for periods prior to 1 January 2006 that does not comply with the GIPS standards, FIRMS MUST disclose the periods of non-compliance.

8.A.4 When FIRMS present COMPOSITE performance to an existing WRAP FEE/SMA sponsor that includes only that sponsor's WRAP FEE/SMA PORTFOLIOS (resulting in a "sponsor-specific COMPOSITE"):

- **a** FIRMS MUST disclose the name of the WRAP FEE/SMA sponsor represented by the sponsor-specific COMPOSITE; and
- **b** If the sponsor-specific COMPOSITE COMPLIANT PRESENTATION is intended for the purpose of generating WRAP FEE/SMA business and does not include performance net of the entire WRAP FEE, the COMPLIANT PRESENTATION MUST disclose that the named sponsor-specific COMPLIANT PRESENTATION is only for the use of the named WRAP FEE/SMA sponsor.

Presentation and Reporting—Requirements (the following provision does not apply: 5.A.3)

8.A.5 When FIRMS present performance to a WRAP FEE/SMA PROSPECTIVE CLIENT, the COMPOSITE presented MUST include the performance of all actual WRAP FEE/SMA PORTFOLIOS, if any, managed according to the COMPOSITE investment mandate, objective, or strategy, regardless of the WRAP FEE/SMA sponsor (resulting in a "style-defined COMPOSITE").

8.A.6 When FIRMS present performance to a WRAP FEE/SMA PROSPECTIVE CLIENT, performance MUST be presented net of the entire WRAP FEE.

8.A.7 FIRMS MUST NOT LINK non-GIPS-compliant performance for periods beginning on or after 1 January 2006 to their GIPS-compliant performance. FIRMS may LINK non-GIPS-compliant performance to their GIPS-compliant performance provided that only GIPS-compliant performance is presented for periods beginning on or after 1 January 2006.

II. GIPS VALUATION PRINCIPLES

The GIPS standards are based on the ethical principles of fair representation and full disclosure. In order for the performance calculations to be meaningful, the valuations of PORTFOLIO investments must have integrity and fairly reflect their value. Effective 1 January 2011, the GIPS standards REQUIRE FIRMS to apply a FAIR VALUE methodology following the definition and REQUIREMENTS listed below. The GIPS Valuation Principles, including the definition of FAIR VALUE, were developed with consideration of the work done by the International Accounting Standards Board (IASB) and the Financial Accounting Standards Board (FASB) as well as other organizations.

The shift to a broader FAIR VALUE REQUIREMENT has implications for all FIRMS claiming compliance with the GIPS standards. For liquid securities in active markets, the change to FAIR VALUE from MARKET VALUE will typically not result in a change to valuations. FIRMS MUST use the objective, observable, unadjusted quoted market prices for identical investments on the measurement date, if available.

Markets are not always liquid and investment prices are not always objective and/or observable. For illiquid or hard to value investments, or for investments where no observable MARKET VALUE or market price is available, additional steps are necessary. A FIRM's valuation policies and procedures MUST address situations where the market prices may be available for similar but not identical investments, inputs to valuations are subjective rather than objective, and/or markets are inactive instead of active. There is a RECOMMENDED valuation hierarchy in Section C below. FIRMS MUST disclose if the COMPOSITE's valuation hierarchy materially differs from the RECOMMENDED valuation hierarchy.

Although a FIRM may use external third parties to value investments, the FIRM still retains responsibility for compliance with the GIPS standards, including the GIPS Valuation Principles.

FIRMS claiming compliance with the GIPS standards MUST adhere to all the REQUIREMENTS and SHOULD comply with the RECOMMENDATIONS below.

Fair Value Definition

FAIR VALUE is defined as the amount at which an investment could be exchanged in a current arm's length transaction between willing parties in which the parties each act knowledgeably and prudently. The valuation MUST be determined using the objective, observable, unadjusted quoted market price for an identical investment in an active market on the measurement date, if available. In the absence of an objective, observable, unadjusted quoted market price for an identical investment in an active market on the measurement date, the valuation MUST represent the FIRM's best estimate of the MARKET VALUE. FAIR VALUE MUST include accrued income.

Valuation Requirements

FIRMS MUST comply with the following valuation REQUIREMENTS:

1 For periods beginning on or after 1 January 2011, PORTFOLIOS MUST be valued in accordance with the definition of FAIR VALUE and the GIPS Valuation Principles (Provision 1.A.2) Chapter II.

2 FIRMS MUST value investments using objective, observable, unadjusted quoted market prices for identical investments in active markets on the measurement date, if available.

3 FIRMS MUST comply with all applicable laws and regulations regarding the calculation and presentation of performance (Provision 0.A.2). Accordingly, FIRMS MUST comply with applicable laws and regulations relating to valuation.

4 If the COMPLIANT PRESENTATION conforms with laws and/or regulations that conflict with the REQUIREMENTS of the GIPS standards, FIRMS MUST disclose this fact and disclose the manner in which the laws and/or regulations conflict with the GIPS standards (Provision 4.A.22). This includes any conflicts between laws and/or regulations and the GIPS Valuation Principles.

5 FIRMS MUST document their policies and procedures used in establishing and maintaining compliance with the GIPS standards, including ensuring the existence and ownership of client assets, and MUST apply them consistently (Provision 0.A.5). Accordingly, FIRMS MUST document their valuation policies, procedures, methodologies, and hierarchy, including any changes, and MUST apply them consistently.

6 FIRMS MUST disclose that policies for valuing PORTFOLIOS, calculating performance, and preparing COMPLIANT PRESENTATIONS are available upon request (Provision 4.A.12).

7 For periods beginning on or after 1 January 2011, FIRMS MUST disclose the use of subjective unobservable inputs for valuing PORTFOLIO investments (as described in the GIPS Valuation Principles) if the PORTFOLIO investments valued using subjective unobservable inputs are material to the COMPOSITE (Provision 4.A.27).

8 For periods beginning on or after 1 January 2011, FIRMS MUST disclose if the COMPOSITE's valuation hierarchy materially differs from the RECOMMENDED hierarchy in the GIPS Valuation Principles (Provision 4.A.28).

Additional Real Estate Valuation Requirements

9 REAL ESTATE investments MUST have an EXTERNAL VALUATION (Provision 6.A.4).

10 The EXTERNAL VALUATION process MUST adhere to practices of the relevant valuation governing and standard setting body.

11 The FIRM MUST NOT use EXTERNAL VALUATIONS where the valuer's or appraiser's fee is contingent upon the investment's appraised value.

12 EXTERNAL VALUATIONS must be performed by an independent external PROFESSIONALLY DESIGNATED, CERTIFIED, OR LICENSED COMMERCIAL PROPERTY VALUER/APPRAISER. In markets where these professionals are not available, the FIRM MUST take necessary steps to ensure that only well-qualified independent property valuers or appraisers are used (Provision 6.A.5).

13 FIRMS MUST disclose the INTERNAL VALUATION methodologies used to value REAL ESTATE investments for the most recent period (Provision 6.A.10.b).

14 For periods beginning on or after 1 January 2011, FIRMS MUST disclose material changes to valuation policies and/or methodologies (Provision 6.A.10.c).

15 For periods beginning on or after 1 January 2011, FIRMS MUST disclose material differences between an EXTERNAL VALUATION and the valuation used in performance reporting and the reason for the differences (Provision 6.A.10.d).

16 FIRMS MUST present, as of each annual period end, the percentage of COMPOSITE assets valued using an EXTERNAL VALUATION during the annual period (Provision 6.A.16.b).

Additional Private Equity Valuation Requirements

17 The valuation methodology selected MUST be the most appropriate for a particular investment based on the nature, facts, and circumstances of the investment.

18 FIRMS MUST disclose the valuation methodologies used to value PRIVATE EQUITY investments for the most recent period (Provision 7.A.13).

19 For periods ending on or after 1 January 2011, FIRMS MUST disclose material changes to valuation policies and/or methodologies (Provision 7.A.14).

20 If the FIRM adheres to any industry valuation guidelines in addition to the GIPS Valuation Principles, the FIRM MUST disclose which guidelines have been applied (Provision 7.A.15).

Valuation Recommendations

FIRMS SHOULD comply with the following valuation RECOMMENDATIONS:

1 **Valuation Hierarchy**: FIRMS SHOULD incorporate the following hierarchy into the policies and procedures for determining FAIR VALUE for PORTFOLIO investments on a COMPOSITE-specific basis.

  a Investments MUST be valued using objective, observable, unadjusted quoted market prices for identical investments in active markets on the measurement date, if available. If not available, then investments SHOULD be valued using;

  b Objective, observable quoted market prices for similar investments in active markets. If not available or appropriate, then investments SHOULD be valued using;

  c Quoted prices for identical or similar investments in markets that are not active (markets in which there are few transactions for the investment, the prices are not current, or price quotations vary substantially over time and/or between market makers). If not available or appropriate, then investments SHOULD be valued based on;

  d Market-based inputs, other than quoted prices, that are observable for the investment. If not available or appropriate, then investments SHOULD be valued based on;

  e. Subjective unobservable inputs for the investment where markets are not active at the measurement date. Unobservable inputs SHOULD only be used to measure FAIR VALUE to the extent that observable inputs and prices are not available or appropriate. Unobservable inputs reflect the FIRM's own assumptions about the assumptions that market participants would use in pricing the investment and SHOULD be developed based on the best information available under the circumstances.

2. FIRMS SHOULD disclose material changes to valuation policies and/or methodologies (Provision 4.B.1).
3. FIRMS SHOULD disclose the key assumptions used to value PORTFOLIO investments (Provision 4.B.4).
4. For periods prior to 1 January 2011, FIRMS SHOULD disclose the use of subjective unobservable inputs for valuing PORTFOLIO investments (as described in the GIPS Valuation Principles in Chapter II) if the PORTFOLIO investments valued using subjective unobservable inputs are material to the COMPOSITE (Provision 4.B.6).
5. Valuations SHOULD be obtained from a qualified independent third party (Provision 1.B.2).

Additional Real Estate Valuation Recommendations

6. Although appraisal standards may allow for a range of estimated values, it is RECOMMENDED that a single value be obtained from external valuers or appraisers because only one value is used in performance reporting.
7. It is RECOMMENDED that the external appraisal firm be rotated every three to five years.
8. FIRMS SHOULD explain and disclose material differences between the valuation used in performance reporting and the valuation used in financial reporting as of each annual period end (Provision 6.B.4).
9. For periods prior to 1 January 2011, FIRMS SHOULD disclose material changes to valuation policies and/or methodologies (Provision 6.B.5).

Additional Private Equity Valuation Recommendations

10. FIRMS SHOULD explain and disclose material differences between the valuations used in performance reporting and the valuations used in financial reporting as of each annual period end (Provision 7.B.3).
11. For periods prior to 1 January 2011, FIRMS SHOULD disclose material changes to valuation policies and/or methodologies (Provision 7.B.4).
12. The following considerations SHOULD be incorporated into the valuation process:
    a. The quality and reliability of the data used in each methodology;
    b. The comparability of enterprise or transaction data;
    c. The stage of development of the enterprise; and
    d. Any additional considerations unique to the enterprise.

III. GIPS ADVERTISING GUIDELINES

Purpose of the GIPS Advertising Guidelines

The GIPS Advertising Guidelines provide FIRMS with options for advertising performance when mentioning the FIRM's claim of compliance. The GIPS Advertising Guidelines do not replace the GIPS standards, nor do they absolve FIRMS from presenting a COMPLIANT PRESENTATION as REQUIRED by the GIPS standards. These guidelines only apply to FIRMS that already satisfy all the REQUIREMENTS of the GIPS standards on a FIRM-wide basis and claim compliance with the GIPS standards in an advertisement. FIRMS that choose to claim compliance in an advertisement MUST follow the GIPS Advertising Guidelines or include a COMPLIANT PRESENTATION in the advertisement.

Definition of Advertisement

For the purposes of these guidelines, an advertisement includes any materials that are distributed to or designed for use in newspapers, magazines, FIRM brochures, letters, media, websites, or any other written or electronic material addressed to more than one PROSPECTIVE CLIENT. Any written material, other than one-on-one presentations and individual client reporting, distributed to maintain existing clients or solicit new clients for a FIRM is considered an advertisement.

Relationship of GIPS Advertising Guidelines to Regulatory Requirements

FIRMS advertising performance MUST adhere to all applicable laws and regulations governing advertisements. FIRMS are encouraged to seek legal or regulatory counsel because additional disclosures may be REQUIRED. In cases where applicable laws and/or regulations conflict with the REQUIREMENTS of the GIPS standards and/or the GIPS Advertising Guidelines, FIRMS are REQUIRED to comply with the law or regulation.

The calculation and advertisement of pooled unitized investment vehicles, such as mutual funds and open-ended investment companies, are regulated in most markets. The GIPS Advertising Guidelines are not intended to replace applicable laws and/or regulations when a FIRM is advertising performance solely for a pooled unitized investment vehicle.

Other Information

The advertisement may include other information beyond what is REQUIRED under the GIPS Advertising Guidelines provided the information is shown with equal or lesser prominence relative to the information REQUIRED by the GIPS Advertising Guidelines and the information does not conflict with the REQUIREMENTS of the GIPS standards and/or the GIPS Advertising Guidelines. FIRMS MUST adhere to the principles of fair representation and full disclosure when advertising and MUST NOT present performance or performance-related information that is false or misleading.

Requirements of the GIPS Advertising Guidelines

All advertisements that include a claim of compliance with the GIPS standards by following the GIPS Advertising Guidelines MUST disclose the following:

1 The definition of the FIRM.

2 How a PROSPECTIVE CLIENT can obtain a COMPLIANT PRESENTATION and/or the FIRM's list of COMPOSITE DESCRIPTIONS.

3 The GIPS compliance statement for advertisements:

"[Insert name of FIRM] claims compliance with the Global Investment Performance Standards (GIPS®)."

All advertisements that include a claim of compliance with the GIPS standards by following the GIPS Advertising Guidelines and that present performance MUST also disclose the following information, which MUST be taken or derived from a COMPLIANT PRESENTATION:

4 The COMPOSITE DESCRIPTION.

5 COMPOSITE TOTAL RETURNS according to one of the following:

a One-, three-, and five-year annualized COMPOSITE returns through the most recent period with the period-end date clearly identified. If the COMPOSITE has been in existence for less than five years, FIRMS MUST also present the annualized returns since the COMPOSITE INCEPTION DATE. (For example, if a COMPOSITE has been in existence for four years, FIRMS MUST present one-, three-, and four-year annualized returns through the most recent period.) Returns for periods of less than one year MUST NOT be annualized.

b Period-to-date COMPOSITE returns in addition to one-, three-, and five-year annualized COMPOSITE returns through the same period of time as presented in the corresponding COMPLIANT PRESENTATION with the period end date clearly identified. If the COMPOSITE has been in existence for less than five years, FIRMS MUST also present the annualized returns since the COMPOSITE INCEPTION DATE (For example, if a COMPOSITE has been in existence for four years, FIRMS MUST present one-, three-, and four-year annualized returns in addition to the period-to-date COMPOSITE return.) Returns for periods of less than one year MUST NOT be annualized.

c Period-to-date COMPOSITE returns in addition to five years of annual COMPOSITE returns (or for each annual period since the COMPOSITE INCEPTION DATE if the COMPOSITE has been in existence for less than five years) with the period end date clearly identified. The annual returns MUST be calculated through the same period of time as presented in the corresponding COMPLIANT PRESENTATION.

6 Whether returns are presented GROSS-OF-FEES and/or NET-OF-FEES.

7 The TOTAL RETURN for the BENCHMARK for the same periods for which the COMPOSITE return is presented. FIRMS MUST present TOTAL RETURNS for the same BENCHMARK as presented in the corresponding COMPLIANT PRESENTATION.

8 The BENCHMARK DESCRIPTION.

9 If the FIRM determines no appropriate BENCHMARK for the COMPOSITE exists, the FIRM MUST disclose why no BENCHMARK is presented.

10 The currency used to express performance.

11 The presence, use, and extent of leverage, derivatives, and short positions, if material, including a description of the frequency of use and characteristics of the instruments sufficient to identify risks.

12 For any performance presented in an advertisement for periods prior to 1 January 2000 that does not comply with the GIPS standards, FIRMS MUST disclose the periods of non-compliance.

13 If the advertisement conforms with laws and/or regulations that conflict with the REQUIREMENTS of the GIPS standards and/or the GIPS Advertising Guidelines, FIRMS MUST disclose this fact and disclose the manner in which the laws and/or regulations conflict with the GIPS standards and/or the GIPS Advertising Guidelines.

IV. VERIFICATION

VERIFICATION is intended to provide a FIRM and its existing clients and PROSPECTIVE CLIENTS additional confidence in the FIRM's claim of compliance with the GIPS standards. VERIFICATION may increase the knowledge of the FIRM's performance measurement team and improve the consistency and quality of the FIRM's COMPLIANT PRESENTATIONS. VERIFICATION may also provide improved internal processes and procedures as well as marketing advantages to the FIRM. Verification does not ensure the accuracy of any specific COMPOSITE presentation.

The GIPS standards RECOMMEND that FIRMS be verified. VERIFICATION brings additional credibility to the claim of compliance and supports the overall guiding principles of fair representation and full disclosure of a FIRM's investment performance.

The VERIFICATION procedures attempt to strike a balance between ensuring the quality, accuracy, and relevance of performance presentations and minimizing the cost to FIRMS.

Scope and Purpose of Verification

1 VERIFICATION MUST be performed by a qualified independent third party.

2 VERIFICATION assesses whether:

  a The FIRM has complied with all the COMPOSITE construction REQUIREMENTS of the GIPS standards on a FIRM-wide basis and

  b The FIRM's policies and procedures are designed to calculate and present performance in compliance with the GIPS standards.

3 A single VERIFICATION REPORT is issued with respect to the whole FIRM. VERIFICATION cannot be carried out on a COMPOSITE and, accordingly, does not provide assurance about the performance of any specific COMPOSITE. FIRMS MUST NOT state that a particular COMPOSITE has been "verified" or make any claim to that effect.

4 The initial minimum period for which VERIFICATION can be performed is one year (or from FIRM inception date through period end if less than one year) of a FIRM's presented performance. The RECOMMENDED period over which VERIFICATION is performed is that part of the FIRM's performance for which compliance with the GIPS standards is claimed.

5 A VERIFICATION REPORT MUST opine that:

  a The FIRM has complied with all the COMPOSITE construction REQUIREMENTS of the GIPS standards on a FIRM-wide basis, and

  b The FIRM's policies and procedures are designed to calculate and present performance in compliance with the GIPS standards.

The FIRM MUST NOT state that it has been verified unless a VERIFICATION REPORT has been issued.

6 A principal verifier may accept the work of another verifier as part of the basis for the principal verifier's opinion. A principal verifier may also choose to rely on the audit and/or internal control work of a qualified and reputable independent third party. In addition, a principal verifier may choose to rely on the other audit and/or internal control work performed by the VERIFICATION firm. If reliance on another party's work is planned, the scope of work, including time period covered, results of procedures performed, qualifications, competency, objectivity, and reputation of the other party, MUST be assessed by the principal verifier when making the determination as to whether to place any reliance on

such work. Reliance considerations and conclusions MUST be documented by the principal verifier. The principal verifier MUST use professional skepticism when deciding whether to place reliance on work performed by another independent third party.

7 Sample PORTFOLIO Selection: Verifiers MUST subject the entire FIRM to testing when performing VERIFICATION procedures unless reliance is placed on work performed by a qualified and reputable independent third party or appropriate alternative control procedures have been performed by the verifier. Verifiers may use a sampling methodology when performing such procedures. Verifiers MUST consider the following criteria when selecting samples:

- **a** Number of COMPOSITES at the FIRM;
- **b** Number of PORTFOLIOS in each COMPOSITE;
- **c** Type of COMPOSITE;
- **d** TOTAL FIRM ASSETS;
- **e** Internal control structure at the FIRM (system of checks and balances in place);
- **f** Number of years being verified; and
- **g** Computer applications, software used in the construction and maintenance of COMPOSITES, the use of external performance measurers, and the method of calculating performance.

This list is not all-inclusive and contains only the minimum criteria that MUST be considered in the selection and evaluation of a sample. For example, one potentially useful approach would be to include in the sample a PORTFOLIO that has the largest impact on COMPOSITE performance because of its size or because of extremely good or bad performance. Missing or incomplete documents, or the presence of errors, would normally be expected to warrant selecting a larger sample or applying additional VERIFICATION procedures.

8 After performing the VERIFICATION, the verifier may conclude that the FIRM is not in compliance with the GIPS standards or that the records of the FIRM cannot support a VERIFICATION. In such situations, the verifier MUST issue a statement to the FIRM clarifying why a VERIFICATION REPORT could not be issued. A VERIFICATION REPORT MUST NOT be issued when the verifier knows that the FIRM is not in compliance with the GIPS standards or the records of the FIRM cannot support a VERIFICATION.

9 The minimum VERIFICATION procedures are described below in Section B. The VERIFICATION REPORT MUST state that the VERIFICATION has been conducted in accordance with these VERIFICATION procedures.

Required Verification Procedures

The following are the minimum procedures that verifiers MUST follow when conducting a VERIFICATION. Verifiers MUST complete the VERIFICATION in accordance with these procedures prior to issuing a VERIFICATION REPORT to the FIRM:

1 Pre-VERIFICATION Procedures:

- **a** Knowledge of the GIPS Standards: Verifiers MUST understand all the REQUIREMENTS and RECOMMENDATIONS of the GIPS standards, including any updates, Guidance Statements, interpretations, Questions & Answers (Q&As), and clarifications published by CFA Institute and the GIPS Executive Committee, which are available on the GIPS standards website (www.gipsstandards.org) as well as in the *GIPS Handbook*.

- **b** Knowledge of Regulations: Verifiers MUST be knowledgeable of applicable laws and regulations regarding the calculation and presentation of performance and MUST consider any differences between these laws and regulations and the GIPS standards.
- **c** Knowledge of the FIRM: Verifiers MUST gain an understanding of the FIRM, including the corporate structure of the FIRM and how it operates.
- **d** Knowledge of the FIRM's Policies and Procedures: Verifiers MUST understand the FIRM's policies and procedures for establishing and maintaining compliance with all the applicable REQUIREMENTS and adopted RECOMMENDATIONS of the GIPS standards. The verifier MUST obtain a copy of the FIRM's policies and procedures used in establishing and maintaining compliance with the GIPS standards and ensure that all applicable policies and procedures are properly included and adequately documented.
- **e** Knowledge of Valuation Basis and Performance Calculations: Verifiers MUST understand the policies, procedures, and methodologies used to value PORTFOLIOS and compute investment performance.

2 VERIFICATION Procedures:

- **a** Fundamentals of Compliance: Verifiers MUST perform sufficient procedures to determine that:
  - **i.** The FIRM is, and has been, appropriately defined;
  - **ii.** The FIRM has defined and maintained COMPOSITES in compliance with the GIPS standards;
  - **iii.** All the FIRM's actual, fee-paying, discretionary PORTFOLIOS are included in at least one COMPOSITE;
  - **iv.** The FIRM's definition of discretion has been consistently applied over time;
  - **v.** At all times, all PORTFOLIOS are included in their respective COMPOSITES and no PORTFOLIOS that belong in a particular COMPOSITE have been excluded;
  - **vi.** The FIRM's policies and procedures for ensuring the existence and ownership of client assets are appropriate and have been consistently applied;
  - **vii.** The COMPOSITE BENCHMARK reflects the investment mandate, objective, or strategy of the COMPOSITE;
  - **viii.** The FIRM's policies and procedures for creating and maintaining COMPOSITES have been consistently applied;
  - **ix.** The FIRM's list of COMPOSITE DESCRIPTIONS is complete; and
  - **x.** TOTAL FIRM ASSETS are appropriately calculated and disclosed.
- **b** Determination of Discretionary Status of PORTFOLIOS: Verifiers MUST obtain a list of all PORTFOLIOS. Verifiers MUST select PORTFOLIOS from this list and perform sufficient procedures to determine that the FIRM's classification of the PORTFOLIOS as discretionary or non-discretionary is appropriate by referring to the PORTFOLIO's investment management agreement and/or investment guidelines and the FIRM's policies and procedures for determining investment discretion.
- **c** Allocation of PORTFOLIOS to COMPOSITES: Verifiers MUST obtain lists of all open (both new and existing) and closed PORTFOLIOS for all COMPOSITES for the periods being verified. Verifiers MUST select PORTFOLIOS from these lists and perform sufficient procedures to determine that:

i. The timing of inclusion in the COMPOSITE is in accordance with policies and procedures of the FIRM.

ii. The timing of exclusion from the COMPOSITE is in accordance with policies and procedures of the FIRM.

iii. The PORTFOLIO's investment mandate, objective, or strategy, as indicated by the PORTFOLIO's investment management agreement, investment guidelines, PORTFOLIO summary, and/or other appropriate documentation, is consistent with the COMPOSITE DEFINITION.

iv. PORTFOLIOS are completely and accurately included in COMPOSITES by tracing selected PORTFOLIOS from:

   a The PORTFOLIO's investment management agreement and/or investment management guidelines to the COMPOSITE(S); and

   b The COMPOSITE(S) to the PORTFOLIO's investment management agreement and/or investment guidelines.

v. PORTFOLIOS sharing the same investment mandate, objective, or strategy are included in the same COMPOSITE.

vi. Movements from one COMPOSITE to another are appropriate and consistent with documented changes to a PORTFOLIO's investment mandate, objective, or strategy or the redefinition of the COMPOSITE.

d Data Review: For selected PORTFOLIOS, verifiers MUST perform sufficient procedures to determine that the treatment of the following items is consistent with the FIRM's policy:

i. Classification of PORTFOLIO flows (e.g., receipts, disbursements, dividends, interest, fees, and taxes);

ii. Accounting treatment of income, interest, and dividend accruals and receipts;

iii. Accounting treatment of taxes, tax reclaims, and tax accruals;

iv. Accounting treatment of purchases, sales, and the opening and closing of other positions; and

v. Accounting treatment and valuation methodologies for investments, including derivatives.

e Performance Measurement Calculation: Recognizing that VERIFICATION does not provide assurance that specific COMPOSITE returns are correctly calculated and presented, verifiers MUST determine that the FIRM has calculated and presented performance in accordance with the FIRM's policies and procedures. Verifiers MUST perform the following procedures:

i. Recalculate rates of return for a sample of PORTFOLIOS, determine that an acceptable return formula as REQUIRED by the GIPS standards is used, and determine that the FIRM's calculations are in accordance with the FIRM's policies and procedures. The verifier MUST also determine that any fees and expenses are treated in accordance with the GIPS standards and the FIRM's policies and procedures.

ii. Take a sample of COMPOSITE and BENCHMARK calculations to determine the accuracy of all required numerical data (e.g., risk measures, INTERNAL DISPERSION).

iii. If a custom BENCHMARK or combination of multiple BENCHMARKS is used, take a sample of the BENCHMARK data used by the FIRM to determine that the calculation methodology has been correctly applied and the data used are consistent with the BENCHMARK disclosure in the COMPLIANT PRESENTATION.

f COMPLIANT PRESENTATIONS: Verifiers MUST perform sufficient procedures on a sample of COMPLIANT PRESENTATIONS to determine that the presentations include all the information and disclosures REQUIRED by the GIPS standards. The information and disclosures MUST be consistent with the FIRM's records, the FIRM's documented policies and procedures, and the results of the verifier's procedures.

g Maintenance of Records: The verifier MUST maintain sufficient documentation to support all procedures performed supporting the issuance of the VERIFICATION REPORT, including all significant judgments and conclusions made by the verifier.

h Representation Letter: The verifier MUST obtain a representation letter from the FIRM confirming that policies and procedures used in establishing and maintaining compliance with the GIPS standards are as described in the FIRM's policies and procedures documents and have been consistently applied throughout the periods being verified. The representation letter MUST confirm that the FIRM complies with the GIPS standards for the period being verified. The representation letter MUST also contain any other specific representations made to the verifier during the VERIFICATION.

Performance Examinations

In addition to a VERIFICATION, a FIRM may choose to have a specifically focused PERFORMANCE EXAMINATION of a particular COMPOSITE COMPLIANT PRESENTATION. However, a PERFORMANCE EXAMINATION REPORT MUST NOT be issued unless a VERIFICATION REPORT has also been issued. The PERFORMANCE EXAMINATION may be performed concurrently with the VERIFICATION.

A PERFORMANCE EXAMINATION is not REQUIRED for a FIRM to be verified. The FIRM MUST NOT state that a COMPOSITE has been examined unless the PERFORMANCE EXAMINATION REPORT has been issued for the specific COMPOSITE.

END OPTIONAL SEGMENT

Please see the Guidance Statement on PERFORMANCE EXAMINATIONS for additional guidance.

V. GIPS GLOSSARY

ACCRUAL ACCOUNTING The recording of financial transactions as they come into existence rather than when they are paid or settled.

ADDITIONAL INFORMATION Information that is REQUIRED or RECOMMENDED under the GIPS standards and is not considered SUPPLEMENTAL INFORMATION.

ADMINISTRATIVE FEE All fees other than TRADING EXPENSES and the INVESTMENT MANAGEMENT FEE. ADMINISTRATIVE FEES include CUSTODY FEES, accounting fees, auditing fees, consulting fees, legal fees, performance measurement fees, and other related fees. (See "BUNDLED FEE")

All-in fee	A type of BUNDLED FEE that can include any combination of INVESTMENT MANAGEMENT FEES, TRADING EXPENSES, CUSTODY FEES, and ADMINISTRATIVE FEES. ALL-IN-FEES are client specific and typically offered in certain jurisdictions where asset management, brokerage, and custody services are offered by the same company.
Benchmark	A point of reference against which the COMPOSITE's performance and/or risk is compared.
Benchmark description	General information regarding the investments, structure, and/or characteristics of the BENCHMARK. The description MUST include the key features of the BENCHMARK or the name of the BENCHMARK for a readily recognized index or other point of reference.
Bundled fee	A fee that combines multiple fees into one total or "bundled" fee. BUNDLED FEES can include any combination of INVESTMENT MANAGEMENT FEES, TRADING EXPENSES, CUSTODY FEES, and/or ADMINISTRATIVE FEES. Two examples of BUNDLED FEES are WRAP FEES and ALL-IN-FEES.
Capital employed (real estate)	The denominator of the return calculations and is defined as the "weighted-average equity" (weighted-average capital) during the measurement period. CAPITAL EMPLOYED does not include any INCOME RETURN or CAPITAL RETURN earned during the measurement period. Beginning capital is adjusted by weighting the EXTERNAL CASH FLOWS that occurred during the period.
Capital return (real estate)	The change in value of the REAL ESTATE investments and cash and/or cash equivalent assets held throughout the measurement period, adjusted for all capital expenditures (subtracted) and net proceeds from sales (added). The CAPITAL RETURN is computed as a percentage of the CAPITAL EMPLOYED. Also known as "capital appreciation return" or "appreciation return."
Carried interest (real estate and private equity)	The profits that GENERAL PARTNERS are allocated from the profits on the investments made by the investment vehicle. Also known as "carry" or "promote."
Carve-out	A portion of a PORTFOLIO that is by itself representative of a distinct investment strategy. It is used to create a track record for a narrower mandate from a multiple-strategy PORTFOLIO managed to a broader mandate. For periods beginning on or after 1 January 2010, a CARVE-OUT MUST be managed separately with its own cash balance.
Closed-end fund (real estate and private equity)	A type of investment vehicle where the number of investors, total COMMITTED CAPITAL, and life are fixed and not open for subscriptions and/or redemptions. CLOSED-END FUNDS have a capital call (drawdown) process in place that is controlled by the GENERAL PARTNER.

(continued)

Committed capital (real estate and private equity)	Pledges of capital to an investment vehicle by investors (LIMITED PARTNERS and the GENERAL PARTNER) or by the FIRM. COMMITTED CAPITAL is typically not drawn down at once but drawn down over a period of time. Also known as "commitments."
Compliant presentation	A presentation for a COMPOSITE that contains all the information REQUIRED by the GIPS standards and may also include ADDITIONAL INFORMATION or SUPPLEMENTAL INFORMATION. (See Sample COMPLIANT PRESENTATIONS in Appendix A)
Composite	An aggregation of one or more PORTFOLIOS managed according to a similar investment mandate, objective, or strategy.
Composite creation date	The date when the FIRM first groups one or more PORTFOLIOS to create a COMPOSITE. The COMPOSITE CREATION DATE is not necessarily the same as the COMPOSITE INCEPTION DATE.
Composite definition	Detailed criteria that determine the assignment of PORTFOLIOS to COMPOSITES. Criteria may include investment mandate, style or strategy, asset class, the use of derivatives, leverage and/or hedging, targeted risk metrics, investment constraints or restrictions, and/or PORTFOLIO type (e.g., segregated or pooled, taxable versus tax exempt.)
Composite description	General information regarding the investment mandate, objective, or strategy of the COMPOSITE. The COMPOSITE DESCRIPTION may be more abbreviated than the COMPOSITE DEFINITION but MUST include all key features of the COMPOSITE and MUST include enough information to allow a PROSPECTIVE CLIENT to understand the key characteristics of the COMPOSITE's investment mandate, objective, or strategy. (See the Sample List of Composite Descriptions in Appendix C)
Composite inception date	The initial date of the COMPOSITE's performance record. The COMPOSITE INCEPTION DATE is not necessarily the same as the COMPOSITE CREATION DATE.
Composite termination date	The date that the last PORTFOLIO exits a COMPOSITE.
Custody fee	The fees payable to the custodian for the safekeeping of PORTFOLIO assets. CUSTODY FEES are considered to be ADMINISTRATIVE FEES and typically contain an asset-based portion and a transaction-based portion. The CUSTODY FEE may also include charges for additional services, including accounting, securities lending, and/or performance measurement. Custodial fees that are charged per transaction SHOULD be included in the CUSTODY FEE and not included as part of TRADING EXPENSES.
Direct investments (private equity)	Investments made directly in PRIVATE EQUITY investments rather than investments made in fund investment vehicles or cash and/or cash equivalents.

Distinct business entity	A unit, division, department, or office that is organizationally and functionally segregated from other units, divisions, departments, or offices and that retains discretion over the assets it manages and that should have autonomy over the investment decision-making process. Possible criteria that can be used to determine this include: ■ being a legal entity, ■ having a distinct market or client type (e.g., institutional, retail, private client, etc.), and ■ using a separate and distinct investment process.
Distribution (real estate and private equity)	Cash or stock distributed to LIMITED PARTNERS (or investors) from an investment vehicle. DISTRIBUTIONS are typically at the discretion of the GENERAL PARTNER (or the FIRM). DISTRIBUTIONS include both recallable and non-recallable DISTRIBUTIONS.
DPI (real estate and private equity)	SINCE INCEPTION DISTRIBUTIONS divided by SINCE INCEPTION PAID-IN CAPITAL. (See "REALIZATION MULTIPLE")
Evergreen fund (private equity)	An OPEN-END FUND that allows for on-going subscriptions and/or redemptions by investors.
Ex-ante	Before the fact.
Ex-post	After the fact.
External cash flow	Capital (cash or investments) that enters or exits a PORTFOLIO.
External valuation (real estate)	An assessment of value performed by an independent external third party who is a qualified, PROFESSIONALLY DESIGNATED, CERTIFIED, OR LICENSED COMMERCIAL PROPERTY VALUER/APPRAISER.
Fair value	The amount at which an investment could be exchanged in a current arm's length transaction between willing parties in which the parties each act knowledgeably and prudently. The valuation MUST be determined using the objective, observable, unadjusted quoted market price for an identical investment in an active market on the measurement date, if available. In the absence of an objective, observable, unadjusted quoted market price for an identical investment in an active market on the measurement date, the valuation MUST represent the FIRM's best estimate of the MARKET VALUE. FAIR VALUE MUST include accrued income.
Fee schedule	The FIRM's current schedule of INVESTMENT MANAGEMENT FEES or BUNDLED FEES relevant to the particular COMPLIANT PRESENTATION.
Final liquidation date (real estate and private equity)	The date when the last PORTFOLIO in a COMPOSITE is fully distributed.
Firm	The entity defined for compliance with the GIPS standards. (See "DISTINCT BUSINESS ENTITY")

(continued)

FUND OF FUNDS (private equity)	An investment vehicle that invests in underlying investment vehicles. PRIVATE EQUITY FUNDS OF FUNDS predominately invest in CLOSED-END FUNDS and may make opportunistic DIRECT INVESTMENTS.
GENERAL PARTNER (real estate and private equity)	A class of partner in a LIMITED PARTNERSHIP. The GENERAL PARTNER (GP) retains liability for the actions of the LIMITED PARTNERSHIP. The GENERAL PARTNER is typically the fund manager, and the LIMITED PARTNERS (LPs) are the other investors in the LIMITED PARTNERSHIP. The GENERAL PARTNER earns an INVESTMENT MANAGEMENT FEE that typically includes a percentage of the LIMITED PARTNERSHIP's profits. (See "CARRIED INTEREST")
GROSS-OF-FEES	The return on investments reduced by any TRADING EXPENSES incurred during the period.
GROSS-OF-FEES (real estate and private equity)	The return on investments reduced by any TRANSACTION EXPENSES incurred during the period.
INCOME RETURN (real estate)	The investment income earned on all investments (including cash and cash equivalents) during the measurement period net of all non-recoverable expenditures, interest expense on debt, and property taxes. The INCOME RETURN is computed as a percentage of the CAPITAL EMPLOYED.
INTERNAL DISPERSION	A measure of the spread of the annual returns of individual PORTFOLIOS within a COMPOSITE. Measures may include, but are not limited to, high/low, range, or STANDARD DEVIATION (asset weighted or equal weighted) of PORTFOLIO returns.
INTERNAL VALUATION (real estate)	A FIRM's best estimate of value based on the most current and accurate information available under the circumstances. INTERNAL VALUATION methodologies include applying a discounted cash flow model, using a sales comparison or replacement cost approach, or conducting a review of all significant events (both general market and asset specific) that could have a material impact on the investment.
INVESTMENT MANAGEMENT FEE	A fee payable to the FIRM for the management of a PORTFOLIO. INVESTMENT MANAGEMENT FEES are typically asset based (percentage of assets), performance based (see "PERFORMANCE-BASED FEE"), or a combination of the two but may take different forms as well. INVESTMENT MANAGEMENT FEES also include CARRIED INTEREST.
INVESTMENT MULTIPLE (TVPI) (real estate and private equity)	TOTAL VALUE divided by SINCE INCEPTION PAID-IN CAPITAL.
LARGE CASH FLOW	The level at which the FIRM determines that an EXTERNAL CASH FLOW may distort performance if the PORTFOLIO is not valued. FIRMS MUST define the amount in terms of the value of cash/asset flow or in terms of a percentage of the PORTFOLIO assets or the COMPOSITE assets.

Limited partner (real estate and private equity)	An investor in a LIMITED PARTNERSHIP. The GENERAL PARTNER is liable for the actions of the LIMITED PARTNERSHIP, and the LIMITED PARTNERS are generally protected from legal actions and any losses beyond their COMMITTED CAPITAL.
Limited partnership (real estate and private equity)	The legal structure used by most PRIVATE EQUITY and REAL ESTATE CLOSED-END FUNDS. LIMITED PARTNERSHIPS are usually fixed life investment vehicles. The GENERAL PARTNER manages the LIMITED PARTNERSHIP pursuant to the partnership agreement.
Link	**1** *Mathematical Linking*: The method by which sub-period returns are geometrically combined to calculate the period return using the following formula: Period return = $[(1 + R_1) \times (1 + R_2) \ldots (1 + R_n)] - 1$, where $R_1, R_2 \ldots R_n$ are the sub-period returns for sub-period 1 through n, respectively. **2** *Presentational Linking*: To be visually connected or otherwise associated within a COMPLIANT PRESENTATION (e.g., two pieces of information are LINKED by placing them next to each other).
Market value	The price at which investors can buy or sell an investment at a given time multiplied by the quantity held plus any accrued income.
Must	A provision, task, or action that is mandatory or REQUIRED to be followed or performed. (See "REQUIRE/REQUIREMENT")
Must not	A task or action that is forbidden or prohibited.
Net-of-fees	The GROSS-OF-FEES return reduced by INVESTMENT MANAGEMENT FEES (including PERFORMANCE-BASED FEES and CARRIED INTEREST).
Open-end fund (real estate and private equity)	A type of investment vehicle where the number of investors and the total COMMITTED CAPITAL is not fixed and is open for subscriptions and/or redemptions. (See "EVERGREEN FUND")
Paid-in capital (real estate and private equity)	Capital inflows to an investment vehicle. COMMITTED CAPITAL is typically drawn down from LIMITED PARTNERS (or investors) over a period of time through a series of capital calls, which are at the discretion of the GENERAL PARTNER or FIRM. PAID-IN CAPITAL is equal to the amount of COMMITTED CAPITAL that has been drawn down SINCE INCEPTION. PAID-IN CAPITAL includes DISTRIBUTIONS that are subsequently recalled by the GENERAL PARTNER or FIRM and reinvested into the investment vehicle.
Performance-based fee	A type of INVESTMENT MANAGEMENT FEE that is typically based on the performance of the PORTFOLIO on an absolute basis or relative to a BENCHMARK.

(continued)

PERFORMANCE EXAMINATION	A detailed examination of a specific COMPOSITE'S COMPLIANT PRESENTATION by an independent verifier.
PERFORMANCE EXAMINATION REPORT	A PERFORMANCE EXAMINATION REPORT is issued after a PERFORMANCE EXAMINATION has been performed and opines that a particular COMPOSITE'S COMPLIANT PRESENTATION has been prepared and presented in compliance with the GIPS standards.
PERIODICITY	The length of the time period over which a variable is measured (e.g., a variable that is measured at a monthly PERIODICITY consists of observations for each month).
PIC MULTIPLE (real estate and private equity)	SINCE INCEPTION PAID-IN CAPITAL divided by cumulative COMMITTED CAPITAL.
PORTFOLIO	An individually managed group of investments. A PORTFOLIO may be an account or pooled investment vehicle.
PRIMARY FUND (private equity)	An investment vehicle that makes DIRECT INVESTMENTS rather than investing in other investment vehicles.
PRIVATE EQUITY	Investment strategies include, but are not limited to, venture capital, leveraged buyouts, consolidations, mezzanine and distressed debt investments, and a varicty of hybrids, such as venture leasing and venture factoring.
PROFESSIONALLY DESIGNATED, CERTIFIED, OR LICENSED COMMERCIAL PROPERTY VALUER/APPRAISER (real estate)	In Europe, Canada, and parts of Southeast Asia, the predominant professional designation is that of the Royal Institution of Chartered Surveyors (RICS). In the United States, the professional designation is Member [of the] Appraisal Institute (MAI). In addition, each state regulates REAL ESTATE appraisers and registers, licenses, or certifies them based on their experience and test results.
PROPRIETARY ASSETS	Investments owned by the FIRM, the FIRM'S management, and/or the FIRM'S parent company that are managed by the FIRM.
PROSPECTIVE CLIENT	Any person or entity that has expressed interest in one of the FIRM'S COMPOSITE strategies and qualifies to invest in the COMPOSITE. Existing clients may also qualify as PROSPECTIVE CLIENTS for any strategy that is different from their current investment strategy. Investment consultants and other third parties are included as PROSPECTIVE CLIENTS if they represent investors that qualify as PROSPECTIVE CLIENTS.
PUBLIC MARKET EQUIVALENT (PME) (private equity)	The performance of a public market index expressed in terms of an internal rate of return (IRR), using the same cash flows and timing as those of the COMPOSITE over the same time period. A PME can be used as a BENCHMARK by comparing the IRR of a PRIVATE EQUITY COMPOSITE with the PME of a public market index.

REAL ESTATE	Investments in: ■ wholly owned or partially owned properties; ■ commingled funds, property unit trusts, and insurance company separate accounts; ■ unlisted, private placement securities issued by private REAL ESTATE investment trusts (REITs) and REAL ESTATE operating companies (REOCs); and ■ equity-oriented debt (e.g., participating mortgage loans) or any private interest in a property where some portion of return to the investor at the time of investment is related to the performance of the underlying REAL ESTATE.
REALIZATION MULTIPLE (DPI) (real estate and private equity)	SINCE INCEPTION DISTRIBUTIONS divided by SINCE INCEPTION PAID-IN CAPITAL.
RECOMMEND/ RECOMMENDATION	A suggested provision, task, or action that SHOULD be followed or performed. A RECOMMENDATION is considered to be best practice but is not a REQUIREMENT. (See "SHOULD")
REQUIRE/REQUIREMENT	A provision, task, or action that MUST be followed or performed. (See "MUST")
RESIDUAL VALUE (private equity and real estate)	The remaining equity that LIMITED PARTNERS (or investors) have in an investment vehicle at the end of the performance reporting period.
RVPI (real estate and private equity)	RESIDUAL VALUE divided by SINCE INCEPTION PAID-IN CAPITAL. (See "UNREALIZED MULTIPLE")
SECONDARY FUND (private equity)	An investment vehicle that buys interests in existing investment vehicles.
SETTLEMENT DATE ACCOUNTING	Recognizing the asset or liability on the date when the exchange of cash and investments is completed.
SHOULD	A provision, task, or action that is RECOMMENDED to be followed or performed and is considered to be best practice but is not REQUIRED. (See "RECOMMEND/RECOMMENDATION")
SIGNIFICANT CASH FLOW	The level at which the FIRM determines that a client-directed EXTERNAL CASH FLOW may temporarily prevent the FIRM from implementing the COMPOSITE strategy. The measure of significance MUST be determined as either a specific monetary amount (e.g., €50,000,000) or a percentage of PORTFOLIO assets (based on the most recent valuation).
SINCE INCEPTION (real estate and private equity)	From the initial cash flow of a COMPOSITE.
SINCE INCEPTION INTERNAL RATE OF RETURN (SI-IRR) (real estate and private equity)	The internal rate of return (IRR) is the implied discount rate or effective compounded rate of return that equates the present value of cash outflows with the present value of cash inflows. The SI-IRR is a special case of the IRR that equates the present value of all cash flows (capital calls and DISTRIBUTIONS) with the period end value. The SI-IRR is always annualized except when the reporting period is less than one year, in which case the SI-IRR is not annualized.

(continued)

Standard deviation A measure of the variability of returns. As a measure of INTERNAL DISPERSION, STANDARD DEVIATION quantifies the distribution of the returns of the individual PORTFOLIOS within the COMPOSITE. As a measure of historical risk, STANDARD DEVIATION quantifies the variability of the COMPOSITE and/or BENCHMARK returns over time. Also referred to as "external STANDARD DEVIATION."

Sub-advisor A third-party investment manager hired by the FIRM to manage some or all of the assets for which a FIRM has investment management responsibility.

Supplemental information Any performance-related information included as part of a COMPLIANT PRESENTATION that supplements or enhances the REQUIRED and/or RECOMMENDED provisions of the GIPS standards.

Temporary new account An account for temporarily holding client-directed EXTERNAL CASH FLOWS until they are invested according to the COMPOSITE strategy or disbursed. FIRMS can use a TEMPORARY NEW ACCOUNT to remove the effect of a SIGNIFICANT CASH FLOW on a PORTFOLIO. When a SIGNIFICANT CASH FLOW occurs in a PORTFOLIO, the FIRM may direct the EXTERNAL CASH FLOW to a TEMPORARY NEW ACCOUNT according to the COMPOSITE'S SIGNIFICANT CASH FLOW policy.

Time-weighted rate of return A method of calculating period-by-period returns that negates the effects of EXTERNAL CASH FLOWS.

Total firm assets All discretionary and non-discretionary assets for which a FIRM has investment management responsibility. TOTAL FIRM ASSETS includes assets assigned to a SUB-ADVISOR provided the FIRM has discretion over the selection of the SUB-ADVISOR.

Total return The rate of return that includes the realized and unrealized gains and losses plus income for the measurement period.

Total return (real estate) The rate of return, including all CAPITAL RETURN and INCOME RETURN components, expressed as a percentage of the CAPITAL EMPLOYED over the measurement period.

Total value (real estate and private equity) RESIDUAL VALUE plus DISTRIBUTIONS.

Trade date accounting Recognizing the asset or liability on the date of the purchase or sale and not on the settlement date. Recognizing the asset or liability within three days of the date the transaction is entered into (trade date, T+1, T+2, or T+3) satisfies the TRADE DATE ACCOUNTING REQUIREMENT for purposes of the GIPS standards. (See "SETTLEMENT DATE ACCOUNTING")

Trading expenses The actual costs of buying or selling investments. These costs typically take the form of brokerage commissions, exchange fees and/or taxes, and/or bid–offer spreads from either internal or external brokers. Custodial fees charged per transaction SHOULD be considered CUSTODY FEES and not TRADING EXPENSES.

TRANSACTION EXPENSES (real estate and private equity) — All actual legal, financial, advisory, and investment banking fees related to buying, selling, restructuring, and/or recapitalizing PORTFOLIO investments as well as TRADING EXPENSES, if any.

TVPI (real estate and private equity) — TOTAL VALUE divided by SINCE INCEPTION PAID-IN CAPITAL. (See "INVESTMENT MULTIPLE")

UNREALIZED MULTIPLE (RVPI) (real estate and private equity) — RESIDUAL VALUE divided by SINCE INCEPTION PAID-IN CAPITAL.

VERIFICATION — A process by which an independent verifier assesses whether

1 the FIRM has complied with all the COMPOSITE construction REQUIREMENTS of the GIPS standards on a FIRM-wide basis and

2 the FIRM's policies and procedures are designed to calculate and present performance in compliance with the GIPS standards.

VERIFICATION REPORT — A VERIFICATION REPORT is issued after a VERIFICATION has been performed and opines that the FIRM has complied with all the COMPOSITE construction REQUIREMENTS of the GIPS standards on a FIRM-wide basis and that the FIRM's policies and procedures are designed to calculate and present performance in compliance with the GIPS standards.

VINTAGE YEAR (real estate and private equity) — Two methods used to determine VINTAGE YEAR are:

1 the year of the investment vehicle's first drawdown or capital call from its investors; or

2 the year when the first COMMITTED CAPITAL from outside investors is closed and legally binding.

WRAP FEE — WRAP FEES are a type of BUNDLED FEE and are specific to a particular investment product. The WRAP FEE is charged by a WRAP FEE sponsor for investment management services and typically includes associated TRADING EXPENSES that cannot be separately identified. WRAP FEES can be all-inclusive, asset-based fees and may include a combination of INVESTMENT MANAGEMENT FEES, TRADING EXPENSES, CUSTODY FEES, and/or ADMINISTRATIVE FEES. A WRAP FEE PORTFOLIO is sometimes referred to as a "separately managed account" (SMA) or "managed account."

APPENDIX A: SAMPLE COMPLIANT PRESENTATIONS

SAMPLE 1 INVESTMENT FIRM BALANCED GROWTH COMPOSITE

1 January 2002 through 31 December 2011

Year	Composite Gross Return (%)	Composite Net Return (%)	Custom Benchmark Return (%)	Composite 3-Yr St Dev (%)	Benchmark 3-Yr St Dev (%)	Number of Portfolios	Internal Dispersion (%)	Composite Assets ($ M)	Firm Assets ($ M)
2002	−10.5	−11.4	−11.8			31	4.5	165	236
2003	16.3	15.1	13.2			34	2.0	235	346
2004	7.5	6.4	8.9			38	5.7	344	529
2005	1.8	0.8	0.3			45	2.8	445	695
2006	11.2	10.1	12.2			48	3.1	520	839
2007	6.1	5.0	7.1			49	2.8	505	1,014
2008	−21.3	−22.1	−24.9			44	2.9	475	964
2009	16.5	15.3	14.7			47	3.1	493	983
2010	10.6	9.5	13.0			51	3.5	549	1,114
2011	2.7	1.7	0.4	7.1	7.4	54	2.5	575	1,236

Sample 1 Investment Firm claims compliance with the Global Investment Performance Standards (GIPS®) and has prepared and presented this report in compliance with the GIPS standards. Sample 1 Investment Firm has been independently verified for the periods 1 January 2000 through 31 December 2010. The verification report is available upon request. Verification assesses whether (1) the firm has complied with all the composite construction requirements of the GIPS standards on a firm-wide basis and (2) the firm's policies and procedures are designed to calculate and present performance in compliance with the GIPS standards. Verification does not ensure the accuracy of any specific composite presentation.

Notes:

1 Sample 1 Investment Firm is a balanced portfolio investment manager that invests solely in US-based securities. Sample 1 Investment Firm is defined as an independent investment management firm that is not affiliated with any parent organization. Policies for valuing portfolios, calculating performance, and preparing compliant presentations are available upon request.

2 The Balanced Growth Composite includes all institutional balanced portfolios that invest in large-cap US equities and investment-grade bonds with the goal of providing long-term capital growth and steady income from a well-diversified strategy. Although the strategy allows for equity exposure ranging between 50–70%, the typical allocation is between 55–65%. The account minimum for the composite is $5 million.

3 The custom benchmark is 60% YYY US Equity Index and 40% ZZZ US Aggregate Bond Index. The benchmark is rebalanced monthly.

4 Valuations are computed and performance is reported in US dollars.

5 Gross-of-fees returns are presented before management and custodial fees but after all trading expenses. Composite and benchmark returns are presented net of non-reclaimable withholding taxes. Net-of-fees returns are calculated by deducting the highest fee of 0.83% from the monthly gross composite return. The management fee schedule is as follows: 1.00% on the first $25 million; 0.60% thereafter.

6 This composite was created in February 2000. A complete list of composite descriptions is available upon request.

7 Internal dispersion is calculated using the equal-weighted standard deviation of annual gross returns of those portfolios that were included in the composite for the entire year.

8 The three-year annualized standard deviation measures the variability of the composite and the benchmark returns over the preceding 36-month period. The standard deviation is not presented for 2002 through 2010 because monthly composite and benchmark returns were not available and is not required for periods prior to 2011.

SAMPLE 2 ASSET MANAGEMENT COMPANY ACTIVE WORLD EQUITY COMPOSITE

Creation Date: 1 July 2005
Reporting Currency: EUR

Year	Gross Return (%)	XYZ World Index Return (%)	Dispersion (Range) (%)	# of Portfolios	Composite Assets (€ M)	% of Firm Assets (%)
2011	−1.9	−0.5	0.2	6	224.9	2.1
2010	16.3	13.5	0.7	8	256.7	2.0
2009	29.0	25.8	1.5	8	205.6	1.9
2008	−39.8	−36.4	1.3	7	164.1	1.5
2007	−2.8	−2.7	n/a	≤ 5	143.7	1.2
2006	9.3	7.5	n/a	≤ 5	62.8	0.4
2005*	14.2	12.6	n/a	≤ 5	16.1	< 0.1

*Returns are for the period from 1 July 2005 (inception date) through 31 December 2005.

Compliance Statement

Sample 2 Asset Management Company claims compliance with the Global Investment Performance Standards (GIPS®) and has prepared and presented this report in compliance with the GIPS standards. Sample 2 Asset Management Company has not been independently verified.

Definition of the Firm

Sample 2 Asset Management Company is an independent investment management firm that was established in 1997. Sample 2 Asset Management Company manages a variety of equity, fixed-income, and balanced assets for primarily European clients.

Policies

Sample 2 Asset Management Company's policies for valuing portfolios, calculating performance, and preparing compliant presentations are available upon request.

Composite Description

The Active World Equity Composite includes accounts whose objective is to exceed the XYZ World Index by 2% over a rolling three-year period. Securities are selected using the firm's proprietary analytics tool, which selects securities expected to be the top performers from within the XYZ World Index universe. Portfolios are more concentrated, typically holding approximately 100–120 securities, versus the benchmark, which reflects the performance of more than 500 holdings. Composite returns may, therefore, have a lower correlation with the benchmark than a more diversified global equity strategy.

Benchmark

The benchmark is the XYZ World Index, which is designed to measure the equity market performance of developed market countries. The benchmark is market-cap weighted and is composed of all XYZ country-specific developed market indexes. Sources of foreign exchange rates may be different between the composite and the benchmark; however, there have not been material differences to date. Benchmark returns are net of withholding taxes.

Fees

Returns are presented gross of management fees, custodial fees, and withholding taxes but net of all trading expenses.

List of Composites

A list of all composite descriptions is available upon request.

Fee Schedule

The standard fixed management fee for accounts with assets under management of up to €50 million is 0.35% per annum; 0.25% thereafter.

Minimum Account Size

The minimum portfolio size for inclusion in the composite is €1 million.

Internal Dispersion

Internal dispersion is calculated using the asset-weighted standard deviation of annual gross-of-fees returns of those portfolios that were included in the composite for the entire year. For those years when less than six portfolios were included in the composite for the full year, no dispersion measure is presented.

Ex-Post Standard Deviation

The three-year annualized ex-post standard deviation of the composite and benchmark as of each year end is as follows:

Year	Composite 3-Yr St Dev (%)	Benchmark 3-Yr St Dev (%)
2011	12.9	14.6
2010	13.2	14.1
2009	17.0	16.3
2008	15.6	14.2

SAMPLE 3 REAL ESTATE: OPEN-END FUNDS/SEPARATE ACCOUNTS

Real Estate Advisors Value-Added Strategy Composite
Schedule of Performance Results 1 January 2002 through 31 December 2011

	Composite Gross-of-Fees Returns					Composite Net-of-Fees Returns	Value-Added Benchmark Returns (Open-End Funds/ Separate Accounts)			Composite Statistics at Year End				
Year	Income Return (%)	Capital Return (%)	Total Return (%)	Low (%)	High (%)	Total Return (%)	Income Return (%)	Capital Return (%)	Total Return (%)	# of Portfolios	Composite Assets (HKD Million)	External Appraisal % of Composite Assets	Total Firm Assets (HKD Million)	Non-Real Estate % of Composite Assets
2002	7.9	1.9	9.9	n/a	n/a	8.8	8.4	−1.6	7.1	≤ 5	3,085	25	13,919	0
2003	8.5	2.9	11.7	5.8	20.4	10.5	8.0	1.0	9.2	6	3,294	25	14,911	0
2004	8.2	2.6	10.9	5.5	19.2	8.3	7.5	6.7	14.4	7	3,348	44	15,144	0
2005	6.6	11.2	18.1	9.0	31.6	16.6	6.8	12.7	19.7	7	3,728	72	19,794	0
2006	6.1	7.9	14.2	7.1	24.9	12.5	6.2	9.9	16.3	8	4,022	46	20,482	0
2007	5.4	8.0	13.7	6.8	23.9	11.8	5.6	9.9	15.6	7	4,348	33	24,219	0
2008	5.2	−11.4	6.6	−9.8	−1.6	−8.2	5.1	−11.1	−5.9	7	3,836	100	21,447	0
2009	7.5	2.7	10.3	5.2	18.1	7.4	7.3	3.2	10.8	7	3,371	52	16,601	0
2010	7.2	1.7	9.0	4.2	19.5	6.9	7.8	3.1	11.1	7	2,852	38	4,516	0
2011	7.2	2.8	10.2	5.1	17.8	8.1	7.1	3.2	10.6	7	3,457	50	17,414	5

Annualized Returns (%)

	Income Return (%)	Capital Return (%)	Total Return (%)	Low (%)	High (%)	Net Total Return (%)	Benchmark Income Return (%)	Benchmark Capital Return (%)	Benchmark Total Return (%)
3 Year	7.3	1.9	9.8			7.5	7.4	3.2	10.8
5 Year	6.5	2.9	7.1			5.0	6.6	1.4	8.2
7 Year	6.4	2.6	9.6			7.6	6.6	4.2	10.9
10 Year	7.0	11.2	10.0			8.1	7.0	3.5	10.7
Since Inception	7.0	7.9	10.0			8.1	7.0	3.5	10.7

Disclosures

Compliance Statement

Sample 3 Real Estate Advisors claims compliance with the Global Investment Performance Standards (GIPS®) and has prepared and presented this report in compliance with the GIPS standards. Sample 3 Real Estate Advisors has been independently verified for the periods 1 January 2006 through 31 December 2011. The verification reports are available upon request.

Verification assesses whether 1) the firm has complied with all the composite construction requirements of the GIPS standards on a firm-wide basis and 2) the firm's policies and procedures are designed to calculate and present performance in compliance with the GIPS standards. Verification does not ensure the accuracy of any specific composite presentation.

The Firm

Sample 3 Real Estate Advisors (the "Firm"), a subsidiary of Sample 3 Capital, Inc., is based in Hong Kong SAR and manages international real estate strategies. A list of the Firm's composite descriptions is available upon request.

The Composite

The Value-Added Strategy Composite consists of all discretionary open-end funds and separate accounts managed by the Firm using a value-added investment strategy with an equal income and appreciation focus and having a minimum portfolio size of HKD 10 million. Portfolio management will invest in only Asian multi-family, office, industrial, and retail property types that require correction or mitigation of the investments' operating, financial, redevelopment, and/or management risk(s). A moderate level of leverage ranging between 30% and 40% is used. Real estate investments are generally illiquid, and the investment outlook may change given the availability of credit or other financing sources.

The composite was created on 1 January 2006. The returns presented for periods prior to 2006 are not in compliance with the GIPS standards. Annual internal dispersion is presented using the high and low gross total returns for those portfolios that have been in the composite for the entire year.

Description of Discretion

The Firm has responsibility for sourcing, valuing, and managing the acquisition and disposition of assets. Although some of the Firm's separate accounts require client approval for the acquisition and disposition of assets, the Firm defines such portfolios as discretionary because its recommendations are consistent with the investment strategy and such client approvals are typically perfunctory.

Valuation

Real estate assets are internally valued by the Firm quarterly. For periods prior to 1 January 2011, assets were externally appraised by an independent appraiser at least every 36 months. Beginning 1 January 2011, assets are externally appraised annually unless client agreements stipulate otherwise, in which case such assets are appraised at least every 36 months or per the client agreement if the client agreement requires external valuation more frequently than every 36 months. The percentage of composite assets valued using an external valuation is shown for each annual period. When market circumstances dictate, the Firm may increase the frequency of external appraisals. All valuations are performed as of calendar quarter-ends.

Internal property valuations are determined by applying market discount rates to future projections of gross cash flows and capitalized terminal values over the expected holding period for each asset. To the extent leverage (debt) is used, the debt is valued separately from the real estate. Property mortgages, notes, and loans are marked to market using prevailing interest rates for comparable property loans if the terms of existing loans preclude the immediate repayment of such loans. Due to the nature of real estate investments, valuations are based upon subjective unobservable inputs.

Basis of Accounting

All funds in the composite report their assets and liabilities on a fair value basis using International Financial Reporting Standards (IFRS).

Calculation of Performance Returns

Returns are presented in Hong Kong dollars and are net of leverage. Net-of-fee returns are net of actual investment management fees including incentive fees, which are recorded on an accrual basis. Returns include cash and cash equivalents and related interest income.

Capital expenditures, tenant improvements, and lease commissions are capitalized, included in the cost of property, and reflected in the capital return component. Income and capital returns may not equal total returns due to the compounding linking of quarterly returns. Composite returns are calculated quarterly on an asset-weighted basis using beginning-of-period values. Annual returns are calculated by linking quarterly composite returns.

Policies for valuing portfolios, calculating performance, and preparing compliant presentations are available upon request.

Investment Management Fees

Some of the funds in the composite pay incentive fees ranging between 10% and 20% of profits in excess of a targeted SI-IRR. The standard annual investment management fee schedule for separately managed institutional accounts is as follows:

Up to HKD 30 million:	1.6%
HKD 30–50 million:	1.3%
Over HKD 50 million:	1.0%

Benchmark

The benchmark is the Value-Added Open-End Fund/Separate Account Index (the "Benchmark"). The Benchmark returns have been taken from published sources. The Benchmark is leveraged, includes various real estate property types, and excludes cash, cash equivalents, and other non-property-related assets, liabilities, income, and expenses. The extent of leverage used by the Benchmark may be different from that of the portfolios in the composite. As of 31 December 2011, the Benchmark leverage was 52%.

SAMPLE 4 REAL ESTATE: CLOSED-END FUND

2006 Value-Added Strategy Closed-End Fund Composite
Schedule of Performance Results 1 April 2006 through 31 December 2011

	Composite Gross TWR			Composite NET TWR	Benchmark			Composite at Year-End						
Year	Income Return (%)	Capital Return (%)	Total Return (%)	Total Return (%)	Income Return (%)	Capital Return (%)	Total Return (%)	# of Portfolios	Composite Assets (U.S. Million)	Leverage (%)	External Appraisal % of Composite Assets	Total Firm Assets (U.S. Million)	% of Firm Assets	Non-Real Estate % of Composite Assets
4/06–12/06	−3.2	0.8	−2.5	−4.0	4.9	2.2	7.2	1	70	40	35	2,641	20	0
2007	2.5	3.4	6.0	4.5	5.8	1.1	7.1	1	164	45	28	3,125	18	0
2008	6.2	1.9	8.2	6.7	6.9	3.8	10.9	1	215	50	100	2,754	18	0
2009	7.4	30.7	38.6	36.1	7.0	10.2	17.4	1	256	53	44	2,142	21	0
2010	6.6	−13.7	−7.3	−8.8	6.1	−8.8	−2.5	1	111	57	28	1,873	19	0
2011	5.8	−1.5	4.3	2.8	5.4	−2.6	3.0	1	112	60	85	2,247	20	15

Year	Gross SI-IRR	Net SI-IRR	Total Committed Capital (U.S. Million)	Paid-In Capital (U.S. Million)	Cumulative Distributions (U.S. Million)	TVPI Multiple	DPI Multiple	RVPI Multiple	PIC Multiple
4/06–12/06	−2.3	−3.1	250	71	0	0.99	0.00	0.99	0.28
2007	3.7	2.2	250	161	1	1.02	0.01	1.02	0.64
2008	5.8	4.2	250	226	26	1.07	0.12	0.95	0.90
2009	18.5	15.2	250	236	76	1.41	0.32	1.08	0.94
2010	11.5	9.8	250	240	201	1.30	0.84	0.46	0.96
2011	10.8	9.1	250	245	208	1.31	0.85	0.46	0.98

TVPI (investment multiple) = total value to paid-in capital
DPI (realization multiple) = cumulative distributions to paid-in capital
RVPI (unrealized multiple) = residual value to paid-in capital
PIC (PIC multiple) = paid-in capital to committed capital

Disclosures

Compliance Statement

Sample 4 Real Estate Managers claims compliance with the Global Investment Performance Standards (GIPS®) and has prepared and presented this report in compliance with the GIPS standards. Sample 4 Real Estate Managers has been independently verified for the periods 1 January 2006 through 31 December 2011. The verification reports are available upon request.

Verification assesses whether (1) the firm has complied with all the composite construction requirements of the GIPS standards on a firm-wide basis and (2) the firm's policies and procedures are designed to calculate and present performance in compliance with the GIPS standards. Verification does not ensure the accuracy of any specific composite presentation.

The Firm

Sample 4 Real Estate Managers (the "Firm") is a registered investment adviser under the Investment Advisers Act of 1940. A list of the Firm's composite descriptions is available upon request.

The Composite

The 2006 Value-Added Strategy Closed-End Fund Composite includes a single closed-end commingled fund managed by the Firm using a value-added investment strategy with a focus on both income and appreciation. Portfolio management intends to invest in properties located in major markets within the United States with higher operational risk than traditional property types. The target level of leverage is 50% with a maximum allowable level of 60%. Real estate investments are generally illiquid, and the investment outlook may change given the availability of credit or other financing sources. If investment opportunities and/or exit strategies become limited, the life of the fund may be extended and capital calls and distributions may be delayed. The composite was created on 1 January 2006. The composite vintage year is 2006, which was determined based on the fund's first capital call in April 2006.

Description of Discretion

The Firm has complete discretion for all investment activities within the fund.

Valuation

Real estate investments are internally valued by the Firm quarterly. For periods prior to 1 January 2011, investments were externally appraised by an independent appraiser at least every 36 months. Beginning 1 January 2011, assets are externally appraised annually. The percentage of composite assets valued using an external valuation is shown for each annual period. When market circumstances dictate, the Firm may increase the frequency of external appraisals. All valuations are performed as of calendar quarter-ends. Internal investment valuations are determined by applying market discount rates to future projections of net cash flows (gross real estate cash flows less debt service) and capitalized terminal values over the expected holding period for each asset. Due to the nature of real estate investments, valuations are based upon subjective unobservable inputs.

Basis of Accounting

All assets and liabilities are reported on a fair value basis using US Generally Accepted Accounting Principles for non-operating companies.

Calculation of Performance Returns and Metrics

Returns are presented in US dollars and are net of leverage. Net-of-fee returns are net of actual investment management fees, including incentive fees, which are recorded on an accrual basis.

Capital expenditures, tenant improvements, and lease commissions are capitalized, included in the cost of property, and reflected in the capital return component. Income and capital returns may not equal total returns due to the compounding linking of quarterly returns. Composite time-weighted returns are calculated quarterly on an asset-weighted basis using beginning-of-period values. Annual returns are calculated by linking quarterly composite returns.

SI-IRRs are calculated using quarterly cash flows through 2010 and daily cash flows starting in 2011.

Policies for valuing portfolios, calculating performance, and preparing presentations are available upon request.

Investment Management Fees

The fund pays an incentive fee of 15% of profits if the SI-IRR exceeds a preferred return to investors of 11%. The incentive fee is calculated annually. The standard annual investment management fee schedule for separately managed institutional accounts is as follows:

Up to $100 million:	1.50%
Over $100 million:	1.25%

Benchmark

The benchmark is the Value-Added Closed-End Fund Index (the "Benchmark"). The Benchmark is a time-weighted return index and returns have been taken from published sources. The Benchmark is leveraged and includes various real estate investment and property types, cash and other non-property-related assets, liabilities, income, and expenses. The extent of leverage used by the Benchmark may be different from that of the fund in the composite. As of 31 December 2011, the Benchmark leverage was 60%. There is no SI-IRR benchmark available for the 2006 vintage year.

SAMPLE 5 PRIVATE EQUITY: FUND OF FUNDS BY INVESTMENT STRATEGY

ABC Fund of Funds Manager, LLC
2006 Buyout Strategy Fund of Funds Composite
Results Reported as of Calendar Year End

Year End	# of Portfolios	Gross-of-Fees SI-IRR (%)	Net-of-Fees SI-IRR (%)	Benchmark SI-IRR (%)	Composite Assets ($ Mil)	Composite % of Firm Assets
2006*	8	26.9	26.4	17.2	2,336	80.8
2007	10	18.5	17.8	10.2	2,512	83.6
2008	11	18.7	18.1	11.0	3,227	84.2
2009	13	19.6	18.9	11.5	4,518	84.8
2010	13	20.7	20.1	11.8	6,330	85.2
2011	13	21.9	21.3	11.8	9,269	86.0

(continued)

(Continued)

Year End	# of Portfolios	Gross-of-Fees SI-IRR (%)	Net-of-Fees SI-IRR (%)	Benchmark SI-IRR (%)	Composite Assets ($ Mil)	Composite % of Firm Assets
2012	14	22.2	21.7	12.3	12,286	86.4
2013	14	15.1	14.4	9.6	12,346	87.7

*Partial year from 15 April 2006 (inception) through 31 December 2006.

Year End	Paid-In Capital ($ Mil)	Cumulative Committed Capital ($ Mil)	Since Inception Distributions	Investment Multiple (TVPI)	Realization Multiple (DPI)	Unrealized Multiple (RVPI)	PIC Multiple (PIC)
2006	1,556	3,177	1,205	1.5	0.8	0.7	0.48
2007	1,908	3,675	1,341	1.3	0.7	0.6	0.51
2008	2,371	5,166	1,623	1.4	0.7	0.7	0.45
2009	3,254	6,401	2,186	1.4	0.7	0.7	0.50
2010	4,400	8,370	2,950	1.4	0.7	0.8	0.51
2011	6,303	11,344	4,138	1.5	0.7	0.8	0.54
2012	8,167	13,713	6,513	1.5	0.8	0.7	0.69
2013	9,651	15,290	7,091	1.3	0.7	0.5	0.71

Aggregate Performance of Underlying Investments by Vintage Year
Results Reported as of 31 December 2013

Vintage Year	Gross-of-Fees Annualized SI-IRR (%)	Benchmark SI-IRR (%)
2006	22.3	2.5
2007	13.4	1.9
2008	26.0	7.1
2009	18.1	3.9
2010	0.7	1.0
2011	−16.2	−7.5
2012	−25.6	−19.9
2013	−49.9	−40.3

Vintage Year	Paid-In Capital ($ Mil)	Cumulative Committed Capital ($ Mil)	Since Inception Distributions ($ Mil)	Investment Multiple (TVPI)	Realization Multiple (DPI)	Unrealized Multiple (RVPI)	PIC Multiple (PIC)
2006	731	724	939	3.0	1.3	1.7	1.0
2007	710	234	294	1.8	0.4	1.3	3.0
2008	1,475	1,220	1,442	2.0	1.0	1.0	1.2

Vintage Year	Paid-In Capital ($ Mil)	Cumulative Committed Capital ($ Mil)	Since Inception Distributions ($ Mil)	Investment Multiple (TVPI)	Realization Multiple (DPI)	Unrealized Multiple (RVPI)	PIC Multiple (PIC)
2009	1,640	1,048	1,156	1.9	0.7	1.2	1.6
2010	1,896	3,695	1,124	1.9	0.6	1.4	0.5
2011	1,984	4,518	1,100	2.1	0.6	1.5	0.4
2012	680	1,998	938	2.2	1.4	0.8	0.3
2013	535	1,853	100	1.1	0.2	0.9	0.3

TVPI (investment multiple) = total value to paid-in capital
DPI (realization multiple) = cumulative distributions to paid-in capital
RVPI (unrealized multiple) = residual value to paid-in capital
PIC (PIC multiple) = paid-in capital to committed capital

Compliance Statement

ABC Fund of Funds Manager, LLC, claims compliance with the Global Investment Performance Standards (GIPS®) and has prepared and presented this report in compliance with the GIPS standards. ABC Fund of Funds Manager, LLC, has been independently verified for the periods 15 April 2006 through 31 December 2012.

Verification assesses whether (1) the firm has complied with all the composite construction requirements of the GIPS standards on a firm-wide basis and (2) the firm's policies and procedures are designed to calculate and present performance in compliance with the GIPS standards. Verification does not ensure the accuracy of any specific composite presentation. The verification report is available upon request.

The Firm

ABC Fund of Funds Manager, LLC, is an independent private equity investment firm with offices in New York, London, and Tokyo. The firm's list of composite descriptions, as well as information regarding the firm's policies for valuing investments, calculating performance, and preparing compliant presentations, are available upon request.

The Composite

The 2006 Buyout Strategy Fund of Funds Composite includes primary and secondary partnership investments with strategies focused on leveraged and growth-oriented buyouts primarily in the United States. Managers of partnerships are expected to focus on reducing costs, preparing companies for downturn, and providing operational improvement rather than financial engineering. Investments may be in small, medium, and large buyout partnerships, aiming to make selective commitments diversifying across stages, industries, and vintage years. Secondary deals take advantage of distressed primary partnership sales providing access to an increased mix of assets. The underlying funds are leveraged 100–300%. Private equity investments are illiquid and, therefore, if investment opportunities and/or exit strategies become limited, the life of the fund may be extended and capital calls and distributions may be delayed. The composite was created on 31 December 2006. The vintage year is 2006 and was determined by the initial subscription date of the fund of funds.

Valuation

The firm uses valuations reported by the general partner of the investment partnerships. Given the nature of the investments, all valuations are determined using both subjective observable and subjective unobservable inputs.

Calculation of Performance Returns

The fund's SI-IRR calculation uses daily cash flows. All cash flows and values used to calculate returns are in, or have been converted to, US dollars. Gross returns are net of all underlying investment partnership expenses, management fees, and carried interest but gross of ABC Fund of Funds Manager's management fees. Net returns are net of all underlying partnership fees and expenses, including ABC Fund of Funds Manager's management fees.

Investment Management Fee

ABC Fund of Funds Manager's management fee varies based on the size of the commitment and structure of the program. The management fee is 100 basis points, based on the total commitment to a fund of funds, plus a 10% carry on total gains. Net returns are calculated using actual management fees of the fund of funds and underlying funds, including performance fees.

Benchmark

The benchmark is derived from private equity dollar-weighted IRRs, and the calculation is based on the overall market return for buyout fund of funds as determined by benchmark provider GHI. Individual vintage year benchmarks are the median SI-IRR for the applicable vintage years, at 31 December 2013.

SAMPLE 6 PRIVATE EQUITY: FUND OF FUNDS BY VINTAGE YEAR

Investments 2002 Fund of Funds Composite
Results Reported as of Calendar Year End

Calendar Year	Gross-of-Fees SI-IRR (%)	Net-of-Fees SI-IRR (%)	Benchmark SI-IRR (%)	Composite Assets ($ Mil)	Total Firm Assets ($ Mil)	# of Portfolios
2002*	2.5	–5.5	8.5	2.6	250	≤ 5
2003	–4.2	–12.3	–3.8	4.7	300	≤ 5
2004	12.5	6.5	14.4	7.5	350	≤ 5
2005	45.8	40.8	42.7	24.2	400	≤ 5
2006	35.6	31.5	30.2	21.6	450	≤ 5
2007	22.2	19.3	13.5	14.7	500	≤ 5
2008	17.4	15.5	8.1	11.8	550	≤ 5
2009	17.3	15.3	7.5	11.0	600	≤ 5
2010	16.5	14.8	8.0	9.3	650	≤ 5
2011	15.9	13.5	8.5	8.1	700	≤ 5
2012	16.8	14.0	10.3	6.5	750	≤ 5

*Returns are for the period from 1 May 2002 (inception date) through 31 December 2002.

Calendar Year	Cumulative Committed Capital ($ Mil)	Paid-In Capital ($ Mil)	Cumulative Distributions ($ Mil)	DPI	RVPI	TVPI	PIC
2002	20	3	0	0.00	1.04	1.04	0.15
2003	20	5	0	0.00	0.93	0.93	0.25
2004	20	8	2	0.22	0.94	1.16	0.40
2005	20	15	4	0.23	1.62	1.85	0.75
2006	20	17	12	0.71	1.25	1.96	0.85
2007	20	18	16	0.89	0.82	1.71	0.90
2008	20	19	17	0.89	0.62	1.51	0.95
2009	20	19	19	0.99	0.57	1.56	0.96
2010	20	20	23	1.18	0.47	1.65	0.98
2011	20	20	25	1.25	0.41	1.66	1.00
2012	20	20	29	1.45	0.33	1.78	1.00

Underlying Partnership Investments by Strategy
Results Reported as of 31 December 2012

Investment Strategy	SI-IRR Gross-of-Fees (%)	Benchmark Return (%)	Committed Capital ($ Mil)	Paid-In Capital ($ Mil)	Cumulative Distributions ($ Mil)	Assets ($ Mil)	DPI Multiple	RVPI Multiple	TVPI Multiple	PIC Multiple
Venture Capital	65.3	32.6	8.0	8.0	16.0	2.0	2.0	0.3	2.3	1.0
Buyout	11.3	10.2	12.0	12.0	13.0	4.5	1.1	0.4	1.5	1.0

Disclosures

Sample 6 Investments claims compliance with the Global Investment Performance Standards (GIPS®) and has prepared and presented this report in compliance with the GIPS standards. Sample 6 Investments has not been independently verified.

Sample 6 Investments is an independent private equity manager of fund of funds strategies with offices in Zurich, Menlo Park, New York, and Hong Kong SAR. The composite was created in May 2002 and includes one closed-end fund that invests in buyout and venture capital funds. The fund of funds has an 8–10 year investment time horizon, but it may be longer based on the life of the underlying funds, which may be extended due to changes in investment and/or exit opportunities. As more fully described in the fund's offering memorandum, primary risks include industry and geographic concentration depending on investment opportunities, and liquidity risks due to the nature of the fund's investments.

The composite's vintage year is 2002, which was determined using the date of the initial capital call of the fund of funds. Returns are presented in US dollars.

The 2002 Fund of Funds Composite complies with PQR's valuation guidelines, which are consistent with the GIPS Valuation Principles. Valuations are normally based on valuations provided by the manager of the underlying investments' partnerships. Because fund investments are not publicly traded, all investments are considered to be valued using subjective unobservable inputs.

All returns for the 2002 Fund of Funds Composite reflect the deduction of administrative expenses (legal, auditing, etc.) of the closed-end fund. Gross returns do not reflect the deduction of Sample 6 Investments' management fees. Net returns reflect the deduction of actual management fees and accrued carried interest, if any.

The fund's SI-IRR calculation incorporates daily cash flows. Sample 6 Investments' annual management fee is 1% on the total committed capital.

The Vendor ABC Private Equity Fund of Funds Index (vintage year 2002) is used as the benchmark.

A complete list of the firm's composite descriptions is available upon request, as are policies for valuing portfolios, calculating performance, and preparing compliant presentations.

SAMPLE 7 PRIVATE EQUITY: PRIMARY FUND VEHICLE

Private Equity Capital Management
2001 Venture Capital Composite
Results Reported as of 31 December

Year End	Paid-In Capital (AUD Mil)	Since Inception Distributions (AUD Mil)	Cumulative Committed Capital (AUD Mil)	Composite Assets (AUD Mil)	% of Firm Assets
2001*	40.3	0.0	175.0	38.5	64.2
2002	82.3	1.0	175.0	78.8	52.5
2003	129.5	29.9	175.0	105.0	58.3
2004	143.5	42.3	175.0	120.8	41.6
2005	157.5	97.0	175.0	119.0	37.8
2006	166.2	129.3	175.0	112.0	31.1
2007	171.5	184.7	175.0	98.0	28.0
2008	182.5	184.7	175.0	78.8	21.0
2009	182.5	184.7	175.0	49.0	11.9
2010	182.5	184.7	175.0	31.5	7.5
2011	182.5	205.8	175.0	5.2	1.1

*Returns are for the period from 3 February 2001 (inception date) through 31 December 2001.

Year End	TVPI	DPI	RVPI	PIC	Composite Gross-of-Fees SI-IRR (%)	Composite Net-of-Fees SI-IRR (%)	Benchmark SI-IRR (%)
2001	0.96	0.00	0.96	0.23	−7.5	−9.5	−12.5
2002	0.97	0.01	0.96	0.47	0.3	−1.6	−3.5
2003	1.04	0.23	0.81	0.74	4.1	2.3	1.2
2004	1.14	0.29	0.84	0.82	8.2	6.4	7.4
2005	1.37	0.62	0.76	0.90	11.0	9.3	8.2
2006	1.45	0.78	0.67	0.95	13.0	10.1	9.7
2007	1.65	1.08	0.57	0.98	18.1	12.3	11.4
2008	1.44	1.01	0.43	1.04	16.9	10.4	10.1

Year End	TVPI	DPI	RVPI	PIC	Composite Gross-of-Fees SI-IRR (%)	Composite Net-of-Fees SI-IRR (%)	Benchmark SI-IRR (%)
2009	1.28	1.01	0.27	1.04	14.9	8.7	7.2
2010	1.18	1.01	0.17	1.04	14.0	7.7	6.8
2011	1.16	1.13	0.03	1.04	11.2	6.2	5.5

TVPI = Total Value to Since Inception Paid-In Capital
DPI = Since Inception Distributions to Since Inception Paid-In Capital
PIC = Since Inception Paid-In Capital to Cumulative Committed Capital
RVPI = Residual Value to Since Inception Paid-In Capital

Disclosures

Compliance Statement

Private Equity Capital Management claims compliance with the Global Investment Performance Standards (GIPS®) and has prepared and presented this report in compliance with the GIPS standards. Private Equity Capital Management has been independently verified for the periods 3 February 2001 through 31 December 2010.

Verification assesses whether (1) the firm has complied with all the composite construction requirements of the GIPS standards on a firm-wide basis and (2) the firm's policies and procedures are designed to calculate and present performance in compliance with the GIPS standards. The 2001 Venture Capital Composite has been examined for the periods 1 January 2005 through 31 December 2010. The verification and performance examination reports are available upon request.

Firm & Composite

Private Equity Capital Management ("PECM") is an independent private equity investment firm with offices in New York, London, and Sydney. The 2001 Venture Capital Composite includes one fund, whose objective is to seek long-term capital appreciation by acquiring minority interests in early-stage technology companies. The fund invests in technology companies in Europe, Asia Pacific, and emerging markets. European venture investments are more concentrated than in the other regions and are focused in a few high-quality companies. Exit opportunities include IPOs, trade sales, and secondary sales. Opportunities in China and India will be targeted for investment, and an allocation to Chinese high-tech will be at least 10% of the invested capital over the life of the fund. International venture capital investments are generally illiquid and are subject to currency risk. If investment opportunities and/or exit strategies become limited, the life of the fund may be extended and capital calls and distributions may be delayed. The 2001 Venture Capital Composite was created in 2001. The vintage year of the composite is 2001 and was determined by the year of the first drawdown. The firm's list of composite descriptions and the firm's policies for calculating performance and preparing compliant presentation are available upon request.

Input Data & Calculation

The 2001 Venture Capital Composite complies with the LMN Venture Capital Association's valuation guidelines as well as the GIPS Valuation Principles. Valuations are prepared by PECM's valuation committee and reviewed by an independent advisory board. All investments within the composite are valued using either a most recent transaction or an earnings multiple. Policies for valuing investments are available upon request. Due to the nature of private equity investments, all investments are valued using subjective unobservable inputs.

The SI-IRR calculation incorporates monthly cash flows for periods prior to 31 December 2009 and daily cash flows thereafter. Performance is expressed in Australian dollars (AUD).

Gross returns are net of transaction expenses and all administrative expenses. Net returns are net of transaction expenses, administrative expenses, management fees, and carried interest. The standard fee schedule currently in effect is as follows:

> The manager will receive an annual management fee equal to 2% of capital commitments. The manager's participation in profits (carried interest) begins after the limited partners have been provided an 8% preferred return. The manager collects 20% of the distributed profits from that point forward. Subsequently, if the amount of cumulative carried interest exceeds 20% of the net cumulative gains, the manager will repay the excess amount to the fund for distribution to the limited partners.

There is only one fund in the composite for all periods; therefore, the internal dispersion of portfolio returns is not applicable.

Benchmark

The benchmark return is derived from private equity dollar-weighted IRRs, and the calculation is based on the overall market return for international venture capital funds as published by Benchmark Provider GHI. Vintage year benchmarks are median returns for the applicable vintage year, as of each year end.

SAMPLE 8 INVESTMENTS LARGE-CAP SMA COMPOSITE

1 January 2001 through 31 December 2010

				As of 31 December			
Year	Net Return (%)	XYZ Index Return (%)	Internal Dispersion (%)	Number of Portfolios	Composite Assets ($ Millions)	Firm Assets ($ Millions)	% of SMA Portfolios
2010	8.4	10.2	0.7	1,834	2,125	18,222	100
2009	21.1	21.1	1.1	1,730	2,130	17,635	100
2008	−39.7	−39.8	1.0	1,631	2,141	19,246	100
2007	1.4	6.2	1.2	1,532	2,127	14,819	100
2006	11.4	10.5	0.9	1,428	2,116	12,362	100
2005	1.0	4.3	0.8	68	1,115	12,051	0
2004	6.8	4.9	1.0	52	1,110	13,419	0
2003	23.9	27.0	1.1	46	990	10,612	0
2002	−24.4	−19.1	0.9	38	975	9,422	0
2001	−17.7	−12.8	0.8	41	870	8,632	0

Notes:

1 Sample 8 Investments claims compliance with the Global Investment Performance Standards (GIPS®) and has prepared and presented this report in compliance with the GIPS standards. Sample 8 Investments has been independently verified for the period from 1 April 1996 through 31 December 2009.

Verification assesses whether (1) the firm has complied with all the composite construction requirements of the GIPS standards on a firm-wide basis and (2) the firm's policies and procedures are designed to calculate and present performance in compliance with the GIPS standards. The Large Cap SMA Composite has been examined for the period from 1 January 2006 through 31 December 2009. The verification and performance examination reports are available upon request.

2 Sample 8 Investments is an independent investment adviser registered under the Investment Advisers Act of 1940, was founded in March 1996, and manages global large-cap equity, fixed-income, and balanced strategies.

3 Beginning 1 January 2006, the composite includes only wrap fee (SMA) portfolios benchmarked to the XYZ Index. Performance results prior to 2006 are based on the Large-Cap Institutional Composite returns.

4 The Large-Cap SMA Composite is composed of portfolios invested in US equities which have a market capitalization greater than $5 billion.

5 The composite was created in February 2006. A list of composite descriptions is available upon request.

6 All returns are expressed in US dollars. Policies for valuing portfolios, calculating performance, and preparing compliant presentations are available upon request.

7 The XYZ Index returns are provided to represent the investment environment existing during the time periods shown. For comparison purposes, the index is fully invested and includes the reinvestment of income. The returns for the index do not include any trading costs, management fees, or other costs. Index returns have been taken from published sources.

8 "Pure" gross returns, presented below as supplemental information, from 2006 through 2010 do not reflect the deduction of any trading costs, fees, or expenses and are presented for comparison purposes only. "Pure" gross returns prior to 2006 reflect the deduction of trading costs. The SMA fee includes all charges for trading costs, portfolio management, custody, and other administrative fees. Net returns are calculated by subtracting the highest applicable SMA fee (2.50% on an annual basis, or 0.21% monthly) on a monthly basis from the "pure" gross composite monthly return. The standard fee schedule in effect is as follows: 2.50% on total assets.

9 The dispersion is measured by the equal-weighted standard deviation of annual returns of those portfolios that are included in the composite for the full year.

10 At 31 December 2010, the three-year annualized ex-post standard deviation of the composite and the benchmark are 12.3% and 13.2%, respectively.

11 Past performance is not an indicator of future results.

Supplemental Information

Year	"Pure" Gross Return* (%)	Net Return (%) Assuming 3% SMA Fees	Net Return (%) Assuming 2% SMA Fees
2010	11.1	7.9	9.0
2009	24.0	20.5	21.7
2008	−38.0	−40.1	−39.4
2007	4.0	0.9	2.0
2006	14.1	10.8	11.9
2005	3.5	0.5	1.5
2004	9.5	6.3	7.4
2003	26.9	23.3	24.5
2002	−22.3	−24.8	−23.9
2001	−15.5	−18.1	−17.2

* "Pure" gross-of-fees returns do not reflect the deduction of any expenses, including trading costs. "Pure" gross-of-fees returns are supplemental to net returns.

OPTIONAL SEGMENT

APPENDIX B: SAMPLE ADVERTISEMENTS

1. SAMPLE ADVERTISEMENT WITHOUT PERFORMANCE

Generic Asset Management

Generic Asset Management is the institutional asset management division of Generic Inc. and is a registered investment advisory firm specializing in qualitative growth-oriented investment management.

Generic Asset Management claims compliance with the Global Investment Performance Standards (GIPS®). To receive a list of composite descriptions of Generic Asset Management and/or a presentation that complies with the GIPS standards, contact Jean Paul at (123) 456-7890, or write to Generic Asset Management, 123 Main Street, Returnsville 12345, or jpaul@genericasset-managment.com.

2. SAMPLE ADVERTISEMENT INCLUDING ONE-, THREE-, AND FIVE-YEAR ANNUALIZED RETURNS

Generic Asset Management: Global Equity Growth Composite

	Ending 31 Mar 2012		
	1-Year	3-Year Annualized	5-Year Annualized
Global Equity Growth Composite	–0.3%	13.7%	0.1%
XYZ World Index	–0.5%	13.8%	–0.6%

Note: Returns are shown in US dollars net of fees.

Generic Asset Management is the institutional asset management subsidiary of Generic Inc. and is a registered investment adviser specializing in qualitative growth-oriented investment management. The Global Equity Growth strategy focuses on earnings, growth of earnings, and key valuation metrics. The benchmark is the XYZ World Index, which is designed to measure the equity market performance of developed market countries. The benchmark is market-cap weighted and is composed of all XYZ developed market indexes.

Generic Asset Management claims compliance with the Global Investment Performance Standards (GIPS®). To receive a list of composite descriptions of Generic Asset Management and/or a presentation that complies with the GIPS standards, contact Jean Paul at (123) 456-7890, or write Generic Asset Management, One Plain Street, Returnsville 12345, or jpaul@genericassetmanagement.com.

3. SAMPLE ADVERTISEMENT INCLUDING PERIOD-TO-DATE AND ONE-, THREE-, AND FIVE-YEAR ANNUALIZED RETURNS

Generic Asset Management: Global Equity Growth Composite

	Ending 31 Mar 2012	Ending 31 Dec 2011		
	Period to Date (3 months)	1-Year	3-Year Annualized	5-Year Annualized
Global Equity Growth Composite	−3.84%	1.3%	15.0%	−1.2%
XYZ World Index	−4.94%	1.5%	14.1%	−0.7%

Note: Returns are shown in US dollars net of fees.

Generic Asset Management is the institutional asset management subsidiary of Generic Inc. and is a registered investment adviser specializing in qualitative growth-oriented investment management. The Global Equity Growth strategy focuses on earnings, growth of earnings, and key valuation metrics. The benchmark is the XYZ World Index, which is designed to measure the equity market performance of developed market countries. The benchmark is market-cap weighted and is composed of all XYZ developed market indexes.

Generic Asset Management claims compliance with the Global Investment Performance Standards (GIPS®). To receive a list of composite descriptions of Generic Asset Management and/or a presentation that complies with the GIPS standards, contact Jean Paul at (123) 456-7890, or write Generic Asset Management, One Plain Street, Returnsville 12345, or jpaul@genericassetmanagement.com.

4. SAMPLE ADVERTISEMENT INCLUDING FIVE YEARS OF ANNUAL RETURNS

Generic Asset Management: Global Equity Growth Composite

	Period to Date	Annual Returns Periods Ended 31 December				
	(3 months to 31 Mar 2012)	2011	2010	2009	2008	2007
Global Equity Growth Composite	−3.84%	1.3%	13.0%	33.0%	−40.6%	9.6%
XYZ World Index	−4.94%	1.5%	11.8%	30.8%	−40.3%	9.6%

Note: Returns are shown in US dollars net of fees.

Generic Asset Management is the institutional asset management subsidiary of Generic Inc. and is a registered investment adviser specializing in qualitative, growth-oriented investment management. The Global Equity Growth strategy focuses on earnings, growth of earnings, and key valuation metrics. The benchmark is the XYZ World Index, which is designed to measure the equity market performance of developed market countries. The benchmark is market-cap weighted and is composed of all XYZ developed market indexes.

Generic Asset Management claims compliance with the Global Investment Performance Standards (GIPS®).

To receive a list of composite descriptions of Generic Asset Management and/or a presentation that complies with the GIPS standards, contact Jean Paul at (123) 456-7890, or write to Generic Asset Management, 123 Main Street, Returnsville 12345, or jpaul@genericassetmanagment.com.

APPENDIX C: SAMPLE LIST OF COMPOSITE DESCRIPTIONS

1 Unconstrained Activist UK Equity Composite

The Unconstrained Activist UK Equity Composite includes all institutional portfolios invested in both listed and unlisted UK equities that pursue an activist investment policy; there is no restriction on the market capitalization of companies held. Portfolios within this composite are highly concentrated, holding approximately 15 securities, so returns may have lower correlation with the benchmark than a fully diversified strategy. In times of increased market volatility, the composite characteristics may change significantly and stock liquidity could be reduced. Due to their more concentrated nature, portfolios will tend to have more stock-specific risk than a more diversified strategy. Portfolios can use both exchange-traded and OTC derivative contracts for efficient portfolio management, which may expose the strategy to counterparty risk. The benchmark is the FTSE All Share® Index.

2 Emerging Market High Yield Fixed Income Composite

The Emerging Market High Yield Fixed Income Composite includes all institutional and retail portfolios invested in high yield debt securities issued by countries outside the OECD. The strategy allows for investment in foreign currency denominated assets over which the manager has full discretion on hedging. The strategy aims to deliver a total return primarily through income but with some capital growth. High yield bonds carry increased levels of credit and default risk and are less liquid than government and investment grade bonds. Investment in less regulated markets carries increased political, economic, and issuer risk. The benchmark is the J.P. Morgan Emerging Market Bond Index (EMBI+).

3 UK Liquidity Plus Composite

The UK Liquidity Plus Composite includes all institutional portfolios invested in a broad range of short-dated interest-bearing deposits, cash equivalents, short-term commercial paper, and other money market investments issued by major UK clearing banks and lending institutions. The strategy has a targeted modified duration of less than one year. The principal investment objectives are preservation of capital, maintenance of liquidity, and provision of yield greater than that available for the benchmark, the three-month Libor rate. The UK Liquidity Plus strategy differs from more conventional cash strategies in that it additionally holds short-term commercial paper, which has a greater exposure to credit risk.

4 Socially Responsible Investment (SRI) Composite

The Socially Responsible Investment Composite includes all segregated institutional and pooled portfolios that invest in global equity securities issued by companies that make a positive contribution to society and the environment through sustainable and socially responsible practices. The strategy aims to provide long-term capital appreciation together with a growing income stream through investment in a portfolio of core equity holdings diversified by economic sector, industry group, and geographic business concentration. All foreign currency exposures are fully hedged back to US dollars.

The SRI process tends to screen out certain companies and sectors, which may result in a more concentrated strategy than a fully diversified strategy. Changes in legislation, scientific thinking, national and supra-national policies, and behaviors could significantly affect the stocks of companies held within the strategy. The benchmark is the Morningstar Ethical/SRI Global GIF Sector peer group.

5 **Leveraged Bond Composite**

The Leveraged Bond Composite includes all institutional segregated portfolios invested in a diversified range of high yield corporate and government bonds with the aim of providing investors with a high level of income while seeking to maximize the total return. The portfolios are invested in domestic and international fixed income securities of varying maturities. The strategy allows investment in exchange-traded and OTC derivative contracts (including, but not limited to, options, futures, swaps, and forward currency contracts) for the purposes of risk, volatility, and currency exposure management. The strategy allows leverage up to but not exceeding twice the value of a portfolio's investments through the use of repurchase financing arrangements with counterparties. Inherent in derivative instrument investments is the risk of counterparty default. Leverage may also magnify losses as well as gains to the extent that leverage is employed. The benchmark is the Bloomberg Barclays Global Aggregate Bond Index.

6 **Global Commodity Composite**

The Global Commodity Composite includes institutional portfolios that globally invest in a diversified range of companies that provide exposure to commodities, energy, and materials. Investment is primarily through the common or ordinary stock of these companies. Investment directly in raw materials is allowable to a maximum exposure of 10%. Exchange-traded funds and exchange-traded commodity securities up to a maximum 20% exposure are also allowed. The base currency is US dollars, and any or all of the currency risk associated with investments in currencies other than dollars may be hedged between 0% and 100% at the manager's discretion. The strategy cannot gear or otherwise deploy leverage but may use exchange-traded derivative instruments for efficient portfolio management.

Investments directly or indirectly in commodities may add to portfolio volatility. Global commodity prices can be affected by changes in legislation, national and supra-national policies, and behaviors. In times of commodity price volatility, the liquidity of directly held commodities and the correlation with the broad market can change quickly. The benchmark is the Dow Jones–UBS Commodity Index Total Return℠.

7 **Large Cap Equity Growth Composite**

The Large Cap Equity Growth Composite includes all institutional portfolios that invest in large capitalization US stocks that are considered to have growth in earnings prospects that is superior to that of the average company within the benchmark, the Russell 3000® Growth Index. The targeted tracking error between the composite and the benchmark is less than 3%.

8 **Balanced Growth Composite**

The Balanced Growth Composite includes all institutional balanced portfolios that invest in large-cap US equities and investment-grade bonds with the goal of providing long-term capital growth and steady income from a well-diversified strategy. Although the strategy allows for equity exposure ranging between 50% and 70%, the typical allocation is between 55% and 65%.

9 **Currency Overlay Composite**

The Currency Overlay Composite includes all institutional and retail portfolios invested in a broad range of foreign-currency-denominated deposits or instruments, such as forward contracts, futures, or foreign exchange derivatives. The principal investment objective is alpha generation through currency appreciation and/or risk mitigation from adverse movements in exchange rates where the original currency exposure stems from a global or international portfolio. Hedging strategies may range from passive to fully active. Currency-related investing carries inherent risks due to changes in macroeconomic policy, which can be amplified in the case of emerging markets, where political regime shifts and changes in the control of capital may be more prevalent. In volatile periods, liquidity and correlations between currencies may change expected returns drastically. Foreign exchange forwards and derivatives traded over the counter have counterparty default risk.

10 Asian Market Neutral Composite

The Asian Market Neutral Composite includes a single hedge fund with a market neutral strategy that invests in publically traded Asian equities with a market capitalization greater than $500 million. The strategy uses a risk controlled quantitative screening and optimization process that invests at least 85% of the net asset value in long equity positions and at least 85% of the net asset value in short equity positions. The long portion of the strategy will overweight those securities that have been quantitatively identified as potentially exhibiting superior and sustainable earnings growth compared with the market; conversely, the short portion of the strategy will consist of securities that have been identified as having inferior growth prospects or that may also be adversely affected by either specific events or by momentum considerations. The principal objective of the strategy is to outperform the return on three-month US Treasury Bills through active trading of long and short equity positions.

The Asian Market Neutral strategy seeks to dollar balance exposures between long and short positions so that broad market movements are neutralized. In certain market conditions, the investment process behind the strategy can give rise to unmatched country, sector, industry, market capitalization, and/or style bias exposures in the portfolio. The active trading strategy will involve significantly greater stock turnover when compared with passive strategies.

11 2001 Venture Capital Composite

The 2001 Venture Capital Composite includes one fund, whose objective is to seek long-term capital appreciation by acquiring minority interests in early-stage technology companies. The fund invests in technology companies in Europe, Asia Pacific, and emerging markets. European venture investments are more concentrated than in the other regions and are focused in a few high-quality companies. Exit opportunities include IPOs, trade sales, and secondary sales. Opportunities in China and India will be targeted for investment, and an allocation to Chinese high-tech will be at least 10% of the invested capital over the life of the fund. International venture capital investments are generally illiquid and are subject to currency risk. If investment opportunities and/or exit strategies become limited, the life of the fund may be extended and capital calls and distributions may be delayed.

12 2006 Buyout Strategy Fund of Funds Composite

The 2006 Buyout Strategy Fund of Funds Composite includes primary and secondary partnership investments with strategies focused on leveraged and growth-oriented buyouts primarily in the United States. Managers of partnerships are expected to focus on reducing costs, preparing companies for downturn, and providing operational improvement rather than financial engineering.

Investments may be in small, medium, and large buyout partnerships, aiming to make selective commitments diversifying across stages, industries, and vintage years. Secondary deals take advantage of distressed primary partnership sales providing access to an increased mix of assets. The underlying funds are leveraged 100–300%. Private equity investments are illiquid and, therefore, if investment opportunities and/or exit strategies become limited, the life of the fund may be extended and capital calls and distributions may be delayed.

13 Value-Added Strategy Non-Closed-End Real Estate Composite

The Value-Added Strategy Composite consists of all discretionary open-end funds and separate accounts managed by the Firm using a value-added investment strategy with an equal income and appreciation focus and having a minimum portfolio size of $10 million. Portfolio management will invest in multi-family, office, industrial, and retail property types only within Asia that require correction or mitigation of the investments' operating, financial, redevelopment, and/or management risk(s). A moderate level of leverage ranging between 30% and 40% is used. Real estate investments are generally illiquid, and the investment outlook may change given the availability of credit or other financing sources.

14 Value-Added Strategy Closed-End Real Estate Composite

The Value-Added Strategy Composite includes a single closed-end commingled fund managed by the Firm using a value-added investment strategy with a focus on both income and appreciation. Portfolio management intends to invest in properties located in major markets within the United States with higher operational risk than traditional property types. The target level of leverage is 50% with a maximum allowable level of 60%. Real estate investments are generally illiquid, and the investment outlook may change given the availability of credit or other financing sources. If investment opportunities and/or exit strategies become limited, the life of the fund may be extended and capital calls and distributions may be delayed.

15 US Core Equity Composite (Terminated Composites)

The US Core Equity Composite includes all institutional portfolios and pooled funds managed to a GARP (growth at a reasonable price) strategy through investment in a high-quality, focused portfolio of domestic, large-capitalization stocks that are expected to generate returns above the S&P 500® Index over a market cycle. Sample Asset Management Firm uses a quantitative screening process together with fundamental research and then overlays macroeconomic factors and economic sector exposures to construct portfolios. The benchmark is the S&P 500 Index. Quantitative-driven investment screening relies on historical stock correlations, which can be adversely affected during periods of severe market volatility. The composite terminated in March 2009.

Detailed composite definitions are available upon request.

END OPTIONAL SEGMENT

PRACTICE PROBLEMS

1 With respect to the Global Investment Performance Standards, which of the following is one of the nine sections containing investment performance provisions?

A Real Estate.

B Derivatives.

C Legal and Ethical Considerations.

2 According to the Fundamentals of Compliance section of the Global Investment Performance Standards, issues that a firm must consider when claiming compliance include all of the following *except*:

A replicating performance.

B properly defining the firm.

C documenting firm policies and procedures used in establishing and maintaining compliance with the Standards.

3 G&F Advisors claims compliance with the Global Investment Performance Standards (GIPS) in its marketing materials. The compliant presentation includes a footnote which indicates that the firm has been verified by an independent third party. An additional note states that G&F is in compliance with the GIPS standards except for its private equity investments. Is it *likely* that G&F violated the GIPS standards?

A No, because the footnotes meet the requirements of the Standards.

B No, because the provisions do not apply to the private equity investments.

C Yes, because they cannot claim compliance unless all requirements of the Standard are met.

4 The GIPS standards are instrumental in:

A enabling regulatory enforcement of investment performance reporting.

B establishing best practices for calculating and presenting investment performance.

C eliminating barriers to entry in markets with no investment performance standards.

5 A key feature of the GIPS standards is that:

A they strive to cover the unique characteristics of each asset class.

B firms must adhere to all requirements of the standards to claim compliance.

C actual, discretionary, fee-paying portfolios may be excluded from a composite under limited conditions.

6 What is the minimum period of compliant performance that a 12-year-old firm must present to comply with the GIPS standards?

A Five years

B Ten years

C Twelve years

7 To claim compliance with the GIPS standards, a firm is required to:

A adhere to certain calculation methodologies.

B conduct an independent third-party verification of its claim of compliance.

C perform periodic internal compliance checks of its investment performance process.

8 Adherence to the GIPS standards is reinforced by:

A the sanctioning authority of sponsoring organizations.

B the higher priority placed on compliance with GIPS over conflicting regulations.

C a strong commitment to ethical integrity in fair representation and full disclosure.

9 Which of the following statements concerning the requirements of GIPS Fundamentals of Compliance is correct?

A Firms claiming compliance have full discretion over the dissemination of their compliant presentation.

B Firms may claim partial compliance with the standards provided the performance presented is not false or misleading.

C The definition of the firm creates defined boundaries whereby total firm assets and the basis for firm-wide compliance are determined.

10 According to the Fundamentals of Compliance—Requirements section of the GIPS standards, a firm must:

A include in total firm assets those assigned to a sub-advisor selected by the firm.

B alter historical composite performance after a significant change in the firm's organization occurs.

C represent that the calculation methodology used by the firm is "in accordance with the Global Investment Performance Standards" when presenting performance.

11 The Fundamentals of Compliance section of the GIPS standards recommends that firms:

A conduct a verification.

B adopt a limited definition of the firm, regardless of the actual name of the individual investment management company.

C annually provide existing clients with compliant presentations for each composite on the firm's list of composite descriptions.

SOLUTIONS

1 A is correct. Real Estate is one of the nine sections in the 2010 edition of the GIPS standards. Derivatives and Legal and Ethical Considerations are not sections of the Standards.

2 A is correct. Replication of performance is not included in the Fundaments of Compliance section within the GIPS standards.

3 C is correct. Firms must meet all the requirements set forth in the GIPS standards and cannot claim partial compliance.

4 B is correct. Given the growth in the types and number of financial entities, the globalization of the investment process, and the increased competition among investment management firms, the establishment of GIPS has led to an accepted set of best practices for calculating and presenting investment performance that is readily comparable among investment firms, regardless of geographic location. A is incorrect because the GIPS standards are a voluntary set of best practices that recognize that investment practices, regulation, performance measurement, and reporting of performance vary considerably from country to country. The standards are based on a "self-regulation" model rather than a legally enforceable regulatory model. C is incorrect because the GIPS standards are designed to encourage fair, global competition among investment firms without creating or eliminating market entry barriers. Presenting performance in accordance with the GIPS standards enables firms to compete on an equal footing regardless of geographic location or the stage of development of local market investment reporting practices.

5 B is correct. To claim compliance, firms must comply with all requirements of the GIPS standards, including any updates. Because meeting the objectives of fair representation and full disclosure is likely to require more than adhering to the minimum requirements, firms should also adhere to the recommendations of the standards to achieve best practice. A is incorrect because the GIPS standards do not address every aspect of performance measurement or cover unique aspects of each asset class. The GIPS standards will continue to evolve over time to address additional areas of investment performance. C is incorrect because the GIPS standards require firms to include all actual, discretionary, fee-paying portfolios in at least one composite defined by investment strategy. There are no exceptions to this requirement for portfolios meeting this definition.

6 B is correct. After a firm presents a minimum of 5 years of GIPS-compliant performance, the firm must present an additional year of performance for each year since its inception, building up to a minimum of 10 years of GIPS-compliant performance. Accordingly, a firm in existence for 12 years must present, at a minimum, 10 years of compliant performance to comply with the GIPS standards.

7 A is correct. The GIPS standards require firms to adhere to certain calculation methodologies and to make specific disclosures along with the firm's performance. B is incorrect because firms may choose (but are not required) to have an independent third-party verification to claim compliance with the GIPS standards. Verification is merely a recommendation of the GIPS standards. Being verified is considered best practice. C is incorrect because the GIPS standards strongly encourage (but do not require) firms to perform periodic

internal compliance checks of their investment performance process. Internal compliance checks do instill confidence in the validity of the performance presented as well as in the claim of compliance.

8 C is correct. Given the voluntary, "self-regulatory" nature of the GIPS standards, adherence to the standards requires firms to be strongly committed to ethical integrity in the reporting of performance that upholds the principles of fair representation and full disclosure. A is incorrect because sponsoring organizations lack the authority to sanction firms that falsely claim compliance with the GIPS standards. Compliance with the standards is voluntary, and firms "self-regulate" their claim of compliance. B is incorrect because where laws or regulations conflict with the GIPS standards, firms are required to comply with the laws and regulations and fully disclose the conflict in the compliant presentation. Complying with regulations takes priority over compliance with GIPS.

9 C is correct. According to Section 0 of the Fundamentals of Compliance, the definition of the firm is the foundation for firm-wide compliance with the GIPS standards and creates defined boundaries whereby total firm assets can be determined. A is incorrect because according to GIPS Provision 0.A.9, to claim compliance with the GIPS standards, firms cannot choose to whom they present a compliant presentation and must make every reasonable effort to provide a compliant presentation to all prospective clients. B is incorrect because according to GIPS Provision 0.A.6, if a firm does not meet all of the requirements of the GIPS standards, it must not represent or make any statements that may indicate partial compliance with the standards.

10 A is correct. According to GIPS Provision 0.A.14, total firm assets must include assets assigned to a sub-advisor provided the firm has discretion over selecting the sub-advisor. B is incorrect because according to GIPS Provision 0.A.15, changes in a firm's organization must not lead to alteration of historical composite performance. C is incorrect because according to GIPS Provision 0.A.7, statements referring to the calculation methodology as being "in accordance", "in compliance", or "consistent" with the Global Investment Performance Standards, or similar statements, are prohibited.

11 A is correct. According to Section 0.B.2 of the Fundamentals of Compliance—Recommendations of the GIPS standards, it is recommended that firms perform an independent, third-party verification of the firm's claim of compliance. B is incorrect because Section 0.B.3 of the Fundamentals of Compliance—Recommendations of the GIPS standards recommends that firms adopt the broadest (rather than limited), most meaningful definition of the firm. The scope of firm definition should include all geographical offices operating under a common brand name regardless of the actual name of the individual investment management company. C is incorrect because Section 0.B.4 of the Fundamentals of Compliance—Recommendations of the GIPS standards recommends that firms annually provide each existing client with a compliant presentation of the composite in which the client's portfolio is included. The standards do not recommend that firms provide compliant presentations for each composite maintained by the firm.

Quantitative Methods

STUDY SESSIONS

Study Session 2	Quantitative Methods (1)
Study Session 3	Quantitative Methods (2)

TOPIC LEVEL LEARNING OUTCOME

The candidate should be able to explain and demonstrate the use of time value of money, data collection and analysis, elementary statistics, probability theory, and probability distribution theory in financial decision-making.

The quantitative concepts and applications that follow are fundamental to financial analysis and are used throughout the CFA Program curriculum. Quantitative methods are used widely in securities and risk analysis and in corporate finance to value capital projects and select investments. Descriptive statistics provide the tools to characterize and assess risk and return and other important financial or economic variables. Probability theory supports investment and risk decision making in the presence of uncertainty.

QUANTITATIVE METHODS

STUDY SESSION 2

Quantitative Methods (1)

This study session introduces quantitative concepts and techniques used in financial analysis and investment decision making. The time value of money and discounted cash flow analysis form the basis for cash flow and security valuation. Descriptive statistics used for conveying important data attributes such as central tendency, location, and dispersion are presented. Characteristics of return distributions such as symmetry, skewness, and kurtosis are also introduced. Finally, all investment forecasts and decisions involve uncertainty: Therefore, probability theory and its application quantifying risk in investment decision making is considered.

READING ASSIGNMENTS

Reading 6	The Time Value of Money by Richard A. DeFusco, PhD, CFA, Dennis W. McLeavey, DBA, CFA, Jerald E. Pinto, PhD, CFA, and David E. Runkle, PhD, CFA
Reading 7	Statistical Concepts and Market Returns by Richard A. DeFusco, PhD, CFA, Dennis W. McLeavey, DBA, CFA, Jerald E. Pinto, PhD, CFA, and David E. Runkle, PhD, CFA
Reading 8	Probability Concepts by Richard A. DeFusco, PhD, CFA, Dennis W. McLeavey, DBA, CFA, Jerald E. Pinto, PhD, CFA, and David E. Runkle, PhD, CFA

READING

6

The Time Value of Money

by Richard A. DeFusco, PhD, CFA, Dennis W. McLeavey, DBA, CFA, Jerald E. Pinto, PhD, CFA, and David E. Runkle, PhD, CFA

Richard A. DeFusco, PhD, CFA, is at the University of Nebraska-Lincoln (USA). Dennis W. McLeavey, DBA, CFA, is at the University of Rhode Island (USA). Jerald E. Pinto, PhD, CFA, is at CFA Institute (USA). David E. Runkle, PhD, CFA, is at Trilogy Global Advisors (USA).

LEARNING OUTCOMES

Mastery	*The candidate should be able to:*
☐	**a.** interpret interest rates as required rates of return, discount rates, or opportunity costs;
☐	**b.** explain an interest rate as the sum of a real risk-free rate and premiums that compensate investors for bearing distinct types of risk;
☐	**c.** calculate and interpret the effective annual rate, given the stated annual interest rate and the frequency of compounding;
☐	**d.** solve time value of money problems for different frequencies of compounding;
☐	**e.** calculate and interpret the future value (FV) and present value (PV) of a single sum of money, an ordinary annuity, an annuity due, a perpetuity (PV only), and a series of unequal cash flows;
☐	**f.** demonstrate the use of a time line in modeling and solving time value of money problems.

INTRODUCTION

1

As individuals, we often face decisions that involve saving money for a future use, or borrowing money for current consumption. We then need to determine the amount we need to invest, if we are saving, or the cost of borrowing, if we are shopping for a loan. As investment analysts, much of our work also involves evaluating transactions with present and future cash flows. When we place a value on any security, for example, we are attempting to determine the worth of a stream of future cash flows. To carry out all the above tasks accurately, we must understand the mathematics of time value of money problems. Money has time value in that individuals value a given amount of money more highly the earlier it is received. Therefore, a smaller amount of money now may be equivalent in value to a larger amount received at a future date. The **time value of money** as a topic in investment mathematics deals with equivalence relationships between cash flows with different dates. Mastery of time value of money concepts and techniques is essential for investment analysts.

The reading[1] is organized as follows: Section 2 introduces some terminology used throughout the reading and supplies some economic intuition for the variables we will discuss. Section 3 tackles the problem of determining the worth at a future point in time of an amount invested today. Section 4 addresses the future worth of a series of cash flows. These two sections provide the tools for calculating the equivalent value at a future date of a single cash flow or series of cash flows. Sections 5 and 6 discuss the equivalent value today of a single future cash flow and a series of future cash flows, respectively. In Section 7, we explore how to determine other quantities of interest in time value of money problems.

2 INTEREST RATES: INTERPRETATION

In this reading, we will continually refer to interest rates. In some cases, we assume a particular value for the interest rate; in other cases, the interest rate will be the unknown quantity we seek to determine. Before turning to the mechanics of time value of money problems, we must illustrate the underlying economic concepts. In this section, we briefly explain the meaning and interpretation of interest rates.

Time value of money concerns equivalence relationships between cash flows occurring on different dates. The idea of equivalence relationships is relatively simple. Consider the following exchange: You pay $10,000 today and in return receive $9,500 today. Would you accept this arrangement? Not likely. But what if you received the $9,500 today and paid the $10,000 one year from now? Can these amounts be considered equivalent? Possibly, because a payment of $10,000 a year from now would probably be worth less to you than a payment of $10,000 today. It would be fair, therefore, to **discount** the $10,000 received in one year; that is, to cut its value based on how much time passes before the money is paid. An **interest rate**, denoted r, is a rate of return that reflects the relationship between differently dated cash flows. If $9,500 today and $10,000 in one year are equivalent in value, then $10,000 – $9,500 = $500 is the required compensation for receiving $10,000 in one year rather than now. The interest rate—the required compensation stated as a rate of return—is $500/$9,500 = 0.0526 or 5.26 percent.

Interest rates can be thought of in three ways. First, they can be considered required rates of return—that is, the minimum rate of return an investor must receive in order to accept the investment. Second, interest rates can be considered discount rates. In the example above, 5.26 percent is that rate at which we discounted the $10,000 future amount to find its value today. Thus, we use the terms "interest rate" and "discount rate" almost interchangeably. Third, interest rates can be considered opportunity costs. An **opportunity cost** is the value that investors forgo by choosing a particular course of action. In the example, if the party who supplied $9,500 had instead decided to spend it today, he would have forgone earning 5.26 percent on the money. So we can view 5.26 percent as the opportunity cost of current consumption.

1 Examples in this reading and other readings in quantitative methods at Level I were updated in 2018 by Professor Sanjiv Sabherwal of the University of Texas, Arlington.

Economics tells us that interest rates are set in the marketplace by the forces of supply and demand, where investors are suppliers of funds and borrowers are demanders of funds. Taking the perspective of investors in analyzing market-determined interest rates, we can view an interest rate r as being composed of a real risk-free interest rate plus a set of four premiums that are required returns or compensation for bearing distinct types of risk:

r = Real risk-free interest rate + Inflation premium + Default risk premium + Liquidity premium + Maturity premium

- The **real risk-free interest rate** is the single-period interest rate for a completely risk-free security if no inflation were expected. In economic theory, the real risk-free rate reflects the time preferences of individuals for current versus future real consumption.
- The **inflation premium** compensates investors for expected inflation and reflects the average inflation rate expected over the maturity of the debt. Inflation reduces the purchasing power of a unit of currency—the amount of goods and services one can buy with it. The sum of the real risk-free interest rate and the inflation premium is the **nominal risk-free interest rate**.[2] Many countries have governmental short-term debt whose interest rate can be considered to represent the nominal risk-free interest rate in that country. The interest rate on a 90-day US Treasury bill (T-bill), for example, represents the nominal risk-free interest rate over that time horizon.[3] US T-bills can be bought and sold in large quantities with minimal transaction costs and are backed by the full faith and credit of the US government.
- The **default risk premium** compensates investors for the possibility that the borrower will fail to make a promised payment at the contracted time and in the contracted amount.
- The **liquidity premium** compensates investors for the risk of loss relative to an investment's fair value if the investment needs to be converted to cash quickly. US T-bills, for example, do not bear a liquidity premium because large amounts can be bought and sold without affecting their market price. Many bonds of small issuers, by contrast, trade infrequently after they are issued; the interest rate on such bonds includes a liquidity premium reflecting the relatively high costs (including the impact on price) of selling a position.
- The **maturity premium** compensates investors for the increased sensitivity of the market value of debt to a change in market interest rates as maturity is extended, in general (holding all else equal). The difference between the interest rate on longer-maturity, liquid Treasury debt and that on short-term Treasury debt reflects a positive maturity premium for the longer-term debt (and possibly different inflation premiums as well).

---

2 Technically, 1 plus the nominal rate equals the product of 1 plus the real rate and 1 plus the inflation rate. As a quick approximation, however, the nominal rate is equal to the real rate plus an inflation premium. In this discussion we focus on approximate additive relationships to highlight the underlying concepts.

3 Other developed countries issue securities similar to US Treasury bills. The French government issues BTFs or negotiable fixed-rate discount Treasury bills (*Bons du Trésor à taux fixe et à intérêts précomptés*) with maturities of up to one year. The Japanese government issues a short-term Treasury bill with maturities of 6 and 12 months. The German government issues at discount both Treasury financing paper (*Finanzierungsschätze des Bundes* or, for short, *Schätze*) and Treasury discount paper (*Bubills*) with maturities up to 24 months. In the United Kingdom, the British government issues gilt-edged Treasury bills with maturities ranging from 1 to 364 days. The Canadian government bond market is closely related to the US market; Canadian Treasury bills have maturities of 3, 6, and 12 months.

Using this insight into the economic meaning of interest rates, we now turn to a discussion of solving time value of money problems, starting with the future value of a single cash flow.

3 THE FUTURE VALUE OF A SINGLE CASH FLOW

In this section, we introduce time value associated with a single cash flow or lump-sum investment. We describe the relationship between an initial investment or **present value (PV)**, which earns a rate of return (the interest rate per period) denoted as r, and its **future value (FV)**, which will be received N years or periods from today.

The following example illustrates this concept. Suppose you invest \$100 (PV = \$100) in an interest-bearing bank account paying 5 percent annually. At the end of the first year, you will have the \$100 plus the interest earned, 0.05 × \$100 = \$5, for a total of \$105. To formalize this one-period example, we define the following terms:

PV = present value of the investment

FV_N = future value of the investment N periods from today

r = rate of interest per period

For $N = 1$, the expression for the future value of amount PV is

$$FV_1 = PV(1 + r) \quad (1)$$

For this example, we calculate the future value one year from today as $FV_1 = \$100(1.05) = \$105$.

Now suppose you decide to invest the initial \$100 for two years with interest earned and credited to your account annually (annual compounding). At the end of the first year (the beginning of the second year), your account will have \$105, which you will leave in the bank for another year. Thus, with a beginning amount of \$105 (PV = \$105), the amount at the end of the second year will be \$105(1.05) = \$110.25. Note that the \$5.25 interest earned during the second year is 5 percent of the amount invested at the beginning of Year 2.

Another way to understand this example is to note that the amount invested at the beginning of Year 2 is composed of the original \$100 that you invested plus the \$5 interest earned during the first year. During the second year, the original principal again earns interest, as does the interest that was earned during Year 1. You can see how the original investment grows:

Original investment	\$100.00
Interest for the first year (\$100 × 0.05)	5.00
Interest for the second year based on original investment (\$100 × 0.05)	5.00
Interest for the second year based on interest earned in the first year (0.05 × \$5.00 interest on interest)	0.25
Total	\$110.25

The \$5 interest that you earned each period on the \$100 original investment is known as **simple interest** (the interest rate times the principal). **Principal** is the amount of funds originally invested. During the two-year period, you earn \$10 of simple interest. The extra \$0.25 that you have at the end of Year 2 is the interest you earned on the Year 1 interest of \$5 that you reinvested.

The interest earned on interest provides the first glimpse of the phenomenon known as **compounding**. Although the interest earned on the initial investment is important, for a given interest rate it is fixed in size from period to period. The compounded interest earned on reinvested interest is a far more powerful force because, for a given interest rate, it grows in size each period. The importance of compounding increases with the magnitude of the interest rate. For example, \$100 invested today would be worth about \$13,150 after 100 years if compounded annually at 5 percent, but worth more than \$20 million if compounded annually over the same time period at a rate of 13 percent.

To verify the \$20 million figure, we need a general formula to handle compounding for any number of periods. The following general formula relates the present value of an initial investment to its future value after N periods:

$$FV_N = PV(1 + r)^N \quad (2)$$

where r is the stated interest rate per period and N is the number of compounding periods. In the bank example, $FV_2 = \$100(1 + 0.05)^2 = \$110.25$. In the 13 percent investment example, $FV_{100} = \$100(1.13)^{100} = \$20{,}316{,}287.42$.

The most important point to remember about using the future value equation is that the stated interest rate, r, and the number of compounding periods, N, must be compatible. Both variables must be defined in the same time units. For example, if N is stated in months, then r should be the one-month interest rate, unannualized.

A time line helps us to keep track of the compatibility of time units and the interest rate per time period. In the time line, we use the time index t to represent a point in time a stated number of periods from today. Thus the present value is the amount available for investment today, indexed as $t = 0$. We can now refer to a time N periods from today as $t = N$. The time line in Figure 1 shows this relationship.

Figure 1 The Relationship between an Initial Investment, PV, and Its Future Value, FV

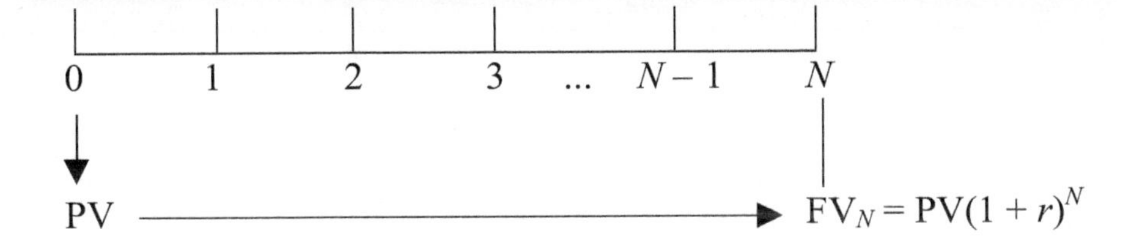

In Figure 1, we have positioned the initial investment, PV, at $t = 0$. Using Equation 2, we move the present value, PV, forward to $t = N$ by the factor $(1 + r)^N$. This factor is called a future value factor. We denote the future value on the time line as FV and position it at $t = N$. Suppose the future value is to be received exactly 10 periods from today's date ($N = 10$). The present value, PV, and the future value, FV, are separated in time through the factor $(1 + r)^{10}$.

The fact that the present value and the future value are separated in time has important consequences:

- We can add amounts of money only if they are indexed at the same point in time.
- For a given interest rate, the future value increases with the number of periods.
- For a given number of periods, the future value increases with the interest rate.

To better understand these concepts, consider three examples that illustrate how to apply the future value formula.

EXAMPLE 1

The Future Value of a Lump Sum with Interim Cash Reinvested at the Same Rate

You are the lucky winner of your state's lottery of \$5 million after taxes. You invest your winnings in a five-year certificate of deposit (CD) at a local financial institution. The CD promises to pay 7 percent per year compounded annually. This institution also lets you reinvest the interest at that rate for the duration of the CD. How much will you have at the end of five years if your money remains invested at 7 percent for five years with no withdrawals?

Solution:

To solve this problem, compute the future value of the \$5 million investment using the following values in Equation 2:

$$\begin{aligned} \text{PV} &= \$5{,}000{,}000 \\ r &= 7\% = 0.07 \\ N &= 5 \\ \text{FV}_N &= \text{PV}(1+r)^N \\ &= \$5{,}000{,}000(1.07)^5 \\ &= \$5{,}000{,}000(1.402552) \\ &= \$7{,}012{,}758.65 \end{aligned}$$

At the end of five years, you will have \$7,012,758.65 if your money remains invested at 7 percent with no withdrawals.

In this and most examples in this reading, note that the factors are reported at six decimal places but the calculations may actually reflect greater precision. For example, the reported 1.402552 has been rounded up from 1.40255173 (the calculation is actually carried out with more than eight decimal places of precision by the calculator or spreadsheet). Our final result reflects the higher number of decimal places carried by the calculator or spreadsheet.[4]

EXAMPLE 2

The Future Value of a Lump Sum with No Interim Cash

An institution offers you the following terms for a contract: For an investment of ¥2,500,000, the institution promises to pay you a lump sum six years from now at an 8 percent annual interest rate. What future amount can you expect?

4 We could also solve time value of money problems using tables of interest rate factors. Solutions using tabled values of interest rate factors are generally less accurate than solutions obtained using calculators or spreadsheets, so practitioners prefer calculators or spreadsheets.

Solution:

Use the following data in Equation 2 to find the future value:

$$\begin{aligned} PV &= ¥2,500,000 \\ r &= 8\% = 0.08 \\ N &= 6 \end{aligned}$$

$$\begin{aligned} FV_N &= PV(1 + r)^N \\ &= ¥2,500,000(1.08)^6 \\ &= ¥2,500,000(1.586874) \\ &= ¥3,967,186 \end{aligned}$$

You can expect to receive ¥3,967,186 six years from now.

Our third example is a more complicated future value problem that illustrates the importance of keeping track of actual calendar time.

EXAMPLE 3

The Future Value of a Lump Sum

A pension fund manager estimates that his corporate sponsor will make a \$10 million contribution five years from now. The rate of return on plan assets has been estimated at 9 percent per year. The pension fund manager wants to calculate the future value of this contribution 15 years from now, which is the date at which the funds will be distributed to retirees. What is that future value?

Solution:

By positioning the initial investment, PV, at $t = 5$, we can calculate the future value of the contribution using the following data in Equation 2:

$$\begin{aligned} PV &= \$10 \text{ million} \\ r &= 9\% = 0.09 \\ N &= 10 \end{aligned}$$

$$\begin{aligned} FV_N &= PV(1 + r)^N \\ &= \$10,000,000(1.09)^{10} \\ &= \$10,000,000(2.367364) \\ &= \$23,673,636.75 \end{aligned}$$

This problem looks much like the previous two, but it differs in one important respect: its timing. From the standpoint of today ($t = 0$), the future amount of \$23,673,636.75 is 15 years into the future. Although the future value is 10 years from its present value, the present value of \$10 million will not be received for another five years.

Figure 2 The Future Value of a Lump Sum, Initial Investment Not at $t = 0$

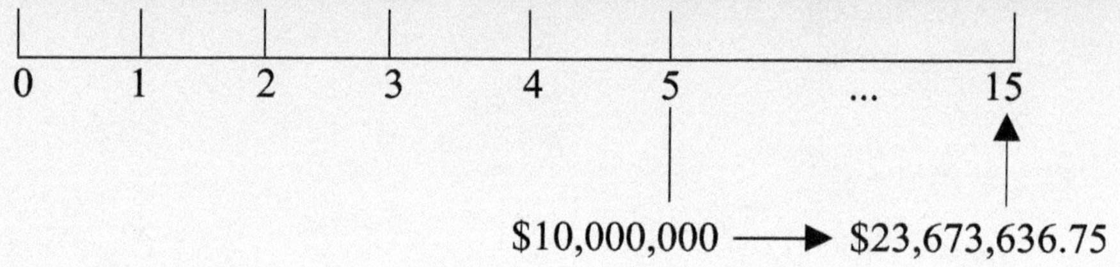

As Figure 2 shows, we have followed the convention of indexing today as $t = 0$ and indexing subsequent times by adding 1 for each period. The additional contribution of $10 million is to be received in five years, so it is indexed as $t = 5$ and appears as such in the figure. The future value of the investment in 10 years is then indexed at $t = 15$; that is, 10 years following the receipt of the $10 million contribution at $t = 5$. Time lines like this one can be extremely useful when dealing with more-complicated problems, especially those involving more than one cash flow.

In a later section of this reading, we will discuss how to calculate the value today of the $10 million to be received five years from now. For the moment, we can use Equation 2. Suppose the pension fund manager in Example 3 above were to receive $6,499,313.86 today from the corporate sponsor. How much will that sum be worth at the end of five years? How much will it be worth at the end of 15 years?

$$\text{PV} = \$6{,}499{,}313.86$$
$$r = 9\% = 0.09$$
$$N = 5$$
$$\begin{aligned} \text{FV}_N &= \text{PV}(1 + r)^N \\ &= \$6{,}499{,}313.86(1.09)^5 \\ &= \$6{,}499{,}313.86(1.538624) \\ &= \$10{,}000{,}000 \text{ at the five-year mark} \end{aligned}$$

and

$$\text{PV} = \$6{,}499{,}313.86$$
$$r = 9\% = 0.09$$
$$N = 15$$
$$\begin{aligned} \text{FV}_N &= \text{PV}(1 + r)^N \\ &= \$6{,}499{,}313.86(1.09)^{15} \\ &= \$6{,}499{,}313.86(3.642482) \\ &= \$23{,}673{,}636.74 \text{ at the 15-year mark} \end{aligned}$$

These results show that today's present value of about $6.5 million becomes $10 million after five years and $23.67 million after 15 years.

3.1 The Frequency of Compounding

In this section, we examine investments paying interest more than once a year. For instance, many banks offer a monthly interest rate that compounds 12 times a year. In such an arrangement, they pay interest on interest every month. Rather than quote the periodic monthly interest rate, financial institutions often quote an annual interest rate that we refer to as the **stated annual interest rate** or **quoted interest rate**. We denote the stated annual interest rate by r_s. For instance, your bank might state that a particular CD pays 8 percent compounded monthly. The stated annual interest rate equals the monthly interest rate multiplied by 12. In this example, the monthly interest rate is 0.08/12 = 0.0067 or 0.67 percent.[5] This rate is strictly a quoting convention because $(1 + 0.0067)^{12} = 1.083$, not 1.08; the term $(1 + r_s)$ is not meant to be a future value factor when compounding is more frequent than annual.

With more than one compounding period per year, the future value formula can be expressed as

$$FV_N = PV\left(1 + \frac{r_s}{m}\right)^{mN} \quad (3)$$

where r_s is the stated annual interest rate, m is the number of compounding periods per year, and N now stands for the number of years. Note the compatibility here between the interest rate used, r_s/m, and the number of compounding periods, mN. The periodic rate, r_s/m, is the stated annual interest rate divided by the number of compounding periods per year. The number of compounding periods, mN, is the number of compounding periods in one year multiplied by the number of years. The periodic rate, r_s/m, and the number of compounding periods, mN, must be compatible.

EXAMPLE 4

The Future Value of a Lump Sum with Quarterly Compounding

Continuing with the CD example, suppose your bank offers you a CD with a two-year maturity, a stated annual interest rate of 8 percent compounded quarterly, and a feature allowing reinvestment of the interest at the same interest rate. You decide to invest \$10,000. What will the CD be worth at maturity?

5 To avoid rounding errors when using a financial calculator, divide 8 by 12 and then press the %*i* key, rather than simply entering 0.67 for %*i*, so we have $(1 + 0.08/12)^{12} = 1.083000$.

Solution:

Compute the future value with Equation 3 as follows:

$$
\begin{aligned}
PV &= \$10{,}000 \\
r_s &= 8\% = 0.08 \\
m &= 4 \\
r_s/m &= 0.08/4 = 0.02 \\
N &= 2 \\
mN &= 4(2) = 8 \text{ interest periods} \\
FV_N &= PV\left(1 + \frac{r_s}{m}\right)^{mN} \\
&= \$10{,}000(1.02)^8 \\
&= \$10{,}000(1.171659) \\
&= \$11{,}716.59
\end{aligned}
$$

At maturity, the CD will be worth $11,716.59.

The future value formula in Equation 3 does not differ from the one in Equation 2. Simply keep in mind that the interest rate to use is the rate per period and the exponent is the number of interest, or compounding, periods.

EXAMPLE 5

The Future Value of a Lump Sum with Monthly Compounding

An Australian bank offers to pay you 6 percent compounded monthly. You decide to invest A$1 million for one year. What is the future value of your investment if interest payments are reinvested at 6 percent?

Solution:

Use Equation 3 to find the future value of the one-year investment as follows:

$$
\begin{aligned}
PV &= A\$1{,}000{,}000 \\
r_s &= 6\% = 0.06 \\
m &= 12 \\
r_s/m &= 0.06/12 = 0.0050 \\
N &= 1 \\
mN &= 12(1) = 12 \text{ interest periods} \\
FV_N &= PV\left(1 + \frac{r_s}{m}\right)^{mN} \\
&= A\$1{,}000{,}000(1.005)^{12} \\
&= A\$1{,}000{,}000(1.061678) \\
&= A\$1{,}061{,}677.81
\end{aligned}
$$

If you had been paid 6 percent with annual compounding, the future amount would be only A$1,000,000(1.06) = A$1,060,000 instead of A$1,061,677.81 with monthly compounding.

3.2 Continuous Compounding

The preceding discussion on compounding periods illustrates discrete compounding, which credits interest after a discrete amount of time has elapsed. If the number of compounding periods per year becomes infinite, then interest is said to compound continuously. If we want to use the future value formula with continuous compounding, we need to find the limiting value of the future value factor for $m \to \infty$ (infinitely many compounding periods per year) in Equation 3. The expression for the future value of a sum in N years with continuous compounding is

$$FV_N = PVe^{r_s N} \quad (4)$$

The term $e^{r_s N}$ is the transcendental number $e \approx 2.7182818$ raised to the power $r_s N$. Most financial calculators have the function e^x.

EXAMPLE 6

The Future Value of a Lump Sum with Continuous Compounding

Suppose a $10,000 investment will earn 8 percent compounded continuously for two years. We can compute the future value with Equation 4 as follows:

$$PV = \$10,000$$
$$r_s = 8\% = 0.08$$
$$N = 2$$
$$\begin{aligned} FV_N &= PVe^{r_s N} \\ &= \$10,000e^{0.08(2)} \\ &= \$10,000(1.173511) \\ &= \$11,735.11 \end{aligned}$$

With the same interest rate but using continuous compounding, the $10,000 investment will grow to $11,735.11 in two years, compared with $11,716.59 using quarterly compounding as shown in Example 4.

Table 1 shows how a stated annual interest rate of 8 percent generates different ending dollar amounts with annual, semiannual, quarterly, monthly, daily, and continuous compounding for an initial investment of $1 (carried out to six decimal places).

As Table 1 shows, all six cases have the same stated annual interest rate of 8 percent; they have different ending dollar amounts, however, because of differences in the frequency of compounding. With annual compounding, the ending amount is $1.08. More frequent compounding results in larger ending amounts. The ending dollar amount with continuous compounding is the maximum amount that can be earned with a stated annual rate of 8 percent.

Table 1 The Effect of Compounding Frequency on Future Value

Frequency	r_s/m	mN	Future Value of $1		
Annual	8%/1 = 8%	1 × 1 = 1	$1.00(1.08)	=	$1.08
Semiannual	8%/2 = 4%	2 × 1 = 2	$\$1.00(1.04)^2$	=	$1.081600
Quarterly	8%/4 = 2%	4 × 1 = 4	$\$1.00(1.02)^4$	=	$1.082432

(continued)

Table 1 (Continued)

Frequency	r_s/m	mN	Future Value of $1		
Monthly	8%/12 = 0.6667%	12 × 1 = 12	$\$1.00(1.006667)^{12}$	=	$1.083000
Daily	8%/365 = 0.0219%	365 × 1 = 365	$\$1.00(1.000219)^{365}$	=	$1.083278
Continuous			$\$1.00e^{0.08(1)}$	=	$1.083287

Table 1 also shows that a $1 investment earning 8.16 percent compounded annually grows to the same future value at the end of one year as a $1 investment earning 8 percent compounded semiannually. This result leads us to a distinction between the stated annual interest rate and the **effective annual rate** (EAR).[6] For an 8 percent stated annual interest rate with semiannual compounding, the EAR is 8.16 percent.

3.3 Stated and Effective Rates

The stated annual interest rate does not give a future value directly, so we need a formula for the EAR. With an annual interest rate of 8 percent compounded semiannually, we receive a periodic rate of 4 percent. During the course of a year, an investment of $1 would grow to $\$1(1.04)^2 = \$1.0816$, as illustrated in Table 1. The interest earned on the $1 investment is $0.0816 and represents an effective annual rate of interest of 8.16 percent. The effective annual rate is calculated as follows:

$$\text{EAR} = (1 + \text{Periodic interest rate})^m - 1 \tag{5}$$

The periodic interest rate is the stated annual interest rate divided by m, where m is the number of compounding periods in one year. Using our previous example, we can solve for EAR as follows: $(1.04)^2 - 1 = 8.16$ percent.

The concept of EAR extends to continuous compounding. Suppose we have a rate of 8 percent compounded continuously. We can find the EAR in the same way as above by finding the appropriate future value factor. In this case, a $1 investment would grow to $\$1e^{0.08(1.0)} = \$1.0833$. The interest earned for one year represents an effective annual rate of 8.33 percent and is larger than the 8.16 percent EAR with semiannual compounding because interest is compounded more frequently. With continuous compounding, we can solve for the effective annual rate as follows:

$$\text{EAR} = e^{r_s} - 1 \tag{6}$$

6 Among the terms used for the effective annual return on interest-bearing bank deposits are annual percentage yield (APY) in the United States and equivalent annual rate (EAR) in the United Kingdom. By contrast, the **annual percentage rate** (APR) measures the cost of borrowing expressed as a yearly rate. In the United States, the APR is calculated as a periodic rate times the number of payment periods per year and, as a result, some writers use APR as a general synonym for the stated annual interest rate. Nevertheless, APR is a term with legal connotations; its calculation follows regulatory standards that vary internationally. Therefore, "stated annual interest rate" is the preferred general term for an annual interest rate that does not account for compounding within the year.

We can reverse the formulas for EAR with discrete and continuous compounding to find a periodic rate that corresponds to a particular effective annual rate. Suppose we want to find the appropriate periodic rate for a given effective annual rate of 8.16 percent with semiannual compounding. We can use Equation 5 to find the periodic rate:

$$0.0816 = (1 + \text{Periodic rate})^2 - 1$$

$$1.0816 = (1 + \text{Periodic rate})^2$$

$$(1.0816)^{1/2} - 1 = \text{Periodic rate}$$

$$(1.04) - 1 = \text{Periodic rate}$$

$$4\% = \text{Periodic rate}$$

To calculate the continuously compounded rate (the stated annual interest rate with continuous compounding) corresponding to an effective annual rate of 8.33 percent, we find the interest rate that satisfies Equation 6:

$$0.0833 = e^{r_s} - 1$$

$$1.0833 = e^{r_s}$$

To solve this equation, we take the natural logarithm of both sides. (Recall that the natural log of e^{r_s} is $\ln e^{r_s} = r_s$.) Therefore, $\ln 1.0833 = r_s$, resulting in r_s = 8 percent. We see that a stated annual rate of 8 percent with continuous compounding is equivalent to an EAR of 8.33 percent.

THE FUTURE VALUE OF A SERIES OF CASH FLOWS

4

In this section, we consider series of cash flows, both even and uneven. We begin with a list of terms commonly used when valuing cash flows that are distributed over many time periods.

- An **annuity** is a finite set of level sequential cash flows.
- An **ordinary annuity** has a first cash flow that occurs one period from now (indexed at $t = 1$).
- An **annuity due** has a first cash flow that occurs immediately (indexed at $t = 0$).
- A **perpetuity** is a perpetual annuity, or a set of level never-ending sequential cash flows, with the first cash flow occurring one period from now.

4.1 Equal Cash Flows—Ordinary Annuity

Consider an ordinary annuity paying 5 percent annually. Suppose we have five separate deposits of \$1,000 occurring at equally spaced intervals of one year, with the first payment occurring at $t = 1$. Our goal is to find the future value of this ordinary annuity after the last deposit at $t = 5$. The increment in the time counter is one year, so the last payment occurs five years from now. As the time line in Figure 3 shows, we find the future value of each \$1,000 deposit as of $t = 5$ with Equation 2, $FV_N = PV(1 + r)^N$. The arrows in Figure 3 extend from the payment date to $t = 5$. For instance, the first \$1,000 deposit made at $t = 1$ will compound over four periods. Using Equation 2, we find that the future value of the first deposit at $t = 5$ is $\$1,000(1.05)^4 = \$1,215.51$. We calculate the future value of all other payments in a similar fashion. (Note that we are finding the future value at $t = 5$, so the last payment does not earn any interest.) With all values now at $t = 5$, we can add the future values to arrive at the future value of the annuity. This amount is \$5,525.63.

Figure 3 The Future Value of a Five-Year Ordinary Annuity

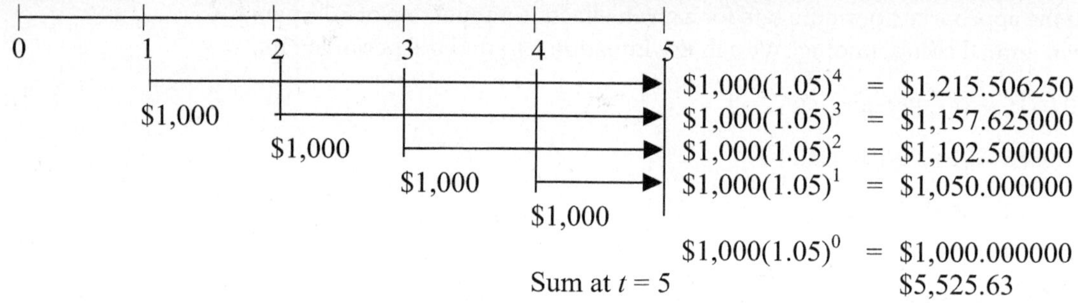

We can arrive at a general annuity formula if we define the annuity amount as A, the number of time periods as N, and the interest rate per period as r. We can then define the future value as

$$FV_N = A\left[(1+r)^{N-1} + (1+r)^{N-2} + (1+r)^{N-3} + \ldots + (1+r)^1 + (1+r)^0\right]$$

which simplifies to

$$FV_N = A\left[\frac{(1+r)^N - 1}{r}\right] \tag{7}$$

The term in brackets is the future value annuity factor. This factor gives the future value of an ordinary annuity of $1 per period. Multiplying the future value annuity factor by the annuity amount gives the future value of an ordinary annuity. For the ordinary annuity in Figure 3, we find the future value annuity factor from Equation 7 as

$$\left[\frac{(1.05)^5 - 1}{0.05}\right] = 5.525631$$

With an annuity amount $A = \$1{,}000$, the future value of the annuity is $1,000(5.525631) = $5,525.63, an amount that agrees with our earlier work.

The next example illustrates how to find the future value of an ordinary annuity using the formula in Equation 7.

EXAMPLE 7

The Future Value of an Annuity

Suppose your company's defined contribution retirement plan allows you to invest up to €20,000 per year. You plan to invest €20,000 per year in a stock index fund for the next 30 years. Historically, this fund has earned 9 percent per year on average. Assuming that you actually earn 9 percent a year, how much money will you have available for retirement after making the last payment?

Solution:

Use Equation 7 to find the future amount:

$$A = €20,000$$
$$r = 9\% = 0.09$$
$$N = 30$$
$$\text{FV annuity factor} = \frac{(1+r)^N - 1}{r} = \frac{(1.09)^{30} - 1}{0.09} = 136.307539$$
$$FV_N = €20,000(136.307539)$$
$$= €2,726,150.77$$

Assuming the fund continues to earn an average of 9 percent per year, you will have €2,726,150.77 available at retirement.

4.2 Unequal Cash Flows

In many cases, cash flow streams are unequal, precluding the simple use of the future value annuity factor. For instance, an individual investor might have a savings plan that involves unequal cash payments depending on the month of the year or lower savings during a planned vacation. One can always find the future value of a series of unequal cash flows by compounding the cash flows one at a time. Suppose you have the five cash flows described in Table 2, indexed relative to the present ($t = 0$).

Table 2 A Series of Unequal Cash Flows and Their Future Values at 5 Percent

Time	Cash Flow ($)	Future Value at Year 5		
$t = 1$	1,000	$1,000(1.05)^4$	=	$1,215.51
$t = 2$	2,000	$2,000(1.05)^3$	=	$2,315.25
$t = 3$	4,000	$4,000(1.05)^2$	=	$4,410.00
$t = 4$	5,000	$5,000(1.05)^1$	=	$5,250.00
$t = 5$	6,000	$6,000(1.05)^0$	=	$6,000.00
		Sum	=	$19,190.76

All of the payments shown in Table 2 are different. Therefore, the most direct approach to finding the future value at $t = 5$ is to compute the future value of each payment as of $t = 5$ and then sum the individual future values. The total future value at Year 5 equals $19,190.76, as shown in the third column. Later in this reading, you will learn shortcuts to take when the cash flows are close to even; these shortcuts will allow you to combine annuity and single-period calculations.

THE PRESENT VALUE OF A SINGLE CASH FLOW 5

5.1 Finding the Present Value of a Single Cash Flow

Just as the future value factor links today's present value with tomorrow's future value, the present value factor allows us to discount future value to present value. For example, with a 5 percent interest rate generating a future payoff of $105 in one year, what current amount invested at 5 percent for one year will grow to \$105? The answer is \$100; therefore, \$100 is the present value of \$105 to be received in one year at a discount rate of 5 percent.

Given a future cash flow that is to be received in N periods and an interest rate per period of r, we can use the formula for future value to solve directly for the present value as follows:

$$FV_N = PV(1 + r)^N$$

$$PV = FV_N\left[\frac{1}{(1 + r)^N}\right] \quad (8)$$

$$PV = FV_N(1 + r)^{-N}$$

We see from Equation 8 that the present value factor, $(1 + r)^{-N}$, is the reciprocal of the future value factor, $(1 + r)^N$.

EXAMPLE 8

The Present Value of a Lump Sum

An insurance company has issued a Guaranteed Investment Contract (GIC) that promises to pay \$100,000 in six years with an 8 percent return rate. What amount of money must the insurer invest today at 8 percent for six years to make the promised payment?

Solution:

We can use Equation 8 to find the present value using the following data:

$$FV_N = \$100{,}000$$

$$r = 8\% = 0.08$$

$$N = 6$$

$$\begin{aligned} PV &= FV_N(1 + r)^{-N} \\ &= \$100{,}000\left[\frac{1}{(1.08)^6}\right] \\ &= \$100{,}000(0.6301696) \\ &= \$63{,}016.96 \end{aligned}$$

We can say that \$63,016.96 today, with an interest rate of 8 percent, is equivalent to \$100,000 to be received in six years. Discounting the \$100,000 makes a future \$100,000 equivalent to \$63,016.96 when allowance is made for the time value of money. As the time line in Figure 4 shows, the \$100,000 has been discounted six full periods.

Figure 4 The Present Value of a Lump Sum to Be Received at Time $t = 6$

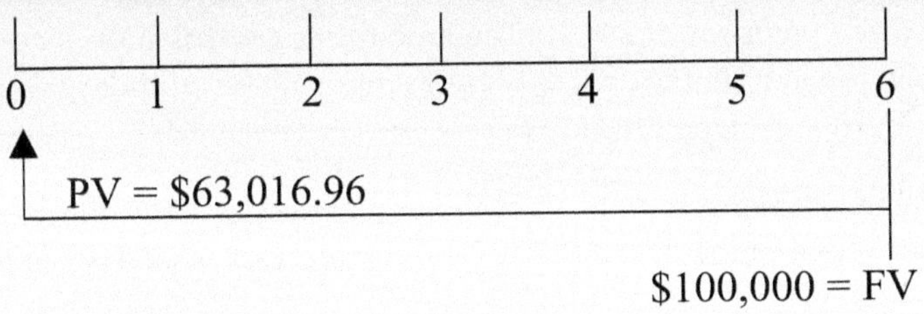

EXAMPLE 9

The Projected Present Value of a More Distant Future Lump Sum

Suppose you own a liquid financial asset that will pay you $100,000 in 10 years from today. Your daughter plans to attend college four years from today, and you want to know what the asset's present value will be at that time. Given an 8 percent discount rate, what will the asset be worth four years from today?

Solution:

The value of the asset is the present value of the asset's promised payment. At $t = 4$, the cash payment will be received six years later. With this information, you can solve for the value four years from today using Equation 8:

$$FV_N = \$100{,}000$$

$$r = 8\% = 0.08$$

$$N = 6$$

$$\begin{aligned} PV &= FV_N(1 + r)^{-N} \\ &= \$100{,}000\frac{1}{(1.08)^6} \\ &= \$100{,}000(0.6301696) \\ &= \$63{,}016.96 \end{aligned}$$

Figure 5 The Relationship between Present Value and Future Value

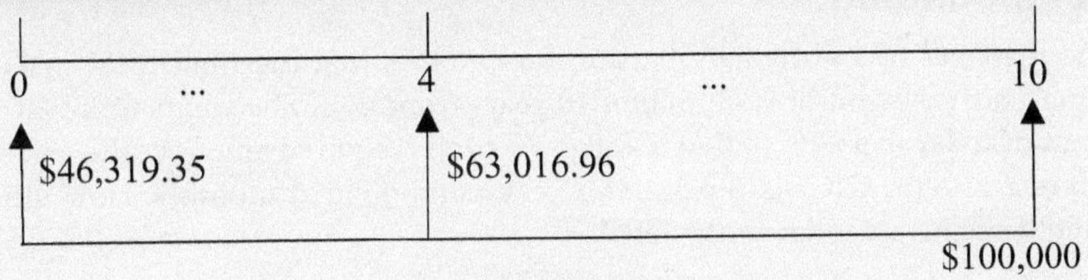

The time line in Figure 5 shows the future payment of \$100,000 that is to be received at $t = 10$. The time line also shows the values at $t = 4$ and at $t = 0$. Relative to the payment at $t = 10$, the amount at $t = 4$ is a projected present value, while the amount at $t = 0$ is the present value (as of today).

Present value problems require an evaluation of the present value factor, $(1 + r)^{-N}$. Present values relate to the discount rate and the number of periods in the following ways:

- For a given discount rate, the farther in the future the amount to be received, the smaller that amount's present value.
- Holding time constant, the larger the discount rate, the smaller the present value of a future amount.

5.2 The Frequency of Compounding

Recall that interest may be paid semiannually, quarterly, monthly, or even daily. To handle interest payments made more than once a year, we can modify the present value formula (Equation 8) as follows. Recall that r_s is the quoted interest rate and equals the periodic interest rate multiplied by the number of compounding periods in each year. In general, with more than one compounding period in a year, we can express the formula for present value as

$$PV = FV_N\left(1 + \frac{r_s}{m}\right)^{-mN} \quad (9)$$

where

m = number of compounding periods per year

r_s = quoted annual interest rate

N = number of years

The formula in Equation 9 is quite similar to that in Equation 8. As we have already noted, present value and future value factors are reciprocals. Changing the frequency of compounding does not alter this result. The only difference is the use of the periodic interest rate and the corresponding number of compounding periods.

The following example illustrates Equation 9.

EXAMPLE 10

The Present Value of a Lump Sum with Monthly Compounding

The manager of a Canadian pension fund knows that the fund must make a lump-sum payment of C\$5 million 10 years from now. She wants to invest an amount today in a GIC so that it will grow to the required amount. The current interest rate on GICs is 6 percent a year, compounded monthly. How much should she invest today in the GIC?

Solution:

Use Equation 9 to find the required present value:

$$\begin{aligned}
FV_N &= C\$5,000,000 \\
r_s &= 6\% = 0.06 \\
m &= 12 \\
r_s/m &= 0.06/12 = 0.005 \\
N &= 10 \\
mN &= 12(10) = 120 \\
PV &= FV_N\left(1 + \frac{r_s}{m}\right)^{-mN} \\
&= C\$5,000,000(1.005)^{-120} \\
&= C\$5,000,000(0.549633) \\
&= C\$2,748,163.67
\end{aligned}$$

In applying Equation 9, we use the periodic rate (in this case, the monthly rate) and the appropriate number of periods with monthly compounding (in this case, 10 years of monthly compounding, or 120 periods).

6 THE PRESENT VALUE OF A SERIES OF CASH FLOWS

Many applications in investment management involve assets that offer a series of cash flows over time. The cash flows may be highly uneven, relatively even, or equal. They may occur over relatively short periods of time, longer periods of time, or even stretch on indefinitely. In this section, we discuss how to find the present value of a series of cash flows.

6.1 The Present Value of a Series of Equal Cash Flows

We begin with an ordinary annuity. Recall that an ordinary annuity has equal annuity payments, with the first payment starting one period into the future. In total, the annuity makes N payments, with the first payment at $t = 1$ and the last at $t = N$. We can express the present value of an ordinary annuity as the sum of the present values of each individual annuity payment, as follows:

$$PV = \frac{A}{(1+r)} + \frac{A}{(1+r)^2} + \frac{A}{(1+r)^3} + \ldots + \frac{A}{(1+r)^{N-1}} + \frac{A}{(1+r)^N} \quad (10)$$

where

A = the annuity amount

r = the interest rate per period corresponding to the frequency of annuity payments (for example, annual, quarterly, or monthly)

N = the number of annuity payments

Because the annuity payment (A) is a constant in this equation, it can be factored out as a common term. Thus the sum of the interest factors has a shortcut expression:

$$PV = A\left[\frac{1 - \frac{1}{(1+r)^N}}{r}\right] \tag{11}$$

In much the same way that we computed the future value of an ordinary annuity, we find the present value by multiplying the annuity amount by a present value annuity factor (the term in brackets in Equation 11).

EXAMPLE 11

The Present Value of an Ordinary Annuity

Suppose you are considering purchasing a financial asset that promises to pay €1,000 per year for five years, with the first payment one year from now. The required rate of return is 12 percent per year. How much should you pay for this asset?

Solution:

To find the value of the financial asset, use the formula for the present value of an ordinary annuity given in Equation 11 with the following data:

A = €1,000

r = 12% = 0.12

N = 5

$$PV = A\left[\frac{1 - \frac{1}{(1+r)^N}}{r}\right]$$

$$= €1,000\left[\frac{1 - \frac{1}{(1.12)^5}}{0.12}\right]$$

$$= €1,000(3.604776)$$

$$= €3,604.78$$

The series of cash flows of €1,000 per year for five years is currently worth €3,604.78 when discounted at 12 percent.

Keeping track of the actual calendar time brings us to a specific type of annuity with level payments: the annuity due. An annuity due has its first payment occurring today (t = 0). In total, the annuity due will make N payments. Figure 6 presents the time line for an annuity due that makes four payments of $100.

Figure 6 An Annuity Due of $100 per Period

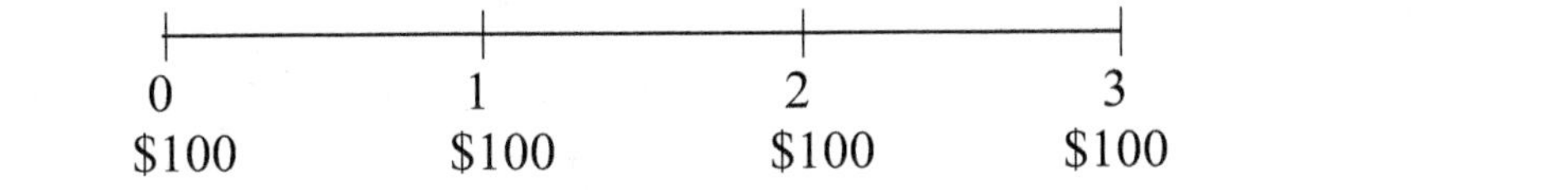

As Figure 6 shows, we can view the four-period annuity due as the sum of two parts: a $100 lump sum today and an ordinary annuity of $100 per period for three periods. At a 12 percent discount rate, the four $100 cash flows in this annuity due example will be worth $340.18.[7]

Expressing the value of the future series of cash flows in today's dollars gives us a convenient way of comparing annuities. The next example illustrates this approach.

EXAMPLE 12

An Annuity Due as the Present Value of an Immediate Cash Flow Plus an Ordinary Annuity

You are retiring today and must choose to take your retirement benefits either as a lump sum or as an annuity. Your company's benefits officer presents you with two alternatives: an immediate lump sum of $2 million or an annuity with 20 payments of $200,000 a year with the first payment starting today. The interest rate at your bank is 7 percent per year compounded annually. Which option has the greater present value? (Ignore any tax differences between the two options.)

Solution:

To compare the two options, find the present value of each at time $t = 0$ and choose the one with the larger value. The first option's present value is $2 million, already expressed in today's dollars. The second option is an annuity due. Because the first payment occurs at $t = 0$, you can separate the annuity benefits into two pieces: an immediate $200,000 to be paid today ($t = 0$) and an ordinary

7 There is an alternative way to calculate the present value of an annuity due. Compared to an ordinary annuity, the payments in an annuity due are each discounted one less period. Therefore, we can modify Equation 11 to handle annuities due by multiplying the right-hand side of the equation by $(1 + r)$:

$$\text{PV}(\text{Annuity due}) = A\left\{\left[1 - (1 + r)^{-N}\right]/r\right\}(1 + r)$$

annuity of \$200,000 per year for 19 years. To value this option, you need to find the present value of the ordinary annuity using Equation 11 and then add \$200,000 to it.

$$A = \$200{,}000$$
$$N = 19$$
$$r = 7\% = 0.07$$

$$\begin{aligned}
\text{PV} &= A\left[\frac{1 - \dfrac{1}{(1+r)^N}}{r}\right]\\
&= \$200{,}000\left[\frac{1 - \dfrac{1}{(1.07)^{19}}}{0.07}\right]\\
&= \$200{,}000(10.335595)\\
&= \$2{,}067{,}119.05
\end{aligned}$$

The 19 payments of \$200,000 have a present value of \$2,067,119.05. Adding the initial payment of \$200,000 to \$2,067,119.05, we find that the total value of the annuity option is \$2,267,119.05. The present value of the annuity is greater than the lump sum alternative of \$2 million.

We now look at another example reiterating the equivalence of present and future values.

EXAMPLE 13

The Projected Present Value of an Ordinary Annuity

A German pension fund manager anticipates that benefits of €1 million per year must be paid to retirees. Retirements will not occur until 10 years from now at time t = 10. Once benefits begin to be paid, they will extend until t = 39 for a total of 30 payments. What is the present value of the pension liability if the appropriate annual discount rate for plan liabilities is 5 percent compounded annually?

Solution:

This problem involves an annuity with the first payment at $t = 10$. From the perspective of $t = 9$, we have an ordinary annuity with 30 payments. We can compute the present value of this annuity with Equation 11 and then look at it on a time line.

$$A = €1{,}000{,}000$$
$$r = 5\% = 0.05$$
$$N = 30$$
$$\text{PV} = A\left[\frac{1 - \frac{1}{(1+r)^N}}{r}\right]$$
$$= €1{,}000{,}000\left[\frac{1 - \frac{1}{(1.05)^{30}}}{0.05}\right]$$
$$= €1{,}000{,}000(15.372451)$$
$$= €15{,}372{,}451.03$$

Figure 7 The Present Value of an Ordinary Annuity with First Payment at Time $t = 10$ (in Millions)

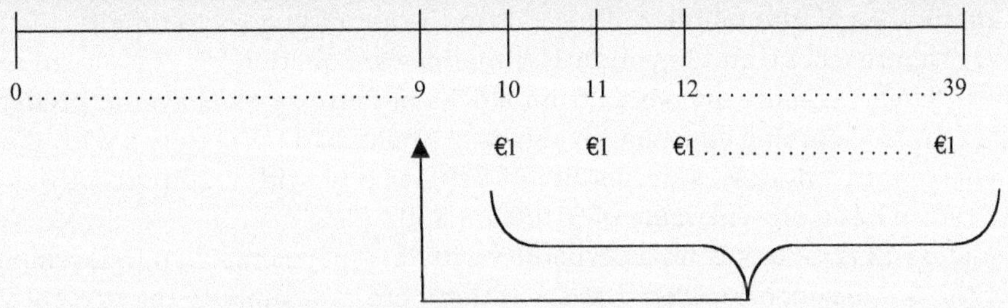

On the time line, we have shown the pension payments of €1 million extending from $t = 10$ to $t = 39$. The bracket and arrow indicate the process of finding the present value of the annuity, discounted back to $t = 9$. The present value of the pension benefits as of $t = 9$ is €15,372,451.03. The problem is to find the present value today (at $t = 0$).

Now we can rely on the equivalence of present value and future value. As Figure 7 shows, we can view the amount at $t = 9$ as a future value from the vantage point of $t = 0$. We compute the present value of the amount at $t = 9$ as follows:

$$\text{FV}_N = €15{,}372{,}451.03 \text{ (the present value at } t = 9)$$
$$N = 9$$
$$r = 5\% = 0.05$$
$$\text{PV} = \text{FV}_N(1 + r)^{-N}$$
$$= €15{,}372{,}451.03(1.05)^{-9}$$
$$= €15{,}372{,}451.03(0.644609)$$
$$= €9{,}909{,}219.00$$

The present value of the pension liability is €9,909,219.00.

Example 13 illustrates three procedures emphasized in this reading:

- finding the present or future value of any cash flow series;
- recognizing the equivalence of present value and appropriately discounted future value; and
- keeping track of the actual calendar time in a problem involving the time value of money.

6.2 The Present Value of an Infinite Series of Equal Cash Flows—Perpetuity

Consider the case of an ordinary annuity that extends indefinitely. Such an ordinary annuity is called a perpetuity (a perpetual annuity). To derive a formula for the present value of a perpetuity, we can modify Equation 10 to account for an infinite series of cash flows:

$$\mathrm{PV} = A\sum_{t=1}^{\infty}\left[\frac{1}{(1+r)^t}\right] \tag{12}$$

As long as interest rates are positive, the sum of present value factors converges and

$$\mathrm{PV} = \frac{A}{r} \tag{13}$$

To see this, look back at Equation 11, the expression for the present value of an ordinary annuity. As N (the number of periods in the annuity) goes to infinity, the term $1/(1 + r)^N$ approaches 0 and Equation 11 simplifies to Equation 13. This equation will reappear when we value dividends from stocks because stocks have no predefined life span. (A stock paying constant dividends is similar to a perpetuity.) With the first payment a year from now, a perpetuity of \$10 per year with a 20 percent required rate of return has a present value of \$10/0.2 = \$50.

Equation 13 is valid only for a perpetuity with level payments. In our development above, the first payment occurred at $t = 1$; therefore, we compute the present value as of $t = 0$.

Other assets also come close to satisfying the assumptions of a perpetuity. Certain government bonds and preferred stocks are typical examples of financial assets that make level payments for an indefinite period of time.

EXAMPLE 14

The Present Value of a Perpetuity

The British government once issued a type of security called a consol bond, which promised to pay a level cash flow indefinitely. If a consol bond paid £100 per year in perpetuity, what would it be worth today if the required rate of return were 5 percent?

Solution:

To answer this question, we can use Equation 13 with the following data:

$$\begin{aligned} A &= £100 \\ r &= 5\% = 0.05 \\ PV &= A/r \\ &= £100/0.05 \\ &= £2{,}000 \end{aligned}$$

The bond would be worth £2,000.

6.3 Present Values Indexed at Times Other than $t = 0$

In practice with investments, analysts frequently need to find present values indexed at times other than $t = 0$. Subscripting the present value and evaluating a perpetuity beginning with \$100 payments in Year 2, we find PV_1 = \$100/0.05 = \$2,000 at a 5 percent discount rate. Further, we can calculate today's PV as PV_0 = \$2,000/1.05 = \$1,904.76.

Consider a similar situation in which cash flows of \$6 per year begin at the end of the 4th year and continue at the end of each year thereafter, with the last cash flow at the end of the 10th year. From the perspective of the end of the third year, we are facing a typical seven-year ordinary annuity. We can find the present value of the annuity from the perspective of the end of the third year and then discount that present value back to the present. At an interest rate of 5 percent, the cash flows of \$6 per year starting at the end of the fourth year will be worth \$34.72 at the end of the third year ($t = 3$) and \$29.99 today ($t = 0$).

The next example illustrates the important concept that an annuity or perpetuity beginning sometime in the future can be expressed in present value terms one period prior to the first payment. That present value can then be discounted back to today's present value.

EXAMPLE 15

The Present Value of a Projected Perpetuity

Consider a level perpetuity of £100 per year with its first payment beginning at $t = 5$. What is its present value today (at $t = 0$), given a 5 percent discount rate?

Solution:

First, we find the present value of the perpetuity at $t = 4$ and then discount that amount back to $t = 0$. (Recall that a perpetuity or an ordinary annuity has its first payment one period away, explaining the $t = 4$ index for our present value calculation.)

i. Find the present value of the perpetuity at $t = 4$:

$$\begin{aligned} A &= £100 \\ r &= 5\% = 0.05 \\ PV &= A/r \\ &= £100/0.05 \\ &= £2{,}000 \end{aligned}$$

ii. Find the present value of the future amount at $t = 4$. From the perspective of $t = 0$, the present value of £2,000 can be considered a future value. Now we need to find the present value of a lump sum:

$$
\begin{aligned}
FV_N &= £2{,}000 \text{ (the present value at } t = 4) \\
r &= 5\% = 0.05 \\
N &= 4 \\
PV &= FV_N(1+r)^{-N} \\
&= £2{,}000(1.05)^{-4} \\
&= £2{,}000(0.822702) \\
&= £1{,}645.40
\end{aligned}
$$

Today's present value of the perpetuity is £1,645.40.

As discussed earlier, an annuity is a series of payments of a fixed amount for a specified number of periods. Suppose we own a perpetuity. At the same time, we issue a perpetuity obligating us to make payments; these payments are the same size as those of the perpetuity we own. However, the first payment of the perpetuity we issue is at $t = 5$; payments then continue on forever. The payments on this second perpetuity exactly offset the payments received from the perpetuity we own at $t = 5$ and all subsequent dates. We are left with level nonzero net cash flows at $t = 1, 2, 3,$ and 4. This outcome exactly fits the definition of an annuity with four payments. Thus we can construct an annuity as the difference between two perpetuities with equal, level payments but differing starting dates. The next example illustrates this result.

EXAMPLE 16

The Present Value of an Ordinary Annuity as the Present Value of a Current Minus Projected Perpetuity

Given a 5 percent discount rate, find the present value of a four-year ordinary annuity of £100 per year starting in Year 1 as the difference between the following two level perpetuities:

Perpetuity 1	£100 per year starting in Year 1 (first payment at $t = 1$)
Perpetuity 2	£100 per year starting in Year 5 (first payment at $t = 5$)

Solution:

If we subtract Perpetuity 2 from Perpetuity 1, we are left with an ordinary annuity of £100 per period for four years (payments at $t = 1, 2, 3, 4$). Subtracting the present value of Perpetuity 2 from that of Perpetuity 1, we arrive at the present value of the four-year ordinary annuity:

$$
\begin{aligned}
PV_0(\text{Perpetuity 1}) &= £100 / 0.05 = £2{,}000 \\
PV_4(\text{Perpetuity 2}) &= £100 / 0.05 = £2{,}000 \\
PV_0(\text{Perpetuity 2}) &= £2{,}000 / (1.05)^4 = £1{,}645.40 \\
PV_0(\text{Annuity}) &= PV_0(\text{Perpetuity 1}) - PV_0(\text{Perpetuity 2}) \\
&= £2{,}000 - £1{,}645.40 \\
&= £354.60
\end{aligned}
$$

The four-year ordinary annuity's present value is equal to £2,000 – £1,645.40 = £354.60.

6.4 The Present Value of a Series of Unequal Cash Flows

When we have unequal cash flows, we must first find the present value of each individual cash flow and then sum the respective present values. For a series with many cash flows, we usually use a spreadsheet. Table 3 lists a series of cash flows with the time periods in the first column, cash flows in the second column, and each cash flow's present value in the third column. The last row of Table 3 shows the sum of the five present values.

Table 3 A Series of Unequal Cash Flows and Their Present Values at 5 Percent

Time Period	Cash Flow ($)	Present Value at Year 0		
1	1,000	$\$1{,}000(1.05)^{-1}$	=	\$952.38
2	2,000	$\$2{,}000(1.05)^{-2}$	=	\$1,814.06
3	4,000	$\$4{,}000(1.05)^{-3}$	=	\$3,455.35
4	5,000	$\$5{,}000(1.05)^{-4}$	=	\$4,113.51
5	6,000	$\$6{,}000(1.05)^{-5}$	=	\$4,701.16
		Sum	=	\$15,036.46

We could calculate the future value of these cash flows by computing them one at a time using the single-payment future value formula. We already know the present value of this series, however, so we can easily apply time-value equivalence. The future value of the series of cash flows from Table 2, \$19,190.76, is equal to the single \$15,036.46 amount compounded forward to $t = 5$:

$$\begin{aligned} \text{PV} &= \$15{,}036.46 \\ N &= 5 \\ r &= 5\% = 0.05 \\ \text{FV}_N &= \text{PV}(1 + r)^N \\ &= \$15{,}036.46(1.05)^5 \\ &= \$15{,}036.46(1.276282) \\ &= \$19{,}190.76 \end{aligned}$$

SOLVING FOR RATES, NUMBER OF PERIODS, OR SIZE OF ANNUITY PAYMENTS 7

In the previous examples, certain pieces of information have been made available. For instance, all problems have given the rate of interest, r, the number of time periods, N, the annuity amount, A, and either the present value, PV, or future value, FV. In real-world applications, however, although the present and future values may be given, you may have to solve for either the interest rate, the number of periods, or the annuity amount. In the subsections that follow, we show these types of problems.

7.1 Solving for Interest Rates and Growth Rates

Suppose a bank deposit of €100 is known to generate a payoff of €111 in one year. With this information, we can infer the interest rate that separates the present value of €100 from the future value of €111 by using Equation 2, $FV_N = PV(1 + r)^N$, with $N = 1$. With PV, FV, and N known, we can solve for r directly:

$$1 + r = FV/PV$$
$$1 + r = €111/€100 = 1.11$$
$$r = 0.11, \text{ or } 11\%$$

The interest rate that equates €100 at $t = 0$ to €111 at $t = 1$ is 11 percent. Thus we can state that €100 grows to €111 with a growth rate of 11 percent.

As this example shows, an interest rate can also be considered a growth rate. The particular application will usually dictate whether we use the term "interest rate" or "growth rate." Solving Equation 2 for r and replacing the interest rate r with the growth rate g produces the following expression for determining growth rates:

$$g = (FV_N/PV)^{1/N} - 1 \quad (14)$$

Below are two examples that use the concept of a growth rate.

EXAMPLE 17

Calculating a Growth Rate (1)

Hyundai Steel, the first Korean steelmaker, was established in 1953. Hyundai Steel's sales increased from ₩14,146.4 billion in 2012 to ₩19,166.0 billion in 2017. However, its net profit declined from ₩796.4 billion in 2012 to ₩727.5 billion in 2017. Calculate the following growth rates for Hyundai Steel for the five-year period from the end of 2012 to the end of 2017:

1 Sales growth rate.
2 Net profit growth rate.

Solution to 1:

To solve this problem, we can use Equation 14, $g = (FV_N/PV)^{1/N} - 1$. We denote sales in 2012 as PV and sales in 2017 as FV_5. We can then solve for the growth rate as follows:

$$g = \sqrt[5]{₩19{,}166.0/₩14{,}146.4} - 1$$
$$= \sqrt[5]{1.354832} - 1$$
$$= 1.062618 - 1$$
$$= 0.062618 \text{ or about } 6.3\%$$

The calculated growth rate of about 6.3 percent a year shows that Hyundai Steel's sales grew during the 2012–2017 period.

Solution to 2:

In this case, we can speak of a positive compound rate of decrease or a negative compound growth rate. Using Equation 14, we find

$$
\begin{aligned}
g &= \sqrt[5]{₩727.5/₩796.4} - 1 \\
&= \sqrt[5]{0.913486} - 1 \\
&= 0.982065 - 1 \\
&= -0.017935 \text{ or about } -1.8\%
\end{aligned}
$$

In contrast to the positive sales growth, the rate of growth in net profit was approximately −1.8 percent during the 2012–2017 period.

EXAMPLE 18

Calculating a Growth Rate (2)

Toyota Motor Corporation, one of the largest automakers in the world, had consolidated vehicle sales of 8.96 million units in 2018 (fiscal year ending 31 March 2018). This is substantially more than consolidated vehicle sales of 7.35 million units six years earlier in 2012. What was the growth rate in number of vehicles sold by Toyota from 2012 to 2018?

Solution:

Using Equation 14, we find

$$
\begin{aligned}
g &= \sqrt[6]{8.96/7.35} - 1 \\
&= \sqrt[6]{1.219048} - 1 \\
&= 1.033563 - 1 \\
&= 0.033563 \text{ or about } 3.4\%
\end{aligned}
$$

The rate of growth in vehicles sold was approximately 3.4 percent during the 2012–2018 period. Note that we can also refer to 3.4 percent as the compound annual growth rate because it is the single number that compounds the number of vehicles sold in 2012 forward to the number of vehicles sold in 2018. Table 4 lists the number of vehicles sold by Toyota from 2012 to 2018.

Table 4 Number of Vehicles Sold, 2012–2018

Year	Number of Vehicles Sold (Millions)	$(1 + g)_t$	t
2012	7.35		0
2013	8.87	8.87/7.35 = 1.1.206803	1
2014	9.12	9.12/8.87 = 1.028185	2
2015	8.97	8.97/9.12 = 0.983553	3
2016	8.68	8.68/8.97 = 0.967670	4
2017	8.97	8.97/8.68 = 1.033410	5
2018	8.96	8.96/8.97 = 0.998885	6

Source: www.toyota.com.

Table 4 also shows 1 plus the one-year growth rate in number of vehicles sold. We can compute the 1 plus six-year cumulative growth in number of vehicles sold from 2012 to 2018 as the product of quantities (1 + one-year growth rate). We arrive at the same result as when we divide the ending number of vehicles sold, 8.96 million, by the beginning number of vehicles sold, 7.35 million:

$$\begin{aligned}\frac{8.96}{7.35} &= \left(\frac{8.87}{7.35}\right)\left(\frac{9.12}{8.87}\right)\left(\frac{8.97}{9.12}\right)\left(\frac{8.68}{8.97}\right)\left(\frac{8.97}{8.68}\right)\left(\frac{8.96}{8.97}\right)\\ &= (1+g_1)(1+g_2)(1+g_3)(1+g_4)(1+g_5)(1+g_6)\\ 1.219048 &= (1.206803)(1.028185)(0.983553)(0.967670)(1.033410)(0.998885)\end{aligned}$$

The right-hand side of the equation is the product of 1 plus the one-year growth rate in number of vehicles sold for each year. Recall that, using Equation 14, we took the sixth root of 8.96/7.35 = 1.219048. In effect, we were solving for the single value of g which, when compounded over six periods, gives the correct product of 1 plus the one-year growth rates.[8]

In conclusion, we do not need to compute intermediate growth rates as in Table 4 to solve for a compound growth rate g. Sometimes, however, the intermediate growth rates are interesting or informative. For example, most of the 21.9 percent increase in vehicles sold by Toyota from 2012 to 2018 occurred in 2013 as sales increased by 20.7 percent from 2012 to 2013. Elsewhere in Toyota Motor's disclosures, the company noted that all regions except Europe showed a substantial increase in sales in 2013. We can also analyze the variability in growth rates when we conduct an analysis as in Table 4. Sales continued to increase in 2014 but then declined in 2015 and 2016. Sales then increased but the sales in 2017 and 2018 are about the same as in 2015.

The compound growth rate is an excellent summary measure of growth over multiple time periods. In our Toyota Motors example, the compound growth rate of 3.4 percent is the single growth rate that, when added to 1, compounded over six years, and multiplied by the 2012 number of vehicles sold, yields the 2018 number of vehicles sold.

7.2 Solving for the Number of Periods

In this section, we demonstrate how to solve for the number of periods given present value, future value, and interest or growth rates.

EXAMPLE 19

The Number of Annual Compounding Periods Needed for an Investment to Reach a Specific Value

You are interested in determining how long it will take an investment of €10,000,000 to double in value. The current interest rate is 7 percent compounded annually. How many years will it take €10,000,000 to double to €20,000,000?

8 The compound growth rate that we calculate here is an example of a geometric mean, specifically the geometric mean of the growth rates. We define the geometric mean in the reading on statistical concepts.

Solution:

Use Equation 2, $FV_N = PV(1 + r)^N$, to solve for the number of periods, N, as follows:

$$
\begin{aligned}
(1 + r)^N &= FV_N/PV = 2 \\
N \ln(1 + r) &= \ln(2) \\
N &= \ln(2)/\ln(1 + r) \\
&= \ln(2)/\ln(1.07) = 10.24
\end{aligned}
$$

With an interest rate of 7 percent, it will take approximately 10 years for the initial €10,000,000 investment to grow to €20,000,000. Solving for N in the expression $(1.07)^N = 2.0$ requires taking the natural logarithm of both sides and using the rule that $\ln(x^N) = N \ln(x)$. Generally, we find that $N = [\ln(FV/PV)]/\ln(1 + r)$. Here, $N = \ln(€20{,}000{,}000/€10{,}000{,}000)/\ln(1.07) = \ln(2)/\ln(1.07) = 10.24$.[9]

7.3 Solving for the Size of Annuity Payments

In this section, we discuss how to solve for annuity payments. Mortgages, auto loans, and retirement savings plans are classic examples of applications of annuity formulas.

EXAMPLE 20

Calculating the Size of Payments on a Fixed-Rate Mortgage

You are planning to purchase a \$120,000 house by making a down payment of \$20,000 and borrowing the remainder with a 30-year fixed-rate mortgage with monthly payments. The first payment is due at $t = 1$. Current mortgage interest rates are quoted at 8 percent with monthly compounding. What will your monthly mortgage payments be?

9 To quickly approximate the number of periods, practitioners sometimes use an ad hoc rule called the **Rule of 72**: Divide 72 by the stated interest rate to get the approximate number of years it would take to double an investment at the interest rate. Here, the approximation gives 72/7 = 10.3 years. The Rule of 72 is loosely based on the observation that it takes 12 years to double an amount at a 6 percent interest rate, giving 6 × 12 = 72. At a 3 percent rate, one would guess it would take twice as many years, 3 × 24 = 72.

Solution:

The bank will determine the mortgage payments such that at the stated periodic interest rate, the present value of the payments will be equal to the amount borrowed (in this case, \$100,000). With this fact in mind, we can use Equation 11, $\text{PV} = A\left[\frac{1 - \frac{1}{(1+r)^N}}{r}\right]$, to solve for the annuity amount, A, as the present value divided by the present value annuity factor:

$$\begin{aligned}
\text{PV} &= \$100{,}000 \\
r_s &= 8\% = 0.08 \\
m &= 12 \\
r_s/m &= 0.08/12 = 0.006667 \\
N &= 30 \\
mN &= 12 \times 30 = 360
\end{aligned}$$

$$\text{Present value annuity factor} = \frac{1 - \frac{1}{\left[1 + (r_s/m)\right]^{mN}}}{r_s/m} = \frac{1 - \frac{1}{(1.006667)^{360}}}{0.006667}$$

$$= 136.283494$$

$$\begin{aligned}
A &= \text{PV/Present value annuity factor} \\
&= \$100{,}000/136.283494 \\
&= \$733.76
\end{aligned}$$

The amount borrowed, \$100,000, is equivalent to 360 monthly payments of \$733.76 with a stated interest rate of 8 percent. The mortgage problem is a relatively straightforward application of finding a level annuity payment.

Next, we turn to a retirement-planning problem. This problem illustrates the complexity of the situation in which an individual wants to retire with a specified retirement income. Over the course of a life cycle, the individual may be able to save only a small amount during the early years but then may have the financial resources to save more during later years. Savings plans often involve uneven cash flows, a topic we will examine in the last part of this reading. When dealing with uneven cash flows, we take maximum advantage of the principle that dollar amounts indexed at the same point in time are additive—the **cash flow additivity principle**.

EXAMPLE 21

The Projected Annuity Amount Needed to Fund a Future-Annuity Inflow

Jill Grant is 22 years old (at $t = 0$) and is planning for her retirement at age 63 (at $t = 41$). She plans to save \$2,000 per year for the next 15 years ($t = 1$ to $t = 15$). She wants to have retirement income of \$100,000 per year for 20 years, with the first retirement payment starting at $t = 41$. How much must Grant save each year from $t = 16$ to $t = 40$ in order to achieve her retirement goal? Assume she plans to invest in a diversified stock-and-bond mutual fund that will earn 8 percent per year on average.

Solution:

To help solve this problem, we set up the information on a time line. As Figure 8 shows, Grant will save \$2,000 (an outflow) each year for Years 1 to 15. Starting in Year 41, Grant will start to draw retirement income of \$100,000 per year for 20 years. In the time line, the annual savings is recorded in parentheses (\$2) to show that it is an outflow. The problem is to find the savings, recorded as X, from Year 16 to Year 40.

Figure 8 Solving for Missing Annuity Payments (in Thousands)

0	1	2	…	15	16	17	…	40	41	42	…	60
	(\$2)	(\$2)	…	(\$2)	(X)	(X)	…	(X)	\$100	\$100	…	\$100

Solving this problem involves satisfying the following relationship: the present value of savings (outflows) equals the present value of retirement income (inflows). We could bring all the dollar amounts to t = 40 or to t = 15 and solve for X.

Let us evaluate all dollar amounts at t = 15 (we encourage the reader to repeat the problem by bringing all cash flows to t = 40). As of t = 15, the first payment of X will be one period away (at t = 16). Thus we can value the stream of Xs using the formula for the present value of an ordinary annuity.

This problem involves three series of level cash flows. The basic idea is that the present value of the retirement income must equal the present value of Grant's savings. Our strategy requires the following steps:

1 Find the future value of the savings of \$2,000 per year and index it at t = 15. This value tells us how much Grant will have saved.

2 Find the present value of the retirement income at t = 15. This value tells us how much Grant needs to meet her retirement goals (as of t = 15). Two substeps are necessary. First, calculate the present value of the annuity of \$100,000 per year at t = 40. Use the formula for the present value of an annuity. (Note that the present value is indexed at t = 40 because the first payment is at t = 41.) Next, discount the present value back to t = 15 (a total of 25 periods).

3 Now compute the difference between the amount Grant has saved (Step 1) and the amount she needs to meet her retirement goals (Step 2). Her savings from t = 16 to t = 40 must have a present value equal to the difference between the future value of her savings and the present value of her retirement income.

Our goal is to determine the amount Grant should save in each of the 25 years from $t = 16$ to $t = 40$. We start by bringing the \$2,000 savings to $t = 15$, as follows:

$$A = \$2{,}000$$
$$r = 8\% = 0.08$$
$$N = 15$$
$$\text{FV} = A\left[\frac{(1+r)^N - 1}{r}\right]$$
$$= \$2{,}000\left[\frac{(1.08)^{15} - 1}{0.08}\right]$$
$$= \$2{,}000(27.152114)$$
$$= \$54{,}304.23$$

At $t = 15$, Grant's initial savings will have grown to \$54,304.23.

Now we need to know the value of Grant's retirement income at $t = 15$. As stated earlier, computing the retirement present value requires two substeps. First, find the present value at $t = 40$ with the formula in Equation 11; second, discount this present value back to $t = 15$. Now we can find the retirement income present value at $t = 40$:

$$A = \$100{,}000$$
$$r = 8\% = 0.08$$
$$N = 20$$
$$\text{PV} = A\left[\frac{1 - \frac{1}{(1+r)^N}}{r}\right]$$
$$= \$100{,}000\left[\frac{1 - \frac{1}{(1.08)^{20}}}{0.08}\right]$$
$$= \$100{,}000(9.818147)$$
$$= \$981{,}814.74$$

The present value amount is as of $t = 40$, so we must now discount it back as a lump sum to $t = 15$:

$$\text{FV}_N = \$981{,}814.74$$
$$N = 25$$
$$r = 8\% = 0.08$$
$$\text{PV} = \text{FV}_N(1+r)^{-N}$$
$$= \$981{,}814.74(1.08)^{-25}$$
$$= \$981{,}814.74(0.146018)$$
$$= \$143{,}362.53$$

Now recall that Grant will have saved \$54,304.23 by $t = 15$. Therefore, in present value terms, the annuity from $t = 16$ to $t = 40$ must equal the difference between the amount already saved (\$54,304.23) and the amount required for retirement (\$143,362.53). This amount is equal to \$143,362.53 − \$54,304.23 =

\$89,058.30. Therefore, we must now find the annuity payment, A, from $t = 16$ to $t = 40$ that has a present value of \$89,058.30. We find the annuity payment as follows:

$$\begin{aligned}
\text{PV} &= \$89{,}058.30 \\
r &= 8\% = 0.08 \\
N &= 25 \\
\text{Present value annuity factor} &= \left[\frac{1-\dfrac{1}{(1+r)^N}}{r}\right] \\
&= \left[\frac{1-\dfrac{1}{(1.08)^{25}}}{0.08}\right] \\
&= 10.674776 \\
A &= \text{PV/Present value annuity factor} \\
&= \$89{,}058.30/10.674776 \\
&= \$8{,}342.87
\end{aligned}$$

Grant will need to increase her savings to \$8,342.87 per year from $t = 16$ to $t = 40$ to meet her retirement goal of having a fund equal to \$981,814.74 after making her last payment at $t = 40$.

7.4 Review of Present and Future Value Equivalence

As we have demonstrated, finding present and future values involves moving amounts of money to different points on a time line. These operations are possible because present value and future value are equivalent measures separated in time. Table 5 illustrates this equivalence; it lists the timing of five cash flows, their present values at $t = 0$, and their future values at $t = 5$.

To interpret Table 5, start with the third column, which shows the present values. Note that each \$1,000 cash payment is discounted back the appropriate number of periods to find the present value at $t = 0$. The present value of \$4,329.48 is exactly equivalent to the series of cash flows. This information illustrates an important point: A lump sum can actually generate an annuity. If we place a lump sum in an account that earns the stated interest rate for all periods, we can generate an annuity that is equivalent to the lump sum. Amortized loans, such as mortgages and car loans, are examples of this principle.

Table 5 The Equivalence of Present and Future Values

Time	Cash Flow (\$)	Present Value at $t = 0$			Future Value at $t = 5$		
1	1,000	$\$1{,}000(1.05)^{-1}$	=	\$952.38	$\$1{,}000(1.05)^{4}$	=	\$1,215.51
2	1,000	$\$1{,}000(1.05)^{-2}$	=	\$907.03	$\$1{,}000(1.05)^{3}$	=	\$1,157.63
3	1,000	$\$1{,}000(1.05)^{-3}$	=	\$863.84	$\$1{,}000(1.05)^{2}$	=	\$1,102.50
4	1,000	$\$1{,}000(1.05)^{-4}$	=	\$822.70	$\$1{,}000(1.05)^{1}$	=	\$1,050.00
5	1,000	$\$1{,}000(1.05)^{-5}$	=	\$783.53	$\$1{,}000(1.05)^{0}$	=	\$1,000.00
		Sum:		\$4,329.48	Sum:		\$5,525.64

To see how a lump sum can fund an annuity, assume that we place \$4,329.48 in the bank today at 5 percent interest. We can calculate the size of the annuity payments by using Equation 11. Solving for A, we find

$$A = \frac{\text{PV}}{\dfrac{1 - \left[1/(1+r)^N\right]}{r}}$$

$$= \frac{\$4{,}329.48}{\dfrac{1 - \left[1/(1.05)^5\right]}{0.05}}$$

$$= \$1{,}000$$

Table 6 shows how the initial investment of \$4,329.48 can actually generate five \$1,000 withdrawals over the next five years.

To interpret Table 6, start with an initial present value of \$4,329.48 at $t = 0$. From $t = 0$ to $t = 1$, the initial investment earns 5 percent interest, generating a future value of \$4,329.48(1.05) = \$4,545.95. We then withdraw \$1,000 from our account, leaving \$4,545.95 − \$1,000 = \$3,545.95 (the figure reported in the last column for time period 1). In the next period, we earn one year's worth of interest and then make a \$1,000 withdrawal. After the fourth withdrawal, we have \$952.38, which earns 5 percent. This amount then grows to \$1,000 during the year, just enough for us to make the last withdrawal. Thus the initial present value, when invested at 5 percent for five years, generates the \$1,000 five-year ordinary annuity. The present value of the initial investment is exactly equivalent to the annuity.

Now we can look at how future value relates to annuities. In Table 5, we reported that the future value of the annuity was \$5,525.64. We arrived at this figure by compounding the first \$1,000 payment forward four periods, the second \$1,000 forward three periods, and so on. We then added the five future amounts at $t = 5$. The annuity is equivalent to \$5,525.64 at $t = 5$ and \$4,329.48 at $t = 0$. These two dollar measures are thus equivalent. We can verify the equivalence by finding the present value of \$5,525.64, which is \$5,525.64 × $(1.05)^{-5}$ = \$4,329.48. We found this result above when we showed that a lump sum can generate an annuity.

Table 6 How an Initial Present Value Funds an Annuity

Time Period	Amount Available at the Beginning of the Time Period (\$)	Ending Amount before Withdrawal			Withdrawal (\$)	Amount Available after Withdrawal (\$)
1	4,329.48	\$4,329.48(1.05)	=	\$4,545.95	1,000	3,545.95
2	3,545.95	\$3,545.95(1.05)	=	\$3,723.25	1,000	2,723.25
3	2,723.25	\$2,723.25(1.05)	=	\$2,859.41	1,000	1,859.41
4	1,859.41	\$1,859.41(1.05)	=	\$1,952.38	1,000	952.38
5	952.38	\$952.38(1.05)	=	\$1,000	1,000	0

To summarize what we have learned so far: A lump sum can be seen as equivalent to an annuity, and an annuity can be seen as equivalent to its future value. Thus present values, future values, and a series of cash flows can all be considered equivalent as long as they are indexed at the same point in time.

7.5 The Cash Flow Additivity Principle

The cash flow additivity principle—the idea that amounts of money indexed at the same point in time are additive—is one of the most important concepts in time value of money mathematics. We have already mentioned and used this principle; this section provides a reference example for it.

Consider the two series of cash flows shown on the time line in Figure 9. The series are denoted A and B. If we assume that the annual interest rate is 2 percent, we can find the future value of each series of cash flows as follows. Series A's future value is \$100(1.02) + \$100 = \$202. Series B's future value is \$200(1.02) + \$200 = \$404. The future value of (A + B) is \$202 + \$404 = \$606 by the method we have used up to this point. The alternative way to find the future value is to add the cash flows of each series, A and B (call it A + B), and then find the future value of the combined cash flow, as shown in Figure 9.

The third time line in Figure 9 shows the combined series of cash flows. Series A has a cash flow of \$100 at $t = 1$, and Series B has a cash flow of \$200 at $t = 1$. The combined series thus has a cash flow of \$300 at $t = 1$. We can similarly calculate the cash flow of the combined series at $t = 2$. The future value of the combined series (A + B) is \$300(1.02) + \$300 = \$606—the same result we found when we added the future values of each series.

The additivity and equivalence principles also appear in another common situation. Suppose cash flows are \$4 at the end of the first year and \$24 (actually separate payments of \$4 and \$20) at the end of the second year. Rather than finding present values of the first year's \$4 and the second year's \$24, we can treat this situation as a \$4 annuity for two years and a second-year \$20 lump sum. If the discount rate were 6 percent, the \$4 annuity would have a present value of \$7.33 and the \$20 lump sum a present value of \$17.80, for a total of \$25.13.

Figure 9 The Additivity of Two Series of Cash Flows

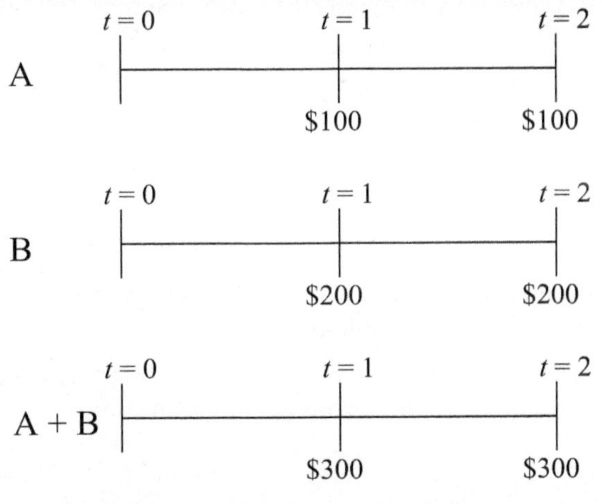

SUMMARY

In this reading, we have explored a foundation topic in investment mathematics, the time value of money. We have developed and reviewed the following concepts for use in financial applications:

- The interest rate, r, is the required rate of return; r is also called the discount rate or opportunity cost.
- An interest rate can be viewed as the sum of the real risk-free interest rate and a set of premiums that compensate lenders for risk: an inflation premium, a default risk premium, a liquidity premium, and a maturity premium.
- The future value, FV, is the present value, PV, times the future value factor, $(1 + r)^N$.
- The interest rate, r, makes current and future currency amounts equivalent based on their time value.
- The stated annual interest rate is a quoted interest rate that does not account for compounding within the year.
- The periodic rate is the quoted interest rate per period; it equals the stated annual interest rate divided by the number of compounding periods per year.
- The effective annual rate is the amount by which a unit of currency will grow in a year with interest on interest included.
- An annuity is a finite set of level sequential cash flows.
- There are two types of annuities, the annuity due and the ordinary annuity. The annuity due has a first cash flow that occurs immediately; the ordinary annuity has a first cash flow that occurs one period from the present (indexed at $t = 1$).
- On a time line, we can index the present as 0 and then display equally spaced hash marks to represent a number of periods into the future. This representation allows us to index how many periods away each cash flow will be paid.
- Annuities may be handled in a similar approach as single payments if we use annuity factors rather than single-payment factors.
- The present value, PV, is the future value, FV, times the present value factor, $(1 + r)^{-N}$.
- The present value of a perpetuity is A/r, where A is the periodic payment to be received forever.
- It is possible to calculate an unknown variable, given the other relevant variables in time value of money problems.
- The cash flow additivity principle can be used to solve problems with uneven cash flows by combining single payments and annuities.

PRACTICE PROBLEMS

1 The table below gives current information on the interest rates for two two-year and two eight-year maturity investments. The table also gives the maturity, liquidity, and default risk characteristics of a new investment possibility (Investment 3). All investments promise only a single payment (a payment at maturity). Assume that premiums relating to inflation, liquidity, and default risk are constant across all time horizons.

Investment	Maturity (in Years)	Liquidity	Default Risk	Interest Rate (%)
1	2	High	Low	2.0
2	2	Low	Low	2.5
3	7	Low	Low	r_3
4	8	High	Low	4.0
5	8	Low	High	6.5

Based on the information in the above table, address the following:

A Explain the difference between the interest rates on Investment 1 and Investment 2.

B Estimate the default risk premium.

C Calculate upper and lower limits for the interest rate on Investment 3, r_3.

2 A couple plans to set aside $20,000 per year in a conservative portfolio projected to earn 7 percent a year. If they make their first savings contribution one year from now, how much will they have at the end of 20 years?

3 Two years from now, a client will receive the first of three annual payments of $20,000 from a small business project. If she can earn 9 percent annually on her investments and plans to retire in six years, how much will the three business project payments be worth at the time of her retirement?

4 To cover the first year's total college tuition payments for his two children, a father will make a $75,000 payment five years from now. How much will he need to invest today to meet his first tuition goal if the investment earns 6 percent annually?

5 A client can choose between receiving 10 annual $100,000 retirement payments, starting one year from today, or receiving a lump sum today. Knowing that he can invest at a rate of 5 percent annually, he has decided to take the lump sum. What lump sum today will be equivalent to the future annual payments?

6 You are considering investing in two different instruments. The first instrument will pay nothing for three years, but then it will pay $20,000 per year for four years. The second instrument will pay $20,000 for three years and $30,000 in the fourth year. All payments are made at year-end. If your required rate of return on these investments is 8 percent annually, what should you be willing to pay for:

A The first instrument?

B The second instrument (use the formula for a four-year annuity)?

7 Suppose you plan to send your daughter to college in three years. You expect her to earn two-thirds of her tuition payment in scholarship money, so you estimate that your payments will be \$10,000 a year for four years. To estimate whether you have set aside enough money, you ignore possible inflation in tuition payments and assume that you can earn 8 percent annually on your investments. How much should you set aside now to cover these payments?

8 A client plans to send a child to college for four years starting 18 years from now. Having set aside money for tuition, she decides to plan for room and board also. She estimates these costs at \$20,000 per year, payable at the beginning of each year, by the time her child goes to college. If she starts next year and makes 17 payments into a savings account paying 5 percent annually, what annual payments must she make?

9 A couple plans to pay their child's college tuition for 4 years starting 18 years from now. The current annual cost of college is C\$7,000, and they expect this cost to rise at an annual rate of 5 percent. In their planning, they assume that they can earn 6 percent annually. How much must they put aside each year, starting next year, if they plan to make 17 equal payments?

10 The nominal risk-free rate is *best* described as the sum of the real risk-free rate and a premium for:

A maturity.

B liquidity.

C expected inflation.

11 Which of the following risk premiums is most relevant in explaining the difference in yields between 30-year bonds issued by the US Treasury and 30-year bonds issued by a small private issuer?

A Inflation

B Maturity

C Liquidity

12 A bank quotes a stated annual interest rate of 4.00%. If that rate is equal to an effective annual rate of 4.08%, then the bank is compounding interest:

A daily.

B quarterly.

C semiannually.

13 The value in six years of \$75,000 invested today at a stated annual interest rate of 7% compounded quarterly is *closest* to:

A \$112,555.

B \$113,330.

C \$113,733.

14 A client requires £100,000 one year from now. If the stated annual rate is 2.50% compounded weekly, the deposit needed today is *closest* to:

A £97,500.

B £97,532.

C £97,561.

15 For a lump sum investment of ¥250,000 invested at a stated annual rate of 3% compounded daily, the number of months needed to grow the sum to ¥1,000,000 is *closest* to:

A 555.

B 563.

C 576.

16 Given a €1,000,000 investment for four years with a stated annual rate of 3% compounded continuously, the difference in its interest earnings compared with the same investment compounded daily is *closest* to:

A €1.

B €6.

C €455.

17 An investment pays €300 annually for five years, with the first payment occurring today. The present value (PV) of the investment discounted at a 4% annual rate is *closest* to:

A €1,336.

B €1,389.

C €1,625.

18 A perpetual preferred stock makes its first quarterly dividend payment of $2.00 in five quarters. If the required annual rate of return is 6% compounded quarterly, the stock's present value is *closest* to:

A $31.

B $126.

C $133.

19 A saver deposits the following amounts in an account paying a stated annual rate of 4%, compounded semiannually:

Year	End of Year Deposits ($)
1	4,000
2	8,000
3	7,000
4	10,000

At the end of Year 4, the value of the account is *closest* to:

A $30,432

B $30,447

C $31,677

20 An investment of €500,000 today that grows to €800,000 after six years has a stated annual interest rate *closest* to:

A 7.5% compounded continuously.

B 7.7% compounded daily.

C 8.0% compounded semiannually.

21 A sweepstakes winner may select either a perpetuity of £2,000 a month beginning with the first payment in one month or an immediate lump sum payment of £350,000. If the annual discount rate is 6% compounded monthly, the present value of the perpetuity is:

A less than the lump sum.

B equal to the lump sum.

C greater than the lump sum.

22 At a 5% interest rate per year compounded annually, the present value (PV) of a 10-year ordinary annuity with annual payments of $2,000 is $15,443.47. The PV of a 10-year annuity due with the same interest rate and payments is *closest* to:

A $14,708.

B $16,216.

C $17,443.

23 Grandparents are funding a newborn's future university tuition costs, estimated at $50,000/year for four years, with the first payment due as a lump sum in 18 years. Assuming a 6% effective annual rate, the required deposit today is *closest* to:

A $60,699.

B $64,341.

C $68,201.

24 The present value (PV) of an investment with the following year-end cash flows (CF) and a 12% required annual rate of return is *closest* to:

Year	Cash Flow (€)
1	100,000
2	150,000
5	−10,000

A €201,747.

B €203,191.

C €227,573.

25 A sports car, purchased for £200,000, is financed for five years at an annual rate of 6% compounded monthly. If the first payment is due in one month, the monthly payment is *closest* to:

A £3,847.

B £3,867.

C £3,957.

26 Given a stated annual interest rate of 6% compounded quarterly, the level amount that, deposited quarterly, will grow to £25,000 at the end of 10 years is *closest* to:

A £461.

B £474.

C £836.

27 Given the following timeline and a discount rate of 4% a year compounded annually, the present value (PV), as of the end of Year 5 (PV_5), of the cash flow received at the end of Year 20 is *closest* to:

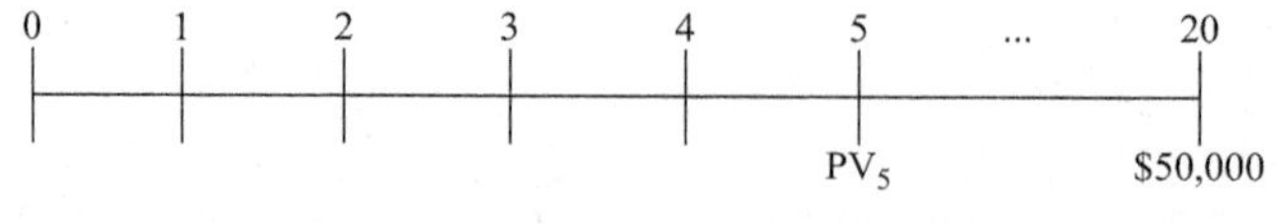

A $22,819.

B $27,763.

C $28,873.

28 A client invests €20,000 in a four-year certificate of deposit (CD) that annually pays interest of 3.5%. The annual CD interest payments are automatically reinvested in a separate savings account at a stated annual interest rate of 2% compounded monthly. At maturity, the value of the combined asset is *closest* to:

A €21,670.

B €22,890.

C €22,950.

SOLUTIONS

1 **A** Investment 2 is identical to Investment 1 except that Investment 2 has low liquidity. The difference between the interest rate on Investment 2 and Investment 1 is 0.5 percentage point. This amount represents the liquidity premium, which represents compensation for the risk of loss relative to an investment's fair value if the investment needs to be converted to cash quickly.

B To estimate the default risk premium, find the two investments that have the same maturity but different levels of default risk. Both Investments 4 and 5 have a maturity of eight years. Investment 5, however, has low liquidity and thus bears a liquidity premium. The difference between the interest rates of Investments 5 and 4 is 2.5 percentage points. The liquidity premium is 0.5 percentage point (from Part A). This leaves 2.5 – 0.5 = 2.0 percentage points that must represent a default risk premium reflecting Investment 5's high default risk.

C Investment 3 has liquidity risk and default risk comparable to Investment 2, but with its longer time to maturity, Investment 3 should have a higher maturity premium. The interest rate on Investment 3, r_3, should thus be above 2.5 percent (the interest rate on Investment 2). If the liquidity of Investment 3 were high, Investment 3 would match Investment 4 except for Investment 3's shorter maturity. We would then conclude that Investment 3's interest rate should be less than the interest rate on Investment 4, which is 4 percent. In contrast to Investment 4, however, Investment 3 has low liquidity. It is possible that the interest rate on Investment 3 exceeds that of Investment 4 despite 3's shorter maturity, depending on the relative size of the liquidity and maturity premiums. However, we expect r_3 to be less than 4.5 percent, the expected interest rate on Investment 4 if it had low liquidity. Thus 2.5 percent < r_3 < 4.5 percent.

2 **i.** Draw a time line.

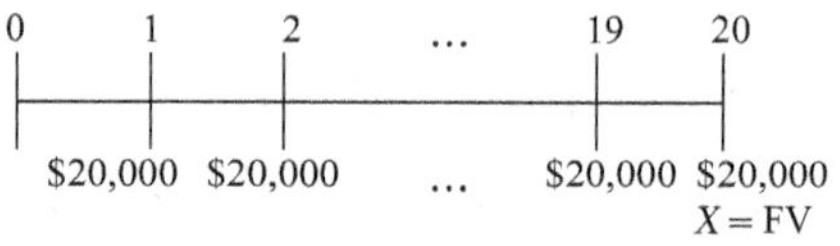

ii. Identify the problem as the future value of an annuity.

iii. Use the formula for the future value of an annuity.

$$
\begin{aligned}
FV_N &= A\left[\frac{(1+r)^N - 1}{r}\right] \\
&= \$20{,}000\left[\frac{(1+0.07)^{20} - 1}{0.07}\right] \\
&= \$819{,}909.85
\end{aligned}
$$

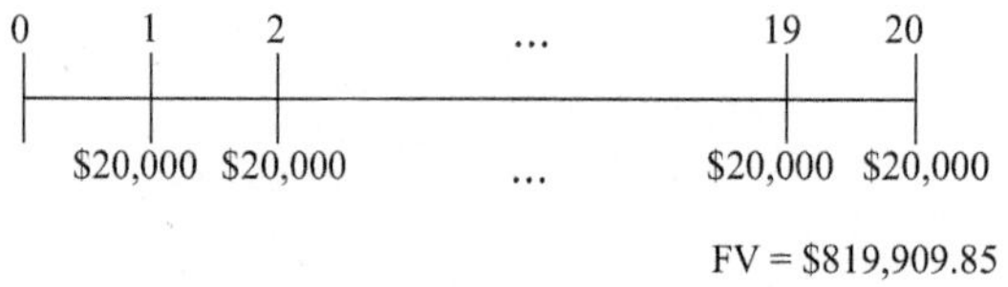

iv. Alternatively, use a financial calculator.

Notation Used on Most Calculators	Numerical Value for This Problem
N	20
$\%i$	7
PV	n/a (= 0)
FV **compute**	X
PMT	\$20,000

Enter 20 for N, the number of periods. Enter 7 for the interest rate and 20,000 for the payment size. The present value is not needed, so enter 0. Calculate the future value. Verify that you get \$819,909.85 to make sure you have mastered your calculator's keystrokes.

In summary, if the couple sets aside \$20,000 each year (starting next year), they will have \$819,909.85 in 20 years if they earn 7 percent annually.

3 **i.** Draw a time line.

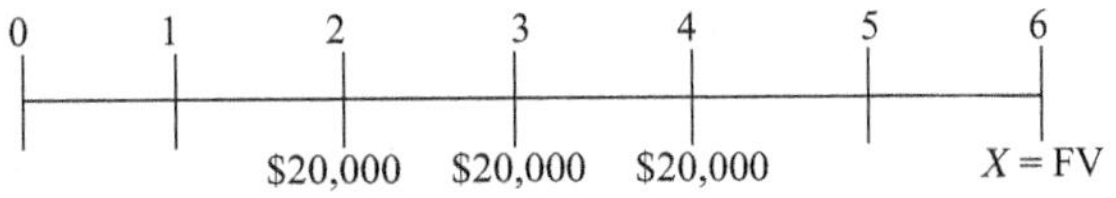

ii. Recognize the problem as the future value of a delayed annuity. Delaying the payments requires two calculations.

iii. Use the formula for the future value of an annuity (Equation 7).

$$FV_N = A\left[\frac{(1+r)^N - 1}{r}\right]$$

to bring the three \$20,000 payments to an equivalent lump sum of \$65,562.00 four years from today.

Notation Used on Most Calculators	Numerical Value for This Problem
N	3
$\%i$	9
PV	n/a (= 0)
FV **compute**	X
PMT	\$20,000

iv. Use the formula for the future value of a lump sum (Equation 2), $FV_N = PV(1 + r)^N$, to bring the single lump sum of \$65,562.00 to an equivalent lump sum of \$77,894.21 six years from today.

Notation Used on Most Calculators	Numerical Value for This Problem
N	2
$\%i$	9
PV	\$65,562.00
FV **compute**	X
PMT	n/a (= 0)

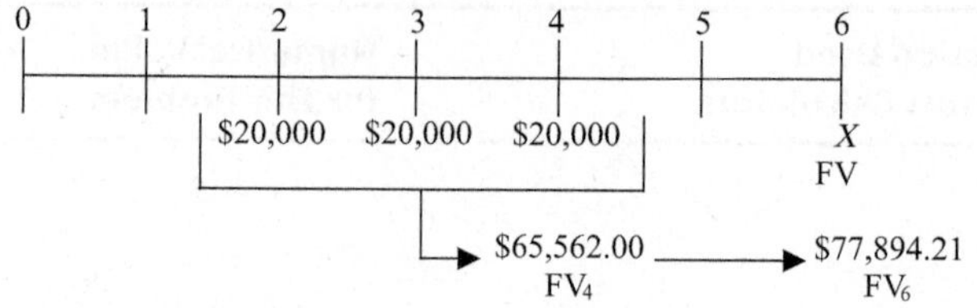

In summary, your client will have $77,894.21 in six years if she receives three yearly payments of $20,000 starting in Year 2 and can earn 9 percent annually on her investments.

4 **i.** Draw a time line.

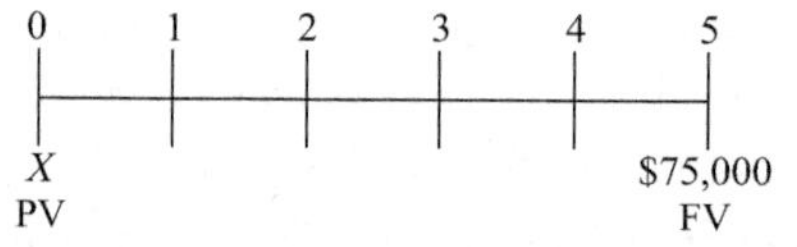

ii. Identify the problem as the present value of a lump sum.

iii. Use the formula for the present value of a lump sum.

$$\begin{aligned} PV &= FV_N(1+r)^{-N} \\ &= \$75{,}000(1+0.06)^{-5} \\ &= \$56{,}044.36 \end{aligned}$$

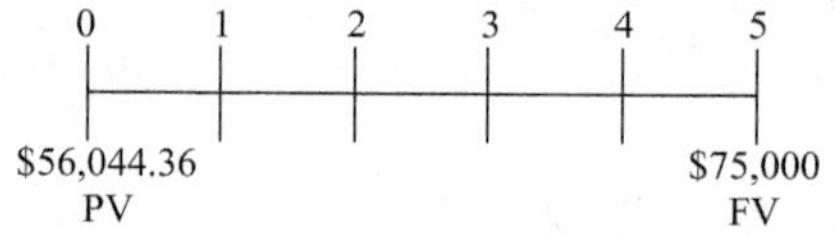

In summary, the father will need to invest $56,044.36 today in order to have $75,000 in five years if his investments earn 6 percent annually.

5 **i.** Draw a time line for the 10 annual payments.

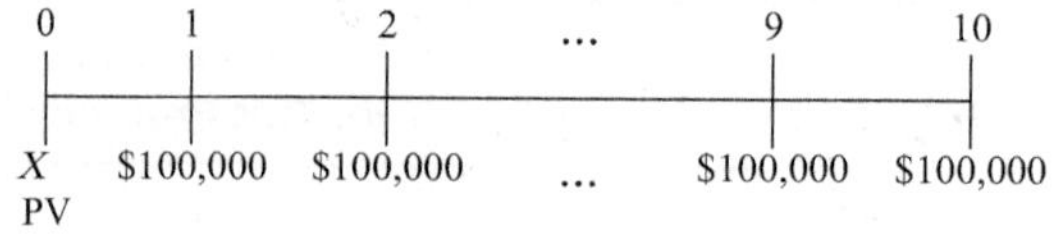

ii. Identify the problem as the present value of an annuity.

iii. Use the formula for the present value of an annuity.

$$\begin{aligned} PV &= A\left[\frac{1-\frac{1}{(1+r)^N}}{r}\right] \\ &= \$100{,}000\left[\frac{1-\frac{1}{(1+0.05)^{10}}}{0.05}\right] \\ &= \$772{,}173.49 \end{aligned}$$

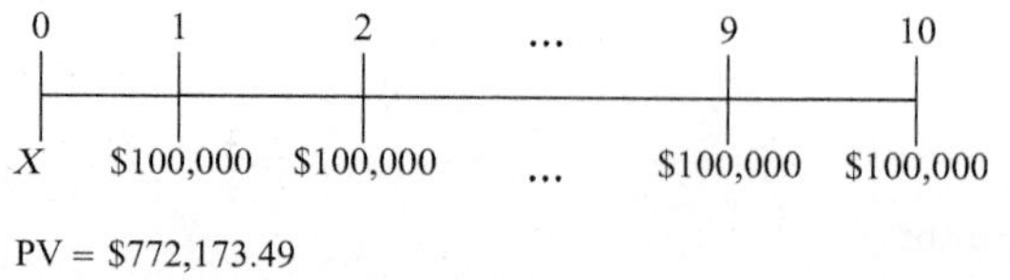

iv. Alternatively, use a financial calculator.

Notation Used on Most Calculators	Numerical Value for This Problem
N	10
$\%i$	5
PV **compute**	X
FV	n/a (= 0)
PMT	$100,000

In summary, the present value of 10 payments of $100,000 is $772,173.49 if the first payment is received in one year and the rate is 5 percent compounded annually. Your client should accept no less than this amount for his lump sum payment.

6 **A** To evaluate the first instrument, take the following steps:

i. Draw a time line.

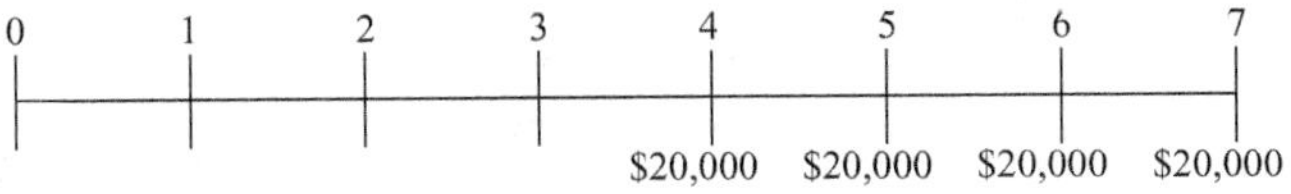

ii.

$$\text{PV}_3 = A\left[\frac{1 - \frac{1}{(1+r)^N}}{r}\right]$$

$$= \$20{,}000\left[\frac{1 - \frac{1}{(1+0.08)^4}}{0.08}\right]$$

$$= \$66{,}242.54$$

iii.

$$\text{PV}_0 = \frac{\text{PV}_3}{(1+r)^N} = \frac{\$66{,}242.54}{1.08^3} = \$52{,}585.46$$

You should be willing to pay $52,585.46 for this instrument.

B To evaluate the second instrument, take the following steps:

i. Draw a time line.

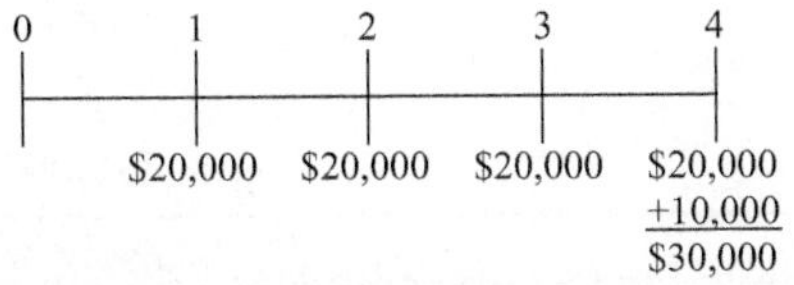

The time line shows that this instrument can be analyzed as an ordinary annuity of $20,000 with four payments (valued in Step ii below) and a $10,000 payment to be received at t = 4 (valued in Step iii below).

ii.

$$PV = A\left[\frac{1-\frac{1}{(1+r)^N}}{r}\right]$$

$$= \$20{,}000\left[\frac{1-\frac{1}{(1+0.08)^4}}{0.08}\right]$$

$$= \$66{,}242.54$$

iii.

$$PV = \frac{FV_4}{(1+r)^N} = \frac{\$10{,}000}{(1+0.08)^4} = \$7{,}350.30$$

iv. Total = \$66,242.54 + \$7,350.30 = \$73,592.84

You should be willing to pay \$73,592.84 for this instrument.

7 **i.** Draw a time line.

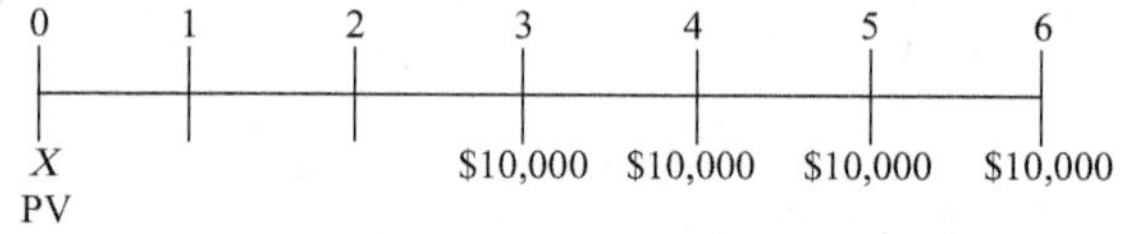

ii. Recognize the problem as a delayed annuity. Delaying the payments requires two calculations.

iii. Use the formula for the present value of an annuity (Equation 11).

$$PV = A\left[\frac{1-\frac{1}{(1+r)^N}}{r}\right]$$

to bring the four payments of \$10,000 back to a single equivalent lump sum of \$33,121.27 at $t = 2$. Note that we use $t = 2$ because the first annuity payment is then one period away, giving an ordinary annuity.

Notation Used on Most Calculators	Numerical Value for This Problem
N	4
$\%i$	8
PV compute	X
PMT	\$10,000

iv. Then use the formula for the present value of a lump sum (Equation 8), $PV = FV_N(1 + r)^{-N}$, to bring back the single payment of \$33,121.27 (at $t = 2$) to an equivalent single payment of \$28,396.15 (at $t = 0$).

Notation Used on Most Calculators	Numerical Value for This Problem
N	2
$\%i$	8
PV compute	X
FV	\$33,121.27
PMT	n/a (= 0)

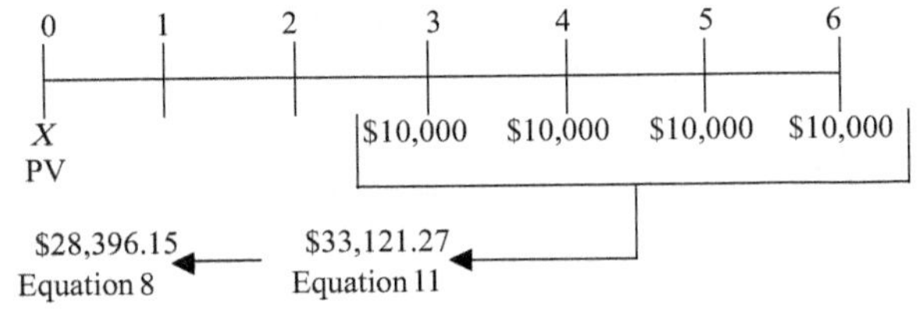

In summary, you should set aside $28,396.15 today to cover four payments of $10,000 starting in three years if your investments earn a rate of 8 percent annually.

8 **i.** Draw a time line.

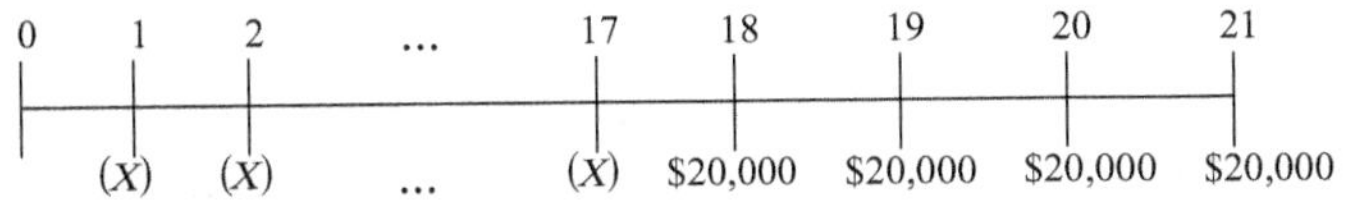

ii. Recognize that you need to equate the values of two annuities.

iii. Equate the value of the four $20,000 payments to a single payment in Period 17 using the formula for the present value of an annuity (Equation 11), with $r = 0.05$. The present value of the college costs as of $t = 17$ is $70,919.

$$\text{PV} = \$20{,}000\left[\frac{1 - \frac{1}{(1.05)^4}}{0.05}\right] = \$70{,}919$$

Notation Used on Most Calculators	Numerical Value for This Problem
N	4
$\%i$	5
PV **compute**	X
FV	n/a (= 0)
PMT	$20,000

iv. Equate the value of the 17 investments of X to the amount calculated in Step iii, college costs as of $t = 17$, using the formula for the future value of an annuity (Equation 7). Then solve for X.

$$\$70{,}919 = \left[\frac{(1.05)^{17} - 1}{0.05}\right] = 25.840366X$$

$$X = \$2{,}744.50$$

Notation Used on Most Calculators	Numerical Value for This Problem
N	17
$\%i$	5
PV	n/a (= 0)
FV	$70,919
PMT **compute**	X

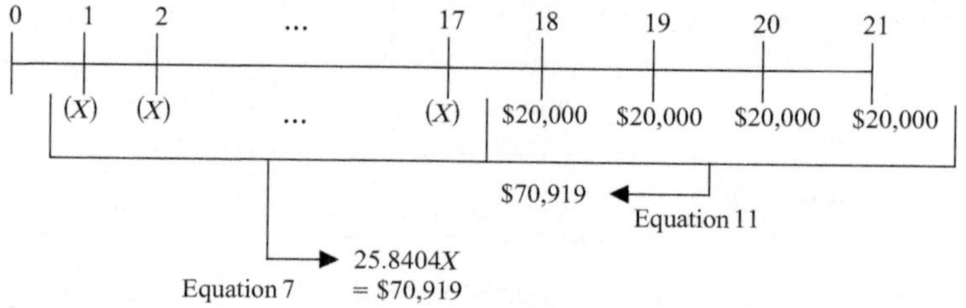

In summary, your client will have to save $2,744.50 each year if she starts next year and makes 17 payments into a savings account paying 5 percent annually.

9 **i.** Draw a time line.

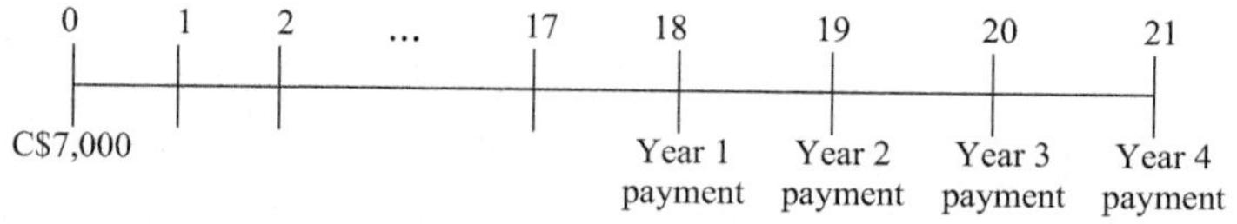

ii. Recognize that the payments in Years 18, 19, 20, and 21 are the future values of a lump sum of C$7,000 in Year 0.

iii. With r = 5%, use the formula for the future value of a lump sum (Equation 2), $FV_N = PV (1 + r)^N$, four times to find the payments. These future values are shown on the time line below.

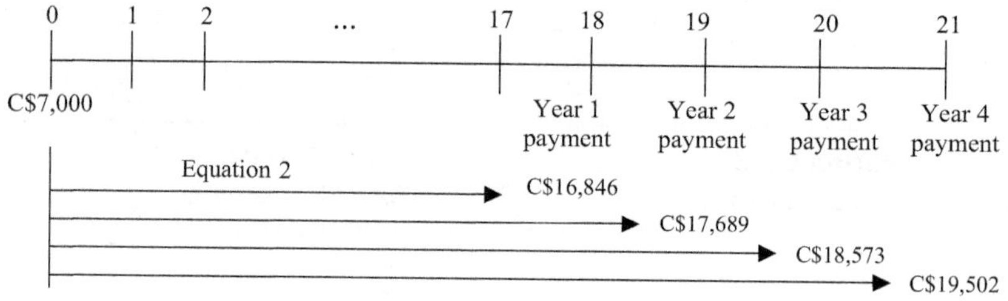

iv. Using the formula for the present value of a lump sum (r = 6%), equate the four college payments to single payments as of t = 17 and add them together. $C\$16{,}846(1.06)^{-1} + C\$17{,}689(1.06)^{-2} + C\$18{,}573(1.06)^{-3} + C\$19{,}502(1.06)^{-4} = C\$62{,}677$

v. Equate the sum of C$62,677 at t = 17 to the 17 payments of X, using the formula for the future value of an annuity (Equation 7). Then solve for X.

$$C\$62{,}677 = X\left[\frac{(1.06)^{17} - 1}{0.06}\right] = 28.21288X$$

$$X = C\$2{,}221.58$$

Notation Used on Most Calculators	Numerical Value for This Problem
N	17
$\%i$	6
PV	n/a (= 0)
FV	C$62,677
PMT **compute**	X

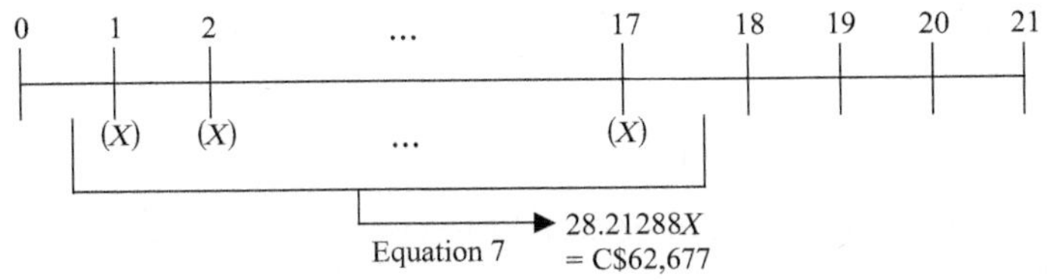

In summary, the couple will need to put aside C$2,221.58 each year if they start next year and make 17 equal payments.

10 C is correct. The sum of the real risk-free interest rate and the inflation premium is the nominal risk-free rate.

11 C is correct. US Treasury bonds are highly liquid, whereas the bonds of small issuers trade infrequently and the interest rate includes a liquidity premium. This liquidity premium reflects the relatively high costs (including the impact on price) of selling a position.

12 A is correct. The effective annual rate (EAR) when compounded daily is 4.08%.

$$\text{EAR} = (1 + \text{Periodic interest rate})^m - 1$$

$$\text{EAR} = (1 + 0.04/365)^{365} - 1$$

$$\text{EAR} = (1.0408) - 1 = 0.04081 \approx 4.08\%.$$

13 C is correct, as shown in the following (where FV is future value and PV is present value):

$$\text{FV} = \text{PV}\left(1 + \frac{r_s}{m}\right)^{mN}$$

$$\text{FV}_6 = \$75{,}000\left(1 + \frac{0.07}{4}\right)^{(4\times 6)}$$

$$\text{FV}_6 = \$113{,}733.21.$$

14 B is correct because £97,531 represents the present value (PV) of £100,000 received one year from today when today's deposit earns a stated annual rate of 2.50% and interest compounds weekly, as shown in the following equation (where FV is future value):

$$\text{PV} = \text{FV}_N\left(1 + \frac{r_s}{m}\right)^{-mN}$$

$$\text{PV} = £100{,}000\left(1 + \frac{0.025}{52}\right)^{-52}$$

$$\text{PV} = £97{,}531.58.$$

15 A is correct. The effective annual rate (EAR) is calculated as follows:

$$\text{EAR} = (1 + \text{Periodic interest rate})^m - 1$$

$$\text{EAR} = (1 + 0.03/365)^{365} - 1$$

$$\text{EAR} = (1.03045) - 1 = 0.030453 \approx 3.0453\%.$$

Solving for N on a financial calculator results in (where FV is future value and PV is present value):

$(1 + 0.030453)^N = FV_N/PV = ¥1,000,000/¥250,000$

= 46.21 years, which multiplied by 12 to convert to months results in 554.5, or ≈ 555 months.

16 B is correct. The difference between continuous compounding and daily compounding is

€127,496.85 – €127,491.29 = €5.56, or ≈ €6, as shown in the following calculations.

With continuous compounding, the investment earns (where PV is present value)

$$\begin{aligned} PVe^{r_s N} - PV &= €1,000,000e^{0.03(4)} - €1,000,000 \\ &= €1,127,496.85 - €1,000,000 \\ &= €127,496.85 \end{aligned}$$

With daily compounding, the investment earns:

$€1,000,000(1 + 0.03/365)^{365(4)} - €1,000,000 = €1,127,491.29 - €1,000,000 =$ €127,491.29.

17 B is correct, as shown in the following calculation for an annuity (A) due:

$$PV = A\left[\frac{1 - \frac{1}{(1+r)^N}}{r}\right](1+r)$$

where A = €300, $r = 0.04$, and $N = 5$.

$$PV = €300\left[\frac{1 - \frac{1}{(1+.04)^5}}{.04}\right](1.04)$$

PV = €1,388.97, or ≈ €1,389.

18 B is correct. The value of the perpetuity one year from now is calculated as: PV = A/r, where PV is present value, A is annuity, and r is expressed as a quarterly required rate of return because the payments are quarterly.

PV = $2.00/(0.06/4)

PV = $133.33.

The value today is (where FV is future value)

$PV = FV_N(1 + r)^{-N}$

$PV = \$133.33(1 + 0.015)^{-4}$

PV = $125.62 ≈ $126.

19 B is correct. To solve for the future value of unequal cash flows, compute the future value of each payment as of Year 4 at the semiannual rate of 2%, and then sum the individual future values, as follows:

Year	End of Year Deposits ($)	Factor	Future Value ($)
1	4,000	$(1.02)^6$	4,504.65
2	8,000	$(1.02)^4$	8,659.46
3	7,000	$(1.02)^2$	7,282.80
4	10,000	$(1.02)^0$	10,000.00
		Sum =	30,446.91

20 C is correct, as shown in the following (where FV is future value and PV is present value):

If:

$$\mathrm{FV}_N = \mathrm{PV}\left(1 + \frac{r_s}{m}\right)^{mN}$$

Then:

$$\left(\frac{\mathrm{FV}_N}{\mathrm{PV}}\right)^{\frac{1}{mN}} - 1 = \frac{r_s}{m}$$

$$\left(\frac{800{,}000}{500{,}000}\right)^{\frac{1}{2\times 6}} - 1 = \frac{r_s}{2}$$

$r_s = 0.07988$ (rounded to 8.0%).

21 C is correct. As shown below, the present value (PV) of a £2,000 per month perpetuity is worth approximately £400,000 at a 6% annual rate compounded monthly. Thus, the present value of the annuity (A) is worth more than the lump sum offers.

A = £2,000

r = (6%/12) = 0.005

PV = (A/r)

PV = (£2,000/0.005)

PV = £400,000

22 B is correct.

The present value of a 10-year annuity (A) due with payments of $2,000 at a 5% discount rate is calculated as follows:

$$\mathrm{PV} = A\left[\frac{1 - \frac{1}{(1+r)^N}}{r}\right] + \$2{,}000$$

$$PV = \$2{,}000\left[\frac{1-\dfrac{1}{(1+0.05)^9}}{0.05}\right] + \$2{,}000$$

$$PV = \$16{,}215.64.$$

Alternatively, the PV of a 10-year annuity due is simply the PV of the ordinary annuity multiplied by 1.05:

$$PV = \$15{,}443.47 \times 1.05$$

$$PV = \$16{,}215.64.$$

23 B is correct. First, find the present value (PV) of an ordinary annuity in Year 17 that represents the tuition costs:

$$\$50{,}000\left[\frac{1-\dfrac{1}{(1+0.06)^4}}{0.06}\right]$$

$$= \$50{,}000 \times 3.4651$$

$$= \$173{,}255.28.$$

Then, find the PV of the annuity in today's dollars (where FV is future value):

$$PV_0 = \frac{FV}{(1+0.06)^{17}}$$

$$PV_0 = \frac{\$173{,}255.28}{(1+0.06)^{17}}$$

$$PV_0 = \$64{,}340.85 \approx \$64{,}341.$$

24 B is correct, as shown in the following table.

Year	Cash Flow (€)	Formula $CF \times (1+r)^t$	PV at Year 0
1	100,000	$100{,}000(1.12)^{-1}$ =	89,285.71
2	150,000	$150{,}000(1.12)^{-2}$ =	119,579.08
5	–10,000	$-10{,}000(1.12)^{-5}$ =	–5,674.27
			203,190.52

25 B is correct, calculated as follows (where A is annuity and PV is present value):

$$A = (\text{PV of annuity}) \Bigg/ \left[\frac{1 - \dfrac{1}{(1 + r_s/m)^{mN}}}{r_s/m} \right]$$

$$= (£200{,}000) \Bigg/ \left[\frac{1 - \dfrac{1}{(1 + r_s/m)^{mN}}}{r_s/m} \right]$$

$$(£200{,}000) \Bigg/ \left[\frac{1 - \dfrac{1}{(1 + 0.06/12)^{12(5)}}}{0.06/12} \right]$$

$$= (£200{,}000)/51.72556$$

$$= £3{,}866.56$$

26 A is correct. To solve for an annuity (A) payment, when the future value (FV), interest rate, and number of periods is known, use the following equation:

$$\text{FV} = A \left[\frac{\left(1 + \dfrac{r_s}{m}\right)^{mN} - 1}{\dfrac{r}{m}} \right]$$

$$£25{,}000 = A \left[\frac{\left(1 + \dfrac{0.06}{4}\right)^{4 \times 10} - 1}{\dfrac{0.06}{4}} \right]$$

$A = £460.68$

27 B is correct. The PV in Year 5 of a \$50,000 lump sum paid in Year 20 is \$27,763.23 (where FV is future value):

$\text{PV} = \text{FV}_N(1 + r)^{-N}$

$\text{PV} = \$50{,}000(1 + 0.04)^{-15}$

$\text{PV} = \$27{,}763.23$

28 B is correct, as the following cash flows show:

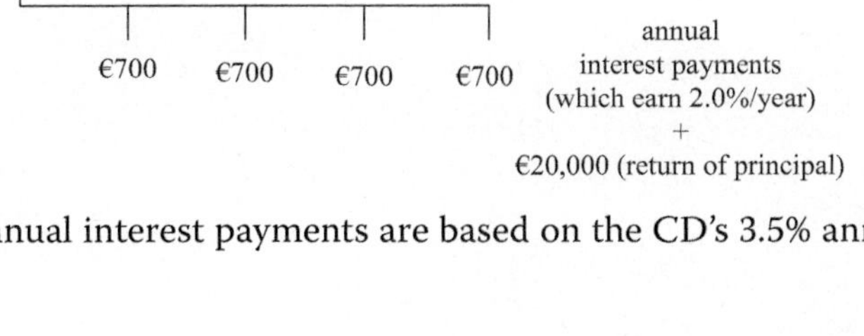

The four annual interest payments are based on the CD's 3.5% annual rate.

The first payment grows at 2.0% compounded monthly for three years (where FV is future value):

$$FV_N = €700\left(1 + \frac{0.02}{12}\right)^{3\times12}$$

$$FV_N = 743.25$$

The second payment grows at 2.0% compounded monthly for two years:

$$FV_N = €700\left(1 + \frac{0.02}{12}\right)^{2\times12}$$

$$FV_N = 728.54$$

The third payment grows at 2.0% compounded monthly for one year:

$$FV_N = €700\left(1 + \frac{0.02}{12}\right)^{1\times12}$$

$$FV_N = 714.13$$

The fourth payment is paid at the end of Year 4. Its future value is €700.

The sum of all future value payments is as follows:

€20,000.00	CD
€743.25	First payment's *FV*
€728.54	Second payment's *FV*
€714.13	Third payment's *FV*
€700.00	Fourth payment's *FV*
€22,885.92	Total *FV*

READING

7

Statistical Concepts and Market Returns

by Richard A. DeFusco, PhD, CFA, Dennis W. McLeavey, DBA, CFA, Jerald E. Pinto, PhD, CFA, and David E. Runkle, PhD, CFA

Richard A. DeFusco, PhD, CFA, is at the University of Lincoln-Nebraska (USA). Dennis W. McLeavey, DBA, CFA, is at the University of Rhode Island (USA). Jerald E. Pinto, PhD, CFA, is at CFA Institute (USA). David E. Runkle, PhD, CFA, is at Trilogy Global Advisors (USA).

LEARNING OUTCOMES

Mastery	*The candidate should be able to:*
☐	**a.** distinguish between descriptive statistics and inferential statistics, between a population and a sample, and among the types of measurement scales;
☐	**b.** define a parameter, a sample statistic, and a frequency distribution;
☐	**c.** calculate and interpret relative frequencies and cumulative relative frequencies, given a frequency distribution;
☐	**d.** describe the properties of a data set presented as a histogram or a frequency polygon;
☐	**e.** calculate and interpret measures of central tendency, including the population mean, sample mean, arithmetic mean, weighted average or mean, geometric mean, harmonic mean, median, and mode;
☐	**f.** calculate and interpret quartiles, quintiles, deciles, and percentiles;
☐	**g.** calculate and interpret 1) a range and a mean absolute deviation and 2) the variance and standard deviation of a population and of a sample;
☐	**h.** calculate and interpret the proportion of observations falling within a specified number of standard deviations of the mean using Chebyshev's inequality;
☐	**i.** calculate and interpret the coefficient of variation;
☐	**j.** explain skewness and the meaning of a positively or negatively skewed return distribution;

(continued)

LEARNING OUTCOMES	
Mastery	***The candidate should be able to:***
☐	k. describe the relative locations of the mean, median, and mode for a unimodal, nonsymmetrical distribution;
☐	l. explain measures of sample skewness and kurtosis;
☐	m. compare the use of arithmetic and geometric means when analyzing investment returns.

1 INTRODUCTION

Statistical methods provide a powerful set of tools for analyzing data and drawing conclusions from them. Whether we are analyzing asset returns, earnings growth rates, commodity prices, or any other financial data, statistical tools help us quantify and communicate the data's important features. This reading presents the basics of describing and analyzing data, the branch of statistics known as descriptive statistics. The reading supplies a set of useful concepts and tools, illustrated in a variety of investment contexts. One theme of our presentation, reflected in the reading's title, is the demonstration of the statistical methods that allow us to summarize return distributions.[1] We explore four properties of return distributions:

- where the returns are centered (central tendency);
- how far returns are dispersed from their center (dispersion);
- whether the distribution of returns is symmetrically shaped or lopsided (skewness); and
- whether extreme outcomes are likely (kurtosis).

These same concepts are generally applicable to the distributions of other types of data, too.

The reading is organized as follows. After defining some basic concepts in Section 2, in Sections 3 and 4 we discuss the presentation of data: Section 3 describes the organization of data in a table format, and Section 4 describes the graphic presentation of data. We then turn to the quantitative description of how data are distributed: Section 5 focuses on measures that quantify where data are centered, or measures of central tendency. Section 6 presents other measures that describe the location of data. Section 7 presents measures that quantify the degree to which data are dispersed. Sections 8 and 9 describe additional measures that provide a more accurate picture of data. Section 10 provides investment applications of concepts introduced in Section 5.

2 SOME FUNDAMENTAL CONCEPTS

Before starting the study of statistics with this reading, it may be helpful to examine a picture of the overall field. In the following, we briefly describe the scope of statistics and its branches of study. We explain the concepts of population and sample. Data

1 Ibbotson Associates (www.ibbotson.com) generously provided some of the data used in this reading. We also draw on Dimson, Marsh, and Staunton's (2011) history and study of world markets as well as other sources.

come in a variety of types, affecting the ways they can be measured and the appropriate statistical methods for analyzing them. We conclude by discussing the basic types of data measurement.

2.1 The Nature of Statistics

The term **statistics** can have two broad meanings, one referring to data and the other to method. A company's average earnings per share (EPS) for the last 20 quarters, or its average returns for the past 10 years, are statistics. We may also analyze historical EPS to forecast future EPS, or use the company's past returns to infer its risk. The totality of methods we employ to collect and analyze data is also called statistics.

Statistical methods include descriptive statistics and statistical inference (inferential statistics). **Descriptive statistics** is the study of how data can be summarized effectively to describe the important aspects of large data sets. By consolidating a mass of numerical details, descriptive statistics turns data into information. **Statistical inference** involves making forecasts, estimates, or judgments about a larger group from the smaller group actually observed. The foundation for statistical inference is probability theory, and both statistical inference and probability theory will be discussed in later readings. Our focus in this reading is solely on descriptive statistics.

2.2 Populations and Samples

Throughout the study of statistics we make a critical distinction between a population and a sample. In this section, we explain these two terms as well as the related terms "parameter" and "sample statistic."[2]

- **Definition of Population.** A **population** is defined as all members of a specified group.

Any descriptive measure of a population characteristic is called a **parameter**. Although a population can have many parameters, investment analysts are usually concerned with only a few, such as the mean value, the range of investment returns, and the variance.

Even if it is possible to observe all the members of a population, it is often too expensive in terms of time or money to attempt to do so. For example, if the population is all telecommunications customers worldwide and an analyst is interested in their purchasing plans, she will find it too costly to observe the entire population. The analyst can address this situation by taking a sample of the population.

- **Definition of Sample.** A **sample** is a subset of a population.

In taking a sample, the analyst hopes it is characteristic of the population. The field of statistics known as sampling deals with taking samples in appropriate ways to achieve the objective of representing the population well. A later reading addresses the details of sampling.

Earlier, we mentioned statistics in the sense of referring to data. Just as a parameter is a descriptive measure of a population characteristic, a sample statistic (statistic, for short) is a descriptive measure of a sample characteristic.

- **Definition of Sample Statistic.** A **sample statistic** (or **statistic**) is a quantity computed from or used to describe a sample.

2 This reading introduces many statistical concepts and formulas. To make it easy to locate them, we have set off some of the more important ones with bullet points.

We devote much of this reading to explaining and illustrating the use of statistics in this sense. The concept is critical also in statistical inference, which addresses such problems as estimating an unknown population parameter using a sample statistic.

2.3 Measurement Scales

To choose the appropriate statistical methods for summarizing and analyzing data, we need to distinguish among different **measurement scales** or levels of measurement. All data measurements are taken on one of four major scales: nominal, ordinal, interval, or ratio.

Nominal scales represent the weakest level of measurement: They categorize data but do not rank them. If we assigned integers to mutual funds that follow different investment strategies, the number 1 might refer to a small-cap value fund, the number 2 to a large-cap value fund, and so on for each possible style. This nominal scale categorizes the funds according to their style but does not rank them.

Ordinal scales reflect a stronger level of measurement. Ordinal scales sort data into categories that are ordered with respect to some characteristic. For example, the Morningstar and Standard & Poor's star ratings for mutual funds represent an ordinal scale in which one star represents a group of funds judged to have had relatively the worst performance, with two, three, four, and five stars representing groups with increasingly better performance, as evaluated by those services.

An ordinal scale may also involve numbers to identify categories. For example, in ranking balanced mutual funds based on their five-year cumulative return, we might assign the number 1 to the top 10 percent of funds, and so on, so that the number 10 represents the bottom 10 percent of funds. The ordinal scale is stronger than the nominal scale because it reveals that a fund ranked 1 performed better than a fund ranked 2. The scale tells us nothing, however, about the difference in performance between funds ranked 1 and 2 compared with the difference in performance between funds ranked 3 and 4, or 9 and 10.

Interval scales provide not only ranking but also assurance that the differences between scale values are equal. As a result, scale values can be added and subtracted meaningfully. The Celsius and Fahrenheit scales are interval measurement scales. The difference in temperature between 10°C and 11°C is the same amount as the difference between 40°C and 41°C. We can state accurately that 12°C = 9°C + 3°C, for example. Nevertheless, the zero point of an interval scale does not reflect complete absence of what is being measured; it is not a true zero point or natural zero. Zero degrees Celsius corresponds to the freezing point of water, not the absence of temperature. As a consequence of the absence of a true zero point, we cannot meaningfully form ratios on interval scales.

As an example, 50°C, although five times as large a number as 10°C, does not represent five times as much temperature. Also, questionnaire scales are often treated as interval scales. If an investor is asked to rank his risk aversion on a scale from 1 (extremely risk-averse) to 7 (extremely risk-loving), the difference between a response of 1 and a response of 2 is sometimes assumed to represent the same difference in risk aversion as the difference between a response of 6 and a response of 7. When that assumption can be justified, the data are measured on an interval scale.

Ratio scales represent the strongest level of measurement. They have all the characteristics of interval measurement scales as well as a true zero point as the origin. With ratio scales, we can meaningfully compute ratios as well as meaningfully add and subtract amounts within the scale. As a result, we can apply the widest range of statistical tools to data measured on a ratio scale. Rates of return are measured on a ratio scale, as is money. If we have twice as much money, then we have twice the purchasing power. Note that the scale has a natural zero—zero means no money.

Now that we have addressed the important preliminaries, we can discuss summarizing and describing data.

EXAMPLE 1

Identifying Scales of Measurement

State the scale of measurement for each of the following:

1 Credit ratings for bond issues.[3]
2 Cash dividends per share.
3 Hedge fund classification types.[4]
4 Bond maturity in years.

Solution to 1:

Credit ratings are measured on an ordinal scale. A rating places a bond issue in a category, and the categories are ordered with respect to the expected probability of default. But the difference in the expected probability of default between AA− and A+, for example, is not necessarily equal to that between BB− and B+. In other words, letter credit ratings are not measured on an interval scale.

Solution to 2:

Cash dividends per share are measured on a ratio scale. For this variable, 0 represents the complete absence of dividends; it is a true zero point.

Solution to 3:

Hedge fund classification types are measured on a nominal scale. Each type groups together hedge funds with similar investment strategies. In contrast to credit ratings for bonds, however, hedge fund classification schemes do not involve a ranking. Thus such classification schemes are not measured on an ordinal scale.

Solution to 4:

Bond maturity is measured on a ratio scale.

SUMMARIZING DATA USING FREQUENCY DISTRIBUTIONS

3

In this section, we discuss one of the simplest ways to summarize data—the frequency distribution.

- **Definition of Frequency Distribution.** A **frequency distribution** is a tabular display of data summarized into a relatively small number of intervals.

3 Credit ratings for a bond issue gauge the bond issuer's ability to meet the promised principal and interest payments on the bond. For example, one rating agency, Standard & Poor's, assigns bond issues to one of the following ratings, given in descending order of credit quality (increasing probability of default): AAA, AA+, AA, AA−, A+, A, A−, BBB+, BBB, BBB−, BB+, BB, BB−, B+, B, B−, CCC+, CCC−, CC, C, D. For more information on credit risk and credit ratings, see the Level I CFA Program curriculum reading "Fixed-Income Securities: Defining Elements."

4 "Hedge fund" refers to investment vehicles with legal structures that result in less regulatory oversight than other pooled investment vehicles such as mutual funds. Hedge fund classification types group hedge funds by the kind of investment strategy they pursue.

Frequency distributions help in the analysis of large amounts of statistical data, and they work with all types of measurement scales.

Rates of return are the fundamental units that analysts and portfolio managers use for making investment decisions and we can use frequency distributions to summarize rates of return. When we analyze rates of return, our starting point is the holding period return (also called the total return).

- **Holding Period Return Formula.** The holding period return for time period t, R_t, is

$$R_t = \frac{P_t - P_{t-1} + D_t}{P_{t-1}} \tag{1}$$

where

P_t = price per share at the end of time period t

P_{t-1} = price per share at the end of time period $t - 1$, the time period immediately preceding time period t

D_t = cash distributions received during time period t

Thus the holding period return for time period t is the capital gain (or loss) plus distributions divided by the beginning-period price. (For common stocks, the distribution is a dividend; for bonds, the distribution is a coupon payment.) Equation 1 can be used to define the holding period return on any asset for a day, week, month, or year simply by changing the interpretation of the time interval between successive values of the time index, t.

The holding period return, as defined in Equation 1, has two important characteristics. First, it has an element of time attached to it. For example, if a monthly time interval is used between successive observations for price, then the rate of return is a monthly figure. Second, rate of return has no currency unit attached to it. For instance, suppose that prices are denominated in euros. The numerator and denominator of Equation 1 would be expressed in euros, and the resulting ratio would not have any units because the units in the numerator and denominator would cancel one another. This result holds regardless of the currency in which prices are denominated.[5]

With these concerns noted, we now turn to the frequency distribution of the holding period returns on the S&P 500 Index.[6] First, we examine annual rates of return; then we look at monthly rates of return. The annual rates of return on the S&P 500 calculated with Equation 1 span the period January 1926 to December 2017, for a total of 92 annual observations. Monthly return data cover the period January 1926 to December 2017, for a total of 1,104 monthly observations.

We can state a basic procedure for constructing a frequency distribution as follows.

Construction of a Frequency Distribution.

1. Sort the data in ascending order.
2. Calculate the range of the data, defined as Range = Maximum value – Minimum value.
3. Decide on the number of intervals in the frequency distribution, k.

---

5 Note, however, that if price and cash distributions in the expression for holding period return were not in one's home currency, one would generally convert those variables to one's home currency before calculating the holding period return. Because of exchange rate fluctuations during the holding period, holding period returns on an asset computed in different currencies would generally differ.

6 For January 1926 to December 2012, we use the total return series on the S&P 500 provided by Ibbotson Associates. For January 2013 to December 2017, we use the total return series on the S&P 500 from S&P Dow Jones Indices LLC (https://us.spindices.com/indices/equity/sp-500, accessed 31 October 2018).

4 Determine interval width as Range/k.

5 Determine the intervals by successively adding the interval width to the minimum value, to determine the ending points of intervals, stopping after reaching an interval that includes the maximum value.

6 Count the number of observations falling in each interval.

7 Construct a table of the intervals listed from smallest to largest that shows the number of observations falling in each interval.

In Step 4, when rounding the interval width, round up rather than down, to ensure that the final interval includes the maximum value of the data.

As the above procedure makes clear, a frequency distribution groups data into a set of intervals.[7] An **interval** is a set of values within which an observation falls. Each observation falls into only one interval, and the total number of intervals covers all the values represented in the data. The actual number of observations in a given interval is called the **absolute frequency**, or simply the frequency. The frequency distribution is the list of intervals together with the corresponding measures of frequency.

To illustrate the basic procedure, suppose we have 12 observations sorted in ascending order: −4.57, −4.04, −1.64, 0.28, 1.34, 2.35, 2.38, 4.28, 4.42, 4.68, 7.16, and 11.43. The minimum observation is −4.57 and the maximum observation is +11.43, so the range is +11.43 − (−4.57) = 16. If we set k = 4, the interval width is 16/4 = 4. Exhibit 1 shows the repeated addition of the interval width of 4 to determine the endpoints for the intervals (Step 5).

Exhibit 1 Endpoints of Intervals

−4.57	+	4.00	=	−0.57
−0.57	+	4.00	=	3.43
3.43	+	4.00	=	7.43
7.4	+	4.00	=	11.43

Thus the intervals are [−4.57 to −0.57), [−0.57 to 3.43), [3.43 to 7.43), and [7.43 to 11.43].[8] Exhibit 2 summarizes Steps 5 through 7.

Exhibit 2 Frequency Distribution

Interval				Absolute Frequency
A	−4.57	≤ observation <	−0.57	3
B	−0.57	≤ observation <	3.43	4
C	3.43	≤ observation <	7.43	4
D	7.43	≤ observation ≤	11.43	1

Note that the intervals do not overlap, so each observation can be placed uniquely into one interval.

7 Intervals are also sometimes called classes, ranges, or bins.

8 The notation [−4.57 to −0.57) means −4.57 ≤ observation < −0.57. In this context, a square bracket indicates that the endpoint is included in the interval.

In practice, we may want to refine the above basic procedure. For example, we may want the intervals to begin and end with whole numbers for ease of interpretation. We also need to explain the choice of the number of intervals, k. We turn to these issues in discussing the construction of frequency distributions for the S&P 500.

We first consider the case of constructing a frequency distribution for the annual returns on the S&P 500 over the period 1926 to 2017. During that period, the return on the S&P 500 had a minimum value of −43.35 percent (in 1931) and a maximum value of +53.97 percent (in 1933). Thus the range of the data was +54% − (−43%) = 97%, approximately. The question now is the number k of intervals into which we should group observations. Although some guidelines for setting k have been suggested in statistical literature, the setting of a useful value for k often involves inspecting the data and exercising judgment. How much detail should we include? If we use too few intervals, we will summarize too much and lose pertinent characteristics. If we use too many intervals, we may not summarize enough.

We can establish an appropriate value for k by evaluating the usefulness of the resulting interval width. A large number of empty intervals may indicate that we are trying to organize the data to present too much detail. Starting with a relatively small interval width, we can see whether or not the intervals are mostly empty and whether or not the value of k associated with that interval width is too large. If intervals are mostly empty or k is very large, we can consider increasingly larger intervals (smaller values of k) until we have a frequency distribution that effectively summarizes the distribution. For the annual S&P 500 series, return intervals of 1 percent width would result in 97 intervals and many of them would be empty because we have only 92 annual observations. We need to keep in mind that the purpose of a frequency distribution is to *summarize* the data. Suppose that for ease of interpretation we want to use an interval width stated in whole rather than fractional percents. A 2 percent interval width would have many fewer empty intervals than a 1 percent interval width and effectively summarize the data. A 2 percent interval width would be associated with 97/2 = 48.5 intervals, which we can round up to 49 intervals. That number of intervals will cover 2% × 49 = 98%. We can confirm that if we start the smallest 2 percent interval at the whole number −44.0 percent, the final interval ends at −44.0% + 98% = 54% and includes the maximum return in the sample, 53.99 percent. In so constructing the frequency distribution, we will also have intervals that end and begin at a value of 0 percent, allowing us to count the negative and positive returns in the data. Without too much work, we have found an effective way to summarize the data. We will use return intervals of 2 percent, beginning with $-44\% \le R_t < -42\%$ (given as "−44% to −42%" in the exhibit) and ending with $52\% \le R_t \le 54\%$. Exhibit 3 shows the frequency distribution for the annual total returns on the S&P 500.

Exhibit 3 includes three other useful ways to present data, which we can compute once we have established the frequency distribution: the relative frequency, the cumulative frequency (also called the cumulative absolute frequency), and the cumulative relative frequency.

- **Definition of Relative Frequency.** The **relative frequency** is the absolute frequency of each interval divided by the total number of observations.

The **cumulative relative frequency** cumulates (adds up) the relative frequencies as we move from the first to the last interval. It tells us the fraction of observations that are less than the upper limit of each interval. Examining the frequency distribution given in Exhibit 3, we see that the first return interval, −44 percent to −42 percent, has one observation; its relative frequency is 1/92 or 1.09 percent. The cumulative frequency for this interval is 1 because only one observation is less than −42 percent. The cumulative relative frequency is thus 1/92 or 1.09 percent. The next return interval has zero observations; therefore, its cumulative frequency is 0 plus 1 and its cumulative relative frequency is 1.09 percent (the cumulative relative frequency from the previous interval). We can find the other cumulative frequencies by adding the (absolute) frequency to the previous cumulative frequency. The cumulative frequency, then, tells us the number of observations that are less than the upper limit of each return interval.

As Exhibit 3 shows, return intervals have frequencies from 0 to 7 in this sample. The interval encompassing returns between −10 percent and −8 percent ($-10\% \leq R_t < -8\%$) has the most observations, seven. Next most frequent are returns between 4 percent and 6 percent ($4\% \leq R_t < 6\%$) and between18 percent and 20 percent ($18\% \leq R_t < 20\%$), with six observations in each interval. From the cumulative frequency column, we see that the number of negative returns is 24. The number of positive returns must then be equal to 92 − 24, or 68. We can express the number of positive and negative outcomes as a percentage of the total to get a sense of the risk inherent in investing in the stock market. During the 92-year period, the S&P 500 had negative annual returns 26.09 percent of the time (that is, 24/92). This result appears in the fifth column of Exhibit 3, which reports the cumulative relative frequency.

The frequency distribution gives us a sense of not only where most of the observations lie but also whether the distribution is evenly distributed, lopsided, or otherwise distinctive. In the case of the S&P 500, we can see that more than half of the outcomes are positive and most of those annual returns are larger than 10 percent. (Only 15 of the 68 positive annual returns—about 16 percent—were between 0 and 10 percent.)

Exhibit 3 permits us to make an important further point about the choice of the number of intervals related to equity returns in particular. From the frequency distribution in Exhibit 3, we can see that only six outcomes fall between −44 percent to −16 percent and only five outcomes fall between 38 percent to 54 percent. Stock return data are frequently characterized by a few very large or small outcomes. We could have collapsed the return intervals in the tails of the frequency distribution by choosing a smaller value of k, but then we would have lost the information about how extremely poorly or well the stock market had performed. A risk manager may need to know the worst possible outcomes and thus may want to have detailed information on the tails (the extreme values). A frequency distribution with a relatively large value of k is useful for that. A portfolio manager or analyst may be equally interested in detailed information on the tails; however, if the manager or analyst wants a picture only of where most of the observations lie, he might prefer to use an interval width of 4 percent (25 intervals beginning at −44 percent), for example.

The frequency distribution for monthly returns on the S&P 500 looks quite different from that for annual returns. The monthly return series from January 1926 to December 2017 has 1,104 observations. Returns range from a minimum of approximately −30 percent to a maximum of approximately +43 percent. With such a large quantity of monthly data we must summarize to get a sense of the distribution, and so we group the data into 37 equally spaced return intervals of 2 percent. The gains from summarizing in this way are substantial. Exhibit 4 presents the resulting frequency distribution. The absolute frequencies appear in the second column, followed by the relative frequencies. The relative frequencies are rounded to two decimal places. The cumulative absolute and cumulative relative frequencies appear in the fourth and fifth columns, respectively.

Exhibit 3 Frequency Distribution for the Annual Total Return on the S&P 500, 1926–2017

Return Interval (%)	Frequency	Relative Frequency (%)	Cumulative Frequency	Cumulative Relative Frequency (%)	Return Interval (%)	Frequency	Relative Frequency (%)	Cumulative Frequency	Cumulative Relative Frequency (%)
−44.0 to −42.0	1	1.09	1	1.09	4.0 to 6.0	6	6.52	34	36.96
−42.0 to −40.0	0	0.00	1	1.09	6.0 to 8.0	4	4.35	38	41.30
−40.0 to −38.0	0	0.00	1	1.09	8.0 to 10.0	1	1.09	39	42.39
−38.0 to −36.0	1	1.09	2	2.17	10.0 to 12.0	5	5.43	44	47.83
−36.0 to −34.0	1	1.09	3	3.26	12.0 to 14.0	2	2.17	46	50.00
−34.0 to −32.0	0	0.00	3	3.26	14.0 to 16.0	4	4.35	50	54.35
−32.0 to −30.0	0	0.00	3	3.26	16.0 to 18.0	2	2.17	52	56.52
−30.0 to −28.0	0	0.00	3	3.26	18.0 to 20.0	6	6.52	58	63.04
−28.0 to −26.0	1	1.09	4	4.35	20.0 to 22.0	4	4.35	62	67.39
−26.0 to −24.0	1	1.09	5	5.43	22.0 to 24.0	5	5.43	67	72.83
−24.0 to −22.0	1	1.09	6	6.52	24.0 to 26.0	2	2.17	69	75.00
−22.0 to −20.0	0	0.00	6	6.52	26.0 to 28.0	2	2.17	71	77.17
−20.0 to −18.0	0	0.00	6	6.52	28.0 to 30.0	2	2.17	73	79.35
−18.0 to −16.0	0	0.00	6	6.52	30.0 to 32.0	5	5.43	78	84.78
−16.0 to −14.0	1	1.09	7	7.61	32.0 to 34.0	5	5.43	83	90.22
−14.0 to −12.0	0	0.00	7	7.61	34.0 to 36.0	0	0.00	83	90.22
−12.0 to −10.0	4	4.35	11	11.96	36.0 to 38.0	4	4.35	87	94.57
−10.0 to −8.0	7	7.61	18	19.57	38.0 to 40.0	0	0.00	87	94.57
−8.0 to −6.0	1	1.09	19	20.65	40.0 to 42.0	0	0.00	87	94.57
−6.0 to −4.0	1	1.09	20	21.74	42.0 to 44.0	2	2.17	89	96.74
−4.0 to −2.0	1	1.09	21	22.83	44.0 to 46.0	0	0.00	89	96.74
−2.0 to 0.0	3	3.26	24	26.09	46.0 to 48.0	1	1.09	90	97.83
0.0 to 2.0	3	3.26	27	29.35	48.0 to 50.0	0	0.00	90	97.83
2.0 to 4.0	1	1.09	28	30.43	50.0 to 52.0	0	0.00	90	97.83
					52.0 to 54.0	2	2.17	92	100.00

Note: The lower class limit is the weak inequality (≤) and the upper class limit is the strong inequality (<). Cumulative relative frequency totals reflect calculations using full precision, with results rounded to two decimal places.

Sources: Ibbotson Associates and S&P Dow Jones Indices LLC.

Exhibit 4 Frequency Distribution for the Monthly Total Return on the S&P 500, January 1926 to December 2017

Return Interval (%)	Absolute Frequency	Relative Frequency (%)	Cumulative Absolute Frequency	Cumulative Relative Frequency (%)
−30.0 to −28.0	1	0.09	1	0.09
−28.0 to −26.0	0	0.00	1	0.09
−26.0 to −24.0	1	0.09	2	0.18
−24.0 to −22.0	1	0.09	3	0.27
−22.0 to −20.0	2	0.18	5	0.45
−20.0 to −18.0	2	0.18	7	0.63
−18.0 to −16.0	3	0.27	10	0.91
−16.0 to −14.0	2	0.18	12	1.09
−14.0 to −12.0	6	0.54	18	1.63
−12.0 to −10.0	7	0.63	25	2.26
−10.0 to −8.0	23	2.08	48	4.35
−8.0 to −6.0	35	3.17	83	7.52
−6.0 to −4.0	60	5.43	143	12.95
−4.0 to −2.0	102	9.24	245	22.19
−2.0 to 0.0	166	15.04	411	37.23
0.0 to 2.0	240	21.74	651	58.97
2.0 to 4.0	190	17.21	841	76.18
4.0 to 6.0	143	12.95	984	89.13
6.0 to 8.0	64	5.80	1,048	94.93
8.0 to 10.0	26	2.36	1,074	97.28
10.0 to 12.0	15	1.36	1,089	98.64
12.0 to 14.0	6	0.54	1,095	99.18
14.0 to 16.0	2	0.18	1,097	99.37
16.0 to 18.0	3	0.27	1,100	99.64
18.0 to 20.0	0	0.00	1,100	99.64
20.0 to 22.0	0	0.00	1,100	99.64
22.0 to 24.0	0	0.00	1,100	99.64
24.0 to 26.0	1	0.09	1,101	99.73
26.0 to 28.0	0	0.00	1,101	99.73
28.0 to 30.0	0	0.00	1,101	99.73
30.0 to 32.0	0	0.00	1,101	99.73
32.0 to 34.0	0	0.00	1,101	99.73
34.0 to 36.0	0	0.00	1,101	99.73
36.0 to 38.0	0	0.00	1,101	99.73
38.0 to 40.0	2	0.18	1,103	99.91
40.0 to 42.0	0	0.00	1,103	99.91
42.0 to 44.0	1	0.09	1,104	100.00

Note: The lower class limit is the weak inequality (≤) and the upper class limit is the strong inequality (<). The relative frequency is the absolute frequency or cumulative frequency divided by the total number of observations. Cumulative relative frequency totals reflect calculations using full precision, with results rounded to two decimal places.

(continued)

Exhibit 4 (Continued)

Sources: Ibbotson Associates and S&P Dow Jones Indices LLC.

The advantage of a frequency distribution is evident in Exhibit 4, which tells us that the vast majority of observations (739/1,104 = 67 percent) lie in the four intervals spanning −2 percent to +6 percent. Altogether, we have 411 negative returns and 693 positive returns. Almost 63 percent of the monthly outcomes are positive. Looking at the cumulative relative frequency in the last column, we see that the interval −2 percent to 0 percent shows a cumulative frequency of 37.23 percent, for an upper return limit of 0 percent. This means that 37.23 percent of the observations lie below the level of 0 percent. We can also see that not many observations are greater than +12 percent or less than −12 percent. Note that the frequency distributions of annual and monthly returns are not directly comparable. On average, we should expect the returns measured at shorter intervals (for example, months) to be smaller than returns measured over longer periods (for example, years).

Next, we construct a frequency distribution of average inflation-adjusted returns over 1900–2010 for 19 major equity markets.

EXAMPLE 2

Constructing a Frequency Distribution

How have equities rewarded investors in different countries in the long run? To answer this question, we could examine the average annual returns directly.[9] The worth of a nominal level of return depends on changes in the purchasing power of money, however, and internationally there have been a variety of experiences with price inflation. It is preferable, therefore, to compare the average real or inflation-adjusted returns earned by investors in different countries. Dimson, Marsh, and Staunton (2011) presented authoritative evidence on asset returns in 19 countries for the 111 years 1900–2010. Exhibit 5 excerpts their findings for average inflation-adjusted returns.

Exhibit 5 Real (Inflation-Adjusted) Equity Returns: Nineteen Major Equity Markets, 1900–2017

Country	Arithmetic Mean (%)
Australia	8.3
Belgium	5.3
Canada	7.1
Denmark	7.4
Finland	9.3
France	5.8
Germany	8.2
Ireland	7.0

9 The average or arithmetic mean of a set of values equals the sum of the values divided by the number of values summed. To find the arithmetic mean of 111 annual returns, for example, we sum the 111 annual returns and then divide the total by 111. Among the most familiar of statistical concepts, the arithmetic mean is explained in more detail later in the reading.

Exhibit 5 (Continued)

Country	Arithmetic Mean (%)
Italy	6.0
Japan	8.8
Netherlands	7.2
New Zealand	8.0
Norway	7.3
South Africa	9.4
Spain	5.8
Sweden	8.0
Switzerland	6.3
United Kingdom	7.3
United States	8.4

Source: Dimson, Marsh, and Staunton (2018), Table 1.

Exhibit 6 summarizes the data in Exhibit 5 into five intervals spanning 5 percent to 10 percent. With nineteen markets, the relative frequency for the 5.0 to 6.0 percent return interval is calculated as 3/19 = 15.79 percent, for example.

Exhibit 6 Frequency Distribution of Average Real Equity Returns

Return Interval (%)	Absolute Frequency	Relative Frequency (%)	Cumulative Absolute Frequency	Cumulative Relative Frequency (%)
5.0 to 6.0	3	15.79	3	15.79
6.0 to 7.0	2	10.53	5	26.32
7.0 to 8.0	6	31.58	11	57.90
8.0 to 9.0	6	31.58	17	89.47
9.0 to 10	2	10.53	19	100.00

As Exhibit 6 shows, there is substantial variation internationally of average real equity returns. Nearly one-third of the observations fall in the 7.0 to 8.0 percent interval and nearly one-third fall in the 8.0 to 9.0 percent interval, each having a relative frequency of 31.58 percent. The other three intervals each has two or three observations.

THE GRAPHIC PRESENTATION OF DATA 4

A graphical display of data allows us to visualize important characteristics quickly. For example, we may see that the distribution is symmetrically shaped, and this finding may influence which probability distribution we use to describe the data. In this section, we discuss the histogram, the frequency polygon, and the cumulative frequency distribution as methods for displaying data graphically. We construct all of these graphic presentations with the information contained in the frequency distribution of the S&P 500 shown in either Exhibit 3 or Exhibit 4.

4.1 The Histogram

A histogram is the graphical equivalent of a frequency distribution.

- **Definition of Histogram.** A **histogram** is a bar chart of data that have been grouped into a frequency distribution.

The advantage of the visual display is that we can see quickly where most of the observations lie. To see how a histogram is constructed, look at the return interval 18% $\leq R_t <$ 20% in Exhibit 3. This interval has an absolute frequency of 6. Therefore, we erect a bar or rectangle with a height of 6 over that return interval on the horizontal axis. Continuing with this process for all other return intervals yields a histogram. Exhibit 7 presents the histogram of the annual total return series on the S&P 500 from 1926 to 2017.

Exhibit 7 Histogram of S&P 500 Annual Total Returns: 1926 to 2017

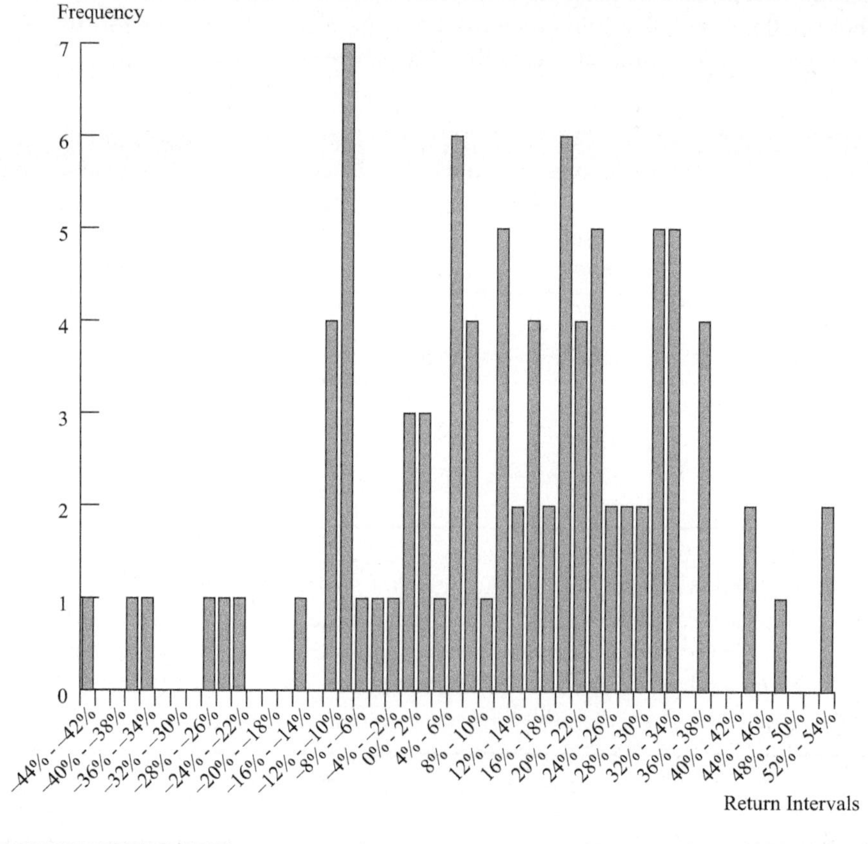

Note: Because of space limitations, only every other return interval is labeled below the horizontal axis.
Sources: Ibbotson Associates and S&P Dow Jones Indices LLC

In the histogram in Exhibit 7, the height of each bar represents the absolute frequency for each return interval. The return interval $-10\% \leq R_t < -8\%$ has a frequency of 7 and is represented by the tallest bar in the histogram. Because there are no gaps between the interval limits, there are no gaps between the bars of the histogram. Many of the return intervals have zero frequency; therefore, they have no height in the histogram.

Exhibit 8 presents the histogram for the distribution of monthly returns on the S&P 500. Somewhat more symmetrically shaped than the histogram of annual returns shown in Exhibit 7, this histogram also appears more bell-shaped than the distribution of annual returns.

Exhibit 8 Histogram of S&P 500 Monthly Total Returns: January 1926 to December 2017

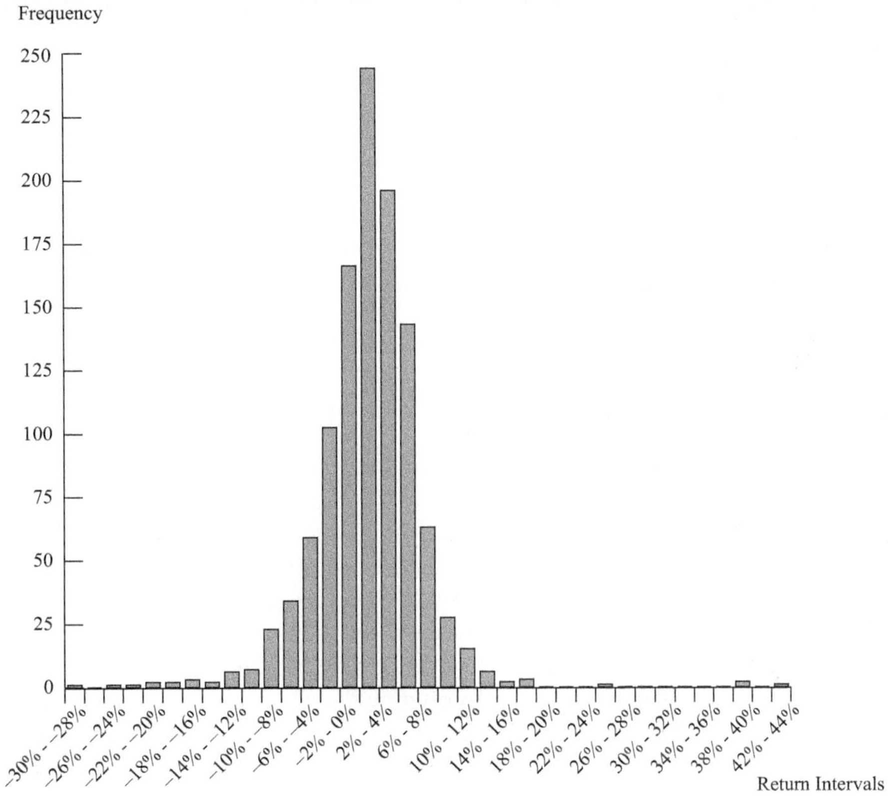

Sources: Ibbotson Associates and S&P Dow Jones Indices LLC

4.2 The Frequency Polygon and the Cumulative Frequency Distribution

Two other graphical tools for displaying data are the frequency polygon and the cumulative frequency distribution. To construct a **frequency polygon**, we plot the midpoint of each interval on the x-axis and the absolute frequency for that interval on the y-axis; we then connect neighboring points with a straight line. Exhibit 9 shows the frequency polygon for the 1,104 monthly returns for the S&P 500 from January 1926 to December 2017.

Exhibit 9 Frequency Polygon of S&P 500 Monthly Total Returns: January 1926 to December 2017

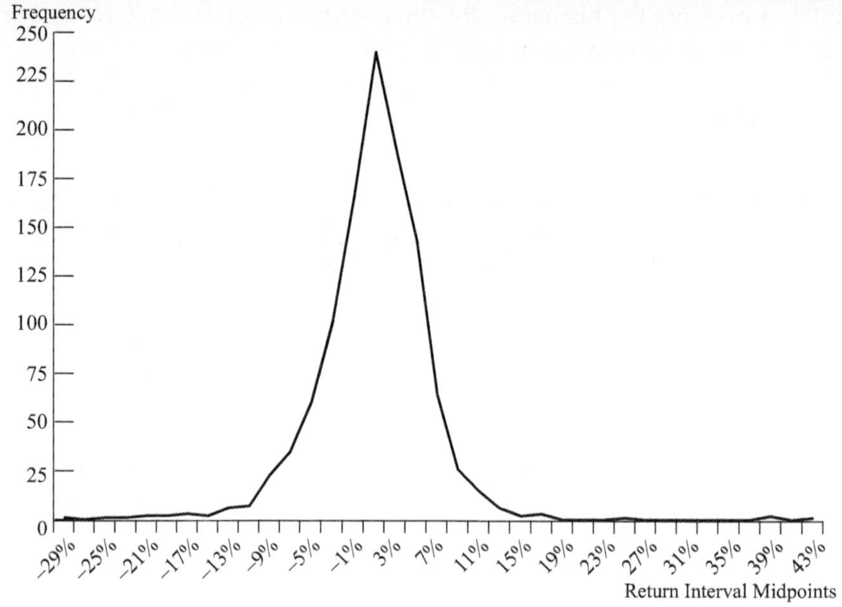

Sources: Ibbotson Associates and S&P Dow Jones Indices LLC

In Exhibit 9, we have replaced the bars in the histogram with points connected with straight lines. For example, the return interval 0 percent to 2 percent has an absolute frequency of 240. In the frequency polygon, we plot the return-interval midpoint of 1 percent and a frequency of 240. We plot all other points in a similar way.[10] This form of visual display adds a degree of continuity to the representation of the distribution.

Another form of line graph is the cumulative frequency distribution. Such a graph can plot either the cumulative absolute or cumulative relative frequency against the upper interval limit. The cumulative frequency distribution allows us to see how many or what percent of the observations lie below a certain value. To construct the cumulative frequency distribution, we graph the returns in the fourth or fifth column of Exhibit 4 against the upper limit of each return interval. Exhibit 10 presents a graph of the cumulative absolute distribution for the monthly returns on the S&P 500. Notice that the cumulative distribution tends to flatten out when returns are extremely negative or extremely positive. The steep slope in the middle of Exhibit 10 reflects the fact that most of the observations lie in the neighborhood of −2 percent to 6 percent.

10 Even though the upper limit on the interval is not a return falling in the interval, we still average it with the lower limit to determine the midpoint.

Exhibit 10 Cumulative Absolute Frequency Distribution of S&P 500 Monthly Total Returns: January 1926 to December 2017

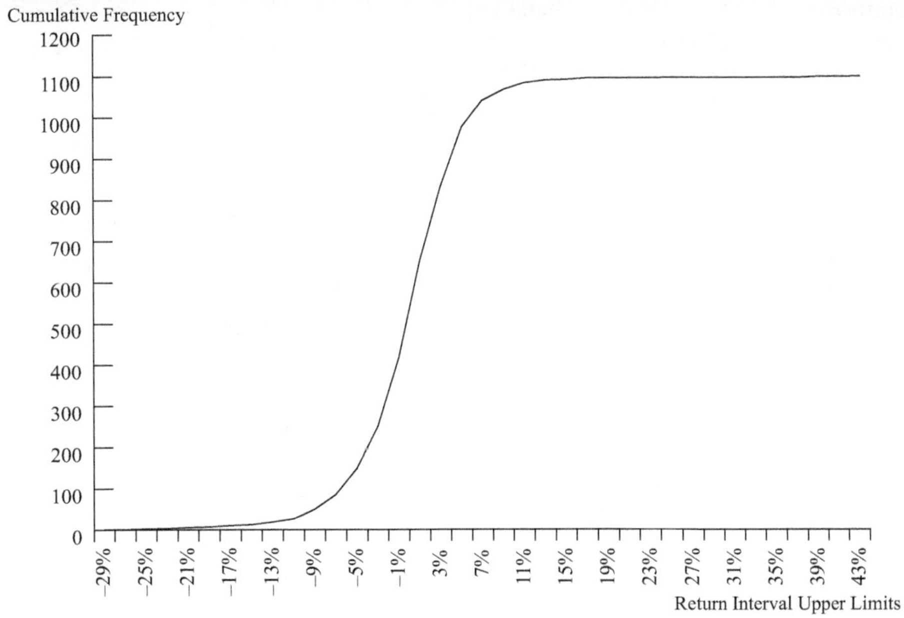

Sources: Ibbotson Associates and S&P Dow Jones Indices LLC

We can further examine the relationship between the relative frequency and the cumulative relative frequency by looking at the two return intervals reproduced in Exhibit 11. The first return interval (0 percent to 2 percent) has a cumulative relative frequency of 58.97 percent. The next return interval (2 percent to 4 percent) has a cumulative relative frequency of 76.18 percent. The change in the cumulative relative frequency as we move from one interval to the next is the next interval's relative frequency. For instance, as we go from the first return interval (0 percent to 2 percent) to the next return interval (2 percent to 4 percent), the change in the cumulative relative frequency is 76.18% − 58.97% = 17.21%. (Values in the exhibit have been rounded to two decimal places.) The fact that the slope is steep indicates that these frequencies are large. As you can see in the graph of the cumulative distribution, the slope of the curve changes as we move from the first return interval to the last. A fairly small slope for the cumulative distribution for the first few return intervals tells us that these return intervals do not contain many observations. You can go back to the frequency distribution in Exhibit 4 and verify that the cumulative absolute frequency is only 25 observations (the cumulative relative frequency is 2.39 percent) up to the 10th return interval (−12 percent to −10 percent). In essence, the slope of the cumulative absolute distribution at any particular interval is proportional to the number of observations in that interval.

Exhibit 11 Selected Class Frequencies for the S&P 500 Monthly Returns

Return Interval (%)	Absolute Frequency	Relative Frequency (%)	Cumulative Absolute Frequency	Cumulative Relative Frequency (%)
0.0 to 2.0	240	21.74	651	58.97
2.0 to 4.0	190	17.21	841	76.18

5 MEASURES OF CENTRAL TENDENCY

So far, we have discussed methods we can use to organize and present data so that they are more understandable. The frequency distribution of an asset class's return series, for example, reveals the nature of the risks that investors may encounter in a particular asset class. As an illustration, the histogram for the annual returns on the S&P 500 clearly shows that large positive and negative annual returns are common. Although frequency distributions and histograms provide a convenient way to summarize a series of observations, these methods are just a first step toward describing the data. In this section we discuss the use of quantitative measures that explain characteristics of data. Our focus is on measures of central tendency and other measures of location or location parameters. A **measure of central tendency** specifies where the data are centered. Measures of central tendency are probably more widely used than any other statistical measure because they can be computed and applied easily. **Measures of location** include not only measures of central tendency but other measures that illustrate the location or distribution of data.

In the following subsections we explain the common measures of central tendency—the arithmetic mean, the median, the mode, the weighted mean, and the geometric mean. We also explain other useful measures of location, including quartiles, quintiles, deciles, and percentiles.

5.1 The Arithmetic Mean

Analysts and portfolio managers often want one number that describes a representative possible outcome of an investment decision. The arithmetic mean is by far the most frequently used measure of the middle or center of data.

- **Definition of Arithmetic Mean.** The **arithmetic mean** is the sum of the observations divided by the number of observations.

We can compute the arithmetic mean for both populations and samples, known as the population mean and the sample mean, respectively.

5.1.1 *The Population Mean*

The population mean is the arithmetic mean computed for a population. If we can define a population adequately, then we can calculate the population mean as the arithmetic mean of all the observations or values in the population. For example, analysts examining the year-over-year growth in same-store sales of major US wholesale clubs might define the population of interest to include only three companies: BJ's Wholesale

Club, Costco Wholesale Corporation, and Sam's Club, part of Wal-Mart Stores.[11] As another example, if a portfolio manager's investment universe (the set of securities he or she must choose from) is the Nikkei 225 Index, the relevant population is the 225 shares on the First Section of the Tokyo Stock Exchange that compose the Nikkei.

- **Population Mean Formula.** The **population mean**, μ, is the arithmetic mean value of a population. For a finite population, the population mean is

$$\mu = \frac{\sum_{i=1}^{N} X_i}{N} \qquad (2)$$

where N is the number of observations in the entire population and X_i is the ith observation.

The population mean is an example of a parameter. The population mean is unique; that is, a given population has only one mean. To illustrate the calculation, we can take the case of the population mean of profit as a percentage of revenue of US companies running major wholesale clubs for 2018. During the year, profit as a percentage of revenue was about 0 percent for BJ's Wholesale club (according to https://investors.bjs.com/), and 2.1 percent and 2.0 percent for Costco Wholesale Corporation, and Wal-Mart Stores, respectively (according to the Fortune 500 list for 2018). Thus the population mean profit as a percentage of revenue was $\mu = (0.0 + 2.1 + 2.0)/3 = 4.1/3 = 1.37$ percent.

5.1.2 *The Sample Mean*

The sample mean is the arithmetic mean computed for a sample. Many times we cannot observe every member of a set; instead, we observe a subset or sample of the population. The concept of the mean can be applied to the observations in a sample with a slight change in notation.

- **Sample Mean Formula.** The **sample mean** or average, $\overline{X}$ (read "X-bar"), is the arithmetic mean value of a sample:

$$\overline{X} = \frac{\sum_{i=1}^{n} X_i}{n} \qquad (3)$$

where n is the number of observations in the sample.

Equation 3 tells us to sum the values of the observations (X_i) and divide the sum by the number of observations. For example, if a sample of price-to-earnings (P/E) multiples for six publicly traded companies contains the values 35, 30, 22, 18, 15, and 12, the sample mean P/E is 132/6 = 22. The sample mean is also called the arithmetic average.[12] As we discussed earlier, the sample mean is a statistic (that is, a descriptive measure of a sample).

Means can be computed for individual units or over time. For instance, the sample might be the return on equity (ROE) in a given year for the 100 companies in the FTSE Eurotop 100, an index of Europe's 100 largest companies. In this case, we calculate mean ROE in that year as an average across 100 individual units. When we examine the characteristics of some units at a specific point in time (such as ROE for the FTSE

11 A wholesale club implements a store format dedicated mostly to bulk sales in warehouse-sized stores to customers who pay membership dues. As of the early 2010s, those three wholesale clubs dominated the segment in the United States.

12 Statisticians prefer the term "mean" to "average." Some writers refer to all measures of central tendency (including the median and mode) as averages. The term "mean" avoids any possibility of confusion.

Eurotop 100), we are examining **cross-sectional data**. The mean of these observations is called a cross-sectional mean. On the other hand, if our sample consists of the historical monthly returns on the FTSE Eurotop 100 for the past five years, then we have **time-series data**. The mean of these observations is called a time-series mean. We will examine specialized statistical methods related to the behavior of time series in the reading on times-series analysis.

Next, we show an example of finding the sample mean return for 16 European equity markets for 2012. In this case, the mean is cross-sectional because we are averaging individual country returns.

EXAMPLE 3

Calculating a Cross-Sectional Mean

The MSCI EAFE (Europe, Australasia, and Far East) Index is a free float-adjusted market capitalization index designed to measure developed-market equity performance excluding the United States and Canada.[13] As of October 2018, the EAFE consisted of 21 developed market country indexes, including indexes for 15 European markets, 2 Australasian markets (Australia and New Zealand), 3 Far Eastern markets (Hong Kong SAR, Japan, and Singapore), and Israel.

Suppose we are interested in the local currency performance over the past five years of the 15 European markets in the EAFE as of 30 October, 2018. We want to find the sample mean total annual return across these 16 markets over the past five years. The return series reported in Exhibit 12 are in local currency (that is, returns are for investors living in the country). Because this return is not stated in any single investor's home currency, it is not a return any single investor would earn. Rather, it is an average of returns in local currencies of the 16 countries.

Exhibit 12 Total Annual Returns over Past Five Years for European Equity Markets, 30 October 2018

Market	Total Return in Local Currency (%)
Austria	5.44
Belgium	5.70
Denmark	10.05
Finland	9.94
France	7.43
Germany	5.01
Ireland	6.81
Italy	2.32
Netherlands	9.14
Norway	7.20
Portugal	−1.35
Spain	1.68
Sweden	8.16

13 The term "free float adjusted" means that the weights of companies in the index reflect the value of the shares actually available for investment.

Exhibit 12 (Continued)

Market	Total Return in Local Currency (%)
Switzerland	5.37
United Kingdom	4.46

Source: www.msci.com.

Using the data in Exhibit 12, calculate the sample mean return for the 15 equity markets.

Solution:

The calculation applies Equation 3 to the returns in Exhibit 12: (5.44 + 5.70 + 10.05 + 9.94 + 7.43 + 5.01 + 6.81 _ 2.32 + 9.14 + 7.20 − 1.35 + 1.68 + 8.16 +5.37 + 4.46)/15 = 187.36/15 = 5.82 percent.

In Example 3, we can verify that eight markets had returns less than the mean and seven had returns that were greater. We should not expect any of the actual observations to equal the mean, because sample means provide only a summary of the data being analyzed. Also, although in this example the number of values below the mean is quite close to the number of values above the mean, that need not be the case. As an analyst, you will often need to find a few numbers that describe the characteristics of the distribution. The mean is generally the statistic that you will use as a measure of the typical outcome for a distribution. You can then use the mean to compare the performance of two different markets. For example, you might be interested in comparing the stock market performance of investments in Pacific Rim countries with investments in European countries. You can use the mean returns in these markets to compare investment results.

5.1.3 *Properties of the Arithmetic Mean*

The arithmetic mean can be likened to the center of gravity of an object. Exhibit 13 expresses this analogy graphically by plotting nine hypothetical observations on a bar. The nine observations are 2, 4, 4, 6, 10, 10, 12, 12, and 12; the arithmetic mean is 72/9 = 8. The observations are plotted on the bar with various heights based on their frequency (that is, 2 is one unit high, 4 is two units high, and so on). When the bar is placed on a fulcrum, it balances only when the fulcrum is located at the point on the scale that corresponds to the arithmetic mean.

Exhibit 13 Center of Gravity Analogy for the Arithmetic Mean

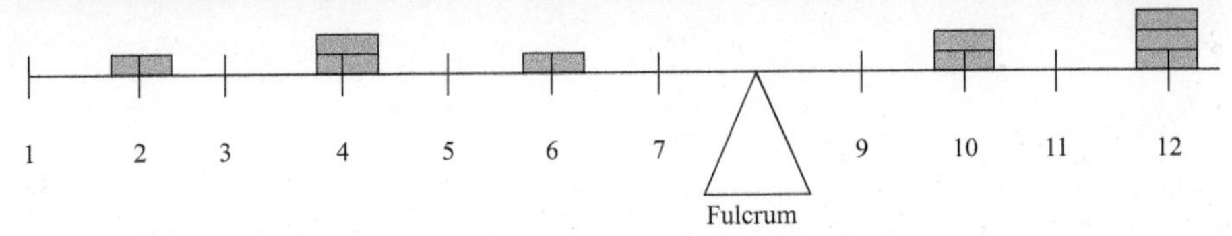

When the fulcrum is placed at 8, the bar is perfectly balanced.

As analysts, we often use the mean return as a measure of the typical outcome for an asset. As in the example above, however, some outcomes are above the mean and some are below it. We can calculate the distance between the mean and each outcome and call it a deviation. Mathematically, it is always true that the sum of the deviations around the mean equals 0. We can see this by using the definition of the arithmetic mean shown in Equation 3, multiplying both sides of the equation by n: $n\overline{X} = \sum_{i=1}^{n} X_i$.

The sum of the deviations from the mean can thus be calculated as follows:

$$\sum_{i=1}^{n}\left(X_i - \overline{X}\right) = \sum_{i=1}^{n} X_i - \sum_{i=1}^{n} \overline{X} = \sum_{i=1}^{n} X_i - n\overline{X} = 0$$

Deviations from the arithmetic mean are important information because they indicate risk. The concept of deviations around the mean forms the foundation for the more complex concepts of variance, skewness, and kurtosis, which we will discuss later in this reading.

An advantage of the arithmetic mean over two other measures of central tendency, the median and mode, is that the mean uses all the information about the size and magnitude of the observations. The mean is also easy to work with mathematically.

A property and potential drawback of the arithmetic mean is its sensitivity to extreme values. Because all observations are used to compute the mean, the arithmetic mean can be pulled sharply upward or downward by extremely large or small observations, respectively. For example, suppose we compute the arithmetic mean of the following seven numbers: 1, 2, 3, 4, 5, 6, and 1,000. The mean is 1,021/7 = 145.86 or approximately 146. Because the magnitude of the mean, 146, is so much larger than that of the bulk of the observations (the first six), we might question how well it represents the location of the data. In practice, although an extreme value or outlier in a financial dataset may only represent a rare value in the population, it may also reflect an error in recording the value of an observation, or an observation generated from a different population from that producing the other observations in the sample. In the latter two cases in particular, the arithmetic mean could be misleading. Perhaps the most common approach in such cases is to report the median in place of or in addition to the mean.[14] We discuss the median next.

14 Other approaches to handling extreme values involve variations of the arithmetic mean. The **trimmed mean** is computed by excluding a stated small percentage of the lowest and highest values and then computing an arithmetic mean of the remaining values. For example, a 5 percent trimmed mean discards the lowest 2.5 percent and the largest 2.5 percent of values and computes the mean of the remaining 95 percent of values. A trimmed mean is used in sports competitions when judges' lowest and highest scores are discarded in computing a contestant's score. A **Winsorized mean** assigns a stated percent of the lowest values equal to one specified low value, and a stated percent of the highest values equal to one specified high value, then computes a mean from the restated data. For example, a 95 percent Winsorized mean sets the bottom 2.5 percent of values equal to the 2.5th percentile value and the upper 2.5 percent of values equal to the 97.5th percentile value. (Percentile values are defined later.)

5.2 The Median

A second important measure of central tendency is the median.

- **Definition of Median.** The **median** is the value of the middle item of a set of items that has been sorted into ascending or descending order. In an odd-numbered sample of n items, the median occupies the $(n + 1)/2$ position. In an even-numbered sample, we define the median as the mean of the values of items occupying the $n/2$ and $(n + 2)/2$ positions (the two middle items).[15]

Earlier we gave the profit as a percentage of revenue of three wholesale clubs as 0.0, 2.0, and 2.1. With an odd number of observations ($n = 3$), the median occupies the $(n + 1)/2 = 4/2 = $ 2nd position. The median was 2.0 percent. The value of 2.0 percent is the "middlemost" observation: One lies above it, and one lies below it. Whether we use the calculation for an even- or odd-numbered sample, an equal number of observations lie above and below the median. A distribution has only one median.

A potential advantage of the median is that, unlike the mean, extreme values do not affect it. The median, however, does not use all the information about the size and magnitude of the observations; it focuses only on the relative position of the ranked observations. Calculating the median is also more complex; to do so, we need to order the observations from smallest to largest, determine whether the sample size is even or odd and, on that basis, apply one of two calculations. Mathematicians express this disadvantage by saying that the median is less mathematically tractable than the mean.

To demonstrate finding the median, we use the data from Example 3, reproduced in Exhibit 14 in ascending order of the annual total return over the past five years for European equities. Because this sample has 15 observations, the median the value in the sorted array that occupies the $(15 + 1)/2 = $ 8thposition.[16] Belgium's return occupies the eighth position with a return of 5.70 percent, and is the median. Note that the median is not influenced by extremely large or small outcomes. Had Portugal's total return been a much lower value or Denmark's total return a much larger value, the median would not have changed. Using a context that arises often in practice, Example 4 shows how to use the mean and median in a sample with extreme values.

Exhibit 14 Total Annual Returns over Past Five Years for European Equity Markets, 30 October 2018 (in Ascending Order)

No.	Market	Total Return in Local Currency (%)
1	Portugal	−1.35
2	Spain	1.68
3	Italy	2.32
4	United Kingdom	4.46
5	Germany	5.01
6	Switzerland	5.37
7	Austria	5.44

(continued)

15 The notation M_d is occasionally used for the median. Just as for the mean, we may distinguish between a population median and a sample median. With the understanding that a population median divides a population in half while a sample median divides a sample in half, we follow general usage in using the term "median" without qualification, for the sake of brevity.

16 If a sample has an even number of observations, the median is the mean of the two values in the middle. For example, if our sample in Example 3 had 16 countries instead of 15, the median would be the mean of the values in the sorted array that occupy the 8th and the 9th positions.

Exhibit 14 (Continued)

No.	Market	Total Return in Local Currency (%)
8	Belgium	5.70
9	Ireland	6.81
10	Norway	7.20
11	France	7.43
12	Sweden	8.16
13	Netherlands	9.14
14	Finland	9.94
15	Denmark	10.05

Source: www.msci.com.

EXAMPLE 4

Median and Arithmetic Mean: The Case of the Price–Earnings Ratio

Suppose a client asks you for a valuation analysis on the seven-stock US common stock portfolio given in Exhibit 15. The stocks are equally weighted in the portfolio. One valuation measure that you use is P/E, the ratio of share price to earnings per share (EPS). Many variations exist for the denominator in the P/E, but you are examining trailing twelve month (TTM) P/E defined as current price divided by the EPS for the company for the last twelve months ("EPS (TTM)" in the exhibit).[17] The values in Exhibit 15 are as of 31 October 2018. For comparison purposes, the average current trailing twelve month P/E on the companies in the S&P 500 index was 22.14 at that time.

Exhibit 15 P/Es for a Client Portfolio

Stock	EPS (TTM)	P/E (TTM)
Caterpillar, Inc.	5.18	23.44
Dunkin' Brands Group, Inc.	4.12	17.62
Ford Motor Company	1.69	5.65
General Dynamics	9.89	17.46
McDonald's Corporation	6.82	25.95
Salesforce.com	0.96	143.11
Spirit Airlines	1.40	22.95

Source: finance.yahoo.com.

17 For more information on price multiples, see the Level I CFA Program curriculum reading "Equity Valuation: Concepts and Basic Tools."

Using the data in Exhibit 15, address the following:

1 Calculate the arithmetic mean P/E.
2 Calculate the median P/E.
3 Evaluate the mean and median P/Es as measures of central tendency for the above portfolio.

Solution to 1:

The mean P/E is (23.44 + 17.62 + 5.65 + 17.46 25.95 + 143.11 + 22.95)/7 = 256.18/7 = 36.60.

Solution to 2:

The P/Es listed in ascending order are:

5.65	17.46	17.62	22.95	23.44	25.95	143.11

The sample has an odd number of observations with $n = 7$, so the median occupies the $(n + 1)/2 = 8/2 = $ 4th position in the sorted list. Therefore, the median P/E is 22.95.

Solution to 3:

Salesforce.com's P/E of approximately 143 tremendously influences the value of the portfolio's arithmetic mean P/E. The mean P/E of about 37 is much larger than the P/E of six of the seven stocks in the portfolio. The mean P/E also misleadingly suggests an orientation to stocks with high P/Es. The mean P/E of the stocks excluding Salesforce.com, or excluding the largest- and smallest-P/E stocks (Salesforce.com and Ford Motor Company), is below the average P/E of 22.14 for the companies in the S&P 500 Index. The median P/E of 22.95 appears to better represent the central tendency of the P/Es than the mean P/E of 36.60.

It frequently happens that when a company's EPS is quite low—at a low point in the business cycle, for example—its P/E is extremely high. The high P/E in those circumstances reflects an anticipated future recovery of earnings. Extreme P/E values need to be investigated and handled with care. For reasons related to this example, analysts often use the median of price multiples to characterize the valuation of industry groups.

5.3 The Mode

The third important measure of central tendency is the mode.

- **Definition of Mode.** The **mode** is the most frequently occurring value in a distribution.[18]

A distribution can have more than one mode, or even no mode. When a distribution has one most frequently occurring value, the distribution is said to be unimodal. If a distribution has two most frequently occurring values, then it has two modes and we say it is bimodal. If the distribution has three most frequently occurring values, then it is trimodal. When all the values in a data set are different, the distribution has no mode because no value occurs more frequently than any other value.

18 The notation M_o is occasionally used for the mode. Just as for the mean and the median, we may distinguish between a population mode and a sample mode. With the understanding that a population mode is the value with the greatest probability of occurrence, while a sample mode is the most frequently occurring value in the sample, we follow general usage in using the term "mode" without qualification, for the sake of brevity.

Stock return data and other data from continuous distributions may not have a modal outcome. When such data are grouped into intervals, however, we often find an interval (possibly more than one) with the highest frequency: the **modal interval** (or intervals). For example, the frequency distribution for the monthly returns on the S&P 500 has a modal interval of 0 percent to 2 percent, as shown in Exhibit 8; this return interval has 240 observations out of a total of 1,104. The modal interval always has the highest bar in the histogram.

The mode is the only measure of central tendency that can be used with nominal data. When we categorize mutual funds into different styles and assign a number to each style, the mode of these categorized data is the most frequent mutual fund style.

5.4 Other Concepts of Mean

Earlier we explained the arithmetic mean, which is a fundamental concept for describing the central tendency of data. Other concepts of mean are very important in investments, however. In the following, we discuss such concepts.

EXAMPLE 5

Calculating a Mode

Exhibit 16 gives the credit ratings on senior unsecured debt as of November 2018 of six US department stores rated by Moody's Investors Service. In descending order of credit quality (increasing expected probability of default), Moody's ratings are Aaa, Aa1, Aa2, Aa3, A1, A2, A3, Baa1, Baa2, Baa3, Ba1, Ba2, Ba3, B1, B2, B3, Caa1, Caa2, Caa3, Ca, and C.[19]

Exhibit 16 Senior Unsecured Debt Ratings: US Department Stores, November 2018

Company	Credit Rating
Dillard's, Inc.	Baa3
Kohl's Corporation	Baa2
Macy's, Inc.	Baa3
Neiman Marcus Group Ltd.	Caa3
Nordstrom, Inc.	Baa1
Penney, JC, Corporation, Inc.	Caa2

Source: www.moodys.com.

Using the data in Exhibit 16, address the following concerning the senior unsecured debt of US department stores:

1 State the modal credit rating.

2 State the median credit rating.

19 For more information on credit risk and credit ratings, see Petitt, Pinto, and Pirie (2015).

Solution to 1:

The group of companies represents six distinct credit ratings, ranging from Baa1 to Caa3. To make our task easy, we first organize the ratings into a frequency distribution.

Exhibit 17 Senior Unsecured Debt Ratings: US Department Stores, Distribution of Credit Ratings

Credit Rating	Frequency
Baa1	1
Baa2	1
Baa3	2
Caa2	1
Caa3	1

Credit rating Baa3 has a frequency of 2, and the other four ratings have a frequency of 1. Therefore, the credit rating of US department stores in November 2018 was unimodal, with Baa3 being the mode. Moody's considers bonds rated Baa to be of moderate credit risk, Ba to be of substantial credit risk, and B to be of high credit risk.

Solution to 2:

For the group $n = 6$, an odd number. The group's median occupies the mean of the $6/2 = 3$rd and $8/2 = 4$th position. We see from Exhibit 17 that Baa3 occupies both the third and the fourth positions. Therefore the median credit rating at November 2018 was Baa3.

5.4.1 *The Weighted Mean*

The concept of weighted mean arises repeatedly in portfolio analysis. In the arithmetic mean, all observations are equally weighted by the factor $1/n$ (or $1/N$). In working with portfolios, we need the more general concept of weighted mean to allow different weights on different observations.

To illustrate the weighted mean concept, an investment manager with $100 million to invest might allocate $70 million to equities and $30 million to bonds. The portfolio has a weight of 0.70 on stocks and 0.30 on bonds. How do we calculate the return on this portfolio? The portfolio's return clearly involves an averaging of the returns on the stock and bond investments. The mean that we compute, however, must reflect the fact that stocks have a 70 percent weight in the portfolio and bonds have a 30 percent weight. The way to reflect this weighting is to multiply the return on the stock investment by 0.70 and the return on the bond investment by 0.30, then sum the two results. This sum is an example of a weighted mean. It would be incorrect to take an arithmetic mean of the return on the stock and bond investments, equally weighting the returns on the two asset classes.

Consider a portfolio invested in Canadian stocks and bonds. The stock component of the portfolio includes the RBC Canadian Index Fund, which tracks the performance of the S&P/TSX Composite Total Return Index. The bond component of the portfolio includes the RBC Bond Fund, which invests in high-quality fixed-income securities issued by Canadian governments and corporations. The portfolio manager allocates 60 percent of the portfolio to the Canadian stock fund and 40 percent to the Canadian bond fund. Exhibit 18 presents total returns for these funds for a five-year period.

Exhibit 18 Returns for Canadian Equity and Bond Funds

Year	Equity Fund (%)	Bond Fund (%)
Year 1	−33.1	−0.1
Year 2	34.1	11.0
Year 3	16.8	6.4
Year 4	−9.2	8.4
Year 5	6.4	3.8

Source: funds.rbcgam.com.

- **Weighted Mean Formula.** The **weighted mean** $\overline{X}_w$ (read "*X*-bar sub-*w*"), for a set of observations $X_1, X_2, ..., X_n$ with corresponding weights of $w_1, w_2, ..., w_n$ is computed as

$$\overline{X}_w = \sum_{i=1}^{n} w_i X_i \tag{4}$$

where the sum of the weights equals 1; that is, $\sum_i w_i = 1$.

In the context of portfolios, a positive weight represents an asset held long and a negative weight represents an asset held short.[20]

The return on the portfolio under consideration is the weighted average of the return on the Canadian stock fund and the Canadian bond fund (the weight of the stock fund is 0.60; that of the bond fund is 0.40). We find, using Equation 4, that

$$\begin{aligned}\text{Portfolio return for Year 1} &= w_{\text{stock}}R_{\text{stock}} + w_{\text{bonds}}R_{\text{bonds}} \\ &= 0.60(-33.1) + 0.40(-0.1) \\ &= -19.9\%\end{aligned}$$

It should be clear that the correct mean to compute in this example is the weighted mean and not the arithmetic mean. If we had computed the arithmetic mean for Year 1, we would have calculated a return equal to ½(−33.1%) + ½(−0.1%) = (−33.1% − 0.1%)/2 = −16.6%. Given that the portfolio manager invested 60 percent in stocks and 40 percent in bonds, the arithmetic mean would underweight the investment in stocks and overweight the investment in bonds, resulting in a number for portfolio return that is too high by 3.3 percentage points (−16.6% − (−19.9%) = −16.6% + 19.9%).

Now suppose that the portfolio manager maintains constant weights of 60 percent in stocks and 40 percent in bonds for all five years. This method is called a constant-proportions strategy. Because value is price multiplied by quantity, price fluctuation causes portfolio weights to change. As a result, the constant-proportions strategy

20 The formula for the weighted mean can be compared to the formula for the arithmetic mean. For a set of observations $X_1, X_2, ..., X_n$, let the weights $w_1, w_2, ..., w_n$ all equal $1/n$. Under this assumption, the formula for the weighted mean is $(1/n)\sum_{i=1}^{n} X_i$. This is the formula for the arithmetic mean. Therefore, the arithmetic mean is a special case of the weighted mean in which all the weights are equal.

requires rebalancing to restore the weights in stocks and bonds to their target levels. Assuming that the portfolio manager is able to accomplish the necessary rebalancing, we can compute the portfolio returns in Years 2, 3, 4, and 5 with Equation 4 as follows:

Portfolio return for Year 2 = 0.60(34.1) + 0.40(11.0) = 24.9%

Portfolio return for Year 3 = 0.60(16.8) + 0.40(6.4) = 12.6%

Portfolio return for Year 4 = 0.60(−9.2) + 0.40(8.4) = −2.2%

Portfolio return for Year 5 = 0.60(6.4) + 0.40(3.8) = 5.4%

We can now find the time-series mean of the returns for Year 1 through Year 5 using Equation 3 for the arithmetic mean. The time-series mean total return for the portfolio is (−19.9 + 24.9 + 12.6 − 2.2 + 5.4)/5 = 20.8/5 = 4.2 percent.

Instead of calculating the portfolio time-series mean return from portfolio annual returns, we can calculate the arithmetic mean stock and bond fund returns for the five years and then apply the portfolio weights of 0.60 and 0.40, respectively, to those values. The mean stock fund return is (−33.1 + 34.1 + 16.8 − 9.2 + 6.4)/5 = 15.0/5 = 3.0 percent. The mean bond fund return is (−0.1 + 11.0 + 6.4 + 8.4 + 3.8)/ 5 = 29.5/5 = 5.9 percent. Therefore, the mean total return for the portfolio is 0.60(3.0) + 0.40(5.9) = 4.2 percent, which agrees with our previous calculation.

EXAMPLE 6

Portfolio Return as a Weighted Mean

Exhibit 19 gives information on the asset allocation of the pension plan of the Canadian Broadcasting Corporation in 2017 as well as the one-year returns on these asset classes in 2017.[21]

Exhibit 19 Asset Allocation for the Pension Plan of the Canadian Broadcasting Corporation in 2017

Asset Class	Asset Allocation (Weight)	Asset Class Return (%)
Cash and short-term investments	4.7	1.2
Nominal bonds	29.0	8.0
Real return bonds	11.8	1.2
Canadian equities	10.5	8.2
Global equities	24.8	15.4
Strategic investments	19.0	15.6
Bond overlay	0.2	5.7

Source: Canadian Broadcasting Corporation Pension Plan, 2017 Annual Report

Using the information in Exhibit 19, calculate the mean return earned by the pension plan in 2017.

21 In Exhibit 19, strategic investments include investments in property, private equity, and hedge fund investments. Bond overlay consists of derivatives used to hedge interest rate and inflation changes.

Solution:

Converting the percent asset allocation to decimal form, we find the mean return as a weighted average of the asset class returns. We have

$$\begin{aligned}\text{Mean portfolio return} &= 0.047(1.2\%) + 0.290(8.0\%) + 0.118(1.2\%)\\ &\quad + 0.105(8.2\%) + 0.248(15.4\%) + 0.190(15.6\%)\\ &\quad + 0.002(5.7\%)\\ &= 0.056\% + 2.320\% + 0.142\% + 0.861\% + 3.819\% +\\ &\quad 2.964\% + 0.011\%\\ &= 10.2 \text{ percent}\end{aligned}$$

The previous examples illustrate the general principle that a portfolio return is a weighted sum. Specifically, a portfolio's return is the weighted average of the returns on the assets in the portfolio; the weight applied to each asset's return is the fraction of the portfolio invested in that asset.

Market indexes are computed as weighted averages. For market-capitalization indexes such as the CAC-40 in France or the TOPIX in Japan or the S&P 500 in the United States, each included stock receives a weight corresponding to its outstanding market value divided by the total market value of all stocks in the index.

Our illustrations of weighted mean use past data, but they might just as well use forward-looking data. When we take a weighted average of forward-looking data, the weighted mean is called **expected value**. Suppose we make one forecast for the year-end level of the S&P 500 assuming economic expansion and another forecast for the year-end level of the S&P 500 assuming economic contraction. If we multiply the first forecast by the probability of expansion and the second forecast by the probability of contraction and then add these weighted forecasts, we are calculating the expected value of the S&P 500 at year-end. If we take a weighted average of possible future returns on the S&P 500, we are computing the S&P 500's expected return. The probabilities must sum to 1, satisfying the condition on the weights in the expression for weighted mean, Equation 4.

5.4.2 *The Geometric Mean*

The geometric mean is most frequently used to average rates of change over time or to compute the growth rate of a variable. In investments, we frequently use the geometric mean to average a time series of rates of return on an asset or a portfolio, or to compute the growth rate of a financial variable such as earnings or sales. In the reading on the time value of money, for instance, we computed a sales growth rate. That growth rate was a geometric mean. Because of the subject's importance, in a later section we will return to the use of the geometric mean and offer practical perspectives on its use. The geometric mean is defined by the following formula.

- **Geometric Mean Formula.** The **geometric mean**, G, of a set of observations $X_1, X_2, \ldots, X_n$ is

$$G = \sqrt[n]{X_1 X_2 X_3 \ldots X_n} \quad \text{with } X_i \geq 0 \text{ for } i = 1,2,\ldots,n. \tag{5}$$

Equation 5 has a solution, and the geometric mean exists, only if the product under the radical sign is non-negative. We impose the restriction that all the observations X_i in Equation 5 are greater than or equal to zero. We can solve for the geometric mean using Equation 5 directly with any calculator that has an exponentiation key (on most calculators, y^x). We can also solve for the geometric mean using natural logarithms. Equation 5 can also be stated as

$$\ln G = \frac{1}{n}\ln\left(X_1 X_2 X_3 \ldots X_n\right)$$

or as

$$\ln G = \frac{\sum_{i=1}^{n} \ln X_i}{n}$$

When we have computed ln G, then $G = e^{\ln G}$ (on most calculators, the key for this step is e^x).

Risky assets can have negative returns up to −100 percent (if their price falls to zero), so we must take some care in defining the relevant variables to average in computing a geometric mean. We cannot just use the product of the returns for the sample and then take the nth root because the returns for any period could be negative. We must redefine the returns to make them positive. We do this by adding 1.0 to the returns expressed as decimals. The term $(1 + R_t)$ represents the year-ending value relative to an initial unit of investment at the beginning of the year. As long as we use $(1 + R_t)$, the observations will never be negative because the biggest negative return is −100 percent. The result is the geometric mean of $1 + R_t$; by then subtracting 1.0 from this result, we obtain the geometric mean of the individual returns R_t. For example, the returns on RBC Canadian Index Fund during a five-year period were given in Exhibit 18 as −0.331, 0.341, 0.168, −0.092, and 0.064, putting the returns into decimal form. Adding 1.0 to those returns produces 0.669, 1.341, 1.168, 0.908, and 1.064. Using Equation 5 we have $\sqrt[5]{(0.669)(1.341)(1.168)(0.908)(1.064)} = \sqrt[5]{1.012337} = 1.002455$.

This number is 1 plus the geometric mean rate of return. Subtracting 1.0 from this result, we have 1.002455 − 1.0 = 0.002455 or approximately 0.25 percent. The geometric mean return of RBC Canadian Index Fund during the five-year period was 0.25 percent.

An equation that summarizes the calculation of the geometric mean return, R_G, is a slightly modified version of Equation 5 in which the X_i represent "1 + return in decimal form." Because geometric mean returns use time series, we use a subscript t indexing time as well.

$$1 + R_G = \sqrt[T]{(1 + R_1)(1 + R_2)\ldots(1 + R_T)}$$

$$1 + R_G = \left[\prod_{t=1}^{T}(1 + R_t)\right]^{\frac{1}{T}}$$

which leads to the following formula.

- **Geometric Mean Return Formula.** Given a time series of holding period returns R_t, t = 1, 2, …, T, the geometric mean return over the time period spanned by the returns R_1 through R_T is

$$R_G = \left[\prod_{t=1}^{T}(1 + R_t)\right]^{\frac{1}{T}} - 1 \tag{6}$$

We can use Equation 6 to solve for the geometric mean return for any return data series. Geometric mean returns are also referred to as compound returns. If the returns being averaged in Equation 6 have a monthly frequency, for example, we may call the geometric mean monthly return the compound monthly return. The next example illustrates the computation of the geometric mean while contrasting the geometric and arithmetic means.

EXAMPLE 7

Geometric and Arithmetic Mean Returns (1)

As a mutual fund analyst, you are examining, in 2018, the most recent five years of total returns for two US large-cap value equity mutual funds.

Exhibit 20 Total Returns for Two Mutual Funds, 2013–2017

Year	Selected American Shares (SLASX)	T. Rowe Price Equity Income (PRFDX)
2013	34.90%	31.69%
2014	6.13	7.75
2015	2.69	−7.56
2016	11.66	18.25
2017	21.77	16.18

Source: performance.morningstar.com.

Based on the data in Exhibit 20, address the following:

1 Calculate the geometric mean return of SLASX.

2 Calculate the arithmetic mean return of SLASX and contrast it to the fund's geometric mean return.

3 Calculate the geometric mean return of PRFDX.

4 Calculate the arithmetic mean return of PRFDX and contrast it to the fund's geometric mean return.

Solution to 1:

Converting the returns on SLASX to decimal form and adding 1.0 to each return produces 1.3490, 1.0613, 1.0269, 1.1166, and 1.2177. We use Equation 6 to find SLASX's geometric mean return:

$$\begin{aligned} R_G &= \sqrt[5]{(1.3490)(1.0613)(1.0269)(1.1166)(1.2177)} - 1 \\ &= \sqrt[5]{1.999016} - 1 \\ &= 1.148585 - 1 \\ &= 14.86\% \end{aligned}$$

Solution to 2:

For SLASX, $\overline{R}$ = (34.90 + 6.13 + 2.69 − 11.66 +21.77)/ 5 = 77.15/5 = 15.43%. The arithmetic mean return for SLASX exceeds the geometric mean return by 15.43 − 14.86 = 0.57% or 57 basis points.

Solution to 3:

Converting the returns on PRFDX to decimal form and adding 1.0 to each return produces 1.3169, 1.0775, 0.9244. 1.1825, and 1.1618. We use Equation 6 to find PRFDX's geometric mean return:

$$R_G = \sqrt[5]{(1.3169)(1.0775)(0.9244)(1.1825)(1.1618)} - 1$$
$$= \sqrt[5]{1.802032} - 1$$
$$= 1.125000 - 1$$
$$= 12.50\%$$

Solution to 4:

PRFDX, $\overline{R}$ = (31.69 + 7.75 − 7.56 + 18.25 + 6.18)/5 = 66.31/5 = 13.26%. The arithmetic mean for PRFDX exceeds the geometric mean return by 13.26 − 12.50 = 0.76% or 76 basis points. The exhibit below summarizes the findings.

Exhibit 21 Mutual Fund Arithmetic and Geometric Mean Returns: Summary of Findings

Fund	Arithmetic Mean (%)	Geometric Mean (%)
SLASX	15.43	14.86
PRFDX	13.26	12.50

In Example 7, for both mutual funds, the geometric mean return was less than the arithmetic mean return. In fact, the geometric mean is always less than or equal to the arithmetic mean.[22] The only time that the two means will be equal is when there is no variability in the observations—that is, when all the observations in the series are the same.[23] In Example 7, there was variability in the funds' returns; thus for both funds, the geometric mean was strictly less than the arithmetic mean. In general, the difference between the arithmetic and geometric means increases with the variability in the period-by-period observations.[24] This relationship is also illustrated by Example 7. Casual inspection suggests that the returns of PRFDX are somewhat more variable than those of SLASX, and consequently, the spread between the arithmetic and geometric mean returns is larger for PRFDX (76 basis points) than for SLASX (57 basis points).[25] Arithmetic and geometric returns need not always rank funds similarly, however, in this example, SLASX has both higher arithmetic and geometric mean returns than PRFDX. However, the difference between the geometric mean returns of the two funds (2.36%) is greater than the difference between the arithmetic mean returns of the two funds (2.17%). How should the analyst interpret these results?

22 This statement can be proved using Jensen's inequality that the average value of a function is less than or equal to the function evaluated at the mean if the function is concave from below—the case for ln(X).

23 For instance, suppose the return for each of the three years is 10 percent. The arithmetic mean is 10 percent. To find the geometric mean, we first express the returns as $(1 + R_t)$ and then find the geometric mean: $[(1.10)(1.10)(1.10)]^{1/3} - 1.0 = 10$ percent. The two means are the same.

24 We will soon introduce standard deviation as a measure of variability. Holding the arithmetic mean return constant, the geometric mean return decreases for an increase in standard deviation.

25 We will introduce formal measures of variability later. But note, for example, the 15.31 percentage point swing in returns between 2013 and 2014 for PRFDX versus the 3.44 percentage point for SLASX.

The geometric mean return represents the growth rate or compound rate of return on an investment. One dollar invested in SLASX at the beginning of 2013 would have grown to (1.3490)(1.0613)(1.0269)(1.1166)(1.2177) = \$1.9990, which is equal to 1 plus the geometric mean return compounded over five periods: $[1 + 0.148585]^5 = (1.148585)^5$ = \$1.9990, confirming that the geometric mean is the compound rate of return. For PRFDX, one dollar would have grown to a smaller amount, (1.3169)(1.0775)(0.9244)(1.1825)(1.1618) = \$1.8020, equal to $(1.125000)^5$. With its focus on the profitability of an investment over a multiperiod horizon, the geometric mean is of key interest to investors. The arithmetic mean return, focusing on average single-period performance, is also of interest. Both arithmetic and geometric means have a role to play in investment management, and both are often reported for return series. Example 8 highlights these points in a simple context.

EXAMPLE 8

Geometric and Arithmetic Mean Returns (2)

A hypothetical investment in a single stock initially costs €100. One year later, the stock is trading at €200. At the end of the second year, the stock price falls back to the original purchase price of €100. No dividends are paid during the two-year period. Calculate the arithmetic and geometric mean annual returns.

Solution:

First, we need to find the Year 1 and Year 2 annual returns with Equation 1.

Return in Year 1 = 200/100 – 1 = 100%

Return in Year 2 = 100/200 – 1 = –50%

The arithmetic mean of the annual returns is (100% – 50%)/2 = 25%.

Before we find the geometric mean, we must convert the percentage rates of return to $(1 + R_t)$. After this adjustment, the geometric mean from Equation 6 is $\sqrt{2.0 \times 0.50} - 1 = 0$ percent.

The geometric mean return of 0 percent accurately reflects that the ending value of the investment in Year 2 equals the starting value in Year 1. The compound rate of return on the investment is 0 percent. The arithmetic mean return reflects the average of the one-year returns.

5.4.3 *The Harmonic Mean*

The arithmetic mean, the weighted mean, and the geometric mean are the most frequently used concepts of mean in investments. A fourth concept, the **harmonic mean**, $\overline{X}_H$, is appropriate in a limited number of applications.[26]

- **Harmonic Mean Formula.** The harmonic mean of a set of observations $X_1, X_2, \ldots, X_n$ is

$$\overline{X}_H = n \Big/ \sum_{i=1}^{n} (1/X_i) \qquad (7)$$

with $X_i > 0$ for $i = 1,2,\ldots,n$

26 The terminology "harmonic" arises from its use relative to a type of series involving reciprocals known as a harmonic series.

The harmonic mean is the value obtained by summing the reciprocals of the observations—terms of the form $1/X_i$—then averaging that sum by dividing it by the number of observations n, and, finally, taking the reciprocal of the average.

The harmonic mean may be viewed as a special type of weighted mean in which an observation's weight is inversely proportional to its magnitude. The harmonic mean is a relatively specialized concept of the mean that is appropriate when averaging ratios ("amount per unit") when the ratios are repeatedly applied to a fixed quantity to yield a variable number of units. The concept is best explained through an illustration. A well-known application arises in the investment strategy known as **cost averaging**, which involves the periodic investment of a fixed amount of money. In this application, the ratios we are averaging are prices per share at purchases dates, and we are applying those prices to a constant amount of money to yield a variable number of shares.

Suppose an investor purchases €1,000 of a security each month for $n = 2$ months. The share prices are €10 and €15 at the two purchase dates. What is the average price paid for the security?

In this example, in the first month we purchase €1,000/€10 = 100 shares and in the second month we purchase €1,000/€15 = 66.67, or 166.67 shares in total. Dividing the total euro amount invested, €2,000, by the total number of shares purchased, 166.67, gives an average price paid of €2,000/166.67 = €12. The average price paid is in fact the harmonic mean of the asset's prices at the purchase dates. Using Equation 7, the harmonic mean price is 2/[(1/10) + (1/15)] = €12. The value €12 is less than the arithmetic mean purchase price (€10 + €15)/2 = €12.5. However, we could find the correct value of €12 using the weighted mean formula, where the weights on the purchase prices equal the shares purchased at a given price as a proportion of the total shares purchased. In our example, the calculation would be (100/166.67)€10.00 + (66.67/166.67)€15.00 = €12. If we had invested varying amounts of money at each date, we could not use the harmonic mean formula. We could, however, still use the weighted mean formula in a manner similar to that just described.

A mathematical fact concerning the harmonic, geometric, and arithmetic means is that unless all the observations in a data set have the same value, the harmonic mean is less than the geometric mean, which in turn is less than the arithmetic mean. In the illustration given, the harmonic mean price was indeed less than the arithmetic mean price.

OTHER MEASURES OF LOCATION: QUANTILES

6

Having discussed measures of central tendency, we now examine an approach to describing the location of data that involves identifying values at or below which specified proportions of the data lie. For example, establishing that 25, 50, and 75 percent of the annual returns on a portfolio are at or below the values –0.05, 0.16, and 0.25, respectively, provides concise information about the distribution of portfolio returns. Statisticians use the word **quantile** (or **fractile**) as the most general term for a value at or below which a stated fraction of the data lies. In the following, we describe the most commonly used quantiles—quartiles, quintiles, deciles, and percentiles—and their application in investments.

6.1 Quartiles, Quintiles, Deciles, and Percentiles

We know that the median divides a distribution in half. We can define other dividing lines that split the distribution into smaller sizes. **Quartiles** divide the distribution into quarters, **quintiles** into fifths, deciles into tenths, and **percentiles** into hundredths.

Given a set of observations, the *y*th percentile is the value at or below which *y* percent of observations lie. Percentiles are used frequently, and the other measures can be defined with respect to them. For example, the first quartile (Q_1) divides a distribution such that 25 percent of the observations lie at or below it; therefore, the first quartile is also the 25th percentile. The second quartile (Q_2) represents the 50th percentile, and the third quartile (Q_3) represents the 75th percentile because 75 percent of the observations lie at or below it.

When dealing with actual data, we often find that we need to approximate the value of a percentile. For example, if we are interested in the value of the 75th percentile, we may find that no observation divides the sample such that exactly 75 percent of the observations lie at or below that value. The following procedure, however, can help us determine or estimate a percentile. The procedure involves first locating the position of the percentile within the set of observations and then determining (or estimating) the value associated with that position.

Let P_y be the value at or below which *y* percent of the distribution lies, or the *y*th percentile. (For example, P_{18} is the point at or below which 18 percent of the observations lie; 100 − 18 = 82 percent are greater than P_{18}.) The formula for the position of a percentile in an array with *n* entries sorted in ascending order is

$$L_y = (n+1)\frac{y}{100} \qquad (8)$$

where *y* is the percentage point at which we are dividing the distribution and L_y is the location (*L*) of the percentile (P_y) in the array sorted in ascending order. The value of L_y may or may not be a whole number. In general, as the sample size increases, the percentile location calculation becomes more accurate; in small samples it may be quite approximate.

As an example of the case in which L_y is not a whole number, suppose that we want to determine the 60th percentile of annual returns for the past five years as of 30 October 2018(Q_3 or P_{75}) for the 15 European equity markets given in Exhibit 12. According to Equation 8, the position of the 60th percentile is L_{60} = (15 + 1)(60/100) = 9.60, or between the 9th and 10th items in Exhibit 14, which ordered the returns into ascending order. The 9th item in Exhibit 14 is the return to equities in Ireland, 6.81 percent. The 10th item is the return to equities in Norway, 7.20 percent. Reflecting the "0.60" in "9.60," we would conclude that P_{60} lies 60 percent of the distance between 6.81 percent and 7.20 percent.

To summarize:

- When the location, L_y, is a whole number, the location corresponds to an actual observation. For example, if we were determining the third quartile, then L_y would have been L_{75} = (15 + 1)(75/100) = 12, and the third quartile would be $P_{75} = X_{12}$, where X_i is defined as the value of the observation in the *i*th ($i = L_{75}$) position of the data sorted in ascending order (i.e., P_{75} =8.16).
- When L_y is not a whole number or integer, L_y lies between the two closest integer numbers (one above and one below), and we use **linear interpolation** between those two places to determine P_y. Interpolation means estimating an unknown value on the basis of two known values that surround it (lie above and below it); the term "linear" refers to a straight-line estimate. Returning to the calculation of P_{60} for the equity returns, we found that L_y = 9.60; the next lower whole number is 9 and the next higher whole number is 10. Using linear interpolation, $P_{60} \approx X_9 + (9.60 - 9)\,(X_{10} - X_9)$. As above, in the 9th position is the return to equities in Ireland, so X_9 = 6.81 percent; X_{10} = 7.20 percent, the return to equities in Norway. Thus our estimate is $P_{60} \approx X_9 + (9.60 - 9.00)(X_{10} - X_9)$ = 6.81 + 0.60 [7.20 − 6.81] = 6.81 + 0.60(0.39) = 6.81 + 0.23 = 7.04 percent. In words, 6.81 and 7.20 bracket P_{60} from below and above, respectively. Because

9.60 − 9 = 0.60, using linear interpolation we move 60 percent of the distance from 6.81 to 7.20 as our estimate of P_{60}. We follow this pattern whenever L_y is a non-integer: The nearest whole numbers below and above L_y establish the positions of observations that bracket P_y and then interpolate between the values of those two observations.

Example 9 illustrates the calculation of various quantiles for the dividend yield on the components of a major European equity index.

EXAMPLE 9

Calculating Percentiles, Quartiles, and Quintiles

The EURO STOXX 50 is an index of 50 publicly traded companies, which provides a blue-chip representation of supersector leaders in the Eurozone. Exhibit 22 shows the market capitalization on the 50 component stocks in the index in November 2018. The market capitalizations are ranked in ascending order.

Exhibit 22 Market Capitalizations of the Components of the EURO STOXX 50

No.	Company	Market Cap (Euro Billion)
1	RWE	9.9
2	Carrefour	12.2
3	E.ON	15.5
4	Inditex	15.5
5	Unibail Rodamco	16.1
6	Deutsche Bank	16.7
7	Saint Gobain	17.7
8	Arcelor Mittal	19.5
9	Repsol S.A.	19.9
10	CRH	20.1
11	Banco Bilbao Vizcaya Argentaria	22.2
12	Assicurazioni Generali	22.2
13	Societe Generale	24.2
14	Engie	26.5
15	Essilor International	27.4
16	Vivendi	28.2
17	Engie	28.4
18	Intesa SanPaolo	30.3
19	Philips	31.5
20	Telefonica SA	33.0
21	Air Liquide	33.4
22	Munchener Ruckversicherungs AG	33.7
23	Banco Santander	35.4
24	Schneider Electric	35.4
25	Orange	36.6

(continued)

Exhibit 22 (Continued)

No.	Company	Market Cap (Euro Billion)
26	Elberdrola	38.4
27	Danone	40.2
28	ING Groep	40.2
29	ENEL	40.8
30	Volkswagon	43.0
31	Vinci	45.5
32	BMW	45.9
33	AXA	52.2
34	Daimler	55.8
35	Bayer	56.1
36	ENI	56.9
37	BNP Paribas	57.8
38	Unilever	61.9
39	BASF	62.5
40	Deutsche Telekom	62.6
41	ASML Holdings	63.4
42	UniCredit	65.5
43	Allianz	83.3
44	Siemens	89.6
45	Anheuser-Busch Inbev	104.7
46	Sanofi-Aventis	104.7
47	SAP AG	116.3
48	LOréal	120.8
49	Total	122.9
50	LVMH	136.5

Source: https://www.dividendmax.com/market-index-constituents/euro-stoxx-50 accessed 01 November 2018.

Using the data in Exhibit 22, address the following:

1 Calculate the 10th and 90th percentiles.
2 Calculate the first, second, and third quartiles.
3 State the value of the median.
4 How many quintiles are there, and to what percentiles do the quintiles correspond?
5 Calculate the value of the first quintile.

Solution to 1:

In this example, $n = 50$. Using Equation 8, $L_y = (n + 1)y/100$ for position of the yth percentile, so for the 10th percentile we have

$$L_{10} = (50 + 1)(10/100) = 5.1$$

L_{10} is between the fifth and sixth observations with values $X_5 = 16.1$ and $X_6 = 16.7$. The estimate of the 10th percentile (first decile) for dividend yield is

$$P_{10} \approx X_5 + (5.1 - 5)(X_6 - X_5) = 16.1 + 0.1(16.7 - 16.1)$$
$$= 16.1 + 0.1(0.6) = 16.16$$

For the 90th percentile,

$$L_{90} = (50 + 1)(90/100) = 45.9$$

L_{90} is between the 45th and 46th observations with values $X_{45} = 104.7$ and $X_{46} = 104.7$, respectively. The two values are the same. Therefore, the estimate of the 90th percentile (ninth decile) is 104.7. If the values were different, we would have computed the 90th percentile using the following formula.

$$P_{90} \approx X_{45} + (45.9 - 45)(X_{46} - X_{45})$$

Solution to 2:

The first, second, and third quartiles correspond to P_{25}, P_{50}, and P_{75}, respectively.

L_{25}	$= (51)(25/100) = 12.75$	L_{25} is between the 12th and 13th entries with values $X_{12} = 22.2$ and $X_{13} = 24.2$.
P_{25}	$= Q_1 \approx X_{12} + (12.75 - 12)(X_{13} - X_{12})$ $= 22.2 + 0.75(24.2 - 22.2)$ $= 22.2 + 0.75(2) = 23.7$	
L_{50}	$= (51)(50/100) = 25.5$	L_{50} is between the 25th and 26th entries with values, $X_{25} = 36.6$ and $X_{26} = 38.4$.
P_{50}	$= Q_2 \approx X_{25} + (25.50 - 25)(X_{26} - X_{25})$ $= 36.6 + 0.50(38.4 - 36.6)$ $= 36.6 + 0.50(1.8) = 37.5$	
L_{75}	$= (51)(75/100) = 38.25$	L_{75} is between the 38th and 39th entries with values $X_{38} = 61.9$ and $X_{39} = 62.5$.
P_{75}	$= Q_3 \approx X_{38} + (38.25 - 38)(X_{39} - X_{38})$ $= 61.9 + 0.25(62.5 - 61.9)$ $= 61.9 + 0.25(0.6) = 62.05$	

Solution to 3:

The median is the 50th percentile, 37.5. This is the same value that we would obtain by taking the mean of the $n/2 = 50/2 = 25$th item and $(n + 2)/2 = 52/2 = 26$th items, consistent with the procedure given earlier for the median of an even-numbered sample.

Solution to 4:

There are five quintiles, and they are specified by P_{20}, P_{40}, P_{60}, and P_{80}.

Solution to 5:

The first quintile is P_{20}.

$L_{20} = (50 + 1)(20/100) = 10.2$ — L_{20} is between the 10th and 11th observations with values $X_{10} = 20.1$ and $X_{11} = 22.2$.

The estimate of the first quintile is

$$P_{20} \approx X_{10} + (10.2 - 10)(X_{11} - X_{10}) = 20.1 + 0.2(22.2 - 20.1)$$
$$= 20.1 + 0.2(2.1) = 20.52.$$

6.2 Quantiles in Investment Practice

In this section, we discuss the use of quantiles in investments. Quantiles are used in portfolio performance evaluation as well as in investment strategy development and research.

Investment analysts use quantiles every day to rank performance—for example, the performance of portfolios. The performance of investment managers is often characterized in terms of the quartile in which they fall relative to the performance of their peer group of managers. The Morningstar mutual fund star rankings, for example, associates the number of stars with percentiles of performance relative to similar-style mutual funds.

Another key use of quantiles is in investment research. Analysts refer to a group defined by a particular quantile as that quantile. For example, analysts often refer to the set of companies with returns falling below the 10th percentile cutoff point as the bottom return decile. Dividing data into quantiles based on some characteristic allows analysts to evaluate the impact of that characteristic on a quantity of interest. For instance, empirical finance studies commonly rank companies based on the market value of their equity and then sort them into deciles. The 1st decile contains the portfolio of those companies with the smallest market values, and the 10th decile contains those companies with the largest market value. Ranking companies by decile allows analysts to compare the performance of small companies with large ones.

We can illustrate the use of quantiles, in particular quartiles, in investment research using the example of Ibbotson et al. (2018). That study is an update of Ibbotson et al. (2013), which proposed an investment style based on liquidity—buying stocks of less liquid stocks and selling stocks of more liquid stocks. These studies compare the performance of this style with three already popular investment styles, which include (1) firm size (buying stocks of small firms and selling stocks of large firms), (2) value/growth (buying stocks of value firms, defined as firms for which the stock price is relatively low in relation to earnings per share, book value per share, or dividends per share, and selling stocks of growth firms, defined as firms for which the stock price is relatively high in relation to those same measures), and (3) momentum (buying stocks of firms with a high momentum in returns, or winners, and selling stocks of firms with a low momentum, or losers.)

Ibbotson et al. (2018) examined the top 3,500 US stocks by market capitalization for the period of 1971–2017. For each stock, they computed yearly measures of liquidity as the annual share turnover (the sum of the 12 monthly volumes divided by each month's shares outstanding), size as the year-end market capitalization, value as the trailing earnings-to-price ratio as of the year end, and momentum as the annual return. They assigned one-fourth of the total sample with the lowest liquidity in a year to Quartile 1 and the one-fourth with the highest liquidity in that year to Quartile 4. The stocks with the second-highest liquidity formed Quartile 3 and the stocks with the second-lowest liquidity, Quartile 2. Treating each quartile group as a portfolio composed of equally weighted stocks, they measured the returns on each liquidity quartile in the following year (so that the quartiles are constructed "before the fact".) The authors repeated this process for each of the other three investment styles (size, value, and momentum.) The results from Table 1 of their study are included in Exhibit 23. We have added a column with the spreads in returns from Quartile 1 to Quartile 4.

Exhibit 23 reports each investment style's geometric and arithmetic mean returns and standard deviation of returns for each quartile grouping. In each style, moving from Quartile 1 to Quartile 4, mean returns decrease. For example, the geometric mean return for the least liquid stocks is 15.16% and for the most liquid stocks is 7.70%. Only for the case of size does standard deviation decrease at each step moving from Quartile 1 to Quartile 4. Thus, the exhibit provides evidence that the investment styles generally having incremental value in explaining returns in relation to standard deviation. The authors conclude that liquidity appears to differentiate the returns approximately as well as the other styles.

Exhibit 23 Cross-Sectional Investment Style Returns (%) and Standard Deviations of Returns (%), 1972–2017

Investment Style	Q_1	Q_2	Q_3	Q_4	Spread in Return, Q1 to Q4
Size *(Q1 = micro; Q4 = large)*					
Geometric Mean	13.40	12.36	12.38	11.61	+1.79
Arithmetic Mean	16.49	14.90	14.40	13.11	+3.38
Standard deviation	26.13	23.63	21.01	17.67	
Value *(Q1 = value; Q4 = growth)*					
Geometric Mean	16.34	14.03	10.73	8.23	+8.11
Arithmetic Mean	18.62	15.70	12.73	11.86	+6.76
Standard deviation	22.47	19.34	20.50	28.24	
Momentum *(Q1 = winners; Q4 = losers)*					
Geometric Mean	13.17	14.60	13.74	7.89	+5.28
Arithmetic Mean	15.49	16.23	15.60	11.58	+3.91
Standard deviation	22.54	18.99	20.31	28.31	
Liquidity *(Q1 = low; Q4 = high)*					
Geometric Mean	15.16	14.19	12.45	7.70	+5.46
Arithmetic Mean	16.89	16.12	14.72	11.17	+5.72
Standard deviation	19.60	20.820	22.22	27.19	

Note: Each investment style portfolio contains as average of 742 stocks a year.
Source: Ibbotson et al. (2018)

To address the concern that liquidity may simply be a proxy for firm size, with investing in less liquid firms being equivalent to investing in small firms, the authors examined how less liquid stocks performed relative to more liquid stocks while controlling for firm size. This step involved constructing equally-weighted double-sorted portfolios in firm size and liquidity quartiles. That is, they constructed 16 different liquidity and size portfolios (4 × 4 = 16) and investigated the interaction between these two styles. The results from Table 2 of their article are included in Exhibit 24. We have added a column with the spreads in returns from Quartile 1 to Quartile 4 for each size category.

Exhibit 24 Mean Annual Returns (%) and Standard Deviations of Returns (%) of Size and Liquidity Quartile Portfolios, 1972–2017

Quartile	Q_1 (Low liquidity)	Q_2	Q_3	Q_4 (High liquidity)	Spread in Return, Q_1 to Q_4
Microcap					
Geometric Mean	16.05	15.68	9.57	0.11	+15.94
Arithmetic Mean	18.38	19.23	14.77	5.23	+13.15
Standard deviation	22.67	28.52	34.54	33.07	
Small cap					
Geometric Mean	15.65	14.32	12.26	6.00	+9.65
Arithmetic Mean	17.29	16.83	15.52	10.11	+7.18
Standard deviation	19.35	23.73	26.86	30.09	
Midcap					
Geometric Mean	14.03	13.88	12.89	8.40	+5.63
Arithmetic Mean	15.38	15.54	14.99	11.87	+3.51
Standard deviation	17.59	19.47	21.54	27.35	
Large cap					
Geometric Mean	11.44	12.28	11.97	9.07	+2.37
Arithmetic Mean	12.66	13.39	13.46	11.99	+0.67
Standard deviation	16.22	15.40	17.61	24.53	

Source: Ibbotson et al. (2018)

The exhibit shows that within the quartile with the smallest firms, the low-liquidity portfolio earned an annual geometric mean return of 16.05%, in contrast to the high-liquidity portfolio return of 0.11%, producing a liquidity effect of 15.94 percentage points (1,594 basis points). While the liquidity effect is strongest for the smallest firms, it does persist in other three size quartiles also. These results indicate that size does not capture liquidity (i.e., the liquidity effect holds regardless of size group).

7 MEASURES OF DISPERSION

As the well-known researcher Fischer Black has written, "[t]he key issue in investments is estimating expected return."[27] Few would disagree with the importance of expected return or mean return in investments: The mean return tells us where returns, and investment results, are centered. To completely understand an investment, however, we also need to know how returns are dispersed around the mean. **Dispersion** is the variability around the central tendency. If mean return addresses reward, dispersion addresses risk.

In this section, we examine the most common measures of dispersion: range, mean absolute deviation, variance, and standard deviation. These are all measures of **absolute dispersion**. Absolute dispersion is the amount of variability present without comparison to any reference point or benchmark.

27 Black (1993).

These measures are used throughout investment practice. The variance or standard deviation of return is often used as a measure of risk pioneered by Nobel laureate Harry Markowitz. Other measures of dispersion, mean absolute deviation and range, are also useful in analyzing data.

7.1 The Range

We encountered range earlier when we discussed the construction of frequency distribution. The simplest of all the measures of dispersion, range can be computed with interval or ratio data.

- **Definition of Range.** The **range** is the difference between the maximum and minimum values in a data set:

$$\text{Range} = \text{Maximum value} - \text{Minimum value} \quad (9)$$

As an illustration of range, the largest monthly return for the S&P 500 in the period from January 1926 to December 2017 is 42.56 percent (in April 1933) and the smallest is −29.73 percent (in September 1931). The range of returns is thus 72.29 percent [42.56 percent − (−29.73 percent)]. An alternative definition of range reports the maximum and minimum values. This alternative definition provides more information than does the range as defined in Equation 9.

One advantage of the range is ease of computation. A disadvantage is that the range uses only two pieces of information from the distribution. It cannot tell us how the data are distributed (that is, the shape of the distribution). Because the range is the difference between the maximum and minimum returns, it can reflect extremely large or small outcomes that may not be representative of the distribution.[28]

7.2 The Mean Absolute Deviation

Measures of dispersion can be computed using all the observations in the distribution rather than just the highest and lowest. The question is, how should we measure dispersion? Our previous discussion on properties of the arithmetic mean introduced the notion of distance or deviation from the mean $(X_i - \overline{X})$ as a fundamental piece of information used in statistics. We could compute measures of dispersion as the arithmetic average of the deviations around the mean, but we would encounter a problem: The deviations around the mean always sum to 0. If we computed the mean of the deviations, the result would also equal 0. Therefore, we need to find a way to address the problem of negative deviations canceling out positive deviations.

One solution is to examine the absolute deviations around the mean as in the mean absolute deviation.

- **Mean Absolute Deviation Formula.** The **mean absolute deviation** (MAD) for a sample is

$$\text{MAD} = \frac{\sum_{i=1}^{n} \left| X_i - \overline{X} \right|}{n} \quad (10)$$

where $\overline{X}$ is the sample mean and n is the number of observations in the sample.

28 Another distance measure of dispersion that we may encounter, the interquartile range, focuses on the middle rather than the extremes. The **interquartile range** (IQR) is the difference between the third and first quartiles of a data set: IQR = $Q_3 - Q_1$. The IQR represents the length of the interval containing the middle 50 percent of the data, with a larger interquartile range indicating greater dispersion, all else equal.

In calculating MAD, we ignore the signs of the deviations around the mean. For example, if $X_i = -11.0$ and $\bar{X} = 4.5$, the absolute value of the difference is $|-11.0 - 4.5| = |-15.5| = 15.5$. The mean absolute deviation uses all of the observations in the sample and is thus superior to the range as a measure of dispersion. One technical drawback of MAD is that it is difficult to manipulate mathematically compared with the next measure we will introduce, variance.[29] Example 10 illustrates the use of the range and the mean absolute deviation in evaluating risk.

EXAMPLE 10

The Range and the Mean Absolute Deviation

Having calculated mean returns for the two mutual funds in Example 7, the analyst is now concerned with evaluating risk.

Exhibit 20 Total Returns for Two Mutual Funds, 2013–2017 (Repeated)

Year	Selected American Shares (SLASX)	T. Rowe Price Equity Income (PRFDX)
2013	34.90%	31.69%
2014	6.13	7.75
2015	2.69	−7.56
2016	11.66	18.25
2017	21.77	16.18

Source: performance.morningstar.com.

Based on the data in Exhibit 20 on the previous page, answer the following:

1 Calculate the range of annual returns for (A) SLASX and (B) PRFDX, and state which mutual fund appears to be riskier based on these ranges.

2 Calculate the mean absolute deviation of returns on (A) SLASX and (B) PRFDX, and state which mutual fund appears to be riskier based on MAD.

Solution to 1:

A For SLASX, the largest return was 34.90 percent and the smallest was 2.69 percent. The range is thus 34.90 − 2.69 = 32.21%.

B For PFRDX, the range is 31.69 − (−7.56) = 39.25%. With a larger range of returns than SLASX, PRFDX appeared to be the riskier fund during the 2013–2017 period.

29 In some analytic work such as optimization, the calculus operation of differentiation is important. Variance as a function can be differentiated, but absolute value cannot.

Solution to 2:

A The arithmetic mean return for SLASX as calculated in Example 7 is 15.43 percent. The MAD of SLASX returns is

$$\text{MAD} = \frac{|34.90 - 15.43| + |6.13 - 15.43| + |2.69 - 15.43| + |11.66 - 15.43| + |21.77 - 15.43|}{5}$$

$$= \frac{19.47 + 9.30 + 12.74 + 3.77 + 6.34}{5}$$

$$= \frac{51.62}{5} = 10.32\%$$

B The arithmetic mean return for PRFDX as calculated in Example 7 is 13.26 percent. The MAD of PRFDX returns is

$$\text{MAD} = \frac{|31.69 - 13.26| + |7.75 - 13.26| + |-7.56 - 13.26| + |18.25 - 13.26| + |16.18 - 13.26|}{5}$$

$$= \frac{18.43 + 5.51 + 20.82 + 4.99 + 2.92}{5}$$

$$= \frac{52.67}{5} = 10.53\%$$

PRFDX, with a MAD of 10.53 percent, appears to be slightly riskier than SLASX, with a MAD of 10.32 percent.

7.3 Population Variance and Population Standard Deviation

The mean absolute deviation addressed the issue that the sum of deviations from the mean equals zero by taking the absolute value of the deviations. A second approach to the treatment of deviations is to square them. The variance and standard deviation, which are based on squared deviations, are the two most widely used measures of dispersion. **Variance** is defined as the average of the squared deviations around the mean. **Standard deviation** is the positive square root of the variance. The following discussion addresses the calculation and use of variance and standard deviation.

7.3.1 *Population Variance*

If we know every member of a population, we can compute the **population variance**. Denoted by the symbol σ^2, the population variance is the arithmetic average of the squared deviations around the mean.

- **Population Variance Formula.** The population variance is

$$\sigma^2 = \frac{\sum_{i=1}^{N}(X_i - \mu)^2}{N} \tag{11}$$

where μ is the population mean and N is the size of the population.

Given knowledge of the population mean, μ, we can use Equation 11 to calculate the sum of the squared differences from the mean, taking account of all N items in the population, and then to find the mean squared difference by dividing the sum by N. Whether a difference from the mean is positive or negative, squaring that difference results in a positive number. Thus variance takes care of the problem of negative deviations from the mean canceling out positive deviations by the operation of squaring those deviations. The profit as a percentage of revenue for BJ's Wholesale Club, Costco, and Walmart was given earlier as 0.0, 2.1, and 2.0, respectively. We calculated the mean profit as a percentage of revenue as 1.37. Therefore, the population variance of the profit as a percentage of revenue is $(1/3)[(0.0 - 1.37)^2 + (2.1 - 1.37)^2 + (2.0 - 1.37)^2] = (1/3)(-1.37^2 + 0.73^2 + 0.63^2) = (1/3)(1.88 + 0.53 + 0.40) = (1/3)(2.81) = 0.94$.

7.3.2 *Population Standard Deviation*

Because the variance is measured in squared units, we need a way to return to the original units. We can solve this problem by using standard deviation, the square root of the variance. Standard deviation is more easily interpreted than the variance because standard deviation is expressed in the same unit of measurement as the observations.

- **Population Standard Deviation Formula.** The **population standard deviation**, defined as the positive square root of the population variance, is

$$\sigma = \sqrt{\frac{\sum_{i=1}^{N}(X_i - \mu)^2}{N}} \quad (12)$$

where μ is the population mean and N is the size of the population.

Using the example of the profit as a percentage of revenue for BJ's Wholesale Club, Costco, and Walmart, according to Equation 12 we would calculate the variance, 0.94, then take the square root: $\sqrt{0.94} = 0.97$.

Both the population variance and standard deviation are examples of parameters of a distribution. In later readings, we will introduce the notion of variance and standard deviation as risk measures.

In investments, we often do not know the mean of a population of interest, usually because we cannot practically identify or take measurements from each member of the population. We then estimate the population mean with the mean from a sample drawn from the population, and we calculate a sample variance or standard deviation using formulas different from Equations 11 and 12. We shall discuss these calculations in subsequent sections. However, in investments we sometimes have a defined group that we can consider to be a population. With well-defined populations, we use Equations 11 and 12, as in the following example.

EXAMPLE 11

Calculating the Population Standard Deviation

Exhibit 25 gives the P/E, the ratio of share price to projected earnings per share (EPS) for 2018 for the 10 US stocks that composed the list of *Barron's* 10 favorite stocks for 2018.[30] The identity of the stocks on the *Barron's* Top 10 list changes from year to year.

Exhibit 25 P/E: *Barron's* 10 Favorite Stocks for 2018

Fund	P/E
Ally Financial	10.7
Alphabet	24.9

30 Toward the end of each year, *Barron's* magazine annually selects its 10 favorite US stocks for the next year.

Exhibit 25 (Continued)

Fund	P/E
Anthem	17.3
Applied Materials	13.0
Berkshire Hathaway	24.6
Delta Airlines	9.7
Enterprise Products Partners	16.7
Pioneer Natural Resources	50.6
US Foods	18.1
Volkswagen	6.5

Source: Barron's (9 December 2017).

Based on the data in Exhibit 25, address the following:

1 Calculate the population mean P/E for the period used by *Barron's* for the 10 favorite stocks.

2 Calculate the population variance and population standard deviation of the P/E.

3 Explain the use of the population formulas in this example.

Solution to 1:

$\mu = (10.7 + 24.9 + 17.3 + 13.0 + 24.6 + 9.7 + 16.7 + 50.6 + 18.1 + 6.5)/10 = 192.1/10 = 19.21.$

Solution to 2:

Having established that $\mu = 19.21$, we can calculate $\sigma^2 = \frac{\sum_{i=1}^{N}(X_i - \mu)^2}{N}$ by first calculating the numerator in the expression and then dividing by $N = 10$. The numerator (the sum of the squared differences from the mean) is

$$(10 - 53)^2 + (360 - 53)^2 + (37 - 53)^2 + (20 - 53)^2 + (49 - 53)^2 + (1 - 53)^2 + (32 - 53)^2 + (72 - 53)^2 + (9 - 53)^2 + (19 - 53)^2 + (16 - 53)^2 + (11 - 53)^2 = 107{,}190$$

Thus $\sigma^2 = 107{,}190/12 = 8{,}932.50$.

$$(10.7 - 19.21)^2 + (24.9 - 19.21)^2 + (17.3 - 19.21)^2 + (13.0 - 19.21)^2 + (24.6 - 19.21)^2 + (9.7 - 19.21)^2 + (16.7 - 19.21)^2 + (50.6 - 19.21)^2 + (18.1 - 19.21)^2 + (6.5 - 19.21)^2 = 1{,}420.9$$

Thus $\sigma^2 = 1{,}420.9/10 = 142.09$.

To calculate standard deviation, $\sigma = \sqrt{142.09} = 11.92$ percent. (The unit of variance is percent squared so the unit of standard deviation is percent.)

Solution to 3:

If the population is clearly defined to be the *Barron's* favorite stocks for one specific year (2018), and if the P/E is understood to refer to the specific one-year period reported upon by *Barron's*, the application of the population formulas to variance and standard deviation is appropriate. The results of 142.09 and 11.92 are, respectively, the cross-sectional variance and standard deviation in the P/E for the 2018 *Barron's* favorite stocks list.[31]

7.4 Sample Variance and Sample Standard Deviation

In the following discussion, note the switch to Roman letters to symbolize sample quantities.

7.4.1 *Sample Variance*

In many instances in investment management, a subset or sample of the population is all that we can observe. When we deal with samples, the summary measures are called statistics. The statistic that measures the dispersion in a sample is called the sample variance.

- **Sample Variance Formula.** The **sample variance** is

$$s^2 = \frac{\sum_{i=1}^{n}\left(X_i - \overline{X}\right)^2}{n-1} \quad (13)$$

where $\overline{X}$ is the sample mean and n is the number of observations in the sample.

Equation 13 tells us to take the following steps to compute the sample variance:

i. Calculate the sample mean, $\overline{X}$.

ii. Calculate each observation's squared deviation from the sample mean, $\left(X_i - \overline{X}\right)^2$.

iii. Sum the squared deviations from the mean: $\sum_{i=1}^{n}\left(X_i - \overline{X}\right)^2$.

iv. Divide the sum of squared deviations from the mean by $n - 1$: $\sum_{i=1}^{n}\left(X_i - \overline{X}\right)^2 / (n-1)$.

We will illustrate the calculation of the sample variance and the sample standard deviation in Example 12.

We use the notation s^2 for the sample variance to distinguish it from population variance, σ^2. The formula for sample variance is nearly the same as that for population variance except for the use of the sample mean, $\overline{X}$, in place of the population mean, μ, and a different divisor. In the case of the population variance, we divide by the size of the population, N. For the sample variance, however, we divide by the sample size minus 1, or $n - 1$. By using $n - 1$ (rather than n) as the divisor, we improve the statistical properties of the sample variance. In statistical terms, the sample variance defined in Equation 13 is an unbiased estimator of the population variance.[32] The quantity $n - 1$ is also known as the number of degrees of freedom in estimating the population variance. To estimate the population variance with s^2, we must first calculate the mean. Once we have computed the sample mean, there are only $n - 1$ independent deviations from it.

---

31 In fact, we could not properly use the Honor Roll funds to estimate the population variance of the P/E (for example) of any other differently defined population, because the favorite stocks are not a random sample from any larger population of US stocks.

32 We discuss this concept further in the reading on sampling.

7.4.2 *Sample Standard Deviation*

Just as we computed a population standard deviation, we can compute a sample standard deviation by taking the positive square root of the sample variance.

- **Sample Standard Deviation Formula.** The **sample standard deviation**, s, is

$$s = \sqrt{\frac{\sum_{i=1}^{n}\left(X_i - \overline{X}\right)^2}{n - 1}} \quad (14)$$

where $\overline{X}$ is the sample mean and n is the number of observations in the sample.

To calculate the sample standard deviation, we first compute the sample variance using the steps given. We then take the square root of the sample variance. Example 12 illustrates the calculation of the sample variance and standard deviation for the two mutual funds introduced earlier.

EXAMPLE 12

Calculating Sample Variance and Sample Standard Deviation

After calculating the geometric and arithmetic mean returns of two mutual funds in Example 7, we calculated two measures of dispersions for those funds, the range and mean absolute deviation of returns, in Example 10. We now calculate the sample variance and sample standard deviation of returns for those same two funds.

Exhibit 20 Total Returns for Two Mutual Funds, 2013–2017 (Repeated)

Year	Selected American Shares (SLASX)	T. Rowe Price Equity Income (PRFDX)
2013	34.90%	31.69%
2014	6.13	7.75
2015	2.69	−7.56
2016	11.66	18.25
2017	21.77	16.18

Source: performance.morningstar.com.

Based on the data in Exhibit 20 repeated above, answer the following:

1 Calculate the sample variance of return for (A) SLASX and (B) PRFDX.

2 Calculate sample standard deviation of return for (A) SLASX and (B) PRFDX.

3 Contrast the dispersion of returns as measured by standard deviation of return and mean absolute deviation of return for each of the two funds.

Solution to 1:

To calculate the sample variance, we use Equation 13. (Deviation answers are all given in percent squared.)

A SLASX

i. The sample mean is

$\overline{R}$ = (34.90 + 6.13 + 2.69 − 11.66 +21.77)/ 5 = 77.15/5 = 15.43%.

ii. The squared deviations from the mean are

$(34.90 - 15.43)^2 = (19.47)^2 = 379.08$

$(6.13 - 15.43)^2 = (-9.30)^2 = 86.49$

$(2.69 - 15.43)^2 = (-12.74)^2 = 162.31$

$(11.66 - 15.43)^2 = (-3.77)^2 = 14.21$

$(21.77 - 15.43)^2 = (6.34)^2 = 40.20$

iii. The sum of the squared deviations from the mean is 379.08 + 86.49 + 162.31 + 14.21 + 40.20 = 682.29.

iv. Divide the sum of the squared deviations from the mean by $n - 1$: 682.29/(5 − 1) = 682.29/4 = 170.57

B PRFDX

i. The sample mean is

$\overline{R}$ = (31.69 + 7.75 − 7.56 + 18.25 + 6.18)/5 = 66.30/5 = 13.26%.

ii. The squared deviations from the mean are

$(31.69 - 13.26)^2 = (18.43)^2 = 339.59$

$(7.75 - 13.26)^2 = (-0.725.51)^2 = 30.38$

$(-7.56 - 13.26)^2 = (-20.82)^2 = 433.56$

$(18.25 - 13.26)^2 = (4.99)^2 = 24.88$

$(16.18 - 13.26)^2 = (2.92)^2 = 8.51$

iii. The sum of the squared deviations from the mean is 339.59 + 30.38 + 433.56 + 24.88 + 8.51 = 836.92.

iv. Divide the sum of the squared deviations from the mean by $n - 1$: 836.92/4 = 209.23

Solution to 2:

To find the standard deviation, we take the positive square root of variance.

A For SLASX, $s = \sqrt{170.57} = 13.1\%$.

B For PRFDX, $s = \sqrt{209.23} = 14.5\%$.

Solution to 3:

Exhibit 26 summarizes the results from Part 2 for standard deviation and incorporates the results for MAD from Example 10.

Exhibit 26 Two Mutual Funds: Comparison of Standard Deviation and Mean Absolute Deviation

Fund	Standard Deviation (%)	Mean Absolute Deviation (%)
SLASX	13.1	10.3
PRFDX	14.5	10.5

Note that the mean absolute deviation is less than the standard deviation. The mean absolute deviation will always be less than or equal to the standard deviation because the standard deviation gives more weight to large deviations than to small ones (remember, the deviations are squared).

Because the standard deviation is a measure of dispersion about the arithmetic mean, we usually present the arithmetic mean and standard deviation together when summarizing data. When we are dealing with data that represent a time series of percent changes, presenting the geometric mean—representing the compound rate of growth—is also very helpful. Exhibit 27 presents the historical geometric and arithmetic mean returns, along with the historical standard deviation of returns, for the S&P 500 annual and monthly returns. We present these statistics for nominal (rather than inflation-adjusted) returns so we can observe the original magnitudes of the returns.

Exhibit 27 Equity Market Returns: Means and Standard Deviations

Return Series	Geometric Mean (%)	Arithmetic Mean (%)	Standard Deviation
1926–2017			
S&P 500 (Annual)	10.16	12.06	19.79
S&P 500 (Monthly)	0.81	0.95	5.39

Sources: Ibbotson Associates and S&P Dow Jones Indices LLC.

7.5 Semivariance, Semideviation, and Related Concepts

An asset's variance or standard deviation of returns is often interpreted as a measure of the asset's risk. Variance and standard deviation of returns take account of returns above and below the mean, but investors are concerned only with downside risk, for example, returns below the mean. As a result, analysts have developed semivariance, semideviation, and related dispersion measures that focus on downside risk. **Semivariance** is defined as the average squared deviation below the mean. **Semideviation** (sometimes called semistandard deviation) is the positive square root of semivariance.[33] To compute the sample semivariance, for example, we take the following steps:

i. Calculate the sample mean.

ii. Identify the observations that are smaller than or equal to the mean (discarding observations greater than the mean).

iii. Compute the sum of the squared negative deviations from the mean (using the observations that are smaller than or equal to the mean).

iv. Divide the sum of the squared negative deviations from Step iii by the *total* sample size minus 1: $n - 1$. A formula for semivariance approximating the unbiased estimator is

$$\sum_{\text{for all } X_i \le \overline{X}} \left(X_i - \overline{X}\right)^2 \Big/ \left(n - 1\right)$$

33 This is an informal treatment of these two measures; see the survey article by N. Fred Choobinbeh (2005) for a rigorous treatment.

To take the case of Selected American Shares with returns (in percent) of 34.90, 6.13, 2.69, 11.66, and 21.77, we earlier calculated a mean return of 15.43 percent. Three returns, 2.69, 6.13, and 11.66, are smaller than 15.43. We compute the sum of the squared negative deviations from the mean as $(2.69 - 15.43)^2 + (6.13 - 15.43)^2 + (11.66 - 15.43)^2 = -12.74^2 + -9.30^2 + -3.77^2 = 162.31 + 86.49 + 14.21 = 263.01$. With $n - 1 = 4$, we conclude that semivariance is 263.01/4 = 65.75 and that semideviation is $\sqrt{65.76} = 8.1$ percent, approximately. The semideviation of 8.1 percent is less than the standard deviation of 13.1 percent. From this downside risk perspective, therefore, standard deviation overstates risk.

In practice, we may be concerned with values of return (or another variable) below some level other than the mean. For example, if our return objective is 11.50 percent annually, we may be concerned particularly with returns below 11.50 percent a year. We can call 11.50 percent the target. The name **target semivariance** has been given to average squared deviation below a stated target, and **target semideviation** is its positive square root. To calculate a sample target semivariance, we specify the target as a first step. After identifying observations below the target, we find the sum of the squared negative deviations from the target and divide that sum by the number of observations minus 1. A formula for target semivariance is

$$\sum_{\text{for all } X_i \leq B} (X_i - B)^2 / (n - 1)$$

where B is the target and n is the number of observations. With a target return of 11.50 percent, we find in the case of Selected American Shares that three returns (2.69 and 6.13) were below the target. The target semivariance is $[(2.69 - 11.50)^2 + (6.13 - 11.50)^2]/(5 - 1) = 26.61$, and the target semideviation is $\sqrt{26.61} = 5.2$ percent, approximately.

When return distributions are symmetric, semivariance and variance are effectively equivalent. For asymmetric distributions, variance and semivariance rank prospects' risk differently.[34] Semivariance (or semideviation) and target semivariance (or target semideviation) have intuitive appeal, but they are harder to work with mathematically than variance.[35] Variance or standard deviation enters into the definition of many of the most commonly used finance risk concepts, such as the Sharpe ratio and beta. Perhaps because of these reasons, variance (or standard deviation) is much more frequently used in investment practice.

7.6 Chebyshev's Inequality

The Russian mathematician Pafnuty Chebyshev developed an inequality using standard deviation as a measure of dispersion. The inequality gives the proportion of values within k standard deviations of the mean.

- **Definition of Chebyshev's Inequality.** According to Chebyshev's inequality, for any distribution with finite variance, the proportion of the observations within k standard deviations of the arithmetic mean is at least $1 - 1/k^2$ for all $k > 1$.

Exhibit 28 illustrates the proportion of the observations that must lie within a certain number of standard deviations around the sample mean.

34 We discuss skewness later in this reading.

35 As discussed in the reading on probability concepts and the various readings on portfolio concepts, we can find a portfolio's variance as a straightforward function of the variances and correlations of the component securities. There is no similar procedure for semivariance and target semivariance. We also cannot take the derivative of semivariance or target semivariance.

Exhibit 28 Proportions from Chebyshev's Inequality

k	Interval around the Sample Mean	Proportion (%)
1.25	$\overline{X} \pm 1.25s$	36
1.50	$\overline{X} \pm 1.50s$	56
2.00	$\overline{X} \pm 2s$	75
2.50	$\overline{X} \pm 2.50s$	84
3.00	$\overline{X} \pm 3s$	89
4.00	$\overline{X} \pm 4s$	94

Note: Standard deviation is denoted as *s*.

When $k = 1.25$, for example, the inequality states that the minimum proportion of the observations that lie within $\pm\ 1.25s$ is $1 - 1/(1.25)^2 = 1 - 0.64 = 0.36$ or 36 percent.

The most frequently cited facts that result from Chebyshev's inequality are that a two-standard-deviation interval around the mean must contain at least 75 percent of the observations, and a three-standard-deviation interval around the mean must contain at least 89 percent of the observations, no matter how the data are distributed.

The importance of Chebyshev's inequality stems from its generality. The inequality holds for samples and populations and for discrete and continuous data regardless of the shape of the distribution. As we shall see in the reading on sampling, we can make much more precise interval statements if we can assume that the sample is drawn from a population that follows a specific distribution called the normal distribution. Frequently, however, we cannot confidently assume that distribution.

The next example illustrates the use of Chebyshev's inequality.

EXAMPLE 13

Applying Chebyshev's Inequality

According to Exhibit 27, the arithmetic mean monthly return and standard deviation of monthly returns on the S&P 500 were 0.95 percent and 5.39 percent, respectively, during the 1926–2017 period, totaling 1,104 monthly observations. Using this information, address the following:

1 Calculate the endpoints of the interval that must contain at least 75 percent of monthly returns according to Chebyshev's inequality.

2 What are the minimum and maximum number of observations that must lie in the interval computed in Part 1, according to Chebyshev's inequality?

Solution to 1:

According to Chebyshev's inequality, at least 75 percent of the observations must lie within two standard deviations of the mean, $\overline{X} \pm 2s$. For the monthly S&P 500 return series, we have 0.95% ± 2(5.39%) = 0.95% ± 10.78%. Thus the lower endpoint of the interval that must contain at least 75 percent of the observations is 0.95% − 10.78% = −9.83%, and the upper endpoint is 0.95% + 10.78% = 11.73%.

Solution to 2:

For a sample size of 1,104, at least 0.75(1,104) = 828 observations must lie in the interval from −9.83% to 11.73% that we computed in Part 1. Chebyshev's inequality gives the minimum percentage of observations that must fall within a given interval around the mean, but it does not give the maximum percentage. Exhibit 4, which gave the frequency distribution of monthly returns on the S&P 500, is excerpted below. The data in the excerpted table are consistent with the prediction of Chebyshev's inequality. The set of intervals running from −10.0% to 12.0% is about equal in width to the two-standard-deviation interval −9.83% to 11.73%. A total of 1,064 observations (approximately 96 percent of observations) fall in the range from −10.0% to 12.0%.

Exhibit 4 Frequency Distribution for the Monthly Total Return on the S&P 500, January 1926 to December 2017 (Excerpt)

Return Interval (%)	Absolute Frequency
−10.0 to −8.0	23
−8.0 to −6.0	35
−6.0 to −4.0	60
−4.0 to −2.0	102
−2.0 to 0.0	166
0.0 to 2.0	240
2.0 to 4.0	190
4.0 to 6.0	143
6.0 to 8.0	64
8.0 to 10.0	26
10.0 to 12.0	15
	1,064

7.7 Coefficient of Variation

We noted earlier that standard deviation is more easily interpreted than variance because standard deviation uses the same units of measurement as the observations. We may sometimes find it difficult to interpret what standard deviation means in terms of the relative degree of variability of different sets of data, however, either because the data sets have markedly different means or because the data sets have different units of measurement. In this section we explain a measure of relative dispersion, the coefficient of variation that can be useful in such situations. **Relative dispersion** is the amount of dispersion relative to a reference value or benchmark.

We can illustrate the problem of interpreting the standard deviation of data sets with markedly different means using two hypothetical samples of companies. The first sample, composed of small companies, includes companies with last year's sales of €50 million, €75 million, €65 million, and €90 million. The second sample, composed of large companies, includes companies with last year's sales of €800 million, €825 million, €815 million, and €840 million. We can verify using Equation 14 that the standard deviation of sales in both samples is €16.8 million.[36] In the first sample, the largest observation, €90 million, is 80 percent larger than the smallest observation, €50 million. In the second sample, the largest observation is only 5 percent larger than the smallest observation. Informally, a standard deviation of €16.8 million represents a high degree of variability relative to the first sample, which reflects mean last year sales of €70 million, but a small degree of variability relative to the second sample, which reflects mean last year sales of €820 million.

The coefficient of variation is helpful in situations such as that just described.

- **Coefficient of Variation Formula.** The **coefficient of variation**, CV, is the ratio of the standard deviation of a set of observations to their mean value:[37]

$$\text{CV} = s/\overline{X} \tag{15}$$

- where s is the sample standard deviation and $\overline{X}$ is the sample mean.

When the observations are returns, for example, the coefficient of variation measures the amount of risk (standard deviation) per unit of mean return. Expressing the magnitude of variation among observations relative to their average size, the coefficient of variation permits direct comparisons of dispersion across different data sets. Reflecting the correction for scale, the coefficient of variation is a scale-free measure (that is, it has no units of measurement).

We can illustrate the application of the coefficient of variation using our earlier example of two samples of companies. The coefficient of variation for the first sample is (€16.8 million)/(€70 million) = 0.24; the coefficient of variation for the second sample is (€16.8 million)/(€820 million) = 0.02. This confirms our intuition that the first sample had much greater variability in sales than the second sample. Note that 0.24 and 0.02 are pure numbers in the sense that they are free of units of measurement (because we divided the standard deviation by the mean, which is measured in the same units as the standard deviation). If we need to compare the dispersion among data sets stated in different units of measurement, the coefficient of variation can be useful because it is free from units of measurement. Example 14 illustrates the calculation of the coefficient of variation.

EXAMPLE 14

Calculating the Coefficient of Variation

Exhibit 29 summarizes annual mean returns and standard deviations computed using monthly return data for major stock market indexes of four Asia-Pacific markets. The indexes are: S&P/ASX 200 Index (Australia), Hang Seng Index (Hong Kong SAR), Nikkei 225 Index (Japan), and KOSPI Composite Index (South Korea).

36 The second sample was created by adding €750 million to each observation in the first sample. Standard deviation (and variance) has the property of remaining unchanged if we add a constant amount to each observation.

37 The reader will also encounter CV defined as $100(s/\overline{X})$, which states CV as a percentage.

Exhibit 29 Arithmetic Mean Annual Return and Standard Deviation of Returns, Asia-Pacific Stock Markets, 2013–2017

Market	Arithmetic Mean Return (%)	Standard Deviation of Return (%)
Australia	5.3	11.9
Hong Kong SAR	5.6	15.8
Japan	15.7	16.3
South Korea	4.2	8.6

Source: finance.yahoo.com, accessed 26 November 2018.

Using the information in Exhibit 29, address the following:

1 Calculate the coefficient of variation for each market given.
2 Rank the markets from most risky to least risky using CV as a measure of relative dispersion.
3 Determine whether there is more difference between the absolute or the relative riskiness of the Australia and South Korea markets. Use the standard deviation as a measure of absolute risk and CV as a measure of relative risk.

Solution to 1:

Australia: CV = 11.9%/5.3% = 2.245

Hong Kong SAR: CV = 15.8%/5.6% = 2.821

Japan: CV = 16.3%/15.7% = 1.038

South Korea: CV = 8.6%/4.2% = 2.048

Solution to 2:

Based on CV, the ranking for the 2013–2017 period examined is Hong Kong SAR (most risky), Australia, South Korea, and Japan (least risky).

Solution to 3:

As measured both by standard deviation and CV, Australia market was riskier than the South Korea market. The standard deviation of Australian returns was (11.9 − 8.6)/8.6 = 0.384 or about 38 percent larger than South Korean returns, compared with a difference in the CV of (2.245 − 2.048)/2.048 = 0.097 or about 10 percent. Thus, the CVs reveal less difference between Australian and South Korean return variability than that suggested by the standard deviations alone.

8 SYMMETRY AND SKEWNESS IN RETURN DISTRIBUTIONS

Mean and variance may not adequately describe an investment's distribution of returns. In calculations of variance, for example, the deviations around the mean are squared, so we do not know whether large deviations are likely to be positive or negative.

We need to go beyond measures of central tendency and dispersion to reveal other important characteristics of the distribution. One important characteristic of interest to analysts is the degree of symmetry in return distributions.

If a return distribution is symmetrical about its mean, then each side of the distribution is a mirror image of the other. Thus equal loss and gain intervals exhibit the same frequencies. Losses from −5 percent to −3 percent, for example, occur with about the same frequency as gains from 3 percent to 5 percent.

One of the most important distributions is the normal distribution, depicted in Exhibit 30. This symmetrical, bell-shaped distribution plays a central role in the mean–variance model of portfolio selection; it is also used extensively in financial risk management. The normal distribution has the following characteristics:

- Its mean and median are equal.
- It is completely described by two parameters—its mean and variance.
- Roughly 68 percent of its observations lie between plus and minus one standard deviation from the mean; 95 percent lie between plus and minus two standard deviations; and 99 percent lie between plus and minus three standard deviations.

A distribution that is not symmetrical is called **skewed**. A return distribution with positive skew has frequent small losses and a few extreme gains. A return distribution with negative skew has frequent small gains and a few extreme losses. Exhibit 31 shows continuous positively and negatively skewed distributions. The continuous positively skewed distribution shown has a long tail on its right side; the continuous negatively skewed distribution shown has a long tail on its left side. For the continuous positively skewed unimodal distribution, the mode is less than the median, which is less than the mean. For the continuous negatively skewed unimodal distribution, the mean is less than the median, which is less than the mode.[38] Investors should be attracted by a positive skew because the mean return falls above the median. Relative to the mean return, positive skew amounts to a limited, though frequent, downside compared with a somewhat unlimited, but less frequent, upside.

38 As a mnemonic, in this case the mean, median, and mode occur in the same order as they would be listed in a dictionary. Von Hippel (2005) explores exceptions to the relationships among these measures for distributions that vary from those shown in Exhibit 31.

Exhibit 30 Properties of a Normal Distribution (EV 5 Expected Value)

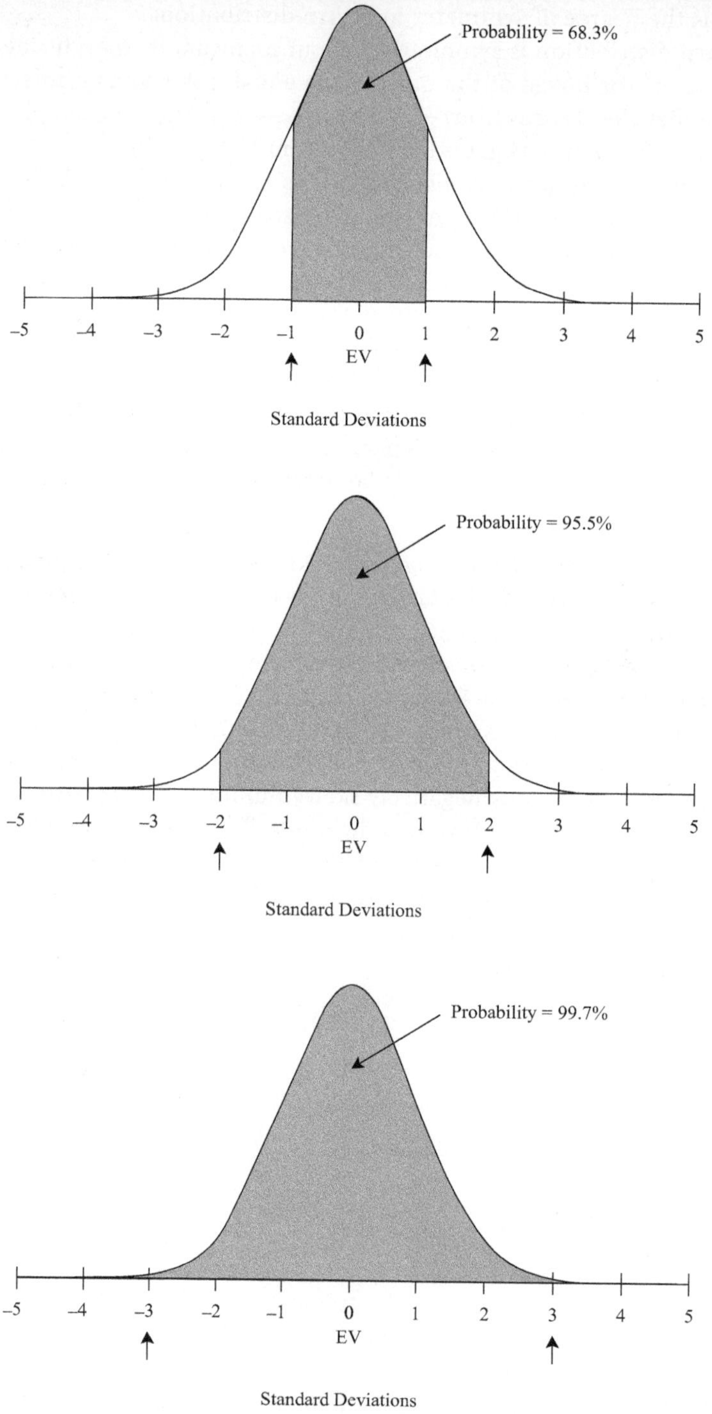

Source: Reprinted from *Fixed Income Analysis.* Copyright CFA Institute.

Exhibit 31 Properties of a Skewed Distribution

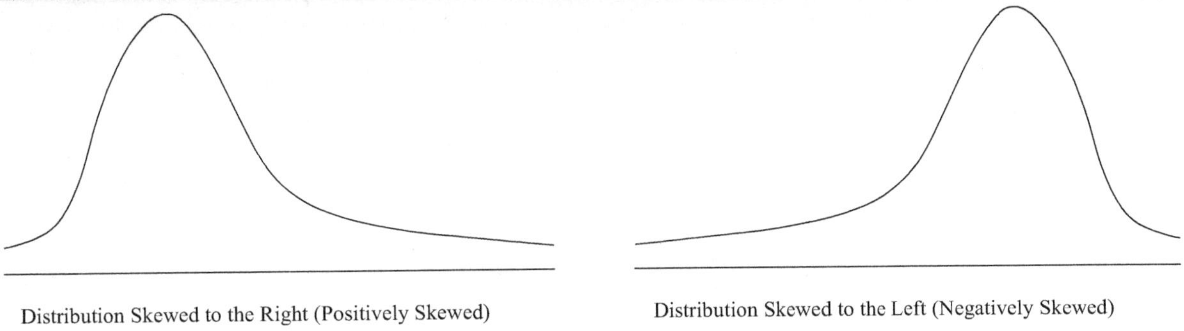

Source: Reprinted from *Fixed Income Analysis.* Copyright CFA Institute.

Skewness is the name given to a statistical measure of skew. (The word "skewness" is also sometimes used interchangeably for "skew.") Like variance, skewness is computed using each observation's deviation from its mean. **Skewness** (sometimes referred to as relative skewness) is computed as the average cubed deviation from the mean standardized by dividing by the standard deviation cubed to make the measure free of scale.[39] A symmetric distribution has skewness of 0, a positively skewed distribution has positive skewness, and a negatively skewed distribution has negative skewness, as given by this measure.

We can illustrate the principle behind the measure by focusing on the numerator. Cubing, unlike squaring, preserves the sign of the deviations from the mean. If a distribution is positively skewed with a mean greater than its median, then more than half of the deviations from the mean are negative and less than half are positive. In order for the sum to be positive, the losses must be small and likely, and the gains less likely but more extreme. Therefore, if skewness is positive, the average magnitude of positive deviations is larger than the average magnitude of negative deviations.

A simple example illustrates that a symmetrical distribution has a skewness measure equal to 0. Suppose we have the following data: 1, 2, 3, 4, 5, 6, 7, 8, and 9. The mean outcome is 5, and the deviations are −4, −3, −2, −1, 0, 1, 2, 3, and 4. Cubing the deviations yields −64, −27, −8, −1, 0, 1, 8, 27, and 64, with a sum of 0. The numerator of skewness (and so skewness itself) is thus equal to 0, supporting our claim. Below we give the formula for computing skewness from a sample.

- **Sample Skewness Formula. Sample skewness** (also called sample relative skewness), S_K, is

$$S_K = \left[\frac{n}{(n-1)(n-2)}\right]\frac{\sum_{i=1}^{n}\left(X_i - \overline{X}\right)^3}{s^3} \qquad (16)$$

where n is the number of observations in the sample and s is the sample standard deviation.[40]

39 We are discussing a moment coefficient of skewness. Some textbooks present the Pearson coefficient of skewness, equal to 3(Mean − Median)/Standard deviation, which has the drawback of involving the calculation of the median.

40 The term $n/[(n-1)(n-2)]$ in Equation 16 corrects for a downward bias in small samples.

The algebraic sign of Equation 16 indicates the direction of skew, with a negative S_K indicating a negatively skewed distribution and a positive S_K indicating a positively skewed distribution. Note that as n becomes large, the expression reduces to the mean cubed deviation, $S_K \approx \left(\frac{1}{n}\right)\frac{\sum_{i=1}^{n}\left(X_i - \bar{X}\right)^3}{s^3}$. As a frame of reference, for a sample size of 100 or larger taken from a normal distribution, a skewness coefficient of ±0.5 would be considered unusually large.

Exhibit 32 shows several summary statistics for the annual and monthly returns on the S&P 500. Earlier we discussed the arithmetic mean return and standard deviation of return, and we shall shortly discuss kurtosis.

Exhibit 32 S&P 500 Annual and Monthly Total Returns, 1926–2017: Summary Statistics

Return Series	Number of Periods	Arithmetic Mean (%)	Standard Deviation (%)	Skewness	Excess Kurtosis
S&P 500 (Annual)	92	12.06	19.79	−0.4019	0.1044
S&P 500 (Monthly)	1,104	0.95	5.5039	0.3387	9.7709

Sources: Ibbotson Associates and S&P Dow Jones Indices LLC.

Exhibit 32 reveals that S&P 500 annual returns during this period were negatively skewed while monthly returns were positively skewed, and the magnitude of skewness was greater for the annual series. We would find for other market series that the shape of the distribution of returns often depends on the holding period examined.

Some researchers believe that investors should prefer positive skewness, all else equal—that is, they should prefer portfolios with distributions offering a relatively large frequency of unusually large payoffs.[41] Different investment strategies may tend to introduce different types and amounts of skewness into returns. Example 15 illustrates the calculation of skewness for a managed portfolio.

EXAMPLE 15

Calculating Skewness for a Mutual Fund

Exhibit 33 presents 10 years of annual returns on the T. Rowe Price Equity Income Fund (PRFDX).

Exhibit 33 Annual Rates of Return: T. Rowe Price Equity Income, 2008–2017

Year	Return (%)
2008	−35.75
2009	25.62
2010	15.15
2011	−0.72

41 For more on the role of skewness in portfolio selection, see Reilly and Brown (2018) and Elton, Gruber, Brown, and Goetzmann (2013) and the references therein.

Exhibit 33 (Continued)

Year	Return (%)
2012	17.25
2013	31.69
2014	7.75
2015	−7.76
2016	18.25
2017	16.18

Source: performance.morningstar.com.

Using the information in Exhibit 33, address the following:

1 Calculate the skewness of PRFDX showing two decimal places.

2 Characterize the shape of the distribution of PRFDX returns based on your answer to Part 1.

Solution to 1:

To calculate skewness, we find the sum of the cubed deviations from the mean, divide by the standard deviation cubed, and then multiply that result by $n/[(n - 1)(n - 2)]$. Exhibit 34 gives the calculations.

Exhibit 34 Calculating Skewness for PRFDX

Year	R_t	$R_t - \overline{R}$	$\left(R_t - \overline{R}\right)^3$
2008	−35.75	−44.52	−88,239.993
2009	25.62	16.85	4,784.094
2010	15.15	6.38	259.694
2011	−0.72	−9.49	−854.670
2012	17.25	8.48	609.800
2013	31.69	22.92	12,040.481
2014	7.75	−1.02	−1.061
2015	−7.76	−16.53	−4,516.672
2016	18.25	9.48	851.971
2017	16.18	7.41	406.869
n =	10		
$\overline{R}$ =	8.77%		
		Sum =	−74,659.487
s =	19.47%	s^3 =	7,380.705
		Sum/s^3 =	−10.1155
		$n/[(n - 1)(n - 2)]$ =	0.1389
		Skewness =	**−1.40**

Source: performance.morningstar.com.

Using Equation 16, the calculation is:

$$S_k = \left[\frac{10}{(9)(8)}\right]\frac{-74{,}659.487}{19.47^3} = -1.40$$

Solution to 2:

Based on this small sample, the distribution of annual returns for the fund appears to be negatively skewed. In this example, four deviations are negative and six are positive. While, there are more positive deviations, they are much more than offset by a huge negative deviation in 2008, when the stock markets sharply went down as a consequence of the global financial crisis. The result is that skewness is a negative number, implying that the distribution is skewed to the left.

9 KURTOSIS IN RETURN DISTRIBUTIONS

In the previous section, we discussed how to determine whether a return distribution deviates from a normal distribution because of skewness. One other way in which a return distribution might differ from a normal distribution is its relative tendency to generate large deviations from the mean. Most investors would perceive a greater chance of extremely large deviations from the mean as increasing risk.

Kurtosis is a measure of the combined weight of the tails of a distribution relative to the rest of the distribution—that is, the proportion of the total probability that is in the tails. A distribution that has fatter tails than the normal distribution is called **leptokurtic**; a distribution that has thinner tails than the normal distribution is called **platykurtic**; and a distribution identical to the normal distribution as concerns relative weight in the tails is called **mesokurtic**. A leptokurtic distribution tends to generate more-frequent extremely large deviations from the mean than the normal distribution.[42]

Exhibit 35 illustrates a leptokurtic distribution. It has fatter tails than the normal distribution. By construction, the leptokurtic and normal distributions have the same mean, standard deviation, and skewness. Note that the leptokurtic distribution is more likely than the normal distribution to generate observations in the tail regions defined by the intersection of graphs near a standard deviation of about ±2.5. The leptokurtic distribution is also more likely to generate observations that are near the mean, defined here as the region ±1 standard deviation around the mean. In compensation, to have probabilities sum to 1, the leptokurtic distribution generates fewer observations in the regions between the central region and the two tail regions.

42 See Wheeler (2011) for definitions and further reading.

Exhibit 35 Leptokurtic: Fat Tailed

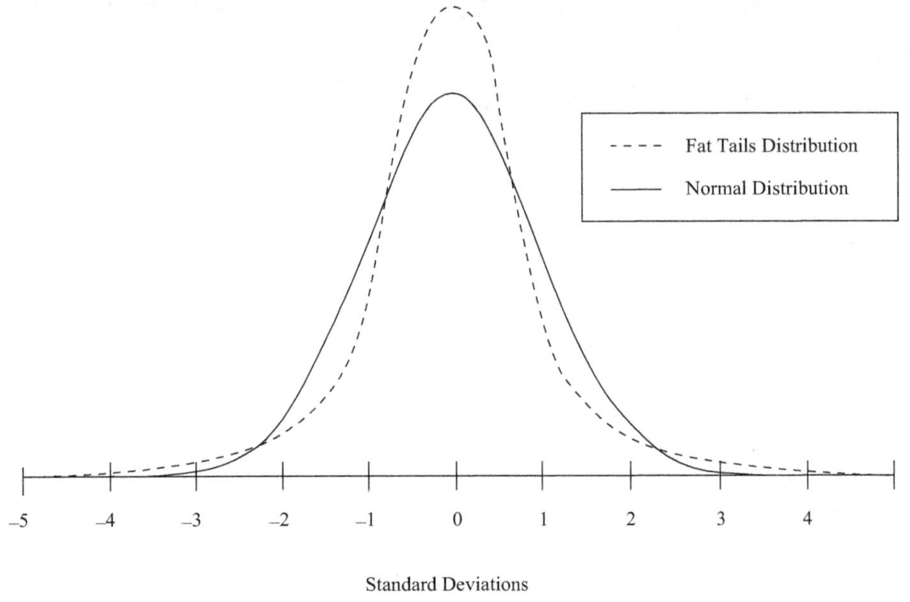

Source: Reprinted from *Fixed Income Analysis.* Copyright CFA Institute.

The calculation for kurtosis involves finding the average of deviations from the mean raised to the fourth power and then standardizing that average by dividing by the standard deviation raised to the fourth power.[43] For all normal distributions, kurtosis is equal to 3. Many statistical packages report estimates of **excess kurtosis**, which is kurtosis minus 3.[44] Excess kurtosis thus characterizes kurtosis relative to the normal distribution. A normal or other mesokurtic distribution has excess kurtosis equal to 0. A leptokurtic distribution has excess kurtosis greater than 0, and a platykurtic distribution has excess kurtosis less than 0. A return distribution with positive excess kurtosis—a leptokurtic return distribution—has more frequent extremely large deviations from the mean than a normal distribution. Below is the expression for computing kurtosis from a sample.

- **Sample Excess Kurtosis Formula.** The **sample excess kurtosis** is

$$K_E = \left(\frac{n(n+1)}{(n-1)(n-2)(n-3)} \frac{\sum_{i=1}^{n}\left(X_i - \bar{X}\right)^4}{s^4}\right) - \frac{3(n-1)^2}{(n-2)(n-3)} \quad (17)$$

where n is the sample size and s is the sample standard deviation.

43 This measure is free of scale. It is always positive because the deviations are raised to the fourth power.

44 Ibbotson and some software packages, such as Microsoft Excel, label "excess kurtosis" as simply "kurtosis." This highlights the fact that one should familiarize oneself with the description of statistical quantities in any software packages that one uses.

In Equation 17, **sample kurtosis** is the first term. Note that as n becomes large, Equation 17 approximately equals $\frac{n^2}{n^3}\frac{\sum\left(X-\bar{X}\right)^4}{s^4}-\frac{3n^2}{n^2}=\frac{1}{n}\frac{\sum\left(X-\bar{X}\right)^4}{s^4}-3$. For a sample of 100 or larger taken from a normal distribution, a sample excess kurtosis of 1.0 or larger would be considered unusually large.

Most equity return series have been found to be leptokurtic. If a return distribution has positive excess kurtosis (leptokurtosis) and we use statistical models that do not account for the fatter tails, we will underestimate the likelihood of very bad or very good outcomes. For example, the return on the S&P 500 for 19 October 1987 was 20 standard deviations away from the mean daily return. Such an outcome is possible with a normal distribution, but its likelihood is almost equal to 0. If daily returns are drawn from a normal distribution, a return four standard deviations or more away from the mean is expected once every 50 years; a return greater than five standard deviations away is expected once every 7,000 years. The return for October 1987 is more likely to have come from a distribution that had fatter tails than from a normal distribution. Looking at Exhibit 32 given earlier, the monthly return series for the S&P 500 has very large excess kurtosis, approximately 9.8. It is extremely fat-tailed relative to the normal distribution. By contrast, the annual return series has about no excess kurtosis. The results for excess kurtosis in the exhibit are consistent with research findings that the normal distribution is a better approximation for US equity returns for annual holding periods than for shorter ones (such as monthly).[45]

The following example illustrates the calculations for sample excess kurtosis for one of the two mutual funds we have been examining.

EXAMPLE 16

Calculating Sample Excess Kurtosis

Having concluded in Example 15 that the annual returns on T. Rowe Price Equity Income Fund were negatively skewed during the 2008–2017 period, what can we say about the kurtosis of the fund's return distribution? Exhibit 33 (repeated below) recaps the annual returns for the fund.

Exhibit 33 Annual Rates of Return: T. Rowe Price Equity Income, 2008–2017 (Repeated)

Year	Return (%)
2008	−35.75
2009	25.62
2010	15.15
2011	−0.72
2012	17.25
2013	31.69
2014	7.75
2015	−7.76

45 See Campbell, Lo, and MacKinlay (1997) for more details.

Exhibit 33 (Continued)

Year	Return (%)
2016	18.25
2017	16.18

Source: performance.morningstar.com.

Using the information from Exhibit 33 repeated above, address the following:

1 Calculate the sample excess kurtosis of PRFDX showing two decimal places.

2 Characterize the shape of the distribution of PRFDX returns based on your answer to Part 1 as leptokurtic, mesokurtic, or platykurtic.

Solution to 1:

To calculate excess kurtosis, we find the sum of the deviations from the mean raised to the fourth power, divide by the standard deviation raised to the fourth power, and then multiply that result by $n(n + 1)/[(n - 1)(n - 2)(n - 3)]$. This calculation determines kurtosis. Excess kurtosis is kurtosis minus $3(n - 1)^2/[(n - 2)(n - 3)]$. Exhibit 36 gives the calculations.

Exhibit 36 Calculating Kurtosis for PRFDX

Year	R_t	$R_t - \overline{R}$	$\left(R_t - \overline{R}\right)^4$
2008	−35.75	−44.52	3,928,444.507
2009	25.62	16.85	80,611.986
2010	15.15	6.38	1,656.848
2011	−0.72	−9.49	8,110.822
2012	17.25	8.48	5,171.106
2013	31.69	22.92	275,967.827
2014	7.75	−1.02	1.082
2015	−7.76	−16.53	74,660.589
2016	18.25	9.48	8,076.689
2017	16.18	7.41	3,014.899
n =	10		
$\overline{R}$ =	8.77%		
		Sum =	4,385,716.355
s =	19.47%	s^4 =	143,702.329
		Sum/s^4 =	30.519
		$n(n + 1)/[(n - 1)(n - 2)(n - 3)]$ =	0.2183
		Kurtosis =	**6.661**
		$3(n - 1)^2/[(n - 2)(n - 3)]$ =	4.34
		Excess Kurtosis =	**2.32**

Source: performance.morningstar.com.

Using Equation 17, the calculation is

$$K_E = \left[\frac{110}{(9)(8)(7)}\right]\frac{4{,}385{,}716.355}{19.47^4} - \frac{3(9)^2}{(8)(7)} = 2.32$$

Solution to 2:

The distribution of PRFDX's annual returns appears to be leptokurtic, based on a positive sample excess kurtosis. The fairly large excess kurtosis of 2.32 indicates that the distribution of PRFDX's annual returns is fat-tailed relative to the normal distribution. With a negative skewness and a positive excess kurtosis, PRFDX's annual returns do not appear to have been normally distributed during the period.[46]

10 USING GEOMETRIC AND ARITHMETIC MEANS

With the concepts of descriptive statistics in hand, we will see why the geometric mean is appropriate for making investment statements about past performance. We will also explore why the arithmetic mean is appropriate for making investment statements in a forward-looking context.

For reporting historical returns, the geometric mean has considerable appeal because it is the rate of growth or return we would have had to earn each year to match the actual, cumulative investment performance. In our simplified Example 8, for instance, we purchased a stock for €100 and two years later it was worth €100, with an intervening year at €200. The geometric mean of 0 percent is clearly the compound rate of growth during the two years. Specifically, the ending amount is the beginning amount times $(1 + R_G)^2$. The geometric mean is an excellent measure of past performance.

Example 8 illustrated how the arithmetic mean can distort our assessment of historical performance. In that example, the total performance for the two-year period was unambiguously 0 percent. With a 100 percent return for the first year and −50 percent for the second, however, the arithmetic mean was 25 percent. As we noted previously, the arithmetic mean is always greater than or equal to the geometric mean. If we want to estimate the average return over a one-period horizon, we should use the arithmetic mean because the arithmetic mean is the average of one-period returns. If we want to estimate the average returns over more than one period, however, we should use the geometric mean of returns because the geometric mean captures how the total returns are linked over time.

As a corollary to using the geometric mean for performance reporting, the use of **semilogarithmic** rather than arithmetic scales is more appropriate when graphing past performance.[47] In the context of reporting performance, a semilogarithmic graph has an arithmetic scale on the horizontal axis for time and a logarithmic scale on the vertical axis for the value of the investment. The vertical axis values are spaced according to the differences between their logarithms. Suppose we want to represent

46 It is useful to know that we can conduct a Jarque–Bera (JB) statistical test of normality based on sample size n, sample skewness, and sample excess kurtosis. We can conclude that a distribution is not normal with no more than a 5 percent chance of being wrong if the quantity $\text{JB} = n\left[\left(S_K^2/6\right) + \left(K_E^2/24\right)\right]$ is 6 or greater for a sample with at least 30 observations. In this mutual fund example, we have only 10 observations and the test described is only correct based on large samples (as a guideline, for $n \geq 30$). Gujarati, Porter, and Gunasekar (2013) provides more details on this test.

47 See Campbell (1974) for more information.

£1, £10, £100, and £1,000 as values of an investment on the vertical axis. Note that each successive value represents a 10-fold increase over the previous value, and each will be equally spaced on the vertical axis because the difference in their logarithms is roughly 2.30; that is, ln 10 – ln 1 = ln 100 – ln 10 = ln 1,000 – ln 100 = 2.30. On a semilogarithmic scale, equal movements on the vertical axis reflect equal percentage changes, and growth at a constant compound rate plots as a straight line. A plot curving upward reflects increasing growth rates over time. The slopes of a plot at different points may be compared in order to judge relative growth rates.

In addition to reporting historical performance, financial analysts need to calculate expected equity risk premiums in a forward-looking context. For this purpose, the arithmetic mean is appropriate.

We can illustrate the use of the arithmetic mean in a forward-looking context with an example based on an investment's future cash flows. In contrasting the geometric and arithmetic means for discounting future cash flows, the essential issue concerns uncertainty. Suppose an investor with $100,000 faces an equal chance of a 100 percent return or a –50 percent return, represented on the tree diagram as a 50/50 chance of a 100 percent return or a –50 percent return per period. With 100 percent return in one period and –50 percent return in the other, the geometric mean return is $\sqrt{2(0.5)} - 1 = 0$.

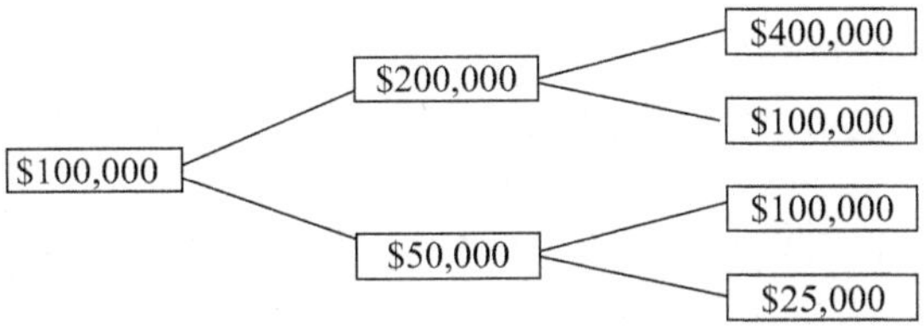

The geometric mean return of 0 percent gives the mode or median of ending wealth after two periods and thus accurately predicts the modal or median ending wealth of $100,000 in this example. Nevertheless, the arithmetic mean return better predicts the arithmetic mean ending wealth. With equal chances of 100 percent or –50 percent returns, consider the four equally likely outcomes of $400,000, $100,000, $100,000, and $25,000 as if they actually occurred. The arithmetic mean ending wealth would be $156,250 = ($400,000 + $100,000 + $100,000 + $25,000)/4. The actual returns would be 300 percent, 0 percent, 0 percent, and –75 percent for a two-period arithmetic mean return of (300 + 0 + 0 –75)/4 = 56.25 percent. This arithmetic mean return predicts the arithmetic mean ending wealth of $100,000 × 1.5625 = $156,250. Noting that 56.25 percent for two periods is 25 percent per period, we then must discount the expected terminal wealth of $156,250 at the 25 percent arithmetic mean rate to reflect the uncertainty in the cash flows.

Uncertainty in cash flows or returns causes the arithmetic mean to be larger than the geometric mean. The more uncertain the returns, the more divergence exists between the arithmetic and geometric means. The geometric mean return approximately equals the arithmetic return minus half the variance of return.[48] Zero variance or zero uncertainty in returns would leave the geometric and arithmetic return approximately equal, but real-world uncertainty presents an arithmetic mean return larger than the geometric. For example, for the nominal annual returns on S&P 500 from 1926 to 2017, Exhibit 32 reports an arithmetic mean of 12.06 percent and standard deviation of 19.79 percent. The geometric mean of these returns is 10.16 percent. We can see the geometric mean is approximately the arithmetic mean minus half of the variance of returns: $R_G \approx 0.1206 - (1/2)(0.1979^2) = 0.1010$, or 10.10 percent.

48 See Bodie, Kane, and Marcus (2017).

SUMMARY

In this reading, we have presented descriptive statistics, the set of methods that permit us to convert raw data into useful information for investment analysis.

- A population is defined as all members of a specified group. A sample is a subset of a population.
- A parameter is any descriptive measure of a population. A sample statistic (statistic, for short) is a quantity computed from or used to describe a sample.
- Data measurements are taken using one of four major scales: nominal, ordinal, interval, or ratio. Nominal scales categorize data but do not rank them. Ordinal scales sort data into categories that are ordered with respect to some characteristic. Interval scales provide not only ranking but also assurance that the differences between scale values are equal. Ratio scales have all the characteristics of interval scales as well as a true zero point as the origin. The scale on which data are measured determines the type of analysis that can be performed on the data.
- A frequency distribution is a tabular display of data summarized into a relatively small number of intervals. Frequency distributions permit us to evaluate how data are distributed.
- The relative frequency of observations in an interval is the number of observations in the interval divided by the total number of observations. The cumulative relative frequency cumulates (adds up) the relative frequencies as we move from the first interval to the last, thus giving the fraction of the observations that are less than the upper limit of each interval.
- A histogram is a bar chart of data that have been grouped into a frequency distribution. A frequency polygon is a graph of frequency distributions obtained by drawing straight lines joining successive points representing the class frequencies.
- Sample statistics such as measures of central tendency, measures of dispersion, skewness, and kurtosis help with investment analysis, particularly in making probabilistic statements about returns.
- Measures of central tendency specify where data are centered and include the (arithmetic) mean, median, and mode (most frequently occurring value). The mean is the sum of the observations divided by the number of observations. The median is the value of the middle item (or the mean of the values of the two middle items) when the items in a set are sorted into ascending or descending order. The mean is the most frequently used measure of central tendency. The median is not influenced by extreme values and is most useful in the case of skewed distributions. The mode is the only measure of central tendency that can be used with nominal data.
- A portfolio's return is a weighted mean return computed from the returns on the individual assets, where the weight applied to each asset's return is the fraction of the portfolio invested in that asset.
- The geometric mean, G, of a set of observations $X_1, X_2, \ldots, X_n$ is $G = \sqrt[n]{X_1 X_2 X_3 \ldots X_n}$ with $X_i \geq 0$ for $i = 1, 2, \ldots, n$. The geometric mean is especially important in reporting compound growth rates for time series data.
- Quantiles such as the median, quartiles, quintiles, deciles, and percentiles are location parameters that divide a distribution into halves, quarters, fifths, tenths, and hundredths, respectively.

- Dispersion measures such as the variance, standard deviation, and mean absolute deviation (MAD) describe the variability of outcomes around the arithmetic mean.
- Range is defined as the maximum value minus the minimum value. Range has only a limited scope because it uses information from only two observations.
- MAD for a sample is $\frac{\sum_{i=1}^{n}\left|X_i - \overline{X}\right|}{n}$ where $\overline{X}$ is the sample mean and n is the number of observations in the sample.
- The variance is the average of the squared deviations around the mean, and the standard deviation is the positive square root of variance. In computing sample variance (s^2) and sample standard deviation, the average squared deviation is computed using a divisor equal to the sample size minus 1.
- The semivariance is the average squared deviation below the mean; semideviation is the positive square root of semivariance. Target semivariance is the average squared deviation below a target level; target semideviation is its positive square root. All these measures quantify downside risk.
- According to Chebyshev's inequality, the proportion of the observations within k standard deviations of the arithmetic mean is at least $1 - 1/k^2$ for all $k > 1$. Chebyshev's inequality permits us to make probabilistic statements about the proportion of observations within various intervals around the mean for any distribution with finite variance. As a result of Chebyshev's inequality, a two-standard-deviation interval around the mean must contain at least 75 percent of the observations, and a three-standard-deviation interval around the mean must contain at least 89 percent of the observations, no matter how the data are distributed.
- The coefficient of variation, CV, is the ratio of the standard deviation of a set of observations to their mean value. A scale-free measure of relative dispersion, by expressing the magnitude of variation among observations relative to their average size, the CV permits direct comparisons of dispersion across different data sets.
- Skew describes the degree to which a distribution is not symmetric about its mean. A return distribution with positive skewness has frequent small losses and a few extreme gains. A return distribution with negative skewness has frequent small gains and a few extreme losses. Zero skewness indicates a symmetric distribution of returns.
- Kurtosis measures combined weight of the tails of a distribution relative to the rest of the distribution. Distributions are characterized as leptokurtic, mesokurtic, or platykurtic according to whether there is relatively more, the same, or less weight in the tails. The calculation for kurtosis involves finding the average of deviations from the mean raised to the fourth power and then standardizing that average by the standard deviation raised to the fourth power. Excess kurtosis is kurtosis minus 3, the value of kurtosis for all normal distributions.

REFERENCES

Black, Fischer. 1993. "Estimating Expected Return." *Financial Analysts Journal*, vol. 49, no. 5:36–38.

Bodie, Zvi, Alex Kane, and Alan J. Marcus. 2017. *Investments*, 11th edition. New York: McGraw-Hill Education.

Campbell, Stephen K. 1974. *Flaws and Fallacies in Statistical Thinking*. Englewood Cliffs, NJ: Prentice-Hall.

Campbell, John, Andrew Lo, and A. Craig MacKinlay. 1997. *The Econometrics of Financial Markets*. Princeton, NJ: Princeton University Press.

Choobinbeh, N. Fred. 2005. "Semivariance" in *The Encyclopedia of Statistical Sciences*. New York: Wiley.

Dimson, Elroy, Paul Marsh, and Mike Staunton. 2011. "Equity Premiums around the World" in *Rethinking the Equity Risk Premium*. Charlottesville, VA: Research Foundation of CFA Institute.

Elton, Edwin J., Martin J. Gruber, Stephen J. Brown, and William N. Goetzmann. 2013. *Modern Portfolio Theory and Investment Analysis*, 9th edition. Hoboken, NJ: Wiley.

Forbes. 16 September 2013. "The Honor Roll." New York: Forbes Management Co., Inc.

Gujarati, Damodar N., Dawn C. Porter, and Sangeetha Gunasekar. 2013. *Basic Econometrics*, 5th edition. New York: McGraw-Hill Irwin.

Ibbotson, Roger G., Zhiwu Chen, Daniel Y.-J. Kim, and Wendy Y. Hu. 2013. "Liquidity as an Investment Style." *Financial Analysts Journal*, vol. 69, no. 3:30–44.

Reilly, Frank K., and Keith C. Brown. 2018. *Investment Analysis and Portfolio Management*, 11th edition. Mason, OH: Cengage South-Western.

Ibbotson, Roger G., and Daniel Y.-J. Kim. 2018. "Liquidity as an Investment Style. 2018 Update" available at research.zebra-capital.com ,

Von Hippel, Paul T. 2005. "Mean, Median, and Skew: Correcting a Textbook Rule." *Journal of Statistics Education*, vol. 13, no. 2. ww2.amstat.org/publications/jse/v13n2/vonhippel.html. Accessed 2 January 2018.

Wheeler, Donald J. 2011. "Problems with Skewness and Kurtosis, Part One: What Do the Shape Parameters Do?" *Quality Digest Daily*, August 1-2, 2011. https://www.spcpress.com/pdf/DJW231.pdf. Accessed 2 January 2018.

PRACTICE PROBLEMS

1 Which of the following groups *best* illustrates a sample?

A The set of all estimates for Exxon Mobil's EPS for next financial year

B The FTSE Eurotop 100 as a representation of the European stock market

C UK shares traded on Wednesday of last week that also closed above £120/share on the London Stock Exchange

2 Published ratings on stocks ranging from 1 (strong sell) to 5 (strong buy) are examples of which measurement scale?

A Ordinal

B Interval

C Nominal

3 Which of the following groups *best* illustrates a population?

A The 500 companies in the S&P 500 Index

B The NYSE-listed stocks in the Dow Jones Industrial Average

C The Lehman Aggregate Bond Index as a representation of the US bond market

4 In descriptive statistics, an example of a parameter is the:

A median of a population.

B mean of a sample of observations.

C standard deviation of a sample of observations.

5 A mutual fund has the return frequency distribution shown in the following table.

Return Interval (%)	Absolute Frequency
−10.0 to −7.0	3
−7.0 to −4.0	7
−4.0 to −1.0	10
−1.0 to +2.0	12
+2.0 to +5.0	23
+5.0 to +8.0	5

Which of the following statements is correct?

A The relative frequency of the interval "−1.0 to +2.0" is 20%.

B The relative frequency of the interval "+2.0 to +5.0" is 23%.

C The cumulative relative frequency of the interval "+5.0 to +8.0" is 91.7%.

6 An analyst is using the data in the following table to prepare a statistical report.

Portfolio's Deviations from Benchmark Return, 2003–2014 (%)			
Year 1	2.48	**Year 7**	−9.19
Year 2	−2.59	**Year 8**	−5.11
Year 3	9.47	**Year 9**	1.33

(continued)

(Continued)

Year 4	−0.55	**Year 10**	6.84
Year 5	−1.69	**Year 11**	3.04
Year 6	−0.89	**Year 12**	4.72

The cumulative relative frequency for the interval −1.71% ≤ x < 2.03% is *closest* to:

A 0.250.

B 0.333.

C 0.583.

7 Frequency distributions summarize data in:

A a tabular display.

B overlapping intervals.

C a relatively large number of intervals.

8 Based on the table below, which of the following statements is correct?

Frequency Distributions of Sample Returns

Interval	Range	Absolute Frequency
A	−10% ≤ Observation ⊠ −5%	2
B	−5% ≤ Observation ⊠ 0%	7
C	0% ≤ Observation < 5%	15
D	5% ≤ Observation < 10%	2

A The relative frequency of Interval C is 15.

B The cumulative frequency of Interval D is 100%.

C The cumulative relative frequency of Interval C is 92.3%.

The following information relates to Questions 9–10

The following histogram shows a distribution of the S&P 500 Index annual returns for a 50-year period:

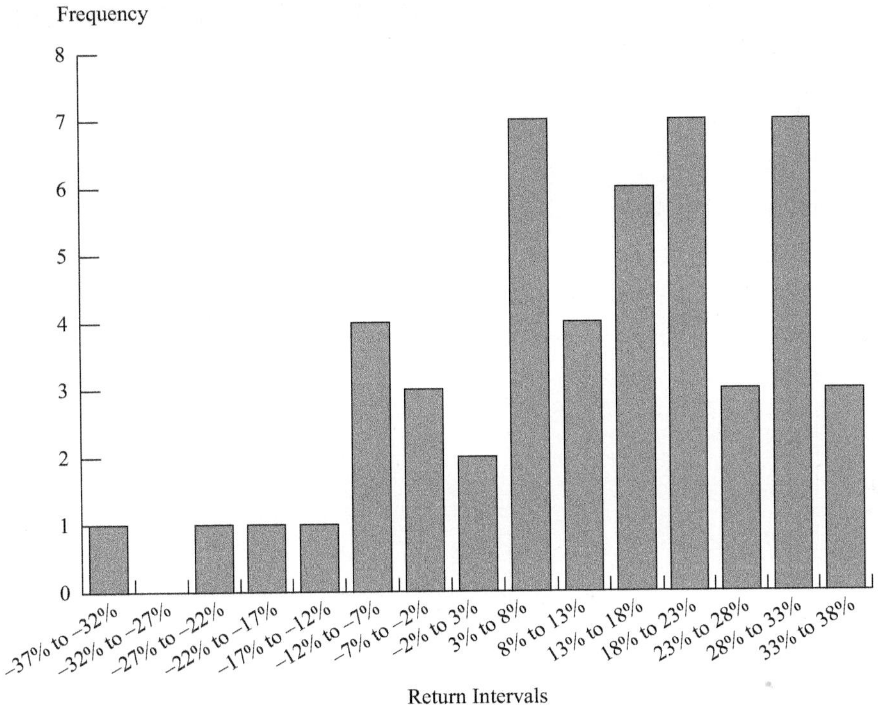

9 The interval containing the median return is:

A 3% to 8%.

B 8% to 13%.

C 13% to 18%.

10 Based on the previous histogram, the distribution is *best* described as having:

A one mode.

B two modes.

C three modes.

---

11 The following is a frequency polygon of monthly exchange rate changes in the US dollar/Japanese yen spot exchange rate for a four-year period. A positive change represents yen appreciation (the yen buys more dollars), and a negative change represents yen depreciation (the yen buys fewer dollars).

Monthly Changes in the US Dollar/Japanese Yen Spot Exchange Rate

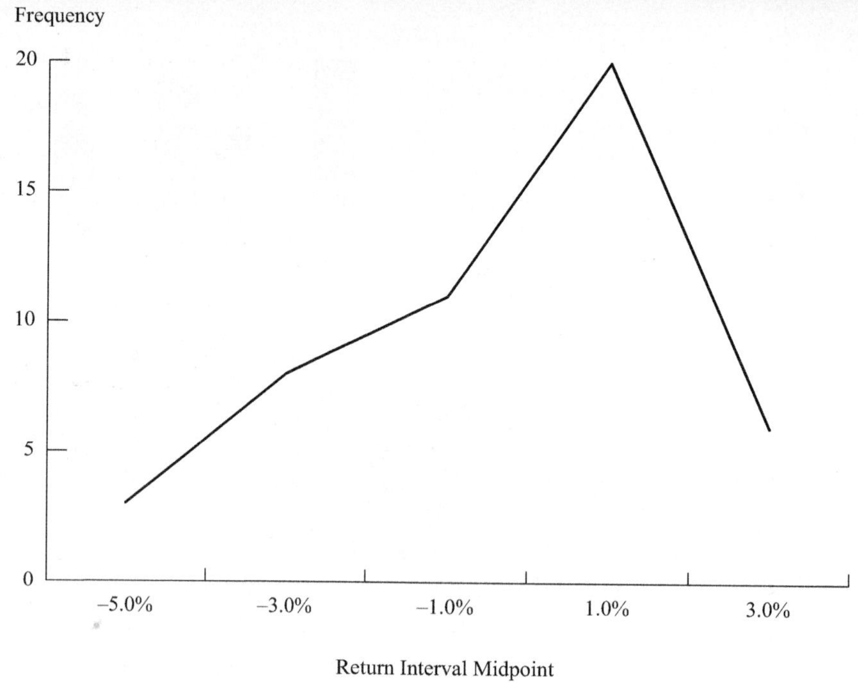

Based on the chart, yen appreciation:

A occurred more than 50% of the time.

B was less frequent than yen depreciation.

C in the 0.0 to 2.0 interval occurred 20% of the time.

12 The height of a bar in a histogram represents the matching data interval's:

A relative frequency.

B absolute frequency.

C cumulative frequency.

The following table relates to Questions 13 and 14

Equity Returns for Six Companies

Company	Total Equity Return (%)
A	–4.53
B	–1.40
C	–1.20
D	–1.20

(Continued)

Company	Total Equity Return (%)
E	0.70
F	8.90

13 Based on the table, the arithmetic mean of the equity returns is *closest* to the return of:

A Company B.

B Company C.

C Company E.

14 Using the data from the table, the difference between the median and the mode is *closest* to:

A −1.41.

B 0.00.

C 1.41.

---

15 The annual returns for three portfolios are shown in the following table. Portfolios P and R were created in Year 1, Portfolio Q in Year 2.

	Annual Portfolio Returns (%)				
	Year 1	Year 2	Year 3	Year 4	Year 5
Portfolio P	−3.0	4.0	5.0	3.0	7.0
Portfolio Q		−3.0	6.0	4.0	8.0
Portfolio R	1.0	−1.0	4.0	4.0	3.0

The median annual return from portfolio creation to 2013 for:

A Portfolio P is 4.5%.

B Portfolio Q is 4.0%.

C Portfolio R is higher than its arithmetic mean annual return.

16 Last year, an investor allocated his retirement savings in the asset classes shown in the following table.

Asset Class	Asset Allocation (%)	Asset Class Return (%)
Large-cap US equities	20.0	8.0
Small-cap US equities	40.0	12.0
Emerging market equities	25.0	−3.0
High-yield bonds	15.0	4.0

The portfolio return in 2015 is *closest to*:

A 5.1%.

B 5.3%.

C 6.3%.

17 The following table shows the annual returns for Fund Y.

	Fund Y (%)
Year 1	19.5
Year 2	−1.9
Year 3	19.7
Year 4	35.0
Year 5	5.7

The geometric mean for Fund Y is *closest* to:

A 14.9%.

B 15.6%.

C 19.5%.

18 A manager invests €5,000 annually in a security for four years at the prices shown in the following table.

	Purchase Price of Security (€)
Year 1	62.00
Year 2	76.00
Year 3	84.00
Year 4	90.00

The average price paid for the security is *closest* to:

A €76.48.

B €77.26.

C €78.00.

The following information relates to Questions 19–20

The following exhibit shows the annual MSCI World Index total returns for a 10-year period.

Year 1	15.25%	**Year 6**	30.79%
Year 2	10.02%	**Year 7**	12.34%
Year 3	20.65%	**Year 8**	−5.02%
Year 4	9.57%	**Year 9**	16.54%
Year 5	−40.33%	**Year 10**	27.37%

19 The fourth quintile return for the MSCI World Index is *closest* to:

A 20.65%.

B 26.03%.

C 27.37%.

20 For Year 6 to Year 10, the mean absolute deviation of the MSCI World Index total returns is *closest* to:

A 10.20%.

B 12.74%.

C 16.40%.

The following table relates to questions 21 and 22

10 Years of S&P 500 Total Returns (in Ascending Order)
Returns
−38.49%
−0.73%
0.00%
9.54%
11.39%
12.78%
13.41%
19.42%
23.45%
29.60%

21 The third quartile percentage of total returns is *closest* to:

A 19.42%.

B 20.43%.

C 23.45%.

22 Complete the missing entries in the table below to answer this question.

Overall Risk Measures, S&P 500 vs. Sample Portfolio

	S&P 500	Sample Portfolio
Mean	8.04%	8.54%
Range	–	67.09%
MAD	–	11.78%

An analyst does a performance measurement to compare the risk of a contemporaneous sample portfolio with that of the S&P 500 by determining the ranges and mean absolute deviations (MAD) of the two investments. The comparison shows that the S&P 500 appears riskier in terms of the:

A range only.

B MAD only.

C MAD and range.

23 Annual returns and summary statistics for three funds are listed in the following table:

Year	Annual Returns (%)		
	Fund ABC	**Fund XYZ**	**Fund PQR**
Year 1	−20.0	−33.0	−14.0
Year 2	23.0	−12.0	−18.0
Year 3	−14.0	−12.0	6.0
Year 4	5.0	−8.0	−2.0
Year 5	−14.0	11.0	3.0
Mean	−4.0	−10.8	−5.0
Standard deviation	17.8	15.6	10.5

The fund that shows the highest dispersion is:

A Fund PQR if the measure of dispersion is the range.

B Fund XYZ if the measure of dispersion is the variance.

C Fund ABC if the measure of dispersion is the mean absolute deviation.

24 Using the information in the following table, the sample standard deviation for VWIGX is *closest* to:

2015–2017 Total Return for VWIGX

Year	Vanguard International Growth Fund (VWIGX)
2015	−0.67%
2016	1.71%
2017	42.96%

A 6.02%.

B 12.04%.

C 24.54%.

25 Over the past 240 months, an investor's portfolio had a mean monthly return of 0.79%, with a standard deviation of monthly returns of 1.16%. According to Chebyshev's inequality, the minimum number of the 240 monthly returns that fall into the range of −0.95% to 2.53% is *closest* to:

A 80.

B 107.

C 133.

26 For a distribution of 2,000 observations with finite variance, sample mean of 10.0%, and standard deviation of 4.0%, what is the minimum number of observations that will lie within 8.0% around the mean according to Chebyshev's Inequality?

A 720

B 1,500

C 1,680

27 The mean monthly return and the standard deviation for three industry sectors are shown in the following exhibit.

Sector	Mean Monthly Return (%)	Standard Deviation of Return (%)
Utilities (UTIL)	2.10	1.23
Materials (MATR)	1.25	1.35
Industrials (INDU)	3.01	1.52

Based on the coefficient of variation, the riskiest sector is:

A utilities.

B materials.

C industrials.

The following information relates to Questions 28–29

The following table shows various statistics for Portfolios 1, 2, and 3.

	Mean Return (%)	Standard Deviation of Returns (%)	Skewness	Excess Kurtosis
Portfolio 1	7.8	15.1	0.0	0.7
Portfolio 2	10.2	20.5	0.9	−1.8
Portfolio 3	12.9	29.3	−1.5	6.2

28 The skewness of Portfolio 1 indicates its mean return is *most likely*:

A less than its median.

B equal to its median.

C greater than its median.

29 Compared with a normal distribution, the distribution of returns for Portfolio 3 *most likely*:

A has less weight in the tails.

B has a greater number of extreme returns.

C has fewer small deviations from its mean.

---

30 Two portfolios have unimodal return distributions. Portfolio 1 has a skewness of 0.77, and Portfolio 2 has a skewness of −1.11.

Which of the following is correct?

A For Portfolio 1, the median is less than the mean.

B For Portfolio 1, the mode is greater than the mean.

C For Portfolio 2, the mean is greater than the median.

31 A return distribution with frequent small gains and a few extreme losses is *most likely* to be called:

A leptokurtic.

B positively skewed.

C negatively skewed.

32 Which of the following sequences *best* represents the relative sizes of the mean, median, and mode for a positively skewed unimodal distribution?

A mode $\leq$ median $\leq$ mean

B mode $<$ median $<$ mean

C mean $<$ median $<$ mode

33 A distribution with excess kurtosis less than zero is termed:

A mesokurtic.

B platykurtic.

C leptokurtic.

34 When analyzing investment returns, which of the following statements is correct?

A The geometric mean will exceed the arithmetic mean for a series with non-zero variance.

B The geometric mean measures an investment's compound rate of growth over multiple periods.

C The arithmetic mean accurately estimates an investment's terminal value over multiple periods.

35 Which of the following statistical means *best* measures a mutual fund's past performance?

A Harmonic

B Geometric

C Arithmetic

SOLUTIONS

1 B is correct. The FTSE Eurotop 100 represents a sample of all European stocks. It is a subset of the population of all European stocks.

2 A is correct. Ordinal scales sort data into categories that are ordered with respect to some characteristic and may involve numbers to identify categories but do not assure that the differences between scale values are equal. The buy rating scale indicates that a stock ranked 5 is expected to perform better than a stock ranked 4, but it tells us nothing about the performance difference between stocks ranked 4 and 5 compared with the performance difference between stocks ranked 1 and 2, and so on.

3 A is correct. A population is defined as all members of a specified group. The S&P 500 Index consists of 500 companies, so this group is the population of companies in the index.

B is incorrect because there are several Dow Jones component stocks that are not traded on the NYSE, making the NYSE group a subset of the total population of stocks included in the Dow Jones average.

C is incorrect because although the Lehman Aggregate Bond Index is representative of the US bond market, it is a sampling of bonds in that market and not the entire population of bonds in that market.

4 A is correct. Any descriptive measure of a population characteristic is referred to as a parameter.

5 A is correct. The relative frequency is the absolute frequency of each interval divided by the total number of observations. Here, the relative frequency is calculated as: (12/60) × 100 = 20%. B is incorrect because the relative frequency of this interval is (23/60) × 100 = 38.33%. C is incorrect because the cumulative relative frequency of the last interval must equal 100%.

6 C is correct. The cumulative relative frequency of an interval identifies the fraction of observations that are less than the upper limit of the given interval. It is determined by summing the relative frequencies from the lowest interval up to and including the given interval. The following exhibit shows the relative frequencies for all the intervals of the data from the previous exhibit:

Lower Limit (%)	Upper Limit (%)	Absolute Frequency	Relative Frequency	Cumulative Relative Frequency
−9.19 ≤	< −5.45	1	0.083	0.083
−5.45 ≤	< −1.71	2	0.167	0.250
−1.71 ≤	< 2.03	4	0.333	0.583
2.03 ≤	< 5.77	3	0.250	0.833
5.77 ≤	≥ 9.51	2	0.167	1.000

The interval −1.71% ≤ x < 2.03% has a cumulative relative frequency of 0.583.

7 A is correct. A frequency distribution is a tabular display of data summarized into a relatively small number of intervals.

B is incorrect because intervals cannot overlap. Each observation is placed uniquely into one interval.

C is incorrect because a frequency distribution is summarized into a relatively small number of intervals.

8 C is correct because the cumulative relative frequency of an interval tells us the fraction of all observations that are less than the upper limit of an interval. For Interval C, that would be (2 + 7 + 15)/26 = 92.3%.

A is incorrect because the relative frequency of an interval is the absolute frequency of that interval divided by the total number of observations, here 15/26 = 57.7%. The number 15 represents Interval C's absolute frequency (also known as frequency), which is simply the actual number of observations in a given interval.

B is incorrect because the cumulative frequency tells us the number of observations that are less than the upper limit of a return interval, not the percentage of observations meeting that criteria. Because Interval D is the uppermost return interval, its cumulative frequency is the total number of observations for all intervals, yielding 2 + 7 + 15 + 2 = 26 and not 100%, which is the cumulative relative frequency for Interval D.

9 C is correct. Because there are 50 data points in the histogram, the median return would be the mean of the 50/2 = 25th and (50 + 2)/2 = 26th positions. The sum of the return interval frequencies to the left of the 13% to 18% interval is 24. As a result, the 25th and 26th returns will fall in the 13% to 18% interval.

10 C is correct. The mode of a distribution with data grouped in intervals is the interval with the highest frequency. The three intervals of 3% to 8%, 18% to 23%, and 28% to 33% all have a high frequency of 7.

11 A is correct. Twenty observations lie in the interval "0.0 to 2.0," and six observations lie in the 2.0 to 4.0 interval. Together, they represent 26/48, or 54.17% of all observations, which is more than 50%.

12 B is correct. In a histogram, the height of each bar represents the absolute frequency of its associated data interval.

A is incorrect because the height of each bar in a histogram represents the absolute (not relative) frequency.

C is incorrect because the height of each bar in a histogram represents the absolute (not cumulative) frequency.

13 C is correct. The arithmetic mean equals the sum of the observations divided by the number of observations. In this case, (–4.53 –1.40 –1.20 –1.20 + 0.70 + 8.90)/6 = 1.27/6 = 0.21.

The arithmetic mean is closest to the total equity return of Company E at 0.70 for a difference of (0.70 – 0.21) = 0.49.

A is incorrect because compared with the arithmetic mean, Company B's total equity return has a difference of (–1.40 –0.21) = –1.61, which is a wider distance from the mean than Company E's total equity return.

B is incorrect because compared with the arithmetic mean, Company C's total equity return has a difference of (–1.20 – 0.21) = –1.41, which is a wider distance from the mean than Company E's total equity return.

14 B is correct. The median is the value of the middle item of a set of items sorted into ascending or descending order. In an even-numbered sample, we define the median as the mean of the values of items occupying the $n/2$ and $(n + 2)/2$ positions (the two middle items). Given Table 2 has six observations, the median is the mean of the third and fourth observations. Because both are–1.20, the median is –1.20.

The mode is the most frequently occurring value in a distribution. The only value occurring more than once is –1.20.

Because the median and the mode both equal –1.20, their difference is zero.

A is incorrect because −1.41 is the difference between both the identical mode and median with the arithmetic mean. Both differences are: [−1.20 − (0.21)] = −1.41.

C is incorrect because 1.41 is the difference between the arithmetic mean with both the identical mode and median. Both differences are: [0.21 − (−1.20)] = 1.41.

15 C is correct. The median of Portfolio R is 0.8% higher than the mean for Portfolio R.

16 C is correct. The portfolio return must be calculated as the weighted mean return, where the weights are the allocations in each asset class:

$$(0.20 \times 8\%) + (0.40 \times 12\%) + (0.25 \times -3\%) + (0.15 \times 4\%) = 6.25\%, \text{ or} \approx 6.3\%.$$

17 A is correct. The geometric mean return for Fund Y is found as follows:

$$\text{Fund Y} = [(1 + 0.195) \times (1 - 0.019) \times (1 + 0.197) \times (1 + 0.350) \times (1 + 0.057)]^{(1/5)} - 1$$
$$= 14.9\%.$$

18 A is correct. The harmonic mean is appropriate for determining the average price per unit. It is calculated by summing the reciprocals of the prices; then averaging that sum by dividing by the number of prices; and finally, taking the reciprocal of the average:

$$4/[(1/62.00) + (1/76.00) + (1/84.00) + (1/90.00)] = €76.48.$$

19 B is correct. Quintiles divide a distribution into fifths, with the fourth quintile occurring at the point at which 80% of the observations lie below it. The fourth quintile is equivalent to the 80th percentile. To find the yth percentile (P_y), we first must determine its location. The formula for the location (L_y) of a yth percentile in an array with n entries sorted in ascending order is $L_y = (n + 1) \times (y/100)$. In this case, $n = 10$ and $y = 80\%$, so

$$L_{80} = (10 + 1) \times (80/100) = 11 \times 0.8 = 8.8.$$

With the data arranged in ascending order (−40.33%, −5.02%, 9.57%, 10.02%, 12.34%, 15.25%, 16.54%, 20.65%, 27.37%, and 30.79%), the 8.8th position would be between the 8th and 9th entries, 20.65% and 27.37%, respectively. Using linear interpolation, $P_{80} = X_8 + (L_y - 8) \times (X_9 - X_8)$,

$$P_{80} = 20.65 + (8.8 - 8) \times (27.37 - 20.65)$$
$$= 20.65 + (0.8 \times 6.72) = 20.65 + 5.38$$
$$= 26.03\%.$$

20 A is correct. The formula for mean absolute deviation (MAD) is

$$\text{MAD} = \frac{\sum_{i=1}^{n} \left| X_i - \bar{X} \right|}{n}$$

Column 1: Sum annual returns and divide by n to find the arithmetic mean $(\bar{X})$ of 16.40%.

Column 2: Calculate the absolute value of the difference between each year's return and the mean from Column 1. Sum the results and divide by n to find the MAD.

These calculations are shown in the following exhibit:

	Column 1		Column 2
Year	**Return**		$\lvert X_i - \overline{X} \rvert$
Year 6	30.79%		14.39%
Year 7	12.34%		4.06%
Year 8	−5.02%		21.42%
Year 9	16.54%		0.14%
Year 10	27.37%		10.97%
Sum:	82.02%	Sum:	50.98%
n:	5	n:	5
$\overline{X}$:	16.40%	MAD:	10.20%

21 B is correct. Quartiles divide a distribution into quarters, with the third quartile occurring at the point at which 75% of the observations lie below it. The third quartile is equivalent to the 75th percentile. The formula for the location (L_y) of the yth percentile in an array with n entries sorted in ascending order is $L_y = (n + 1) \times (y/100)$. In this case, $n = 10$ and $y = 75$, so $L_{75} = (11) \times (75/100) = 11 \times 0.75 = 8.25$.

Rearranging the data in ascending order (i.e., with the lowest value at the top), the 8.25th position would be between the eighth and ninth rank order entries, 19.42% and 23.45%, respectively. Using linear interpolation, $P_{75} = X_8 + (L_{75} - 8) \times (X_9 - X_8)$, so P_{75} = 19.42% + (8.25 − 8) × (23.45% − 19.42%) = 20.428%, or 20.43%.

A is incorrect because it is the non-interpolated value of the eighth observation without the adjustment for placement at the location of the third quartile.

C is incorrect because it is the non-interpolated value of the ninth observation without the adjustment for placement at the location of the third quartile.

22 C is correct. Both the range and MAD of the S&P 500 are greater than the range and MAD of the sample portfolio. Thus both measures indicate the S&P 500 is riskier.

The range for the S&P 500 equals the distance between the lowest and highest values in the dataset. That distance for the S&P 500 is [29.60% − (−38.49%)] = 68.09%. Given that this range is larger than the range of the sample portfolio at 67.09%, the S&P 500 appears riskier than the sample portfolio.

The MAD for the S&P 500 returns equals the sum of the absolute deviations from the mean return divided by the number of observations.

$$\text{MAD} = \frac{\sum_{i=1}^{n} \lvert X_i - \overline{X} \rvert}{n}$$, where $\overline{X}$ is the sample mean and n is the number of observations in the sample.

Use the 10 observed S&P 500 returns from the table (sample mean = 8.04%) to calculate the MAD for the S&P 500 as follows:

$$\text{MAD}_{\text{S\&P500}} = \frac{\lvert 19.42 - \bar{x} \rvert + \lvert 9.54 - \bar{x} \rvert + \lvert -0.73 - \bar{x} \rvert + \lvert 11.39 - \bar{x} \rvert + \lvert 29.60 - \bar{x} \rvert + \lvert 13.41 - \bar{x} \rvert + \lvert 0.00 - \bar{x} \rvert + \lvert 12.78 - \bar{x} \rvert + \lvert 23.45 - \bar{x} \rvert + \lvert -38.49 - }{10}$$

$$\text{MAD}_{\text{S\&P500}} = 12.67\%$$

Given that the MAD for the S&P 500 is greater than the MAD for the sample portfolio (12.67% versus 11.78%), the S&P 500 appears riskier than the sample portfolio.

A is incorrect because although the S&P 500 is correctly identified as having the larger range, the sample portfolio has a smaller MAD.

B is incorrect because although the S&P 500 is correctly identified as having the larger MAD, the Sample Portfolio has a smaller range.

23 C is correct. The mean absolute deviation (MAD) of Fund ABC's returns is greater than the MAD of both of the other funds.

$$\text{MAD} = \frac{\sum_{i=1}^{n}\left|X_i - \bar{X}\right|}{n}, \text{ where } \bar{X} \text{ is the arithmetic mean of the series.}$$

MAD for Fund ABC =

$$\frac{\left|-20-(-4)\right| + \left|23-(-4)\right| + \left|-14-(-4)\right| + \left|5-(-4)\right| + \left|-14-(-4)\right|}{5} = 14.4\%$$

MAD for Fund XYZ =

$$\frac{\left|-33-(-10.8)\right| + \left|-12-(-10.8)\right| + \left|-12-(-10.8)\right| + \left|-8-(-10.8)\right| + \left|11-(-10.8)\right|}{5} = 9.8\%$$

MAD for Fund PQR =

$$\frac{\left|-14-(-5)\right| + \left|-18-(-5)\right| + \left|6-(-5)\right| + \left|-2-(-5)\right| + \left|3-(-5)\right|}{5} = 8.8\%$$

A and B are incorrect because the range and variance of the three funds are as follows:

	Fund ABC	Fund XYZ	Fund PQR
Range	43%	44%	24%
Variance	317	243	110

The numbers shown for variance are understood to be in "percent squared" terms so that when taking the square root, the result is standard deviation in percentage terms. Alternatively, by expressing standard deviation and variance in decimal form, one can avoid the issue of units; in decimal form, the variances for Fund ABC, Fund XYZ, and Fund PQR are 0.0317, 0.0243, and 0.0110, respectively.

24 C is correct. The sample variance is defined as sum of the squared deviations from the sample mean divided by the sample size minus one, and the sample standard deviation equals the square root of the sample variance.

The following figure summarizes the inputs for the calculation of VWGIX sample variance.

Year	VWIGX	$(X_i - \bar{X})^2$
2015	–0.67%	2.35
2016	1.71%	1.68
2017	42.96%	8.00

(continued)

Year	VWIGX	$(X_i - \bar{X})^2$
Sample mean $(\bar{X})$	14.67%	
$\sum(X - \bar{X})^2$		12.04
$\left[\sum(X - \bar{X})^2\right]/(n-1) = \sigma^2$	[12.04/2]	6.02
$\sqrt{\left[\sum(X - \bar{X})^2\right]/(n-1)} = \sigma$	$\sqrt{(12.04/2)}$	24.54%

The sample variance is thus calculated as $\dfrac{\left[\sum(X - \bar{X})^2\right]}{(n-1)} = \dfrac{12.04}{2} = 6.02$.

The square root of the sample variance is the sample standard deviation.

That number is $\left(\sqrt{6.02}\right) = 24.54\%$.

A is incorrect because it is the sample variance for VWGIX, not its sample standard deviation.

B is incorrect because it represents the sum of the squared deviations from the mean, not the sample standard deviation.

25 C is correct. According to Chebyshev's inequality, the proportion of the observations within k standard deviations of the arithmetic mean is at least $1 - 1/k^2$ for all $k > 1$.

The upper limit of the range is 2.53%, which is 2.53 − 0.79 = 1.74% above the mean. The lower limit is −0.95, which is 0.79 − (−0.95) = 1.74% below the mean. As a result, k = 1.74/1.16 = 1.50 standard deviations.

Because k = 1.50, the proportion of observations within the interval is at least 1 − $1/1.5^2$ = 1 − 0.444 = 0.556, or 55.6%. Thus, the number of observations in the given range is at least 240 × 55.6%, which is ≈ 133.

26 B is correct. Observations within 8% of the sample mean will cover an interval of 8/4 or two standard deviations. Chebyshev's Inequality says the proportion of the observations P within k standard deviations of the arithmetic mean is at least $1 - 1/k^2$ for all $k > 1$. So, solving for k = 2: P = 1 − ¼ = 75%. Given 2,000 observations, this implies at least 1,500 will lie within 8.0% of the mean.

A is incorrect because 720 shows P = 720/2,000 = 36.0% of the observations. Using P to solve for k implies 36.0% = $1 - 1/k^2$, where k = 1.25. This result would cover an interval only 4% × 1.25 or 5% around the mean (i.e. less than two standard deviations).

C is incorrect because 1,680 shows P = 1,680/2,000 = 84.0% of the observations. Using P to solve for k implies 84.0% = $1 - 1/k^2$, where k = 2.50. This result would cover an interval of 4% × 2.5, or 10% around the mean (i.e., more than two standard deviations).

27 B is correct. The coefficient of variation (CV) is the ratio of the standard deviation to the mean, where a higher CV implies greater risk per unit of return.

$$CV_{UTIL} = \frac{s}{\bar{X}} = \frac{1.23\%}{2.10\%} = 0.59$$

$$CV_{MATR} = \frac{s}{\overline{X}} = \frac{1.35\%}{1.25\%} = 1.08$$

$$CV_{INDU} = \frac{s}{\overline{X}} = \frac{1.52\%}{3.01\%} = 0.51$$

28 B is correct. Portfolio 1 has a skewness of 0.0, which indicates that the portfolio's return distribution is symmetrical and thus its mean and median are equal.

29 B is correct. Portfolio 3 has positive excess kurtosis (i.e., kurtosis greater than 3), which indicates that its return distribution is leptokurtic and has fatter tails than the normal. The fatter tails mean Portfolio 3 has a greater number of extreme returns.

30 A is correct. Portfolio 1 is positively skewed, so the mean is greater than the median, which is greater than the mode.

31 C is correct. A return distribution with negative skew has frequent small gains and a few extreme losses.

A is incorrect because a leptokurtic distribution is more peaked with fatter tails, which exhibit both extreme gains and losses.

B is incorrect because a return distribution with positive skew has frequent small losses and a few extreme gains.

32 B is correct. For the positively skewed unimodal distribution, the mode is less than the median, which is less than the mean.

A is incorrect because, for the positively skewed unimodal distribution, the mode is less than the median (not less than or equal to), which is less than (not less than or equal to) the mean.

C is incorrect because, for the negatively (not positively) skewed unimodal distribution, the mean is less than the median, which is less than the mode.

33 B is correct. A platykurtic distribution has excess kurtosis less than zero.

A is incorrect because a normal or other mesokurtic distribution has excess kurtosis equal to zero.

C is incorrect because a leptokurtic distribution has excess kurtosis greater than zero.

34 B is correct. The geometric mean compounds the periodic returns of every period, giving the investor a more accurate measure of the terminal value of an investment.

35 B is correct. The geometric mean is an excellent measure of past performance. For reporting historical returns, the geometric mean has considerable appeal because it is the rate of growth or return a fund would have had to earn each year to match the actual, cumulative investment performance. To estimate the average returns over more than one period, the geometric mean captures how the total returns are linked over time.

A is incorrect because the harmonic mean is more appropriate for determining the average price per unit, not evaluating a mutual fund's return history. The average price paid is in fact the harmonic mean of the asset's prices at the purchase dates. The harmonic mean is applicable when ratios are repeatedly applied to a fixed quantity to yield a variable number of units, such as in cost averaging, which involves the periodic investment of a fixed amount of money.

C is incorrect because the arithmetic mean is more appropriate for making investment statements in a forward-looking context, not for historical returns. It can distort the assessment of historical performance, so it is better applied to estimate the average return over a one-period horizon.

READING

8

Probability Concepts

by Richard A. DeFusco, PhD, CFA, Dennis W. McLeavey, DBA, CFA, Jerald E. Pinto, PhD, CFA, and David E. Runkle, PhD, CFA

Richard A. DeFusco, PhD, CFA, is at the University of Nebraska-Lincoln (USA). Dennis W. McLeavey, DBA, CFA, is at the University of Rhode Island (USA). Jerald E. Pinto, PhD, CFA, is at CFA Institute (USA). David E. Runkle, PhD, CFA, is at Trilogy Global Advisors (USA).

LEARNING OUTCOMES

Mastery	*The candidate should be able to:*
☐	**a.** define a random variable, an outcome, an event, mutually exclusive events, and exhaustive events;
☐	**b.** state the two defining properties of probability and distinguish among empirical, subjective, and a priori probabilities;
☐	**c.** state the probability of an event in terms of odds for and against the event;
☐	**d.** distinguish between unconditional and conditional probabilities;
☐	**e.** explain the multiplication, addition, and total probability rules;
☐	**f.** calculate and interpret 1) the joint probability of two events, 2) the probability that at least one of two events will occur, given the probability of each and the joint probability of the two events, and 3) a joint probability of any number of independent events;
☐	**g.** distinguish between dependent and independent events;
☐	**h.** calculate and interpret an unconditional probability using the total probability rule;
☐	**i.** explain the use of conditional expectation in investment applications;
☐	**j.** explain the use of a tree diagram to represent an investment problem;
☐	**k.** calculate and interpret covariance and correlation and interpret a scatterplot;
☐	**l.** calculate and interpret the expected value, variance, and standard deviation of a random variable and of returns on a portfolio;

(continued)

LEARNING OUTCOMES	
Mastery	**The candidate should be able to:**
☐	**m.** calculate and interpret covariance given a joint probability function;
☐	**n.** calculate and interpret an updated probability using Bayes' formula;
☐	**o.** identify the most appropriate method to solve a particular counting problem and solve counting problems using factorial, combination, and permutation concepts.

1 INTRODUCTION

All investment decisions are made in an environment of risk. The tools that allow us to make decisions with consistency and logic in this setting come under the heading of probability. This reading presents the essential probability tools needed to frame and address many real-world problems involving risk. We illustrate how these tools apply to such issues as predicting investment manager performance, forecasting financial variables, and pricing bonds so that they fairly compensate bondholders for default risk. Our focus is practical. We explore in detail the concepts that are most important to investment research and practice. One such concept is independence, as it relates to the predictability of returns and financial variables. Another is expectation, as analysts continually look to the future in their analyses and decisions. Analysts and investors must also cope with variability. We present variance, or dispersion around expectation, as a risk concept important in investments. The reader will acquire specific skills in using portfolio expected return and variance.

The basic tools of probability, including expected value and variance, are set out in Section 2 of this reading. Section 3 introduces covariance and correlation (measures of relatedness between random quantities) and the principles for calculating portfolio expected return and variance. It also discusses scatter plots, a graphical depiction of the relatedness between two random variables. Two topics end the reading: Bayes' formula and outcome counting. Bayes' formula is a procedure for updating beliefs based on new information. In several areas, including a widely used option-pricing model, the calculation of probabilities involves defining and counting outcomes. The reading ends with a discussion of principles and shortcuts for counting.

2 PROBABILITY, EXPECTED VALUE, AND VARIANCE

The probability concepts and tools necessary for most of an analyst's work are relatively few and simple but require thought to apply. This section presents the essentials for working with probability, expectation, and variance, drawing on examples from equity and fixed income analysis.

An investor's concerns center on returns. The return on a risky asset is an example of a **random variable**, a quantity whose **outcomes** (possible values) are uncertain. For example, a portfolio may have a return objective of 10 percent a year. The portfolio manager's focus at the moment may be on the likelihood of earning a return that is less than 10 percent over the next year. Ten percent is a particular value or outcome of the random variable "portfolio return." Although we may be concerned about a single outcome, frequently our interest may be in a set of outcomes: The concept of "event" covers both.

- **Definition of Event.** An **event** is a specified set of outcomes.

We may specify an event to be a single outcome—for example, *the portfolio earns a return of 10 percent.* (We use italics to highlight statements that define events.) We can capture the portfolio manager's concerns by defining the event as *the portfolio earns a return below 10 percent.* This second event, referring as it does to all possible returns greater than or equal to −100 percent (the worst possible return) but less than 10 percent, contains an infinite number of outcomes. To save words, it is common to use a capital letter in italics to represent a defined event. We could define A = *the portfolio earns a return of 10 percent* and B = *the portfolio earns a return below 10 percent.*

To return to the portfolio manager's concern, how likely is it that the portfolio will earn a return below 10 percent?

The answer to this question is a **probability**: a number between 0 and 1 that measures the chance that a stated event will occur. If the probability is 0.40 that the portfolio earns a return below 10 percent, there is a 40 percent chance of that event happening. If an event is impossible, it has a probability of 0. If an event is certain to happen, it has a probability of 1. If an event is impossible or a sure thing, it is not random at all. So, 0 and 1 bracket all the possible values of a probability.

Probability has two properties, which together constitute its definition.

- **Definition of Probability.** The two defining properties of a probability are as follows:
  1. The probability of any event E is a number between 0 and 1: $0 \le P(E) \le 1$.
  2. The sum of the probabilities of any set of mutually exclusive and **exhaustive** events equals 1.

P followed by parentheses stands for "the probability of (the event in parentheses)," as in $P(E)$ for "the probability of event E." We can also think of P as a rule or function that assigns numerical values to events consistent with Properties 1 and 2.

In the above definition, the term mutually exclusive means that only one event can occur at a time; **exhaustive** means that the events cover all possible outcomes. The events A = *the portfolio earns a return of 10 percent* and B = *the portfolio earns a return below 10 percent* are mutually exclusive because A and B cannot both occur at the same time. For example, a return of 8.1 percent means that B has occurred and A has not occurred. Although events A and B are mutually exclusive, they are not exhaustive because they do not cover outcomes such as a return of 11 percent. Suppose we define a third event: C = *the portfolio earns a return above 10 percent.* Clearly, A, B, and C are mutually exclusive and exhaustive events. Each of $P(A)$, $P(B)$, and $P(C)$ is a number between 0 and 1, and $P(A) + P(B) + P(C) = 1$.

The most basic kind of mutually exclusive and exhaustive events is the set of all the distinct possible outcomes of the random variable. If we know both that set and the assignment of probabilities to those outcomes—the probability distribution of the random variable—we have a complete description of the random variable, and we can assign a probability to any event that we might describe.[1] The probability of any event is the sum of the probabilities of the distinct outcomes included in the definition of the event. Suppose the event of interest is D = *the portfolio earns a return above the risk-free rate,* and we know the probability distribution of portfolio returns. Assume

1 In the reading on common probability distributions, we describe some of the probability distributions most frequently used in investment applications.

the risk-free rate is 4 percent. To calculate $P(D)$, the probability of D, we would sum the probabilities of the outcomes that satisfy the definition of the event; that is, we would sum the probabilities of portfolio returns greater than 4 percent.

Earlier, to illustrate a concept, we assumed a probability of 0.40 for a portfolio earning less than 10 percent, without justifying the particular assumption. We also talked about using a probability distribution of outcomes to calculate the probability of events, without explaining how a probability distribution might be estimated. Making actual financial decisions using inaccurate probabilities might have grave consequences. How, in practice, do we estimate probabilities? This topic is a field of study in itself, but there are three broad approaches to estimating probabilities. In investments, we often estimate the probability of an event as a relative frequency of occurrence based on historical data. This method produces an **empirical probability**. For example, Thanatawee (2013) reports that of his sample of 1,927 yearly observations for nonfinancial SET (Stock Exchange of Thailand) firms during the years 2002 to 2010, 1,382 were dividend paying firms and 545 were non dividend paying firms. The empirical probability of a Thai firm paying a dividend is thus 1,382/1,927 = 0.72, approximately. We will point out empirical probabilities in several places as they appear in this reading.

Relationships must be stable through time for empirical probabilities to be accurate. We cannot calculate an empirical probability of an event not in the historical record or a reliable empirical probability for a very rare event. There are cases, then, in which we may adjust an empirical probability to account for perceptions of changing relationships. In other cases, we have no empirical probability to use at all. We may also make a personal assessment of probability without reference to any particular data. Each of these three types of probability is a **subjective probability**, one drawing on personal or subjective judgment. Subjective probabilities are of great importance in investments. Investors, in making buy and sell decisions that determine asset prices, often draw on subjective probabilities. Subjective probabilities appear in various places in this reading, notably in our discussion of Bayes' formula.

In a more narrow range of well-defined problems, we can sometimes deduce probabilities by reasoning about the problem. The resulting probability is an **a priori probability**, one based on logical analysis rather than on observation or personal judgment. We will use this type of probability in Example 6. The counting methods we discuss later are particularly important in calculating an a priori probability. Because a priori and empirical probabilities generally do not vary from person to person, they are often grouped as **objective probabilities**.

In business and elsewhere, we often encounter probabilities stated in terms of odds—for instance, "the odds for E" or the "odds against E." For example, as of August 2018, analysts' fiscal year 2019 EPS forecasts for JetBlue Airways ranged from \$1.50 to \$2.20. Suppose one analyst asserts that the odds for the company beating the highest estimate, \$2.20, are 1 to 7. Suppose a second analyst argues that the odds against that happening are 15 to 1. What do those statements imply about the probability of the company's EPS beating the highest estimate? We interpret probabilities stated in terms of odds as follows:

- **Probability Stated as Odds.** Given a probability $P(E)$,
  1. Odds for $E = P(E)/[1 - P(E)]$. The odds for E are the probability of E divided by 1 minus the probability of E. Given odds for E of "a to b," the implied probability of E is $a/(a + b)$.

In the example, the statement that the odds for *the company's EPS for FY2019 beating \$2.20* are 1 to 7 means that the speaker believes the probability of the event is $1/(1 + 7) = 1/8 = 0.125$.

2 Odds against $E = [1 - P(E)]/P(E)$, the reciprocal of odds for E. Given odds against E of "a to b," the implied probability of E is $b/(a + b)$.

The statement that the odds against *the company's EPS for FY2019 beating $2.20* are 15 to 1 is consistent with a belief that the probability of the event is $1/(1 + 15) = 1/16 = 0.0625$.

To further explain odds for an event, if $P(E) = 1/8$, the odds for E are $(1/8)/(7/8) = (1/8)(8/7) = 1/7$, or "1 to 7." For each occurrence of E, we expect seven cases of non-occurrence; out of eight cases in total, therefore, we expect E to happen once, and the probability of E is 1/8. In wagering, it is common to speak in terms of the odds against something, as in Statement 2. For odds of "15 to 1" against E (an implied probability of E of 1/16), a $1 wager on E, if successful, returns $15 in profits plus the $1 staked in the wager. We can calculate the bet's anticipated profit as follows:

Win: Probability = 1/16; Profit =$15

Loss: Probability = 15/16; Profit =−$1

Anticipated profit = (1/16)($15) + (15/16)(−$1) = $0

Weighting each of the wager's two outcomes by the respective probability of the outcome, if the odds (probabilities) are accurate, the anticipated profit of the bet is $0.

EXAMPLE 1

Profiting from Inconsistent Probabilities

You are examining the common stock of two companies in the same industry in which an important antitrust decision will be announced next week. The first company, SmithCo Corporation, will benefit from a governmental decision that there is no antitrust obstacle related to a merger in which it is involved. You believe that SmithCo's share price reflects a 0.85 probability of such a decision. A second company, Selbert Corporation, will equally benefit from a "go ahead" ruling. Surprisingly, you believe Selbert stock reflects only a 0.50 probability of a favorable decision. Assuming your analysis is correct, what investment strategy would profit from this pricing discrepancy?

Consider the logical possibilities. One is that the probability of 0.50 reflected in Selbert's share price is accurate. In that case, Selbert is fairly valued but SmithCo is overvalued, as its current share price overestimates the probability of a "go ahead" decision. The second possibility is that the probability of 0.85 is accurate. In that case, SmithCo shares are fairly valued, but Selbert shares, which build in a lower probability of a favorable decision, are undervalued. You diagram the situation as shown in Table 1.

Table 1 Worksheet for Investment Problem

	True Probability of a "Go Ahead" Decision	
	0.50	**0.85**
SmithCo	Shares Overvalued	Shares Fairly Valued
Selbert	Shares Fairly Valued	Shares Undervalued

The 0.50 probability column shows that Selbert shares are a better value than SmithCo shares. Selbert shares are also a better value if a 0.85 probability is accurate. Thus SmithCo shares are overvalued relative to Selbert shares.

Your investment actions depend on your confidence in your analysis and on any investment constraints you face (such as constraints on selling stock short).[2] A conservative strategy would be to buy Selbert shares and reduce or eliminate any current position in SmithCo. The most aggressive strategy is to short SmithCo stock (relatively overvalued) and simultaneously buy the stock of Selbert (relatively undervalued). This strategy is known as **pairs arbitrage trade**: a trade in two closely related stocks involving the short sale of one and the purchase of the other.

The prices of SmithCo and Selbert shares reflect probabilities that are not **consistent**. According to one of the most important probability results for investments, the **Dutch Book Theorem**,[3] inconsistent probabilities create profit opportunities. In our example, investors, by their buy and sell decisions to exploit the inconsistent probabilities, should eliminate the profit opportunity and inconsistency.

To understand the meaning of a probability in investment contexts, we need to distinguish between two types of probability: unconditional and conditional. Both unconditional and conditional probabilities satisfy the definition of probability stated earlier, but they are calculated or estimated differently and have different interpretations. They provide answers to different questions.

The probability in answer to the straightforward question "What is the probability of this event A?" is an **unconditional probability**, denoted $P(A)$. Unconditional probability is also frequently referred to as **marginal probability**.[4]

Suppose the question is "What is the probability that *the stock earns a return above the risk-free rate* (event A)?" The answer is an unconditional probability that can be viewed as the ratio of two quantities. The numerator is the sum of the probabilities of stock returns above the risk-free rate. Suppose that sum is 0.70. The denominator is 1, the sum of the probabilities of all possible returns. The answer to the question is $P(A) = 0.70$.

Contrast the question "What is the probability of A?" with the question "What is the probability of A, given that B has occurred?" The probability in answer to this last question is a **conditional probability**, denoted $P(A \mid B)$ (read: "the probability of A given B").

Suppose we want to know the probability that *the stock earns a return above the risk-free rate* (event A), given that *the stock earns a positive return* (event B). With the words "given that," we are restricting returns to those larger than 0 percent—a new element in contrast to the question that brought forth an unconditional probability. The conditional probability is calculated as the ratio of two quantities. The numerator is the sum of the probabilities of stock returns above the risk-free rate; in this particular case, the numerator is the same as it was in the unconditional case, which we gave as 0.70. The denominator, however, changes from 1 to the sum of the probabilities for all outcomes (returns) above 0 percent. Suppose that number is 0.80, a

2 *Selling short* or *shorting stock* means selling borrowed shares in the hope of repurchasing them later at a lower price.

3 The theorem's name comes from the terminology of wagering. Suppose someone places a \$100 bet on X at odds of 10 to 1 against X, and later he is able to place a \$600 bet against X at odds of 1 to 1 against X. Whatever the outcome of X, that person makes a riskless profit (equal to \$400 if X occurs or \$500 if X does not occur) because the implied probabilities are inconsistent. Ramsey (1931) presented the problem of inconsistent probabilities. See also Lo (1999).

4 In analyses of probabilities presented in tables, unconditional probabilities usually appear at the ends or *margins* of the table, hence the term *marginal probability*. Because of possible confusion with the way *marginal* is used in economics (roughly meaning *incremental*), we use the term *unconditional probability* throughout this discussion.

larger number than 0.70 because returns between 0 and the risk-free rate have some positive probability of occurring. Then $P(A \mid B) = 0.70/0.80 = 0.875$. If we observe that the stock earns a positive return, the probability of a return above the risk-free rate is greater than the unconditional probability, which is the probability of the event given no other information. The result is intuitive.[5] To review, an unconditional probability is the probability of an event without any restriction; it might even be thought of as a stand-alone probability. A conditional probability, in contrast, is a probability of an event given that another event has occurred.

In discussing approaches to calculating probability, we gave one empirical estimate of the probability that a change in dividends is a dividend decrease. That probability was an unconditional probability. Given additional information on company characteristics, could an investor refine that estimate? Investors continually seek an information edge that will help improve their forecasts. In mathematical terms, they are attempting to frame their view of the future using probabilities conditioned on relevant information or events. Investors do not ignore useful information; they adjust their probabilities to reflect it. Thus, the concepts of conditional probability (which we analyze in more detail below), as well as related concepts discussed further on, are extremely important in investment analysis and financial markets.

To state an exact definition of conditional probability, we first need to introduce the concept of joint probability. Suppose we ask the question "What is the probability of both A and B happening?" The answer to this question is a **joint probability**, denoted $P(AB)$ (read: "the probability of A and B"). If we think of the probability of A and the probability of B as sets built of the outcomes of one or more random variables, the joint probability of A and B is the sum of the probabilities of the outcomes they have in common. For example, consider two events: *the stock earns a return above the risk-free rate* (A) and *the stock earns a positive return* (B). The outcomes of A are contained within (a subset of) the outcomes of B, so $P(AB)$ equals $P(A)$. We can now state a formal definition of conditional probability that provides a formula for calculating it.

- **Definition of Conditional Probability.** The conditional probability of A given that B has occurred is equal to the joint probability of A and B divided by the probability of B (assumed not to equal 0).

$$P(A \mid B) = P(AB)/P(B),\ P(B) \neq 0 \qquad (1)$$

Sometimes we know the conditional probability $P(A \mid B)$ and we want to know the joint probability $P(AB)$. We can obtain the joint probability from the following **multiplication rule for probabilities**, which is Equation 1 rearranged.

- **Multiplication Rule for Probability.** The joint probability of A and B can be expressed as

$$P(AB) = P(A \mid B)P(B) \qquad (2)$$

5 In this example, the conditional probability is greater than the unconditional probability. The conditional probability of an event may, however, be greater than, equal to, or less than the unconditional probability, depending on the facts. For instance, the probability that *the stock earns a return above the risk-free rate* given that *the stock earns a negative return* is 0.

EXAMPLE 2

Conditional Probabilities and Predictability of Mutual Fund Performance (1)

Vidal-Garcia (2013) examined whether historical performance predicts future performance for a sample of mutual funds that included 1,050 actively managed equity funds in six European countries over a 13-year period. Funds were classified into nine investment styles based on combinations of investment focus (growth, blend, and value) and funds' market capitalization (small, mid, and large cap). One approach Vidal-Garcia used involved calculating each fund's annual benchmark-adjusted return by subtracting a benchmark return from the annual return of the fund. MSCI (Morgan Stanley Capital International) style indexes were used as benchmarks. For each style of fund in each country, funds were classified as winners or losers for each of two consecutive years. The top 50 percent of funds by benchmark-adjusted return for a given year were labeled winners; the bottom 50 percent were labeled losers. An excerpt from the results of the study for 135 French funds classified as large value funds is given in Table 2. It shows the percentage of those funds that were winners in two consecutive years, winner in one year and then loser in the next year, losers then winners, and losers in both years. The winner–winner entry, for example, shows that 65.5% of the first-year winner funds were also winners in the second year. Note that the four entries in the table can be viewed as conditional probabilities.

Table 2 Persistence of Returns for Large Value Funds in France over a 13-Year Period

	Year 2 Winner	Year 2 Loser
Year 1 winner	65.5%	34.5%
Year 1 loser	15.5%	84.5%

Source: Vidal-Garcia (2013), Table 4.

Based on the data in Table 2, answer the following questions:

1 State the four events needed to define the four conditional probabilities.

2 State the four entries of the table as conditional probabilities using the form *P*(*this event* | *that event*) = number.

3 Are the conditional probabilities in Part 2 empirical, a priori, or subjective probabilities?

4 Using information in the table, calculate the probability of the event a *fund is a loser in both Year 1 and Year 2.* (Note that because 50 percent of funds are categorized as losers in each year, the unconditional probability that a fund is labeled a loser in either year is 0.5.)

Solution to 1:

The four events needed to define the conditional probabilities are as follows:

Fund is a Year 1 winner

Fund is a Year 1 loser

Fund is a Year 2 loser

Fund is a Year 2 winner

Solution to 2:

From Row 1:

$P(\textit{fund is a Year 2 winner} \mid \textit{fund is a Year 1 winner}) = 0.655$

$P(\textit{fund is a Year 2 loser} \mid \textit{fund is a Year 1 winner}) = 0.345$

From Row 2:

$P(\textit{fund is a Year 2 winner} \mid \textit{fund is a Year 1 loser}) = 0.155$

$P(\textit{fund is a Year 2 loser} \mid \textit{fund is a Year 1 loser}) = 0.845$

Solution to 3:

These probabilities are calculated from data, so they are empirical probabilities.

Solution to 4:

The estimated probability is 0.423. Let A represent the event that a *fund is a Year 2 loser*, and let B represent the event that *the fund is a Year 1 loser*. Therefore, the event AB is the event that a *fund is a loser in both Year 1 and Year 2*. From Table 2, $P(A \mid B) = 0.845$ and $P(B) = 0.50$. Thus, using Equation 2, we find that

$$P(AB) = P(A \mid B)P(B) = 0.845(0.50) = 0.4225$$

or a probability of approximately 0.423.

Equation 2 states that the joint probability of A and B equals the probability of A given B times the probability of B. Because $P(AB) = P(BA)$, the expression $P(AB) = P(BA) = P(B \mid A)P(A)$ is equivalent to Equation 2.

When we have two events, A and B, that we are interested in, we often want to know the probability that either A or B occurs. Here the word "or" is inclusive, meaning that either A or B occurs or that both A and B occur. Put another way, the probability of A or B is the probability that at least one of the two events occurs. Such probabilities are calculated using the **addition rule for probabilities**.

- **Addition Rule for Probabilities.** Given events A and B, the probability that A or B occurs, or both occur, is equal to the probability that A occurs, plus the probability that B occurs, minus the probability that both A and B occur.

$$P(A \text{ or } B) = P(A) + P(B) - P(AB) \qquad (3)$$

If we think of the individual probabilities of A and B as sets built of outcomes of one or more random variables, the first step in calculating the probability of A or B is to sum the probabilities of the outcomes in A to obtain $P(A)$. If A and B share any outcomes, then if we now added $P(B)$ to $P(A)$, we would count twice the probabilities of those shared outcomes. So we add to $P(A)$ the quantity $[P(B) - P(AB)]$, which is the probability of outcomes in B net of the probability of any outcomes already counted when we computed $P(A)$. Figure 1 illustrates this process; we avoid double-counting the outcomes in the intersection of A and B by subtracting $P(AB)$. As an example of the calculation, if $P(A) = 0.50$, $P(B) = 0.40$, and $P(AB) = 0.20$, then $P(A \text{ or } B) = 0.50 + 0.40 - 0.20 = 0.70$. Only if the two events A and B were mutually exclusive, so that $P(AB) = 0$, would it be correct to state that $P(A \text{ or } B) = P(A) + P(B)$.

Figure 1 Addition Rule for Probabilities

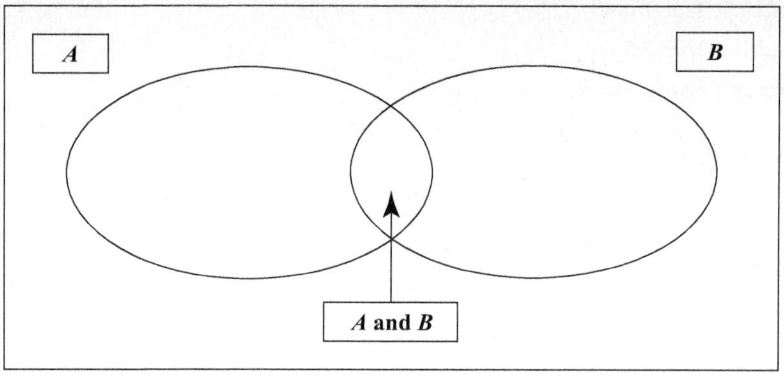

The next example shows how much useful information can be obtained using the few probability rules presented to this point.

EXAMPLE 3

Probability of a Limit Order Executing

You have two buy limit orders outstanding on the same stock. A limit order to buy stock at a stated price is an order to buy at that price or lower. A number of vendors, including an internet service that you use, supply the estimated probability that a limit order will be filled within a stated time horizon, given the current stock price and the price limit. One buy order (Order 1) was placed at a price limit of $10. The probability that it will execute within one hour is 0.35. The second buy order (Order 2) was placed at a price limit of $9.75; it has a 0.25 probability of executing within the same one-hour time frame.

1 What is the probability that either Order 1 or Order 2 will execute?

2 What is the probability that Order 2 executes, given that Order 1 executes?

Solution to 1:

The probability is 0.35. The two probabilities that are given are *P*(*Order 1 executes*) = 0.35 and *P*(*Order 2 executes*) = 0.25. Note that if Order 2 executes, it is certain that Order 1 also executes because the price must pass through $10 to reach $9.75. Thus,

$$P(\textit{Order 1 executes} \mid \textit{Order 2 executes}) = 1$$

and

$$P(\textit{Order 1 executes} \text{ and } \textit{Order 2 executes}) = P(\textit{Order 1 executes} \mid \textit{Order 2 executes})P(\textit{Order 2 executes}) = 1(0.25) = 0.25$$

To answer the question, we use the addition rule for probabilities:

$$P(\textit{Order 1 executes} \text{ or } \textit{Order 2 executes}) = P(\textit{Order 1 executes}) + P(\textit{Order 2 executes}) - P(\textit{Order 1 executes} \text{ and } \textit{Order 2 executes}) = 0.35 + 0.25 - 0.25 = 0.35$$

Note that the outcomes for which Order 2 executes are a subset of the outcomes for which Order 1 executes. After you count the probability that Order 1 executes, you have counted the probability of the outcomes for which Order 2 also executes. Therefore, the answer to the question is the probability that Order 1 executes, 0.35.

Solution to 2:

If the first order executes, the probability that the second order executes is 0.714. In the solution to Part 1, you found that $P(\textit{Order 1 executes} \text{ and } \textit{Order 2 executes}) = P(\textit{Order 1 executes} \mid \textit{Order 2 executes})P(\textit{Order 2 executes}) = 1(0.25) = 0.25$. An equivalent way to state this joint probability is useful here:

$$P(\textit{Order 1 executes} \text{ and } \textit{Order 2 executes}) = 0.25$$
$$= P(\textit{Order 2 executes} \mid \textit{Order 1 executes})P(\textit{Order 1 executes})$$

Because $P(\textit{Order 1 executes}) = 0.35$ was a given, you have one equation with one unknown:

$$0.25 = P(\textit{Order 2 executes} \mid \textit{Order 1 executes})(0.35)$$

You conclude that $P(\textit{Order 2 executes} \mid \textit{Order 1 executes}) = 0.25/0.35 = 5/7$, or about 0.714. You can also use Equation 1 to obtain this answer.

Of great interest to investment analysts are the concepts of independence and dependence. These concepts bear on such basic investment questions as which financial variables are useful for investment analysis, whether asset returns can be predicted, and whether superior investment managers can be selected based on their past records.

Two events are independent if the occurrence of one event does not affect the probability of occurrence of the other event.

- **Definition of Independent Events.** Two events A and B are **independent** if and only if $P(A \mid B) = P(A)$ or, equivalently, $P(B \mid A) = P(B)$.

When two events are not independent, they are **dependent**: The probability of occurrence of one is related to the occurrence of the other. If we are trying to forecast one event, information about a dependent event may be useful, but information about an independent event will not be useful.

When two events are independent, the multiplication rule for probabilities, Equation 2, simplifies because $P(A \mid B)$ in that equation then equals $P(A)$.

- **Multiplication Rule for Independent Events.** When two events are independent, the joint probability of A and B equals the product of the individual probabilities of A and B.

$$P(AB) = P(A)P(B) \tag{4}$$

Therefore, if we are interested in two independent events with probabilities of 0.75 and 0.50, respectively, the probability that both will occur is $0.375 = 0.75(0.50)$. The multiplication rule for independent events generalizes to more than two events; for example, if A, B, and C are independent events, then $P(ABC) = P(A)P(B)P(C)$.

EXAMPLE 4

BankCorp's Earnings per Share (1)

As part of your work as a banking industry analyst, you build models for forecasting earnings per share of the banks you cover. Today you are studying BankCorp. The historical record shows that in 55 percent of recent quarters BankCorp's

EPS has increased sequentially, and in 45 percent of quarters EPS has decreased or remained unchanged sequentially.[6] At this point in your analysis, you are assuming that changes in sequential EPS are independent.

Earnings per share for 2Q:Year 1 (that is, EPS for the second quarter of Year 1) were larger than EPS for 1Q:Year 1.

1 What is the probability that 3Q:Year 1 EPS will be larger than 2Q:Year 1 EPS (a positive change in sequential EPS)?

2 What is the probability that EPS decreases or remains unchanged in the next two quarters?

Solution to 1:

Under the assumption of independence, the probability that 3Q:Year 1 EPS will be larger than 2Q:Year 1 EPS is the unconditional probability of positive change, 0.55. The fact that 2Q:Year 1 EPS was larger than 1Q:Year 1 EPS is not useful information, as the next change in EPS is independent of the prior change.

Solution to 2:

The probability is 0.2025 = 0.45(0.45).

The following example illustrates how difficult it is to satisfy a set of independent criteria even when each criterion by itself is not necessarily stringent.

EXAMPLE 5

Screening Stocks for Investment

You have developed a stock screen—a set of criteria for selecting stocks. Your investment universe (the set of securities from which you make your choices) is the Russell 1000 Index, an index of 1,000 large-capitalization US equities. Your criteria capture different aspects of the selection problem; you believe that the criteria are independent of each other, to a close approximation.

Criterion	Fraction of Russell 1000 Stocks Meeting Criterion
First valuation criterion	0.50
Second valuation criterion	0.50
Analyst coverage criterion	0.25
Profitability criterion for company	0.55
Financial strength criterion for company	0.67

How many stocks do you expect to pass your screen?

Only 23 stocks out of 1,000 pass through your screen. If you define five events—*the stock passes the first valuation criterion, the stock passes the second valuation criterion, the stock passes the analyst coverage criterion, the company*

6 *Sequential* comparisons of quarterly EPS are with the immediate prior quarter. A sequential comparison stands in contrast to a comparison with the same quarter one year ago (another frequent type of comparison).

passes the profitability criterion, the company passes the financial strength criterion (say events A, B, C, D, and E, respectively)—then the probability that a stock will pass all five criteria, under independence, is

$$P(ABCDE) = P(A)P(B)P(C)P(D)P(E) = (0.50)(0.50)(0.25)(0.55)(0.67)$$
$$= 0.023031$$

Although only one of the five criteria is even moderately strict (the strictest lets 25 percent of stocks through), the probability that a stock can pass all five is only 0.023031, or about 2 percent. The size of the list of candidate investments is 0.023031(1,000) = 23.031, or 23 stocks.

An area of intense interest to investment managers and their clients is whether records of past performance are useful in identifying repeat winners and losers. The following example shows how this issue relates to the concept of independence.

EXAMPLE 6

Conditional Probabilities and Predictability of Mutual Fund Performance (2)

The purpose of the Vidal-Garcia (2013) study, introduced in Example 2, was to address the question of repeat European mutual fund winners and losers. If the status of a fund as a winner or a loser in one year is independent of whether it is a winner in the next year, the practical value of performance ranking is questionable. Using the four events defined in Example 2 as building blocks, we can define the following events to address the issue of predictability of mutual fund performance:

Fund is a Year 1 winner and *fund is a Year 2 winner*

Fund is a Year 1 winner and *fund is a Year 2 loser*

Fund is a Year 1 loser and *fund is a Year 2 winner*

Fund is a Year 1 loser and *fund is a Year 2 loser*

In Part 4 of Example 2, you calculated that

P(*fund is a Year 2 loser* and *fund is a Year 1 loser*) = 0.423

If the ranking in one year is independent of the ranking in the next year, what will you expect P(*fund is a Year 2 loser* and *fund is a Year 1 loser*) to be? Interpret the empirical probability 0.423.

By the multiplication rule for independent events, P(*fund is a Year 2 loser* and *fund is a Year 1 loser*) = P(*fund is a Year 2 loser*)P(*fund is a Year 1 loser*). Because 50 percent of funds are categorized as losers in each year, the unconditional probability that a fund is labeled a loser in either year is 0.50. Thus P(*fund is a Year 2 loser*)P(*fund is a Year 1 loser*) = 0.50(0.50) = 0.25. If the status of a fund as a loser in one year is independent of whether it is a loser in the prior year, we conclude that P(*fund is a Year 2 loser* and *fund is a Year 1 loser*) = 0.25. This probability is a priori because it is obtained from reasoning about the problem. You could also reason that the four events described above define categories and that if funds are randomly assigned to the four categories, there is a 1/4 probability of *fund is a Year 1 loser* and *fund is a Year 2 loser.* If the classifications in Year 1 and Year 2 were dependent, then the assignment of funds to categories would not be random. The empirical probability of 0.423 is above 0.25. Is this apparent predictability the result of chance? A test conducted by Vidal-Garcia indicated a less than 1 percent chance of observing the tabled data if the Year 1 and Year 2 rankings were independent.

In investments, the question of whether one event (or characteristic) provides information about another event (or characteristic) arises in both time-series settings (through time) and cross-sectional settings (among units at a given point in time). Examples 4 and 6 examined independence in a time-series setting. Example 5 illustrated independence in a cross-sectional setting. Independence/dependence relationships are often also explored in both settings using regression analysis, a technique we discuss in a later reading.

In many practical problems, we logically analyze a problem as follows: We formulate scenarios that we think affect the likelihood of an event that interests us. We then estimate the probability of the event, given the scenario. When the scenarios (conditioning events) are mutually exclusive and exhaustive, no possible outcomes are left out. We can then analyze the event using the **total probability rule**. This rule explains the unconditional probability of the event in terms of probabilities conditional on the scenarios.

The total probability rule is stated below for two cases. Equation 5 gives the simplest case, in which we have two scenarios. One new notation is introduced: If we have an event or scenario S, the event not-S, called the **complement** of S, is written S^C.[7] Note that $P(S) + P(S^C) = 1$, as either S or not-S must occur. Equation 6 states the rule for the general case of n mutually exclusive and exhaustive events or scenarios.

- **The Total Probability Rule.**

$$\begin{aligned} P(A) &= P(AS) + P\left(AS^C\right) \\ &= P(A \mid S)P(S) + P\left(A \mid S^C\right)P\left(S^C\right) \end{aligned} \tag{5}$$

$$\begin{aligned} P(A) &= P(AS_1) + P(AS_2) + \ldots + P(AS_n) \\ &= P(A \mid S_1)P(S_1) + P(A \mid S_2)P(S_2) + \ldots + P(A \mid S_n)P(S_n) \end{aligned} \tag{6}$$

where $S_1, S_2, \ldots, S_n$ are mutually exclusive and exhaustive scenarios or events.

Equation 6 states the following: The probability of any event [$P(A)$] can be expressed as a weighted average of the probabilities of the event, given scenarios [terms such $P(A \mid S_1)$]; the weights applied to these conditional probabilities are the respective probabilities of the scenarios [terms such as $P(S_1)$ multiplying $P(A \mid S_1)$], and the scenarios must be mutually exclusive and exhaustive. Among other applications, this rule is needed to understand Bayes' formula, which we discuss later in the reading.

In the next example, we use the total probability rule to develop a consistent set of views about BankCorp's earnings per share.

EXAMPLE 7

BankCorp's Earnings per Share (2)

You are continuing your investigation into whether you can predict the direction of changes in BankCorp's quarterly EPS. You define four events:

7 For readers familiar with mathematical treatments of probability, S, a notation usually reserved for a concept called the sample space, is being appropriated to stand for *scenario.*

Event	Probability
A = *Change in sequential EPS is positive next quarter*	0.55
A^C = *Change in sequential EPS is 0 or negative next quarter*	0.45
S = *Change in sequential EPS is positive in the prior quarter*	0.55
S^C = *Change in sequential EPS is 0 or negative in the prior quarter*	0.45

On inspecting the data, you observe some persistence in EPS changes: Increases tend to be followed by increases, and decreases by decreases. The first probability estimate you develop is *P*(*change in sequential EPS is positive next quarter* | *change in sequential EPS is 0 or negative in the prior quarter*) = $P(A \mid S^C)$ = 0.40. The most recent quarter's EPS (2Q:Year 1) is announced, and the change is a positive sequential change (the event S). You are interested in forecasting EPS for 3Q:Year 1.

1 Write this statement in probability notation: "the probability that the change in sequential EPS is positive next quarter, given that the change in sequential EPS is positive the prior quarter."

2 Calculate the probability in Part 1. (Calculate the probability that is consistent with your other probabilities or beliefs.)

Solution to 1:

In probability notation, this statement is written $P(A \mid S)$.

Solution to 2:

The probability is 0.673 that the change in sequential EPS is positive for 3Q:Year 1, given the positive change in sequential EPS for 2Q:Year 1, as shown below.

According to Equation 5, $P(A) = P(A \mid S)P(S) + P(A \mid S^C)P(S^C)$. The values of the probabilities needed to calculate $P(A \mid S)$ are already known: $P(A) = 0.55$, $P(S) = 0.55$, $P(S^C) = 0.45$, and $P(A \mid S^C) = 0.40$. Substituting into Equation 5,

$$0.55 = P(A \mid S)(0.55) + 0.40(0.45)$$

Solving for the unknown, $P(A \mid S) = [0.55 - 0.40(0.45)]/0.55 = 0.672727$, or 0.673.

You conclude that *P*(*change in sequential EPS is positive next quarter* | *change in sequential EPS is positive the prior quarter*) = 0.673. Any other probability is not consistent with your other estimated probabilities. Reflecting the persistence in EPS changes, this conditional probability of a positive EPS change, 0.673, is greater than the unconditional probability of an EPS increase, 0.55.

In the reading on statistical concepts and market returns, we discussed the concept of a weighted average or weighted mean. The example highlighted in that reading was that portfolio return is a weighted average of the returns on the individual assets in the portfolio, where the weight applied to each asset's return is the fraction of the portfolio invested in that asset. The total probability rule, which is a rule for stating an unconditional probability in terms of conditional probabilities, is also a weighted average. In that formula, probabilities of scenarios are used as weights. Part of the definition of weighted average is that the weights sum to 1. The probabilities of mutually exclusive and exhaustive events do sum to 1 (this is part of the definition of probability). The next weighted average we discuss, the expected value of a random variable, also uses probabilities as weights.

The expected value of a random variable is an essential quantitative concept in investments. Investors continually make use of expected values—in estimating the rewards of alternative investments, in forecasting EPS and other corporate financial variables and ratios, and in assessing any other factor that may affect their financial position. The expected value of a random variable is defined as follows:

- **Definition of Expected Value.** The **expected value** of a random variable is the probability-weighted average of the possible outcomes of the random variable. For a random variable X, the expected value of X is denoted $E(X)$.

Expected value (for example, expected stock return) looks either to the future, as a forecast, or to the "true" value of the mean (the population mean, discussed in the reading on statistical concepts and market returns). We should distinguish expected value from the concepts of historical or sample mean. The sample mean also summarizes in a single number a central value. However, the sample mean presents a central value for a particular set of observations as an equally weighted average of those observations. To summarize, the contrast is forecast versus historical, or population versus sample.

EXAMPLE 8

BankCorp's Earnings per Share (3)

You continue with your analysis of BankCorp's EPS. In Table 3, you have recorded a probability distribution for BankCorp's EPS for the current fiscal year.

Table 3 Probability Distribution for BankCorp's EPS

Probability	EPS ($)
0.15	2.60
0.45	2.45
0.24	2.20
0.16	2.00
1.00	

What is the expected value of BankCorp's EPS for the current fiscal year?

Following the definition of expected value, list each outcome, weight it by its probability, and sum the terms.

$$E(\text{EPS}) = 0.15(\$2.60) + 0.45(\$2.45) + 0.24(\$2.20) + 0.16(\$2.00)$$
$$= \$2.3405$$

The expected value of EPS is $2.34.

An equation that summarizes your calculation in Example 8 is

$$E(X) = P(X_1)X_1 + P(X_2)X_2 + \ldots + P(X_n)X_n = \sum_{i=1}^{n} P(X_i)X_i \quad (7)$$

where X_i is one of n possible outcomes of the random variable X.[8]

The expected value is our forecast. Because we are discussing random quantities, we cannot count on an individual forecast being realized (although we hope that, on average, forecasts will be accurate). It is important, as a result, to measure the risk we face. Variance and standard deviation measure the dispersion of outcomes around the expected value or forecast.

- **Definition of Variance.** The **variance** of a random variable is the expected value (the probability-weighted average) of squared deviations from the random variable's expected value:

$$\sigma^2(X) = E\left\{\left[X - E(X)\right]^2\right\} \quad (8)$$

- The two notations for variance are $\sigma^2(X)$ and Var(X).

Variance is a number greater than or equal to 0 because it is the sum of squared terms. If variance is 0, there is no dispersion or risk. The outcome is certain, and the quantity X is not random at all. Variance greater than 0 indicates dispersion of outcomes. Increasing variance indicates increasing dispersion, all else equal. Variance of X is a quantity in the squared units of X. For example, if the random variable is return in percent, variance of return is in units of percent squared. Standard deviation is easier to interpret than variance, as it is in the same units as the random variable. If the random variable is return in percent, standard deviation of return is also in units of percent. In the following example, when the variance of returns is stated as a percent or amount of money, to conserve space the reading may suppress showing the unit squared. Note that when the variance of returns is stated as a decimal, the complication of dealing with units of "percent squared" does not arise.

- **Definition of Standard Deviation. Standard deviation** is the positive square root of variance.

The best way to become familiar with these concepts is to work examples.

EXAMPLE 9

BankCorp's Earnings per Share (4)

In Example 8, you calculated the expected value of BankCorp's EPS as \$2.34, which is your forecast. Now you want to measure the dispersion around your forecast. Table 4 shows your view of the probability distribution of EPS for the current fiscal year.

Table 4 Probability Distribution for BankCorp's EPS

Probability	EPS ($)
0.15	2.60
0.45	2.45
0.24	2.20

(continued)

8 For simplicity, we model all random variables in this reading as discrete random variables, which have a countable set of outcomes. For continuous random variables, which are discussed along with discrete random variables in the reading on common probability distributions, the operation corresponding to summation is integration.

Table 4 (Continued)

Probability	EPS ($)
0.16	2.00
1.00	

What are the variance and standard deviation of BankCorp's EPS for the current fiscal year?

The order of calculation is always expected value, then variance, then standard deviation. Expected value has already been calculated. Following the definition of variance above, calculate the deviation of each outcome from the mean or expected value, square each deviation, weight (multiply) each squared deviation by its probability of occurrence, and then sum these terms.

$$\begin{aligned}\sigma^2(\text{EPS}) &= P(\$2.60)[\$2.60 - E(\text{EPS})]^2 + P(\$2.45)[\$2.45 - E(\text{EPS})]^2 \\ &\quad + P(\$2.20)[\$2.20 - E(\text{EPS})]^2 + P(\$2.00)[\$2.00 - E(\text{EPS})]^2 \\ &= 0.15(2.60 - 2.34)^2 + 0.45(2.45 - 2.34)^2 \\ &\quad + 0.24(2.20 - 2.34)^2 + 0.16(2.00 - 2.34)^2 \\ &= 0.01014 + 0.005445 + 0.004704 + 0.018496 = 0.038785\end{aligned}$$

Standard deviation is the positive square root of 0.038785:

$\sigma(\text{EPS}) = 0.038785^{1/2} = 0.196939$, or approximately 0.20.

An equation that summarizes your calculation of variance in Example 9 is

$$\begin{aligned}\sigma^2(X) &= P(X_1)[X_1 - E(X)]^2 + P(X_2)[X_2 - E(X)]^2 \\ &\quad + \ldots + P(X_n)[X_n - E(X)]^2 = \sum_{i=1}^{n} P(X_i)[X_i - E(X)]^2\end{aligned} \quad (9)$$

where X_i is one of n possible outcomes of the random variable X.

In investments, we make use of any relevant information available in making our forecasts. When we refine our expectations or forecasts, we are typically making adjustments based on new information or events; in these cases we are using **conditional expected values**. The expected value of a random variable X given an event or scenario S is denoted $E(X \mid S)$. Suppose the random variable X can take on any one of n distinct outcomes $X_1, X_2, \ldots, X_n$ (these outcomes form a set of mutually exclusive and exhaustive events). The expected value of X conditional on S is the first outcome, X_1, times the probability of the first outcome given S, $P(X_1 \mid S)$, plus the second outcome, X_2, times the probability of the second outcome given S, $P(X_2 \mid S)$, and so forth.

$$E(X \mid S) = P(X_1 \mid S)X_1 + P(X_2 \mid S)X_2 + \ldots + P(X_n \mid S)X_n \quad (10)$$

We will illustrate this equation shortly.

Parallel to the total probability rule for stating unconditional probabilities in terms of conditional probabilities, there is a principle for stating (unconditional) expected values in terms of conditional expected values. This principle is the **total probability rule for expected value**.

- **The Total Probability Rule for Expected Value.**

$$E(X) = E(X \mid S)P(S) + E(X \mid S^C)P(S^C) \quad (11)$$

$$E(X) = E(X \mid S_1)P(S_1) + E(X \mid S_2)P(S_2) + \ldots + E(X \mid S_n)P(S_n) \quad (12)$$

where S_1, S_2, ..., S_n are mutually exclusive and exhaustive scenarios or events.

The general case, Equation 12, states that the expected value of X equals the expected value of X given Scenario 1, $E(X \mid S_1)$, times the probability of Scenario 1, $P(S_1)$, plus the expected value of X given Scenario 2, $E(X \mid S_2)$, times the probability of Scenario 2, $P(S_2)$, and so forth.

To use this principle, we formulate mutually exclusive and exhaustive scenarios that are useful for understanding the outcomes of the random variable. This approach was employed in developing the probability distribution of BankCorp's EPS in Examples 8 and 9, as we now discuss.

The earnings of BankCorp are interest rate sensitive, benefiting from a declining interest rate environment. Suppose there is a 0.60 probability that BankCorp will operate in a *declining interest rate environment* in the current fiscal year and a 0.40 probability that it will operate in a *stable interest rate environment* (assessing the chance of an increasing interest rate environment as negligible). If a *declining interest rate environment* occurs, the probability that EPS will be \$2.60 is estimated at 0.25, and the probability that EPS will be \$2.45 is estimated at 0.75. Note that 0.60, the probability of *declining interest rate environment,* times 0.25, the probability of \$2.60 EPS given a *declining interest rate environment,* equals 0.15, the (unconditional) probability of \$2.60 given in the table in Examples 8 and 9. The probabilities are consistent. Also, 0.60(0.75) = 0.45, the probability of \$2.45 EPS given in Tables 3 and 4. The **tree diagram** in Figure 2 shows the rest of the analysis.

Figure 2 BankCorp's Forecasted EPS

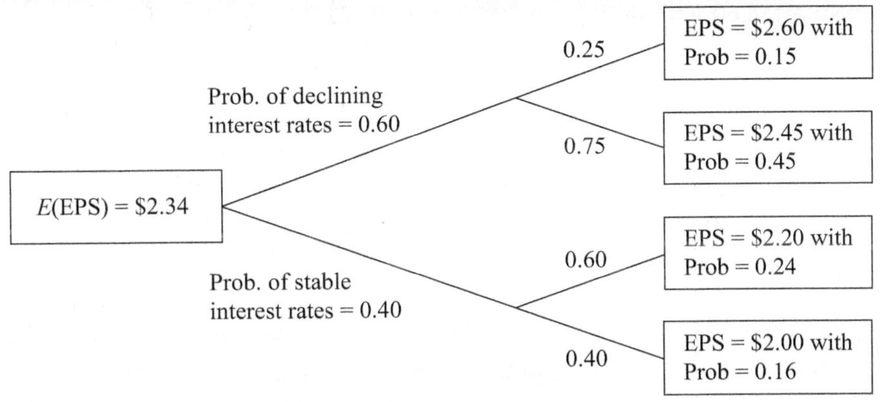

A declining interest rate environment points us to the **node** of the tree that branches off into outcomes of \$2.60 and \$2.45. We can find expected EPS given a declining interest rate environment as follows, using Equation 10:

$$\begin{aligned} E(\text{EPS} \mid \textit{declining interest rate environment}) &= 0.25(\$2.60) + 0.75(\$2.45) \\ &= \$2.4875 \end{aligned}$$

If interest rates are stable,

$$\begin{aligned} E(\text{EPS} \mid \textit{stable interest rate environment}) &= 0.60(\$2.20) + 0.40(\$2.00) \\ &= \$2.12 \end{aligned}$$

Once we have the new piece of information that interest rates are stable, for example, we revise our original expectation of EPS from \$2.34 downward to \$2.12. Now using the total probability rule for expected value,

$$E(\text{EPS}) = E(\text{EPS} \mid \textit{declining interest rate environment})P(\textit{declining interest rate environment}) + E(\text{EPS} \mid \textit{stable interest rate environment})P(\textit{stable interest rate environment})$$

So $E(\text{EPS})$ = \$2.4875(0.60) + \$2.12(0.40) = \$2.3405 or about \$2.34.

This amount is identical to the estimate of the expected value of EPS calculated directly from the probability distribution in Example 8. Just as our probabilities must be consistent, so must our expected values, unconditional and conditional; otherwise our investment actions may create profit opportunities for other investors at our expense.

To review, we first developed the factors or scenarios that influence the outcome of the event of interest. After assigning probabilities to these scenarios, we formed expectations conditioned on the different scenarios. Then we worked backward to formulate an expected value as of today. In the problem just worked, EPS was the event of interest, and the interest rate environment was the factor influencing EPS.

We can also calculate the variance of EPS given each scenario:

$$\begin{aligned}
&\sigma^2(\text{EPS} \mid \textit{declining interest rate environment})\\
&\quad = P(\$2.60 \mid \textit{declining interest rate environment})\\
&\quad \times\left[\$2.60 - E(\text{EPS} \mid \textit{declining interest rate environment})\right]^2\\
&\quad + P(\$2.45 \mid \textit{declining interest rate environment})\\
&\quad \times\left[\$2.45 - E(\text{EPS} \mid \textit{declining interest rate environment})\right]^2\\
&\quad = 0.25(\$2.60 - \$2.4875)^2 + 0.75(\$2.45 - \$2.4875)^2\\
&\quad = 0.004219
\end{aligned}$$

$$\begin{aligned}
&\sigma^2(\text{EPS} \mid \textit{stable interest rate environment})\\
&\quad = P(\$2.20 \mid \textit{stable interest rate environment})\\
&\quad \times\left[\$2.20 - E(\text{EPS} \mid \textit{stable interest rate environment})\right]^2\\
&\quad + P(\$2.00 \mid \textit{stable interest rate environment})\\
&\quad \times\left[\$2.00 - E(\text{EPS} \mid \textit{stable interest rate environment})\right]^2\\
&\quad = 0.60(\$2.20 - \$2.12)^2 + 0.40(\$2.00 - \$2.12)^2 = 0.0096
\end{aligned}$$

These are **conditional variances**, the variance of EPS given a *declining interest rate environment* and the variance of EPS given a *stable interest rate environment*. The relationship between unconditional variance and conditional variance is a relatively advanced topic.[9] The main points are 1) that variance, like expected value, has a conditional counterpart to the unconditional concept and 2) that we can use conditional variance to assess risk given a particular scenario.

---

9 The unconditional variance of EPS is the sum of two terms: 1) the expected value (probability-weighted average) of the conditional variances (parallel to the total probability rules) and 2) the variance of conditional expected values of EPS. The second term arises because the variability in conditional expected value is a source of risk. Term 1 is $\sigma^2(\text{EPS}) = P(\textit{declining interest rate environment})\ \sigma^2(\text{EPS} \mid \textit{declining interest rate environment}) + P(\textit{stable interest rate environment})\ \sigma^2(\text{EPS} \mid \textit{stable interest rate environment})$ = 0.60(0.004219) + 0.40(0.0096) = 0.006371. Term 2 is $\sigma^2[E(\text{EPS} \mid \text{interest rate environment})]$ = 0.60(\$2.4875 − \$2.34)^2 + 0.40(\$2.12 − \$2.34)^2 = 0.032414. Summing the two terms, unconditional variance equals 0.006371 + 0.032414 = 0.038785.

EXAMPLE 10

BankCorp's Earnings per Share (5)

Continuing with BankCorp, you focus now on BankCorp's cost structure. One model you are researching for BankCorp's operating costs is

$$\hat{Y} = a + bX$$

where $\hat{Y}$ is a forecast of operating costs in millions of dollars and X is the number of branch offices. $\hat{Y}$ represents the expected value of Y given X, or $E(Y \mid X)$. ($\hat{Y}$ is a notation used in regression analysis, which we discuss in a later reading.) You interpret the intercept a as fixed costs and b as variable costs. You estimate the equation as

$$\hat{Y} = 12.5 + 0.65X$$

BankCorp currently has 66 branch offices, and the equation estimates that 12.5 + 0.65(66) = \$55.4 million. You have two scenarios for growth, pictured in the tree diagram in Figure 3.

Figure 3 BankCorp's Forecasted Operating Costs

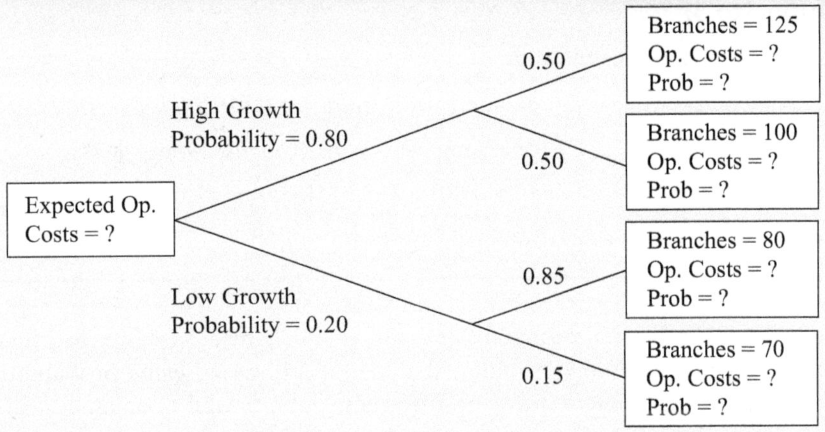

1 Compute the forecasted operating costs given the different levels of operating costs, using $\hat{Y} = 12.5 + 0.65X$. State the probability of each level of the number of branch offices. These are the answers to the questions in the terminal boxes of the tree diagram.

2 Compute the expected value of operating costs under the high growth scenario. Also calculate the expected value of operating costs under the low growth scenario.

3 Answer the question in the initial box of the tree: What are BankCorp's expected operating costs?

Solution to 1:

Using $\hat{Y} = 12.5 + 0.65X$, from top to bottom, we have

Operating Costs	Probability
$\hat{Y} = 12.5 + 0.65(125) = \$93.75$ million	$0.80(0.50) = 0.40$
$\hat{Y} = 12.5 + 0.65(100) = \$77.50$ million	$0.80(0.50) = 0.40$
$\hat{Y} = 12.5 + 0.65(80) = \$64.50$ million	$0.20(0.85) = 0.17$
$\hat{Y} = 12.5 + 0.65(70) = \$58.00$ million	$0.20(0.15) = 0.03$
	Sum = 1.00

Solution to 2:

Dollar amounts are in millions.

$$E(\text{operating costs} \mid \textit{high growth}) = 0.50(\$93.75) + 0.50(\$77.50) = \$85.625$$

$$E(\text{operating costs} \mid \textit{low growth}) = 0.85(\$64.50) + 0.15(\$58.00) = \$63.525$$

Solution to 3:

Dollar amounts are in millions.

$$\begin{aligned} E(\text{operating costs}) &= E(\text{operating costs} \mid \textit{high growth})P(\textit{high growth}) \\ &\quad + E(\text{operating costs} \mid \textit{low growth})P(\textit{low growth}) \\ &= \$85.625(0.80) + \$63.525(0.20) = \$81.205 \end{aligned}$$

BankCorp's expected operating costs are \$81.205 million.

We will see conditional probabilities again when we discuss Bayes' formula. This section has introduced a few problems that can be addressed using probability concepts. The following problem draws on these concepts, as well as on analytical skills.

EXAMPLE 11

The Default Risk Premium for a One-Period Debt Instrument

As the co-manager of a short-term bond portfolio, you are reviewing the pricing of a speculative-grade, one-year-maturity, zero-coupon bond. For this type of bond, the return is the difference between the amount paid and the principal value received at maturity. Your goal is to estimate an appropriate default risk premium for this bond. You define the default risk premium as the extra return above the risk-free return that will compensate investors for default risk. If R is the promised return (yield-to-maturity) on the debt instrument and R_F is the risk-free rate, the default risk premium is $R - R_F$. You assess the probability that the bond defaults as $P(\textit{the bond defaults}) = 0.06$. Looking at current money market yields, you find that one-year US Treasury bills (T-bills) are offering a return of 2 percent, an estimate of R_F. As a first step, you make the simplifying assumption that bondholders will recover nothing in the event of a default. What is the minimum default risk premium you should require for this instrument?

The challenge in this type of problem is to find a starting point. In many problems, including this one, an effective first step is to divide up the possible outcomes into mutually exclusive and exhaustive events in an economically logical way. Here, from the viewpoint of a bondholder, the two events that affect returns are *the bond defaults* and *the bond does not default*. These two events cover all outcomes. How do these events affect a bondholder's returns? A second step is to compute the value of the bond for the two events. We have no specifics on bond **face value**, but we can compute value per \$1 or one unit of currency invested.

	The Bond Defaults	*The Bond Does Not Default*
Bond value	\$0	\$(1 + R)

The third step is to find the expected value of the bond (per \$1 invested).

$$E(\text{bond}) = \$0 \times P(\textit{the bond defaults}) + \$(1 + R)[1 - P(\textit{the bond defaults})]$$

So $E(\text{bond}) = \$(1 + R)[1 - P(\textit{the bond defaults})]$. The expected value of the T-bill per \$1 invested is $(1 + R_F)$. In fact, this value is certain because the T-bill is risk free. The next step requires economic reasoning. You want the default premium to be large enough so that you expect to at least break even compared with investing in the T-bill. This outcome will occur if the expected value of the bond equals the expected value of the T-bill per \$1 invested.

$$\begin{array}{ccc} \textit{Expected Value of Bond} & = & \textit{Expected Value of T-Bill} \\ \$(1 + R)\left[1 - P(\textit{the bond defaults})\right] & = & (1 + R_F) \end{array}$$

Solving for the promised return on the bond, you find $R = \{(1 + R_F)/[1 - P(\textit{the bond defaults})]\} - 1$. Substituting the values in the statement of the problem, $R = [1.02/(1 - 0.06)] - 1 = 1.08511 - 1 = 0.08511$ or about 8.51 percent, and default risk premium is $R - R_F = 8.51\% - 2\% = 6.51\%$.

You require a default risk premium of at least 651 basis points. You can state the matter as follows: If the bond is priced to yield 8.51 percent, you will earn a 651 basis-point spread and receive the bond principal with 94 percent probability. If the bond defaults, however, you will lose everything. With a premium of 651 basis points, you expect to just break even relative to an investment in T-bills. Because an investment in the zero-coupon bond has variability, if you are risk averse you will demand that the premium be larger than 651 basis points.

This analysis is a starting point. Bondholders usually recover part of their investment after a default. A next step would be to incorporate a recovery rate.

In this section, we have treated random variables such as EPS as stand-alone quantities. We have not explored how descriptors such as expected value and variance of EPS may be functions of other random variables. Portfolio return is one random variable that is clearly a function of other random variables, the random returns on the individual securities in the portfolio. To analyze a portfolio's expected return and variance of return, we must understand these quantities are a function of characteristics of the individual securities' returns. Looking at the dispersion or variance of portfolio return, we see that the way individual security returns move together or covary is important. To understand the significance of these movements, we need to explore some new concepts, covariance and correlation. The next section, which deals with portfolio expected return and variance of return, introduces these concepts.

3 PORTFOLIO EXPECTED RETURN AND VARIANCE OF RETURN

Modern portfolio theory makes frequent use of the idea that investment opportunities can be evaluated using expected return as a measure of reward and variance of return as a measure of risk. The calculation and interpretation of portfolio expected return and variance of return are fundamental skills. In this section, we will develop an understanding of portfolio expected return and variance of return.[10] Portfolio return is determined by the returns on the individual holdings. As a result, the calculation of portfolio variance, as a function of the individual asset returns, is more complex than the variance calculations illustrated in the previous section.

We work with an example of a portfolio that is 50 percent invested in an S&P 500 Index fund, 25 percent invested in a US long-term corporate bond fund, and 25 percent invested in a fund indexed to the MSCI EAFE Index (representing equity markets in Europe, Australasia, and the Far East). Table 5 shows these weights.

Table 5 Portfolio Weights

Asset Class	Weights
S&P 500	0.50
US long-term corporate bonds	0.25
MSCI EAFE	0.25

We first address the calculation of the expected return on the portfolio. In the previous section, we defined the expected value of a random variable as the probability-weighted average of the possible outcomes. Portfolio return, we know, is a weighted average of the returns on the securities in the portfolio. Similarly, the expected return on a portfolio is a weighted average of the expected returns on the securities in the portfolio, using exactly the same weights. When we have estimated the expected returns on the individual securities, we immediately have portfolio expected return. This convenient fact follows from the properties of expected value.

- **Properties of Expected Value.** Let w_i be any constant and R_i be a random variable.
  1. The expected value of a constant times a random variable equals the constant times the expected value of the random variable.

     $$E(w_iR_i) = w_iE(R_i)$$

  2. The expected value of a weighted sum of random variables equals the weighted sum of the expected values, using the same weights.

     $$E(w_1R_1 + w_2R_2 + \ldots + w_nR_n) = w_1E(R_1) + w_2E(R_2) + \ldots + w_nE(R_n) \quad (13)$$

10 Although we outline a number of basic concepts in this section, we do not present mean–variance analysis per se. For a presentation of mean–variance analysis, see the readings on portfolio concepts, as well as the extended treatments in standard investment textbooks such as Bodie, Kane, and Marcus (2017), Elton, Gruber, Brown, and Goetzmann (2013), and Reilly and Brown (2018).

Suppose we have a random variable with a given expected value. If we multiply each outcome by 2, for example, the random variable's expected value is multiplied by 2 as well. That is the meaning of Part 1. The second statement is the rule that directly leads to the expression for portfolio expected return. A portfolio with n securities is defined by its portfolio weights, $w_1, w_2, \ldots, w_n$, which sum to 1. So portfolio return, R_p, is $R_p = w_1R_1 + w_2R_2 + \ldots + w_nR_n$. We can state the following principle:

- **Calculation of Portfolio Expected Return.** Given a portfolio with n securities, the expected return on the portfolio is a weighted average of the expected returns on the component securities:

$$\begin{aligned} E(R_p) &= E(w_1R_1 + w_2R_2 + \ldots + w_nR_n) \\ &= w_1E(R_1) + w_2E(R_2) + \ldots + w_nE(R_n) \end{aligned}$$

Suppose we have estimated expected returns on the assets in the portfolio, as given in Table 6.

Table 6 Weights and Expected Returns

Asset Class	Weight	Expected Return (%)
S&P 500	0.50	13
US long-term corporate bonds	0.25	6
MSCI EAFE	0.25	15

We calculate the expected return on the portfolio as 11.75 percent:

$$\begin{aligned} E(R_p) &= w_1E(R_1) + w_2E(R_2) + w_3E(R_3) \\ &= 0.50(13\%) + 0.25(6\%) + 0.25(15\%) = 11.75\% \end{aligned}$$

In the previous section, we studied variance as a measure of dispersion of outcomes around the expected value. Here we are interested in portfolio variance of return as a measure of investment risk. Letting R_p stand for the return on the portfolio, portfolio variance is $\sigma^2(R_p) = E\{[R_p - E(R_p)]^2\}$ according to Equation 8. How do we implement this definition? In the reading on statistical concepts and market returns, we learned how to calculate a historical or sample variance based on a sample of returns. Now we are considering variance in a forward-looking sense. We will use information about the individual assets in the portfolio to obtain portfolio variance of return. To avoid clutter in notation, we write ER_p for $E(R_p)$. We need the concept of covariance.

- **Definition of Covariance.** Given two random variables R_i and R_j, the covariance between R_i and R_j is

$$\text{Cov}(R_i,R_j) = E\left[(R_i - ER_i)(R_j - ER_j)\right] \quad (14)$$

Alternative notations are $\sigma(R_i,R_j)$ and σ_{ij}.

Equation 14 states that the covariance between two random variables is the probability-weighted average of the cross-products of each random variable's deviation from its own expected value. The above measure is the population covariance and it is forward-looking. Sometimes analysts look at historical covariance for guidance on developing expectations for the future. For this purpose, the sample covariance, which is computed using a sample of historical data about the two variables, is appropriate. The sample covariance between two random variables R_i and R_j, based on a sample of past data of size n is

$$\text{Cov}\left(R_i,R_j\right) = \sum_{i=1}^{n}\left(R_{i,t} - \bar{R}_i\right)\left(R_{j,t} - \bar{R}_j\right)/(n-1) \quad (15)$$

The sample covariance is the average value of the product of the deviations of observations on two random variables from their sample means.[11] If the random variables are returns, the units of both forward-looking covariance and historical variance would be returns squared. In this reading, we will consider covariance in a forward-looking sense, unless mentioned otherwise.

We will return to discuss covariance after we establish the need for the concept. Working from the definition of variance, we find

$$\sigma^2\left(R_p\right) = E\left[\left(R_p - ER_p\right)^2\right]$$

$$= E\left\{\left[w_1R_1 + w_2R_2 + w_3R_3 - E\left(w_1R_1 + w_2R_2 + w_3R_3\right)\right]^2\right\}$$

$$= E\left\{\left[w_1R_1 + w_2R_2 + w_3R_3 - w_1ER_1 - w_2ER_2 - w_3ER_3\right]^2\right\}$$

(using Equation 13)

$$= E\left\{\left[w_1\left(R_1 - ER_1\right) + w_2\left(R_2 - ER_2\right) + w_3\left(R_3 - ER_3\right)\right]^2\right\}$$

(rearranging)

$$= E\left\{\left[w_1\left(R_1 - ER_1\right) + w_2\left(R_2 - ER_2\right) + w_3\left(R_3 - ER_3\right)\right] \times\left[w_1\left(R_1 - ER_1\right) + w_2\left(R_2 - ER_2\right) + w_3\left(R_3 - ER_3\right)\right]\right\}$$

(what squaring means)

$$\begin{aligned} &= E\left[w_1w_1\left(R_1 - ER_1\right)\left(R_1 - ER_1\right) + w_1w_2\left(R_1 - ER_1\right)\left(R_2 - ER_2\right)\right.\\ &\quad + w_1w_3\left(R_1 - ER_1\right)\left(R_3 - ER_3\right) + w_2w_1\left(R_2 - ER_2\right)\left(R_1 - ER_1\right)\\ &\quad + w_2w_2\left(R_2 - ER_2\right)\left(R_2 - ER_2\right) + w_2w_3\left(R_2 - ER_2\right)\left(R_3 - ER_3\right)\\ &\quad + w_3w_1\left(R_3 - ER_3\right)\left(R_1 - ER_1\right) + w_3w_2\left(R_3 - ER_3\right)\left(R_2 - ER_2\right)\\ &\quad \left.+ w_3w_3\left(R_3 - ER_3\right)\left(R_3 - ER_3\right)\right] \end{aligned}$$

(doing the multiplication)

$$\begin{aligned} &= w_1^2E\left[\left(R_1 - ER_1\right)^2\right] + w_1w_2E\left[\left(R_1 - ER_1\right)\left(R_2 - ER_2\right)\right]\\ &\quad + w_1w_3E\left[\left(R_1 - ER_1\right)\left(R_3 - ER_3\right)\right] + w_2w_1E\left[\left(R_2 - ER_2\right)\left(R_1 - ER_1\right)\right]\\ &\quad + w_2^2E\left[\left(R_2 - ER_2\right)^2\right] + w_2w_3E\left[\left(R_2 - ER_2\right)\left(R_3 - ER_3\right)\right]\\ &\quad + w_3w_1E\left[\left(R_3 - ER_3\right)\left(R_1 - ER_1\right)\right] + w_3w_2E\left[\left(R_3 - ER_3\right)\left(R_2 - ER_2\right)\right]\\ &\quad + w_3^2E\left[\left(R_3 - ER_3\right)^2\right] \end{aligned}$$

(recalling that the w_i terms are constants)

11 The use of $n - 1$ in the denominator is a technical point; it ensures that the sample covariance is an unbiased estimate of population covariance.

$$= w_1^2\sigma^2(R_1) + w_1w_2\text{Cov}(R_1,R_2) + w_1w_3\text{Cov}(R_1,R_3)$$
$$+ w_1w_2\textit{Cov}(R_1,R_2) + w_2^2\sigma^2(R_2) + w_2w_3\text{Cov}(R_2,R_3) \quad \textbf{(16)}$$
$$+ w_1w_3\textit{Cov}(R_1,R_3) + w_2w_3\textit{Cov}(R_2,R_3) + w_3^2\sigma^2(R_3)$$

The last step follows from the definitions of variance and covariance.[12] For the italicized covariance terms in Equation 16, we used the fact that the order of variables in covariance does not matter: $\text{Cov}(R_2,R_1) = \text{Cov}(R_1,R_2)$, for example. As we will show, the diagonal variance terms $\sigma^2(R_1)$, $\sigma^2(R_2)$, and $\sigma^2(R_3)$ can be expressed as $\text{Cov}(R_1,R_1)$, $\text{Cov}(R_2,R_2)$, and $\text{Cov}(R_3,R_3)$, respectively. Using this fact, the most compact way to state Equation 16 is $\sigma^2(R_p) = \sum_{i=1}^{3}\sum_{j=1}^{3} w_iw_j\text{Cov}(R_i,R_j)$. The double summation signs say: "Set $i = 1$ and let j run from 1 to 3; then set $i = 2$ and let j run from 1 to 3; next set $i = 3$ and let j run from 1 to 3; finally, add the nine terms." This expression generalizes for a portfolio of any size n to

$$\sigma^2(R_p) = \sum_{i=1}^{n}\sum_{j=1}^{n} w_iw_j\text{Cov}(R_i,R_j) \quad \textbf{(17)}$$

We see from Equation 16 that individual variances of return constitute part, but not all, of portfolio variance. The three variances are actually outnumbered by the six covariance terms off the diagonal. For three assets, the ratio is 1 to 2, or 50 percent. If there are 20 assets, there are 20 variance terms and $20(20) - 20 = 380$ off-diagonal covariance terms. The ratio of variance terms to off-diagonal covariance terms is less than 6 to 100, or 6 percent. A first observation, then, is that as the number of holdings increases, covariance[13] becomes increasingly important, all else equal.

What exactly is the effect of covariance on portfolio variance? The covariance terms capture how the co-movements of returns affect portfolio variance. For example, consider two stocks: One tends to have high returns (relative to its expected return) when the other has low returns (relative to its expected return). The returns on one stock tend to offset the returns on the other stock, lowering the variability or variance of returns on the portfolio. Like variance, the units of covariance are hard to interpret, and we will introduce a more intuitive concept shortly. Meanwhile, from the definition of covariance, we can establish two essential observations about covariance.

1. We can interpret the sign of covariance as follows:

   Covariance of returns is negative if, when the return on one asset is above its expected value, the return on the other asset tends to be below its expected value (an average inverse relationship between returns).

   Covariance of returns is 0 if returns on the assets are unrelated.

   Covariance of returns is positive when the returns on both assets tend to be on the same side (above or below) their expected values at the same time (an average positive relationship between returns).

2. The covariance of a random variable with itself (*own covariance*) is its own variance: $\text{Cov}(R,R) = E\{[R - E(R)][R - E(R)]\} = E\{[R - E(R)]^2\} = \sigma^2(R)$.

---

12 Useful facts about variance and covariance include: 1) The variance of a constant *times* a random variable equals the constant squared times the variance of the random variable, or $\sigma^2(wR) = w^2\sigma^2(R)$; 2) The variance of a constant *plus* a random variable equals the variance of the random variable, or $\sigma^2(w + R) = \sigma^2(R)$ because a constant has zero variance; 3) The covariance between a constant and a random variable is zero.

13 When the meaning of covariance as "off-diagonal covariance" is obvious, as it is here, we omit the qualifying words. Covariance is usually used in this sense.

A complete list of the covariances constitutes all the statistical data needed to compute portfolio variance of return. Covariances are often presented in a square format called a **covariance matrix**. Table 7 summarizes the inputs for portfolio expected return and variance of return.

Table 7 Inputs to Portfolio Expected Return and Variance

A. Inputs to Portfolio Expected Return

Asset	A	B	C
	$E(R_A)$	$E(R_B)$	$E(R_C)$

B. Covariance Matrix: The Inputs to Portfolio Variance of Return

Asset	A	B	C
A	**$\text{Cov}(R_A,R_A)$**	$\text{Cov}(R_A,R_B)$	$\text{Cov}(R_A,R_C)$
B	$\text{Cov}(R_B,R_A)$	**$\text{Cov}(R_B,R_B)$**	$\text{Cov}(R_B,R_C)$
C	$\text{Cov}(R_C,R_A)$	$\text{Cov}(R_C,R_B)$	**$\text{Cov}(R_C,R_C)$**

With three assets, the covariance matrix has $3^2 = 3 \times 3 = 9$ entries, but it is customary to treat the diagonal terms, the variances, separately from the off-diagonal terms. These diagonal terms are bolded in Table 7. This distinction is natural, as security variance is a single-variable concept. So there are $9 - 3 = 6$ covariances, excluding variances. But $\text{Cov}(R_B,R_A) = \text{Cov}(R_A,R_B)$, $\text{Cov}(R_C,R_A) = \text{Cov}(R_A,R_C)$, and $\text{Cov}(R_C,R_B) = \text{Cov}(R_B,R_C)$. The covariance matrix below the diagonal is the mirror image of the covariance matrix above the diagonal. As a result, there are only $6/2 = 3$ distinct covariance terms to estimate. In general, for n securities, there are $n(n - 1)/2$ distinct covariances to estimate and n variances to estimate.

Suppose we have the covariance matrix shown in Table 8. We will be working in returns stated as percents and the table entries are in units of percent squared ($\%^2$). The terms $38\%^2$ and $400\%^2$ are 0.0038 and 0.0400, respectively, stated as decimals; correctly working in percents and decimals leads to identical answers.

Table 8 Covariance Matrix

	S&P 500	US Long-Term Corporate Bonds	MSCI EAFE
S&P 500	400	45	189
US long-term corporate bonds	45	81	38
MSCI EAFE	189	38	441

Taking Equation 16 and grouping variance terms together produces the following:

$$\begin{aligned}\sigma^2(R_p) &= w_1^2\sigma^2(R_1) + w_2^2\sigma^2(R_2) + w_3^2\sigma^2(R_3) + 2w_1w_2\mathrm{Cov}(R_1,R_2)\\ &\quad + 2w_1w_3\mathrm{Cov}(R_1,R_3) + 2w_2w_3\mathrm{Cov}(R_2,R_3)\\ &= (0.50)^2(400) + (0.25)^2(81) + (0.25)^2(441)\\ &\quad + 2(0.50)(0.25)(45) + 2(0.50)(0.25)(189)\\ &\quad + 2(0.25)(0.25)(38)\\ &= 100 + 5.0625 + 27.5625 + 11.25 + 47.25 + 4.75 = 195.875\end{aligned} \tag{18}$$

The variance is 195.875. Standard deviation of return is $195.875^{1/2} = 14$ percent. To summarize, the portfolio has an expected annual return of 11.75 percent and a standard deviation of return of 14 percent.

Let us look at the first three terms in the calculation above. Their sum, 100 + 5.0625 + 27.5625 = 132.625, is the contribution of the individual variances to portfolio variance. If the returns on the three assets were independent, covariances would be 0 and the standard deviation of portfolio return would be $132.625^{1/2} = 11.52$ percent as compared to 14 percent before. The portfolio would have less risk. Suppose the covariance terms were negative. Then a negative number would be added to 132.625, so portfolio variance and risk would be even smaller. At the same time, we have not changed expected return. For the same expected portfolio return, the portfolio has less risk. This risk reduction is a diversification benefit, meaning a risk-reduction benefit from holding a portfolio of assets. The diversification benefit increases with decreasing covariance. This observation is a key insight of modern portfolio theory. It is even more intuitively stated when we can use the concept of **correlation**. Then we can say that as long as security returns are not perfectly positively correlated, diversification benefits are possible. Furthermore, the smaller the correlation between security returns, the greater the cost of not diversifying (in terms of risk-reduction benefits forgone), all else equal.

- **Definition of Correlation.** The correlation between two random variables, R_i and R_j, is defined as $\rho(R_i,R_j) = \mathrm{Cov}(R_i,R_j)/[\sigma(R_i)\sigma(R_j)]$. Alternative notations are $\mathrm{Corr}(R_i,R_j)$ and ρ_{ij}.

The above definition of correlation is forward-looking because it involves dividing the forward-looking covariance by the product of forward-looking standard deviations. We can similarly compute an historical or sample correlation by dividing historical or sample covariance between two variables by the product of sample standard deviations of the two variables.[14]

Frequently, covariance is substituted out using the relationship $\mathrm{Cov}(R_i,R_j) = \rho(R_i,R_j)\sigma(R_i)\sigma(R_j)$. Like covariance, the correlation coefficient is a measure of linear association. However, the division indicated in the definition of correlation makes correlation a pure number (one without a unit of measurement) and places bounds on its largest and smallest possible values. Using the above definition, we can state a correlation matrix from data in the covariance matrix alone. Table 9 shows the correlation matrix.

14 Sample covariance is discussed earlier in this reading. Sample standard deviation is discussed in the reading on statistical concepts and market returns.

Table 9 Correlation Matrix of Returns

	S&P 500	US Long-Term Corporate Bonds	MSCI EAFE
S&P 500	1.00	0.25	0.45
US long-term corporate bonds	0.25	1.00	0.20
MSCI EAFE	0.45	0.20	1.00

For example, the covariance between long-term bonds and MSCI EAFE is 38, from Table 8. The standard deviation of long-term bond returns is $81^{1/2} = 9$ percent, that of MSCI EAFE returns is $441^{1/2} = 21$ percent, from diagonal terms in Table 8. The correlation ρ(Return on long-term bonds, Return on EAFE) is 38/[(9%)(21%)] = 0.201, rounded to 0.20. The correlation of the S&P 500 with itself equals 1: The calculation is its own covariance divided by its standard deviation squared.

- **Properties of Correlation.**
  1. Correlation may range from −1 and +1 for two random variables, X and Y:

     $$-1 \leq \rho(X,Y) \leq +1$$

  2. A correlation of 0 (uncorrelated variables) indicates an absence of any linear (straight-line) relationship between the variables.[15] Increasingly positive correlation indicates an increasingly strong positive linear relationship (up to 1, which indicates a perfect linear relationship). Increasingly negative correlation indicates an increasingly strong negative (inverse) linear relationship (down to −1, which indicates a perfect inverse linear relationship).[16]

We will make use of scatter plots to illustrate correlation. A **scatter plot** is a graph that shows the relationship between the observations for two data series in two dimensions. In contrast to correlation analysis, which expresses the relationship between two data series using a single number, a scatter plot depicts this same relationship graphically. Each observation in a scatter plot is represented as a point, and the points are not connected. A scatter plot shows only the actual observations of both data series plotted as pairs and does not include specifics about the observations.

Figure 4 shows some scatter plots. Part A of the figure shows the scatter plot of two variables with a correlation of 1. Note that all the points on the scatter plot in Part A lie on a straight line with a positive slope. Whenever variable X increases by one unit, variable Y increases by half a unit. Because all of the points in the graph lie on a straight line, an increase of one unit in X is associated with exactly the same half-unit increase in Y, regardless of the level of X. Even if the slope of the line in the figure were different (but positive), the correlation between the two variables would be 1 as long as all the points lie on that straight line.

Part B shows a scatter plot for two variables with a correlation coefficient of −1. Once again, the plotted observations fall on a straight line. In this graph, however, the line has a negative slope. As X increases by one unit, Y decreases by half a unit, regardless of the initial value of X.

Part C shows a scatter plot of two variables with a correlation of 0; they have no linear relation. This graph shows that the value of variable X tells us absolutely nothing about the value of variable Y.

15 If the correlation is 0, $R_1 = a + bR_2$ + error, with $b = 0$.

16 If the correlation is positive, $R_1 = a + bR_2$ + error, with $b > 0$. If the correlation is negative, $b < 0$.

Figure 4 Scatter Plots

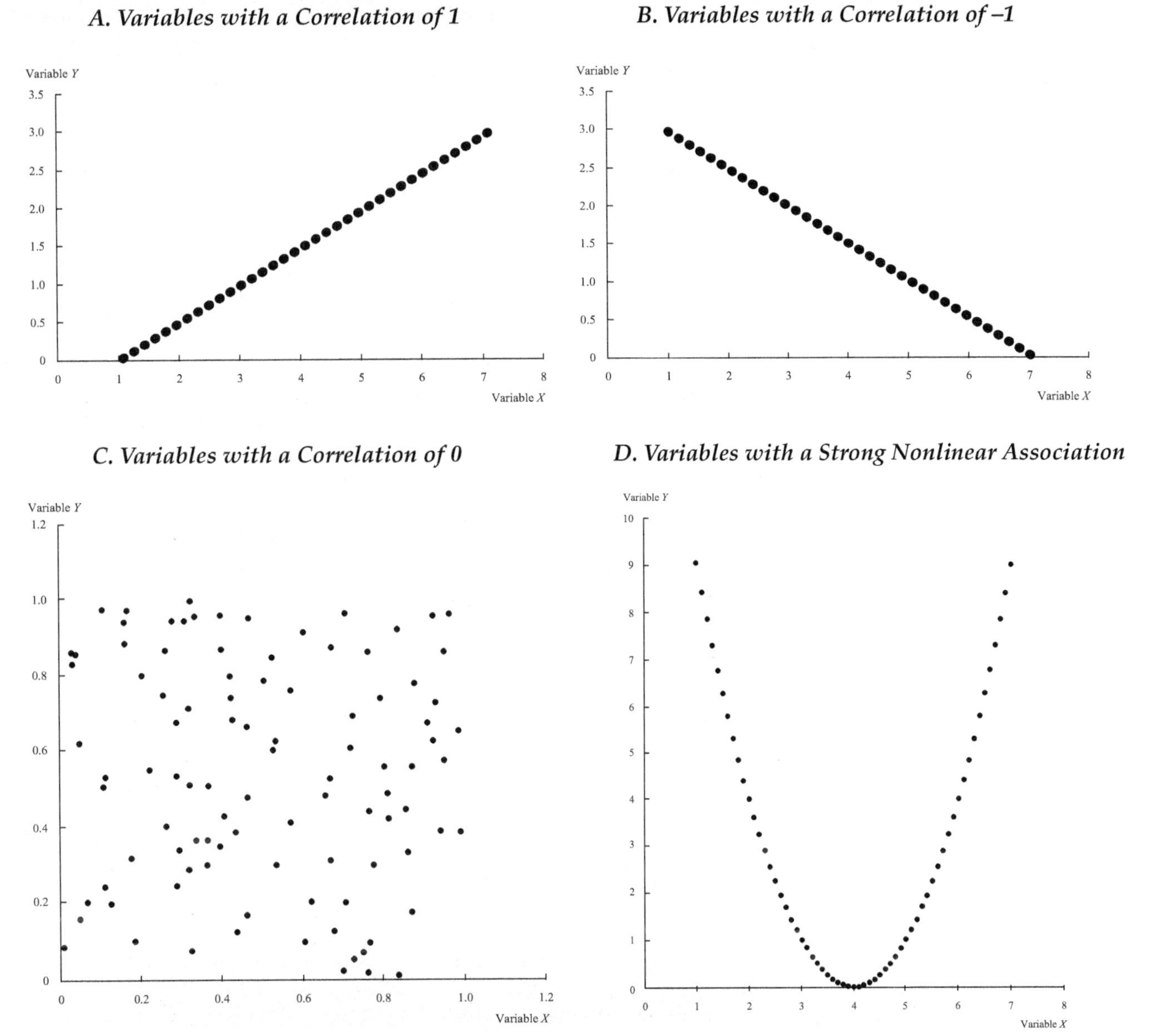

Limitations of Correlation Analysis.

Part D of Figure 4 illustrates that correlation measures the linear association between two variables, but it may not always be reliable. Two variables can have a strong nonlinear relation and still have a very low correlation. For example, the relation $Y = (X - 4)^2$ is a nonlinear relation contrasted to the linear relation $Y = 2X - 4$. The nonlinear relation between variables X and Y is shown in Part D of Figure 4. Below a level of 4 for X, variable Y decreases with increasing values of X. When X is 4 or greater, however, Y increases whenever X increases. Even though these two variables are perfectly associated, there is no linear association between them.[17]

17 The perfect association is the quadratic relationship $Y = (X - 4)^2$.

Correlation also may be an unreliable measure when outliers are present in one or both of the series. Outliers are small numbers of observations at either extreme (small or large) of a sample. The correlation may be quite sensitive to excluding outliers. In such a situation, we should consider whether it makes sense to exclude those outlier observations, and whether they are noise or news. As a general rule, we must determine whether a computed sample correlation changes greatly by removing a few outliers. But we must also use judgment to determine whether those outliers contain information about the two variables' relationship (and should thus be included in the correlation analysis) or contain no information (and should thus be excluded).

Keep in mind that correlation does not imply causation. Even if two variables are highly correlated, one does not necessarily cause the other in the sense that certain values of one variable bring about the occurrence of certain values of the other. Furthermore, correlations can be spurious in the sense of misleadingly pointing towards associations between variables.

The term **spurious correlation** has been used to refer to 1) correlation between two variables that reflects chance relationships in a particular data set, 2) correlation induced by a calculation that mixes each of two variables with a third, and 3) correlation between two variables arising not from a direct relation between them but from their relation to a third variable. As an example of the second kind of spurious correlation, two variables that are uncorrelated may be correlated if divided by a third variable. As an example of the third kind of spurious correlation, height may be positively correlated with the extent of a person's vocabulary, but the underlying relationships are between age and height and between age and vocabulary. Investment professionals must be cautious in basing investment strategies on high correlations. Spurious correlation may suggest investment strategies that appear profitable but actually would not be so, if implemented.

EXAMPLE 12

Portfolio Expected Return and Variance of Return

You have a portfolio of two mutual funds, A and B, 75 percent invested in A, as shown in Table 10.

Table 10 Mutual Fund Expected Returns, Return Variances, and Covariances

Fund	A $E(R_A) = 20\%$	B $E(R_B) = 12\%$
	Covariance Matrix	
Fund	A	B
A	625	120
B	120	196

1 Calculate the expected return of the portfolio.

2 Calculate the correlation matrix for this problem. Carry out the answer to two decimal places.

3 Compute portfolio standard deviation of return.

Solution to 1:

$E(R_p) = w_A E(R_A) + (1 - w_A)E(R_B) = 0.75(20\%) + 0.25(12\%) = 18\%$. Portfolio weights must sum to 1: $w_B = 1 - w_A$.

Solution to 2:

$\sigma(R_A) = 625^{1/2} = 25$ percent $\sigma(R_B) = 196^{1/2} = 14$ percent. There is one distinct covariance and thus one distinct correlation: $\rho(R_A,R_B) = \text{Cov}(R_A,R_B)/[\sigma(R_A)\sigma(R_B)] = 120/[25(14)] = 0.342857$, or 0.34 Table 11 shows the correlation matrix.

Table 11 Correlation Matrix

	A	B
A	1.00	0.34
B	0.34	1.00

Diagonal terms are always equal to 1 in a correlation matrix.

Solution to 3:

$$\begin{aligned}\sigma^2(R_p) &= w_A^2\sigma^2(R_A) + w_B^2\sigma^2(R_B) + 2w_A w_B \text{Cov}(R_A,R_B)\\ &= (0.75)^2(625) + (0.25)^2(196) + 2(0.75)(0.25)(120)\\ &= 351.5625 + 12.25 + 45 = 408.8125\end{aligned}$$

$$\sigma(R_p) = 408.8125^{1/2} = 20.22 \text{ percent}$$

How do we estimate return covariance and correlation? Frequently, we make forecasts on the basis of historical covariance or use other methods based on historical return data, such as a market model regression.[18] We can also calculate covariance using the **joint probability function** of the random variables, if that can be estimated. The joint probability function of two random variables X and Y, denoted $P(X,Y)$, gives the probability of joint occurrences of values of X and Y. For example, $P(3, 2)$, is the probability that X equals 3 and Y equals 2.

Suppose that the joint probability function of the returns on BankCorp stock (R_A) and the returns on NewBank stock (R_B) has the simple structure given in Table 12.

Table 12 Joint Probability Function of BankCorp and NewBank Returns (Entries Are Joint Probabilities)

	$R_B = 20\%$	$R_B = 16\%$	$R_B = 10\%$
$R_A = 25\%$	0.20	0	0
$R_A = 12\%$	0	0.50	0
$R_A = 10\%$	0	0	0.30

18 See any of the textbooks mentioned in Footnote 10.

The expected return on BankCorp stock is 0.20(25%) + 0.50(12%) + 0.30(10%) = 14%. The expected return on NewBank stock is 0.20(20%) + 0.50(16%) + 0.30(10%) = 15%. The joint probability function above might reflect an analysis based on whether banking industry conditions are good, average, or poor. Table 13 presents the calculation of covariance.

Table 13 Covariance Calculations

Banking Industry Condition	Deviations BankCorp	Deviations NewBank	Product of Deviations	Probability of Condition	Probability-Weighted Product
Good	25–14	20–15	55	0.20	11
Average	12–14	16–15	−2	0.50	−1
Poor	10–14	10–15	20	0.30	6
					$\text{Cov}(R_A,R_B) = 16$

Note: Expected return for BankCorp is 14% and for NewBank, 15%.

The first and second columns of numbers show, respectively, the deviations of BankCorp and NewBank returns from their mean or expected value. The next column shows the product of the deviations. For example, for good industry conditions, (25 – 14)(20 – 15) = 11(5) = 55. Then 55 is multiplied or weighted by 0.20, the probability that banking industry conditions are good: 55(0.20) = 11. The calculations for average and poor banking conditions follow the same pattern. Summing up these probability-weighted products, we find that $\text{Cov}(R_A,R_B) = 16$.

A formula for computing the covariance between random variables R_A and R_B is

$$\text{Cov}(R_A,R_B) = \sum_i \sum_j P(R_{A,i},R_{B,j})(R_{A,i} - ER_A)(R_{B,j} - ER_B) \quad (19)$$

The formula tells us to sum all possible deviation cross-products weighted by the appropriate joint probability. In the example we just worked, as Table 12 shows, only three joint probabilities are nonzero. Therefore, in computing the covariance of returns in this case, we need to consider only three cross-products:

$$\begin{aligned}\text{Cov}(R_A,R_B) &= P(25,20)[(25-14)(20-15)] + P(12,16)[(12-14)\\ &\qquad (16-15)] + P(10,10)[(10-14)(10-15)]\\ &= 0.20(11)(5) + 0.50(-2)(1) + 0.30(-4)(-5)\\ &= 11 - 1 + 6 = 16\end{aligned}$$

One theme of this reading has been independence. Two random variables are independent when every possible pair of events—one event corresponding to a value of X and another event corresponding to a value of Y—are independent events. When two random variables are independent, their joint probability function simplifies.

- **Definition of Independence for Random Variables.** Two random variables X and Y are independent if and only if $P(X,Y) = P(X)P(Y)$.

For example, given independence, $P(3,2) = P(3)P(2)$. We multiply the individual probabilities to get the joint probabilities. *Independence* is a stronger property than *uncorrelatedness* because correlation addresses only linear relationships. The following condition holds for independent random variables and, therefore, also holds for uncorrelated random variables.

- **Multiplication Rule for Expected Value of the Product of Uncorrelated Random Variables.** The expected value of the product of uncorrelated random variables is the product of their expected values.

  $E(XY) = E(X)E(Y)$ if X and Y are uncorrelated.

Many financial variables, such as revenue (price times quantity), are the product of random quantities. When applicable, the above rule simplifies calculating expected value of a product of random variables.[19]

TOPICS IN PROBABILITY

4

In the remainder of the reading we discuss two topics that can be important in solving investment problems. We start with Bayes' formula: what probability theory has to say about learning from experience. Then we move to a discussion of shortcuts and principles for counting.

4.1 Bayes' Formula

When we make decisions involving investments, we often start with viewpoints based on our experience and knowledge. These viewpoints may be changed or confirmed by new knowledge and observations. Bayes' formula is a rational method for adjusting our viewpoints as we confront new information.[20] Bayes' formula and related concepts have been applied in many business and investment decision-making contexts, including the evaluation of mutual fund performance.[21]

Bayes' formula makes use of Equation 6, the total probability rule. To review, that rule expressed the probability of an event as a weighted average of the probabilities of the event, given a set of scenarios. Bayes' formula works in reverse; more precisely, it reverses the "given that" information. Bayes' formula uses the occurrence of the event to infer the probability of the scenario generating it. For that reason, Bayes' formula is sometimes called an inverse probability. In many applications, including the one illustrating its use in this section, an individual is updating his beliefs concerning the causes that may have produced a new observation.

- **Bayes' Formula.** Given a set of prior probabilities for an event of interest, if you receive new information, the rule for updating your probability of the event is

$$\text{Updated probability of event given the new information} = \frac{\text{Probability of the new information given event}}{\text{Unconditional probability of the new information}} \times \text{Prior probability of event}$$

19 Otherwise, the calculation depends on conditional expected value; the calculation can be expressed as $E(XY) = E(X)\,E(Y \mid X)$.
20 Named after the Reverend Thomas Bayes (1702–61).
21 See Huij and Verbeek (2007).

In probability notation, this formula can be written concisely as:

$$P(\text{Event} \mid \text{Information}) = \frac{P(\text{Information} \mid \text{Event})}{P(\text{Information})} P(\text{Event})$$

To illustrate Bayes' formula, we work through an investment example that can be adapted to any actual problem. Suppose you are an investor in the stock of DriveMed, Inc. Positive earnings surprises relative to consensus EPS estimates often result in positive stock returns, and negative surprises often have the opposite effect. DriveMed is preparing to release last quarter's EPS result, and you are interested in which of these three events happened: *last quarter's EPS exceeded the consensus EPS estimate,* or *last quarter's EPS exactly met the consensus EPS estimate,* or *last quarter's EPS fell short of the consensus EPS estimate.* This list of the alternatives is mutually exclusive and exhaustive.

On the basis of your own research, you write down the following **prior probabilities** (or priors, for short) concerning these three events:

- *P*(*EPS exceeded consensus*) = 0.45
- *P*(*EPS met consensus*) = 0.30
- *P*(*EPS fell short of consensus*) = 0.25

These probabilities are "prior" in the sense that they reflect only what you know now, before the arrival of any new information.

The next day, DriveMed announces that it is expanding factory capacity in Singapore and Ireland to meet increased sales demand. You assess this new information. The decision to expand capacity relates not only to current demand but probably also to the prior quarter's sales demand. You know that sales demand is positively related to EPS. So now it appears more likely that last quarter's EPS will exceed the consensus.

The question you have is, "In light of the new information, what is the updated probability that the prior quarter's EPS exceeded the consensus estimate?"

Bayes' formula provides a rational method for accomplishing this updating. We can abbreviate the new information as *DriveMed expands.* The first step in applying Bayes' formula is to calculate the probability of the new information (here: *DriveMed expands*), given a list of events or scenarios that may have generated it. The list of events should cover all possibilities, as it does here. Formulating these conditional probabilities is the key step in the updating process. Suppose your view is

P(*DriveMed expands* | *EPS exceeded consensus*) = 0.75

P(*DriveMed expands* | *EPS met consensus*) = 0.20

P(*DriveMed expands* | *EPS fell short of consensus*) = 0.05

Conditional probabilities of an observation (here: *DriveMed expands*) are sometimes referred to as **likelihoods**. Again, likelihoods are required for updating the probability.

Next, you combine these conditional probabilities or likelihoods with your prior probabilities to get the unconditional probability for DriveMed expanding, *P(DriveMed expands)*, as follows:

$$\begin{aligned}
&P(DriveMed\ expands)\\
&= P(DriveMed\ expands \mid EPS\ exceeded\ consensus)\\
&\quad \times P(EPS\ exceeded\ consensus)\\
&+ P(DriveMed\ expands \mid EPS\ met\ consensus)\\
&\quad \times P(EPS\ met\ consensus)\\
&+ P(DriveMed\ expands \mid EPS\ fell\ short\ of\ consensus)\\
&\quad \times P(EPS\ fell\ short\ of\ consensus)\\
&= 0.75(0.45) + 0.20(0.30) + 0.05(0.25) = 0.41, \text{ or } 41\%
\end{aligned}$$

This is Equation 6, the total probability rule, in action. Now you can answer your question by applying Bayes' formula:

$$\begin{aligned}
&P(EPS\ exceeded\ consensus \mid DriveMed\ expands)\\
&= \frac{P(DriveMed\ expands \mid EPS\ exceeded\ consensus)}{P(DriveMed\ expands)} P(EPS\ exceeded\ consensus)\\
&= (0.75/0.41)(0.45) = 1.829268(0.45) = 0.823171
\end{aligned}$$

Prior to DriveMed's announcement, you thought the probability that DriveMed would beat consensus expectations was 45 percent. On the basis of your interpretation of the announcement, you update that probability to 82.3 percent. This updated probability is called your **posterior probability** because it reflects or comes after the new information.

The Bayes' calculation takes the prior probability, which was 45 percent, and multiplies it by a ratio—the first term on the right-hand side of the equal sign. The denominator of the ratio is the probability that DriveMed expands, as you view it without considering (conditioning on) anything else. Therefore, this probability is unconditional. The numerator is the probability that DriveMed expands, if last quarter's EPS actually exceeded the consensus estimate. This last probability is larger than unconditional probability in the denominator, so the ratio (1.83 roughly) is greater than 1. As a result, your updated or posterior probability is larger than your prior probability. Thus, the ratio reflects the impact of the new information on your prior beliefs.

EXAMPLE 13

Inferring whether DriveMed's EPS Met Consensus EPS

You are still an investor in DriveMed stock. To review the givens, your prior probabilities are *P(EPS exceeded consensus)* = 0.45, *P(EPS met consensus)* = 0.30, and *P(EPS fell short of consensus)* = 0.25. You also have the following conditional probabilities:

$P(DriveMed\ expands \mid EPS\ exceeded\ consensus) = 0.75$

$P(DriveMed\ expands \mid EPS\ met\ consensus) = 0.20$

$P(DriveMed\ expands \mid EPS\ fell\ short\ of\ consensus) = 0.05$

Recall that you updated your probability that last quarter's EPS exceeded the consensus estimate from 45 percent to 82.3 percent after DriveMed announced it would expand. Now you want to update your other priors.

1 Update your prior probability that DriveMed's EPS met consensus.

2 Update your prior probability that DriveMed's EPS fell short of consensus.

3 Show that the three updated probabilities sum to 1. (Carry each probability to four decimal places.)

4 Suppose, because of lack of prior beliefs about whether DriveMed would meet consensus, you updated on the basis of prior probabilities that all three possibilities were equally likely: *P(EPS exceeded consensus)* = *P(EPS met consensus)* = *P(EPS fell short of consensus)* = 1/3. What is your estimate of the probability *P(EPS exceeded consensus | DriveMed expands)*?

Solution to 1:

The probability is *P(EPS met consensus | DriveMed expands)* =

$$\frac{P(DriveMed\ expands \mid EPS\ met\ consensus)}{P(DriveMed\ expands)}P(EPS\ met\ consensus)$$

The probability *P(DriveMed expands)* is found by taking each of the three conditional probabilities in the statement of the problem, such as *P(DriveMed expands | EPS exceeded consensus)*; multiplying each one by the prior probability of the conditioning event, such as *P(EPS exceeded consensus)*; then adding the three products. The calculation is unchanged from the problem in the text above: *P(DriveMed expands)* = 0.75(0.45) + 0.20(0.30) + 0.05(0.25) = 0.41, or 41 percent. The other probabilities needed, *P(DriveMed expands | EPS met consensus)* = 0.20 and *P(EPS met consensus)* = 0.30, are givens. So

$$\begin{aligned}&P(EPS\ met\ consensus \mid DriveMed\ expands)\\&\quad = [P(DriveMed\ expands \mid EPS\ met\ consensus)/P(DriveMed\ expands)]\\&\quad\quad P(EPS\ met\ consensus)\\&\quad = (0.20/0.41)(0.30) = 0.487805(0.30) = 0.146341\end{aligned}$$

After taking account of the announcement on expansion, your updated probability that last quarter's EPS for DriveMed just met consensus is 14.6 percent compared with your prior probability of 30 percent.

Solution to 2:

P(DriveMed expands) was already calculated as 41 percent. Recall that *P(DriveMed expands | EPS fell short of consensus)* = 0.05 and *P(EPS fell short of consensus)* = 0.25 are givens.

$$\begin{aligned}&P(EPS\ fell\ short\ of\ consensus \mid DriveMed\ expands)\\&\quad = \left[P(DriveMed\ expands \mid EPS\ fell\ short\ of\ consensus)\ /\right.\\&\quad\quad \left.P(DriveMed\ expands)\right]P(EPS\ fell\ short\ of\ consensus)\\&\quad = (0.05\ /\ 0.41)(0.25) = 0.121951(0.25) = 0.030488\end{aligned}$$

As a result of the announcement, you have revised your probability that DriveMed's EPS fell short of consensus from 25 percent (your prior probability) to 3 percent.

Solution to 3:

The sum of the three updated probabilities is

$$\begin{aligned}&P(EPS\ exceeded\ consensus \mid DriveMed\ expands) + P(EPS\ met\ consensus \mid\\&\quad DriveMed\ expands) + P(EPS\ fell\ short\ of\ consensus \mid DriveMed\ expands)\\&\quad = 0.8232 + 0.1463 + 0.0305 = 1.0000\end{aligned}$$

The three events (*EPS exceeded consensus, EPS met consensus, EPS fell short of consensus*) are mutually exclusive and exhaustive: One of these events or statements must be true, so the conditional probabilities must sum to 1. Whether we are talking about conditional or unconditional probabilities, whenever we have a complete set of the distinct possible events or outcomes, the probabilities must sum to 1. This calculation serves as a check on your work.

Solution to 4:

Using the probabilities given in the question,

$$\begin{aligned}&P(DriveMed\ expands)\\&= P(DriveMed\ expands \mid EPS\ exceeded\ consensus)\\&\quad P(EPS\ exceeded\ consensus) + P(DriveMed\ expands \mid\\&\quad EPS\ met\ consensus)P(EPS\ met\ consensus) + P(DriveMed\ expands \mid\\&\quad EPS\ fell\ short\ of\ consensus)P(EPS\ fell\ short\ of\ consensus)\\&= 0.75(1/3) + 0.20(1/3) + 0.05(1/3) = 1/3\end{aligned}$$

Not surprisingly, the probability of DriveMed expanding is 1/3 because the decision maker has no prior beliefs or views regarding how well EPS performed relative to the consensus estimate. Now we can use Bayes' formula to find *P(EPS exceeded consensus | DriveMed expands)* = [*P(DriveMed expands | EPS exceeded consensus)*/*P(DriveMed expands)*] *P(EPS exceeded consensus)* = [(0.75/(1/3)](1/3) = 0.75 or 75 percent. This probability is identical to your estimate of *P(DriveMed expands | EPS exceeded consensus)*.

When the prior probabilities are equal, the probability of information given an event equals the probability of the event given the information. When a decision-maker has equal prior probabilities (called **diffuse priors**), the probability of an event is determined by the information.

4.2 Principles of Counting

The first step in addressing a question often involves determining the different logical possibilities. We may also want to know the number of ways that each of these possibilities can happen. In the back of our mind is often a question about probability. How likely is it that I will observe this particular possibility? Records of success and failure are an example. When we evaluate a market timer's record, one well-known evaluation method uses counting methods presented in this section.[22] An important investment model, the binomial option pricing model, incorporates the combination formula that we will cover shortly. We can also use the methods in this section to calculate what we called a priori probabilities in Section 2. When we can assume that the possible outcomes of a random variable are equally likely, the probability of an event equals the number of possible outcomes favorable for the event divided by the total number of outcomes.

22 Henriksson and Merton (1981).

In counting, enumeration (counting the outcomes one by one) is of course the most basic resource. What we discuss in this section are shortcuts and principles. Without these shortcuts and principles, counting the total number of outcomes can be very difficult and prone to error. The first and basic principle of counting is the multiplication rule.

- **Multiplication Rule of Counting.** If one task can be done in n_1 ways, and a second task, given the first, can be done in n_2 ways, and a third task, given the first two tasks, can be done in n_3 ways, and so on for k tasks, then the number of ways the k tasks can be done is $(n_1)(n_2)(n_3) \ldots (n_k)$.

Suppose we have three steps in an investment decision process. The first step can be done in two ways, the second in four ways, and the third in three ways. Following the multiplication rule, there are (2)(4)(3) = 24 ways in which we can carry out the three steps.

Another illustration is the assignment of members of a group to an equal number of positions. For example, suppose you want to assign three security analysts to cover three different industries. In how many ways can the assignments be made? The first analyst may be assigned in three different ways. Then two industries remain. The second analyst can be assigned in two different ways. Then one industry remains. The third and last analyst can be assigned in only one way. The total number of different assignments equals (3)(2)(1) = 6. The compact notation for the multiplication we have just performed is 3! (read: 3 factorial). If we had n analysts, the number of ways we could assign them to n tasks would be

$$n! = n(n - 1)(n - 2)(n - 3)\ldots1$$

or ***n* factorial**. (By convention, 0! = 1.) To review, in this application we repeatedly carry out an operation (here, job assignment) until we use up all members of a group (here, three analysts). With n members in the group, the multiplication formula reduces to n factorial.[23]

The next type of counting problem can be called labeling problems.[24] We want to give each object in a group a label, to place it in a category. The following example illustrates this type of problem.

A mutual fund guide ranked 18 bond mutual funds by total returns for the last year. The guide also assigned each fund one of five risk labels: *high risk* (four funds), *above-average risk* (four funds), *average risk* (three funds), *below-average risk* (four funds), and *low risk* (three funds); as 4 + 4 + 3 + 4 + 3 = 18, all the funds are accounted for. How many different ways can we take 18 mutual funds and label 4 of them high risk, 4 above-average risk, 3 average risk, 4 below-average risk, and 3 low risk, so that each fund is labeled?

The answer is close to 13 billion. We can label any of 18 funds *high risk* (the first slot), then any of 17 remaining funds, then any of 16 remaining funds, then any of 15 remaining funds (now we have 4 funds in the *high risk* group); then we can label any of 14 remaining funds *above-average risk*, then any of 13 remaining funds, and so forth. There are 18! possible sequences. However, order of assignment within a category does not matter. For example, whether a fund occupies the first or third slot of the four funds labeled *high risk*, the fund has the same label (*high risk*). Thus there are 4! ways to assign a given group of four funds to the four *high risk* slots. Making the same argument for the other categories, in total there are (4!)(4!)(3!)(4!)(3!) equivalent

---

23 The shortest explanation of n factorial is that it is the number of ways to order n objects in a row. In all the problems to which we apply this counting method, we must use up all the members of a group (sampling without replacement).

24 This discussion follows Kemeny, Schleifer, Snell, and Thompson (1972) in terminology and approach.

sequences. To eliminate such redundancies from the 18! total, we divide 18! by (4!)(4!)(3!)(4!)(3!). We have 18!/[(4!)(4!)(3!)(4!)(3!)] = 18!/[(24)(24)(6)(24)(6)] = 12,864,852,000. This procedure generalizes as follows.

- **Multinomial Formula (General Formula for Labeling Problems).** The number of ways that n objects can be labeled with k different labels, with n_1 of the first type, n_2 of the second type, and so on, with $n_1 + n_2 + \ldots + n_k = n$, is given by

$$\frac{n!}{n_1!n_2!\ldots n_k!}$$

The multinomial formula with two different labels ($k = 2$) is especially important. This special case is called the combination formula. A **combination** is a listing in which the order of the listed items does not matter. We state the combination formula in a traditional way, but no new concepts are involved. Using the notation in the formula below, the number of objects with the first label is $r = n_1$ and the number with the second label is $n - r = n_2$ (there are just two categories, so $n_1 + n_2 = n$). Here is the formula:

- **Combination Formula (Binomial Formula).** The number of ways that we can choose r objects from a total of n objects, when the order in which the r objects are listed does not matter, is

$${}_nC_r = \binom{n}{r} = \frac{n!}{(n-r)!r!}$$

Here ${}_nC_r$ and $\binom{n}{r}$ are shorthand notations for $n!/(n - r)!r!$ (read: n choose r, or n combination r).

If we label the r objects as *belongs to the group* and the remaining objects as *does not belong to the group*, whatever the group of interest, the combination formula tells us how many ways we can select a group of size r. We can illustrate this formula with the binomial option pricing model. This model describes the movement of the underlying asset as a series of moves, price up (U) or price down (D). For example, two sequences of five moves containing three up moves, such as UUUDD and UDUUD, result in the same final stock price. At least for an option with a payoff dependent on final stock price, the number but not the order of up moves in a sequence matters. How many sequences of five moves *belong to the group with three up moves?* The answer is 10, calculated using the combination formula ("5 choose 3"):

$$\begin{aligned} {}_5C_3 &= 5!/[(5-3)!3!] \\ &= [(5)(4)(3)(2)(1)]/[(2)(1)(3)(2)(1)] = 120/12 = 10 \text{ ways} \end{aligned}$$

A useful fact can be illustrated as follows: ${}_5C_3 = 5!/(2!3!)$ equals ${}_5C_2 = 5!/(3!2!)$, as $3 + 2 = 5$; ${}_5C_4 = 5!/(1!4!)$ equals ${}_5C_1 = 5!/(4!1!)$, as $4 + 1 = 5$. This symmetrical relationship can save work when we need to calculate many possible combinations.

Suppose jurors want to select three companies out of a group of five to receive the first-, second-, and third-place awards for the best annual report. In how many ways can the jurors make the three awards? Order does matter if we want to distinguish among the three awards (the rank within the group of three); clearly the question makes order important. On the other hand, if the question were "In how many ways can the jurors choose three winners, without regard to place of finish?" we would use the combination formula.

To address the first question above, we need to count ordered listings such as *first place, New Company; second place, Fir Company; third place, Well Company*. An ordered listing is known as a **permutation**, and the formula that counts the number of permutations is known as the permutation formula.[25]

- **Permutation Formula.** The number of ways that we can choose r objects from a total of n objects, when the order in which the r objects are listed does matter, is

$$_nP_r = \frac{n!}{(n-r)!}$$

So the jurors have $_5P_3 = 5!/(5-3)! = [(5)(4)(3)(2)(1)]/[(2)(1)] = 120/2 = 60$ ways in which they can make their awards. To see why this formula works, note that [(5)(4)(3)(2)(1)]/[(2)(1)] reduces to (5)(4)(3), after cancellation of terms. This calculation counts the number of ways to fill three slots choosing from a group of five people, according to the multiplication rule of counting. This number is naturally larger than it would be if order did not matter (compare 60 to the value of 10 for "5 choose 3" that we calculated above). For example, *first place, Well Company; second place, Fir Company; third place, New Company* contains the same three companies as *first place, New Company; second place, Fir Company; third place, Well Company*. If we were concerned only with award winners (without regard to place of finish), the two listings would count as one combination. But when we are concerned with the order of finish, the listings count as two permutations.

Answering the following questions may help you apply the counting methods we have presented in this section.

1. Does the task that I want to measure have a finite number of possible outcomes? If the answer is yes, you may be able to use a tool in this section, and you can go to the second question. If the answer is no, the number of outcomes is infinite, and the tools in this section do not apply.
2. Do I want to assign every member of a group of size n to one of n slots (or tasks)? If the answer is yes, use n factorial. If the answer is no, go to the third question.
3. Do I want to count the number of ways to apply one of three or more labels to each member of a group? If the answer is yes, use the multinomial formula. If the answer is no, go to the fourth question.
4. Do I want to count the number of ways that I can choose r objects from a total of n, when the order in which I list the r objects does not matter (can I give the r objects a label)? If the answer to these questions is yes, the combination formula applies. If the answer is no, go to the fifth question.
5. Do I want to count the number of ways I can choose r objects from a total of n, when the order in which I list the r objects is important? If the answer is yes, the permutation formula applies. If the answer is no, go to question 6.
6. Can the multiplication rule of counting be used? If it cannot, you may have to count the possibilities one by one, or use more advanced techniques than those presented here.[26]

25 A more formal definition states that a permutation is an ordered subset of n distinct objects.
26 Feller (1957) contains a very full treatment of counting problems and solution methods.

SUMMARY

In this reading, we have discussed the essential concepts and tools of probability. We have applied probability, expected value, and variance to a range of investment problems.

- A random variable is a quantity whose outcome is uncertain.
- Probability is a number between 0 and 1 that describes the chance that a stated event will occur.
- An event is a specified set of outcomes of a random variable.
- Mutually exclusive events can occur only one at a time. Exhaustive events cover or contain all possible outcomes.
- The two defining properties of a probability are, first, that $0 \leq P(E) \leq 1$ (where $P(E)$ denotes the probability of an event E), and second, that the sum of the probabilities of any set of mutually exclusive and exhaustive events equals 1.
- A probability estimated from data as a relative frequency of occurrence is an empirical probability. A probability drawing on personal or subjective judgment is a subjective probability. A probability obtained based on logical analysis is an a priori probability.
- A probability of an event E, $P(E)$, can be stated as odds for $E = P(E)/[1 - P(E)]$ or odds against $E = [1 - P(E)]/P(E)$.
- Probabilities that are inconsistent create profit opportunities, according to the Dutch Book Theorem.
- A probability of an event *not* conditioned on another event is an unconditional probability. The unconditional probability of an event A is denoted $P(A)$. Unconditional probabilities are also called marginal probabilities.
- A probability of an event given (conditioned on) another event is a conditional probability. The probability of an event A given an event B is denoted $P(A \mid B)$.
- The probability of both A and B occurring is the joint probability of A and B, denoted $P(AB)$.
- $P(A \mid B) = P(AB)/P(B)$, $P(B) \neq 0$.
- The multiplication rule for probabilities is $P(AB) = P(A \mid B)P(B)$.
- The probability that A or B occurs, or both occur, is denoted by $P(A \text{ or } B)$.
- The addition rule for probabilities is $P(A \text{ or } B) = P(A) + P(B) - P(AB)$.
- When events are independent, the occurrence of one event does not affect the probability of occurrence of the other event. Otherwise, the events are dependent.
- The multiplication rule for independent events states that if A and B are independent events, $P(AB) = P(A)P(B)$. The rule generalizes in similar fashion to more than two events.
- According to the total probability rule, if $S_1, S_2, \ldots, S_n$ are mutually exclusive and exhaustive scenarios or events, then $P(A) = P(A \mid S_1)P(S_1) + P(A \mid S_2)P(S_2) + \ldots + P(A \mid S_n)P(S_n)$.
- The expected value of a random variable is a probability-weighted average of the possible outcomes of the random variable. For a random variable X, the expected value of X is denoted $E(X)$.
- The total probability rule for expected value states that $E(X) = E(X \mid S_1)P(S_1) + E(X \mid S_2)P(S_2) + \ldots + E(X \mid S_n)P(S_n)$, where $S_1, S_2, \ldots, S_n$ are mutually exclusive and exhaustive scenarios or events.

- The variance of a random variable is the expected value (the probability-weighted average) of squared deviations from the random variable's expected value $E(X)$: $\sigma^2(X) = E\{[X - E(X)]^2\}$, where $\sigma^2(X)$ stands for the variance of X.
- Variance is a measure of dispersion about the mean. Increasing variance indicates increasing dispersion. Variance is measured in squared units of the original variable.
- Standard deviation is the positive square root of variance. Standard deviation measures dispersion (as does variance), but it is measured in the same units as the variable.
- Covariance is a measure of the co-movement between random variables.
- The covariance between two random variables R_i and R_j in a forward-looking sense is the expected value of the cross-product of the deviations of the two random variables from their respective means: $\text{Cov}(R_i,R_j) = E\{[R_i - E(R_i)][R_j - E(R_j)]\}$. The covariance of a random variable with itself is its own variance.
- The historical or sample covariance between two random variables R_i and R_j based on a sample of past data of size n is the average value of the product of the deviations of observations on two random variables from their sample means:

$$\text{Cov}(R_i,R_j) = \sum_{i=1}^{n}(R_{i,t} - \bar{R}_i)(R_{j,t} - \bar{R}_j)/(n-1)$$

- Correlation is a number between −1 and +1 that measures the co-movement (linear association) between two random variables: $\rho(R_i,R_j) = \text{Cov}(R_i,R_j)/[\sigma(R_i)\ \sigma(R_j)]$.
- If two variables have a very strong linear relation, then the absolute value of their correlation will be close to 1. If two variables have a weak linear relation, then the absolute value of their correlation will be close to 0.
- If the correlation coefficient is positive, the two variables are directly related; if the correlation coefficient is negative, the two variables are inversely related.
- A scatter plot shows graphically the relationship between two variables. If the points on the scatter plot cluster together in a straight line, the two variables have a strong linear relation.
- Even one outlier can greatly affect the correlation between two variables. Analysts should examine a scatter plot for the variables to determine whether outliers might affect a particular correlation.
- Correlations can be spurious in the sense of misleadingly pointing toward associations between variables.
- To calculate the variance of return on a portfolio of n assets, the inputs needed are the n expected returns on the individual assets, n variances of return on the individual assets, and $n(n - 1)/2$ distinct covariances.
- Portfolio variance of return is $\sigma^2(R_p) = \sum_{i=1}^{n}\sum_{j=1}^{n} w_i w_j \text{Cov}(R_i,R_j)$.
- The calculation of covariance in a forward-looking sense requires the specification of a joint probability function, which gives the probability of joint occurrences of values of the two random variables.
- When two random variables are independent, the joint probability function is the product of the individual probability functions of the random variables.
- Bayes' formula is a method for updating probabilities based on new information.

- Bayes' formula is expressed as follows: Updated probability of event given the new information = [(Probability of the new information given event)/(Unconditional probability of the new information)] × Prior probability of event.
- The multiplication rule of counting says, for example, that if the first step in a process can be done in 10 ways, the second step, given the first, can be done in 5 ways, and the third step, given the first two, can be done in 7 ways, then the steps can be carried out in (10)(5)(7) = 350 ways.
- The number of ways to assign every member of a group of size n to n slots is $n! = n(n-1)(n-2)(n-3) \ldots 1$. (By convention, $0! = 1$.)
- The number of ways that n objects can be labeled with k different labels, with n_1 of the first type, n_2 of the second type, and so on, with $n_1 + n_2 + \ldots + n_k = n$, is given by $n!/(n_1!n_2! \ldots n_k!)$. This expression is the multinomial formula.
- A special case of the multinomial formula is the combination formula. The number of ways to choose r objects from a total of n objects, when the order in which the r objects are listed does not matter, is

$$_nC_r = \binom{n}{r} = \frac{n!}{(n-r)!r!}$$

- The number of ways to choose r objects from a total of n objects, when the order in which the r objects are listed does matter, is

$$_nP_r = \frac{n!}{(n-r)!}$$

This expression is the permutation formula.

REFERENCES

Bodie, Zvi, Alex Kane, and Alan J. Marcus. 2017. *Essentials of Investments*, 11th edition. New York: McGraw-Hill Irwin.

Elton, Edwin J., Martin J. Gruber, Stephen J. Brown, and William N. Goetzmann. 2013. *Modern Portfolio Theory and Investment Analysis*, 9th edition. Hoboken, NJ: Wiley.

Feller, William. 1957. *An Introduction to Probability Theory and Its Applications, Vol. I*, 2nd edition. New York: Wiley.

Henriksson, Roy D., and Robert C. Merton. 1981. "On Market Timing and Investment Performance, II. Statistical Procedures for Evaluating Forecasting Skills." *Journal of Business*, vol. 54, no. 4:513–533.

Huij, Joop, and Marno Verbeek. 2007. "Cross-sectional learning and short-run persistence in mutual fund performance." *Journal of Banking & Finance*, vol. 31:973–997.

Kemeny, John G., Arthur Schleifer, Jr, J. Laurie Snell, and Gerald L. Thompson. 1972. *Finite Mathematics with Business Applications*, 2nd edition. Englewood Cliffs, NJ: Prentice-Hall.

Lo, Andrew W. 1999. "The Three P's of Total Risk Management." *Financial Analysts Journal*, vol. 55, no. 1:13–26.

Ramsey, Frank P. 1931. "Truth and Probability." In *The Foundations of Mathematics and Other Logical Essays*, edited by R.B. Braithwaite. London: Routledge and Keegan Paul.

Reilly, Frank K., and Keith C. Brown. 2018. *Investment Analysis and Portfolio Management*, 11th edition. Mason, OH: Cengage South-Western.

Thanatawee, Yordying. 2013. "Ownership Structure with Dividend Policy: Evidence from Thailand." *International Journal of Economics and Finance*, vol. 5, no. 1:121–132.

Vidal-Garcia, Javier. 2013. "The Persistence of European Mutual Fund Performance." *Research in International Business and Finance*, vol. 28:45–67.

PRACTICE PROBLEMS

1 Suppose that 5 percent of the stocks meeting your stock-selection criteria are in the telecommunications (telecom) industry. Also, dividend-paying telecom stocks are 1 percent of the total number of stocks meeting your selection criteria. What is the probability that a stock is dividend paying, given that it is a telecom stock that has met your stock selection criteria?

2 You are using the following three criteria to screen potential acquisition targets from a list of 500 companies:

Criterion	Fraction of the 500 Companies Meeting the Criterion
Product lines compatible	0.20
Company will increase combined sales growth rate	0.45
Balance sheet impact manageable	0.78

If the criteria are independent, how many companies will pass the screen?

3 You apply both valuation criteria and financial strength criteria in choosing stocks. The probability that a randomly selected stock (from your investment universe) meets your valuation criteria is 0.25. Given that a stock meets your valuation criteria, the probability that the stock meets your financial strength criteria is 0.40. What is the probability that a stock meets both your valuation and financial strength criteria?

4 Suppose the prospects for recovering principal for a defaulted bond issue depend on which of two economic scenarios prevails. Scenario 1 has probability 0.75 and will result in recovery of \$0.90 per \$1 principal value with probability 0.45, or in recovery of \$0.80 per \$1 principal value with probability 0.55. Scenario 2 has probability 0.25 and will result in recovery of \$0.50 per \$1 principal value with probability 0.85, or in recovery of \$0.40 per \$1 principal value with probability 0.15.

A Compute the probability of each of the four possible recovery amounts: \$0.90, \$0.80, \$0.50, and \$0.40.

B Compute the expected recovery, given the first scenario.

C Compute the expected recovery, given the second scenario.

D Compute the expected recovery.

E Graph the information in a tree diagram.

5 You have developed a set of criteria for evaluating distressed credits. Companies that do not receive a passing score are classed as likely to go bankrupt within 12 months. You gathered the following information when validating the criteria:

- Forty percent of the companies to which the test is administered will go bankrupt within 12 months: $P(nonsurvivor) = 0.40$.
- Fifty-five percent of the companies to which the test is administered pass it: $P(pass\ test) = 0.55$.
- The probability that a company will pass the test given that it will subsequently survive 12 months, is 0.85: $P(pass\ test \mid survivor) = 0.85$.

A What is $P(pass\ test \mid nonsurvivor)$?

B Using Bayes' formula, calculate the probability that a company is a survivor, given that it passes the test; that is, calculate $P(\text{survivor} \mid \text{pass test})$.

C What is the probability that a company is a *nonsurvivor*, given that it fails the test?

D Is the test effective?

6 In probability theory, exhaustive events are *best* described as events:

A with a probability of zero.

B that are mutually exclusive.

C that include all potential outcomes.

7 Which probability estimate *most likely* varies greatly between people?

A An *a priori* probability

B An empirical probability

C A subjective probability

8 If the probability that Zolaf Company sales exceed last year's sales is 0.167, the odds for exceeding sales are *closest* to:

A 1 to 5.

B 1 to 6.

C 5 to 1.

9 The probability of an event given that another event has occurred is a:

A joint probability.

B marginal probability.

C conditional probability.

10 After estimating the probability that an investment manager will exceed his benchmark return in each of the next two quarters, an analyst wants to forecast the probability that the investment manager will exceed his benchmark return over the two-quarter period in total. Assuming that each quarter's performance is independent of the other, which probability rule should the analyst select?

A Addition rule

B Multiplication rule

C Total probability rule

11 Which of the following is a property of two dependent events?

A The two events must occur simultaneously.

B The probability of one event influences the probability of the other event.

C The probability of the two events occurring is the product of each event's probability.

12 Which of the following *best* describes how an analyst would estimate the expected value of a firm under the scenarios of bankruptcy and survivorship? The analyst would use:

A the addition rule.

B conditional expected values.

C the total probability rule for expected value.

13 An analyst developed two scenarios with respect to the recovery of $100,000 principal from defaulted loans:

Scenario	Probability of Scenario (%)	Amount Recovered ($)	Probability of Amount (%)
1	40	50,000	60
		30,000	40
2	60	80,000	90
		60,000	10

The amount of the expected recovery is *closest* to:

A $36,400.

B $63,600.

C $81,600.

14 US and Spanish bonds have return standard deviations of 0.64 and 0.56, respectively. If the correlation between the two bonds is 0.24, the covariance of returns is *closest* to:

A 0.086.

B 0.670.

C 0.781.

15 The covariance of returns is positive when the returns on two assets tend to:

A have the same expected values.

B be above their expected value at different times.

C be on the same side of their expected value at the same time.

16 Which of the following correlation coefficients indicates the weakest linear relationship between two variables?

A −0.67

B −0.24

C 0.33

17 An analyst develops the following covariance matrix of returns:

	Hedge Fund	Market Index
Hedge fund	256	110
Market index	110	81

The correlation of returns between the hedge fund and the market index is *closest* to:

A 0.005.

B 0.073.

C 0.764.

18 All else being equal, as the correlation between two assets approaches +1.0, the diversification benefits:

A decrease.

B stay the same.

C increase.

19 Given a portfolio of five stocks, how many unique covariance terms, excluding variances, are required to calculate the portfolio return variance?

A 10

B 20

C 25

20 The probability distribution for a company's sales is:

Probability	Sales ($ millions)
0.05	70
0.70	40
0.25	25

The standard deviation of sales is *closest* to:

A $9.81 million.

B $12.20 million.

C $32.40 million.

21 Which of the following statements is *most* accurate? If the covariance of returns between two assets is 0.0023, then:

A the assets' risk is near zero.

B the asset returns are unrelated.

C the asset returns have a positive relationship.

22 An analyst produces the following joint probability function for a foreign index (FI) and a domestic index (DI).

	R_{DI} = 30%	R_{DI} = 25%	R_{DI} = 15%
R_{FI} = 25%	0.25		
R_{FI} = 15%		0.50	
R_{FI} = 10%			0.25

The covariance of returns on the foreign index and the returns on the domestic index is *closest* to:

A 26.39.

B 26.56.

C 28.12.

23 A manager will select 20 bonds out of his universe of 100 bonds to construct a portfolio. Which formula provides the number of possible portfolios?

A Permutation formula

B Multinomial formula

C Combination formula

24 A firm will select two of four vice presidents to be added to the investment committee. How many different groups of two are possible?

A 6

B 12

C 24

25 From an approved list of 25 funds, a portfolio manager wants to rank 4 mutual funds from most recommended to least recommended. Which formula is *most* appropriate to calculate the number of possible ways the funds could be ranked?

A Permutation formula

B Multinomial formula

C Combination formula

SOLUTIONS

1 Use Equation 1 to find this conditional probability: *P(stock is dividend paying | telecom stock that meets criteria) = P(stock is dividend paying and telecom stock that meets criteria)/P(telecom stock that meets criteria)* = 0.01/0.05 = 0.20.

2 According to the multiplication rule for independent events, the probability of a company meeting all three criteria is the product of the three probabilities. Labeling the event that a company passes the first, second, and third criteria, *A*, *B*, and *C*, respectively $P(ABC) = P(A)P(B)P(C) = (0.20)(0.45)(0.78) = 0.0702$. As a consequence, (0.0702)(500) = 35.10, so 35 companies pass the screen.

3 Use Equation 2, the multiplication rule for probabilities $P(AB) = P(A \mid B)P(B)$, defining *A* as the event that *a stock meets the financial strength criteria* and defining *B* as the event that *a stock meets the valuation criteria.* Then $P(AB) = P(A \mid B)P(B) = 0.40 \times 0.25 = 0.10$. The probability that a stock meets both the financial and valuation criteria is 0.10.

4 **A** *Outcomes associated with Scenario 1:* With a 0.45 probability of a \$0.90 recovery per \$1 principal value, given Scenario 1, and with the probability of Scenario 1 equal to 0.75, the probability of recovering \$0.90 is 0.45 (0.75) = 0.3375. By a similar calculation, the probability of recovering \$0.80 is 0.55(0.75) = 0.4125.

Outcomes associated with Scenario 2: With a 0.85 probability of a \$0.50 recovery per \$1 principal value, given Scenario 2, and with the probability of Scenario 2 equal to 0.25, the probability of recovering \$0.50 is 0.85(0.25) = 0.2125. By a similar calculation, the probability of recovering \$0.40 is 0.15(0.25) = 0.0375.

B *E(recovery | Scenario 1)* = 0.45(\$0.90) + 0.55(\$0.80) = \$0.845

C *E(recovery | Scenario 2)* = 0.85(\$0.50) + 0.15(\$0.40) = \$0.485

D *E(recovery)* = 0.75(\$0.845) + 0.25(\$0.485) = \$0.755

E

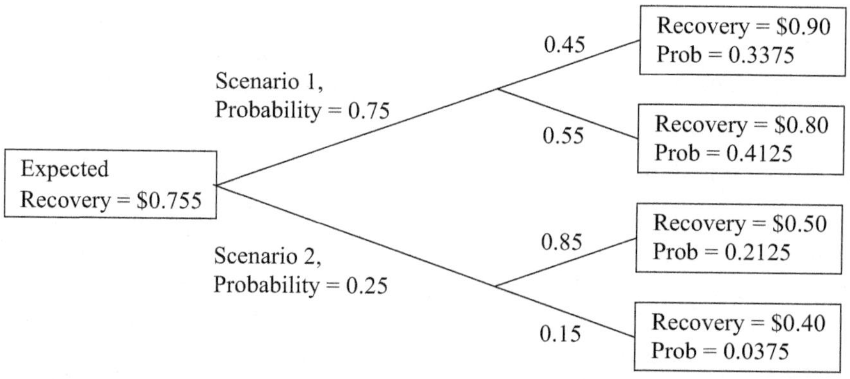

5 **A** We can set up the equation using the total probability rule:

$$P(\textit{pass test}) = P(\textit{pass test} \mid \textit{survivor})P(\textit{survivor}) + P(\textit{pass test} \mid \textit{nonsurvivor})P(\textit{nonsurvivor})$$

We know that *P(survivor)* = 1 – *P(nonsurvivor)* = 1 – 0.40 = 0.60. Therefore, *P(pass test)* = 0.55 = 0.85(0.60) + *P(pass test | nonsurvivor)*(0.40). Thus *P(pass test | nonsurvivor)* = [0.55 – 0.85(0.60)]/0.40 = 0.10.

B $P(survivor \mid pass\ test) = \left[P(pass\ test \mid survivor)/P(pass\ test)\right]P(survivor)$

$$= (0.85/0.55)0.60 = 0.927273$$

The information that a company passes the test causes you to update your probability that it is a survivor from 0.60 to approximately 0.927.

C According to Bayes' formula, $P(nonsurvivor \mid fail\ test) = [P(fail\ test \mid nonsurvivor)/\ P(fail\ test)]P(nonsurvivor) = [P(fail\ test \mid nonsurvivor)/0.45]0.40$.

We can set up the following equation to obtain $P(fail\ test \mid nonsurvivor)$:

$$P(fail\ test) = P(fail\ test \mid nonsurvivor)P(nonsurvivor) + P(fail\ test \mid survivor)P(survivor)$$

$$0.45 = P(fail\ test \mid nonsurvivor)0.40 + 0.15(0.60)$$

where $P(fail\ test \mid survivor) = 1 - P(pass\ test \mid survivor) = 1 - 0.85 = 0.15$. So $P(fail\ test \mid nonsurvivor) = [0.45 - 0.15(0.60)]/0.40 = 0.90$. Using this result with the formula above, we find $P(nonsurvivor \mid fail\ test) = (0.90/0.45)0.40 = 0.80$. Seeing that a company fails the test causes us to update the probability that it is a nonsurvivor from 0.40 to 0.80.

D A company passing the test greatly increases our confidence that it is a survivor. A company failing the test doubles the probability that it is a nonsurvivor. Therefore, the test appears to be useful.

6 C is correct. The term "exhaustive" means that the events cover all possible outcomes.

7 C is correct. A subjective probability draws on personal or subjective judgment that may be without reference to any particular data.

8 A is correct. Given odds for E of a to b, the implied probability of $E = a/(a + b)$. Stated in terms of odds a to b with $a = 1$, $b = 5$, the probability of $E = 1/(1 + 5) = 1/6 = 0.167$. This result confirms that a probability of 0.167 for beating sales is odds of 1 to 5.

9 C is correct. A conditional probability is the probability of an event given that another event has occurred.

10 B is correct. Because the events are independent, the multiplication rule is most appropriate for forecasting their joint probability. The multiplication rule for independent events states that the joint probability of both A and B occurring is P(AB) = P(A)P(B).

11 B is correct. The probability of the occurrence of one is related to the occurrence of the other. If we are trying to forecast one event, information about a dependent event may be useful.

12 C is correct. The total probability rule for expected value is used to estimate an expected value based on mutually exclusive and exhaustive scenarios.

13 B is correct. If Scenario 1 occurs, the expected recovery is 60% (\$50,000) + 40% (\$30,000) = \$42,000, and if Scenario 2 occurs, the expected recovery is 90% (\$80,000) + 10%(\$60,000) = \$78,000. Weighting by the probability of each scenario, the expected recovery is 40%(\$42,000) + 60%(\$78,000) = \$63,600. Alternatively, first calculating the probability of each amount occurring, the expected recovery is (40%)(60%)(\$50,000) + (40%)(40%)(\$30,000) + (60%)(90%)(\$80,000) + (60%)(10%)(\$60,000) = \$63,600.

14 A is correct. The covariance is the product of the standard deviations and correlation using the formula Cov(US bond returns, Spanish bond returns) = σ(US bonds) × σ (Spanish bonds) × ρ(US bond returns, Spanish bond returns) = 0.64 × 0.56 × 0.24 = 0.086.

15 C is correct. The covariance of returns is positive when the returns on both assets tend to be on the same side (above or below) their expected values at the same time, indicating an average positive relationship between returns.

16 B is correct. Correlations near +1 exhibit strong positive linearity, whereas correlations near −1 exhibit strong negative linearity. A correlation of 0 indicates an absence of any linear relationship between the variables. The closer the correlation is to 0, the weaker the linear relationship.

17 C is correct. The correlation between two random variables R_i and R_j is defined as $\rho(R_i,R_j) = \text{Cov}(R_i,R_j)/[\sigma(R_i)\sigma(R_j)]$. Using the subscript i to represent hedge funds and the subscript j to represent the market index, the standard deviations are $\sigma(R_i) = 256^{1/2} = 16$ and $\sigma(R_j) = 81^{1/2} = 9$. Thus, $\rho(R_i,R_j) = \text{Cov}(R_i,R_j)/[\sigma(R_i)\sigma(R_j)] = 110/(16 \times 9) = 0.764$.

18 A is correct. As the correlation between two assets approaches +1, diversification benefits decrease. In other words, an increasingly positive correlation indicates an increasingly strong positive linear relationship and fewer diversification benefits.

19 A is correct. A covariance matrix for five stocks has 5 × 5 = 25 entries. Subtracting the 5 diagonal variance terms results in 20 off-diagonal entries. Because a covariance matrix is symmetrical, only 10 entries are unique (20/2 = 10).

20 A is correct. The analyst must first calculate expected sales as 0.05 × \$70 + 0.70 × \$40 + 0.25 × \$25 = \$3.50 million + \$28.00 million + \$6.25 million = \$37.75 million.

After calculating expected sales, we can calculate the variance of sales:

$$
\begin{aligned}
&= \sigma^2 \text{ (Sales)} \\
&= P(\$70)[\$70 - E(\text{Sales})]^2 + P(\$40)[\$40 - E(\text{Sales})]^2 + P(\$25) \\
&\quad [\$25 - E(\text{Sales})]^2 \\
&= 0.05(\$70 - 37.75)^2 + 0.70(\$40 - 37.75)^2 + 0.25(\$25 - 37.75)^2 \\
&= \$52.00 \text{ million} + \$3.54 \text{ million} + \$40.64 \text{ million} = \$96.18 \text{ million.}
\end{aligned}
$$

The standard deviation of sales is thus $\sigma = (\$96.18)^{1/2} = \$9.81$ million.

21 C is correct. The covariance of returns is positive when the returns on both assets tend to be on the same side (above or below) their expected values at the same time.

22 B is correct. The covariance is 26.56, calculated as follows. First, expected returns are

$$
\begin{aligned}
E(R_{FI}) &= (0.25 \times 25) + (0.50 \times 15) + (0.25 \times 10) \\
&= 6.25 + 7.50 + 2.50 = 16.25 \text{ and} \\
E(R_{DI}) &= (0.25 \times 30) + (0.50 \times 25) + (0.25 \times 15) \\
&= 7.50 + 12.50 + 3.75 = 23.75.
\end{aligned}
$$

Covariance is

$$
\begin{aligned}
\text{Cov}(R_{FI},R_{DI}) &= \sum_i \sum_j P(R_{FI,i},R_{DI,j})(R_{FI,i} - ER_{FI})(R_{DI,j} - ER_{DI}) \\
&= 0.25[(25 - 16.25)(30 - 23.75)] + 0.50[(15 - 16.25) \\
&\quad (25 - 23.75)] + 0.25[(10 - 16.25)(15 - 23.75)] \\
&= 13.67 + (-0.78) + 13.67 = 26.56.
\end{aligned}
$$

23 C is correct. The combination formula provides the number of ways that r objects can be chosen from a total of n objects, when the order in which the r objects are listed does not matter. The order of the bonds within the portfolio does not matter.

24 A is correct. The answer is found using the combination formula

$$_nC_r = \binom{n}{r} = \frac{n!}{(n-r)!r!}$$

Here, $n = 4$ and $r = 2$, so the answer is $4!/[(4-2)!2!] = 24/[(2) \times (2)] = 6$. This result can be verified by assuming there are four vice presidents, VP1–VP4. The six possible additions to the investment committee are VP1 and VP2, VP1 and VP3, VP1 and VP4, VP2 and VP3, VP2 and VP4, and VP3 and VP4.

25 A is correct. The permutation formula is used to choose r objects from a total of n objects when order matters. Because the portfolio manager is trying to rank the four funds from most recommended to least recommended, the order of the funds matters; therefore, the permutation formula is most appropriate.

QUANTITATIVE METHODS

STUDY SESSION

3

Quantitative Methods (2)

This study session introduces the common probability distributions used to describe the behavior of random variables, such as asset prices and returns. How to estimate measures of a population (mean, standard deviation) based on a population sample is shown. The study session ends with a framework for hypothesis testing, used for validating dataset hypotheses, along with techniques to test a hypothesis.

READING ASSIGNMENTS

Reading 9	Common Probability Distributions by Richard A. DeFusco, PhD, CFA, Dennis W. McLeavey, DBA, CFA, Jerald E. Pinto, PhD, CFA, and David E. Runkle, PhD, CFA
Reading 10	Sampling and Estimation by Richard A. DeFusco, PhD, CFA, Dennis W. McLeavey, DBA, CFA, Jerald E. Pinto, PhD, CFA, and David E. Runkle, PhD, CFA
Reading 11	Hypothesis Testing by Richard A. DeFusco, PhD, CFA, Dennis W. McLeavey, DBA, CFA, Jerald E. Pinto, PhD, CFA, and David E. Runkle, PhD, CFA

READING

9

Common Probability Distributions

by Richard A. DeFusco, PhD, CFA, Dennis W. McLeavey, DBA, CFA, Jerald E. Pinto, PhD, CFA, and David E. Runkle, PhD, CFA

Richard A. DeFusco, PhD, CFA, is at the University of Nebraska-Lincoln (USA). Dennis W. McLeavey, DBA, CFA, is at the University of Rhode Island (USA). Jerald E. Pinto, PhD, CFA, is at CFA Institute (USA). David E. Runkle, PhD, CFA, is at Trilogy Global Advisors (USA).

LEARNING OUTCOMES

Mastery	*The candidate should be able to:*
☐	**a.** define a probability distribution and distinguish between discrete and continuous random variables and their probability functions;
☐	**b.** describe the set of possible outcomes of a specified discrete random variable;
☐	**c.** interpret a cumulative distribution function;
☐	**d.** calculate and interpret probabilities for a random variable, given its cumulative distribution function;
☐	**e.** define a discrete uniform random variable, a Bernoulli random variable, and a binomial random variable;
☐	**f.** calculate and interpret probabilities given the discrete uniform and the binomial distribution functions;
☐	**g.** construct a binomial tree to describe stock price movement;
☐	**h.** define the continuous uniform distribution and calculate and interpret probabilities, given a continuous uniform distribution;
☐	**i.** explain the key properties of the normal distribution;
☐	**j.** distinguish between a univariate and a multivariate distribution and explain the role of correlation in the multivariate normal distribution;
☐	**k.** determine the probability that a normally distributed random variable lies inside a given interval;
☐	**l.** define the standard normal distribution, explain how to standardize a random variable, and calculate and interpret probabilities using the standard normal distribution;
☐	**m.** define shortfall risk, calculate the safety-first ratio, and select an optimal portfolio using Roy's safety-first criterion;

(continued)

LEARNING OUTCOMES

Mastery	The candidate should be able to:
☐	**n.** explain the relationship between normal and lognormal distributions and why the lognormal distribution is used to model asset prices;
☐	**o.** distinguish between discretely and continuously compounded rates of return and calculate and interpret a continuously compounded rate of return, given a specific holding period return;
☐	**p.** explain Monte Carlo simulation and describe its applications and limitations;
☐	**q.** compare Monte Carlo simulation and historical simulation.

1 INTRODUCTION TO COMMON PROBABILITY DISTRIBUTIONS

In nearly all investment decisions we work with random variables. The return on a stock and its earnings per share are familiar examples of random variables. To make probability statements about a random variable, we need to understand its probability distribution. A **probability distribution** specifies the probabilities of the possible outcomes of a random variable.

In this reading, we present important facts about four probability distributions and their investment uses. These four distributions—the uniform, binomial, normal, and lognormal—are used extensively in investment analysis. They are used in such basic valuation models as the Black–Scholes–Merton option pricing model, the binomial option pricing model, and the capital asset pricing model. With the working knowledge of probability distributions provided in this reading, you will also be better prepared to study and use other quantitative methods such as hypothesis testing, regression analysis, and time-series analysis.

After discussing probability distributions, we end the reading with an introduction to Monte Carlo simulation, a computer-based tool for obtaining information on complex problems. For example, an investment analyst may want to experiment with an investment idea without actually implementing it. Or she may need to price a complex option for which no simple pricing formula exists. In these cases and many others, Monte Carlo simulation is an important resource. To conduct a Monte Carlo simulation, the analyst must identify risk factors associated with the problem and specify probability distributions for them. Hence, Monte Carlo simulation is a tool that requires an understanding of probability distributions.

Before we discuss specific probability distributions, we define basic concepts and terms. We then illustrate the operation of these concepts through the simplest distribution, the uniform distribution. That done, we address probability distributions that have more applications in investment work but also greater complexity.

DISCRETE RANDOM VARIABLES

2

A **random variable** is a quantity whose future outcomes are uncertain. The two basic types of random variables are discrete random variables and continuous random variables. A **discrete random variable** can take on at most a countable number of possible values. For example, a discrete random variable X can take on a limited number of outcomes $x_1, x_2, ..., x_n$ (n possible outcomes), or a discrete random variable Y can take on an unlimited number of outcomes $y_1, y_2, ...$ (without end).[1] Because we can count all the possible outcomes of X and Y (even if we go on forever in the case of Y), both X and Y satisfy the definition of a discrete random variable. By contrast, we cannot count the outcomes of a **continuous random variable**. We cannot describe the possible outcomes of a continuous random variable Z with a list $z_1, z_2, ...$ because the outcome $(z_1 + z_2)/2$, not in the list, would always be possible. Rate of return is an example of a continuous random variable.

In working with a random variable, we need to understand its possible outcomes. For example, a majority of the stocks traded on the New Zealand Stock Exchange are quoted in ticks of NZ$0.01. Quoted stock price is thus a discrete random variable with possible values NZ$0, NZ$0.01, NZ$0.02, ... But we can also model stock price as a continuous random variable (as a lognormal random variable, to look ahead). In many applications, we have a choice between using a discrete or a continuous distribution. We are usually guided by which distribution is most efficient for the task we face. This opportunity for choice is not surprising, as many discrete distributions can be approximated with a continuous distribution, and vice versa. In most practical cases, a probability distribution is only a mathematical idealization, or approximate model, of the relative frequencies of a random variable's possible outcomes.

EXAMPLE 1

The Distribution of Bond Price

You are researching a probability model for bond price, and you begin by thinking about the characteristics of bonds that affect price. What are the lowest and the highest possible values for bond price? Why? What are some other characteristics of bonds that may affect the distribution of bond price?

The lowest possible value of bond price is 0, when the bond is worthless. Identifying the highest possible value for bond price is more challenging. The promised payments on a coupon bond are the coupons (interest payments) plus the face amount (principal). The price of a bond is the present discounted value of these promised payments. Because investors require a return on their investments, 0 percent is the lower limit on the discount rate that investors would use to discount a bond's promised payments. At a discount rate of 0 percent, the price of a bond is the sum of the face value and the remaining coupons without any discounting. The discount rate thus places the upper limit on bond price. Suppose, for example, that face value is $1,000 and two $40 coupons remain; the interval $0 to $1,080 captures all possible values of the bond's price. This upper limit decreases through time as the number of remaining payments decreases.

1 We follow the convention that an uppercase letter represents a random variable and a lowercase letter represents an outcome or specific value of the random variable. Thus X refers to the random variable, and x refers to an outcome of X. We subscript outcomes, as in x_1 and x_2, when we need to distinguish among different outcomes in a list of outcomes of a random variable.

Other characteristics of a bond also affect its price distribution. Pull to par value is one such characteristic: As the maturity date approaches, the standard deviation of bond price tends to grow smaller as bond price converges to par value. Embedded options also affect bond price. For example, with bonds that are currently callable, the issuer may retire the bonds at a prespecified premium above par; this option of the issuer cuts off part of the bond's upside. Modeling bond price distribution is a challenging problem.

Every random variable is associated with a probability distribution that describes the variable completely. We can view a probability distribution in two ways. The basic view is the **probability function**, which specifies the probability that the random variable takes on a specific value: $P(X = x)$ is the probability that a random variable X takes on the value x. (Note that capital X represents the random variable and lowercase x represents a specific value that the random variable may take.) For a discrete random variable, the shorthand notation for the probability function is $p(x) = P(X = x)$. For continuous random variables, the probability function is denoted $f(x)$ and called the **probability density function** (pdf), or just the density.[2]

A probability function has two key properties (which we state, without loss of generality, using the notation for a discrete random variable):

- $0 \le p(x) \le 1$, because probability is a number between 0 and 1.
- The sum of the probabilities $p(x)$ over all values of X equals 1. If we add up the probabilities of all the distinct possible outcomes of a random variable, that sum must equal 1.

We are often interested in finding the probability of a range of outcomes rather than a specific outcome. In these cases, we take the second view of a probability distribution, the cumulative distribution function (cdf). The **cumulative distribution function**, or distribution function for short, gives the probability that a random variable X is less than or equal to a particular value x, $P(X \le x)$. For both discrete and continuous random variables, the shorthand notation is $F(x) = P(X \le x)$. How does the cumulative distribution function relate to the probability function? The word "cumulative" tells the story. To find $F(x)$, we sum up, or cumulate, values of the probability function for all outcomes less than or equal to x. The function of the cdf is parallel to that of cumulative relative frequency, which we discussed in the reading on statistical concepts and market returns.

Next, we illustrate these concepts with examples and show how we use discrete and continuous distributions. We start with the simplest distribution, the discrete uniform.

2.1 The Discrete Uniform Distribution

The simplest of all probability distributions is the discrete uniform distribution. Suppose that the possible outcomes are the integers (whole numbers) 1 to 8, inclusive, and the probability that the random variable takes on any of these possible values is the same for all outcomes (that is, it is uniform). With eight outcomes, $p(x) = 1/8$, or 0.125, for all values of X ($X = 1, 2, 3, 4, 5, 6, 7, 8$); the statement just made is a complete description of this discrete uniform random variable. The distribution has a finite number of specified outcomes, and each outcome is equally likely. Table 1 summarizes the two views of this random variable, the probability function and the cumulative distribution function.

2 The technical term for the probability function of a discrete random variable, probability mass function (pmf), is used less frequently.

Table 1 Probability Function and Cumulative Distribution Function for a Discrete Uniform Random Variable

$X = x$	Probability Function $p(x) = P(X = x)$	Cumulative Distribution Function $F(x) = P(X \le x)$
1	0.125	0.125
2	0.125	0.250
3	0.125	0.375
4	0.125	0.500
5	0.125	0.625
6	0.125	0.750
7	0.125	0.875
8	0.125	1.000

We can use Table 1 to find three probabilities: $P(X \le 7)$, $P(4 \le X \le 6)$, and $P(4 < X \le 6)$. The following examples illustrate how to use the cdf to find the probability that a random variable will fall in any interval (for any random variable, not only the uniform).

- The probability that X is less than or equal to 7, $P(X \le 7)$, is the next-to-last entry in the third column, 0.875 or 87.5 percent.
- To find $P(4 \le X \le 6)$, we need to find the sum of three probabilities: $p(4)$, $p(5)$, and $p(6)$. We can find this sum in two ways. We can add $p(4)$, $p(5)$, and $p(6)$ from the second column. Or we can calculate the probability as the difference between two values of the cumulative distribution function:

  $$F(6) = P(X \le 6) = p(6) + p(5) + p(4) + p(3) + p(2) + p(1)$$

  $$F(3) = P(X \le 3) = p(3) + p(2) + p(1)$$

  so

  $$P(4 \le X \le 6) = F(6) - F(3) = p(6) + p(5) + p(4) = 3/8$$

  So we calculate the second probability as $F(6) - F(3) = 3/8$.
- The third probability, $P(4 < X \le 6)$, the probability that X is less than or equal to 6 but greater than 4, is $p(5) + p(6)$. We compute it as follows, using the cdf:

  $$P(4 < X \le 6) = P(X \le 6) - P(X \le 4) = F(6) - F(4) = p(6) + p(5) = 2/8$$

  So we calculate the third probability as $F(6) - F(4) = 2/8$.

Suppose we want to check that the discrete uniform probability function satisfies the general properties of a probability function given earlier. The first property is $0 \le p(x) \le 1$. We see that $p(x) = 1/8$ for all x in the first column of the table. (Note that $p(x)$ equals 0 for numbers x such as −14 or 12.215 that are not in that column.) The first property is satisfied. The second property is that the probabilities sum to 1. The entries in the second column of Table 1 do sum to 1.

The cdf has two other characteristic properties:

- The cdf lies between 0 and 1 for any x: $0 \le F(x) \le 1$.
- As we increase x, the cdf either increases or remains constant.

Check these statements by looking at the third column in Table 1.

We now have some experience working with probability functions and cdfs for discrete random variables. Later in this reading, we will discuss Monte Carlo simulation, a methodology driven by random numbers. As we will see, the uniform distribution has an important technical use: It is the basis for generating random numbers, which in turn produce random observations for all other probability distributions.[3]

2.2 The Binomial Distribution

In many investment contexts, we view a result as either a success or a failure, or as binary (twofold) in some other way. When we make probability statements about a record of successes and failures, or about anything with binary outcomes, we often use the binomial distribution. What is a good model for how a stock price moves through time? Different models are appropriate for different uses. Cox, Ross, and Rubinstein (1979) developed an option pricing model based on binary moves, price up or price down, for the asset underlying the option. Their binomial option pricing model was the first of a class of related option pricing models that have played an important role in the development of the derivatives industry. That fact alone would be sufficient reason for studying the binomial distribution, but the binomial distribution has uses in decision-making as well.

The building block of the binomial distribution is the **Bernoulli random variable**, named after the Swiss probabilist Jakob Bernoulli (1654–1704). Suppose we have a trial (an event that may repeat) that produces one of two outcomes. Such a trial is a **Bernoulli trial**. If we let Y equal 1 when the outcome is success and Y equal 0 when the outcome is failure, then the probability function of the Bernoulli random variable Y is

$$p(1) = P(Y = 1) = p$$

$$p(0) = P(Y = 0) = 1 - p$$

where p is the probability that the trial is a success. Our next example is the very first step on the road to understanding the binomial option pricing model.

EXAMPLE 2

One-Period Stock Price Movement as a Bernoulli Random Variable

Suppose we describe stock price movement in the following way. Stock price today is S. Next period stock price can move up or down. The probability of an up move is p, and the probability of a down move is $1 - p$. Thus, stock price is a Bernoulli random variable with probability of success (an up move) equal to p. When the stock moves up, ending price is uS, with u equal to 1 plus the rate of return if the stock moves up. For example, if the stock earns 0.01 or 1 percent on an up move, $u = 1.01$. When the stock moves down, ending price is dS, with d equal to 1 plus the rate of return if the stock moves down. For example, if the stock earns −0.01 or −1 percent on a down move, $d = 0.99$. Figure 1 shows a diagram of this model of stock price dynamics.

3 See Hillier (2014). Random numbers initially generated by computers are usually random positive integer numbers that are converted to approximate continuous uniform random numbers between 0 and 1. Then the continuous uniform random numbers are used to produce random observations on other distributions, such as the normal, using various techniques. We will discuss random observation generation further in the section on Monte Carlo simulation.

Figure 1 One-Period Stock Price as a Bernoulli Random Variable

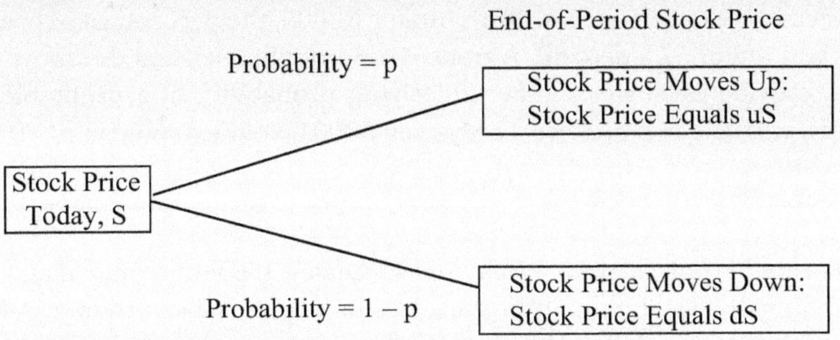

We will continue with the above example later. In the model of stock price movement in Example 2, success and failure at a given trial relate to up moves and down moves, respectively. In the following example, success is a profitable trade and failure is an unprofitable one.

EXAMPLE 3

A Trading Desk Evaluates Block Brokers (1)

You work in equities trading at an institutional money manager that regularly trades with several block brokers. Blocks are orders to sell or buy that are too large for the liquidity ordinarily available in dealer networks or stock exchanges. Your firm has known interests in certain kinds of stock. Block brokers call your trading desk when they want to sell blocks of stocks that they think your firm may be interested in buying. You know that these transactions have definite risks. For example, if the broker's client (the seller of the shares) has unfavorable information on the stock, or if the total amount he is selling through all channels is not truthfully communicated to you, you may see an immediate loss on the trade. From time to time, your firm audits the performance of block brokers. Your firm calculates the post-trade, market-risk-adjusted dollar returns on stocks purchased from block brokers. On that basis, you classify each trade as unprofitable or profitable. You have summarized the performance of the brokers in a spreadsheet, excerpted in Table 2 for November of last year. (The broker names are coded BB001 and BB002.)

Table 2 Block Trading Gains and Losses

	Profitable Trades	Losing Trades
BB001	3	9
BB002	5	3

View each trade as a Bernoulli trial. Calculate the percentage of profitable trades with the two block brokers for last November. These are estimates of p, the underlying probability of a successful (profitable) trade with each broker.

Your firm has logged 3 + 9 = 12 trades (the row total) with block broker BB001. Because 3 of the 12 trades were profitable, the percentage of profitable trades was 3/12 or 25 percent. With broker BB002, the percentage of profitable trades was 5/8 or 62.5 percent. A trade is a Bernoulli trial, and the above calculations provide estimates of the underlying probability of a profitable trade (success) with the two brokers. For broker BB001, your estimate is $\hat{p} = 0.25$; for broker BB002, your estimate is $\hat{p} = 0.625$.[4]

In n Bernoulli trials, we can have 0 to n successes. If the outcome of an individual trial is random, the total number of successes in n trials is also random. A **binomial random variable** X is defined as the number of successes in n Bernoulli trials. A binomial random variable is the sum of Bernoulli random variables Y_i, $i = 1, 2, \ldots, n$:

$$X = Y_1 + Y_2 + \ldots + Y_n$$

where Y_i is the outcome on the ith trial (1 if a success, 0 if a failure). We know that a Bernoulli random variable is defined by the parameter p. The number of trials, n, is the second parameter of a binomial random variable. The binomial distribution makes these assumptions:

- The probability, p, of success is constant for all trials.
- The trials are independent.

The second assumption has great simplifying force. If individual trials were correlated, calculating the probability of a given number of successes in n trials would be much more complicated.

Under the above two assumptions, a binomial random variable is completely described by two parameters, n and p. We write

$$X \sim B(n,p)$$

which we read as "X has a binomial distribution with parameters n and p." You can see that a Bernoulli random variable is a binomial random variable with $n = 1$: $Y \sim B(1, p)$.

Now we can find the general expression for the probability that a binomial random variable shows x successes in n trials. We can think in terms of a model of stock price dynamics that can be generalized to allow any possible stock price movements if the periods are made extremely small. Each period is a Bernoulli trial: With probability p, the stock price moves up; with probability $1 - p$, the price moves down. A success is an up move, and x is the number of up moves or successes in n periods (trials). With each period's moves independent and p constant, the number of up moves in n periods is a binomial random variable. We now develop an expression for $P(X = x)$, the probability function for a binomial random variable.

Any sequence of n periods that shows exactly x up moves must show $n - x$ down moves. We have many different ways to order the up moves and down moves to get a total of x up moves, but given independent trials, any sequence with x up moves must occur with probability $p^x(1 - p)^{n-x}$. Now we need to multiply this probability by the number of different ways we can get a sequence with x up moves. Using a basic result in counting from the reading on probability concepts, there are

$$\frac{n!}{(n-x)!x!}$$

4 The "hat" over p indicates that it is an estimate of p, the underlying probability of a profitable trade with the broker.

different sequences in n trials that result in x up moves (or successes) and $n - x$ down moves (or failures). Recall from the reading on probability concepts that n factorial ($n!$) is defined as $n(n - 1)(n - 2) \ldots 1$ (and $0! = 1$ by convention). For example, $5! = (5)(4)(3)(2)(1) = 120$. The combination formula $n!/[(n - x)!x!]$ is denoted by

$$\binom{n}{x}$$

(read "n combination x" or "n choose x"). For example, over three periods, exactly three different sequences have two up moves: UUD, UDU, and DUU. We confirm this by

$$\binom{3}{2} = \frac{3!}{(3-2)!2!} = \frac{(3)(2)(1)}{(1)(2)(1)} = 3$$

If, hypothetically, each sequence with two up moves had a probability of 0.15, then the total probability of two up moves in three periods would be $3 \times 0.15 = 0.45$. This example should persuade you that for X distributed $B(n, p)$, the probability of x successes in n trials is given by

$$p(x) = P(X = x) = \binom{n}{x} p^x (1-p)^{n-x} = \frac{n!}{(n-x)!x!} p^x (1-p)^{n-x} \quad (1)$$

Some distributions are always symmetric, such as the normal, and others are always asymmetric or skewed, such as the lognormal. The binomial distribution is symmetric when the probability of success on a trial is 0.50, but it is asymmetric or skewed otherwise.

We illustrate Equation 1 (the probability function) and the cdf through the symmetrical case. Consider a random variable distributed $B(n = 5, p = 0.50)$. Table 3 contains a complete description of this random variable. The fourth column of Table 3 is Column 2, n combination x, times Column 3, $p^x(1 - p)^{n-x}$; Column 4 gives the probability for each value of the number of up moves from the first column. The fifth column, cumulating the entries in the fourth column, is the cumulative distribution function.

Table 3 Binomial Probabilities, $p = 0.50$ and $n = 5$

Number of Up Moves, x (1)	Number of Possible Ways to Reach x Up Moves (2)	Probability for Each Way (3)	Probability for x, $p(x)$ (4) = (2) × (3)	$F(x) = P(X \le x)$ (5)
0	1	$0.50^0(1 - 0.50)^5 = 0.03125$	0.03125	0.03125
1	5	$0.50^1(1 - 0.50)^4 = 0.03125$	0.15625	0.18750
2	10	$0.50^2(1 - 0.50)^3 = 0.03125$	0.31250	0.50000
3	10	$0.50^3(1 - 0.50)^2 = 0.03125$	0.31250	0.81250
4	5	$0.50^4(1 - 0.50)^1 = 0.03125$	0.15625	0.96875
5	1	$0.50^5(1 - 0.50)^0 = 0.03125$	0.03125	1.00000

What would happen if we kept $n = 5$ but sharply lowered the probability of success on a trial to 10 percent? "Probability for Each Way" for $X = 0$ (no up moves) would then be about 59 percent: $0.10^0(1 - 0.10)^5 = 0.59049$. Because zero successes could still happen one way (Column 2), $p(0) = 59$ percent. You may want to check that given $p = 0.10$, $P(X \le 2) = 99.14$ percent: The probability of two or fewer up moves would be more than 99 percent. The random variable's probability would be massed on 0, 1, and 2 up moves, and the probability of larger outcomes would be minute. The outcomes of 3 and larger would be the long right tail, and the distribution would be right skewed. On the other hand, if we set $p = 0.90$, we would have the mirror image of the distribution with $p = 0.10$. The distribution would be left skewed.

With an understanding of the binomial probability function in hand, we can continue with our example of block brokers.

EXAMPLE 4

A Trading Desk Evaluates Block Brokers (2)

You now want to evaluate the performance of the block brokers in Example 3. You begin with two questions:

1 If you are paying a fair price on average in your trades with a broker, what should be the probability of a profitable trade?

2 Did each broker meet or miss that expectation on probability?

You also realize that the brokers' performance has to be evaluated in light of the sample's size, and for that you need to use the binomial probability function (Equation 1). You thus address the following (referring to the data in Example 3):

3 Under the assumption that the prices of trades were fair,

A calculate the probability of three or fewer profitable trades with broker BB001.

B calculate the probability of five or more profitable trades with broker BB002.

Solution to 1 and 2:

If the price you trade at is fair, 50 percent of the trades you do with a broker should be profitable.[5] The rate of profitable trades with broker BB001 was 25 percent. Therefore, broker BB001 missed your performance expectation. Broker BB002, at 62.5 percent profitable trades, exceeded your expectation.

Solution to 3:

A For broker BB001, the number of trades (the trials) was $n = 12$, and 3 were profitable. You are asked to calculate the probability of three or fewer profitable trades, $F(3) = p(3) + p(2) + p(1) + p(0)$.

Suppose the underlying probability of a profitable trade with BB001 is $p = 0.50$. With $n = 12$ and $p = 0.50$, according to Equation 1 the probability of three profitable trades is

$$p(3) = \binom{n}{x} p^x (1-p)^{n-x} = \binom{12}{3}\left(0.50^3\right)\left(0.50^9\right)$$

$$= \frac{12!}{(12-3)!3!} 0.50^{12} = 220(0.000244) = 0.053711$$

5 Of course, you need to adjust for the direction of the overall market after the trade (any broker's record will be helped by a bull market) and perhaps make other risk adjustments. Assume that these adjustments have been made.

The probability of exactly 3 profitable trades out of 12 is 5.4 percent if broker BB001 were giving you fair prices. Now you need to calculate the other probabilities:

$$p(2) = [12!/(12 - 2)!2!](0.50^2)(0.50^{10}) = 66(0.000244) = 0.016113$$

$$p(1) = [12!/(12 - 1)!1!](0.50^1)(0.50^{11}) = 12(0.000244) = 0.00293$$

$$p(0) = [12!/(12 - 0)!0!](0.50^0)(0.50^{12}) = 1(0.000244) = 0.000244$$

Adding all the probabilities, $F(3) = 0.053711 + 0.016113 + 0.00293 + 0.000244 = 0.072998$ or 7.3 percent. The probability of doing 3 or fewer profitable trades out of 12 would be 7.3 percent if your trading desk were getting fair prices from broker BB001.

B For broker BB002, you are assessing the probability that the underlying probability of a profitable trade with this broker was 50 percent, despite the good results. The question was framed as the probability of doing five or more profitable trades if the underlying probability is 50 percent: $1 - F(4) = p(5) + p(6) + p(7) + p(8)$. You could calculate $F(4)$ and subtract it from 1, but you can also calculate $p(5) + p(6) + p(7) + p(8)$ directly.

You begin by calculating the probability that exactly 5 out of 8 trades would be profitable if BB002 were giving you fair prices:

$$\begin{aligned} p(5) &= \binom{8}{5}\left(0.50^5\right)\left(0.50^3\right) \\ &= 56(0.003906) = 0.21875 \end{aligned}$$

The probability is about 21.9 percent. The other probabilities are

$$p(6) = 28(0.003906) = 0.109375$$

$$p(7) = 8(0.003906) = 0.03125$$

$$p(8) = 1(0.003906) = 0.003906$$

So $p(5) + p(6) + p(7) + p(8) = 0.21875 + 0.109375 + 0.03125 + 0.003906 = 0.363281$ or 36.3 percent.[6] A 36.3 percent probability is substantial; the underlying probability of executing a fair trade with BB002 might well have been 0.50 despite your success with BB002 in November of last year. If one of the trades with BB002 had been reclassified from profitable to unprofitable, exactly half the trades would have been profitable. In summary, your trading desk is getting at least fair prices from BB002; you will probably want to accumulate additional evidence before concluding that you are trading at better-than-fair prices.

The magnitude of the profits and losses in these trades is another important consideration. If all profitable trades had small profits but all unprofitable trades had large losses, for example, you might lose money on your trades even if the majority of them were profitable.

In the next example, the binomial distribution helps in evaluating the performance of an investment manager.

6 In this example all calculations were worked through by hand, but binomial probability and cdf functions are also available in computer spreadsheet programs.

EXAMPLE 5

Meeting a Tracking Objective

You work for a pension fund sponsor. You have assigned a new money manager to manage a $500 million portfolio indexed on the MSCI EAFE (Europe, Australasia, and Far East) Index, which is designed to measure developed-market equity performance excluding the United States and Canada. After research, you believe it is reasonable to expect that the manager will keep portfolio return within a band of 75 basis points (bps) of the benchmark's return, on a quarterly basis.[7] To quantify this expectation further, you will be satisfied if portfolio return is within the 75 bps band 90 percent of the time. The manager meets the objective in six out of eight quarters. Of course, six out of eight quarters is a 75 percent success rate. But how does the manager's record precisely relate to your expectation of a 90 percent success rate and the sample size, 8 observations? To answer this question, you must find the probability that, given an assumed true or underlying success rate of 90 percent, performance could be as bad as or worse than that delivered. Calculate the probability (by hand or with a spreadsheet).

Specifically, you want to find the probability that portfolio return is within the 75 bps band in six or fewer quarters out of the eight in the sample. With $n = 8$ and $p = 0.90$, this probability is $F(6) = p(6) + p(5) + p(4) + p(3) + p(2) + p(1) + p(0)$. Start with

$$p(6) = (8!/6!2!)(0.90^6)(0.10^2) = 28(0.005314) = 0.148803$$

and work through the other probabilities:

$$p(5) = (8!/5!3!)(0.90^5)(0.10^3) = 56(0.00059) = 0.033067$$

$$p(4) = (8!/4!4!)(0.90^4)(0.10^4) = 70(0.000066) = 0.004593$$

$$p(3) = (8!/3!5!)(0.90^3)(0.10^5) = 56(0.000007) = 0.000408$$

$$p(2) = (8!/2!6!)(0.90^2)(0.10^6) = 28(0.000001) = 0.000023$$

$$p(1) = (8!/1!7!)(0.90^1)(0.10^7) = 8(0.00000009) = 0.00000072$$

$$p(0) = (8!/0!8!)(0.90^0)(0.10^8) = 1(0.00000001) = 0.00000001$$

Summing all these probabilities, you conclude that $F(6) = 0.148803 + 0.033067 + 0.004593 + 0.000408 + 0.000023 + 0.00000072 + 0.00000001 = 0.186895$ or 18.7 percent. There is a moderate 18.7 percent probability that the manager would show the record he did (or a worse record) if he had the skill to meet your expectations 90 percent of the time.

You can use other evaluation concepts such as tracking error or tracking risk, defined as the standard deviation of return differences between a portfolio and its benchmark, to assess the manager's performance. The calculation above would be only one input into any conclusions that you reach concerning the manager's performance. But to answer problems involving success rates, you need to be skilled in using the binomial distribution.

7 A basis point is one-hundredth of 1 percent (0.01 percent).

Two descriptors of a distribution that are often used in investments are the mean and the variance (or the standard deviation, the positive square root of variance).[8] Table 4 gives the expressions for the mean and variance of binomial random variables.

Table 4 Mean and Variance of Binomial Random Variables

	Mean	Variance
Bernoulli, $B(1, p)$	p	$p(1 - p)$
Binomial, $B(n, p)$	np	$np(1 - p)$

Because a single Bernoulli random variable, $Y \sim B(1, p)$, takes on the value 1 with probability p and the value 0 with probability $1 - p$, its mean or weighted-average outcome is p. Its variance is $p(1 - p)$.[9] A general binomial random variable, $B(n, p)$, is the sum of n Bernoulli random variables, and so the mean of a $B(n, p)$ random variable is np. Given that a $B(1, p)$ variable has variance $p(1 - p)$, the variance of a $B(n, p)$ random variable is n times that value, or $np(1 - p)$, assuming that all the trials (Bernoulli random variables) are independent. We can illustrate the calculation for two binomial random variables with differing probabilities as follows:

Random Variable	Mean	Variance
$B(n = 5, p = 0.50)$	2.50 = 5(0.50)	1.25 = 5(0.50)(0.50)
$B(n = 5, p = 0.10)$	0.50 = 5(0.10)	0.45 = 5(0.10)(0.90)

For a $B(n = 5, p = 0.50)$ random variable, the expected number of successes is 2.5 with a standard deviation of $1.118 = (1.25)^{1/2}$; for a $B(n = 5, p = 0.10)$ random variable, the expected number of successes is 0.50 with a standard deviation of $0.67 = (0.45)^{1/2}$.

EXAMPLE 6

The Expected Number of Defaults in a Bond Portfolio

Suppose as a bond analyst you are asked to estimate the number of bond issues expected to default over the next year in an unmanaged high-yield bond portfolio with 25 US issues from distinct issuers. The credit ratings of the bonds in the portfolio are tightly clustered around Moody's B2/Standard & Poor's B, meaning that the bonds are speculative with respect to the capacity to pay interest and repay principal. The estimated annual default rate for B2/B rated bonds is 10.7 percent.

1 Over the next year, what is the expected number of defaults in the portfolio, assuming a **binomial model** for defaults?

2 Estimate the standard deviation of the number of defaults over the coming year.

3 Critique the use of the binomial probability model in this context.

8 The mean (or arithmetic mean) is the sum of all values in a distribution or dataset, divided by the number of values summed. The variance is a measure of dispersion about the mean. See the reading on statistical concepts and market returns for further details on these concepts.

9 We can show that $p(1 - p)$ is the variance of a Bernoulli random variable as follows, noting that a Bernoulli random variable can take on only one of two values, 1 or 0: $\sigma^2(Y) = E[(Y - EY)^2] = E[(Y - p)^2] = (1 - p)^2 p + (0 - p)^2(1 - p) = (1 - p)[(1 - p)p + p^2] = p(1 - p)$.

Solution to 1:

For each bond, we can define a Bernoulli random variable equal to 1 if the bond defaults during the year and zero otherwise. With 25 bonds, the expected number of defaults over the year is np = 25(0.107) = 2.675 or approximately 3.

Solution to 2:

The variance is $np(1 - p)$ = 25(0.107)(0.893) = 2.388775. The standard deviation is $(2.388775)^{1/2}$ = 1.55. Thus, a two standard deviation confidence interval about the expected number of defaults would run from approximately 0 to approximately 6, for example.

Solution to 3:

An assumption of the binomial model is that the trials are independent. In this context, a trial relates to whether an individual bond issue will default over the next year. Because the issuing companies probably share exposure to common economic factors, the trials may not be independent. Nevertheless, for a quick estimate of the expected number of defaults, the binomial model may be adequate.

Earlier, we looked at a simple one-period model for stock price movement. Now we extend the model to describe stock price movement on three consecutive days. Each day is an independent trial. The stock moves up with constant probability p (the **up transition probability**); if it moves up, u is 1 plus the rate of return for an up move. The stock moves down with constant probability $1 - p$ (the **down transition probability**); if it moves down, d is 1 plus the rate of return for a down move. We graph stock price movement in Figure 2, where we now associate each of the n = 3 stock price moves with time indexed by t. The shape of the graph suggests why it is a called a **binomial tree**. Each boxed value from which successive moves or outcomes branch in the tree is called a **node**; in this example, a node is potential value for the stock price at a specified time.

Figure 2 A Binomial Model of Stock Price Movement

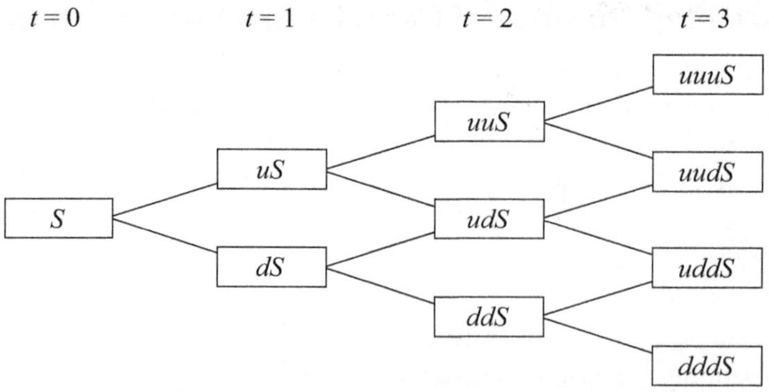

We see from the tree that the stock price at t = 3 has four possible values: $uuuS$, $uudS$, $uddS$, and $dddS$. The probability that the stock price equals *any* one of these four values is given by the binomial distribution. For example, three sequences of moves result in a final stock price of $uudS$: These are uud, udu, and duu. These sequences have two up moves out of three moves in total; the combination formula confirms that the number of ways to get two up moves (successes) in three periods (trials)

is $3!/(3 - 2)!2! = 3$. Next note that each of these sequences, *uud*, *udu*, and *duu*, has probability $p^2(1 - p)$. So $P(S_3 = uudS) = 3p^2(1 - p)$, where S_3 indicates the stock's price after three moves.

The binomial random variable in this application is the number of up moves. Final stock price distribution is a function of the initial stock price, the *number* of up moves, and the *size* of the up moves and down moves. We cannot say that stock price itself is a binomial random variable; rather, it is a function of a binomial random variable, as well as of u and d, and initial price. This richness is actually one key to why this way of modeling stock price is useful: It allows us to choose values of these parameters to approximate various distributions for stock price (using a large number of time periods).[10] One distribution that can be approximated is the lognormal, an important continuous distribution model for stock price that we will discuss later. The flexibility extends further. In the tree shown above, the transition probabilities are the same at each node: p for an up move and $1 - p$ for a down move. That standard formula describes a process in which stock return volatility is constant through time. Option experts, however, sometimes model changing volatility through time using a binomial tree in which the probabilities for up and down moves differ at different nodes.

The binomial tree also supplies the possibility of testing a condition or contingency at any node. This flexibility is useful in investment applications such as option pricing. Consider an American call option on a dividend-paying stock. (Recall that an American option can be exercised at any time before expiration, at any node on the tree.) Just before an ex-dividend date, it may be optimal to exercise an American call option on stock to buy the stock and receive the dividend.[11] If we model stock price with a binomial tree, we can test, at each node, whether exercising the option is optimal. Also, if we know the value of the call at the four terminal nodes at $t = 3$ and we have a model for discounting values by one period, we can step backward one period to $t = 2$ to find the call's value at the three nodes there. Continuing back recursively, we can find the call's value today. This type of recursive operation is easily programmed on a computer. As a result, binomial trees can value options even more complex than American calls on stock.[12]

CONTINUOUS RANDOM VARIABLES

3

In the previous section, we considered discrete random variables (i.e., random variables whose set of possible outcomes is countable). In contrast, the possible outcomes of continuous random variables are never countable. If 1.250 is one possible value of a continuous random variable, for example, we cannot name the next higher or lower possible value. Technically, the range of possible outcomes of a continuous random variable is the real line (all real numbers between $-\infty$ and $+\infty$) or some subset of the real line.

In this section, we focus on the two most important continuous distributions in investment work, the normal and lognormal. As we did with discrete distributions, we introduce the topic through the uniform distribution.

10 For example, we can split 20 days into 100 subperiods, taking care to use compatible values for u and d.

11 Cash dividends represent a reduction of a company's assets. Early exercise may be optimal because the exercise price of options is typically not reduced by the amount of cash dividends, so cash dividends negatively affect the position of an American call option holder.

12 See Chance and Brooks (2016) for more information on option pricing models.

3.1 Continuous Uniform Distribution

The continuous uniform distribution is the simplest continuous probability distribution. The uniform distribution has two main uses. As the basis of techniques for generating random numbers, the uniform distribution plays a role in Monte Carlo simulation. As the probability distribution that describes equally likely outcomes, the uniform distribution is an appropriate probability model to represent a particular kind of uncertainty in beliefs in which all outcomes appear equally likely.

The pdf for a uniform random variable is

$$f(x) = \begin{cases} \dfrac{1}{b - a} & \text{for } a < x < b \\ 0 & \text{otherwise} \end{cases}$$

For example, with $a = 0$ and $b = 8$, $f(x) = 1/8$ or 0.125. We graph this density in Figure 3.

Figure 3 Continuous Uniform Distribution

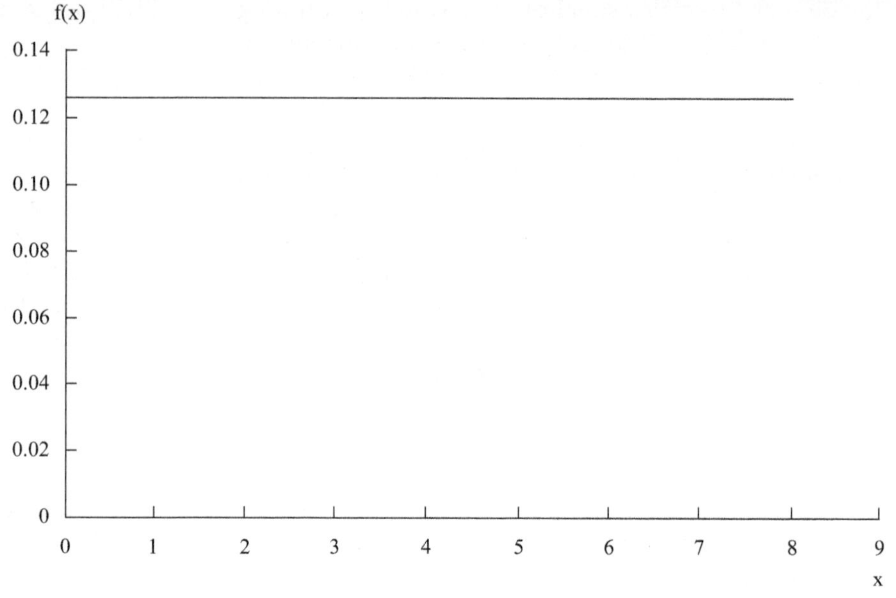

The graph of the density function plots as a horizontal line with a value of 0.125.

What is the probability that a uniform random variable with limits $a = 0$ and $b = 8$ is less than or equal to 3, or $F(3) = P(X \le 3)$? When we were working with the discrete uniform random variable with possible outcomes 1, 2, …, 8, we summed individual probabilities: $p(1) + p(2) + p(3) = 0.375$. In contrast, the probability that a continuous uniform random variable, or any continuous random variable, assumes any given fixed value is 0. To illustrate this point, consider the narrow interval 2.510 to 2.511. Because that interval holds an infinity of possible values, the sum of the probabilities of values in that interval alone would be infinite if each individual value in it had a positive probability. To find the probability $F(3)$, we find the area under the curve graphing the pdf, between 0 to 3 on the x axis. In calculus, this operation is called integrating the probability function $f(x)$ from 0 to 3. This area under the curve is a rectangle with base $3 - 0 = 3$ and height 1/8. The area of this rectangle equals base times height: $3(1/8) = 3/8$ or 0.375. So $F(3) = 3/8$ or 0.375.

The interval from 0 to 3 is three-eighths of the total length between the limits of 0 and 8, and $F(3)$ is three-eighths of the total probability of 1. The middle line of the expression for the cdf captures this relationship.

$$F(x) = \begin{cases} 0 \text{ for } x \le a \\ \dfrac{x-a}{b-a} \text{ for } a < x < b \\ 1 \text{ for } x \ge b \end{cases}$$

For our problem, $F(x) = 0$ for $x \le 0$, $F(x) = x/8$ for $0 < x < 8$, and $F(x) = 1$ for $x \ge 8$. We graph this cdf in Figure 4.

Figure 4 Continuous Uniform Cumulative Distribution

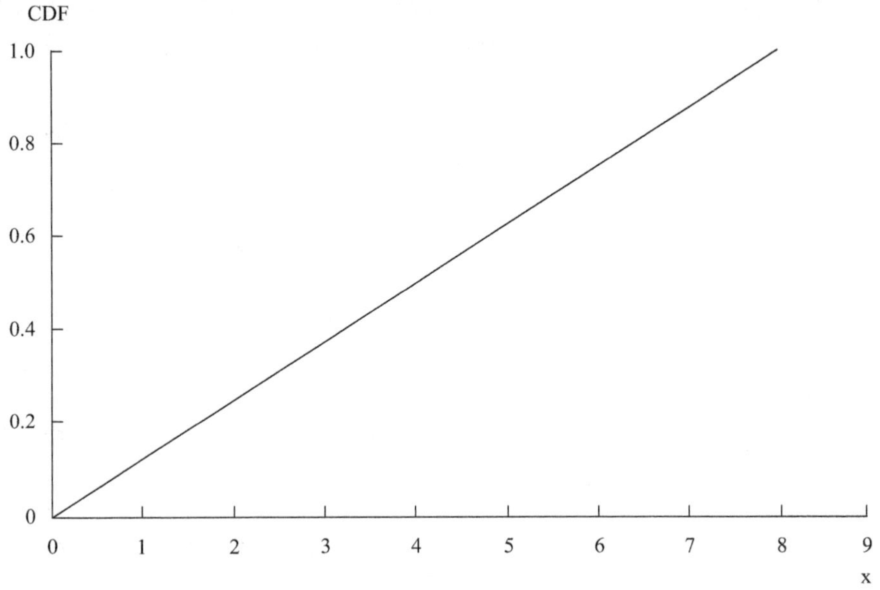

The mathematical operation that corresponds to finding the area under the curve of a pdf $f(x)$ from a to b is the integral of $f(x)$ from a to b:

$$P(a \le X \le b) = \int_a^b f(x)dx \tag{2}$$

where $\int dx$ is the symbol for summing $\int$ over small changes dx, and the limits of integration (a and b) can be any real numbers or $-\infty$ and $+\infty$. All probabilities of continuous random variables can be computed using Equation 2. For the uniform distribution example considered above, $F(7)$ is Equation 2 with lower limit $a = 0$ and upper limit $b = 7$. The integral corresponding to the cdf of a uniform distribution reduces to the three-line expression given previously. To evaluate Equation 2 for nearly all other continuous distributions, including the normal and lognormal, we rely on spreadsheet functions, computer programs, or tables of values to calculate probabilities. Those tools use various numerical methods to evaluate the integral in Equation 2.

Recall that the probability of a continuous random variable equaling any fixed point is 0. This fact has an important consequence for working with the cumulative distribution function of a continuous random variable: For any continuous random variable X, $P(a \le X \le b) = P(a < X \le b) = P(a \le X < b) = P(a < X < b)$, because the probabilities at the endpoints a and b are 0. For discrete random variables, these relations of equality are not true, because probability accumulates at points.

EXAMPLE 7

Probability That a Lending Facility Covenant Is Breached

You are evaluating the bonds of a below-investment-grade borrower at a low point in its business cycle. You have many factors to consider, including the terms of the company's bank lending facilities. The contract creating a bank lending facility such as an unsecured line of credit typically has clauses known as covenants. These covenants place restrictions on what the borrower can do. The company will be in breach of a covenant in the lending facility if the interest coverage ratio, EBITDA/interest, calculated on EBITDA over the four trailing quarters, falls below 2.0. EBITDA is earnings before interest, taxes, depreciation, and amortization.[13] Compliance with the covenants will be checked at the end of the current quarter. If the covenant is breached, the bank can demand immediate repayment of all borrowings on the facility. That action would probably trigger a liquidity crisis for the company. With a high degree of confidence, you forecast interest charges of \$25 million. Your estimate of EBITDA runs from \$40 million on the low end to \$60 million on the high end.

Address two questions (treating projected interest charges as a constant):

1 If the outcomes for EBITDA are equally likely, what is the probability that EBITDA/interest will fall below 2.0, breaching the covenant?

2 Estimate the mean and standard deviation of EBITDA/interest. For a continuous uniform random variable, the mean is given by $\mu = (a + b)/2$ and the variance is given by $\sigma^2 = (b - a)^2/12$.

Solution to 1:

EBITDA/interest is a continuous uniform random variable because all outcomes are equally likely. The ratio can take on values between 1.6 = (\$40 million)/(\$25 million) on the low end and 2.4 = (\$60 million/\$25 million) on the high end. The range of possible values is 2.4 – 1.6 = 0.8. What fraction of the possible values falls below 2.0, the level that triggers default? The distance between 2.0 and 1.6 is 0.40; the value 0.40 is one-half the total length of 0.8, or 0.4/0.8 = 0.50. So, the probability that the covenant will be breached is 50 percent.

Solution to 2:

In Solution 1, we found that the lower limit of EBITDA/interest is 1.6. This lower limit is a. We found that the upper limit is 2.4. This upper limit is b. Using the formula given above,

$$\mu = (a + b)/2 = (1.6 + 2.4)/2 = 2.0$$

The variance of the interest coverage ratio is

$$\sigma^2 = (b - a)^2/12 = (2.4 - 1.6)^2/12 = 0.053333$$

The standard deviation is the positive square root of the variance, $0.230940 = (0.053333)^{1/2}$. The standard deviation is not particularly useful as a risk measure for a uniform distribution, however. The probability that lies within various standard deviation bands around the mean is sensitive to different specifications of the upper and lower limits (although Chebyshev's inequality is always satisfied).[14] Here, a one standard deviation interval around the mean of 2.0 runs from 1.769

13 For a detailed discussion on EBITDA, see the Level I CFA Program curriculum reading "Financial Reporting Quality."

14 Chebyshev's inequality is discussed in the reading on statistical concepts and market returns.

to 2.231 and captures 0.462/0.80 = 0.5775 or 57.8 percent of the probability. A two standard deviation interval runs from 1.538 to 2.462, which extends past both the lower and upper limits of the random variable.

3.2 The Normal Distribution

The normal distribution may be the most extensively used probability distribution in quantitative work. It plays key roles in modern portfolio theory and in several risk management technologies. Because it has so many uses, the normal distribution must be thoroughly understood by investment professionals.

The role of the normal distribution in statistical inference and regression analysis is vastly extended by a crucial result known as the central limit theorem. The central limit theorem states that the sum (and mean) of a large number of independent random variables is approximately normally distributed.[15]

The French mathematician Abraham de Moivre (1667–1754) introduced the normal distribution in 1733 in developing a version of the central limit theorem. As Figure 5 shows, the normal distribution is symmetrical and bell-shaped. The range of possible outcomes of the normal distribution is the entire real line: all real numbers lying between $-\infty$ and $+\infty$. The tails of the bell curve extend without limit to the left and to the right.

Figure 5 Two Normal Distributions

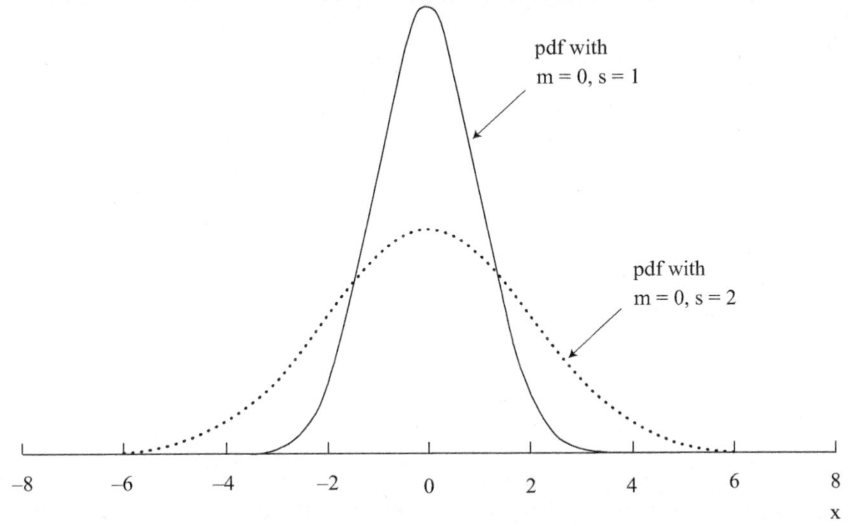

The defining characteristics of a normal distribution are as follows:

- The normal distribution is completely described by two parameters—its mean, μ, and variance, σ^2. We indicate this as $X \sim N(\mu, \sigma^2)$ (read "X follows a normal distribution with mean μ and variance σ^2"). We can also define a normal distribution in terms of the mean and the standard deviation, σ (this is often convenient because σ is measured in the same units as X and μ). As a consequence, we can answer any probability question about a normal random variable if we know its mean and variance (or standard deviation).

15 The central limit theorem is discussed further in the reading on sampling.

- The normal distribution has a skewness of 0 (it is symmetric). The normal distribution has a kurtosis of 3; its excess kurtosis (kurtosis – 3.0) equals 0.[16] As a consequence of symmetry, the mean, median, and the mode are all equal for a normal random variable.
- A linear combination of two or more normal random variables is also normally distributed.

These bullet points concern a single variable or univariate normal distribution: the distribution of one normal random variable. A **univariate distribution** describes a single random variable. A **multivariate distribution** specifies the probabilities for a group of related random variables. You will encounter the **multivariate normal distribution** in investment work and reading and should know the following about it.

When we have a group of assets, we can model the distribution of returns on each asset individually, or the distribution of returns on the assets as a group. "As a group" means that we take account of all the statistical interrelationships among the return series. One model that has often been used for security returns is the multivariate normal distribution. A multivariate normal distribution for the returns on n stocks is completely defined by three lists of parameters:

- the list of the mean returns on the individual securities (n means in total);
- the list of the securities' variances of return (n variances in total); and
- the list of all the distinct pairwise return correlations: $n(n - 1)/2$ distinct correlations in total.[17]

The need to specify correlations is a distinguishing feature of the multivariate normal distribution in contrast to the univariate normal distribution.

The statement "assume returns are normally distributed" is sometimes used to mean a joint normal distribution. For a portfolio of 30 securities, for example, portfolio return is a weighted average of the returns on the 30 securities. A weighted average is a linear combination. Thus, portfolio return is normally distributed if the individual security returns are (joint) normally distributed. To review, in order to specify the normal distribution for portfolio return, we need the means, variances, and the distinct pairwise correlations of the component securities.

With these concepts in mind, we can return to the normal distribution for one random variable. The curves graphed in Figure 5 are the normal density function:

$$f(x) = \frac{1}{\sigma\sqrt{2\pi}}\exp\left(\frac{-(x-\mu)^2}{2\sigma^2}\right) \text{ for } -\infty < x < +\infty \quad (3)$$

The two densities graphed in Figure 5 correspond to a mean of $\mu = 0$ and standard deviations of $\sigma = 1$ and $\sigma = 2$. The normal density with $\mu = 0$ and $\sigma = 1$ is called the **standard normal distribution** (or **unit normal distribution**). Plotting two normal distributions with the same mean and different standard deviations helps us appreciate why standard deviation is a good measure of dispersion for the normal distribution: Observations are much more concentrated around the mean for the normal distribution with $\sigma = 1$ than for the normal distribution with $\sigma = 2$.

16 If we have a sample of size n from a normal distribution, we may want to know the possible variation in sample skewness and kurtosis. For a normal random variable, the standard deviation of sample skewness is $6/n$ and the standard deviation of sample kurtosis is $24/n$.

17 For example, a distribution with two stocks (a bivariate normal distribution) has two means, two variances, and one correlation: 2(2 – 1)/2. A distribution with 30 stocks has 30 means, 30 variances, and 435 distinct correlations: 30(30 – 1)/2. The return correlation of Dow Chemical with American Express stock is the same as the correlation of American Express with Dow Chemical stock, so these are counted as one distinct correlation.

Although not literally accurate, the normal distribution can be considered an approximate model for returns. Nearly all the probability of a normal random variable is contained within three standard deviations of the mean. For realistic values of mean return and return standard deviation for many assets, the normal probability of outcomes below −100 percent is very small. Whether the approximation is useful in a given application is an empirical question. For example, the normal distribution is a closer fit for quarterly and yearly holding period returns on a diversified equity portfolio than it is for daily or weekly returns.[18] A persistent departure from normality in most equity return series is kurtosis greater than 3, the fat-tails problem. So when we approximate equity return distributions with the normal distribution, we should be aware that the normal distribution tends to underestimate the probability of extreme returns.[19] Option returns are skewed. Because the normal is a symmetrical distribution, we should be cautious in using the normal distribution to model the returns on portfolios containing significant positions in options.

The normal distribution, however, is less suitable as a model for asset prices than as a model for returns. A normal random variable has no lower limit. This characteristic has several implications for investment applications. An asset price can drop only to 0, at which point the asset becomes worthless. As a result, practitioners generally do not use the normal distribution to model the distribution of asset prices. Also note that moving from any level of asset price to 0 translates into a return of −100 percent. Because the normal distribution extends below 0 without limit, it cannot be literally accurate as a model for asset returns.

Having established that the normal distribution is the appropriate model for a variable of interest, we can use it to make the following probability statements:

- Approximately 50 percent of all observations fall in the interval $\mu \pm (2/3)\sigma$.
- Approximately 68 percent of all observations fall in the interval $\mu \pm \sigma$.
- Approximately 95 percent of all observations fall in the interval $\mu \pm 2\sigma$.
- Approximately 99 percent of all observations fall in the interval $\mu \pm 3\sigma$.

One, two, and three standard deviation intervals are illustrated in Figure 6. The intervals indicated are easy to remember but are only approximate for the stated probabilities. More-precise intervals are $\mu \pm 1.96\sigma$ for 95 percent of the observations and $\mu \pm 2.58\sigma$ for 99 percent of the observations.

18 See Fama (1976) and Campbell, Lo, and MacKinlay (1997).

19 Fat tails can be modeled by a mixture of normal random variables or by a Student's *t*-distribution with a relatively small number of degrees of freedom. See Kon (1984) and Campbell, Lo, and MacKinlay (1997). We discuss the Student's *t*-distribution in the reading on sampling and estimation.

Figure 6 Units of Standard Deviation

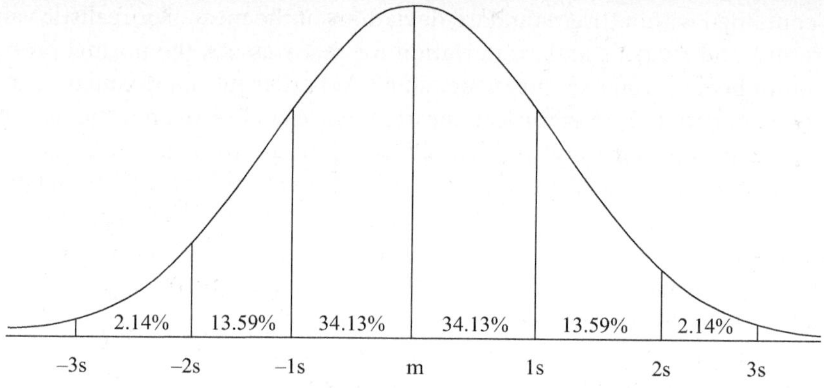

In general, we do not observe the population mean or the population standard deviation of a distribution, so we need to estimate them.[20] We estimate the population mean, μ, using the sample mean, $\overline{X}$ (sometimes denoted as $\hat{\mu}$) and estimate the population standard deviation, σ, using the sample standard deviation, s (sometimes denoted as $\hat{\sigma}$).

There are as many different normal distributions as there are choices for mean (μ) and variance (σ^2). We can answer all of the above questions in terms of any normal distribution. Spreadsheets, for example, have functions for the normal cdf for any specification of mean and variance. For the sake of efficiency, however, we would like to refer all probability statements to a single normal distribution. The standard normal distribution (the normal distribution with $\mu = 0$ and $\sigma = 1$) fills that role.

There are two steps in **standardizing** a random variable X: Subtract the mean of X from X, then divide that result by the standard deviation of X. If we have a list of observations on a normal random variable, X, we subtract the mean from each observation to get a list of deviations from the mean, then divide each deviation by the standard deviation. The result is the standard normal random variable, Z. (Z is the conventional symbol for a standard normal random variable.) If we have $X \sim N(\mu,\sigma^2)$ (read "X follows the normal distribution with parameters μ and σ^2"), we standardize it using the formula

$$Z = (X - \mu)/\sigma \tag{4}$$

Suppose we have a normal random variable, X, with $\mu = 5$ and $\sigma = 1.5$. We standardize X with $Z = (X - 5)/1.5$. For example, a value $X = 9.5$ corresponds to a standardized value of 3, calculated as $Z = (9.5 - 5)/1.5 = 3$. The probability that we will observe a value as small as or smaller than 9.5 for $X \sim N(5,1.5)$ is exactly the same as the probability that we will observe a value as small as or smaller than 3 for $Z \sim N(0,1)$. We can answer all probability questions about X using standardized values and probability tables for Z. We generally do not know the population mean and standard deviation, so we often use the sample mean $\overline{X}$ for μ and the sample standard deviation s for σ.

20 A population is all members of a specified group, and the population mean is the arithmetic mean computed for the population. A sample is a subset of a population, and the sample mean is the arithmetic mean computed for the sample. For more information on these concepts, see the reading on statistical concepts and market returns.

Standard normal probabilities can also be computed with spreadsheets, statistical and econometric software, and programming languages. Tables of the cumulative distribution function for the standard normal random variable are in the back of this book. Table 5 shows an excerpt from those tables. $N(x)$ is a conventional notation for the cdf of a standard normal variable.[21]

Table 5 $P(Z \le x) = N(x)$ for $x \ge 0$ or $P(Z \le z) = N(z)$ for $z \ge 0$

x or z	0	0.01	0.02	0.03	0.04	0.05	0.06	0.07	0.08	0.09
0.00	0.5000	0.5040	0.5080	0.5120	0.5160	0.5199	0.5239	0.5279	0.5319	0.5359
0.10	0.5398	0.5438	0.5478	0.5517	0.5557	0.5596	0.5636	0.5675	0.5714	0.5753
0.20	0.5793	0.5832	0.5871	0.5910	0.5948	0.5987	0.6026	0.6064	0.6103	0.6141
0.30	0.6179	0.6217	0.6255	0.6293	0.6331	0.6368	0.6406	0.6443	0.6480	0.6517
0.40	0.6554	0.6591	0.6628	0.6664	0.6700	0.6736	0.6772	0.6808	0.6844	0.6879
0.50	0.6915	0.6950	0.6985	0.7019	0.7054	0.7088	0.7123	0.7157	0.7190	0.7224

To find the probability that a standard normal variable is less than or equal to 0.24, for example, locate the row that contains 0.20, look at the 0.04 column, and find the entry 0.5948. Thus, $P(Z \le 0.24) = 0.5948$ or 59.48 percent.

The following are some of the most frequently referenced values in the standard normal table:

- The 90th percentile point is 1.282: $P(Z \le 1.282) = N(1.282) = 0.90$ or 90 percent, and 10 percent of values remain in the right tail.
- The 95th percentile point is 1.65: $P(Z \le 1.65) = N(1.65) = 0.95$ or 95 percent, and 5 percent of values remain in the right tail. Note the difference between the use of a percentile point when dealing with one tail rather than two tails. Earlier, we used 1.65 standard deviations for the 90 percent confidence interval, where 5 percent of values lie outside that interval on each of the two sides. Here we use 1.65 because we are concerned with the 5 percent of values that lie only on one side, the right tail.
- The 99th percentile point is 2.327: $P(Z \le 2.327) = N(2.327) = 0.99$ or 99 percent, and 1 percent of values remain in the right tail.

The tables that we give for the normal cdf include probabilities for $x \le 0$. Many sources, however, give tables only for $x \ge 0$. How would one use such tables to find a normal probability? Because of the symmetry of the normal distribution, we can find all probabilities using tables of the cdf of the standard normal random variable, $P(Z \le x) = N(x)$, for $x \ge 0$. The relations below are helpful for using tables for $x \ge 0$, as well as in other uses:

- For a non-negative number x, use $N(x)$ from the table. Note that for the probability to the right of x, we have $P(Z \ge x) = 1.0 - N(x)$.
- For a negative number $-x$, $N(-x) = 1.0 - N(x)$: Find $N(x)$ and subtract it from 1. All the area under the normal curve to the left of x is $N(x)$. The balance, $1.0 - N(x)$, is the area and probability to the right of x. By the symmetry of the normal distribution around its mean, the area and the probability to the right of x are equal to the area and the probability to the left of $-x$, $N(-x)$.
- For the probability to the right of $-x$, $P(Z \ge -x) = N(x)$.

21 Another often-seen notation for the cdf of a standard normal variable is $\Phi(x)$.

EXAMPLE 8

Probabilities for a Common Stock Portfolio

Assume the portfolio mean return is 12 percent and the standard deviation of return estimate is 22 percent per year.

You want to calculate the following probabilities, assuming that a normal distribution describes returns. (You can use the excerpt from the table of normal probabilities to answer these questions.)

1 What is the probability that portfolio return will exceed 20 percent?

2 What is the probability that portfolio return will be between 12 percent and 20 percent? In other words, what is P(12% ≤ Portfolio return ≤ 20%)?

3 You can buy a one-year T-bill that yields 5.5 percent. This yield is effectively a one-year risk-free interest rate. What is the probability that your portfolio's return will be equal to or less than the risk-free rate?

If X is portfolio return, standardized portfolio return is $Z = (X - \overline{X})/s = (X - 12\%)/22\%$. We use this expression throughout the solutions.

Solution to 1:

For $X = 20\%$, $Z = (20\% - 12\%)/22\% = 0.363636$. You want to find $P(Z > 0.363636)$. First note that $P(Z > x) = P(Z \geq x)$ because the normal is a continuous distribution. Recall that $P(Z \geq x) = 1.0 - P(Z \leq x)$ or $1 - N(x)$. Rounding 0.363636 to 0.36, according to the table, $N(0.36) = 0.6406$. Thus, $1 - 0.6406 = 0.3594$. The probability that portfolio return will exceed 20 percent is about 36 percent if your normality assumption is accurate.

Solution to 2:

P(12% ≤ Portfolio return ≤ 20%) = N(Z corresponding to 20%) − N(Z corresponding to 12%). For the first term, $Z = (20\% - 12\%)/22\% = 0.36$ approximately, and $N(0.36) = 0.6406$ (as in Solution 1). To get the second term immediately, note that 12 percent is the mean, and for the normal distribution 50 percent of the probability lies on either side of the mean. Therefore, N(Z corresponding to 12%) must equal 50 percent. So P(12% ≤ Portfolio return ≤ 20%) = 0.6406 − 0.50 = 0.1406 or approximately 14 percent.

Solution to 3:

If X is portfolio return, then we want to find P(Portfolio return ≤ 5.5%). This question is more challenging than Parts 1 or 2, but when you have studied the solution below you will have a useful pattern for calculating other shortfall probabilities.

There are three steps, which involve standardizing the portfolio return: First, subtract the portfolio mean return from each side of the inequality: P(Portfolio return − 12% ≤ 5.5% − 12%). Second, divide each side of the inequality by the standard deviation of portfolio return: P[(Portfolio return − 12%)/22% ≤ (5.5% − 12%)/22%] = $P(Z \leq -0.295455) = N(-0.295455)$. Third, recognize that on the left-hand side we have a standard normal variable, denoted by Z. As we pointed out above, $N(-x) = 1 - N(x)$. Rounding −0.29545 to −0.30 for use with the excerpted table, we have $N(-0.30) = 1 - N(0.30) = 1 - 0.6179 = 0.3821$, roughly 38 percent. The probability that your portfolio will underperform the one-year risk-free rate is about 38 percent.

We can get the answer above quickly by subtracting the mean portfolio return from 5.5 percent, dividing by the standard deviation of portfolio return, and evaluating the result (−0.295455) with the standard normal cdf.

3.3 Applications of the Normal Distribution

Modern portfolio theory (MPT) makes wide use of the idea that the value of investment opportunities can be meaningfully measured in terms of mean return and variance of return. In economic theory, **mean–variance analysis** holds exactly when investors are risk averse; when they choose investments so as to maximize expected utility, or satisfaction; and when either 1) returns are normally distributed, or 2) investors have quadratic utility functions.[22] Mean–variance analysis can still be useful, however—that is, it can hold approximately—when either assumption 1 or 2 is violated. Because practitioners prefer to work with observables such as returns, the proposition that returns are at least approximately normally distributed has played a key role in much of MPT.

Mean–variance analysis generally considers risk symmetrically in the sense that standard deviation captures variability both above and below the mean.[23] An alternative approach evaluates only downside risk. We discuss one such approach, safety-first rules, as it provides an excellent illustration of the application of normal distribution theory to practical investment problems. **Safety-first rules** focus on **shortfall risk**, the risk that portfolio value will fall below some minimum acceptable level over some time horizon. The risk that the assets in a defined benefit plan will fall below plan liabilities is an example of a shortfall risk.

Suppose an investor views any return below a level of R_L as unacceptable. Roy's safety-first criterion states that the optimal portfolio minimizes the probability that portfolio return, R_P, falls below the threshold level, R_L.[24] In symbols, the investor's objective is to choose a portfolio that minimizes $P(R_P < R_L)$. When portfolio returns are normally distributed, we can calculate $P(R_P < R_L)$ using the number of standard deviations that R_L lies below the expected portfolio return, $E(R_P)$. The portfolio for which $E(R_P) - R_L$ is largest relative to standard deviation minimizes $P(R_P < R_L)$. Therefore, if returns are normally distributed, the safety-first optimal portfolio *maximizes* the safety-first ratio (SFRatio):

$$\text{SFRatio} = [E(R_P) - R_L]/\sigma_P$$

The quantity $E(R_P) - R_L$ is the distance from the mean return to the shortfall level. Dividing this distance by σ_P gives the distance in units of standard deviation. There are two steps in choosing among portfolios using Roy's criterion (assuming normality):[25]

1 Calculate each portfolio's SFRatio.

2 Choose the portfolio with the highest SFRatio.

For a portfolio with a given safety-first ratio, the probability that its return will be less than R_L is $N(-\text{SFRatio})$, and the safety-first optimal portfolio has the lowest such probability. For example, suppose an investor's threshold return, R_L, is 2 percent. He is presented with two portfolios. Portfolio 1 has an expected return of 12 percent with a standard deviation of 15 percent. Portfolio 2 has an expected return of 14 percent with a standard deviation of 16 percent. The SFRatios are $0.667 = (12 - 2)/15$ and $0.75 = (14 - 2)/16$ for Portfolios 1 and 2, respectively. For the superior Portfolio 2, the probability that portfolio return will be less than 2 percent is $N(-0.75) = 1 - N(0.75) = 1 - 0.7734 = 0.227$ or about 23 percent, assuming that portfolio returns are normally distributed.

22 Utility functions are mathematical representations of attitudes toward risk and return.

23 We shall discuss mean–variance analysis in detail in the readings on portfolio concepts.

24 A.D. Roy (1952) introduced this criterion.

25 If there is an asset offering a risk-free return over the time horizon being considered, and if R_L is less than or equal to that risk-free rate, then it is optimal to be fully invested in the risk-free asset. Holding the risk-free asset in this case eliminates the chance that the threshold return is not met.

You may have noticed the similarity of SFRatio to the Sharpe ratio. If we substitute the risk-free rate, R_F, for the critical level R_L, the SFRatio becomes the Sharpe ratio. The safety-first approach provides a new perspective on the Sharpe ratio: When we evaluate portfolios using the Sharpe ratio, the portfolio with the highest Sharpe ratio is the one that minimizes the probability that portfolio return will be less than the risk-free rate (given a normality assumption).

EXAMPLE 9

The Safety-First Optimal Portfolio for a Client

You are researching asset allocations for a client in Canada with a C$800,000 portfolio. Although her investment objective is long-term growth, at the end of a year she may want to liquidate C$30,000 of the portfolio to fund educational expenses. If that need arises, she would like to be able to take out the C$30,000 without invading the initial capital of C$800,000. Table 6 shows three alternative allocations.

Table 6 Mean and Standard Deviation for Three Allocations (in Percent)

	A	B	C
Expected annual return	25	11	14
Standard deviation of return	27	8	20

Address these questions (assume normality for Parts 2 and 3):

1 Given the client's desire not to invade the C$800,000 principal, what is the shortfall level, R_L? Use this shortfall level to answer Part 2.

2 According to the safety-first criterion, which of the three allocations is the best?

3 What is the probability that the return on the safety-first optimal portfolio will be less than the shortfall level?

Solution to 1:

Because C$30,000/C$800,000 is 3.75 percent, for any return less than 3.75 percent the client will need to invade principal if she takes out C$30,000. So R_L = 3.75 percent.

Solution to 2:

To decide which of the three allocations is safety-first optimal, select the alternative with the highest ratio $[E(R_P) - R_L]/\sigma_P$:

Allocation A: 0.787037 = (25 – 3.75)/27

Allocation B: 0.90625 = (11 – 3.75)/8

Allocation C: 0.5125 = (14 – 3.75)/20

Allocation B, with the largest ratio (0.90625), is the best alternative according to the safety-first criterion.

Solution to 3:

To answer this question, note that $P(R_B < 3.75) = N(-0.90625)$. We can round 0.90625 to 0.91 for use with tables of the standard normal cdf. First, we calculate $N(-0.91) = 1 - N(0.91) = 1 - 0.8186 = 0.1814$ or about 18.1 percent. Using a spreadsheet function for the standard normal cdf on −0.90625 without rounding, we get 18.24 percent or about 18.2 percent. The safety-first optimal portfolio has a roughly 18 percent chance of not meeting a 3.75 percent return threshold.

Several points are worth noting. First, if the inputs were even slightly different, we could get a different ranking. For example, if the mean return on B were 10 rather than 11 percent, A would be superior to B. Second, if meeting the 3.75 percent return threshold were a necessity rather than a wish, C$830,000 in one year could be modeled as a liability. Fixed income strategies such as cash flow matching could be used to offset or immunize the C$830,000 quasi-liability.

Roy's safety-first rule was the earliest approach to addressing shortfall risk. The standard mean-variance portfolio selection process can also accommodate a shortfall risk constraint.[26]

In many investment contexts besides Roy's safety-first criterion, we use the normal distribution to estimate a probability. For example, Kolb, Gay, and Hunter (1985) developed an expression based on the standard normal distribution for the probability that a futures trader will exhaust his liquidity because of losses in a futures contract. Another arena in which the normal distribution plays an important role is financial risk management. Financial institutions such as investment banks, security dealers, and commercial banks have formal systems to measure and control financial risk at various levels, from trading positions to the overall risk for the firm.[27] Two mainstays in managing financial risk are Value at Risk (VaR) and stress testing/scenario analysis. **Stress testing/scenario analysis**, a complement to VaR, refers to a set of techniques for estimating losses in extremely unfavorable combinations of events or scenarios. **Value at Risk** (VaR) is a money measure of the minimum value of losses expected over a specified time period (for example, a day, a quarter, or a year) at a given level of probability (often 0.05 or 0.01). Suppose we specify a one-day time horizon and a level of probability of 0.05, which would be called a 95 percent one-day VaR.[28] If this VaR equaled €5 million for a portfolio, there would be a 0.05 probability that the portfolio would lose €5 million or more in a single day (assuming our assumptions were correct). One of the basic approaches to estimating VaR, the variance-covariance or analytical method, assumes that returns follow a normal distribution. For more information on VaR, see Chance and Brooks (2016).

3.4 The Lognormal Distribution

Closely related to the normal distribution, the lognormal distribution is widely used for modeling the probability distribution of share and other asset prices. For example, the lognormal appears in the Black–Scholes–Merton option pricing model. The Black–Scholes–Merton model assumes that the price of the asset underlying the option is lognormally distributed.

26 See Leibowitz and Henriksson (1989), for example.

27 **Financial risk** is risk relating to asset prices and other financial variables. The contrast is to other, non-financial risks (for example, relating to operations and technology), which require different tools to manage.

28 In 95 percent one-day VaR, the 95 percent refers to the confidence in the value of VaR and is equal to 1 − 0.05; this is a traditional way to state VaR.

A random variable Y follows a lognormal distribution if its natural logarithm, ln Y, is normally distributed. The reverse is also true: If the natural logarithm of random variable Y, ln Y, is normally distributed, then Y follows a lognormal distribution. If you think of the term lognormal as "the log is normal," you will have no trouble remembering this relationship.

The two most noteworthy observations about the lognormal distribution are that it is bounded below by 0 and it is skewed to the right (it has a long right tail). Note these two properties in the graphs of the pdfs of two lognormal distributions in Figure 7. Asset prices are bounded from below by 0. In practice, the lognormal distribution has been found to be a usefully accurate description of the distribution of prices for many financial assets. On the other hand, the normal distribution is often a good approximation for returns. For this reason, both distributions are very important for finance professionals.

Figure 7 Two Lognormal Distributions

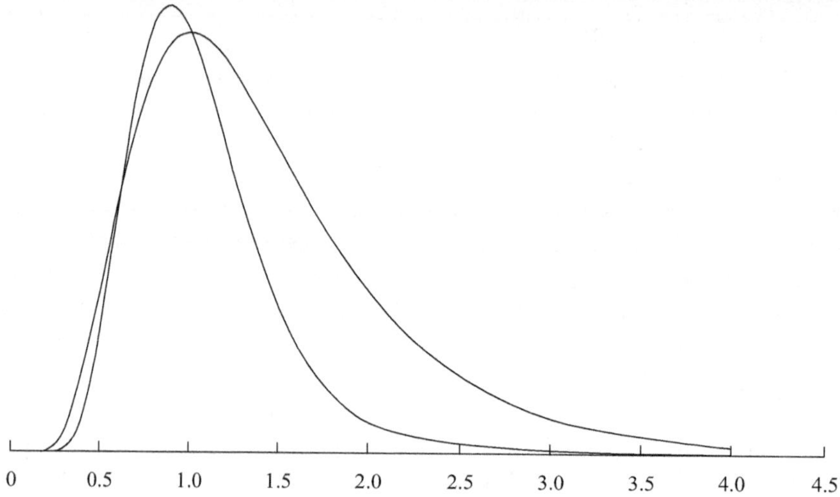

Like the normal distribution, the lognormal distribution is completely described by two parameters. Unlike the other distributions we have considered, a lognormal distribution is defined in terms of the parameters of a *different* distribution. The two parameters of a lognormal distribution are the mean and standard deviation (or variance) of its associated normal distribution: the mean and variance of ln Y, given that Y is lognormal. Remember, we must keep track of two sets of means and standard deviations (or variances): the mean and standard deviation (or variance) of the associated normal distribution (these are the parameters), and the mean and standard deviation (or variance) of the lognormal variable itself.

The expressions for the mean and variance of the lognormal variable itself are challenging. Suppose a normal random variable X has expected value μ and variance σ^2. Define $Y = \exp(X)$. Remember that the operation indicated by $\exp(X)$ or e^X is the opposite operation from taking logs.[29] Because $\ln Y = \ln[\exp(X)] = X$ is normal (we assume X is normal), Y is lognormal. What is the expected value of $Y = \exp(X)$? A guess might be that the expected value of Y is $\exp(\mu)$. The expected value is actually $\exp(\mu + 0.50\sigma^2)$, which is larger than $\exp(\mu)$ by a factor of $\exp(0.50\sigma^2) > 1$.[30] To get some

29 The quantity $e \approx 2.7182818$.
30 Note that $\exp(0.50\sigma^2) > 1$ because $\sigma^2 > 0$.

insight into this concept, think of what happens if we increase σ^2. The distribution spreads out; it can spread upward, but it cannot spread downward past 0. As a result, the center of its distribution is pushed to the right—the distribution's mean increases.[31]

The expressions for the mean and variance of a lognormal variable are summarized below, where μ and σ^2 are the mean and variance of the associated normal distribution (refer to these expressions as needed, rather than memorizing them):

- Mean (μ_L) of a lognormal random variable = $\exp(\mu + 0.50\sigma^2)$
- Variance ($\sigma_L{}^2$) of a lognormal random variable = $\exp(2\mu + \sigma^2) \times [\exp(\sigma^2) - 1]$

We now explore the relationship between the distribution of stock return and stock price. In the following we show that if a stock's continuously compounded return is normally distributed, then future stock price is necessarily lognormally distributed.[32] Furthermore, we show that stock price may be well described by the lognormal distribution even when continuously compounded returns do not follow a normal distribution. These results provide the theoretical foundation for using the lognormal distribution to model prices.

To outline the presentation that follows, we first show that the stock price at some future time T, S_T, equals the current stock price, S_0, multiplied by e raised to power $r_{0,T}$, the continuously compounded return from 0 to T; this relationship is expressed as $S_T = S_0\exp(r_{0,T})$. We then show that we can write $r_{0,T}$ as the sum of shorter-term continuously compounded returns and that if these shorter-period returns are normally distributed, then $r_{0,T}$ is normally distributed (given certain assumptions) or approximately normally distributed (not making those assumptions). As S_T is proportional to the log of a normal random variable, S_T is lognormal.

To supply a framework for our discussion, suppose we have a series of equally spaced observations on stock price: S_0, S_1, S_2, ..., S_T. Current stock price, S_0, is a known quantity and so is nonrandom. The future prices (such as S_1), however, are random variables. The **price relative**, S_1/S_0, is an ending price, S_1, over a beginning price, S_0; it is equal to 1 plus the holding period return on the stock from $t = 0$ to $t = 1$:

$$S_1/S_0 = 1 + R_{0,1}$$

For example, if S_0 = \$30 and S_1 = \$34.50, then S_1/S_0 = \$34.50/\$30 = 1.15. Therefore, $R_{0,1}$ = 0.15 or 15 percent. In general, price relatives have the form

$$S_{t+1}/S_t = 1 + R_{t,t+1}$$

where $R_{t,t+1}$ is the rate of return from t to $t + 1$.

An important concept is the continuously compounded return associated with a holding period return such as $R_{0,1}$. The **continuously compounded return** associated with a holding period is the natural logarithm of 1 plus that holding period return, or equivalently, the natural logarithm of the ending price over the beginning price (the price relative).[33] For example, if we observe a one-week holding period return of 0.04, the equivalent continuously compounded return, called the one-week continuously compounded return, is ln(1.04) = 0.039221; €1.00 invested for one week at 0.039221 continuously compounded gives €1.04, equivalent to a 4 percent one-week holding period return. The continuously compounded return from t to $t + 1$ is

$$r_{t,t+1} = \ln(S_{t+1}/S_t) = \ln(1 + R_{t,t+1}) \tag{5}$$

31 Luenberger (1998) is the source of this explanation.

32 Continuous compounding treats time as essentially continuous or unbroken, in contrast to discrete compounding, which treats time as advancing in discrete finite intervals. Continuously compounded returns are the model for returns in so-called **continuous time** finance models such as the Black–Scholes–Merton option pricing model. See the reading on the time value of money for more information on compounding.

33 In this reading we use lowercase r to refer specifically to continuously compounded returns.

For our example, $r_{0,1} = \ln(S_1/S_0) = \ln(1 + R_{0,1}) = \ln(\$34.50/\$30) = \ln(1.15) = 0.139762$. Thus, 13.98 percent is the continuously compounded return from $t = 0$ to $t = 1$. The continuously compounded return is smaller than the associated holding period return. If our investment horizon extends from $t = 0$ to $t = T$, then the continuously compounded return to T is

$$r_{0,T} = \ln(S_T/S_0)$$

Applying the function exp to both sides of the equation, we have $\exp(r_{0,T}) = \exp[\ln(S_T/S_0)] = S_T/S_0$, so

$$S_T = S_0\exp(r_{0,T})$$

We can also express S_T/S_0 as the product of price relatives:

$$S_T/S_0 = (S_T/S_{T-1})(S_{T-1}/S_{T-2})\ldots(S_1/S_0)$$

Taking logs of both sides of this equation, we find that continuously compounded return to time T is the sum of the one-period continuously compounded returns:

$$r_{0,T} = r_{T-1,T} + r_{T-2,T-1} + \ldots r_{0,1} \quad (6)$$

Using holding period returns to find the ending value of a \$1 investment involves the multiplication of quantities (1 + holding period return). Using continuously compounded returns involves addition.

A key assumption in many investment applications is that returns are **independently and identically distributed (IID)**. Independence captures the proposition that investors cannot predict future returns using past returns (i.e., weak-form market efficiency). Identical distribution captures the assumption of stationarity.[34]

Assume that the one-period continuously compounded returns (such as $r_{0,1}$) are IID random variables with mean μ and variance σ^2 (but making no normality or other distributional assumption). Then

$$E(r_{0,T}) = E(r_{T-1,T}) + E(r_{T-2,T-1}) + \ldots + E(r_{0,1}) = \mu T \quad (7)$$

(we add up μ for a total of T times) and

$$\sigma^2(r_{0,T}) = \sigma^2 T \quad (8)$$

(as a consequence of the independence assumption). The variance of the T holding period continuously compounded return is T multiplied by the variance of the one-period continuously compounded return; also, $\sigma(r_{0,T}) = \sigma\sqrt{T}$. If the one-period continuously compounded returns on the right-hand side of Equation 6 are normally distributed, then the T holding period continuously compounded return, $r_{0,T}$, is also normally distributed with mean μT and variance $\sigma^2 T$. This relationship is so because a linear combination of normal random variables is also normal. But even if the one-period continuously compounded returns are not normal, their sum, $r_{0,T}$, is approximately normal according to a result in statistics known as the central limit theorem.[35] Now compare $S_T = S_0\exp(r_{0,T})$ to $Y = \exp(X)$, where X is normal and Y is lognormal (as we discussed above). Clearly, we can model future stock price S_T as a lognormal random variable because $r_{0,T}$ should be at least approximately normal. This assumption of normally distributed returns is the basis in theory for the lognormal distribution as a model for the distribution of prices of shares and other assets.

---

34 Stationarity implies that the mean and variance of return do not change from period to period.

35 We mentioned the central limit theorem earlier in our discussion of the normal distribution. To give a somewhat fuller statement of it, according to the central limit theorem the sum (as well as the mean) of a set of independent, identically distributed random variables with finite variances is normally distributed, whatever distribution the random variables follow. We discuss the central limit theorem in the reading on sampling.

Continuously compounded returns play a role in many option pricing models, as mentioned earlier. An estimate of volatility is crucial for using option pricing models such as the Black–Scholes–Merton model. **Volatility** measures the standard deviation of the continuously compounded returns on the underlying asset.[36] In practice, we very often estimate volatility using a historical series of continuously compounded daily returns. We gather a set of daily holding period returns and then use Equation 5 to convert them into continuously compounded daily returns. We then compute the standard deviation of the continuously compounded daily returns and annualize that number using Equation 8.[37] (By convention, volatility is stated as an annualized measure.)[38] Example 10 illustrates the estimation of volatility for the shares of Astra International.

EXAMPLE 10

Volatility as Used in Option Pricing Models

Suppose you are researching Astra International (Indonesia Stock Exchange: ASII) and are interested in Astra's price action in a week in which international economic news had significantly affected the Indonesian stock market. You decide to use volatility as a measure of the variability of Astra shares during that week. Table 7 shows closing prices during that week.

Table 7 Astra International Daily Closing Prices

Day	Closing Price (IDR)
Monday	6,950
Tuesday	7,000
Wednesday	6,850
Thursday	6,600
Friday	6,350

Use the data in Table 7 to do the following:

1 Estimate the volatility of Astra shares. (Annualize volatility based on 250 days in a year.)

2 Identify the probability distribution for Astra share prices if continuously compounded daily returns follow the normal distribution.

36 Volatility is also called the instantaneous standard deviation, and as such is denoted σ. The underlying asset, or simply the underlying, is the asset underlying the option. For more information on these concepts, see Chance and Brooks (2016).

37 To compute the standard deviation of a set or sample of n returns, we sum the squared deviation of each return from the mean return and then divide that sum by $n - 1$. The result is the sample variance. Taking the square root of the sample variance gives the sample standard deviation. To review the calculation of standard deviation, see the reading on statistical concepts and market returns.

38 Annualizing is often done on the basis of 250 days in a year, the approximate number of days markets are open for trading. The 250-day number may lead to a better estimate of volatility than the 365-day number. Thus if daily volatility were 0.01, we would state volatility (on an annual basis) as $0.01\sqrt{250} = 0.1581$.

Solution to 1:

First, use Equation 5 to calculate the continuously compounded daily returns; then find their standard deviation in the usual way. (In the calculation of sample variance to get sample standard deviation, use a divisor of 1 less than the sample size.)

$\ln(7{,}000/6{,}950) = 0.007168$

$\ln(6{,}850/7{,}000) = -0.021661$

$\ln(6{,}600/6{,}850) = -0.037179$

$\ln(6{,}350/6{,}600) = -0.038615$

Sum = −0.090287

Mean = −0.022572

Variance = 0.000452

Standard Deviation = 0.021261

The standard deviation of continuously compounded daily returns is 0.021261. Equation 8 states that $\hat{\sigma}(r_{0,T}) = \hat{\sigma}\sqrt{T}$. In this example, $\hat{\sigma}$ is the sample standard deviation of one-period continuously compounded returns. Thus, $\hat{\sigma}$ refers to 0.021261. We want to annualize, so the horizon T corresponds to one year. As $\hat{\sigma}$ is in days, we set T equal to the number of trading days in a year (250).

We find that annualized volatility for Astra stock that week was 33.6 percent, calculated as $0.021261\sqrt{250} = 0.336165$.

Note that the sample mean, −0.022572, is a possible estimate of the mean, μ, of the continuously compounded one-period or daily returns. The sample mean can be translated into an estimate of the expected continuously compounded annual return using Equation 7: $\hat{\mu}T = -0.022572(250)$ (using 250 to be consistent with the calculation of volatility). But four observations are far too few to estimate expected returns. The variability in the daily returns overwhelms any information about expected return in a series this short.

Solution to 2:

Astra share prices should follow the lognormal distribution if the continuously compounded daily returns on Astra shares follow the normal distribution.

We have shown that the distribution of stock price is lognormal, given certain assumptions. What are the mean and variance of S_T if S_T follows the lognormal distribution? Earlier in this section, we gave bullet-point expressions for the mean and variance of a lognormal random variable. In the bullet-point expressions, the $\hat{\mu}$ and $\hat{\sigma}^2$ would refer, in the context of this discussion, to the mean and variance of the T horizon (not the one-period) continuously compounded returns (assumed to follow a normal distribution), compatible with the horizon of S_T.[39] Related to the use of mean and variance (or standard deviation), earlier in this reading we used those quantities to construct intervals in which we expect to find a certain percentage of the observations of a normally distributed random variable. Those intervals were symmetric about the mean. Can we state similar, symmetric intervals for a lognormal random variable?

39 The expression for the mean is $E(S_T) = S_0 \exp[E(r_{0,T}) + 0.5\sigma^2(r_{0,T})]$, for example.

Unfortunately, we cannot. Because the lognormal distribution is not symmetric, such intervals are more complicated than for the normal distribution, and we will not discuss this specialist topic here.[40]

Finally, we have presented the relation between the mean and variance of continuously compounded returns associated with different time horizons (see Equations 7 and 8), but how are the means and variances of holding period returns and continuously compounded returns related? As analysts, we typically think in terms of holding period returns rather than continuously compounded returns, and we may desire to convert means and standard deviations of holding period returns to means and standard deviations of continuously compounded returns for an option application, for example. To effect such conversions (and those in the other direction, from a continuous compounding to a holding period basis), we can use the expressions in Ferguson (1993).

MONTE CARLO SIMULATION

4

With an understanding of probability distributions, we are now prepared to learn about a computer-based technique in which probability distributions play an integral role. The technique is called Monte Carlo simulation. **Monte Carlo simulation** in finance involves the use of a computer to represent the operation of a complex financial system. A characteristic feature of Monte Carlo simulation is the generation of a large number of random samples from a specified probability distribution or distributions to represent the role of risk in the system.

Monte Carlo simulation has several quite distinct uses. One use is in planning. Stanford University researcher Sam Savage provided the following neat picture of that role: "What is the last thing you do before you climb on a ladder? You shake it, and that is Monte Carlo simulation."[41] Just as shaking a ladder helps us assess the risks in climbing it, Monte Carlo simulation allows us to experiment with a proposed policy before actually implementing it. For example, investment performance can be evaluated with reference to a benchmark or a liability. Defined benefit pension plans often invest assets with reference to plan liabilities. Pension liabilities are a complex random process. In a Monte Carlo asset-liability financial planning study, the functioning of pension assets and liabilities is simulated over time, given assumptions about how assets are invested, the work force, and other variables. A key specification in this and all Monte Carlo simulations is the probability distributions of the various sources of risk (including interest rates and security market returns, in this case). The implications of different investment policy decisions on the plan's funded status can be assessed through simulated time. The experiment can be repeated for another set of assumptions. We can view Example 11 below as coming under this heading. In that example, market return series are not long enough to address researchers' questions on stock market timing, so the researchers simulate market returns to find answers to their questions.

Monte Carlo simulation is also widely used to develop estimates of VaR. In this application, we simulate the portfolio's profit and loss performance for a specified time horizon. Repeated trials within the simulation (each trial involving a draw of random observations from a probability distribution) produce a frequency distribution for changes in portfolio value. The point that defines the cutoff for the least favorable 5 percent of simulated changes is an estimate of 95 percent VaR, for example.

40 See Hull (2017) for a discussion of lognormal confidence intervals.

41 *Business Week*, 22 January 2001.

In an extremely important use, Monte Carlo simulation is a tool for valuing complex securities, particularly some European-style options for which no analytic pricing formula is available.[42] For other securities, such as mortgage-backed securities with complex embedded options, Monte Carlo simulation is also an important modeling resource.

Researchers use Monte Carlo simulation to test their models and tools. How critical is a particular assumption to the performance of a model? Because we control the assumptions when we do a simulation, we can run the model through a Monte Carlo simulation to examine a model's sensitivity to a change in our assumptions.

To understand the technique of Monte Carlo simulation, let us present the process as a series of steps.[43] To illustrate the steps, we take the case of using Monte Carlo simulation to value a type of option for which no analytic pricing formula is available, an Asian call option on a stock. An **Asian call option** is a European-style option with a value at maturity equal to the difference between the stock price at maturity and the average stock price during the life of the option, or \$0, whichever is greater. For instance, if the final stock price is \$34 with an average value of \$31 over the life of the option, the value of the option at maturity is \$3 (the greater of \$34 − \$31 = \$3 and \$0). Steps 1 through 3 of the process describe specifying the simulation; Steps 4 through 7 describe running the simulation.

1 Specify the quantities of interest (option value, for example, or the funded status of a pension plan) in terms of underlying variables. The underlying variable or variables could be stock price for an equity option, the market value of pension assets, or other variables relating to the pension benefit obligation for a pension plan. Specify the starting values of the underlying variables.

   To illustrate the steps, we are using the case of valuing an Asian call option on stock. We use C_{iT} to represent the value of the option at maturity T. The subscript i in C_{iT} indicates that C_{iT} is a value resulting from the ith **simulation trial**, each simulation trial involving a drawing of random values (an iteration of Step 4).

2 Specify a time grid. Take the horizon in terms of calendar time and split it into a number of subperiods, say K in total. Calendar time divided by the number of subperiods, K, is the time increment, Δt.

3 Specify distributional assumptions for the risk factors that drive the underlying variables. For example, stock price is the underlying variable for the Asian call, so we need a model for stock price movement. Say we choose the following model for changes in stock price, where Z_k stands for the standard normal random variable:

$$\Delta(\text{Stock price}) = (\mu \times \text{Prior stock price} \times \Delta t) + (\sigma \times \text{Prior stock price} \times Z_k)$$

   In the way that we are using the term, Z_k is a risk factor in the simulation. Through our choice of μ and σ, we control the distribution of stock price. Although this example has one risk factor, a given simulation may have multiple risk factors.

4 Using a computer program or spreadsheet function, draw K random values of each risk factor. In our example, the spreadsheet function would produce a draw of K values of the standard normal variable Z_k: $Z_1, Z_2, Z_3, \ldots, Z_K$.

42 A **European-style** option or **European option** is an option exercisable only at maturity.

43 The steps should be viewed as providing an overview of Monte Carlo simulation rather than as a detailed recipe for implementing a Monte Carlo simulation in its many varied applications.

5 Calculate the underlying variables using the random observations generated in Step 4. Using the above model of stock price dynamics, the result is K observations on changes in stock price. An additional calculation is needed to convert those changes into K stock prices (using initial stock price, which is given). Another calculation produces the average stock price during the life of the option (the sum of K stock prices divided by K).

6 Compute the quantities of interest. In our example, the first calculation is the value of an Asian call at maturity, C_{iT}. A second calculation discounts this terminal value back to the present to get the call value as of today, C_{i0}. We have completed one simulation trial. (The subscript i in C_{i0} stands for the ith simulation trial, as it does in C_{iT}.) In a Monte Carlo simulation, a running tabulation is kept of statistics relating to the distribution of the quantities of interest, including their mean value and standard deviation, over the simulation trials to that point.

7 Iteratively go back to Step 4 until a specified number of trials, I, is completed. Finally, produce statistics for the simulation. The key value for our example is the mean value of C_{i0} for the total number of simulation trials. This mean value is the Monte Carlo estimate of the value of the Asian call.

How many simulation trials should be specified? In general, we need to increase the number of trials by a factor of 100 to get each extra digit of accuracy. Depending on the problem, tens of thousands of trials may be needed to obtain accuracy to two decimal places (as required for option value, for example). Conducting a large number of trials is not necessarily a problem, given today's computing power. The number of trials needed can be reduced using variance reduction procedures, a topic outside the scope of this reading.[44]

In Step 4 of our example, a computer function produced a set of random observations on a standard normal random variable. Recall that for a uniform distribution, all possible numbers are equally likely. The term **random number generator** refers to an algorithm that produces uniformly distributed random numbers between 0 and 1. In the context of computer simulations, the term **random number** refers to an observation drawn from a uniform distribution.[45] For other distributions, the term "random observation" is used in this context.

It is a remarkable fact that random observations from any distribution can be produced using the uniform random variable with endpoints 0 and 1. To see why this is so, consider the inverse transformation method of producing random observations. Suppose we are interested in obtaining random observations for a random variable, X, with cumulative distribution function $F(x)$. Recall that $F(x)$ evaluated at x is a number between 0 and 1. Suppose a random outcome of this random variable is 3.21 and that $F(3.21) = 0.25$ or 25 percent. Define an inverse of F, call it F^{-1}, that can do the following: Substitute the probability 0.25 into F^{-1} and it returns the random outcome 3.21. In other words, $F^{-1}(0.25) = 3.21$. To generate random observations on X, the steps are 1) generate a uniform random number, r, between 0 and 1 using the random number generator and 2) evaluate $F^{-1}(r)$ to obtain a random observation on X. Random observation generation is a field of study in itself, and we have briefly discussed the inverse transformation method here just to illustrate a point. As a generalist

44 For details on this and other technical aspects of Monte Carlo simulation, see Hillier (2014).

45 The numbers that random number generators produce depend on a seed or initial value. If the same seed is fed to the same generator, it will produce the same sequence. All sequences eventually repeat. Because of this predictability, the technically correct name for the numbers produced by random number generators is **pseudo-random numbers**. Pseudo-random numbers have sufficient qualities of randomness for most practical purposes.

you do not need to address the technical details of converting random numbers into random observations, but you do need to know that random observations from any distribution can be generated using a uniform random variable.

In Examples 11 and 12, we give an application of Monte Carlo simulation to a question of great interest to investment practice: the potential gains from market timing.

EXAMPLE 11

Potential Gains from Market Timing: A Monte Carlo Simulation (1)

All active investors want to achieve superior performance. One possible source of superior performance is market timing ability. How accurate does an investor need to be as a bull- and bear-market forecaster for market timing to be profitable? What size gains compared with a buy-and-hold strategy accrue to a given level of accuracy? Because of the variability in asset returns, a huge amount of return data is needed to find statistically reliable answers to these questions. Chua, Woodward, and To (1987) thus selected Monte Carlo simulation to address the potential gains from market timing. They were interested in the perspective of a Canadian investor.

To understand their study, suppose that at the beginning of a year, an investor predicts that the next year will see either a bull market or bear market. If the prediction is *bull market,* the investor puts all her money in stocks and earns the market return for that year. On the other hand, if the prediction is *bear market,* the investor holds T-bills and earns the T-bill return. After the fact, a market is categorized as *bull market* if the stock market return, R_{Mt}, minus T-bill return, R_{Ft}, is positive for the year; otherwise, the market is classed as *bear market.* The investment results of a market timer can be compared with those of a buy-and-hold investor. A buy-and-hold investor earns the market return every year. For Chua et al., one quantity of interest was the gain from market timing. They defined this quantity as the market timer's average return minus the average return to a buy-and-hold investor.

To simulate market returns, Chua et al. generated 10,000 random standard normal observations, Z_t. At the time of the study, Canadian stocks had a historical mean annual return of 12.95 percent with a standard deviation of 18.30 percent. To reflect these parameters, the simulated market returns are $R_{Mt} = 0.1830Z_t + 0.1295$, $t = 1, 2, \ldots, 10{,}000$. Using a second set of 10,000 random standard normal observations, historical return parameters for Canadian T-bills, as well as the historical correlation of T-bill and stock returns, the authors generated 10,000 T-bill returns.

An investor can have different skills in forecasting bull and bear markets. Chua et al. characterized market timers by accuracy in forecasting bull markets and accuracy in forecasting bear markets. For example, bull market forecasting accuracy of 50 percent means that when the timer forecasts *bull market* for the next year, she is right just half the time, indicating no skill. Suppose an investor has 60 percent accuracy in forecasting *bull market* and 80 percent accuracy in forecasting *bear market* (a 60–80 timer). We can simulate how an investor would fare. After generating the first observation on $R_{Mt} - R_{Ft}$, we know whether that observation is a bull or bear market. If the observation is *bull market,* then 0.60 (forecast accuracy for bull markets) is compared with a random number (between 0 and 1). If the random number is less than 0.60, which occurs with a 60 percent probability, then the market timer is assumed to have correctly predicted *bull market* and her return for that first observation is the market return. If the random number is greater than 0.60, then the market timer is assumed to have made an error and predicted *bear market;* her return for that observation is the risk-free rate. In a similar fashion, if that first observation is *bear market,* the timer has an 80 percent chance of being right in forecasting *bear market* based on a random number draw. In either case, her return is compared with the market return to record her gain versus a buy-and-hold strategy. That process is one simulation trial. The simulated mean return earned by the timer is the average return earned by the timer over all trials in the simulation.

To increase our understanding of the process, consider a hypothetical Monte Carlo simulation with four trials for the 60–80 timer (who, to reiterate, has 60 percent accuracy in forecasting bull markets and 80 percent accuracy in forecasting bear markets). Table 8 gives data for the simulation. Let us look at Trials 1 and 2. In Trial 1, the first random number drawn leads to a market return of 0.121. Because the market return, 0.121, exceeded the T-bill return, 0.050, we have a bull market. We generate a random number, 0.531, which we then compare with the timer's bull market accuracy, 0.60. Because 0.531 is less than 0.60, the timer is assumed to have made a correct bull market forecast and thus to have invested in stocks. Thus the timer earns the stock market return, 0.121, for that trial. In the second trial we observe another bull market, but because the random number 0.725 is greater than 0.60, the timer is assumed to have made an error and predicted a bear market; therefore, the timer earned the T-bill return, 0.081, rather than higher stock market return.

Table 8 Hypothetical Simulation for a 60–80 Market Timer

	After Draws for Z_t and for the T-bill Return			Simulation Results		
Trial	R_{Mt}	R_{Ft}	Bull or Bear Market?	Value of X	Timer's Prediction Correct?	Return Earned by Timer
1	0.121	0.050	Bull	0.531	Yes	0.121
2	0.092	0.081	Bull	0.725	No	0.081
3	−0.020	0.034	Bear	0.786	Yes	0.034
4	0.052	0.055	*A*	0.901	*B*	*C*
						$\bar{R} = D$

Note: $\bar{R}$ is the mean return earned by the timer over the four simulation trials.

Using the data in Table 8, determine the values of *A*, *B*, *C*, and *D*.

Solution:

The value of *A* is *Bear* because the stock market return was less than the T-bill return in Trial 4. The value of *B* is *No.* Because we observe a bear market, we compare the random number 0.901 with 0.80, the timer's bear-market forecasting accuracy. Because 0.901 is greater than 0.8, the timer is assumed to have made an error. The value of *C* is 0.052, the return on the stock market, because the timer made an error and invested in the stock market and earned 0.052 rather than the higher T-bill return of 0.055. The value of *D* is $\bar{R}$ = (0.121 + 0.081 + 0.034 + 0.052) = 0.288/4 = 0.072. Note that we could calculate other statistics besides the mean, such as the standard deviation of the returns earned by the timer over the four trials in the simulation.

EXAMPLE 12

Potential Gains from Market Timing: A Monte Carlo Simulation (2)

Having discussed the plan of the Chua et al. study and illustrated the method for a hypothetical Monte Carlo simulation with four trials, we conclude our presentation of the study.

The hypothetical simulation in Example 11 had four trials, far too few to reach statistically precise conclusions. The simulation of Chua et al. incorporated 10,000 trials. Chua et al. specified bull- and bear-market prediction skill levels of 50, 60, 70, 80, 90, and 100 percent. Table 9 presents a very small excerpt from their simulation results for the no transaction costs case (transaction costs were also examined). Reading across the row, the timer with 60 percent bull market and 80 percent bear market forecasting accuracy had a mean annual gain from market timing of −1.12 percent per year. On average, the buy-and-hold investor out-earned this skillful timer by 1.12 percentage points. There was substantial variability in gains across the simulation trials, however: The standard deviation of the gain was 14.77 percent, so in many trials (but not on average) the gain was positive. Row 3 (win/loss) is the ratio of profitable switches between stocks and T-bills to unprofitable switches. This ratio was a favorable 1.2070 for the 60–80 timer. (When transaction costs were considered, however, fewer switches are profitable: The win–loss ratio was 0.5832 for the 60–80 timer.)

Table 9 Gains from Stock Market Timing (No Transaction Costs)

Bull Market Accuracy (%)		Bear Market Accuracy (%)					
		50	60	70	80	90	100
60	Mean (%)	−2.50	−1.99	−1.57	−1.12	−0.68	−0.22
	S.D. (%)	13.65	14.11	14.45	14.77	15.08	15.42
	Win/Loss	0.7418	0.9062	1.0503	1.2070	1.3496	1.4986

Source: Chua, Woodward, and To (1987), Table II (excerpt).

The authors concluded that the cost of not being invested in the market during bull market years is high. Because a buy-and-hold investor never misses a bull market year, she has 100 percent forecast accuracy for bull markets (at the cost of 0 percent accuracy for bear markets). Given their definitions and assumptions, the authors also concluded that successful market timing requires a minimum accuracy of 80 percent in forecasting both bull and bear markets. Market timing is a continuing area of interest and study, and other perspectives exist. However, this example illustrates how Monte Carlo simulation is used to address important investment issues.

The analyst chooses the probability distributions in Monte Carlo simulation. By contrast, **historical simulation** samples from a historical record of returns (or other underlying variables) to simulate a process. The concept underlying historical simulation (also called **back simulation**) is that the historical record provides the most direct evidence on distributions (and that the past applies to the future). For example, refer to Step 2 in the outline of Monte Carlo simulation above and suppose the time increment is one day. Further, suppose we base the simulation on the record of daily stock returns over the last five years. In one type of historical simulation, we randomly draw K returns from that record to generate one simulation trial. We put back the observations into the sample, and in the next trial we again randomly sample with replacement. The simulation results directly reflect frequencies in the data. A drawback of this approach is that any risk not represented in the time period selected (for example, a stock market crash) will not be reflected in the simulation. Compared with Monte Carlo simulation, historical simulation does not lend itself to "what if" analyses. Nevertheless, historic simulation is an established alternative simulation methodology.

Monte Carlo simulation is a complement to analytical methods. It provides only statistical estimates, not exact results. Analytical methods, where available, provide more insight into cause-and-effect relationships. For example, the Black–Scholes–Merton option pricing model for the value of a European call option is an analytical method, expressed as a formula. It is a much more efficient method for valuing such a call than is Monte Carlo simulation. As an analytical expression, the Black–Scholes–Merton model permits the analyst to quickly gauge the sensitivity of call value to changes in current stock price and the other variables that determine call value. In contrast, Monte Carlo simulations do not directly provide such precise insights. However, only some types of options can be priced with analytical expressions. As financial product innovations proceed, the field of applications for Monte Carlo simulation continues to grow.

SUMMARY

In this reading, we have presented the most frequently used probability distributions in investment analysis and the Monte Carlo simulation.

- A probability distribution specifies the probabilities of the possible outcomes of a random variable.
- The two basic types of random variables are discrete random variables and continuous random variables. Discrete random variables take on at most a countable number of possible outcomes that we can list as x_1, x_2, ... In contrast, we cannot describe the possible outcomes of a continuous random variable Z with a list z_1, z_2, ... because the outcome $(z_1 + z_2)/2$, not in the list, would always be possible.
- The probability function specifies the probability that the random variable will take on a specific value. The probability function is denoted $p(x)$ for a discrete random variable and $f(x)$ for a continuous random variable. For any probability function $p(x)$, $0 \leq p(x) \leq 1$, and the sum of $p(x)$ over all values of X equals 1.
- The cumulative distribution function, denoted $F(x)$ for both continuous and discrete random variables, gives the probability that the random variable is less than or equal to x.
- The discrete uniform and the continuous uniform distributions are the distributions of equally likely outcomes.
- The binomial random variable is defined as the number of successes in n Bernoulli trials, where the probability of success, p, is constant for all trials and the trials are independent. A Bernoulli trial is an experiment with two outcomes, which can represent success or failure, an up move or a down move, or another binary (two-fold) outcome.

- A binomial random variable has an expected value or mean equal to np and variance equal to $np(1 - p)$.
- A binomial tree is the graphical representation of a model of asset price dynamics in which, at each period, the asset moves up with probability p or down with probability $(1 - p)$. The binomial tree is a flexible method for modeling asset price movement and is widely used in pricing options.
- The normal distribution is a continuous symmetric probability distribution that is completely described by two parameters: its mean, μ, and its variance, σ^2.
- A univariate distribution specifies the probabilities for a single random variable. A multivariate distribution specifies the probabilities for a group of related random variables.
- To specify the normal distribution for a portfolio when its component securities are normally distributed, we need the means, standard deviations, and all the distinct pairwise correlations of the securities. When we have those statistics, we have also specified a multivariate normal distribution for the securities.
- For a normal random variable, approximately 68 percent of all possible outcomes are within a one standard deviation interval about the mean, approximately 95 percent are within a two standard deviation interval about the mean, and approximately 99 percent are within a three standard deviation interval about the mean.
- A normal random variable, X, is standardized using the expression $Z = (X - \mu)/\sigma$, where μ and σ are the mean and standard deviation of X. Generally, we use the sample mean $\overline{X}$ as an estimate of μ and the sample standard deviation s as an estimate of σ in this expression.
- The standard normal random variable, denoted Z, has a mean equal to 0 and variance equal to 1. All questions about any normal random variable can be answered by referring to the cumulative distribution function of a standard normal random variable, denoted $N(x)$ or $N(z)$.
- Shortfall risk is the risk that portfolio value will fall below some minimum acceptable level over some time horizon.
- Roy's safety-first criterion, addressing shortfall risk, asserts that the optimal portfolio is the one that minimizes the probability that portfolio return falls below a threshold level. According to Roy's safety-first criterion, if returns are normally distributed, the safety-first optimal portfolio P is the one that maximizes the quantity $[E(R_P) - R_L]/\sigma_P$, where R_L is the minimum acceptable level of return.
- A random variable follows a lognormal distribution if the natural logarithm of the random variable is normally distributed. The lognormal distribution is defined in terms of the mean and variance of its associated normal distribution. The lognormal distribution is bounded below by 0 and skewed to the right (it has a long right tail).
- The lognormal distribution is frequently used to model the probability distribution of asset prices because it is bounded below by zero.
- Continuous compounding views time as essentially continuous or unbroken; discrete compounding views time as advancing in discrete finite intervals.
- The continuously compounded return associated with a holding period is the natural log of 1 plus the holding period return, or equivalently, the natural log of ending price over beginning price.

- If continuously compounded returns are normally distributed, asset prices are lognormally distributed. This relationship is used to move back and forth between the distributions for return and price. Because of the central limit theorem, continuously compounded returns need not be normally distributed for asset prices to be reasonably well described by a lognormal distribution.
- Monte Carlo simulation involves the use of a computer to represent the operation of a complex financial system. A characteristic feature of Monte Carlo simulation is the generation of a large number of random samples from specified probability distribution(s) to represent the operation of risk in the system. Monte Carlo simulation is used in planning, in financial risk management, and in valuing complex securities. Monte Carlo simulation is a complement to analytical methods but provides only statistical estimates, not exact results.
- Historical simulation is an established alternative to Monte Carlo simulation that in one implementation involves repeated sampling from a historical data series. Historical simulation is grounded in actual data but can reflect only risks represented in the sample historical data. Compared with Monte Carlo simulation, historical simulation does not lend itself to "what if" analyses.

REFERENCES

Campbell, John, Andrew Lo, and A. Craig MacKinlay. 1997. *The Econometrics of Financial Markets*. Princeton, NJ: Princeton University Press.

Chance, Don M., and Robert Brooks. 2016. *An Introduction to Derivatives and Risk Management*, 10th ed. Mason, OH: South-Western.

Chua, Jess H., Richard S. Woodward, and Eric C. To. 1987. "Potential Gains from Stock Market Timing in Canada." *Financial Analysts Journal*, vol. 43, no. 5:50–56.

Cox, Jonathan, Stephen Ross, and Mark Rubinstein. 1979. "Options Pricing: A Simplified Approach." *Journal of Financial Economics*, vol. 7:229–263.

Fama, Eugene. 1976. *Foundations of Finance*. New York: Basic Books.

Ferguson, Robert. 1993. "Some Formulas for Evaluating Two Popular Option Strategies." *Financial Analysts Journal*, vol. 49, no. 5:71–76.

Hillier, Frederick S. 2014. *Introduction to Operations Research*, 10th edition. New York: McGraw-Hill.

Hull, John. 2017. *Options, Futures, and Other Derivatives*, 10th edition. Upper Saddle River, NJ: Pearson.

Kolb, Robert W., Gerald D. Gay, and William C. Hunter. 1985. "Liquidity Requirements for Financial Futures Investments." *Financial Analysts Journal*, vol. 41, no. 3:60–68.

Kon, Stanley J. 1984. "Models of Stock Returns—A Comparison." *Journal of Finance*, vol. 39:147–165.

Leibowitz, Martin, and Roy Henriksson. 1989. "Portfolio Optimization with Shortfall Constraints: A Confidence-Limit Approach to Managing Downside Risk." *Financial Analysts Journal*, vol. 45, no. 2:34–41.

Luenberger, David G. 1998. *Investment Science*. New York: Oxford University Press.

Roy, A.D. 1952. "Safety-First and the Holding of Assets." *Econometrica*, vol. 20:431–439.

PRACTICE PROBLEMS

1 A European put option on stock conveys the right to sell the stock at a prespecified price, called the exercise price, at the maturity date of the option. The value of this put at maturity is (exercise price – stock price) or $0, whichever is greater. Suppose the exercise price is $100 and the underlying stock trades in ticks of $0.01. At any time before maturity, the terminal value of the put is a random variable.

A Describe the distinct possible outcomes for terminal put value. (Think of the put's maximum and minimum values and its minimum price increments.)

B Is terminal put value, at a time before maturity, a discrete or continuous random variable?

C Letting Y stand for terminal put value, express in standard notation the probability that terminal put value is less than or equal to $24. No calculations or formulas are necessary.

2 Define the term "binomial random variable." Describe the types of problems for which the binomial distribution is used.

3 The value of the cumulative distribution function $F(x)$, where x is a particular outcome, for a discrete uniform distribution:

A sums to 1.

B lies between 0 and 1.

C decreases as x increases.

4 For a binomial random variable with five trials, and a probability of success on each trial of 0.50, the distribution will be:

A skewed.

B uniform.

C symmetric.

5 In a discrete uniform distribution with 20 potential outcomes of integers 1 to 20, the probability that X is greater than or equal to 3 but less than 6, $P(3 \leq X < 6)$, is:

A 0.10.

B 0.15.

C 0.20.

6 Over the last 10 years, a company's annual earnings increased year over year seven times and decreased year over year three times. You decide to model the number of earnings increases for the next decade as a binomial random variable.

A What is your estimate of the probability of success, defined as an increase in annual earnings?

For Parts B, C, and D of this problem, assume the estimated probability is the actual probability for the next decade.

B What is the probability that earnings will increase in exactly 5 of the next 10 years?

C Calculate the expected number of yearly earnings increases during the next 10 years.

D Calculate the variance and standard deviation of the number of yearly earnings increases during the next 10 years.

E The expression for the probability function of a binomial random variable depends on two major assumptions. In the context of this problem, what must you assume about annual earnings increases to apply the binomial distribution in Part B? What reservations might you have about the validity of these assumptions?

7 A portfolio manager annually outperforms her benchmark 60% of the time. Assuming independent annual trials, what is the probability that she will outperform her benchmark four or more times over the next five years?

A 0.26

B 0.34

C 0.48

8 You are examining the record of an investment newsletter writer who claims a 70 percent success rate in making investment recommendations that are profitable over a one-year time horizon. You have the one-year record of the newsletter's seven most recent recommendations. Four of those recommendations were profitable. If all the recommendations are independent and the newsletter writer's skill is as claimed, what is the probability of observing four or fewer profitable recommendations out of seven in total?

9 You are forecasting sales for a company in the fourth quarter of its fiscal year. Your low-end estimate of sales is €14 million, and your high-end estimate is €15 million. You decide to treat all outcomes for sales between these two values as equally likely, using a continuous uniform distribution.

A What is the expected value of sales for the fourth quarter?

B What is the probability that fourth-quarter sales will be less than or equal to €14,125,000?

10 State the approximate probability that a normal random variable will fall within the following intervals:

A Mean plus or minus one standard deviation.

B Mean plus or minus two standard deviations.

C Mean plus or minus three standard deviations.

11 Find the area under the normal curve up to $z = 0.36$; that is, find $P(Z \leq 0.36)$. Interpret this value.

12 If the probability that a portfolio outperforms its benchmark in any quarter is 0.75, the probability that the portfolio outperforms its benchmark in three or fewer quarters over the course of a year is *closest* to:

A 0.26

B 0.42

C 0.68

13 In futures markets, profits or losses on contracts are settled at the end of each trading day. This procedure is called marking to market or daily resettlement. By preventing a trader's losses from accumulating over many days, marking to market reduces the risk that traders will default on their obligations. A futures markets trader needs a liquidity pool to meet the daily mark to market. If liquidity is exhausted, the trader may be forced to unwind his position at an unfavorable time.

Suppose you are using financial futures contracts to hedge a risk in your portfolio. You have a liquidity pool (cash and cash equivalents) of λ dollars per contract and a time horizon of T trading days. For a given size liquidity pool, λ, Kolb, Gay, and Hunter (1985) developed an expression for the probability stating that you will exhaust your liquidity pool within a T-day horizon as a result of the daily mark to market. Kolb et al. assumed that the expected change in futures price is 0 and that futures price changes are normally distributed. With σ representing the standard deviation of daily futures price changes, the standard deviation of price changes over a time horizon to day T is $\sigma\sqrt{T}$, given continuous compounding. With that background, the Kolb et al. expression is

$$\text{Probability of exhausting liquidity pool} = 2[1 - N(x)]$$

where $x = \lambda/\left(\sigma\sqrt{T}\right)$. Here x is a standardized value of λ. $N(x)$ is the standard normal cumulative distribution function. For some intuition about $1 - N(x)$ in the expression, note that the liquidity pool is exhausted if losses exceed the size of the liquidity pool at any time up to and including T; the probability of that event happening can be shown to be proportional to an area in the right tail of a standard normal distribution, $1 - N(x)$.

Using the Kolb et al. expression, answer the following questions:

A Your hedging horizon is five days, and your liquidity pool is \$2,000 per contract. You estimate that the standard deviation of daily price changes for the contract is \$450. What is the probability that you will exhaust your liquidity pool in the five-day period?

B Suppose your hedging horizon is 20 days, but all the other facts given in Part A remain the same. What is the probability that you will exhaust your liquidity pool in the 20-day period?

14 Which of the following is characteristic of the normal distribution?

A Asymmetry

B Kurtosis of 3

C Definitive limits or boundaries

15 Which of the following assets *most likely* requires the use of a multivariate distribution for modeling returns?

A A call option on a bond

B A portfolio of technology stocks

C A stock in a market index

16 The total number of parameters that fully characterizes a multivariate normal distribution for the returns on two stocks is:

A 3.

B 4.

C 5.

17 A client has a portfolio of common stocks and fixed-income instruments with a current value of £1,350,000. She intends to liquidate £50,000 from the portfolio at the end of the year to purchase a partnership share in a business. Furthermore, the client would like to be able to withdraw the £50,000 without reducing the initial capital of £1,350,000. The following table shows four alternative asset allocations.

Mean and Standard Deviation for Four Allocations (in Percent)				
	A	B	C	D
Expected annual return	16	12	10	9
Standard deviation of return	24	17	12	11

Address the following questions (assume normality for Parts B and C):

A Given the client's desire not to invade the £1,350,000 principal, what is the shortfall level, R_L? Use this shortfall level to answer Part B.

B According to the safety-first criterion, which of the allocations is the best?

C What is the probability that the return on the safety-first optimal portfolio will be less than the shortfall level, R_L?

Please refer to Exhibit 1 for Questions 18 and 19

Exhibit 1 *Z*-Table Values, $P(Z \leq z) = N(z)$ for $z \geq 0$

Z	0.00	0.01	0.02	0.03	0.04	0.05	0.06	0.07	0.08	0.09
0.00	0.5000	0.5040	0.5080	0.5120	0.5160	0.5199	0.5239	0.5279	0.5319	0.5359
0.1	0.5398	0.5438	0.5478	0.5517	0.5557	0.5596	0.5636	0.5675	0.5714	0.5753
0.2	0.5793	0.5832	0.5871	0.5910	0.5948	0.5987	0.6026	0.6064	0.6103	0.6141
0.3	0.6179	0.6217	0.6255	0.6293	0.6331	0.6368	0.6406	0.6443	0.6480	0.6517
0.4	0.6554	0.6591	0.6628	0.6664	0.6700	0.6736	0.6772	0.6808	0.6844	0.6879
0.5	0.6915	0.6950	0.6985	0.7019	0.7054	0.7088	0.7123	0.7157	0.7190	0.7224

18 A portfolio has an expected mean return of 8 percent and standard deviation of 14 percent. The probability that its return falls between 8 and 11 percent is *closest* to:

A 8.3%

B 14.8%.

C 58.3%.

19 A portfolio has an expected return of 7% with a standard deviation of 13%. For an investor with a minimum annual return target of 4%, the probability that the portfolio return will fail to meet the target is *closest* to:

A 33%.

B 41%.

C 59%.

20 **A** Define Monte Carlo simulation and explain its use in finance.

B Compared with analytical methods, what are the strengths and weaknesses of Monte Carlo simulation for use in valuing securities?

21 A standard lookback call option on stock has a value at maturity equal to (Value of the stock at maturity – Minimum value of stock during the life of the option prior to maturity) or \$0, whichever is greater. If the minimum value reached prior to maturity was \$20.11 and the value of the stock at maturity is \$23, for example, the call is worth \$23 – \$20.11 = \$2.89. Briefly discuss how you might use Monte Carlo simulation in valuing a lookback call option.

22 Which of the following is a continuous random variable?

A The value of a futures contract quoted in increments of \$0.05

B The total number of heads recorded in 1 million tosses of a coin

C The rate of return on a diversified portfolio of stocks over a three-month period

23 X is a discrete random variable with possible outcomes $X = \{1,2,3,4\}$. Three functions $f(x)$, $g(x)$, and $h(x)$ are proposed to describe the probabilities of the outcomes in X.

	Probability Function		
X = x	**f(x) = P(X = x)**	**g(x) = P(X = x)**	**h(x) = P(X = x)**
1	–0.25	0.20	0.20
2	0.25	0.25	0.25
3	0.50	0.50	0.30
4	0.25	0.05	0.35

The conditions for a probability function are satisfied by:

A $f(x)$.

B $g(x)$.

C $h(x)$.

24 The cumulative distribution function for a discrete random variable is shown in the following table.

X = x	Cumulative Distribution Function F(x) = P(X ≤ x)
1	0.15
2	0.25
3	0.50
4	0.60
5	0.95
6	1.00

The probability that X will take on a value of either 2 or 4 is *closest* to:

A 0.20.

B 0.35.

C 0.85.

25 Which of the following events can be represented as a Bernoulli trial?

A The flip of a coin

B The closing price of a stock

C The picking of a random integer between 1 and 10

26 The weekly closing prices of Mordice Corporation shares are as follows:

Date	Closing Price (€)
1 August	112
8 August	160
15 August	120

The continuously compounded return of Mordice Corporation shares for the period August 1 to August 15 is *closest to*:

A 6.90%

B 7.14%

C 8.95%

27 A stock is priced at \$100.00 and follows a one-period binomial process with an up move that equals 1.05 and a down move that equals 0.97. If 1 million Bernoulli trials are conducted, and the average terminal stock price is \$102.00, the probability of an up move (p) is *closest* to:

A 0.375.

B 0.500.

C 0.625.

28 A call option on a stock index is valued using a three-step binomial tree with an up move that equals 1.05 and a down move that equals 0.95. The current level of the index is \$190, and the option exercise price is \$200. If the option value is positive when the stock price exceeds the exercise price at expiration and \$0 otherwise, the number of terminal nodes with a positive payoff is:

A one.

B two.

C three.

29 A random number between zero and one is generated according to a continuous uniform distribution. What is the probability that the first number generated will have a value of exactly 0.30?

A 0%

B 30%

C 70%

30 A Monte Carlo simulation can be used to:

A directly provide precise valuations of call options.

B simulate a process from historical records of returns.

C test the sensitivity of a model to changes in assumptions.

31 A limitation of Monte Carlo simulation is:

A its failure to do "what if" analysis.

B that it requires historical records of returns

C its inability to independently specify cause-and-effect relationships.

32 Which parameter equals zero in a normal distribution?

A Kurtosis

B Skewness

C Standard deviation

33 An analyst develops the following capital market projections.

	Stocks	Bonds
Mean Return	10%	2%
Standard Deviation	15%	5%

Assuming the returns of the asset classes are described by normal distributions, which of the following statements is correct?

A Bonds have a higher probability of a negative return than stocks.

B On average, 99% of stock returns will fall within two standard deviations of the mean.

C The probability of a bond return less than or equal to 3% is determined using a Z-score of 0.25.

34 A client holding a £2,000,000 portfolio wants to withdraw £90,000 in one year without invading the principal. According to Roy's safety-first criterion, which of the following portfolio allocations is optimal?

	Allocation A	Allocation B	Allocation C
Expected annual return	6.5%	7.5%	8.5%
Standard deviation of returns	8.35%	10.21%	14.34%

A Allocation A

B Allocation B

C Allocation C

35 In contrast to normal distributions, lognormal distributions:

A are skewed to the left.

B have outcomes that cannot be negative.

C are more suitable for describing asset returns than asset prices.

36 The lognormal distribution is a more accurate model for the distribution of stock prices than the normal distribution because stock prices are:

A symmetrical.

B unbounded.

C non-negative.

37 The price of a stock at $t = 0$ is \$208.25 and at $t = 1$ is \$186.75. The continuously compounded rate of return for the stock from $t = 0$ to $t = 1$ is *closest* to:

A −10.90%.

B −10.32%.

C 11.51%.

SOLUTIONS

1 **A** The put's minimum value is \$0. The put's value is \$0 when the stock price is at or above \$100 at the maturity date of the option. The put's maximum value is \$100 = \$100 (the exercise price) – \$0 (the lowest possible stock price). The put's value is \$100 when the stock is worthless at the option's maturity date. The put's minimum price increments are \$0.01. The possible outcomes of terminal put value are thus \$0.00, \$0.01, \$0.02, ..., \$100.

B The price of the underlying has minimum price fluctuations of \$0.01: These are the minimum price fluctuations for terminal put value. For example, if the stock finishes at \$98.20, the payoff on the put is \$100 – \$98.20 = \$1.80. We can specify that the nearest values to \$1.80 are \$1.79 and \$1.81. With a continuous random variable, we cannot specify the nearest values. So, we must characterize terminal put value as a discrete random variable.

C The probability that terminal put value is less than or equal to \$24 is $P(Y \leq 24)$ or $F(24)$, in standard notation, where F is the cumulative distribution function for terminal put value.

2 A binomial random variable is defined as the number of successes in n Bernoulli trials (a trial that produces one of two outcomes). The binomial distribution is used to make probability statements about a record of successes and failures or about anything with binary (twofold) outcomes.

3 B is correct. The value of the cumulative distribution function lies between 0 and 1 for any x: $0 \leq F(x) \leq 1$.

4 C is correct. The binomial distribution is symmetric when the probability of success on a trial is 0.50, but it is asymmetric or skewed otherwise. Here it is given that $p = 0.50$

5 B is correct. The probability of any outcome is 0.05, $P(1) = 1/20 = 0.05$. The probability that X is greater than or equal to 3 but less than 6, which is expressed as $P(3 \leq X < 6) = P(3) + P(4) + P(5) = 0.05 + 0.05 + 0.05 = 0.15$

6 **A** The probability of an earnings increase (success) in a year is estimated as 7/10 = 0.70 or 70 percent, based on the record of the past 10 years.

B The probability that earnings will increase in 5 out of the next 10 years is about 10.3 percent. Define a binomial random variable X, counting the number of earnings increases over the next 10 years. From Part A, the probability of an earnings increase in a given year is $p = 0.70$ and the number of trials (years) is $n = 10$. Equation 1 gives the probability that a binomial random variable has x successes in n trials, with the probability of success on a trial equal to p.

$$P(X = x) = \binom{n}{x} p^x (1 - p)^{n-x} = \frac{n!}{(n - x)!x!} p^x (1 - p)^{n-x}$$

For this example,

$$\binom{10}{5} 0.7^5 0.3^{10-5} = \frac{10!}{(10 - 5)!5!} 0.7^5 0.3^{10-5}$$
$$= 252 \times 0.16807 \times 0.00243 = 0.102919$$

We conclude that the probability that earnings will increase in exactly 5 of the next 10 years is 0.1029, or approximately 10.3 percent.

C The expected number of yearly increases is $E(X) = np = 10 \times 0.70 = 7$.

D The variance of the number of yearly increases over the next 10 years is $\sigma^2 = np(1 - p) = 10 \times 0.70 \times 0.30 = 2.1$. The standard deviation is 1.449 (the positive square root of 2.1).

E You must assume that 1) the probability of an earnings increase (success) is constant from year to year and 2) earnings increases are independent trials. If current and past earnings help forecast next year's earnings, Assumption 2 is violated. If the company's business is subject to economic or industry cycles, neither assumption is likely to hold.

7 B is correct. To calculate the probability of 4 years of outperformance, use the formula:

$$p(x) = P(X = x) = \binom{n}{x} p^x (1 - p)^{n-x} = \frac{n!}{(n - x)!x!} p^x (1 - p)^{n-x}$$

Using this formula to calculate the probability in 4 of 5 years, $n = 5$, $x = 4$ and $p = 0.60$.

Therefore,

$$p(4) = \frac{5!}{(5 - 4)!4!} 0.6^4 (1 - 0.6)^{5-4} = [120/24](0.1296)(0.40) = 0.2592$$

$$p(5) = \frac{5!}{(5 - 5)!5!} 0.6^5 (1 - 0.6)^{5-5} = [120/120](0.0778)(1) = 0.0778$$

The probability of outperforming 4 or more times is $p(4) + p(5) = 0.2592 + 0.0778 = 0.3370$

8 The observed success rate is 4/7 = 0.571, or 57.1 percent. The probability of four or fewer successes is $F(4) = p(4) + p(3) + p(2) + p(1) + p(0)$, where $p(4)$, $p(3)$, $p(2)$, $p(1)$, and $p(0)$ are respectively the probabilities of 4, 3, 2, 1, and 0 successes, according to the binomial distribution with $n = 7$ and $p = 0.70$. We have

$p(4) = (7!/4!3!)(0.70^4)(0.30^3) = 35(0.006483) = 0.226895$

$p(3) = (7!/3!4!)(0.70^3)(0.30^4) = 35(0.002778) = 0.097241$

$p(2) = (7!/2!5!)(0.70^2)(0.30^5) = 21(0.001191) = 0.025005$

$p(1) = (7!/1!6!)(0.70^1)(0.30^6) = 7(0.000510) = 0.003572$

$p(0) = (7!/0!7!)(0.70^0)(0.30^7) = 1(0.000219) = 0.000219$

Summing all these probabilities, you conclude that $F(4) = 0.226895 + 0.097241 + 0.025005 + 0.003572 + 0.000219 = 0.352931$, or 35.3 percent.

9 A The expected value of fourth-quarter sales is €14,500,000, calculated as (€14,000,000 + €15,000,000)/2. With a continuous uniform random variable, the mean or expected value is the midpoint between the smallest and largest values. (See Example 7.)

B The probability that fourth-quarter sales will be less than €14,125,000 is 0.125 or 12.5 percent, calculated as (€14,125,000 – €14,000,000)/(€15,000,000 – €14,000,000).

10 A Approximately 68 percent of all outcomes of a normal random variable fall within plus or minus one standard deviation of the mean.

B Approximately 95 percent of all outcomes of a normal random variable fall within plus or minus two standard deviations of the mean.

C Approximately 99 percent of all outcomes of a normal random variable fall within plus or minus three standard deviations of the mean.

11 The area under the normal curve for $z = 0.36$ is 0.6406 or 64.06 percent. The following table presents an excerpt from the tables of the standard normal cumulative distribution function in the back of this volume. To locate $z = 0.36$, find 0.30 in the fourth row of numbers, then look at the column for 0.06 (the second decimal place of 0.36). The entry is 0.6406.

$P(Z \le x) = N(x)$ for $x \ge 0$ or $P(Z \le z) = N(z)$ for $z \ge 0$

x or z	0	0.01	0.02	0.03	0.04	0.05	0.06	0.07	0.08	0.09
0.00	0.5000	0.5040	0.5080	0.5120	0.5160	0.5199	0.5239	0.5279	0.5319	0.5359
0.10	0.5398	0.5438	0.5478	0.5517	0.5557	0.5596	0.5636	0.5675	0.5714	0.5753
0.20	0.5793	0.5832	0.5871	0.5910	0.5948	0.5987	0.6026	0.6064	0.6103	0.6141
0.30	0.6179	0.6217	0.6255	0.6293	0.6331	0.6368	**0.6406**	0.6443	0.6480	0.6517
0.40	0.6554	0.6591	0.6628	0.6664	0.6700	0.6736	0.6772	0.6808	0.6844	0.6879
0.50	0.6915	0.6950	0.6985	0.7019	0.7054	0.7088	0.7123	0.7157	0.7190	0.7224

The interpretation of 64.06 percent for $z = 0.36$ is that 64.06 percent of observations on a standard normal random variable are smaller than or equal to the value 0.36. (So 100% – 64.06% = 35.94% of the values are greater than 0.36.)

12 C is correct. The probability that the performance is at or below the expectation is calculated by finding $F(3) = p(3) + p(2) + p(1)$ using the formula:

$$p(x) = P(X = x) = \binom{n}{x} p^x (1-p)^{n-x} = \frac{n!}{(n-x)!x!} p^x (1-p)^{n-x}$$

Using this formula,

$$p(3) = \frac{4!}{(4-3)!3!} 0.75^3 (1-0.75)^{4-3} = [24/6](0.42)(0.25) = 0.42$$

$$p(2) = \frac{4!}{(4-2)!2!} 0.75^2 (1-0.75)^{4-2} = [24/4](0.56)(0.06) = 0.20$$

$$p(1) = \frac{4!}{(4-1)!1!} 0.75^1 (1-0.75)^{4-1} = [24/6](0.75)(0.02) = 0.06$$

$$p(0) = \frac{4!}{(4-0)!0!} 0.75^0 (1-0.75)^{4-0} = [24/24](1)(0.004) = 0.004$$

Therefore,

$F(3) = p(3) + p(2) + p(1) + p(0) = 0.42 + 0.20 + 0.06 + 0.004 = 0.684$ or approximately 68 percent

13 **A** The probability of exhausting the liquidity pool is 4.7 percent. First calculate $x = \lambda / \left(\sigma \sqrt{T}\right) = \$2{,}000 / \left(\$450\sqrt{5}\right) = 1.987616$. We can round this value to 1.99 to use the standard normal tables in the back of this book. Using those tables, we find that $N(1.99) = 0.9767$. Thus, the probability of exhausting the liquidity pool is $2[1 - N(1.99)] = 2(1 - 0.9767) = 0.0466$ or about 4.7 percent.

B The probability of exhausting the liquidity pool is now 32.2 percent. The calculation follows the same steps as those in Part A. We calculate $x = \lambda/\left(\sigma\sqrt{T}\right) = \$2{,}000/\left(\$450\sqrt{20}\right) = 0.993808$. We can round this value to 0.99 to use the standard normal tables in the back of this book. Using those tables, we find that $N(0.99) = 0.8389$. Thus, the probability of exhausting the liquidity pool is $2[1 - N(0.99)] = 2(1 - 0.8389) = 0.3222$ or about 32.2 percent. This is a substantial probability that you will run out of funds to meet mark to market.

In their paper, Kolb et al. call the probability of exhausting the liquidity pool the probability of ruin, a traditional name for this type of calculation.

14 B is correct. The normal distribution has a skewness of 0, a kurtosis of 3, and a mean, median and mode that are all equal.

15 B is correct. Multivariate distributions specify the probabilities for a group of related random variables. A portfolio of technology stocks represents a group of related assets. Accordingly, statistical interrelationships must be considered, resulting in the need to use a multivariate normal distribution.

16 C is correct. A bivariate normal distribution (two stocks) will have two means, two variances and one correlation. A multivariate normal distribution for the returns on n stocks will have n means, n variances and $n(n - 1)/2$ distinct correlations.

17 **A** Because £50,000/£1,350,000 is 3.7 percent, for any return less than 3.7 percent the client will need to invade principal if she takes out £50,000. So R_L = 3.7 percent.

B To decide which of the allocations is safety-first optimal, select the alternative with the highest ratio $[E(R_P) - R_L]/\sigma_P$:

Allocation A: 0.5125 = (16 – 3.7)/24

Allocation B: 0.488235 = (12 – 3.7)/17

Allocation C: 0.525 = (10 – 3.7)/12

Allocation D: 0.481818 = (9 – 3.7)/11

Allocation C, with the largest ratio (0.525), is the best alternative according to the safety-first criterion.

C To answer this question, note that $P(R_C < 3.7) = N(-0.525)$. We can round 0.525 to 0.53 for use with tables of the standard normal cdf. First, we calculate $N(-0.53) = 1 - N(0.53) = 1 - 0.7019 = 0.2981$ or about 30 percent. The safety-first optimal portfolio has a roughly 30 percent chance of not meeting a 3.7 percent return threshold.

18 A is correct. $P(8\% \le \text{Portfolio return} \le 11\%) = N(Z \text{ corresponding to } 11\%) - N(Z \text{ corresponding to } 8\%)$. For the first term, $Z = (11\% - 8\%)/14\% = 0.21$ approximately, and using the table of cumulative normal distribution given in the problem, $N(0.21) = 0.5832$. To get the second term immediately, note that 8 percent is the mean, and for the normal distribution 50 percent of the probability lies on either side of the mean. Therefore, $N(Z$ corresponding to 8%) must equal 50 percent. So $P(8\% \le \text{Portfolio return} \le 11\%) = 0.5832 - 0.50 = 0.0832$ or approximately 8.3 percent.

19 B is correct. There are three steps, which involve standardizing the portfolio return: First, subtract the portfolio mean return from each side of the inequality: $P(\text{Portfolio return} - 7\%) \le 4\% - 7\%)$. Second, divide each side of the inequality by the standard deviation of portfolio return: $P[(\text{Portfolio return}$

– 7%)/13% ≤ (4% – 7%)/13%] = $P(Z \leq -0.2308) = N(-0.2308)$. Third, recognize that on the left-hand side we have a standard normal variable, denoted by Z and $N(-x) = 1 - N(x)$. Rounding –0.2308 to –0.23 for use with the cumulative distribution function (cdf) table, we have $N(-0.23) = 1 - N(0.23) = 1 - 0.5910 = 0.409$, approximately 41 percent. The probability that the portfolio will underperform the target is about 41 percent.

20 A Elements that should appear in a definition of Monte Carlo simulation are that it makes use of a computer; that it is used to represent the operation of a complex system, or in some applications, to find an approximate solution to a problem; and that it involves the generation of a large number of random samples from a specified probability distribution. The exact wording can vary, but one definition follows:

Monte Carlo simulation in finance involves the use of a computer to represent the operation of a complex financial system. In some important applications, Monte Carlo simulation is used to find an approximate solution to a complex financial problem. An integral part of Monte Carlo simulation is the generation of a large number of random samples from a probability distribution.

B *Strengths.* Monte Carlo simulation can be used to price complex securities for which no analytic expression is available, particularly European-style options.

Weaknesses. Monte Carlo simulation provides only statistical estimates, not exact results. Analytic methods, when available, provide more insight into cause-and-effect relationships than does Monte Carlo simulation.

21 In the text, we described how we could use Monte Carlo simulation to value an Asian option, a complex European-style option. Just as we can calculate the average value of the stock over a simulation trial to value an Asian option, we can also calculate the minimum value of the stock over a simulation trial. Then, for a given simulation trial, we can calculate the terminal value of the call, given the minimum value of the stock for the simulation trial. We can then discount back this terminal value to the present to get the value of the call today ($t = 0$). The average of these $t = 0$ values over all simulation trials is the Monte Carlo simulated value of the lookback call option.

22 C is correct. The rate of return is a random variable because the future outcomes are uncertain, and it is continuous because it can take on an unlimited number of outcomes.

23 B is correct. The function $g(x)$ satisfies the conditions of a probability function. All of the values of $g(x)$ are between 0 and 1, and the values of $g(x)$ all sum to 1.

24 A is correct. The probability that X will take on a value of 4 or less is: $F(4) = P(X \leq 4) = p(1) + p(2) + p(3) + p(4) = 0.60$. The probability that X will take on a value of 3 or less is: $F(3) = P(X \leq 3) = p(1) + p(2) + p(3) = 0.50$. So, the probability that X will take on a value of 4 is: $F(4) - F(3) = p(4) = 0.10$. The probability of $X = 2$ can be found using the same logic: $F(2) - F(1) = p(2) = 0.25 - 0.15 = 0.10$. The probability of X taking on a value of 2 or 4 is: $p(2) + p(4) = 0.10 + 0.10 = 0.20$.

25 A is correct. A trial, such as a coin flip, will produce one of two outcomes. Such a trial is a Bernoulli trial.

26 A is correct. The continuously compounded return of an asset over a period is equal to the natural log of period's change. In this case:

$$\ln(120/112) = 6.90\%$$

27 C is correct. The probability of an up move (p) can be found by solving the equation: $(p)uS + (1 - p)dS = (p)105 + (1 - p)97 = 102$. Solving for p gives $8p = 5$, so that $p = 0.625$.

28 A is correct. Only the top node value of \$219.9488 exceeds \$200.

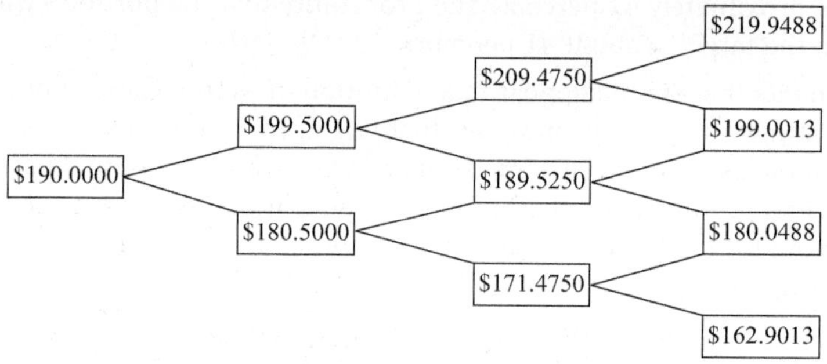

29 A is correct. The probability of generating a random number equal to any fixed point under a continuous uniform distribution is zero.

30 C is correct. A characteristic feature of Monte Carlo simulation is the generation of a large number of random samples from a specified probability distribution or distributions to represent the role of risk in the system.

31 C is correct. Monte Carlo simulation is a complement to analytical methods. Monte Carlo simulation provides statistical estimates and not exact results. Analytical methods, when available, provide more insight into cause-and-effect relationships

32 B is correct. A normal distribution has a skewness of zero (it is symmetrical around the mean). A non-zero skewness implies asymmetry in a distribution.

33 A is correct. The chance of a negative return falls in the area to the left of 0% under a standard normal curve. By standardizing the returns and standard deviations of the two assets, the likelihood of either asset experiencing a negative return may be determined: Z-score (standardized value) = $(X - \mu)/\sigma$

Z-score for a bond return of 0% = $(0 - 2)/5 = -0.40$.

Z-score for a stock return of 0% = $(0 - 10)/15 = -0.67$.

For bonds, a 0% return falls 0.40 standard deviations below the mean return of 2%. In contrast, for stocks, a 0% return falls 0.67 standard deviations below the mean return of 10%. A standard deviation of 0.40 is less than a standard deviation of 0.67. Negative returns thus occupy more of the left tail of the bond distribution than the stock distribution. Thus, bonds are more likely than stocks to experience a negative return.

34 B is correct. Allocation B has the highest safety-first ratio. The threshold return level R_L for the portfolio is £90,000/£2,000,000 = 4.5%, thus any return less than R_L = 4.5% will invade the portfolio principal. To compute the allocation that is safety-first optimal, select the alternative with the highest ratio:

$$\frac{\left[E\left(R_P - R_L\right)\right]}{\sigma_P}$$

$$\text{Allocation A} = \frac{6.5 - 4.5}{8.35} = 0.240$$

$$\text{Allocation B} = \frac{7.5 - 4.5}{10.21} = 0.294$$

$$\text{Allocation C} = \frac{8.5 - 4.5}{14.34} = 0.279$$

35 B is correct. By definition, lognormal random variables cannot have negative values.

36 C is correct. A lognormal distributed variable has a lower bound of zero. The lognormal distribution is also right skewed, which is a useful property in describing asset prices.

37 A is correct. The continuously compounded return from $t = 0$ to $t = 1$ is $r_{0,1} = \ln(S_1/S_0) = \ln(186.75/208.25) = -0.10897 = -10.90\%$.

READING

10

Sampling and Estimation

by Richard A. DeFusco, PhD, CFA, Dennis W. McLeavey, DBA, CFA, Jerald E. Pinto, PhD, CFA, and David E. Runkle, PhD, CFA

Richard A. DeFusco, PhD, CFA, is at the University of Nebraska-Lincoln (USA). Dennis W. McLeavey, DBA, CFA, is at the University of Rhode Island (USA). Jerald E. Pinto, PhD, CFA, is at CFA Institute (USA). David E. Runkle, PhD, CFA, is at Trilogy Global Advisors (USA).

LEARNING OUTCOMES

Mastery	*The candidate should be able to:*
☐	**a.** define simple random sampling and a sampling distribution;
☐	**b.** explain sampling error;
☐	**c.** distinguish between simple random and stratified random sampling;
☐	**d.** distinguish between time-series and cross-sectional data;
☐	**e.** explain the central limit theorem and its importance;
☐	**f.** calculate and interpret the standard error of the sample mean;
☐	**g.** identify and describe desirable properties of an estimator;
☐	**h.** distinguish between a point estimate and a confidence interval estimate of a population parameter;
☐	**i.** describe properties of Student's t-distribution and calculate and interpret its degrees of freedom;
☐	**j.** calculate and interpret a confidence interval for a population mean, given a normal distribution with 1) a known population variance, 2) an unknown population variance, or 3) an unknown population variance and a large sample size;
☐	**k.** describe the issues regarding selection of the appropriate sample size, data-mining bias, sample selection bias, survivorship bias, look-ahead bias, and time-period bias.

1 INTRODUCTION

Each day, we observe the high, low, and close of stock market indexes from around the world. Indexes such as the S&P 500 Index and the Nikkei-Dow Jones Average are samples of stocks. Although the S&P 500 and the Nikkei do not represent the populations of US or Japanese stocks, we view them as valid indicators of the whole population's behavior. As analysts, we are accustomed to using this sample information to assess how various markets from around the world are performing. Any statistics that we compute with sample information, however, are only estimates of the underlying population parameters. A sample, then, is a subset of the population—a subset studied to infer conclusions about the population itself.

This reading explores how we sample and use sample information to estimate population parameters. In the next section, we discuss **sampling**—the process of obtaining a sample. In investments, we continually make use of the mean as a measure of central tendency of random variables, such as return and earnings per share. Even when the probability distribution of the random variable is unknown, we can make probability statements about the population mean using the central limit theorem. In Section 3, we discuss and illustrate this key result. Following that discussion, we turn to statistical estimation. Estimation seeks precise answers to the question "What is this parameter's value?"

The central limit theorem and estimation are the core of the body of methods presented in this reading. In investments, we apply these and other statistical techniques to financial data; we often interpret the results for the purpose of deciding what works and what does not work in investments. We end this reading with a discussion of the interpretation of statistical results based on financial data and the possible pitfalls in this process.

2 SAMPLING

In this section, we present the various methods for obtaining information on a population (all members of a specified group) through samples (part of the population). The information on a population that we try to obtain usually concerns the value of a **parameter**, a quantity computed from or used to describe a population of data. When we use a sample to estimate a parameter, we make use of sample statistics (statistics, for short). A **statistic** is a quantity computed from or used to describe a sample of data.

We take samples for one of two reasons. In some cases, we cannot possibly examine every member of the population. In other cases, examining every member of the population would not be economically efficient. Thus, savings of time and money are two primary factors that cause an analyst to use sampling to answer a question about a population. In this section, we discuss two methods of random sampling: simple random sampling and stratified random sampling. We then define and illustrate the two types of data an analyst uses: cross-sectional data and time-series data.

2.1 Simple Random Sampling

Suppose a telecommunications equipment analyst wants to know how much major customers will spend on average for equipment during the coming year. One strategy is to survey the population of telecom equipment customers and inquire what their purchasing plans are. In statistical terms, the characteristics of the population of customers' planned expenditures would then usually be expressed by descriptive measures such as the mean and variance. Surveying all companies, however, would be very costly in terms of time and money.

Alternatively, the analyst can collect a representative sample of companies and survey them about upcoming telecom equipment expenditures. In this case, the analyst will compute the sample mean expenditure, $\overline{X}$, a statistic. This strategy has a substantial advantage over polling the whole population because it can be accomplished more quickly and at lower cost.

Sampling, however, introduces error. The error arises because not all the companies in the population are surveyed. The analyst who decides to sample is trading time and money for sampling error.

When an analyst chooses to sample, he must formulate a sampling plan. A **sampling plan** is the set of rules used to select a sample. The basic type of sample from which we can draw statistically sound conclusions about a population is the **simple random sample** (random sample, for short).

- **Definition of Simple Random Sample.** A simple random sample is a subset of a larger population created in such a way that each element of the population has an equal probability of being selected to the subset.

The procedure of drawing a sample to satisfy the definition of a simple random sample is called **simple random sampling**. How is simple random sampling carried out? We need a method that ensures randomness—the lack of any pattern—in the selection of the sample. For a finite (limited) population, the most common method for obtaining a random sample involves the use of random numbers (numbers with assured properties of randomness). First, we number the members of the population in sequence. For example, if the population contains 500 members, we number them in sequence with three digits, starting with 001 and ending with 500. Suppose we want a simple random sample of size 50. In that case, using a computer random-number generator or a table of random numbers, we generate a series of three-digit random numbers. We then match these random numbers with the number codes of the population members until we have selected a sample of size 50.

Sometimes we cannot code (or even identify) all the members of a population. We often use **systematic sampling** in such cases. With systematic sampling, we select every *k*th member until we have a sample of the desired size. The sample that results from this procedure should be approximately random. Real sampling situations may require that we take an approximately random sample.

Suppose the telecommunications equipment analyst polls a random sample of telecom equipment customers to determine the average equipment expenditure. The sample mean will provide the analyst with an estimate of the population mean expenditure. Any difference between the sample mean and the population mean is called **sampling error**.

- **Definition of Sampling Error.** Sampling error is the difference between the observed value of a statistic and the quantity it is intended to estimate.

A random sample reflects the properties of the population in an unbiased way, and sample statistics, such as the sample mean, computed on the basis of a random sample are valid estimates of the underlying population parameters.

A sample statistic is a random variable. In other words, not only do the original data from the population have a distribution but so does the sample statistic.

This distribution is the statistic's **sampling distribution**.

- **Definition of Sampling Distribution of a Statistic.** The sampling distribution of a statistic is the distribution of all the distinct possible values that the statistic can assume when computed from samples of the same size randomly drawn from the same population.

In the case of the sample mean, for example, we refer to the "sampling distribution of the sample mean" or the distribution of the sample mean. We will have more to say about sampling distributions later in this reading. Next, however, we look at another sampling method that is useful in investment analysis.

2.2 Stratified Random Sampling

The simple random sampling method just discussed may not be the best approach in all situations. One frequently used alternative is stratified random sampling.

- **Definition of Stratified Random Sampling.** In stratified random sampling, the population is divided into subpopulations (strata) based on one or more classification criteria. Simple random samples are then drawn from each stratum in sizes proportional to the relative size of each stratum in the population. These samples are then pooled to form a stratified random sample.

In contrast to simple random sampling, stratified random sampling guarantees that population subdivisions of interest are represented in the sample. Another advantage is that estimates of parameters produced from stratified sampling have greater precision—that is, smaller variance or dispersion—than estimates obtained from simple random sampling.

Bond indexing is one area in which stratified sampling is frequently applied. **Indexing** is an investment strategy in which an investor constructs a portfolio to mirror the performance of a specified index. In pure bond indexing, also called the full-replication approach, the investor attempts to fully replicate an index by owning all the bonds in the index in proportion to their market value weights. Many bond indexes consist of thousands of issues, however, so pure bond indexing is difficult to implement. In addition, transaction costs would be high because many bonds do not have liquid markets. Although a simple random sample could be a solution to the cost problem, the sample would probably not match the index's major risk factors—interest rate sensitivity, for example. Because the major risk factors of fixed-income portfolios are well known and quantifiable, stratified sampling offers a more effective approach. In this approach, we divide the population of index bonds into groups of similar duration (interest rate sensitivity), cash flow distribution, sector, credit quality, and call exposure. We refer to each group as a stratum or cell (a term frequently used in this context). Then, we choose a sample from each stratum proportional to the relative market weighting of the stratum in the index to be replicated.

EXAMPLE 1

Bond Indexes and Stratified Sampling

Suppose you are the manager of a mutual fund indexed to the Bloomberg Barclays US Government/Credit Index. You are exploring several approaches to indexing, including a stratified sampling approach. You first distinguish among agency bonds, US Treasury bonds, and investment grade corporate bonds. For each of these three groups, you define 10 maturity intervals—1 to 2 years, 2 to 3 years, 3 to 4 years, 4 to 6 years, 6 to 8 years, 8 to 10 years, 10 to 12 years,

12 to 15 years, 15 to 20 years, and 20 to 30 years—and also separate the bonds with coupons (annual interest rates) of 6 percent or less from the bonds with coupons of more than 6 percent.

1 How many cells or strata does this sampling plan entail?

2 If you use this sampling plan, what is the minimum number of issues the indexed portfolio can have?

3 Suppose that in selecting among the securities that qualify for selection within each cell, you apply a criterion concerning the liquidity of the security's market. Is the sample obtained random? Explain your answer.

Solution to 1:

We have 3 issuer classifications, 10 maturity classifications, and 2 coupon classifications. So, in total, this plan entails 3(10)(2) = 60 different strata or cells. (This answer is an application of the multiplication rule of counting discussed in the reading on probability concepts.)

Solution to 2:

You cannot have fewer than one issue for each cell, so the portfolio must include at least 60 issues.

Solution to 3:

If you apply any additional criteria to the selection of securities for the cells, not every security that might be included has an equal probability of being selected. As a result, the sampling is not random. In practice, indexing using stratified sampling usually does not strictly involve random sampling because the selection of bond issues within cells is subject to various additional criteria. Because the purpose of sampling in this application is not to make an inference about a population parameter but rather to index a portfolio, lack of randomness is not in itself a problem in this application of stratified sampling.

In the next section, we discuss the kinds of data used by financial analysts in sampling and practical issues that arise in selecting samples.

2.3 Time-Series and Cross-Sectional Data

Investment analysts commonly work with both time-series and cross-sectional data. A time series is a sequence of returns collected at discrete and equally spaced intervals of time (such as a historical series of monthly stock returns). Cross-sectional data are data on some characteristic of individuals, groups, geographical regions, or companies at a single point in time. The book value per share at the end of a given year for all New York Stock Exchange-listed companies is an example of cross-sectional data.

Economic or financial theory offers no basis for determining whether a long or short time period should be selected to collect a sample. As analysts, we might have to look for subtle clues. For example, combining data from a period of fixed exchange rates with data from a period of floating exchange rates would be inappropriate. The variance of exchange rates when exchange rates were fixed would certainly be less than when rates were allowed to float. As a consequence, we would not be sampling from a population described by a single set of parameters.[1] Tight versus loose **monetary**

1 When the mean or variance of a time series is not constant through time, the time series is not stationary.

policy also influences the distribution of returns to stocks; thus, combining data from tight-money and loose-money periods would be inappropriate. Example 2 illustrates the problems that can arise when sampling from more than one distribution.

EXAMPLE 2

Calculating Sharpe Ratios: One or Two Years of Quarterly Data

Analysts often use the Sharpe ratio to evaluate the performance of a managed portfolio. The **Sharpe ratio** is the average return in excess of the risk-free rate divided by the standard deviation of returns. This ratio measures the excess return earned per unit of standard deviation of return.

To compute the Sharpe ratio, suppose that an analyst collects eight quarterly excess returns (i.e., total return in excess of the risk-free rate). During the first year, the investment manager of the portfolio followed a low-risk strategy, and during the second year, the manager followed a high-risk strategy. For each of these years, the analyst also tracks the quarterly excess returns of some benchmark against which the manager will be evaluated. For each of the two years, the Sharpe ratio for the benchmark is 0.21. Table 1 gives the calculation of the Sharpe ratio of the portfolio.

Table 1 Calculation of Sharpe Ratios: Low-Risk and High-Risk Strategies

Quarter/Measure	Year 1 Excess Returns	Year 2 Excess Returns
Quarter 1	−3%	−12%
Quarter 2	5	20
Quarter 3	−3	−12
Quarter 4	5	20
Quarterly average	1%	4%
Quarterly standard deviation	4.62%	18.48%
Sharpe ratio = 0.22 = 1/4.62 = 4/18.48		

For the first year, during which the manager followed a low-risk strategy, the average quarterly return in excess of the risk-free rate was 1 percent with a standard deviation of 4.62 percent. The Sharpe ratio is thus 1/4.62 = 0.22. The second year's results mirror the first year except for the higher average return and volatility. The Sharpe ratio for the second year is 4/18.48 = 0.22. The Sharpe ratio for the benchmark is 0.21 during the first and second years. Because larger Sharpe ratios are better than smaller ones (providing more return per unit of risk), the manager appears to have outperformed the benchmark.

Now, suppose the analyst believes a larger sample to be superior to a small one. She thus decides to pool the two years together and calculate a Sharpe ratio based on eight quarterly observations. The average quarterly excess return for the two years is the average of each year's average excess return. For the two-year period, the average excess return is (1 + 4)/2 = 2.5 percent per quarter. The standard deviation for all eight quarters measured from the sample mean of 2.5 percent is 12.57 percent. The portfolio's Sharpe ratio for the two-year period is now 2.5/12.57 = 0.199; the Sharpe ratio for the benchmark remains 0.21. Thus, when returns for the two-year period are pooled, the manager appears to have provided less return per unit of risk than the benchmark and less when compared with the separate yearly results.

The problem with using eight quarters of return data is that the analyst has violated the assumption that the sampled returns come from the same population. As a result of the change in the manager's investment strategy, returns in Year 2 followed a different distribution than returns in Year 1. Clearly, during Year 1, returns were generated by an underlying population with lower mean and variance than the population of the second year. Combining the results for the first and second years yielded a sample that was representative of no population. Because the larger sample did not satisfy model assumptions, any conclusions the analyst reached based on the larger sample are incorrect. For this example, she was better off using a smaller sample than a larger sample because the smaller sample represented a more homogeneous distribution of returns.

The second basic type of data is cross-sectional data.[2] With cross-sectional data, the observations in the sample represent a characteristic of individuals, groups, geographical regions, or companies at a single point in time. The telecommunications analyst discussed previously is essentially collecting a cross-section of planned capital expenditures for the coming year.

Whenever we sample cross-sectionally, certain assumptions must be met if we wish to summarize the data in a meaningful way. Again, a useful approach is to think of the observation of interest as a random variable that comes from some underlying population with a given mean and variance. As we collect our sample and begin to summarize the data, we must be sure that all the data do, in fact, come from the same underlying population. For example, an analyst might be interested in how efficiently companies use their inventory assets. Some companies, however, turn over their inventory more quickly than others because of differences in their operating environments (e.g., grocery stores turn over inventory more quickly than automobile manufacturers, in general). So the distribution of inventory turnover rates may not be characterized by a single distribution with a given mean and variance. Therefore, summarizing inventory turnover across all companies might be inappropriate. If random variables are generated by different underlying distributions, the sample statistics computed from combined samples are not related to one underlying population parameter. The size of the sampling error in such cases is unknown.

In instances such as these, analysts often summarize company-level data by industry. Attempting to summarize by industry partially addresses the problem of differing underlying distributions, but large corporations are likely to be in more than one industrial sector, so analysts should be sure they understand how companies are assigned to the industry groups.

Whether we deal with time-series data or cross-sectional data, we must be sure to have a random sample that is representative of the population we wish to study. With the objective of inferring information from representative samples, we now turn to the next part of this reading, which focuses on the central limit theorem as well as point and interval estimates of the population mean.

---

2 The reader may also encounter two types of datasets that have both time-series and cross-sectional aspects. **Panel data** consist of observations through time on a single characteristic of multiple observational units. For example, the annual inflation rate of the Eurozone countries over a five-year period would represent panel data. **Longitudinal data** consist of observations on characteristic(s) of the same observational unit through time. Observations on a set of financial ratios for a single company over a 10-year period would be an example of longitudinal data. Both panel and longitudinal data may be represented by arrays (matrixes) in which successive rows represent the observations for successive time periods.

3 DISTRIBUTION OF THE SAMPLE MEAN

Earlier in this reading, we presented a telecommunications equipment analyst who decided to sample in order to estimate mean planned capital expenditures by his customers. Supposing that the sample is representative of the underlying population, how can the analyst assess the sampling error in estimating the population mean? Viewed as a formula that takes a function of the random outcomes of a random variable, the sample mean is itself a random variable with a probability distribution. That probability distribution is called the statistic's sampling distribution.[3] To estimate how closely the sample mean can be expected to match the underlying population mean, the analyst needs to understand the sampling distribution of the mean. Fortunately, we have a result, the central limit theorem, that helps us understand the sampling distribution of the mean for many of the estimation problems we face.

3.1 The Central Limit Theorem

One of the most practically useful theorems in probability theory, the central limit theorem has important implications for how we construct confidence intervals and test hypotheses. Formally, it is stated as follows:

- **The Central Limit Theorem.** Given a population described by any probability distribution having mean μ and finite variance σ^2, the sampling distribution of the sample mean $\overline{X}$ computed from samples of size n from this population will be approximately normal with mean μ (the population mean) and variance σ^2/n (the population variance divided by n) when the sample size n is large.

The central limit theorem allows us to make quite precise probability statements about the population mean by using the sample mean, *whatever the distribution of the population* (so long as it has finite variance), because the sample mean follows an approximate normal distribution for large-size samples. The obvious question is, "When is a sample's size large enough that we can assume the sample mean is normally distributed?" In general, when sample size n is greater than or equal to 30, we can assume that the sample mean is approximately normally distributed.[4]

The central limit theorem states that the variance of the distribution of the sample mean is σ^2/n. The positive square root of variance is standard deviation. The standard deviation of a sample statistic is known as the standard error of the statistic. The standard error of the sample mean is an important quantity in applying the central limit theorem in practice.

- **Definition of the Standard Error of the Sample Mean.** For sample mean $\overline{X}$ calculated from a sample generated by a population with standard deviation σ, the standard error of the sample mean is given by one of two expressions:

$$\sigma_{\overline{X}} = \frac{\sigma}{\sqrt{n}} \quad (1)$$

---

3 Sometimes confusion arises because "sample mean" is also used in another sense. When we calculate the sample mean for a particular sample, we obtain a definite number, say 8. If we state that "the sample mean is 8" we are using "sample mean" in the sense of a particular outcome of sample mean as a random variable. The number 8 is of course a constant and does not have a probability distribution. In this discussion, we are not referring to "sample mean" in the sense of a constant number related to a particular sample.

4 When the underlying population is very nonnormal, a sample size well in excess of 30 may be required for the normal distribution to be a good description of the sampling distribution of the mean.

when we know σ, the population standard deviation, or by

$$s_{\overline{X}} = \frac{s}{\sqrt{n}} \quad (2)$$

when we do not know the population standard deviation and need to use the sample standard deviation, s, to estimate it.[5]

In practice, we almost always need to use Equation 2. The estimate of s is given by the square root of the sample variance, s^2, calculated as follows:

$$s^2 = \frac{\sum_{i=1}^{n}\left(X_i - \overline{X}\right)^2}{n-1} \quad (3)$$

We will soon see how we can use the sample mean and its standard error to make probability statements about the population mean by using the technique of confidence intervals. First, however, we provide an illustration of the central limit theorem's force.

EXAMPLE 3

The Central Limit Theorem

It is remarkable that the sample mean for large sample sizes will be distributed normally regardless of the distribution of the underlying population. To illustrate the central limit theorem in action, we specify in this example a distinctly nonnormal distribution and use it to generate a large number of random samples of size 100. We then calculate the sample mean for each sample. The frequency distribution of the calculated sample means is an approximation of the sampling distribution of the sample mean for that sample size. Does that sampling distribution look like a normal distribution?

We return to the telecommunications analyst studying the capital expenditure plans of telecom businesses. Suppose that capital expenditures for communications equipment form a continuous uniform random variable with a **lower bound** equal to \$0 and an upper bound equal to \$100—for short, call this a uniform (0, 100) random variable. The probability function of this continuous uniform random variable has a rather simple shape that is anything but normal. It is a horizontal line with a vertical intercept equal to 1/100. Unlike a normal random variable, for which outcomes close to the mean are most likely, all possible outcomes are equally likely for a uniform random variable.

To illustrate the power of the central limit theorem, we conduct a Monte Carlo simulation to study the capital expenditure plans of telecom businesses.[6] In this simulation, we collect 200 random samples of the capital expenditures of 100 companies (200 random draws, each consisting of the capital expenditures of 100 companies with $n = 100$). In each simulation trial, 100 values for capital

5 We need to note a technical point: When we take a sample of size n from a finite population of size N, we apply a shrinkage factor to the estimate of the standard error of the sample mean that is called the finite population correction factor (fpc). The fpc is equal to $[(N - n)/(N - 1)]^{1/2}$. Thus, if $N = 100$ and $n = 20$, $[(100 - 20)/(100 - 1)]^{1/2} = 0.898933$. If we have estimated a standard error of, say, 20, according to Equation 1 or Equation 2, the new estimate is $20(0.898933) = 17.978663$. The fpc applies only when we sample from a finite population without replacement; most practitioners also do not apply the fpc if sample size n is very small relative to N (say, less than 5 percent of N). For more information on the finite population correction factor, see Daniel and Terrell (1995).

6 Monte Carlo simulation involves the use of a computer to represent the operation of a system subject to risk. An integral part of Monte Carlo simulation is the generation of a large number of random samples from a specified probability distribution or distributions.

expenditure are generated from the uniform (0, 100) distribution. For each random sample, we then compute the sample mean. We conduct 200 simulation trials in total. Because we have specified the distribution generating the samples, we know that the population mean capital expenditure is equal to (\$0 + \$100 million)/2 = \$50 million; the population variance of capital expenditures is equal to $(100 - 0)^2/12 = 833.33$; thus, the standard deviation is \$28.87 million and the standard error is $28.87/\sqrt{100} = 2.887$ under the central limit theorem.[7]

The results of this Monte Carlo experiment are tabulated in Table 2 in the form of a frequency distribution. This distribution is the estimated sampling distribution of the sample mean.

Table 2 Frequency Distribution: 200 Random Samples of a Uniform (0,100) Random Variable

Range of Sample Means (\$ Million)	Absolute Frequency
$42.5 \le \bar{X} < 44$	1
$44 \le \bar{X} < 45.5$	6
$45.5 \le \bar{X} < 47$	22
$47 \le \bar{X} < 48.5$	39
$48.5 \le \bar{X} < 50$	41
$50 \le \bar{X} < 51.5$	39
$51.5 \le \bar{X} < 53$	23
$53 \le \bar{X} < 54.5$	12
$54.5 \le \bar{X} < 56$	12
$56 \le \bar{X} < 57.5$	5

Note: $\bar{X}$ is the mean capital expenditure for each sample.

The frequency distribution can be described as bell-shaped and centered close to the population mean of 50. The most frequent, or modal, range, with 41 observations, is 48.5 to 50. The overall average of the sample means is \$49.92, with a standard error equal to \$2.80. The calculated standard error is close to the value of 2.887 given by the central limit theorem. The discrepancy between calculated and expected values of the mean and standard deviation under the central limit theorem is a result of random chance (sampling error).

In summary, although the distribution of the underlying population is very nonnormal, the simulation has shown that a normal distribution well describes the estimated sampling distribution of the sample mean, with mean and standard error consistent with the values predicted by the central limit theorem.

7 If a is the lower limit of a uniform random variable and b is the upper limit, then the random variable's mean is given by $(a + b)/2$ and its variance is given by $(b - a)^2/12$. The reading on common probability distributions fully describes continuous uniform random variables.

To summarize, according to the central limit theorem, when we sample from any distribution, the distribution of the sample mean will have the following properties as long as our sample size is large:

- The distribution of the sample mean $\overline{X}$ will be approximately normal.
- The mean of the distribution of $\overline{X}$ will be equal to the mean of the population from which the samples are drawn.
- The variance of the distribution of $\overline{X}$ will be equal to the variance of the population divided by the sample size.

We next discuss the concepts and tools related to estimating the population parameters, with a special focus on the population mean. We focus on the population mean because analysts are more likely to meet interval estimates for the population mean than any other type of interval estimate.

POINT AND INTERVAL ESTIMATES OF THE POPULATION MEAN

4

Statistical inference traditionally consists of two branches, hypothesis testing and estimation. Hypothesis testing addresses the question "Is the value of this parameter (say, a population mean) equal to some specific value (0, for example)?" In this process, we have a hypothesis concerning the value of a parameter, and we seek to determine whether the evidence from a sample supports or does not support that hypothesis. We discuss hypothesis testing in detail in the reading on hypothesis testing.

The second branch of statistical inference, and the focus of this reading, is estimation. Estimation seeks an answer to the question "What is this parameter's (for example, the population mean's) value?" In estimating, unlike in hypothesis testing, we do not start with a hypothesis about a parameter's value and seek to test it. Rather, we try to make the best use of the information in a sample to form one of several types of estimates of the parameter's value. With estimation, we are interested in arriving at a rule for best calculating a single number to estimate the unknown population parameter (a point estimate). Together with calculating a point estimate, we may also be interested in calculating a range of values that brackets the unknown population parameter with some specified level of probability (a confidence interval). In Section 4.1 we discuss point estimates of parameters and then, in Section 4.2, the formulation of confidence intervals for the population mean.

4.1 Point Estimators

An important concept introduced in this reading is that sample statistics viewed as formulas involving random outcomes are random variables. The formulas that we use to compute the sample mean and all the other sample statistics are examples of estimation formulas or **estimators**. The particular value that we calculate from sample observations using an estimator is called an **estimate**. An estimator has a sampling distribution; an estimate is a fixed number pertaining to a given sample and thus has no sampling distribution. To take the example of the mean, the calculated value of the sample mean in a given sample, used as an estimate of the population mean, is called a **point estimate** of the population mean. As Example 3 illustrated, the formula for the sample mean can and will yield different results in repeated samples as different samples are drawn from the population.

In many applications, we have a choice among a number of possible estimators for estimating a given parameter. How do we make our choice? We often select estimators because they have one or more desirable statistical properties. Following is a brief description of three desirable properties of estimators: unbiasedness (lack of bias), efficiency, and consistency.[8]

- **Definition of Unbiasedness.** An unbiased estimator is one whose expected value (the mean of its sampling distribution) equals the parameter it is intended to estimate.

For example, the expected value of the sample mean, $\overline{X}$, equals μ, the population mean, so we say that the sample mean is an unbiased estimator (of the population mean). The sample variance, s^2, which is calculated using a divisor of $n - 1$ (Equation 3), is an unbiased estimator of the population variance, σ^2. If we were to calculate the sample variance using a divisor of n, the estimator would be biased: Its expected value would be smaller than the population variance. We would say that sample variance calculated with a divisor of n is a biased estimator of the population variance.

Whenever one unbiased estimator of a parameter can be found, we can usually find a large number of other unbiased estimators. How do we choose among alternative unbiased estimators? The criterion of efficiency provides a way to select from among unbiased estimators of a parameter.

- **Definition of Efficiency.** An unbiased estimator is efficient if no other unbiased estimator of the same parameter has a sampling distribution with smaller variance.

To explain the definition, in repeated samples we expect the estimates from an efficient estimator to be more tightly grouped around the mean than estimates from other unbiased estimators. Efficiency is an important property of an estimator.[9] Sample mean $\overline{X}$ is an efficient estimator of the population mean; sample variance s^2 is an efficient estimator of σ^2.

Recall that a statistic's sampling distribution is defined for a given sample size. Different sample sizes define different sampling distributions. For example, the variance of sampling distribution of the sample mean is smaller for larger sample sizes. Unbiasedness and efficiency are properties of an estimator's sampling distribution that hold for any size sample. An unbiased estimator is unbiased equally in a sample of size 10 and in a sample of size 1,000. In some problems, however, we cannot find estimators that have such desirable properties as unbiasedness in small samples.[10] In this case, statisticians may justify the choice of an estimator based on the properties of the estimator's sampling distribution in extremely large samples, the estimator's so-called asymptotic properties. Among such properties, the most important is consistency.

- **Definition of Consistency.** A consistent estimator is one for which the probability of estimates close to the value of the population parameter increases as sample size increases.

Somewhat more technically, we can define a consistent estimator as an estimator whose sampling distribution becomes concentrated on the value of the parameter it is intended to estimate as the sample size approaches infinity. The sample mean, in addition to being an efficient estimator, is also a consistent estimator of the population mean: As sample size n goes to infinity, its standard error, $\sigma/\sqrt{n}$, goes to 0 and its sampling distribution becomes concentrated right over the value of population mean,

8 See Daniel and Terrell (1995) or Greene (2018) for a thorough treatment of the properties of estimators.
9 An efficient estimator is sometimes referred to as the best unbiased estimator.
10 Such problems frequently arise in regression and time-series analyses.

μ. To summarize, we can think of a consistent estimator as one that tends to produce more and more accurate estimates of the population parameter as we increase the sample's size. If an estimator is consistent, we may attempt to increase the accuracy of estimates of a population parameter by calculating estimates using a larger sample. For an inconsistent estimator, however, increasing sample size does not help to increase the probability of accurate estimates.

4.2 Confidence Intervals for the Population Mean

When we need a single number as an estimate of a population parameter, we make use of a point estimate. However, because of sampling error, the point estimate is not likely to equal the population parameter in any given sample. Often, a more useful approach than finding a point estimate is to find a range of values that we expect to bracket the parameter with a specified level of probability—an interval estimate of the parameter. A confidence interval fulfills this role.

- **Definition of Confidence Interval.** A confidence interval is a range for which one can assert with a given probability $1 - \alpha$, called the **degree of confidence**, that it will contain the parameter it is intended to estimate. This interval is often referred to as the $100(1 - \alpha)\%$ confidence interval for the parameter.

The endpoints of a confidence interval are referred to as the lower and upper confidence limits. In this reading, we are concerned only with two-sided confidence intervals—confidence intervals for which we calculate both lower and upper limits.[11]

Confidence intervals are frequently given either a probabilistic interpretation or a practical interpretation. In the probabilistic interpretation, we interpret a 95 percent confidence interval for the population mean as follows. In repeated sampling, 95 percent of such confidence intervals will, in the long run, include or bracket the population mean. For example, suppose we sample from the population 1,000 times, and based on each sample, we construct a 95 percent confidence interval using the calculated sample mean. Because of random chance, these confidence intervals will vary from each other, but we expect 95 percent, or 950, of these intervals to include the unknown value of the population mean. In practice, we generally do not carry out such repeated sampling. Therefore, in the practical interpretation, we assert that we are 95 percent confident that a single 95 percent confidence interval contains the population mean. We are justified in making this statement because we know that 95 percent of all possible confidence intervals constructed in the same manner will contain the population mean. The confidence intervals that we discuss in this reading have structures similar to the following basic structure:

- **Construction of Confidence Intervals.** A $100(1 - \alpha)\%$ confidence interval for a parameter has the following structure:

  Point estimate ± Reliability factor × Standard error

11 It is also possible to define two types of one-sided confidence intervals for a population parameter. A lower one-sided confidence interval establishes a lower limit only. Associated with such an interval is an assertion that with a specified degree of confidence the population parameter equals or exceeds the lower limit. An upper one-sided confidence interval establishes an upper limit only; the related assertion is that the population parameter is less than or equal to that upper limit, with a specified degree of confidence. Investment researchers rarely present one-sided confidence intervals, however.

where

Point estimate = a point estimate of the parameter (a value of a sample statistic)

Reliability factor = a number based on the assumed distribution of the point estimate and the degree of confidence $(1 - \alpha)$ for the confidence interval

Standard error = the standard error of the sample statistic providing the point estimate[12]

The most basic confidence interval for the population mean arises when we are sampling from a normal distribution with known variance. The reliability factor in this case is based on the standard normal distribution, which has a mean of 0 and a variance of 1. A standard normal random variable is conventionally denoted by Z. The notation z_α denotes the point of the standard normal distribution such that α of the probability remains in the right tail. For example, 0.05 or 5 percent of the possible values of a standard normal random variable are larger than $z_{0.05} = 1.65$.

Suppose we want to construct a 95 percent confidence interval for the population mean and, for this purpose, we have taken a sample of size 100 from a normally distributed population with known variance of $\sigma^2 = 400$ (so, $\sigma = 20$). We calculate a sample mean of $\overline{X} = 25$. Our point estimate of the population mean is, therefore, 25. If we move 1.96 standard deviations above the mean of a normal distribution, 0.025 or 2.5 percent of the probability remains in the right tail; by symmetry of the normal distribution, if we move 1.96 standard deviations below the mean, 0.025 or 2.5 percent of the probability remains in the left tail. In total, 0.05 or 5 percent of the probability is in the two tails and 0.95 or 95 percent lies in between. So, $z_{0.025} = 1.96$ is the reliability factor for this 95 percent confidence interval. Note the relationship $100(1 - \alpha)\%$ for the confidence interval and the $z_{\alpha/2}$ for the reliability factor. The standard error of the sample mean, given by Equation 1, is $\sigma_{\overline{X}} = 20/\sqrt{100} = 2$. The confidence interval, therefore, has a lower limit of $\overline{X} - 1.96\sigma_{\overline{X}} = 25 - 1.96(2) = 25 - 3.92 = 21.08$. The upper limit of the confidence interval is $\overline{X} + 1.96\sigma_{\overline{X}} = 25 + 1.96(2) = 25 + 3.92 = 28.92$. The 95 percent confidence interval for the population mean spans 21.08 to 28.92.

- **Confidence Intervals for the Population Mean (Normally Distributed Population with Known Variance).** A $100(1 - \alpha)\%$ confidence interval for population mean μ when we are sampling from a normal distribution with known variance σ^2 is given by

$$\overline{X} \pm z_{\alpha/2}\frac{\sigma}{\sqrt{n}} \tag{4}$$

The reliability factors for the most frequently used confidence intervals are as follows.

- **Reliability Factors for Confidence Intervals Based on the Standard Normal Distribution.** We use the following reliability factors when we construct confidence intervals based on the standard normal distribution:[13]
  - 90 percent confidence intervals: Use $z_{0.05} = 1.65$

12 The quantity (reliability factor) × (standard error) is sometimes called the precision of the estimator; larger values of the product imply lower precision in estimating the population parameter.

13 Most practitioners use values for $z_{0.05}$ and $z_{0.005}$ that are carried to two decimal places. For reference, more exact values for $z_{0.05}$ and $z_{0.005}$ are 1.645 and 2.575, respectively. For a quick calculation of a 95 percent confidence interval, $z_{0.025}$ is sometimes rounded from 1.96 to 2.

- 95 percent confidence intervals: Use $z_{0.025} = 1.96$
- 99 percent confidence intervals: Use $z_{0.005} = 2.58$

These reliability factors highlight an important fact about all confidence intervals. As we increase the degree of confidence, the confidence interval becomes wider and gives us less precise information about the quantity we want to estimate. "The surer we want to be, the less we have to be sure of."[14]

In practice, the assumption that the sampling distribution of the sample mean is at least approximately normal is frequently reasonable, either because the underlying distribution is approximately normal or because we have a large sample and the central limit theorem applies. However, rarely do we know the population variance in practice. When the population variance is unknown but the sample mean is at least approximately normally distributed, we have two acceptable ways to calculate the confidence interval for the population mean. We will soon discuss the more conservative approach, which is based on Student's *t*-distribution (the *t*-distribution, for short).[15] In investment literature, it is the most frequently used approach in both estimation and hypothesis tests concerning the mean when the population variance is not known, whether sample size is small or large.

A second approach to confidence intervals for the population mean, based on the standard normal distribution, is the *z*-alternative. It can be used only when sample size is large. (In general, a sample size of 30 or larger may be considered large.) In contrast to the confidence interval given in Equation 4, this confidence interval uses the sample standard deviation, *s*, in computing the standard error of the sample mean (Equation 2).

- **Confidence Intervals for the Population Mean—The *z*-Alternative (Large Sample, Population Variance Unknown).** A $100(1 - \alpha)\%$ confidence interval for population mean μ when sampling from any distribution with unknown variance and when sample size is large is given by

$$\overline{X} \pm z_{\alpha/2}\frac{s}{\sqrt{n}} \quad (5)$$

Because this type of confidence interval appears quite often, we illustrate its calculation in Example 4.

EXAMPLE 4

Confidence Interval for the Population Mean of Sharpe Ratios—*z*-Statistic

Suppose an investment analyst takes a random sample of US equity mutual funds and calculates the average Sharpe ratio. The sample size is 100, and the average Sharpe ratio is 0.45. The sample has a standard deviation of 0.30. Calculate and interpret the 90 percent confidence interval for the population mean of all US equity mutual funds by using a reliability factor based on the standard normal distribution.

14 Freund and Williams (1977), p. 266.

15 The distribution of the statistic *t* is called Student's *t*-distribution after the pen name "Student" used by W. S. Gosset, who published his work in 1908.

The reliability factor for a 90 percent confidence interval, as given earlier, is $z_{0.05} = 1.65$. The confidence interval will be

$$\overline{X} \pm z_{0.05}\frac{s}{\sqrt{n}} = 0.45 \pm 1.65\frac{0.30}{\sqrt{100}} = 0.45 \pm 1.65(0.03) = 0.45 \pm 0.0495$$

The confidence interval spans 0.4005 to 0.4995, or 0.40 to 0.50, carrying two decimal places. The analyst can say with 90 percent confidence that the interval includes the population mean.

In this example, the analyst makes no specific assumption about the probability distribution describing the population. Rather, the analyst relies on the central limit theorem to produce an approximate normal distribution for the sample mean.

As Example 4 shows, even if we are unsure of the underlying population distribution, we can still construct confidence intervals for the population mean as long as the sample size is large because we can apply the central limit theorem.

We now turn to the conservative alternative, using the t-distribution, for constructing confidence intervals for the population mean when the population variance is not known. For confidence intervals based on samples from normally distributed populations with unknown variance, the theoretically correct reliability factor is based on the t-distribution. Using a reliability factor based on the t-distribution is essential for a small sample size. Using a t reliability factor is appropriate when the population variance is unknown, even when we have a large sample and could use the central limit theorem to justify using a z reliability factor. In this large sample case, the t-distribution provides more-conservative (wider) confidence intervals.

The t-distribution is a symmetrical probability distribution defined by a single parameter known as **degrees of freedom (df)**. Each value for the number of degrees of freedom defines one distribution in this family of distributions. We will shortly compare t-distributions with the standard normal distribution, but first we need to understand the concept of degrees of freedom. We can do so by examining the calculation of the sample variance.

Equation 3 gives the unbiased estimator of the sample variance that we use. The term in the denominator, $n - 1$, which is the sample size minus 1, is the number of degrees of freedom in estimating the population variance when using Equation 3. We also use $n - 1$ as the number of degrees of freedom for determining reliability factors based on the t-distribution. The term "degrees of freedom" is used because in a random sample, we assume that observations are selected independently of each other. The numerator of the sample variance, however, uses the sample mean. How does the use of the sample mean affect the number of observations collected independently for the sample variance formula? With a sample of size 10 and a mean of 10 percent, for example, we can freely select only 9 observations. Regardless of the 9 observations selected, we can always find the value for the 10th observation that gives a mean equal to 10 percent. From the standpoint of the sample variance formula, then, there are 9 degrees of freedom. Given that we must first compute the sample mean from the total of n independent observations, only $n - 1$ observations can be chosen independently for the calculation of the sample variance. The concept of degrees of freedom comes up frequently in statistics, and you will see it often in later readings.

Suppose we sample from a normal distribution. The ratio $z = \left(\overline{X} - \mu\right)/\left(\sigma/\sqrt{n}\right)$ is distributed normally with a mean of 0 and standard deviation of 1; however, the ratio $t = \left(\overline{X} - \mu\right)/\left(s/\sqrt{n}\right)$ follows the t-distribution with a mean of 0 and $n - 1$ degrees of freedom. The ratio represented by t is not normal because t is the ratio of two random variables, the sample mean and the sample standard deviation. The definition of the standard normal random variable involves only one random variable, the sample mean. As degrees of freedom increase, however, the *t*-distribution approaches the standard normal distribution. Figure 1 shows the standard normal distribution and two *t*-distributions, one with df = 2 and one with df = 8.

Figure 1 Student's *t*-Distribution versus the Standard Normal Distribution

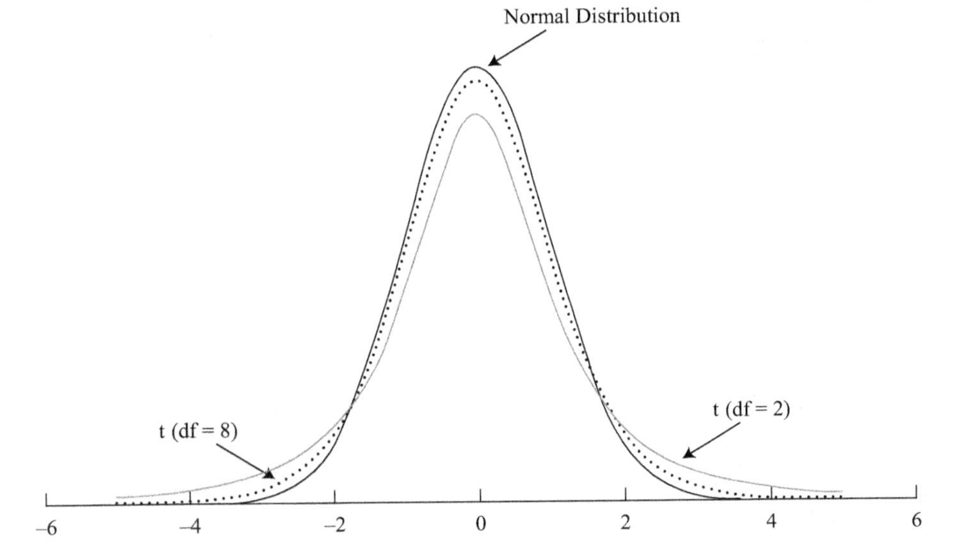

Of the three distributions shown in Figure 1, the standard normal distribution has tails that approach zero faster than the tails of the two *t*-distributions. The *t*-distribution is also symmetrically distributed around its mean value of zero, just like the normal distribution. As the degrees of freedom increase, the *t*-distribution approaches the standard normal. The *t*-distribution with df = 8 is closer to the standard normal than the *t*-distribution with df = 2.

Beyond plus and minus four standard deviations from the mean, the area under the standard normal distribution appears to approach 0; both *t*-distributions continue to show some area under each curve beyond four standard deviations, however. The *t*-distributions have fatter tails, but the tails of the *t*-distribution with df = 8 more closely resemble the normal distribution's tails. As the degrees of freedom increase, the tails of the *t*-distribution become less fat.

Frequently referred to values for the *t*-distribution are presented in tables at the end of the book. For each degree of freedom, five values are given: $t_{0.10}$, $t_{0.05}$, $t_{0.025}$, $t_{0.01}$, and $t_{0.005}$. The values for $t_{0.10}$, $t_{0.05}$, $t_{0.025}$, $t_{0.01}$, and $t_{0.005}$ are such that, respectively, 0.10, 0.05, 0.025, 0.01, and 0.005 of the probability remains in the right tail, for the specified number of degrees of freedom.[16] For example, for df = 30, $t_{0.10} = 1.310$, $t_{0.05} = 1.697$, $t_{0.025} = 2.042$, $t_{0.01} = 2.457$, and $t_{0.005} = 2.750$.

We now give the form of confidence intervals for the population mean using the *t*-distribution.

- **Confidence Intervals for the Population Mean (Population Variance Unknown)—*t*-Distribution.** If we are sampling from a population with unknown variance and either of the conditions below holds:

16 The values $t_{0.10}$, $t_{0.05}$, $t_{0.025}$, $t_{0.01}$, and $t_{0.005}$ are also referred to as one-sided critical values of *t* at the 0.10, 0.05, 0.025, 0.01, and 0.005 significance levels, for the specified number of degrees of freedom.

- the sample is large, or
- the sample is small, but the population is normally distributed, or approximately normally distributed,

then a 100(1 – α)% confidence interval for the population mean μ is given by

$$\bar{X} \pm t_{\alpha/2}\frac{s}{\sqrt{n}} \tag{6}$$

where the number of degrees of freedom for $t_{\alpha/2}$ is $n - 1$ and n is the sample size.

Example 5 reprises the data of Example 4 but uses the *t*-statistic rather than the *z*-statistic to calculate a confidence interval for the population mean of Sharpe ratios.

EXAMPLE 5

Confidence Interval for the Population Mean of Sharpe Ratios—*t*-Statistic

As in Example 4, an investment analyst seeks to calculate a 90 percent confidence interval for the population mean Sharpe ratio of US equity mutual funds based on a random sample of 100 US equity mutual funds. The sample mean Sharpe ratio is 0.45, and the sample standard deviation of the Sharpe ratios is 0.30. Now recognizing that the population variance of the distribution of Sharpe ratios is unknown, the analyst decides to calculate the confidence interval using the theoretically correct *t*-statistic.

Because the sample size is 100, df = 99. In the tables in the back of the book, the closest value is df = 100. Using df = 100 and reading down the 0.05 column, we find that $t_{0.05} = 1.66$. This reliability factor is slightly larger than the reliability factor $z_{0.05} = 1.65$ that was used in Example 4. The confidence interval will be

$$\bar{X} \pm t_{0.05}\frac{s}{\sqrt{n}} = 0.45 \pm 1.66\frac{0.30}{\sqrt{100}} = 0.45 \pm 1.66(0.03) = 0.45 \pm 0.0498$$

The confidence interval spans 0.4002 to 0.4998, or 0.40 to 0.50, carrying two decimal places. To two decimal places, the confidence interval is unchanged from the one computed in Example 4.

Table 3 summarizes the various reliability factors that we have used.

Table 3 Basis of Computing Reliability Factors

Sampling from:	Statistic for Small Sample Size	Statistic for Large Sample Size
Normal distribution with known variance	z	z
Normal distribution with unknown variance	t	t^*

Table 3 (Continued)

Sampling from:	Statistic for Small Sample Size	Statistic for Large Sample Size
Nonnormal distribution with known variance	not available	z
Nonnormal distribution with unknown variance	not available	t*

* Use of z also acceptable.

4.3 Selection of Sample Size

What choices affect the width of a confidence interval? To this point we have discussed two factors that affect width: the choice of statistic (t or z) and the choice of degree of confidence (affecting which specific value of t or z we use). These two choices determine the reliability factor. (Recall that a confidence interval has the structure Point estimate ± Reliability factor × Standard error.)

The choice of sample size also affects the width of a confidence interval. All else equal, a larger sample size decreases the width of a confidence interval. Recall the expression for the standard error of the sample mean:

$$\text{Standard error of the sample mean} = \frac{\text{Sample standard deviation}}{\sqrt{\text{Sample size}}}$$

We see that the standard error varies inversely with the square root of sample size. As we increase sample size, the standard error decreases and consequently the width of the confidence interval also decreases. The larger the sample size, the greater precision with which we can estimate the population parameter.[17] All else equal, larger samples are good, in that sense. In practice, however, two considerations may operate against increasing sample size. First, as we saw in Example 2 concerning the Sharpe ratio, increasing the size of a sample may result in sampling from more than one population. Second, increasing sample size may involve additional expenses that outweigh the value of additional precision. Thus three issues that the analyst should weigh in selecting sample size are the need for precision, the risk of sampling from more than one population, and the expenses of different sample sizes.

EXAMPLE 6

A Money Manager Estimates Net Client Inflows

A money manager wants to obtain a 95 percent confidence interval for fund inflows and outflows over the next six months for his existing clients. He begins by calling a random sample of 10 clients and inquiring about their planned additions to and withdrawals from the fund. The manager then computes the change in cash flow for each client sampled as a percentage change in total funds placed with the manager. A positive percentage change indicates a net cash inflow to the

17 A formula exists for determining the sample size needed to obtain a desired width for a confidence interval. Define E = Reliability factor × Standard error. The smaller E is, the smaller the width of the confidence interval, because $2E$ is the confidence interval's width. The sample size to obtain a desired value of E at a given degree of confidence $(1 - \alpha)$ is $n = [(t_{\alpha/2}s)/E]^2$.

client's account, and a negative percentage change indicates a net cash outflow from the client's account. The manager weights each response by the relative size of the account within the sample and then computes a weighted average.

As a result of this process, the money manager computes a weighted average of 5.5 percent. Thus, a point estimate is that the total amount of funds under management will increase by 5.5 percent in the next six months. The standard deviation of the observations in the sample is 10 percent. A histogram of past data looks fairly close to normal, so the manager assumes the population is normal.

1 Calculate a 95 percent confidence interval for the population mean and interpret your findings.

The manager decides to see what the confidence interval would look like if he had used a sample size of 20 or 30 and found the same mean (5.5 percent) and standard deviation (10 percent).

2 Using the sample mean of 5.5 percent and standard deviation of 10 percent, compute the confidence interval for sample sizes of 20 and 30. For the sample size of 30, use Equation 6.

3 Interpret your results from Parts 1 and 2.

Solution to 1:

Because the population variance is unknown and the sample size is small, the manager must use the t-statistic in Equation 6 to calculate the confidence interval. Based on the sample size of 10, df = $n - 1 = 10 - 1 = 9$. For a 95 percent confidence interval, he needs to use the value of $t_{0.025}$ for df = 9. According to the tables in Appendix B at the end of this volume, this value is 2.262. Therefore, a 95 percent confidence interval for the population mean is

$$\begin{aligned}\overline{X} \pm t_{0.025}\frac{s}{\sqrt{n}} &= 5.5\% \pm 2.262\frac{10\%}{\sqrt{10}}\\ &= 5.5\% \pm 2.262(3.162)\\ &= 5.5\% \pm 7.15\%\end{aligned}$$

The confidence interval for the population mean spans −1.65 percent to +12.65 percent.[18] The manager can be confident at the 95 percent level that this range includes the population mean.

Solution to 2:

Table 4 gives the calculations for the three sample sizes.

Table 4 The 95 Percent Confidence Interval for Three Sample Sizes

Distribution	95% Confidence Interval	Lower Bound	Upper Bound	Relative Size
$t(n = 10)$	5.5% ± 2.262(3.162)	−1.65%	12.65%	100.0%
$t(n = 20)$	5.5% ± 2.093(2.236)	0.82	10.18	65.5
$t(n = 30)$	5.5% ± 2.045(1.826)	1.77	9.23	52.2

18 We assumed in this example that sample size is sufficiently small compared with the size of the client base that we can disregard the finite population correction factor (mentioned in Footnote 6).

Solution to 3:

The width of the confidence interval decreases as we increase the sample size. This decrease is a function of the standard error becoming smaller as n increases. The reliability factor also becomes smaller as the number of degrees of freedom increases. The last column of Table 4 shows the relative size of the width of confidence intervals based on $n = 10$ to be 100 percent. Using a sample size of 20 reduces the confidence interval's width to 65.5 percent of the interval width for a sample size of 10. Using a sample size of 30 cuts the width of the interval almost in half. Comparing these choices, the money manager would obtain the most precise results using a sample of 30.

Having covered many of the fundamental concepts of sampling and estimation, we are in a good position to focus on sampling issues of special concern to analysts. The quality of inferences depends on the quality of the data as well as on the quality of the sampling plan used. Financial data pose special problems, and sampling plans frequently reflect one or more biases. The next section of this reading discusses these issues.

MORE ON SAMPLING

5

We have already seen that the selection of sample period length may raise the issue of sampling from more than one population. There are, in fact, a range of challenges to valid sampling that arise in working with financial data. In this section we discuss four such sampling-related issues: data-mining bias, sample selection bias, look-ahead bias, and time-period bias. All of these issues are important for point and interval estimation and hypothesis testing. As we will see, if the sample is biased in any way, then point and interval estimates and any other conclusions that we draw from the sample will be in error.

5.1 Data-Mining Bias

Data mining relates to overuse of the same or related data in ways that we shall describe shortly. Data-mining bias refers to the errors that arise from such misuse of data. Investment strategies that reflect data-mining biases are often not successful in the future. Nevertheless, both investment practitioners and researchers have frequently engaged in data mining. Analysts thus need to understand and guard against this problem.

Data-mining is the practice of determining a model by extensive searching through a dataset for statistically significant patterns (that is, repeatedly "drilling" in the same data until finding something that appears to work).[19] In exercises involving statistical significance we set a significance level, which is the probability of rejecting the hypothesis we are testing when the hypothesis is in fact correct.[20] Because rejecting a true hypothesis is undesirable, the investigator often sets the significance level at

19 Some researchers use the term "data snooping" instead of data mining.

20 To convey an understanding of data mining, it is very helpful to introduce some basic concepts related to hypothesis testing. The reading on hypothesis testing contains further discussion of significance levels and tests of significance.

a relatively small number such as 0.05 or 5 percent.[21] Suppose we test the hypothesis that a variable does not predict stock returns, and we test in turn 100 different variables. Let us also suppose that in truth none of the 100 variables has the ability to predict stock returns. Using a 5 percent significance level in our tests, we would still expect that 5 out of 100 variables would appear to be significant predictors of stock returns because of random chance alone. We have mined the data to find some apparently significant variables. In essence, we have explored the same data again and again until we found some after-the-fact pattern or patterns in the dataset. This is the sense in which data mining involves overuse of data. If we were to just report the significant variables, without also reporting the total number of variables that we tested that were unsuccessful as predictors, we would be presenting a very misleading picture of our findings. Our results would appear to be far more significant than they actually were, because a series of tests such as the one just described invalidates the conventional interpretation of a given significance level (such as 5 percent), according to the theory of inference.

How can we investigate the presence of data-mining bias? With most financial data, the most ready means is to conduct out-of-sample tests of the proposed variable or strategy. An **out-of-sample test** uses a sample that does not overlap the time period(s) of the sample(s) on which a variable, strategy, or model, was developed. If a variable or investment strategy is the result of data mining, it should generally not be significant in out-of-sample tests. A variable or investment strategy that is statistically and economically significant in out-of-sample tests, and that has a plausible economic basis, may be the basis for a valid investment strategy. Caution is still warranted, however. The most crucial out-of-sample test is future investment success. If the strategy becomes known to other investors, prices may adjust so that the strategy, however well tested, does not work in the future. To summarize, the analyst should be aware that many apparently profitable investment strategies may reflect data-mining bias and thus be cautious about the future applicability of published investment research results.

Untangling the extent of data mining can be complex. To assess the significance of an investment strategy, we need to know how many unsuccessful strategies were tried not only by the current investigator but also by *previous* investigators using the same or related datasets. Much research, in practice, closely builds on what other investigators have done, and so reflects intergenerational data mining, to use the terminology of McQueen and Thorley (1999). **Intergenerational data mining** involves using information developed by previous researchers using a dataset to guide current research using the same or a related dataset.[22] Analysts have accumulated many observations about the peculiarities of many financial datasets, and other analysts may develop models or investment strategies that will tend to be supported within a dataset based on their familiarity with the prior experience of other analysts. As a consequence, the importance of those new results may be overstated. Research has suggested that the magnitude of this type of data-mining bias may be considerable.[23]

With the background of the above definitions and explanations, we can understand McQueen and Thorley's (1999) cogent exploration of data mining in the context of the popular Motley Fool "Foolish Four" investment strategy. The Foolish Four strategy, first

21 In terms of our previous discussion of confidence intervals, significance at the 5 percent level corresponds to a hypothesized value for a population statistic falling outside a 95 percent confidence interval based on an appropriate sample statistic (e.g., the sample mean, when the hypothesis concerns the population mean).

22 The term "intergenerational" comes from viewing each round of researchers as a generation. Campbell, Lo, and MacKinlay (1997) have called intergenerational data mining "data snooping." The latter phrase, however, is commonly used as a synonym of data mining; thus McQueen and Thorley's terminology is less ambiguous. The term "intragenerational data mining" is available when we want to highlight that the reference is to an investigator's new or independent data mining.

23 For example, Lo and MacKinlay (1990) concluded that the magnitude of this type of bias on tests of the capital asset pricing model was considerable.

presented in 1996, was a version of the Dow Dividend Strategy that was tuned by its developers to exhibit an even higher arithmetic mean return than the Dow Dividend Strategy over 1973 to 1993.[24] From 1973 to 1993, the Foolish Four portfolio had an average annual return of 25 percent, and the claim was made in print that the strategy should have similar returns in the future. As McQueen and Thorley discussed, however, the Foolish Four strategy was very much subject to data-mining bias, including bias from intergenerational data mining, as the strategy's developers exploited observations about the dataset made by earlier workers. McQueen and Thorley highlighted the data-mining issues by taking the Foolish Four portfolio one step further. They mined the data to create a "Fractured Four" portfolio that earned nearly 35 percent over 1973 to 1996, beating the Foolish Four strategy by almost 8 percentage points. Observing that all of the Foolish Four stocks did well in even years but not odd years and that the second-to-lowest-priced high-yielding stock was relatively the best-performing stock in odd years, the strategy of the Fractured Four portfolio was to hold the Foolish Four stocks with equal weights in even years and hold only the second-to-lowest-priced stock in odd years. How likely is it that a performance difference between even and odd years reflected underlying economic forces, rather than a chance pattern of the data over the particular time period? Probably, very unlikely. Unless an investment strategy reflected underlying economic forces, we would not expect it to have any value in a forward-looking sense. Because the Foolish Four strategy also partook of data mining, the same issues applied to it. McQueen and Thorley found that in an out-of-sample test over the 1949–72 period, the Foolish Four strategy had about the same mean return as buying and holding the DJIA, but with higher risk. If the higher taxes and transaction costs of the Foolish Four strategy were accounted for, the comparison would have been even more unfavorable.

McQueen and Thorley presented two signs that can warn analysts about the potential existence of data mining:

- *Too much digging/too little confidence.* The testing of many variables by the researcher is the "too much digging" warning sign of a data-mining problem. Unfortunately, many researchers do not disclose the number of variables examined in developing a model. Although the number of variables examined may not be reported, we should look closely for verbal hints that the researcher searched over many variables. The use of terms such as "we noticed (or noted) that" or "someone noticed (or noted) that," with respect to a pattern in a dataset, should raise suspicions that the researchers were trying out variables based on their own or others' observations of the data.
- *No story/no future.* The absence of an explicit economic rationale for a variable or trading strategy is the "no story" warning sign of a data-mining problem. Without a plausible economic rationale or story for why a variable should work, the variable is unlikely to have predictive power. In a demonstration exercise using an extensive search of variables in an international financial database, Leinweber (1997) found that butter production in a particular country remote from the United States explained 75 percent of the variation in US stock returns as represented by the S&P 500. Such a pattern, with no plausible economic rationale, is highly likely to be a random pattern particular to a specific time

---

24 The Dow Dividend Strategy, also known as Dogs of the Dow Strategy, consists of holding an equally weighted portfolio of the 10 highest-yielding DJIA stocks as of the beginning of a year. At the time of McQueen and Thorley's research, the Foolish Four strategy was as follows: At the beginning of each year, the Foolish Four portfolio purchases a 4-stock portfolio from the 5 lowest-priced stocks of the 10 highest-yielding DJIA stocks. The lowest-priced stock of the five is excluded, and 40 percent is invested in the second-to-lowest-priced stock, with 20 percent weights in the remaining three.

period.[25] What if we do have a plausible economic explanation for a significant variable? McQueen and Thorley caution that a plausible economic rationale is a necessary but not a sufficient condition for a trading strategy to have value. As we mentioned earlier, if the strategy is publicized, market prices may adjust to reflect the new information as traders seek to exploit it; as a result, the strategy may no longer work.

5.2 Sample Selection Bias

When researchers look into questions of interest to analysts or portfolio managers, they may exclude certain stocks, bonds, portfolios, or time periods from the analysis for various reasons—perhaps because of data availability. When data availability leads to certain assets being excluded from the analysis, we call the resulting problem **sample selection bias**. For example, you might sample from a database that tracks only companies currently in existence. Many mutual fund databases, for instance, provide historical information about only those funds that currently exist. Databases that report historical balance sheet and income statement information suffer from the same sort of bias as the mutual fund databases: Funds or companies that are no longer in business do not appear there. So, a study that uses these types of databases suffers from a type of sample selection bias known as **survivorship bias**.

Dimson, Marsh, and Staunton (2002) raised the issue of survivorship bias in international indexes:

> An issue that has achieved prominence is the impact of market survival on estimated long-run returns. Markets can experience not only disappointing performance but also total loss of value through confiscation, hyperinflation, nationalization, and market failure. By measuring the performance of markets that survive over long intervals, we draw inferences that are conditioned on survival. Yet, as pointed out by Brown, Goetzmann, and Ross (1995) and Goetzmann and Jorion (1999), one cannot determine in advance which markets will survive and which will perish. (p. 41)

Survivorship bias sometimes appears when we use both stock price and accounting data. For example, many studies in finance have used the ratio of a company's market price to book equity per share (i.e., the price-to-book ratio, P/B) and found that P/B is inversely related to a company's returns (see Fama and French 1992, 1993). P/B is also used to create many popular value and growth indexes. If the database that we use to collect accounting data excludes failing companies, however, a survivorship bias might result. Kothari, Shanken, and Sloan (1995) investigated just this question and argued that failing stocks would be expected to have low returns and low P/Bs. If we exclude failing stocks, then those stocks with low P/Bs that are included will have returns that are higher on average than if all stocks with low P/Bs were included. Kothari, Shanken, and Sloan suggested that this bias is responsible for the previous findings of an inverse relationship between average return and P/B.[26] The only advice we can offer at this point is to be aware of any biases potentially inherent in a sample. Clearly, sample selection biases can cloud the results of any study.

---

25 In the finance literature, such a random but irrelevant-to-the-future pattern is sometimes called an artifact of the dataset.

26 See Fama and French (1996, p. 80) for discussion of data snooping and survivorship bias in their tests.

A sample can also be biased because of the removal (or delisting) of a company's stock from an exchange.[27] For example, the Center for Research in Security Prices at the University of Chicago is a major provider of return data used in academic research. When a delisting occurs, CRSP attempts to collect returns for the delisted company, but many times, it cannot do so because of the difficulty involved; CRSP must simply list delisted company returns as missing. A study in the *Journal of Finance* by Shumway and Warther (1999) documented the bias caused by delisting for CRSP NASDAQ return data. The authors showed that delistings associated with poor company performance (e.g., bankruptcy) are missed more often than delistings associated with good or neutral company performance (e.g., merger or moving to another exchange). In addition, delistings occur more frequently for small companies.

Sample selection bias occurs even in markets where the quality and consistency of the data are quite high. Newer asset classes such as hedge funds may present even greater problems of sample selection bias. Hedge funds are a heterogeneous group of investment vehicles typically organized so as to be free from regulatory oversight. In general, hedge funds are not required to publicly disclose performance (in contrast to, say, mutual funds). Hedge funds themselves decide whether they want to be included in one of the various databases of hedge fund performance. Hedge funds with poor track records clearly may not wish to make their records public, creating a problem of self-selection bias in hedge fund databases. Further, as pointed out by Fung and Hsieh (2002), because only hedge funds with good records will volunteer to enter a database, in general, overall past hedge fund industry performance will tend to appear better than it really is. Furthermore, many hedge fund databases drop funds that go out of business, creating survivorship bias in the database. Even if the database does not drop defunct hedge funds, in the attempt to eliminate survivorship bias, the problem remains of hedge funds that stop reporting performance because of poor results.[28]

5.3 Look-Ahead Bias

A test design is subject to **look-ahead bias** if it uses information that was not available on the test date. For example, tests of trading rules that use stock market returns and accounting balance sheet data must account for look-ahead bias. In such tests, a company's book value per share is commonly used to construct the P/B variable. Although the market price of a stock is available for all market participants at the same point in time, fiscal year-end book equity per share might not become publicly available until sometime in the following quarter.

5.4 Time-Period Bias

A test design is subject to **time-period bias** if it is based on a time period that may make the results time-period specific. A short time series is likely to give period specific results that may not reflect a longer period. A long time series may give a more accurate picture of true investment performance; its disadvantage lies in the potential for a structural change occurring during the time frame that would result in two different return distributions. In this situation, the distribution that would reflect conditions before the change differs from the distribution that would describe conditions after the change.

27 Delistings occur for a variety of reasons: merger, bankruptcy, liquidation, or migration to another exchange.

28 See Fung and Hsieh (2002) and ter Horst and Verbeek (2007) for more details on the problems of interpreting hedge fund performance. Note that an offsetting type of bias may occur if successful funds stop reporting performance because they no longer want new cash inflows.

EXAMPLE 7

Biases in Investment Research

An analyst is reviewing the empirical evidence on historical US equity returns. She finds that value stocks (i.e., those with low P/Bs) outperformed growth stocks (i.e., those with high P/Bs) in some recent time periods. After reviewing the US market, the analyst wonders whether value stocks might be attractive in the United Kingdom. She investigates the performance of value and growth stocks in the UK market for a 14-year period. To conduct this research, the analyst does the following:

- obtains the current composition of the Financial Times Stock Exchange (FTSE) All Share Index, which is a market-capitalization-weighted index;
- eliminates the few companies that do not have December fiscal year-ends;
- uses year-end book values and market prices to rank the remaining universe of companies by P/Bs at the end of the year;
- based on these rankings, divides the universe into 10 portfolios, each of which contains an equal number of stocks;
- calculates the equal-weighted return of each portfolio and the return for the FTSE All Share Index for the 12 months following the date each ranking was made; and
- subtracts the FTSE returns from each portfolio's returns to derive excess returns for each portfolio.

Describe and discuss each of the following biases introduced by the analyst's research design:

- survivorship bias;
- look-ahead bias; and
- time-period bias.

Survivorship Bias.

A test design is subject to survivorship bias if it fails to account for companies that have gone bankrupt, merged, or otherwise departed the database. In this example, the analyst used the current list of FTSE stocks rather than the actual list of stocks that existed at the start of each year. To the extent that the computation of returns excluded companies removed from the index, the performance of the portfolios with the lowest P/B is subject to survivorship bias and may be overstated. At some time during the testing period, those companies not currently in existence were eliminated from testing. They would probably have had low prices (and low P/Bs) and poor returns.

Look-Ahead Bias.

A test design is subject to look-ahead bias if it uses information unavailable on the test date. In this example, the analyst conducted the test under the assumption that the necessary accounting information was available at the end of the fiscal year. For example, the analyst assumed that book value per share for a given fiscal year was available on 31 December of that year. Because this information is not released until several months after the close of a fiscal year, the test may have contained look-ahead bias. This bias would make a strategy based on the information appear successful, but it assumes perfect forecasting ability.

Time-Period Bias.

A test design is subject to time-period bias if it is based on a time period that may make the results time-period specific. Although the test covered a period extending more than 10 years, that period may be too short for testing an anomaly. Ideally, an analyst should test market anomalies over several business cycles to ensure that results are not period specific. This bias can favor a proposed strategy if the time period chosen was favorable to the strategy.

SUMMARY

In this reading, we have presented basic concepts and results in sampling and estimation. We have also emphasized the challenges faced by analysts in appropriately using and interpreting financial data. As analysts, we should always use a critical eye when evaluating the results from any study. The quality of the sample is of the utmost importance: If the sample is biased, the conclusions drawn from the sample will be in error.

- To draw valid inferences from a sample, the sample should be random.
- In simple random sampling, each observation has an equal chance of being selected. In stratified random sampling, the population is divided into subpopulations, called strata or cells, based on one or more classification criteria; simple random samples are then drawn from each stratum.
- Stratified random sampling ensures that population subdivisions of interest are represented in the sample. Stratified random sampling also produces more-precise parameter estimates than simple random sampling.
- Time-series data are a collection of observations at equally spaced intervals of time. Cross-sectional data are observations that represent individuals, groups, geographical regions, or companies at a single point in time.
- The central limit theorem states that for large sample sizes, for any underlying distribution for a random variable, the sampling distribution of the sample mean for that variable will be approximately normal, with mean equal to the population mean for that random variable and variance equal to the population variance of the variable divided by sample size.
- Based on the central limit theorem, when the sample size is large, we can compute confidence intervals for the population mean based on the normal distribution regardless of the distribution of the underlying population. In general, a sample size of 30 or larger can be considered large.
- An estimator is a formula for estimating a parameter. An estimate is a particular value that we calculate from a sample by using an estimator.
- Because an estimator or statistic is a random variable, it is described by some probability distribution. We refer to the distribution of an estimator as its sampling distribution. The standard deviation of the sampling distribution of the sample mean is called the standard error of the sample mean.
- The desirable properties of an estimator are *unbiasedness* (the expected value of the estimator equals the population parameter), *efficiency* (the estimator has the smallest variance), and *consistency* (the probability of accurate estimates increases as sample size increases).

- The two types of estimates of a parameter are point estimates and interval estimates. A point estimate is a single number that we use to estimate a parameter. An interval estimate is a range of values that brackets the population parameter with some probability.
- A confidence interval is an interval for which we can assert with a given probability $1 - \alpha$, called the degree of confidence, that it will contain the parameter it is intended to estimate. This measure is often referred to as the $100(1 - \alpha)\%$ confidence interval for the parameter.
- A $100(1 - \alpha)\%$ confidence interval for a parameter has the following structure: Point estimate ± Reliability factor × Standard error, where the reliability factor is a number based on the assumed distribution of the point estimate and the degree of confidence $(1 - \alpha)$ for the confidence interval and where standard error is the standard error of the sample statistic providing the point estimate.
- A $100(1 - \alpha)\%$ confidence interval for population mean μ when sampling from a normal distribution with known variance σ^2 is given by $\bar{X} \pm z_{\alpha/2}\frac{\sigma}{\sqrt{n}}$, where $z_{\alpha/2}$ is the point of the standard normal distribution such that $\alpha/2$ remains in the right tail.
- Student's *t*-distribution is a family of symmetrical distributions defined by a single parameter, degrees of freedom.
- A random sample of size n is said to have $n - 1$ degrees of freedom for estimating the population variance, in the sense that there are only $n - 1$ independent deviations from the mean on which to base the estimate.
- The degrees of freedom number for use with the *t*-distribution is also $n - 1$.
- The *t*-distribution has fatter tails than the standard normal distribution but converges to the standard normal distribution as degrees of freedom go to infinity.
- A $100(1 - \alpha)\%$ confidence interval for the population mean μ when sampling from a normal distribution with unknown variance (a *t*-distribution confidence interval) is given by $\bar{X} \pm t_{\alpha/2}\left(s/\sqrt{n}\right)$, where $t_{\alpha/2}$ is the point of the *t*-distribution such that $\alpha/2$ remains in the right tail and s is the sample standard deviation. This confidence interval can also be used, because of the central limit theorem, when dealing with a large sample from a population with unknown variance that may not be normal.
- We may use the confidence interval $\bar{X} \pm z_{\alpha/2}\left(s/\sqrt{n}\right)$ as an alternative to the *t*-distribution confidence interval for the population mean when using a large sample from a population with unknown variance. The confidence interval based on the *z*-statistic is less conservative (narrower) than the corresponding confidence interval based on a *t*-distribution.
- Three issues in the selection of sample size are the need for precision, the risk of sampling from more than one population, and the expenses of different sample sizes.
- Sample data in investments can have a variety of problems. *Survivorship bias* occurs if companies are excluded from the analysis because they have gone out of business or because of reasons related to poor performance. *Data-mining bias* comes from finding models by repeatedly searching through databases for patterns. *Look-ahead bias* exists if the model uses data not available to market participants at the time the market participants act in the model. Finally, time-period bias is present if the time period used makes the results time-period specific or if the time period used includes a point of structural change.

REFERENCES

Brown, Stephen, William Goetzmann, and Stephen Ross. 1995. "Survival." *Journal of Finance*, vol. 50:853–873.

Campbell, John, Andrew Lo, and A. Craig MacKinlay. 1997. *The Econometrics of Financial Markets*. Princeton, NJ: Princeton University Press.

Daniel, Wayne W., and James C. Terrell. 1995. *Business Statistics for Management & Economics*, 7th edition. Boston: Houghton-Mifflin.

Dimson, Elroy, Paul Marsh, and Mike Staunton. 2002. *Triumphs of the Optimists: 101 Years of Global Investment Returns*. Princeton, NJ: Princeton University Press.

Fama, Eugene F., and Kenneth R. French. 1996. "Multifactor Explanations of Asset Pricing Anomalies." *Journal of Finance*, vol. 51, no. 1:55–84.

Freund, John E, and Frank J. Williams. 1977. *Elementary Business Statistics*, 3rd edition. Englewood Cliffs, NJ: Prentice-Hall.

Fung, William, and David Hsieh. 2002. "Hedge-Fund Benchmarks: Information Content and Biases." *Financial Analysts Journal*, vol. 58, no. 1:22–34.

Goetzmann, William, and Philippe Jorion. 1999. "Re-Emerging Markets." *Journal of Financial and Quantitative Analysis*, vol. 34, no. 1:1–32.

Greene, William H. 2018. *Econometric Analysis*, 8th edition. Upper Saddle River, NJ: Prentice-Hall.

Kothari, S.P., Jay Shanken, and Richard G. Sloan. 1995. "Another Look at the Cross-Section of Expected Stock Returns." *Journal of Finance*, vol. 50, no. 1:185–224.

Leinweber, David. 1997. *Stupid Data Mining Tricks: Over-Fitting the S&P 500*. Monograph. Pasadena, CA: First Quadrant.

Lo, Andrew W., and A. Craig MacKinlay. 1990. "Data Snooping Biases in Tests of Financial Asset Pricing Models." *Review of Financial Studies*, vol. 3:175–208.

McQueen, Grant, and Steven Thorley. 1999. "Mining Fools Gold." *Financial Analysts Journal*, vol. 55, no. 2:61–72.

Shumway, Tyler, and Vincent A. Warther. 1999. "The Delisting Bias in CRSP's Nasdaq Data and Its Implications for the Size Effect." *Journal of Finance*, vol. 54, no. 6:2361–2379.

ter Horst, Jenke, and Marno Verbeek. 2007. "Fund Liquidation, Self-selection, and Look-ahead Bias in the Hedge Fund Industry." *Review of Finance*, vol. 11:605–632.

PRACTICE PROBLEMS

1 Peter Biggs wants to know how growth managers performed last year. Biggs assumes that the population cross-sectional standard deviation of growth manager returns is 6 percent and that the returns are independent across managers.

A How large a random sample does Biggs need if he wants the standard deviation of the sample means to be 1 percent?

B How large a random sample does Biggs need if he wants the standard deviation of the sample means to be 0.25 percent?

2 Petra Munzi wants to know how value managers performed last year. Munzi estimates that the population cross-sectional standard deviation of value manager returns is 4 percent and assumes that the returns are independent across managers.

A Munzi wants to build a 95 percent confidence interval for the mean return. How large a random sample does Munzi need if she wants the 95 percent confidence interval to have a total width of 1 percent?

B Munzi expects a cost of about $10 to collect each observation. If she has a $1,000 budget, will she be able to construct the confidence interval she wants?

3 Assume that the equity risk premium is normally distributed with a population mean of 6 percent and a population standard deviation of 18 percent. Over the last four years, equity returns (relative to the risk-free rate) have averaged −2.0 percent. You have a large client who is very upset and claims that results this poor should *never* occur. Evaluate your client's concerns.

A Construct a 95 percent confidence interval around the population mean for a sample of four-year returns.

B What is the probability of a −2.0 percent or lower average return over a four-year period?

4 Compare the standard normal distribution and Student's *t*-distribution.

5 Find the reliability factors based on the *t*-distribution for the following confidence intervals for the population mean (df = degrees of freedom, n = sample size):

A A 99 percent confidence interval, df = 20.

B A 90 percent confidence interval, df = 20.

C A 95 percent confidence interval, n = 25.

D A 95 percent confidence interval, n = 16.

6 Assume that monthly returns are normally distributed with a mean of 1 percent and a sample standard deviation of 4 percent. The population standard deviation is unknown. Construct a 95 percent confidence interval for the sample mean of monthly returns if the sample size is 24.

7 Ten analysts have given the following fiscal year earnings forecasts for a stock:

Forecast (X_i)	Number of Analysts (n_i)
1.40	1
1.43	1
1.44	3

Forecast (X_i)	Number of Analysts (n_i)
1.45	2
1.47	1
1.48	1
1.50	1

Because the sample is a small fraction of the number of analysts who follow this stock, assume that we can ignore the finite population correction factor. Assume that the analyst forecasts are normally distributed.

A What are the mean forecast and standard deviation of forecasts?

B Provide a 95 percent confidence interval for the population mean of the forecasts.

8 Thirteen analysts have given the following fiscal-year earnings forecasts for a stock:

Forecast (X_i)	Number of Analysts (n_i)
0.70	2
0.72	4
0.74	1
0.75	3
0.76	1
0.77	1
0.82	1

Because the sample is a small fraction of the number of analysts who follow this stock, assume that we can ignore the finite population correction factor.

A What are the mean forecast and standard deviation of forecasts?

B What aspect of the data makes us uncomfortable about using t-tables to construct confidence intervals for the population mean forecast?

9 Explain the differences between constructing a confidence interval when sampling from a normal population with a known population variance and sampling from a normal population with an unknown variance.

10 An exchange rate has a given expected future value and standard deviation.

A Assuming that the exchange rate is normally distributed, what are the probabilities that the exchange rate will be at least 2 or 3 standard deviations away from its mean?

B Assume that you do not know the distribution of exchange rates. Use Chebyshev's inequality (that at least $1 - 1/k^2$ proportion of the observations will be within k standard deviations of the mean for any positive integer k greater than 1) to calculate the maximum probabilities that the exchange rate will be at least 2 or 3 standard deviations away from its mean.

11 Although he knows security returns are not independent, a colleague makes the claim that because of the central limit theorem, if we diversify across a large number of investments, the portfolio standard deviation will eventually approach zero as n becomes large. Is he correct?

12 Why is the central limit theorem important?

13 What is wrong with the following statement of the central limit theorem?

Central Limit Theorem. "If the random variables $X_1, X_2, X_3, \ldots, X_n$ are a random sample of size n from any distribution with finite mean μ and variance σ^2, then the distribution of $\overline{X}$ will be approximately normal, with a standard deviation of $\sigma/\sqrt{n}$."

14 Suppose we take a random sample of 30 companies in an industry with 200 companies. We calculate the sample mean of the ratio of cash flow to total debt for the prior year. We find that this ratio is 23 percent. Subsequently, we learn that the population cash flow to total debt ratio (taking account of all 200 companies) is 26 percent. What is the explanation for the discrepancy between the sample mean of 23 percent and the population mean of 26 percent?

A Sampling error.

B Bias.

C A lack of consistency.

15 Alcorn Mutual Funds is placing large advertisements in several financial publications. The advertisements prominently display the returns of 5 of Alcorn's 30 funds for the past 1-, 3-, 5-, and 10-year periods. The results are indeed impressive, with all of the funds beating the major market indexes and a few beating them by a large margin. Is the Alcorn family of funds superior to its competitors?

16 Julius Spence has tested several predictive models in order to identify undervalued stocks. Spence used about 30 company-specific variables and 10 market-related variables to predict returns for about 5,000 North American and European stocks. He found that a final model using eight variables applied to telecommunications and computer stocks yields spectacular results. Spence wants you to use the model to select investments. Should you? What steps would you take to evaluate the model?

17 The *best* approach for creating a stratified random sample of a population involves:

A drawing an equal number of simple random samples from each subpopulation.

B selecting every *k*th member of the population until the desired sample size is reached.

C drawing simple random samples from each subpopulation in sizes proportional to the relative size of each subpopulation.

18 A population has a non-normal distribution with mean μ and variance σ^2. The sampling distribution of the sample mean computed from samples of large size from that population will have:

A the same distribution as the population distribution.

B its mean approximately equal to the population mean.

C its variance approximately equal to the population variance.

19 A sample mean is computed from a population with a variance of 2.45. The sample size is 40. The standard error of the sample mean is *closest* to:

A 0.039.

B 0.247.

C 0.387.

20 An estimator with an expected value equal to the parameter that it is intended to estimate is described as:

A efficient.

B unbiased.

C consistent.

21 If an estimator is consistent, an increase in sample size will increase the:

A accuracy of estimates.

B efficiency of the estimator.

C unbiasedness of the estimator.

22 For a two-sided confidence interval, an increase in the degree of confidence will result in:

A a wider confidence interval.

B a narrower confidence interval.

C no change in the width of the confidence interval.

23 As the t-distribution's degrees of freedom decrease, the t-distribution *most likely*:

A exhibits tails that become fatter.

B approaches a standard normal distribution.

C becomes asymmetrically distributed around its mean value.

24 For a sample size of 17, with a mean of 116.23 and a variance of 245.55, the width of a 90% confidence interval using the appropriate t-distribution is *closest to*:

A 13.23.

B 13.27.

C 13.68.

25 For a sample size of 65 with a mean of 31 taken from a normally distributed population with a variance of 529, a 99% confidence interval for the population mean will have a lower limit *closest* to:

A 23.64.

B 25.41.

C 30.09.

26 An increase in sample size is *most likely* to result in a:

A wider confidence interval.

B decrease in the standard error of the sample mean.

C lower likelihood of sampling from more than one population.

27 A report on long-term stock returns focused exclusively on all currently publicly traded firms in an industry is *most likely* susceptible to:

A look-ahead bias.

B survivorship bias.

C intergenerational data mining.

28 Which sampling bias is *most likely* investigated with an out-of-sample test?

A Look-ahead bias

B Data-mining bias

C Sample selection bias

29 Which of the following characteristics of an investment study *most likely* indicates time-period bias?

A The study is based on a short time-series.

B Information not available on the test date is used.

C A structural change occurred prior to the start of the study's time series.

SOLUTIONS

1 **A** The standard deviation or standard error of the sample mean is $\sigma_{\bar{X}} = \sigma/\sqrt{n}$. Substituting in the values for $\sigma_{\bar{X}}$ and σ, we have 1% = $6\%/\sqrt{n}$, or $\sqrt{n}$ = 6. Squaring this value, we get a random sample of n = 36.

B As in Part A, the standard deviation of sample mean is $\sigma_{\bar{X}} = \sigma/\sqrt{n}$. Substituting in the values for $\sigma_{\bar{X}}$ and σ, we have 0.25% = $6\%/\sqrt{n}$, or $\sqrt{n}$ = 24. Squaring this value, we get a random sample of n = 576, which is substantially larger than for Part A of this question.

2 **A** Assume the sample size will be large and thus the 95 percent confidence interval for the mean of a sample of manager returns is $\bar{X} \pm 1.96 s_{\bar{X}}$, where $s_{\bar{X}} = s/\sqrt{n}$. Munzi wants the distance between the upper limit and lower limit in the confidence interval to be 1 percent, which is

$$\left(\bar{X} + 1.96 s_{\bar{X}}\right) - \left(\bar{X} - 1.96 s_{\bar{X}}\right) = 1\%$$

Simplifying this equation, we get $2\left(1.96 s_{\bar{X}}\right)$ = 1%. Finally, we have $3.92 s_{\bar{X}}$ = 1%, which gives us the standard deviation of the sample mean, $s_{\bar{X}}$ = 0.255%. The distribution of sample means is $s_{\bar{X}} = s/\sqrt{n}$. Substituting in the values for $s_{\bar{X}}$ and s, we have 0.255% = $4\%/\sqrt{n}$, or $\sqrt{n}$ = 15.69. Squaring this value, we get a random sample of n = 246.

B With her budget, Munzi can pay for a sample of up to 100 observations, which is far short of the 246 observations needed. Munzi can either proceed with her current budget and settle for a wider confidence interval or she can raise her budget (to around $2,460) to get the sample size for a 1 percent width in her confidence interval.

3 **A** This is a small-sample problem in which the sample comes from a normal population with a known standard deviation; thus we use the z-distribution in the solution. For a 95 percent confidence interval (and 2.5 percent in each tail), the critical z-value is 1.96. For returns that are normally distributed, a 95 percent confidence interval is of the form

$$\mu + 1.96\frac{\sigma}{\sqrt{n}}$$

The lower limit is $X_l = \mu - 1.96\frac{\sigma}{\sqrt{n}} = 6\% - 1.96\frac{18\%}{\sqrt{4}} = 6\% - 1.96(9\%) =$ −11.64%.

The upper limit is $X_u = \mu + 1.96\frac{\sigma}{\sqrt{n}} = 6\% + 1.96\frac{18\%}{\sqrt{4}} = 6\% + 1.96(9\%) =$ 23.64%.

There is a 95 percent probability that four-year average returns will be between −11.64 percent and +23.64 percent.

B The critical z-value associated with the −2.0 percent return is

$$Z = \frac{\bar{X} - \mu}{\sigma/\sqrt{n}} = \frac{-2\% - 6\%}{18\%/\sqrt{4}} = \frac{-8\%}{9\%} = -0.89$$

Using a normal table, the probability of a z-value less than −0.89 is $P(Z < -0.89) = 0.1867$. Unfortunately, although your client is unhappy with the investment result, a four-year average return of −2.0 percent or lower should occur 18.67 percent of the time.

4 (Refer to Figure 1 to help visualize the answer to this question.) Basically, only one standard normal distribution exists, but many t-distributions exist—one for every different number of degrees of freedom. The normal distribution and the t-distribution for a large number of degrees of freedom are practically the same. The lower the degrees of freedom, the flatter the t-distribution becomes. The t-distribution has less mass (lower probabilities) in the center of the distribution and more mass (higher probabilities) out in both tails. Therefore, the confidence intervals based on t-values will be wider than those based on the normal distribution. Stated differently, the probability of being within a given number of standard deviations (such as within ±1 standard deviation or ±2 standard deviations) is lower for the t-distribution than for the normal distribution.

5 **A** For a 99 percent confidence interval, the reliability factor we use is $t_{0.005}$; for df = 20, this factor is 2.845.

B For a 90 percent confidence interval, the reliability factor we use is $t_{0.05}$; for df = 20, this factor is 1.725.

C Degrees of freedom equals $n - 1$, or in this case $25 - 1 = 24$. For a 95 percent confidence interval, the reliability factor we use is $t_{0.025}$; for df = 24, this factor is 2.064.

D Degrees of freedom equals $16 - 1 = 15$. For a 95 percent confidence interval, the reliability factor we use is $t_{0.025}$; for df = 15, this factor is 2.131.

6 Because this is a small sample from a normal population and we have only the sample standard deviation, we use the following model to solve for the confidence interval of the population mean:

$$\overline{X} \pm t_{\alpha/2}\frac{s}{\sqrt{n}}$$

where we find $t_{0.025}$ (for a 95 percent confidence interval) for df = $n - 1 = 24 - 1 = 23$; this value is 2.069. Our solution is $1\% \pm 2.069(4\%)/\sqrt{24} = 1\% \pm 2.069(0.8165) = 1\% \pm 1.69$. The 95 percent confidence interval spans the range from −0.69 percent to +2.69 percent.

7 The following table summarizes the calculations used in the answers.

Forecast (X_i)	Number of Analysts (n_i)	$X_i n_i$	$(X_i - \overline{X})$	$(X_i - \overline{X})^2$	$(X_i - \overline{X})^2 n_i$
1.40	1	1.40	−0.05	0.0025	0.0025
1.43	1	1.43	−0.02	0.0004	0.0004
1.44	3	4.32	−0.01	0.0001	0.0003
1.45	2	2.90	0.00	0.0000	0.0000
1.47	1	1.47	0.02	0.0004	0.0004
1.48	1	1.48	0.03	0.0009	0.0009
1.50	1	1.50	0.05	0.0025	0.0025
Sums	10	14.50			0.0070

A With $n = 10, \bar{X} = \sum_{i=1}^{10} X_i/n = 14.50/10 = 1.45$. The variance is $s^2 = \left[\sum_{i=1}^{10}(X_i - \bar{X})^2\right]\Big/(n-1) = 0.0070/9 = 0.0007778$. The sample standard deviation is $s = \sqrt{0.0007778} = 0.02789$.

B The confidence interval for the mean can be estimated by using $\bar{X} \pm t_{\alpha/2}\left(s/\sqrt{n}\right)$. For 9 degrees of freedom, the reliability factor, $t_{0.025}$, equals 2.262 and the confidence interval is

$$1.45 \pm 2.262 \times 0.02789/\sqrt{10} = 1.45 \pm 2.262(0.00882)$$
$$= 1.45 \pm 0.02$$

The confidence interval for the population mean ranges from 1.43 to 1.47.

8 The following table summarizes the calculations used in the answers.

Forecast (X_i)	Number of Analysts (n_i)	X_in_i	$(X_i - \bar{X})$	$(X_i - \bar{X})^2$	$(X_i - \bar{X})^2 n_i$
0.70	2	1.40	−0.04	0.0016	0.0032
0.72	4	2.88	−0.02	0.0004	0.0016
0.74	1	0.74	0.00	0.0000	0.0000
0.75	3	2.25	0.01	0.0001	0.0003
0.76	1	0.76	0.02	0.0004	0.0004
0.77	1	0.77	0.03	0.0009	0.0009
0.82	1	0.82	0.08	0.0064	0.0064
Sums	13	9.62			0.0128

A With $n = 13, \bar{X} = \sum_{i=1}^{13} X_i/n = 9.62/13 = 0.74$. The variance is $s^2 = \left[\sum_{i=1}^{13}(X_i - \bar{X})^2\right]\Big/(n-1) = 0.0128/12 = 0.001067$. The sample standard deviation is $s = \sqrt{0.001067} = 0.03266$.

B The sample is small, and the distribution appears to be bimodal. We cannot compute a confidence interval for the population mean because we have probably sampled from a distribution that is not normal.

9 If the population variance is known, the confidence interval is

$$\bar{X} \pm z_{\alpha/2}\frac{\sigma}{\sqrt{n}}$$

The confidence interval for the population mean is centered at the sample mean, $\bar{X}$. The population standard deviation is σ, and the sample size is n. The population standard deviation divided by the square root of n is the standard error of the estimate of the mean. The value of z depends on the desired degree of confidence. For a 95 percent confidence interval, $z_{0.025} = 1.96$ and the confidence interval estimate is

$$\bar{X} \pm 1.96\frac{\sigma}{\sqrt{n}}$$

If the population variance is not known, we make two changes to the technique used when the population variance is known. First, we must use the sample standard deviation instead of the population standard deviation. Second, we use the t-distribution instead of the normal distribution. The critical t-value will depend on degrees of freedom $n - 1$. If the sample size is large, we have the alternative of using the z-distribution with the sample standard deviation.

10 A The probabilities can be taken from a normal table, in which the critical z-values are 2.00 or 3.00 and we are including the probabilities in both tails. The probabilities that the exchange rate will be at least 2 or 3 standard deviations away from the mean are

$$P(|X - \mu| \geq 2\sigma) = 0.0456$$

$$P(|X - \mu| \geq 3\sigma) = 0.0026$$

B With Chebyshev's inequality, the maximum probability of the exchange rate being at least k standard deviations from the mean is $P(| X - \mu | \geq k\sigma) \leq (1/k)^2$. The maximum probabilities of the rate being at least 2 or 3 standard deviations away from the mean are

$$P(|X - \mu| \geq 2\sigma) \leq (1/2)^2 = 0.2500$$

$$P(|X - \mu| \geq 3\sigma) \leq (1/3)^2 = 0.1111$$

The probability of the rate being outside 2 or 3 standard deviations of the mean is much smaller with a known normal distribution than when the distribution is unknown and we are relying on Chebyshev's inequality.

11 No. First the conclusion on the limit of zero is wrong; second, the support cited for drawing the conclusion (i.e., the central limit theorem) is not relevant in this context.

12 In many instances, the distribution that describes the underlying population is not normal or the distribution is not known. The central limit theorem states that if the sample size is large, regardless of the shape of the underlying population, the distribution of the sample mean is approximately normal. Therefore, even in these instances, we can still construct confidence intervals (and conduct tests of inference) as long as the sample size is large (generally $n \geq 30$).

13 The statement makes the following mistakes:

- Given the conditions in the statement, the distribution of $\bar{X}$ will be approximately normal only for large sample sizes.
- The statement omits the important element of the central limit theorem that the distribution of $\bar{X}$ will have mean μ.

14 A is correct. The discrepancy arises from sampling error. Sampling error exists whenever one fails to observe every element of the population, because a sample statistic can vary from sample to sample. As stated in the reading, the sample mean is an unbiased estimator, a consistent estimator, and an efficient estimator of the population mean. Although the sample mean is an unbiased estimator of the population mean—the expected value of the sample mean equals the population mean—because of sampling error, we do not expect the sample mean to exactly equal the population mean in any one sample we may take.

15 No, we cannot say that Alcorn Mutual Funds as a group is superior to competitors. Alcorn Mutual Funds' advertisement may easily mislead readers because the advertisement does not show the performance of all its funds. In particular, Alcorn Mutual Funds is engaging in sample selection bias by presenting the investment results from its best-performing funds only.

16 Spence may be guilty of data mining. He has used so many possible combinations of variables on so many stocks, it is not surprising that he found some instances in which a model worked. In fact, it would have been more surprising if he had not found any. To decide whether to use his model, you should do two things: First, ask that the model be tested on out-of-sample data—that is, data that were not used in building the model. The model may not be successful with out-of-sample data. Second, examine his model to make sure that the relationships in the model make economic sense, have a story, and have a future.

17 C is correct. Stratified random sampling involves dividing a population into subpopulations based on one or more classification criteria. Then, simple random samples are drawn from each subpopulation in sizes proportional to the relative size of each subpopulation. These samples are then pooled to form a stratified random sample.

18 B is correct. Given a population described by any probability distribution (normal or non-normal) with finite variance, the central limit theorem states that the sampling distribution of the sample mean will be approximately normal, with the mean approximately equal to the population mean, when the sample size is large.

19 B is correct. Taking the square root of the known population variance to determine the population standard deviation (σ) results in:

$$\sigma = \sqrt{2.45} = 1.565$$

The formula for the standard error of the sample mean (σ_X), based on a known sample size (n), is:

$$\sigma_X = \frac{\sigma}{\sqrt{n}}$$

Therefore,

$$\sigma_X = \frac{1.565}{\sqrt{40}} = 0.247$$

20 B is correct. An unbiased estimator is one for which the expected value equals the parameter it is intended to estimate.

21 A is correct. A consistent estimator is one for which the probability of estimates close to the value of the population parameter increases as sample size increases. More specifically, a consistent estimator's sampling distribution becomes concentrated on the value of the parameter it is intended to estimate as the sample size approaches infinity.

22 A is correct. As the degree of confidence increases (e.g., from 95% to 99%), a given confidence interval will become wider. A confidence interval is a range for which one can assert with a given probability $1 - \alpha$, called the degree of confidence, that it will contain the parameter it is intended to estimate.

23 A is correct. A standard normal distribution has tails that approach zero faster than the *t*-distribution. As degrees of freedom increase, the tails of the *t*-distribution become less fat and the *t*-distribution begins to look more like a standard normal distribution. But as degrees of freedom decrease, the tails of the *t*-distribution become fatter.

24 B is correct. The confidence interval is calculated using the following equation:

$$\overline{X} \pm t_{\alpha/2}\frac{s}{\sqrt{n}}$$

Sample standard deviation (s) = $\sqrt{245.55}$ = 15.670.

For a sample size of 17, degrees of freedom equal 16, so $t_{0.05}$ = 1.746.

The confidence interval is calculated as

$$116.23 \pm 1.746\frac{15.67}{\sqrt{17}} = 116.23 \pm 6.6357$$

Therefore, the interval spans 109.5943 to 122.8656, meaning its width is equal to approximately 13.271. (This interval can be alternatively calculated as 6.6357 × 2).

25 A is correct. To solve, use the structure of Confidence interval = Point estimate ± Reliability factor × Standard error, which, for a normally distributed population with known variance, is represented by the following formula:

$$\overline{X} \pm z_{\alpha/2}\frac{\sigma}{\sqrt{n}}$$

For a 99% confidence interval, use $z_{0.005}$ = 2.58.

Also, $\sigma = \sqrt{529} = 23$.

Therefore, the lower limit = $31 - 2.58\frac{23}{\sqrt{65}} = 23.6398$.

26 B is correct. All else being equal, as the sample size increases, the standard error of the sample mean decreases and the width of the confidence interval also decreases.

27 B is correct. A report that uses a current list of stocks does not account for firms that failed, merged, or otherwise disappeared from the public equity market in previous years. As a consequence, the report is biased. This type of bias is known as survivorship bias.

28 B is correct. An out-of-sample test is used to investigate the presence of data-mining bias. Such a test uses a sample that does not overlap the time period of the sample on which a variable, strategy, or model was developed.

29 A is correct. A short time series is likely to give period-specific results that may not reflect a longer time period.

READING

11

Hypothesis Testing

by Richard A. DeFusco, PhD, CFA, Dennis W. McLeavey, DBA, CFA, Jerald E. Pinto, PhD, CFA, and David E. Runkle, PhD, CFA

Richard A. DeFusco, PhD, CFA, is at the University of Nebraska-Lincoln (USA). Dennis W. McLeavey, DBA, CFA, is at the University of Rhode Island (USA). Jerald E. Pinto, PhD, CFA, is at CFA Institute (USA). David E. Runkle, PhD, CFA, is at Trilogy Global Advisors (USA).

LEARNING OUTCOMES

Mastery	*The candidate should be able to:*
☐	**a.** define a hypothesis, describe the steps of hypothesis testing, and describe and interpret the choice of the null and alternative hypotheses;
☐	**b.** distinguish between one-tailed and two-tailed tests of hypotheses;
☐	**c.** explain a test statistic, Type I and Type II errors, a significance level, and how significance levels are used in hypothesis testing;
☐	**d.** explain a decision rule, the power of a test, and the relation between confidence intervals and hypothesis tests;
☐	**e.** distinguish between a statistical result and an economically meaningful result;
☐	**f.** explain and interpret the *p*-value as it relates to hypothesis testing;
☐	**g.** identify the appropriate test statistic and interpret the results for a hypothesis test concerning the population mean of both large and small samples when the population is normally or approximately normally distributed and the variance is 1) known or 2) unknown;
☐	**h.** identify the appropriate test statistic and interpret the results for a hypothesis test concerning the equality of the population means of two at least approximately normally distributed populations, based on independent random samples with 1) equal or 2) unequal assumed variances;
☐	**i.** identify the appropriate test statistic and interpret the results for a hypothesis test concerning the mean difference of two normally distributed populations;

(continued)

LEARNING OUTCOMES

Mastery	The candidate should be able to:
☐	**j.** identify the appropriate test statistic and interpret the results for a hypothesis test concerning 1) the variance of a normally distributed population, and 2) the equality of the variances of two normally distributed populations based on two independent random samples;
☐	**k.** formulate a test of the hypothesis that the population correlation coefficient equals zero and determine whether the hypothesis is rejected at a given level of significance;
☐	**l.** distinguish between parametric and nonparametric tests and describe situations in which the use of nonparametric tests may be appropriate.

1 INTRODUCTION

Analysts often confront competing ideas about how financial markets work. Some of these ideas develop through personal research or experience with markets; others come from interactions with colleagues; and many others appear in the professional literature on finance and investments. In general, how can an analyst decide whether statements about the financial world are probably true or probably false?

When we can reduce an idea or assertion to a definite statement about the value of a quantity, such as an underlying or population mean, the idea becomes a statistically testable statement or hypothesis. The analyst may want to explore questions such as the following:

- Is the underlying mean return on this mutual fund different from the underlying mean return on its benchmark?
- Did the volatility of returns on this stock change after the stock was added to a stock market index?
- Are a security's bid-ask spreads related to the number of dealers making a market in the security?
- Do data from a national bond market support a prediction of an economic theory about the term structure of interest rates (the relationship between yield and maturity)?

To address these questions, we use the concepts and tools of hypothesis testing. Hypothesis testing is part of statistical inference, the process of making judgments about a larger group (a population) on the basis of a smaller group actually observed (a sample). The concepts and tools of hypothesis testing provide an objective means to gauge whether the available evidence supports the hypothesis. After a statistical test of a hypothesis we should have a clearer idea of the probability that a hypothesis is true or not, although our conclusion always stops short of certainty. Hypothesis testing has been a powerful tool in the advancement of investment knowledge and science. As Robert L. Kahn of the Institute for Social Research (Ann Arbor, Michigan) has written, "The mill of science grinds only when hypothesis and data are in continuous and abrasive contact."

The main emphases of this reading are the framework of hypothesis testing and tests concerning mean, variance, and correlation, three quantities frequently used in investments. We give an overview of the procedure of hypothesis testing in the next section. We then address testing hypotheses about the mean and hypotheses about the differences between means. In the fourth section of this reading, we address testing hypotheses about a single variance, the differences between variances, and a correlation coefficient. We end the reading with an overview of some other important issues and techniques in statistical inference.

HYPOTHESIS TESTING

2

Hypothesis testing, as we have mentioned, is part of the branch of statistics known as statistical inference. Traditionally, the field of statistical inference has two subdivisions: **estimation** and **hypothesis testing**. Estimation addresses the question "What is this parameter's (e.g., the population mean's) value?" The answer is in the form of a confidence interval built around a point estimate. Take the case of the mean: We build a confidence interval for the population mean around the sample mean as a point estimate. For the sake of specificity, suppose the sample mean is 50 and a 95 percent confidence interval for the population mean is 50 ± 10 (the confidence interval runs from 40 to 60). If this confidence interval has been properly constructed, there is a 95 percent probability that the interval from 40 to 60 contains the population mean's value.[1] The second branch of statistical inference, hypothesis testing, has a somewhat different focus. A hypothesis testing question is "Is the value of the parameter (say, the population mean) 45 (or some other specific value)?" The assertion "the population mean is 45" is a hypothesis. A **hypothesis** is defined as a statement about one or more populations.

This section focuses on the concepts of hypothesis testing. The process of hypothesis testing is part of a rigorous approach to acquiring knowledge known as the scientific method. The scientific method starts with observation and the formulation of a theory to organize and explain observations. We judge the correctness of the theory by its ability to make accurate predictions—for example, to predict the results of new observations.[2] If the predictions are correct, we continue to maintain the theory as a possibly correct explanation of our observations. When risk plays a role in the outcomes of observations, as in finance, we can only try to make unbiased, probability-based judgments about whether the new data support the predictions. Statistical hypothesis testing fills that key role of testing hypotheses when chance plays a role. In an analyst's day-to-day work, he may address questions to which he might give answers of varying quality. When an analyst correctly formulates the question into a testable hypothesis and carries out and reports on a hypothesis test, he has provided an element of support to his answer consistent with the standards of the scientific method. Of course, the analyst's logic, economic reasoning, information sources, and perhaps other factors also play a role in our assessment of the answer's quality.[3]

We organize this introduction to hypothesis testing around the following list of seven steps.

- **Steps in Hypothesis Testing.** The steps in testing a hypothesis are as follows:[4]

1 We discussed the construction and interpretation of confidence intervals in the reading on sampling and estimation.

2 To be testable, a theory must be capable of making predictions that can be shown to be wrong.

3 See Freeley and Steinberg (2013) for a discussion of critical thinking applied to reasoned decision making.

4 This list is based on one in Daniel and Terrell (1995).

1 Stating the hypotheses.
2 Identifying the appropriate test statistic and its probability distribution.
3 Specifying the significance level.
4 Stating the decision rule.
5 Collecting the data and calculating the test statistic.
6 Making the statistical decision.
7 Making the economic or investment decision.

We will explain each of these steps using as illustration a hypothesis test concerning the sign of the risk premium on US stocks. The steps above constitute a traditional approach to hypothesis testing. We will end the section with a frequently used alternative to those steps, the *p*-value approach.

The first step in hypothesis testing is stating the hypotheses. We always state two hypotheses: the null hypothesis (or null), designated H_0, and the alternative hypothesis, designated H_a.

- **Definition of Null Hypothesis.** The null hypothesis is the hypothesis to be tested. For example, we could hypothesize that the population mean risk premium for US equities is less than or equal to zero.

The null hypothesis is a proposition that is considered true unless the sample we use to conduct the hypothesis test gives convincing evidence that the null hypothesis is false. When such evidence is present, we are led to the alternative hypothesis.

- **Definition of Alternative Hypothesis.** The alternative hypothesis is the hypothesis accepted when the null hypothesis is rejected. Our alternative hypothesis is that the population mean risk premium for US equities is greater than zero.

Suppose our question concerns the value of a population parameter, θ, in relation to one possible value of the parameter, θ_0 (these are read, respectively, "theta" and "theta sub zero").[5] Examples of a population parameter include the population mean, μ, and the population variance, σ^2. We can formulate three different sets of hypotheses, which we label according to the assertion made by the alternative hypothesis.

- **Formulations of Hypotheses.** In the following discussion we formulate the null and alternative hypotheses in three different ways:
  1 H_0: $\theta = \theta_0$ versus H_a: $\theta \neq \theta_0$ (a "not equal to" alternative hypothesis)
  2 H_0: $\theta \leq \theta_0$ versus H_a: $\theta > \theta_0$ (a "greater than" alternative hypothesis)
  3 H_0: $\theta \geq \theta_0$ versus H_a: $\theta < \theta_0$ (a "less than" alternative hypothesis)

In our US example, $\theta = \mu_{RP}$ and represents the population mean risk premium on US equities. Also, $\theta_0 = 0$ and we are using the second of the above three formulations.

The first formulation is a **two-sided hypothesis test** (or **two-tailed hypothesis test**): We reject the null in favor of the alternative if the evidence indicates that the population parameter is either smaller or larger than θ_0. In contrast, Formulations 2 and 3 are each a **one-sided hypothesis test** (or **one-tailed hypothesis test**). For Formulations 2 and 3, we reject the null only if the evidence indicates that the population parameter is respectively greater than or less than θ_0. The alternative hypothesis has one side.

---

5 Greek letters, such as σ, are reserved for population parameters; Roman letters in italics, such as *s*, are used for sample statistics.

Notice that in each case above, we state the null and alternative hypotheses such that they account for all possible values of the parameter. With Formulation 1, for example, the parameter is either equal to the hypothesized value θ_0 (under the null hypothesis) or not equal to the hypothesized value θ_0 (under the alternative hypothesis). Those two statements logically exhaust all possible values of the parameter.

Despite the different ways to formulate hypotheses, we always conduct a test of the null hypothesis at the point of equality, $\theta = \theta_0$. Whether the null is H_0: $\theta = \theta_0$, H_0: $\theta \leq \theta_0$, or H_0: $\theta \geq \theta_0$, we actually test $\theta = \theta_0$. The reasoning is straightforward. Suppose the hypothesized value of the parameter is 5. Consider H_0: $\theta \leq 5$, with a "greater than" alternative hypothesis, H_a: $\theta > 5$. If we have enough evidence to reject H_0: $\theta = 5$ in favor of H_a: $\theta > 5$, we definitely also have enough evidence to reject the hypothesis that the parameter, θ, is some smaller value, such as 4.5 or 4. To review, the calculation to test the null hypothesis is the same for all three formulations. What is different for the three formulations, we will see shortly, is how the calculation is evaluated to decide whether or not to reject the null.

How do we choose the null and alternative hypotheses? Probably most common are "not equal to" alternative hypotheses. We reject the null because the evidence indicates that the parameter is either larger or smaller than θ_0. Sometimes, however, we may have a "suspected" or "hoped for" condition for which we want to find supportive evidence.[6] In that case, we can formulate the alternative hypothesis as the statement that this condition is true; the null hypothesis that we test is the statement that this condition is not true. If the evidence supports rejecting the null and accepting the alternative, we have statistically confirmed what we thought was true. For example, economic theory suggests that investors require a positive risk premium on stocks (the **risk premium** is defined as the expected return on stocks minus the risk-free rate). Following the principle of stating the alternative as the "hoped for" condition, we formulate the following hypotheses:

H_0: The population mean risk premium on US stocks is less than or equal to 0.

H_a: The population mean risk premium on US stocks is positive.

Note that "greater than" and "less than" alternative hypotheses reflect the beliefs of the researcher more strongly than a "not equal to" alternative hypothesis. To emphasize an attitude of neutrality, the researcher may sometimes select a "not equal to" alternative hypothesis when a one-sided alternative hypothesis is also reasonable.

The second step in hypothesis testing is identifying the appropriate test statistic and its probability distribution.

- **Definition of Test Statistic.** A test statistic is a quantity, calculated based on a sample, whose value is the basis for deciding whether or not to reject the null hypothesis.

The focal point of our statistical decision is the value of the test statistic. Frequently, the test statistic has the form[7]

$$\text{Test statistic} = \frac{\text{Sample statistic} - \text{Value of the population parameter under } H_0}{\text{Standard error of the sample statistic}} \quad (1)$$

---

6 Part of this discussion of the selection of hypotheses follows Bowerman, O'Connell, and Murphree (2016).

7 In some cases, the test statistic may have a different form. For example, as we discuss in Section 4.3, the form of the test statistic for correlation coefficient is different.

For our risk premium example, the population parameter of interest is the population mean risk premium, μ_{RP}. We label the hypothesized value of the population mean under H_0 as μ_0. Restating the hypotheses using symbols, we test H_0: $\mu_{RP} \le \mu_0$ versus H_a: $\mu_{RP} > \mu_0$. However, because under the null we are testing $\mu_0 = 0$, we write H_0: $\mu_{RP} \le 0$ versus H_a: $\mu_{RP} > 0$.

The sample mean provides an estimate of the population mean. Therefore, we can use the sample mean risk premium calculated from historical data, $\overline{X}_{RP}$, as the sample statistic in Equation 1. The standard deviation of the sample statistic, known as the "standard error" of the statistic, is the denominator in Equation 1. For this example, the sample statistic is a sample mean. For a sample mean, $\overline{X}$, calculated from a sample generated by a population with standard deviation σ, the standard error is given by one of two expressions:

$$\sigma_{\overline{X}} = \frac{\sigma}{\sqrt{n}} \tag{2}$$

when we know σ (the population standard deviation), or

$$s_{\overline{X}} = \frac{s}{\sqrt{n}} \tag{3}$$

when we do not know the population standard deviation and need to use the sample standard deviation s to estimate it. For this example, because we do not know the population standard deviation of the process generating the return, we use Equation 3. The test statistic is thus

$$\frac{\overline{X}_{RP} - \mu_0}{s_{\overline{X}}} = \frac{\overline{X}_{RP} - 0}{s/\sqrt{n}}$$

In making the substitution of 0 for μ_0, we use the fact already highlighted that we test any null hypothesis at the point of equality, as well as the fact that $\mu_0 = 0$ here.

We have identified a test statistic to test the null hypothesis. What probability distribution does it follow? We will encounter four distributions for test statistics in this reading:

- the t-distribution (for a t-test);
- the standard normal or z-distribution (for a z-test);
- the chi-square (χ^2) distribution (for a chi-square test); and
- the F-distribution (for an F-test).

We will discuss the details later, but assume we can conduct a z-test based on the central limit theorem because our US sample has many observations.[8] To summarize, the test statistic for the hypothesis test concerning the mean risk premium is $\overline{X}_{RP}/s_{\overline{X}}$. We can conduct a z-test because we can plausibly assume that the test statistic follows a standard normal distribution.

The third step in hypothesis testing is specifying the significance level. When the test statistic has been calculated, two actions are possible: 1) We reject the null hypothesis or 2) we do not reject the null hypothesis. The action we take is based on comparing the calculated test statistic to a specified possible value or values. The comparison values we choose are based on the level of significance selected. The level of significance reflects how much sample evidence we require to reject the null. Analogous to

8 The central limit theorem says that the sampling distribution of the sample mean will be approximately normal with mean μ and variance σ^2/n when the sample size is large. The sample we will use for this example has 118 observations.

its counterpart in a court of law, the required standard of proof can change according to the nature of the hypotheses and the seriousness of the consequences of making a mistake. There are four possible outcomes when we test a null hypothesis:

1 We reject a false null hypothesis. This is a correct decision.
2 We reject a true null hypothesis. This is called a **Type I error**.
3 We do not reject a false null hypothesis. This is called a **Type II error**.
4 We do not reject a true null hypothesis. This is a correct decision.

We illustrate these outcomes in Exhibit 1.

Exhibit 1 Type I and Type II Errors in Hypothesis Testing

	True Situation	
Decision	**H_0 True**	**H_0 False**
Do not reject H_0	Correct Decision	Type II Error
Reject H_0 (accept H_a)	Type I Error	Correct Decision

When we make a decision in a hypothesis test, we run the risk of making either a Type I or a Type II error. These are mutually exclusive errors: If we mistakenly reject the null, we can only be making a Type I error; if we mistakenly fail to reject the null, we can only be making a Type II error.

The probability of a Type I error in testing a hypothesis is denoted by the Greek letter alpha, α. This probability is also known as the **level of significance** of the test. For example, a level of significance of 0.05 for a test means that there is a 5 percent probability of rejecting a true null hypothesis. The probability of a Type II error is denoted by the Greek letter beta, β.

Controlling the probabilities of the two types of errors involves a trade-off. All else equal, if we decrease the probability of a Type I error by specifying a smaller significance level (say 0.01 rather than 0.05), we increase the probability of making a Type II error because we will reject the null less frequently, including when it is false. The only way to reduce the probabilities of both types of errors simultaneously is to increase the sample size, n.

Quantifying the trade-off between the two types of error in practice is usually impossible because the probability of a Type II error is itself hard to quantify. Consider H_0: $\theta \le 5$ versus H_a: $\theta > 5$. Because every true value of θ greater than 5 makes the null hypothesis false, each value of θ greater than 5 has a different β (Type II error probability). In contrast, it is sufficient to state a Type I error probability for $\theta = 5$, the point at which we conduct the test of the null hypothesis. Thus, in general, we specify only α, the probability of a Type I error, when we conduct a hypothesis test. Whereas the significance level of a test is the probability of incorrectly rejecting the null, the **power of a test** is the probability of *correctly* rejecting the null—that is, the probability of rejecting the null when it is false.[9] When more than one test statistic is available to conduct a hypothesis test, we should prefer the most powerful, all else equal.[10]

9 The power of a test is, in fact, 1 minus the probability of a Type II error.
10 We do not always have information on the relative power of the test for competing test statistics, however.

To summarize, the standard approach to hypothesis testing involves specifying a level of significance (probability of Type I error) only. It is most appropriate to specify this significance level prior to calculating the test statistic. If we specify it after calculating the test statistic, we may be influenced by the result of the calculation, which detracts from the objectivity of the test.

We can use three conventional significance levels to conduct hypothesis tests: 0.10, 0.05, and 0.01. Qualitatively, if we can reject a null hypothesis at the 0.10 level of significance, we have *some evidence* that the null hypothesis is false. If we can reject a null hypothesis at the 0.05 level, we have *strong evidence* that the null hypothesis is false. And if we can reject a null hypothesis at the 0.01 level, we have *very strong evidence* that the null hypothesis is false. For the risk premium example, we will specify a 0.05 significance level.

The fourth step in hypothesis testing is stating the decision rule. The general principle is simply stated. When we test the null hypothesis, if we find that the calculated value of the test statistic is more extreme than a given value or values determined by the specified level of significance, α, we reject the null hypothesis. We say the result is **statistically significant**. Otherwise, we do not reject the null hypothesis and we say the result is not statistically significant. The value or values with which we compare the calculated test statistic to make our decision are the rejection points (critical values) for the test.[11]

- **Definition of a Rejection Point (Critical Value) for the Test Statistic.** A rejection point (critical value) for a test statistic is a value with which the computed test statistic is compared to decide whether to reject or not reject the null hypothesis.

For a one-tailed test, we indicate a rejection point using the symbol for the test statistic with a subscript indicating the specified probability of a Type I error, α; for example, z_α. For a two-tailed test, we indicate $z_{\alpha/2}$. To illustrate the use of rejection points, suppose we are using a z-test and have chosen a 0.05 level of significance.

- For a test of H_0: $\theta = \theta_0$ versus H_a: $\theta \neq \theta_0$, two rejection points exist, one negative and one positive. For a two-sided test at the 0.05 level, the total probability of a Type I error must sum to 0.05. Thus, 0.05/2 = 0.025 of the probability should be in each tail of the distribution of the test statistic under the null. Consequently, the two rejection points are $z_{0.025} = 1.96$ and $-z_{0.025} = -1.96$. Let z represent the calculated value of the test statistic. We reject the null if we find that $z < -1.96$ or $z > 1.96$. We do not reject if $-1.96 \leq z \leq 1.96$.
- For a test of H_0: $\theta \leq \theta_0$ versus H_a: $\theta > \theta_0$ at the 0.05 level of significance, the rejection point is $z_{0.05} = 1.645$. We reject the null hypothesis if $z > 1.645$. The value of the standard normal distribution such that 5 percent of the outcomes lie to the right is $z_{0.05} = 1.645$.
- For a test of H_0: $\theta \geq \theta_0$ versus H_a: $\theta < \theta_0$, the rejection point is $-z_{0.05} = -1.645$. We reject the null hypothesis if $z < -1.645$.

Exhibit 2 illustrates a test H_0: $\mu = \mu_0$ versus H_a: $\mu \neq \mu_0$ at the 0.05 significance level using a z-test. The "acceptance region" is the traditional name for the set of values of the test statistic for which we do not reject the null hypothesis. (The traditional name, however, is inaccurate. We should avoid using phrases such as "accept the null hypothesis" because such a statement implies a greater degree of conviction about the

11 "Rejection point" is a descriptive synonym for the more traditional term "critical value."

null than is warranted when we fail to reject it.)[12] On either side of the acceptance region is a rejection region (or critical region). If the null hypothesis that $\mu = \mu_0$ is true, the test statistic has a 2.5 percent chance of falling in the left rejection region and a 2.5 percent chance of falling in the right rejection region. Any calculated value of the test statistic that falls in either of these two regions causes us to reject the null hypothesis at the 0.05 significance level. The rejection points of 1.96 and −1.96 are seen to be the dividing lines between the acceptance and rejection regions.

Exhibit 2 Rejection Points (Critical Values), 0.05 Significance Level, Two-Sided Test of the Population Mean Using a *z*-Test

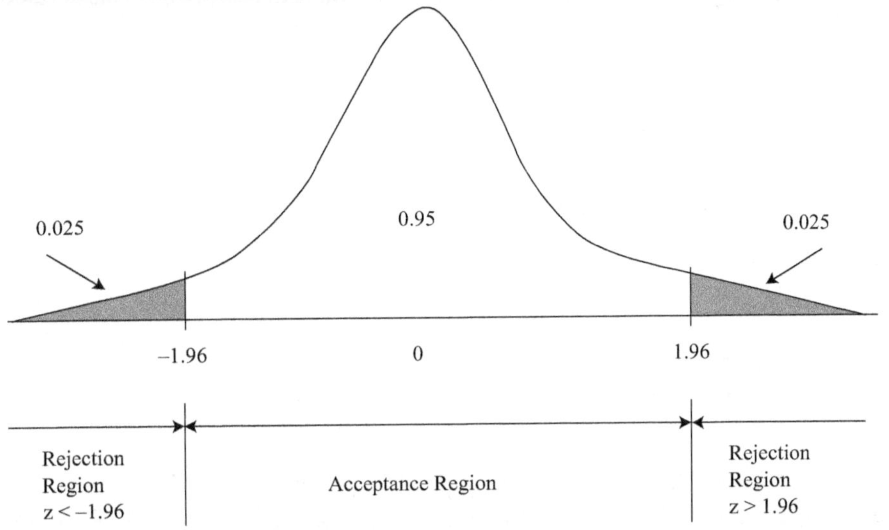

Exhibit 2 affords a good opportunity to highlight the relationship between confidence intervals and hypothesis tests. A 95 percent confidence interval for the population mean, μ, based on sample mean, $\overline{X}$, is given by $\overline{X} - 1.96s_{\overline{X}}$ to $\overline{X} + 1.96s_{\overline{X}}$, where $s_{\overline{X}}$ is the standard error of the sample mean (Equation 3).[13]

Now consider one of the conditions for rejecting the null hypothesis:

$$\frac{\overline{X} - \mu_0}{s_{\overline{X}}} > 1.96$$

Here, μ_0 is the hypothesized value of the population mean. The condition states that rejection is warranted if the test statistic exceeds 1.96. Multiplying both sides by $s_{\overline{X}}$, we have $\overline{X} - \mu_0 > 1.96s_{\overline{X}}$, or after rearranging, $\overline{X} - 1.96s_{\overline{X}} > \mu_0$, which we can also write as $\mu_0 < \overline{X} - 1.96s_{\overline{X}}$. This expression says that if the hypothesized population mean, μ_0, is less than the lower limit of the 95 percent confidence interval based on the sample mean, we must reject the null hypothesis at the 5 percent significance level (the test statistic falls in the rejection region to the right).

12 The analogy in some courts of law (for example, in the United States) is that if a jury does not return a verdict of guilty (the alternative hypothesis), it is most accurate to say that the jury has failed to reject the null hypothesis, namely, that the defendant is innocent.

13 Just as with the hypothesis test, we can use this confidence interval, based on the standard normal distribution, when we have large samples. An alternative hypothesis test and confidence interval uses the *t*-distribution, which requires concepts that we introduce in the next section.

Now, we can take the other condition for rejecting the null hypothesis:

$$\frac{\overline{X} - \mu_0}{s_{\overline{X}}} < -1.96$$

and, using algebra as before, rewrite it as $\mu_0 > \overline{X} + 1.96 s_{\overline{X}}$. If the hypothesized population mean is larger than the upper limit of the 95 percent confidence interval, we reject the null hypothesis at the 5 percent level (the test statistic falls in the rejection region to the left). Thus, an α significance level in a two-sided hypothesis test can be interpreted in exactly the same way as a $(1 - \alpha)$ confidence interval.

In summary, when the hypothesized value of the population parameter under the null is outside the corresponding confidence interval, the null hypothesis is rejected. We could use confidence intervals to test hypotheses; practitioners, however, usually do not. Computing a test statistic (one number, versus two numbers for the usual confidence interval) is more efficient. Also, analysts encounter actual cases of one-sided confidence intervals only rarely. Furthermore, only when we compute a test statistic can we obtain a *p*-value, a useful quantity relating to the significance of our results (we will discuss *p*-values shortly).

To return to our risk premium test, we stated hypotheses H_0: $\mu_{RP} \le 0$ versus H_a: $\mu_{RP} > 0$. We identified the test statistic as $\overline{X}_{RP} / s_{\overline{X}}$ and stated that it follows a standard normal distribution. We are, therefore, conducting a one-sided *z*-test. We specified a 0.05 significance level. For this one-sided *z*-test, the rejection point at the 0.05 level of significance is 1.645. We will reject the null if the calculated *z*-statistic is larger than 1.645. Exhibit 3 illustrates this test.

Exhibit 3 Rejection Point (Critical Value), 0.05 Significance Level, One-Sided Test of the Population Mean Using a *z*-Test

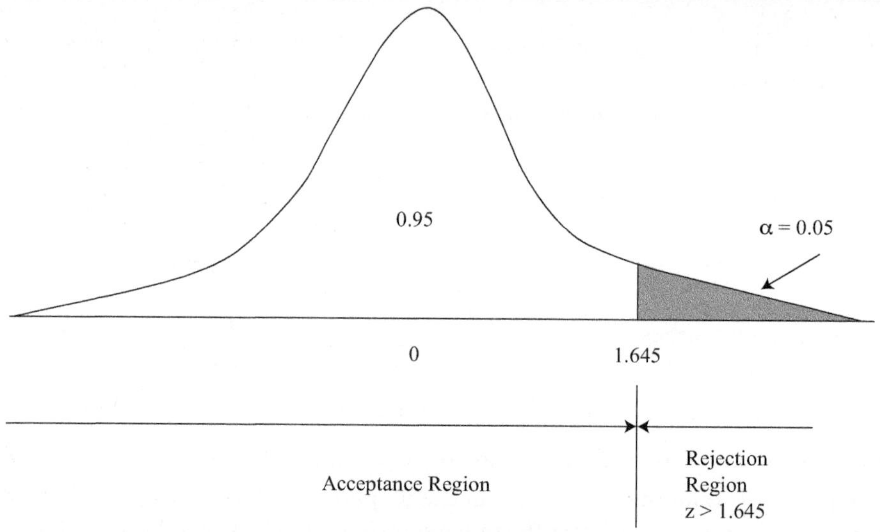

The fifth step in hypothesis testing is collecting the data and calculating the test statistic. The quality of our conclusions depends not only on the appropriateness of the statistical model but also on the quality of the data we use in conducting the test. We first need to check for measurement errors in the recorded data. Some other issues to be aware of include sample selection bias and time-period bias. Sample selection bias refers to bias introduced by systematically excluding some members of the population according to a particular attribute. One type of sample selection bias is survivorship bias. For example, if we define our sample as US bond mutual funds currently operating and we collect returns for just these funds, we will systematically exclude funds that have not survived to the present date. Nonsurviving funds are likely to have underperformed surviving funds, on average; as a result the performance reflected in the sample may be biased upward. Time-period bias refers to the possibility that when we use a time-series sample, our statistical conclusion may be sensitive to the starting and ending dates of the sample.[14]

To continue with the risk premium hypothesis, we focus on US equities. According to Dimson, Marsh, and Staunton (2018) for the period 1900 to 2017 inclusive (118 annual observations), the arithmetic mean equity risk premium for US stocks relative to bill returns, $\overline{X}_{RP}$, was 7.5 percent per year. The sample standard deviation of the annual risk premiums was 19.5 percent. Using Equation 3, the standard error of the sample mean is $s_{\overline{X}} = s/\sqrt{n} = 19.5\%/\sqrt{118} = 1.795\%$. The test statistic is $z = \overline{X}_{RP}/s_{\overline{X}} = 7.5\%/1.795\% = 4.18$.

The sixth step in hypothesis testing is making the statistical decision. For our example, because the test statistic $z = 4.18$ is larger than the rejection point of 1.645, we reject the null hypothesis in favor of the alternative hypothesis that the risk premium on US stocks is positive. The first six steps are the statistical steps. The final decision concerns our use of the statistical decision.

The seventh and final step in hypothesis testing is making the economic or investment decision. The economic or investment decision takes into consideration not only the statistical decision but also all pertinent economic issues. In the sixth step, we found strong statistical evidence that the US risk premium is positive. The magnitude of the estimated risk premium, 7.5 percent a year, is economically very meaningful as well. Based on these considerations, an investor might decide to commit funds to US equities. A range of nonstatistical considerations, such as the investor's tolerance for risk and financial position, might also enter the decision-making process.

The preceding discussion raises an issue that often arises in this decision-making step. We frequently find that slight differences between a variable and its hypothesized value are statistically significant but not economically meaningful. For example, we may be testing an investment strategy and reject a null hypothesis that the mean return to the strategy is zero based on a large sample. Equation 1 shows that the smaller the standard error of the sample statistic (the divisor in the formula), the larger the value of the test statistic and the greater the chance the null will be rejected, all else equal. The standard error decreases as the sample size, n, increases, so that for very large samples, we can reject the null for small departures from it. We may find that although a strategy provides a statistically significant positive mean return, the results are not economically significant when we account for transaction costs, taxes, and risk. Even if we conclude that a strategy's results are economically meaningful, we should explore the logic of why the strategy might work in the future before actually implementing it. Such considerations cannot be incorporated into a hypothesis test.

Before leaving the subject of the process of hypothesis testing, we should discuss an important alternative approach called the p-value approach to hypothesis testing. Analysts and researchers often report the p-value (also called the marginal significance level) associated with hypothesis tests.

- **Definition of p-Value.** The p-value is the smallest level of significance at which the null hypothesis can be rejected.

For the value of the test statistic of 4.18 in the risk premium hypothesis test, using a spreadsheet function for the standard normal distribution, we calculate a p-value of 0.000015. We can reject the null hypothesis at that level of significance. The smaller

14 These issues are discussed further in the reading on sampling.

the p-value, the stronger the evidence against the null hypothesis and in favor of the alternative hypothesis. The p-value for a two-sided test that a parameter equals zero is frequently generated automatically by statistical and econometric software programs.[15]

We can use p-values in the hypothesis testing framework presented above as an alternative to using rejection points. If the p-value is less than our specified level of significance, we reject the null hypothesis. Otherwise, we do not reject the null hypothesis. Using the p-value in this fashion, we reach the same conclusion as we do using rejection points. For example, because 0.000015 is less than 0.05, we would reject the null hypothesis in the risk premium test. The p-value, however, provides more precise information on the strength of the evidence than does the rejection points approach. The p-value of 0.000015 indicates that the null is rejected at a far smaller level of significance than 0.05.

If one researcher examines a question using a 0.05 significance level and another researcher uses a 0.01 significance level, the reader may have trouble comparing the findings. This concern has given rise to an approach to presenting the results of hypothesis tests that features p-values and omits specification of the significance level (Step 3). The interpretation of the statistical results is left to the consumer of the research. This has sometimes been called the p-value approach to hypothesis testing.[16]

3 HYPOTHESIS TESTS CONCERNING THE MEAN

Hypothesis tests concerning the mean are among the most common in practice. In this section we discuss such tests for several distinct types of problems. In one type (discussed in Section 3.1), we test whether the population mean of a single population is equal to (or greater or less than) some hypothesized value. Then, in Sections 3.2 and 3.3, we address inference on means based on two samples. Is an observed difference between two sample means due to chance or different underlying (population) means? When we have two random samples that are independent of each other—no relationship exists between the measurements in one sample and the measurements in the other—the techniques of Section 3.2 apply. When the samples are dependent, the methods of Section 3.3 are appropriate.[17]

3.1 Tests Concerning a Single Mean

An analyst who wants to test a hypothesis concerning the value of an underlying or population mean will conduct a t-test in the great majority of cases. A **t-test** is a hypothesis test using a statistic (t-statistic) that follows a t-distribution. The t-distribution is a probability distribution defined by a single parameter known as degrees of freedom (df). Each value of degrees of freedom defines one distribution in this family of

15 We can use spreadsheets to calculate p-values as well. In Microsoft Excel, for example, we may use the worksheet functions TDIST, NORMSDIST, CHIDIST, and FDIST to calculate p-values for t-tests, z-tests, chi-square tests, and F-tests, respectively.

16 Davidson and MacKinnon (1993) argued the merits of this approach: "The P value approach does not necessarily force us to make a decision about the null hypothesis. If we obtain a P value of, say, 0.000001, we will almost certainly want to reject the null. But if we obtain a P value of, say, 0.04, or even 0.004, we are not *obliged* to reject it. We may simply file the result away as information that casts some doubt on the null hypothesis, but that is not, by itself, conclusive. We believe that this somewhat agnostic attitude toward test statistics, in which they are merely regarded as pieces of information that we may or may not want to act upon, is usually the most sensible one to take." (p. 80)

17 When we want to test whether the population means of more than two populations are equal, we use analysis of variance (ANOVA). We introduce ANOVA in its most common application, regression analysis, in the reading on linear regression.

distributions. The t-distribution is closely related to the standard normal distribution. Like the standard normal distribution, a t-distribution is symmetrical with a mean of zero. However, the t-distribution is more spread out: It has a standard deviation greater than 1 (compared to 1 for the standard normal)[18] and more probability for outcomes distant from the mean (it has fatter tails than the standard normal distribution). As the number of degrees of freedom increases with sample size, the spread decreases and the t-distribution approaches the standard normal distribution as a limit.

Why is the t-distribution the focus for the hypothesis tests of this section? In practice, investment analysts need to estimate the population standard deviation by calculating a sample standard deviation. That is, the population variance (or standard deviation) is unknown. For hypothesis tests concerning the population mean of a normally distributed population with unknown variance, the theoretically correct test statistic is the t-statistic. What if a normal distribution does not describe the population? The t-test is **robust** to moderate departures from normality, except for outliers and strong skewness.[19] When we have large samples, departures of the underlying distribution from the normal are of increasingly less concern. The sample mean is approximately normally distributed in large samples according to the central limit theorem, whatever the distribution describing the population. In general, a sample size of 30 or more usually can be treated as a large sample and a sample size of 29 or less is treated as a small sample.[20]

- **Test Statistic for Hypothesis Tests of the Population Mean (Practical Case—Population Variance Unknown).** If the population sampled has unknown variance and either of the conditions below holds:

  1. the sample is large, or
  2. the sample is small but the population sampled is normally distributed, or approximately normally distributed,

  then the test statistic for hypothesis tests concerning a single population mean, μ, is

$$t_{n-1} = \frac{\overline{X} - \mu_0}{s/\sqrt{n}} \tag{4}$$

  where

  t_{n-1} = t-statistic with $n - 1$ degrees of freedom (n is the sample size)

  $\overline{X}$ = the sample mean

  μ_0 = the hypothesized value of the population mean

  s = the sample standard deviation

---

18 The formula for the variance of a t-distribution is df/(df – 2).

19 See Moore, McCabe, and Craig (2016). A statistic is robust if the required probability calculations are insensitive to violations of the assumptions.

20 Although this generalization is useful, we caution that the sample size needed to obtain an approximately normal sampling distribution for the sample mean depends on how non-normal the original population is. For some populations, "large" may be a sample size well in excess of 30.

The denominator of the t-statistic is an estimate of the sample mean standard error, $s_{\overline{X}} = s/\sqrt{n}$.[21]

In Example 1, because the sample size is small, the test is called a small sample test concerning the population mean.

EXAMPLE 1

Risk and Return Characteristics of an Equity Mutual Fund (1)

You are analyzing Sendar Equity Fund, a midcap growth fund that has been in existence for 24 months. During this period, it has achieved a mean monthly return of 1.50 percent with a sample standard deviation of monthly returns of 3.60 percent. Given its level of systematic (market) risk and according to a pricing model, this mutual fund was expected to have earned a 1.10 percent mean monthly return during that time period. Assuming returns are normally distributed, are the actual results consistent with an underlying or population mean monthly return of 1.10 percent?

1 Formulate null and alternative hypotheses consistent with the description of the research goal.

2 Identify the test statistic for conducting a test of the hypotheses in Part 1.

3 Identify the rejection point or points for the hypothesis tested in Part 1 at the 0.10 level of significance.

4 Determine whether the null hypothesis is rejected or not rejected at the 0.10 level of significance. (Use the tables in the back of this book.)

Solution to 1:

We have a "not equal to" alternative hypothesis, where μ is the underlying mean return on Sendar Equity Fund—H_0: $\mu = 1.10$ versus H_a: $\mu \neq 1.10$.

Solution to 2:

Because the population variance is not known, we use a t-test with 24 – 1 = 23 degrees of freedom.

Solution to 3:

Because this is a two-tailed test, we have the rejection point $t_{\alpha/2,n-1} = t_{0.05,23}$. In the table for the t-distribution, we look across the row for 23 degrees of freedom to the 0.05 column, to find 1.714. The two rejection points for this two-sided test are –1.714 and 1.714. We will reject the null if we find that $t < -1.714$ or $t > 1.714$.

Solution to 4:

$$t_{23} = \frac{1.50 - 1.10}{3.60/\sqrt{24}} = \frac{0.40}{0.734847} = 0.544331 \text{ or } 0.544$$

21 A technical note, for reference, is required. When the sample comes from a finite population, estimates of the standard error of the mean, whether from Equation 2 or Equation 3, overestimate the true standard error. To address this, the computed standard error is multiplied by a shrinkage factor called the finite population correction factor (fpc), equal to $\sqrt{(N-n)/(N-1)}$, where N is the population size and n is the sample size. When the sample size is small relative to the population size (less than 5 percent of the population size), the fpc is usually ignored. The overestimation problem arises only in the usual situation of sampling without replacement (after an item is selected, it cannot be picked again) as opposed to sampling with replacement.

Because 0.544 does not satisfy either $t > 1.714$ or $t < -1.714$, we do not reject the null hypothesis.

The confidence interval approach provides another perspective on this hypothesis test. The theoretically correct $100(1 - \alpha)\%$ confidence interval for the population mean of a normal distribution with unknown variance, based on a sample of size n, is

$$\overline{X} - t_{\alpha/2}s_{\overline{X}} \text{ to } \overline{X} + t_{\alpha/2}s_{\overline{X}}$$

where $t_{\alpha/2}$ is the value of t such that $\alpha/2$ of the probability remains in the right tail and where $-t_{\alpha/2}$ is the value of t such that $\alpha/2$ of the probability remains in the left tail, for $n - 1$ degrees of freedom. Here, the 90 percent confidence interval runs from $1.5 - (1.714)(0.734847) = 0.240$ to $1.5 + (1.714)(0.734847) = 2.760$, compactly [0.240, 2.760]. The hypothesized value of mean return, 1.10, falls within this confidence interval, and we see from this perspective also that the null hypothesis is not rejected. At a 10 percent level of significance, we conclude that a population mean monthly return of 1.10 percent is consistent with the 24-month observed data series. Note that 10 percent is a relatively high probability of rejecting the hypothesis of a 1.10 percent population mean monthly return when it is true.

EXAMPLE 2

A Slowdown in Payments of Receivables

FashionDesigns, a supplier of casual clothing to retail chains, is concerned about a possible slowdown in payments from its customers. The controller's office measures the rate of payment by the average number of days in receivables.[22] FashionDesigns has generally maintained an average of 45 days in receivables. Because it would be too costly to analyze all of the company's receivables frequently, the controller's office uses sampling to track customers' payment rates. A random sample of 50 accounts shows a mean number of days in receivables of 49 with a standard deviation of 8 days.

1 Formulate null and alternative hypotheses consistent with determining whether the evidence supports the suspected condition that customer payments have slowed.

2 Identify the test statistic for conducting a test of the hypotheses in Part 1.

3 Identify the rejection point or points for the hypothesis tested in Part 1 at the 0.05 and 0.01 levels of significance.

4 Determine whether the null hypothesis is rejected or not rejected at the 0.05 and 0.01 levels of significance.

Solution to 1:

The suspected condition is that the number of days in receivables has increased relative to the historical rate of 45 days, which suggests a "greater than" alternative hypothesis. With μ as the population mean number of days in receivables, the hypotheses are H_0: $\mu \le 45$ versus H_a: $\mu > 45$.

---

22 This measure represents the average length of time that the business must wait after making a sale before receiving payment. The calculation is (Accounts receivable)/(Average sales per day).

Solution to 2:

Because the population variance is not known, we use a t-test with 50 − 1 = 49 degrees of freedom.

Solution to 3:

The rejection point is found across the row for degrees of freedom of 49. To find the one-tailed rejection point for a 0.05 significance level, we use the 0.05 column: The value is 1.677. To find the one-tailed rejection point for a 0.01 level of significance, we use the 0.01 column: The value is 2.405. To summarize, at a 0.05 significance level, we reject the null if we find that $t > 1.677$; at a 0.01 significance level, we reject the null if we find that $t > 2.405$.

Solution to 4:

$$t_{49} = \frac{49 - 45}{8/\sqrt{50}} = \frac{4}{1.131371} = 3.536$$

Because 3.536 > 1.677, the null hypothesis is rejected at the 0.05 level. Because 3.536 > 2.405, the null hypothesis is also rejected at the 0.01 level. We can say with a high level of confidence that FashionDesigns has experienced a slowdown in customer payments. The level of significance, 0.01, is a relatively low probability of rejecting the hypothesized mean of 45 days or less. Rejection gives us confidence that the mean has increased above 45 days.

We stated above that when population variance is not known, we use a t-test for tests concerning a single population mean. Given at least approximate normality, the t-test is always called for when we deal with small samples and do not know the population variance. For large samples, the central limit theorem states that the sample mean is approximately normally distributed, whatever the distribution of the population. So the t-test is still appropriate, but an alternative test may be more useful when sample size is large.

For large samples, practitioners sometimes use a z-test in place of a t-test for tests concerning a mean.[23] The justification for using the z-test in this context is twofold. First, in large samples, the sample mean should follow the normal distribution at least approximately, as we have already stated, fulfilling the normality assumption of the z-test. Second, the difference between the rejection points for the t-test and z-test becomes quite small when sample size is large. For a two-sided test at the 0.05 level of significance, the rejection points for a z-test are 1.96 and −1.96. For a t-test, the rejection points are 2.045 and −2.045 for df = 29 (about a 4 percent difference between the z and t rejection points) and 2.009 and −2.009 for df = 50 (about a 2.5 percent difference between the z and t rejection points). Because the t-test is readily available as statistical program output and theoretically correct for unknown population variance, we present it as the test of choice.

In a very limited number of cases, we may know the population variance; in such cases, the z-test is theoretically correct.[24]

- **The z-Test Alternative.**

---

23 These practitioners choose between t-tests and z-tests based on sample size. For small samples ($n < 30$), they use a t-test, and for large samples, a z-test.

24 For example, in Monte Carlo simulation, we prespecify the probability distributions for the risk factors. If we use a normal distribution, we know the true values of mean and variance. Monte Carlo simulation involves the use of a computer to represent the operation of a system subject to risk; we discuss Monte Carlo simulation in the reading on common probability distributions.

1 If the population sampled is normally distributed with known variance σ^2, then the test statistic for a hypothesis test concerning a single population mean, μ, is

$$z = \frac{\overline{X} - \mu_0}{\sigma/\sqrt{n}} \tag{5}$$

2 If the population sampled has unknown variance and the sample is large, in place of a t-test, an alternative test statistic (relying on the central limit theorem) is

$$z = \frac{\overline{X} - \mu_0}{s/\sqrt{n}} \tag{6}$$

In the above equations,

σ = the known population standard deviation
s = the sample standard deviation
μ_0 = the hypothesized value of the population mean

When we use a z-test, we most frequently refer to a rejection point in the list below.

- **Rejection Points for a z-Test.**

A Significance level of $\alpha = 0.10$.

1 H_0: $\theta = \theta_0$ versus H_a: $\theta \neq \theta_0$. The rejection points are $z_{0.05} = 1.645$ and $-z_{0.05} = -1.645$.
Reject the null hypothesis if $z > 1.645$ or if $z < -1.645$.

2 H_0: $\theta \leq \theta_0$ versus H_a: $\theta > \theta_0$. The rejection point is $z_{0.10} = 1.28$.
Reject the null hypothesis if $z > 1.28$.

3 H_0: $\theta \geq \theta_0$ versus H_a: $\theta < \theta_0$. The rejection point is $-z_{0.10} = -1.28$.
Reject the null hypothesis if $z < -1.28$.

B Significance level of $\alpha = 0.05$.

1 H_0: $\theta = \theta_0$ versus H_a: $\theta \neq \theta_0$. The rejection points are $z_{0.025} = 1.96$ and $-z_{0.025} = -1.96$.
Reject the null hypothesis if $z > 1.96$ or if $z < -1.96$.

2 H_0: $\theta \leq \theta_0$ versus H_a: $\theta > \theta_0$. The rejection point is $z_{0.05} = 1.645$.
Reject the null hypothesis if $z > 1.645$.

3 H_0: $\theta \geq \theta_0$ versus H_a: $\theta < \theta_0$. The rejection point is $-z_{0.05} = -1.645$.
Reject the null hypothesis if $z < -1.645$.

C Significance level of $\alpha = 0.01$.

1 H_0: $\theta = \theta_0$ versus H_a: $\theta \neq \theta_0$. The rejection points are $z_{0.005} = 2.575$ and $-z_{0.005} = -2.575$.
Reject the null hypothesis if $z > 2.575$ or if $z < -2.575$.

2 H_0: $\theta \leq \theta_0$ versus H_a: $\theta > \theta_0$. The rejection point is $z_{0.01} = 2.33$.
Reject the null hypothesis if $z > 2.33$.

3 H_0: $\theta \geq \theta_0$ versus H_a: $\theta < \theta_0$. The rejection point is $-z_{0.01} = -2.33$.
Reject the null hypothesis if $z < -2.33$.

Next, we present a historical example of conducting a hypothesis test on the potential impact of negative internal control disclosure by a company on its stock price.

EXAMPLE 3

The Effect of Control Deficiency Disclosures under the Sarbanes–Oxley Act on Share Prices

The Sarbanes–Oxley Act came into effect in 2002 and introduced major changes to the regulation of corporate governance and financial practice in the United States. One of the requirements of this Act is for firms to periodically assess and report certain types of internal control deficiencies to the audit committee, external auditors, and to the Securities and Exchange Commission (SEC). When a company makes an internal control weakness disclosure, does it convey information that affects the market value of the firm's stock?

Gupta and Nayar (2007) addressed this question by studying a number of voluntary disclosures made in the very early days of Sarbanes–Oxley implementation. Their final sample for this study consisted of 90 firms that had made control deficiency disclosures to the SEC from March 2003 to July 2004. This 90-firm sample was termed the "full sample". These firms were further examined to see if there were any other contemporaneous announcements, such as earnings announcements, associated with the control deficiency disclosures. Of the 90 firms, 45 did not have any such confounding announcements, and the sample of these firms was termed the "clean sample".

The announcement day of the internal control weakness was designated $t = 0$. If these announcements provide *new* information useful for equity valuation, the information should cause a change in stock prices and returns once it is available. Only one component of stock returns is of interest: the return in excess of that predicted given a stock's market risk or beta, called the abnormal return. Significant negative (positive) abnormal returns indicate that investors perceive unfavorable (favorable) corporate news in the internal control weakness announcement. Although Gupta and Nayar examined abnormal returns for various time horizons or event windows, we report a selection of their findings for the window [0, +1], which includes a two-day period of the day of and the day after the announcement. The researchers chose to use z-tests for statistical significance.

Full sample (90 firms). The null hypothesis that the average abnormal stock return during [0, +1] was 0 would be true if stock investors did not find either positive or negative information in the announcement.

Mean abnormal return = –3.07 percent.

z-statistic for abnormal return = –5.938.

Clean sample (45 firms). The null hypothesis that the average abnormal stock return during [0, +1] was 0 would be true if stock investors did not find either positive or negative information in the announcement.

Mean abnormal return = –1.87 percent.

z-statistic for abnormal return = –3.359.

1 With respect to both of the cases, suppose that the null hypothesis reflects the belief that investors do not, on average, perceive either positive or negative information in control deficiency disclosures. State one set of hypotheses (a null hypothesis and an alternative hypothesis) that covers both cases.

2 Determine whether the null hypothesis formulated in Part 1 is rejected or not rejected at the 0.05 and 0.01 levels of significance for the *full sample* case. Interpret the results.

3 Determine whether the null hypothesis formulated in Part 1 is rejected or not rejected at the 0.05 and 0.01 levels of significance for the *clean sample* case. Interpret the results.

Solution to 1:

A set of hypotheses consistent with no information in control deficiency disclosures relevant to stock investors is

H_0: The population mean abnormal return during [0, +1] equals 0.

H_a: The population mean abnormal return during [0, +1] does not equal 0.

Solution to 2:

From the information on rejection points for *z*-tests, we know that we reject the null hypothesis at the 0.05 significance level if $z > 1.96$ or if $z < -1.96$, and at the 0.01 significance level if $z > 2.575$ or if $z < -2.575$. The *z*-statistic reported by the researchers is −5.938, which is significant at the 0.05 and 0.01 levels. The null is rejected. The control deficiency disclosures appear to contain valuation-relevant information.

Because it is possible that significant results could be due to outliers, the researchers also reported the number of cases of positive and negative abnormal returns. The ratio of cases of positive to negative abnormal returns was 32:58, which tends to support the conclusion from the *z*-test of statistically significant negative abnormal returns.

Solution to 3:

The *z*-statistic reported by the researchers for the clean sample is −3.359, which is significant at the 0.05 and 0.01 levels. Although both the mean abnormal return and the *z*-statistic are smaller in magnitude for the clean sample than for the full sample, the results continue to be statistically significant.

The ratio of cases of positive to negative abnormal returns was 16:29, which tends to support the conclusion from the *z*-test of statistically significant negative abnormal returns.

Nearly all practical situations involve an unknown population variance. Exhibit 4 summarizes our discussion for tests concerning the population mean when the population variance is unknown.

Exhibit 4 Test Concerning the Population Mean (Population Variance Unknown)

	Large Sample ($n \geq 30$)	Small Sample ($n < 30$)
Population normal	*t*-Test (*z*-Test alternative)	*t*-Test
Population non-normal	*t*-Test (*z*-Test alternative)	Not Available

3.2 Tests Concerning Differences between Means

We often want to know whether a mean value—for example, a mean return—differs between two groups. Is an observed difference due to chance or to different underlying values for the mean? We have two samples, one for each group. When it is reasonable to believe that the samples are from populations at least approximately normally distributed and that the samples are also independent of each other, the techniques of this section apply. We discuss two *t*-tests for a test concerning differences between the means of two populations. In one case, the population variances, although unknown, can be assumed to be equal. Then, we efficiently combine the observations from both samples to obtain a pooled estimate of the common but unknown population variance. A pooled estimate is an estimate drawn from the combination of two different samples. In the second case, we do not assume that the unknown population variances are equal, and an approximate *t*-test is then available. Letting μ_1 and μ_2 stand, respectively, for the population means of the first and second populations, we most often want to test whether the population means, although unknown, are equal or whether one is larger than the other. Thus we usually formulate the following hypotheses:

1 H_0: $\mu_1 - \mu_2 = 0$ versus H_a: $\mu_1 - \mu_2 \neq 0$ (the alternative is that $\mu_1 \neq \mu_2$)

2 H_0: $\mu_1 - \mu_2 \leq 0$ versus H_a: $\mu_1 - \mu_2 > 0$ (the alternative is that $\mu_1 > \mu_2$)

3 H_0: $\mu_1 - \mu_2 \geq 0$ versus H_a: $\mu_1 - \mu_2 < 0$ (the alternative is that $\mu_1 < \mu_2$)

We can, however, formulate other hypotheses, such as H_0: $\mu_1 - \mu_2 = 2$ versus H_a: $\mu_1 - \mu_2 \neq 2$. The procedure is the same.

The definition of the *t*-test follows.

- **Test Statistic for a Test of the Difference between Two Population Means (Normally Distributed Populations, Population Variances Unknown but Assumed Equal).** When we can assume that the two populations are normally distributed and that the unknown population variances are equal, a *t*-test based on independent random samples is given by

$$t = \frac{(\bar{X}_1 - \bar{X}_2) - (\mu_1 - \mu_2)}{\left(\frac{s_p^2}{n_1} + \frac{s_p^2}{n_2}\right)^{1/2}} \tag{7}$$

where $s_p^2 = \frac{(n_1 - 1)s_1^2 + (n_2 - 1)s_2^2}{n_1 + n_2 - 2}$ is a pooled estimator of the common variance.

The number of degrees of freedom is $n_1 + n_2 - 2$.

EXAMPLE 4

Mean Returns on the S&P BSE SENSEX: A Test of Equality across Two Time Periods

The S&P BSE SENSEX is an index designed to measure the performance of the Indian stock market. The realized mean monthly return on this index in years 2012–2014 appears to have been substantially different than the mean return in years 2015–2017. Was the difference statistically significant? The data, shown in Exhibit 5, indicate that the difference in standard deviations during these two periods is small. Therefore, assuming equal population variances for returns in the two periods is not unreasonable.

Exhibit 5 S&P BSE SENSEX Monthly Return and Standard Deviation for Two Time Periods

Time Period	Number of Months (n)	Mean Monthly Return (%)	Standard Deviation
2012 through 2014	36	1.694	4.115
2015 through 2017	36	0.665	3.779

Source of data returns: https://www.asiaindex.co.in/indices/equity/sp-bse-sensex accessed 18 August 2018.

1 Formulate null and alternative hypotheses consistent with a two-sided hypothesis test.

2 Identify the test statistic for conducting a test of the hypotheses in Part 1.

3 Identify the rejection point or points for the hypothesis tested in Part 1 at the 0.10, 0.05, and 0.01 levels of significance.

4 Determine whether the null hypothesis is rejected or not rejected at the 0.10, 0.05, and 0.01 levels of significance.

Solution to 1:

Letting μ_1 represent the population mean return for the 2012 through 2014 and μ_2 represent the population mean return for the 2015 through 2017, we formulate the following hypotheses:

$$H_0: \mu_1 - \mu_2 = 0 \text{ versus } H_a: \mu_1 - \mu_2 \neq 0$$

Solution to 2:

Because the two samples are drawn from two different time periods, they are independent samples. The population variances are not known but can be assumed to be equal. Given all these considerations, the t-test given in Equation 7 has 36 + 36 − 2 = 70 degrees of freedom.

Solution to 3:

In the tables (Appendix B), for a two-sided test, the rejection points are ±1.667, ±1.994, and ±2.648 for, respectively, the 0.10, 0.05, and 0.01 levels for df = 70. To summarize, at the 0.10 level, we will reject the null if $t < -1.667$ or $t > 1.667$; at the 0.05 level, we will reject the null if $t < -1.994$ or $t > 1.994$; and at the 0.01 level, we will reject the null if $t < -2.648$ or $t > 2.648$.

Solution to 4:

In calculating the test statistic, the first step is to calculate the pooled estimate of variance:

$$\begin{aligned} s_p^2 &= \frac{(n_1 - 1)s_1^2 + (n_2 - 1)s_2^2}{n_1 + n_2 - 2} \\ &= \frac{(36 - 1)(4.115)^2 + (36 - 1)(3.779)^2}{36 + 36 - 2} \\ &= \frac{1{,}092.4923}{70} \\ &= 15.6070 \end{aligned}$$

$$t = \frac{(\bar{X}_1 - \bar{X}_2) - (\mu_1 - \mu_2)}{\left(\frac{s_p^2}{n_1} + \frac{s_p^2}{n_2}\right)^{1/2}}$$

$$= \frac{(1.694 - 0.665) - 0}{\left(\frac{15.6070}{36} + \frac{15.6070}{36}\right)^{1/2}}$$

$$= \frac{1.029}{0.9312}$$

$$= 1.11$$

The calculated t statistic of 1.11 is not significant at the 0.10 level, so it is also not significant at the 0.05 and 0.01 levels. Therefore, we do not reject the null hypothesis at any of the three levels.

In many cases of practical interest, we cannot assume that population variances are equal. The following test statistic is often used in the investment literature in such cases:

- **Test Statistic for a Test of the Difference between Two Population Means (Normally Distributed Populations, Unequal and Unknown Population Variances).** When we can assume that the two populations are normally distributed but do not know the population variances and cannot assume that they are equal, an approximate t-test based on independent random samples is given by

$$t = \frac{(\bar{X}_1 - \bar{X}_2) - (\mu_1 - \mu_2)}{\left(\frac{s_1^2}{n_1} + \frac{s_2^2}{n_2}\right)^{1/2}} \quad (8)$$

where we use tables of the t-distribution using "modified" degrees of freedom computed with the formula

$$\text{df} = \frac{\left(\frac{s_1^2}{n_1} + \frac{s_2^2}{n_2}\right)^2}{\frac{(s_1^2/n_1)^2}{n_1} + \frac{(s_2^2/n_2)^2}{n_2}} \quad (9)$$

A practical tip is to compute the t-statistic before computing the degrees of freedom. Whether or not the t-statistic is significant will sometimes be obvious.

EXAMPLE 5

Recovery Rates on Defaulted Bonds: A Hypothesis Test

How are the required yields on risky corporate bonds determined? Two key factors are the expected probability of default and the expected amount that will be recovered in the event of default, or the recovery rate. Jankowitsch, Nagler, and Subrahmanyam (2014) examine the recovery rates of defaulted bonds in the US corporate bond market based on an extensive set of traded prices and volumes around various types of default events. For their study period, 2002 to

2012, Jankowitsch et al. confirm that the type of default event (e.g., distressed exchanges and formal bankruptcy filings), the seniority of the bond, and the industry of the firm are important in explaining the recovery rate. In one of their analyses, they focus on non-financial firms, and find that electricity firms recover more in default than firms in the retail industry. We want to test if the difference in recovery rates between those two types of firms is statistically significant. With μ_1 denoting the population mean recovery rate for the bonds of electricity firms and μ_2 denoting the population mean recovery rate for the bonds of retail firms, the hypotheses are H_0: $\mu_1 - \mu_2 = 0$ versus H_a: $\mu_1 - \mu_2 \neq 0$.

Exhibit 6 excerpts from their findings.

Exhibit 6 Recovery Rates by Industry of Firm

Electricity			Retail		
Number of Observations	Average Price[a]	Standard Deviation	Number of Observations	Average Price[a]	Standard Deviation
39	\$48.03	\$22.67	33	\$33.40	\$34.19

[a] This is the average traded price over the default day and the following 30 days after default; the average price provides an indication of the amount of money that can be recovered.

Source: Jankowitsch, Nagler, and Subrahmanyam (2013), Table 2.

We assume that the populations (recovery rates) are normally distributed and that the samples are independent. Based on the data in the table, address the following:

1 Discuss whether we should choose a test based on Equation 8 or Equation 7.

2 Calculate the test statistic to test the null hypothesis given above.

3 What is the value of the test's modified degrees of freedom?

4 Determine whether to reject the null hypothesis at the 0.10 level.

Solution to 1:

The sample standard deviation for the recovery rate on the bonds of electricity firms (\$22.67) appears much smaller than the sample standard deviation of the bonds for retail firms (\$34.19). Therefore, we should not assume equal variances, and accordingly, we should employ the approximate *t*-test given in Equation 8.

Solution to 2:

The test statistic is

$$t = \frac{\left(\bar{X}_1 - \bar{X}_2\right)}{\left(\frac{s_1^2}{n_1} + \frac{s_2^2}{n_2}\right)^{1/2}}$$

where

$\bar{X}_1$ = sample mean recovery rate for electricity firms = 48.03

$\bar{X}_2$ = sample mean recovery rate for retail firms = 33.40

s_1^2 = sample variance for electricity firms = 22.67^2 = 513.9289

s_2^2 = sample variance for retail firms = 34.19^2 = 1,168.9561

n_1 = sample size of the electricity firms sample = 39

n_2 = sample size of the retail firms sample = 33

Thus, $t = (48.03 - 33.40)/[(513.9289/39) + (1{,}168.9561/33)]^{1/2} = 14.63/(13.177664 + 35.422912)^{1/2} = 14.63/6.971411 = 2.099$. The calculated t-statistic is thus 2.099.

Solution to 3:

$$\text{df} = \frac{\left(\dfrac{s_1^2}{n_1} + \dfrac{s_2^2}{n_2}\right)^2}{\dfrac{\left(s_1^2/n_1\right)^2}{n_1} + \dfrac{\left(s_2^2/n_2\right)^2}{n_2}} = \frac{\left(\dfrac{513.9289}{39} + \dfrac{1{,}168.9561}{33}\right)^2}{\dfrac{(513.9289/39)^2}{39} + \dfrac{(1{,}168.9561/33)^2}{33}}$$

$$= \frac{2362.016009}{42.476304} = 55.61 \text{ or } 56 \text{ degrees of freedom}$$

Solution to 4:

The closest entry to df = 56 in the tables for the t-distribution is df = 60. For α = 0.10, we find $t_{\alpha/2}$ = 1.671. Thus, we reject the null if $t < -1.671$ or $t > 1.671$. Based on the computed value of 2.099, we reject the null hypothesis at the 0.10 level. Some evidence exists that recovery rates differ between electricity and retail industries. Why? Studies on recovery rates suggest that the higher recovery rates of electricity firms may be explained by their higher levels of tangible assets.

3.3 Tests Concerning Mean Differences

In the previous section, we presented two t-tests for discerning differences between population means. The tests were based on two samples. An assumption for those tests' validity was that the samples were independent—i.e., unrelated to each other. When we want to conduct tests on two means based on samples that we believe are dependent, the methods of this section apply.

The t-test in this section is based on data arranged in **paired observations**, and the test itself is sometimes called a **paired comparisons test**. Paired observations are observations that are dependent because they have something in common. A paired comparisons test is a statistical test for differences in dependent items. For example, we may be concerned with the dividend policy of companies before and after a change in the tax law affecting the taxation of dividends. We then have pairs of "before" and "after" observations for the same companies. We may test a hypothesis about the mean of the differences (mean differences) that we observe across companies. In other cases, the paired observations are not on the same units. For example, we may be testing whether the mean returns earned by two investment strategies were equal over a study period. The observations here are dependent in the sense that there is one observation for each strategy in each month, and both observations depend on underlying market risk factors. Because the returns to both strategies are likely to be related to some common risk factors, such as the market return, the samples are dependent. By calculating a standard error based on differences, the t-test presented below takes account of correlation between the observations.

Letting A represent "after" and B "before," suppose we have observations for the random variables X_A and X_B and that the samples are dependent. We arrange the observations in pairs. Let d_i denote the difference between two paired observations. We can use the notation $d_i = x_{Ai} - x_{Bi}$, where x_{Ai} and x_{Bi} are the ith pair of observations, $i = 1, 2, \ldots, n$ on the two variables. Let μ_d stand for the population mean difference. We can formulate the following hypotheses, where μ_{d0} is a hypothesized value for the population mean difference:

1 H_0: $\mu_d = \mu_{d0}$ versus H_a: $\mu_d \neq \mu_{d0}$
2 H_0: $\mu_d \leq \mu_{d0}$ versus H_a: $\mu_d > \mu_{d0}$
3 H_0: $\mu_d \geq \mu_{d0}$ versus H_a: $\mu_d < \mu_{d0}$

In practice, the most commonly used value for μ_{d0} is 0.

As usual, we are concerned with the case of normally distributed populations with unknown population variances, and we will formulate a t-test. To calculate the t-statistic, we first need to find the sample mean difference:

$$\bar{d} = \frac{1}{n}\sum_{i=1}^{n} d_i \quad (10)$$

where n is the number of pairs of observations. The sample variance, denoted by s_d^2, is

$$s_d^2 = \frac{\sum_{i=1}^{n}\left(d_i - \bar{d}\right)^2}{n-1} \quad (11)$$

Taking the square root of this quantity, we have the sample standard deviation, s_d, which then allows us to calculate the standard error of the mean difference as follows:[25]

$$s_{\bar{d}} = \frac{s_d}{\sqrt{n}} \quad (12)$$

- **Test Statistic for a Test of Mean Differences (Normally Distributed Populations, Unknown Population Variances).** When we have data consisting of paired observations from samples generated by normally distributed populations with unknown variances, a t-test is based on

$$t = \frac{\bar{d} - \mu_{d0}}{s_{\bar{d}}} \quad (13)$$

with $n - 1$ degrees of freedom, where n is the number of paired observations, $\bar{d}$ is the sample mean difference (as given by Equation 10), and $s_{\bar{d}}$ is the standard error of $\bar{d}$ (as given by Equation 12).

Exhibit 7 reports the quarterly returns for a six-year period for two managed portfolios specializing in precious metals. The two portfolios were closely similar in risk (as measured by standard deviation of return and other measures) and had nearly identical expense ratios. A major investment services company rated Portfolio B more

25 We can also use the following equivalent expression, which makes use of the correlation between the two variables: $s_{\bar{d}} = \sqrt{s_A^2 + s_B^2 - 2r(X_A, X_B)s_A s_B}\,/\sqrt{n}$ where s_A^2 is the sample variance of X_A, s_B^2 is the sample variance of X_B, and $r(X_A, X_B)$ is the sample correlation between X_A and X_B.

highly than Portfolio A. In investigating the portfolios' relative performance, suppose we want to test the hypothesis that the mean quarterly return on Portfolio A equaled the mean quarterly return on Portfolio B during the six-year period. Because the two portfolios shared essentially the same set of risk factors, their returns were not independent, so a paired comparisons test is appropriate. Let μ_d stand for the population mean value of difference between the returns on the two portfolios during this period. We test H_0: $\mu_d = 0$ versus H_a: $\mu_d \neq 0$ at a 0.05 significance level.

Exhibit 7 Quarterly Returns on Two Managed Portfolios

Quarter	Portfolio A (%)	Portfolio B (%)	Difference (Portfolio A – Portfolio B)
4Q:Year 6	11.40	14.64	−3.24
3Q:Year 6	−2.17	0.44	−2.61
2Q:Year 6	10.72	19.51	−8.79
1Q:Year 6	38.91	50.40	−11.49
4Q:Year 5	4.36	1.01	3.35
3Q:Year 5	5.13	10.18	−5.05
2Q:Year 5	26.36	17.77	8.59
1Q:Year 5	−5.53	4.76	−10.29
4Q:Year 4	5.27	−5.36	10.63
3Q:Year 4	−7.82	−1.54	−6.28
2Q:Year 4	2.34	0.19	2.15
1Q:Year 4	−14.38	−12.07	−2.31
4Q:Year 3	−9.80	−9.98	0.18
3Q:Year 3	19.03	26.18	−7.15
2Q:Year 3	4.11	−2.39	6.50
1Q:Year 3	−4.12	−2.51	−1.61
4Q:Year 2	−0.53	−11.32	10.79
3Q:Year 2	5.06	0.46	4.60
2Q:Year 2	−14.01	−11.56	−2.45
1Q:Year 2	12.50	3.52	8.98
4Q:Year 1	−29.05	−22.45	−6.60
3Q:Year 1	3.60	0.10	3.50
2Q:Year 1	−7.97	−8.96	0.99
1Q:Year 1	−8.62	−0.66	−7.96
Mean	1.87	2.52	−0.65

Sample standard deviation of differences = 6.71

The sample mean difference, $\bar{d}$, between Portfolio A and Portfolio B is −0.65 percent per quarter. The standard error of the sample mean difference is $s_{\bar{d}} = 6.71/\sqrt{24} = 1.369673$. The calculated test statistic is $t = (-0.65 - 0)/1.369673 = -0.475$ with $n - 1 = 24 - 1 = 23$ degrees of freedom. At the 0.05 significance level, we reject the null if $t > 2.069$ or if $t < -2.069$. Because −0.475 is not less than −2.069, we fail to reject the null. At the 0.10 significance level, we reject the null if $t > 1.714$ or if $t < -1.714$. Thus, the difference in mean quarterly returns is not significant at any conventional significance level.

The following example illustrates the application of this test to evaluate two competing investment strategies.

EXAMPLE 6

A Comparison of Two Portfolios

You are investigating whether the performance of a portfolio of stocks from the entire world differs from the performance of a portfolio of only US stocks. For the worldwide portfolio, you choose to focus on Vanguard Total World Stock Index ETF. This ETF seeks to track the performance of the FTSE Global All Cap Index, which is a market-capitalization-weighted index designed to measure the market performance of stock of companies from both developed and emerging markets. For the US portfolio, you choose to focus on SPDR S&P 500, an ETF that seeks to track the performance of the S&P 500 Index. You analyze the monthly returns on both ETFs from August 2013 to July 2018 and prepare the following summary table.

Exhibit 8 Montly Return Summary for Vanguard Total World Stock Index ETF and SPDR S&P 500 ETF: August 2013 to July 2018 ($n = 60$)

Strategy	Mean Return	Standard Deviation
Worldwide	0.79%	2.93%
US	1.06	2.81
Difference	−0.27	1.00[a]

[a] Sample standard deviation of differences.
Source of data returns: finance.yahoo.com accessed 18 August 2018.

From Exhibit 8 we have $\overline{d} = -0.27\%$ and $s_d = 1.00\%$.

1 Formulate null and alternative hypotheses consistent with a two-sided test that the mean difference between the worldwide and only US strategies equals 0.

2 Identify the test statistic for conducting a test of the hypotheses in Part 1.

3 Identify the rejection point or points for the hypothesis tested in Part 1 at the 0.01 level of significance.

4 Determine whether the null hypothesis is rejected or not rejected at the 0.01 level of significance. (Use the tables in the back of this volume.)

5 Discuss the choice of a paired comparisons test.

Solution to 1:

With μ_d as the underlying mean difference between the worldwide and US strategies, we have H_0: $\mu_d = 0$ versus H_a: $\mu_d \neq 0$.

Solution to 2:

Because the population variance is unknown, the test statistic is a t-test with $60 - 1 = 59$ degrees of freedom.

Solution to 3:

In the table for the t-distribution, the closest entry to df = 59 is df = 60. We look across the row for 60 degrees of freedom to the 0.005 column, to find 2.66. We will reject the null if we find that $t > 2.66$ or $t < -2.66$.

Solution to 4:

$$t_{59} = \frac{-0.27}{1.00/\sqrt{60}} = \frac{-0.27}{0.129099} = -2.09$$

Because −2.09 > −2.66, we cannot reject the null hypothesis. Accordingly, we conclude that the difference in mean returns for the two strategies is not statistically significant.

Solution to 5:

Several US stocks that are part of the S&P 500 index are also included in the Vanguard Total World Stock Index ETF. The profile of the World ETF indicates that nine of the top ten holdings in the ETF are US stocks. As a result, they are not independent samples; in general, the correlation of returns on the Vanguard Total World Stock Index ETF and SPDR S&P 500 ETF should be positive. Because the samples are dependent, a paired comparisons test was appropriate.

4 HYPOTHESIS TESTS CONCERNING VARIANCE AND CORRELATION

Because variance and standard deviation are widely used quantitative measures of risk in investments, analysts should be familiar with hypothesis tests concerning variance. The correlation between two variables is also widely used in investments. For example, investment managers often need to understand the correlations among returns on different assets. Therefore, analysts should also be familiar with hypothesis tests concerning correlation. The tests of variance and correlation discussed in this section make regular appearances in investment literature. Next, we examine two types of tests concerning variance: tests concerning the value of a single population variance and tests concerning the differences between two population variances. We then examine how to test the significance of a correlation coefficient.

4.1 Tests Concerning a Single Variance

In this section, we discuss testing hypotheses about the value of the variance, σ^2, of a single population. We use σ_0^2 to denote the hypothesized value of σ^2. We can formulate hypotheses as follows:

1 $H_0: \sigma^2 = \sigma_0^2$ versus $H_a: \sigma^2 \neq \sigma_0^2$ (a "not equal to" alternative hypothesis)

2 $H_0: \sigma^2 \leq \sigma_0^2$ versus $H_a: \sigma^2 > \sigma_0^2$ (a "greater than" alternative hypothesis)

3 $H_0: \sigma^2 \geq \sigma_0^2$ versus $H_a: \sigma^2 < \sigma_0^2$ (a "less than" alternative hypothesis)

In tests concerning the variance of a single normally distributed population, we make use of a chi-square test statistic, denoted χ^2. The chi-square distribution, unlike the normal and t-distributions, is asymmetrical. Like the t-distribution, the chi-square distribution is a family of distributions. A different distribution exists for each possible value of degrees of freedom, $n - 1$ (n is sample size). Unlike the t-distribution, the chi-square distribution is bounded below by 0; χ^2 does not take on negative values.

- **Test Statistic for Tests Concerning the Value of a Population Variance (Normal Population).** If we have n independent observations from a normally distributed population, the appropriate test statistic is

$$\chi^2 = \frac{(n-1)s^2}{\sigma_0^2} \tag{14}$$

with $n - 1$ degrees of freedom. In the numerator of the expression is the sample variance, calculated as

$$s^2 = \frac{\sum_{i=1}^{n}\left(X_i - \overline{X}\right)^2}{n-1} \tag{15}$$

In contrast to the t-test, for example, the chi-square test is sensitive to violations of its assumptions. If the sample is not actually random or if it does not come from a normally distributed population, inferences based on a chi-square test are likely to be faulty.

If we choose a level of significance, α, the rejection points for the three kinds of hypotheses are as follows:

- **Rejection Points for Hypothesis Tests on the Population Variance.**
  1. "Not equal to" H_a: Reject the null hypothesis if the test statistic is greater than the upper α/2 point (denoted $\chi^2_{\alpha/2}$) or less than the lower α/2 point (denoted $\chi^2_{1-\alpha/2}$) of the chi-square distribution with df = $n - 1$.[26]
  2. "Greater than" H_a: Reject the null hypothesis if the test statistic is greater than the upper α point of the chi-square distribution with df = $n - 1$.
  3. "Less than" H_a: Reject the null hypothesis if the test statistic is less than the lower α point of the chi-square distribution with df = $n - 1$.

EXAMPLE 7

Risk and Return Characteristics of an Equity Mutual Fund (2)

You continue with your analysis of Sendar Equity Fund, a midcap growth fund that has been in existence for only 24 months. Recall that during this period, Sendar Equity achieved a sample standard deviation of monthly returns of 3.60 percent. You now want to test a claim that the specific investment approach followed by Sendar result in a standard deviation of monthly returns of less than 4 percent.

1. Formulate null and alternative hypotheses consistent with the verbal description of the research goal.

---

26 Just as with other hypothesis tests, the chi-square test can be given a confidence interval interpretation. Unlike confidence intervals based on z- or t-statistics, however, chi-square confidence intervals for variance are asymmetric. A two-sided confidence interval for population variance, based on a sample of size n, has a lower limit $L = (n-1)s^2/\chi^2_{\alpha/2}$ and an upper limit $U = (n-1)s^2/\chi^2_{1-\alpha/2}$. Under the null hypothesis, the hypothesized value of the population variance should fall within these two limits.

2 Identify the test statistic for conducting a test of the hypotheses in Part 1.

3 Identify the rejection point or points for the hypothesis tested in Part 1 at the 0.05 level of significance.

4 Determine whether the null hypothesis is rejected or not rejected at the 0.05 level of significance. (Use the tables in the back of this volume.)

Solution to 1:

We have a "less than" alternative hypothesis, where σ is the underlying standard deviation of return on Sendar Equity Fund. Being careful to square standard deviation to obtain a test in terms of variance, the hypotheses are H_0: $\sigma^2 \geq 16.0$ versus H_a: $\sigma^2 < 16.0$.

Solution to 2:

The test statistic is χ^2 with 24 – 1 = 23 degrees of freedom.

Solution to 3:

The lower 0.05 rejection point is found on the line for df = 23, under the 0.95 column (95 percent probability in the right tail, to give 0.95 probability of getting a test statistic this large or larger). The rejection point is 13.091. We will reject the null if we find that χ^2 is less than 13.091.

Solution to 4:

$$\chi^2 = \frac{(n-1)s^2}{\sigma_0^2} = \frac{23 \times 3.60^2}{4^2} = \frac{298.08}{16} = 18.63$$

Because 18.63 (the calculated value of the test statistic) is not less than 13.091, we do not reject the null hypothesis. We cannot conclude that Sendar's investment disciplines result in a standard deviation of monthly returns of less than 4 percent.

4.2 Tests Concerning the Equality (Inequality) of Two Variances

Suppose we have a hypothesis about the relative values of the variances of two normally distributed populations with means μ_1 and μ_2 and variances σ_1^2 and σ_2^2. We can formulate all hypotheses as one of the choices below:

1 $H_0: \sigma_1^2 = \sigma_2^2$ versus $H_a: \sigma_1^2 \neq \sigma_2^2$

2 $H_0: \sigma_1^2 \leq \sigma_2^2$ versus $H_a: \sigma_1^2 > \sigma_2^2$

3 $H_0: \sigma_1^2 \geq \sigma_2^2$ versus $H_a: \sigma_1^2 < \sigma_2^2$

Note that at the point of equality, the null hypothesis $\sigma_1^2 = \sigma_2^2$ implies that the ratio of population variances equals 1: $\sigma_1^2/\sigma_2^2 = 1$. Given independent random samples from these populations, tests related to these hypotheses are based on an *F*-test, which is the ratio of sample variances. Suppose we use n_1 observations in calculating the sample variance s_1^2 and n_2 observations in calculating the sample variance s_2^2. Tests concerning the difference between the variances of two populations make use of the *F*-distribution. Like the chi-square distribution, the *F*-distribution is a family of asymmetrical distributions bounded from below by 0. Each *F*-distribution is defined by two values of degrees of freedom, called the numerator and denominator degrees of freedom.[27] The F-test, like the chi-square test, is not robust to violations of its assumptions.

- **Test Statistic for Tests Concerning Differences between the Variances of Two Populations (Normally Distributed Populations).** Suppose we have two samples, the first with n_1 observations and sample variance s_1^2, the second with n_2 observations and sample variance s_2^2. The samples are random, independent of each other, and generated by normally distributed populations. A test concerning differences between the variances of the two populations is based on the ratio of sample variances

$$F = \frac{s_1^2}{s_2^2} \tag{16}$$

with $\text{df}_1 = n_1 - 1$ numerator degrees of freedom and $\text{df}_2 = n_2 - 1$ denominator degrees of freedom. Note that df_1 and df_2 are the divisors used in calculating s_1^2 and s_2^2, respectively.

A convention, or usual practice, is to use the larger of the two ratios s_1^2/s_2^2 or s_2^2/s_1^2 as the actual test statistic. When we follow this convention, the value of the test statistic is always greater than or equal to 1; tables of critical values of F then need include only values greater than or equal to 1. Under this convention, the rejection point for any formulation of hypotheses is a single value in the right-hand side of the relevant F-distribution. Note that the labeling of populations as "1" or "2" is arbitrary in any case.

- **Rejection Points for Hypothesis Tests on the Relative Values of Two Population Variances.** Follow the convention of using the larger of the two ratios s_1^2/s_2^2 and s_2^2/s_1^2 and consider two cases:
  1. A "not equal to" alternative hypothesis: Reject the null hypothesis at the α significance level if the test statistic is greater than the upper $\alpha/2$ point of the F-distribution with the specified numerator and denominator degrees of freedom.
  2. A "greater than" or "less than" alternative hypothesis: Reject the null hypothesis at the α significance level if the test statistic is greater than the upper α point of the F-distribution with the specified number of numerator and denominator degrees of freedom.

Thus, if we conduct a two-sided test at the $\alpha = 0.01$ level of significance, we need to find the rejection point in F-tables at the $\alpha/2 = 0.01/2 = 0.005$ significance level for a one-sided test (Case 1). But a one-sided test at 0.01 uses rejection points in F-tables for $\alpha = 0.01$ (Case 2). As an example, suppose we are conducting a two-sided test at the 0.05 significance level. We calculate a value of F of 2.77 with 12 numerator and 19 denominator degrees of freedom. Using the F-tables for $0.05/2 = 0.025$ in the back of the volume, we find that the rejection point is 2.72. Because the value 2.77 is greater than 2.72, we reject the null hypothesis at the 0.05 significance level.

---

27 The relationship between the chi-square and F-distributions is as follows: If χ_1^2 is one chi-square random variable with m degrees of freedom and χ_2^2 is another chi-square random variable with n degrees of freedom, then $F = \left(\chi_1^2/m\right)/\left(\chi_2^2/n\right)$ follows an F-distribution with m numerator and n denominator degrees of freedom.

If the convention stated above is not followed and we are given a calculated value of F less than 1, can we still use F-tables? The answer is yes; using a reciprocal property of F-statistics, we can calculate the needed value. The easiest way to present this property is to show a calculation. Suppose our chosen level of significance is 0.05 for a two-tailed test and we have a value of F of 0.11, with 7 numerator degrees of freedom and 9 denominator degrees of freedom. We take the reciprocal, 1/0.11 = 9.09. Then we look up this value in the F-tables for 0.025 (because it is a two-tailed test) with degrees of freedom reversed: F for 9 numerator and 7 denominator degrees of freedom. In other words, $F_{9,7} = 1/F_{7,9}$ and 9.09 exceeds the critical value of 4.82, so $F_{7,9} = 0.11$ is significant at the 0.05 level.

EXAMPLE 8

Volatility and the Global Financial Crisis of the Late 2000s

You are investigating whether the population variance of returns on the KOSPI Index of the South Korean stock market changed subsequent to the global financial crisis that peaked in 2008. For this investigation, you are considering 1999 to 2006 as the pre-crisis period and 2010 to 2017 as the post-crisis period. You gather the data in Exhibit 9 for 418 weeks of returns during 1999 to 2006 and 418 weeks of returns during 2010 to 2017. You have specified a 0.01 level of significance.

Exhibit 9 KOSPI Index Returns and Variance before and after the Global Financial Crisis of the Late 2000s

	n	Mean Weekly Return (%)	Variance of Returns
Before crisis: 1999 to 2006	418	0.307	18.203
After crisis: 2010 to 2017	418	0.114	3.919

Source of data for returns: finance.yahoo.com accessed 19 August 2018.

1 Formulate null and alternative hypotheses consistent with the verbal description of the research goal.

2 Identify the test statistic for conducting a test of the hypotheses in Part 1.

3 Determine whether or not to reject the null hypothesis at the 0.01 level of significance. (Use the F-tables in the back of this volume.)

Solution to 1:

We have a "not equal to" alternative hypothesis:

$$H_0: \sigma^2_{\text{Before}} = \sigma^2_{\text{After}} \text{ versus } H_a: \sigma^2_{\text{Before}} \neq \sigma^2_{\text{After}}$$

Solution to 2:

To test a null hypothesis of the equality of two variances, we use $F = s_1^2/s_2^2$ with 418 – 1 = 417 numerator and denominator degrees of freedom.

Solution to 3:

The "before" sample variance is larger, so following a convention for calculating F-statistics, the "before" sample variance goes in the numerator: F = 18.203/3.919 = 4.645. Because this is a two-tailed test, we use F-tables for the 0.005 level (= 0.01/2) to give a 0.01 significance level. In the tables in the back of the volume, the closest value to 417 degrees of freedom is 120 degrees of freedom. At the 0.01 level, the rejection point is 1.61. Because 4.645 is greater than the critical value 1.61, we reject the null hypothesis that the population variance of returns is the same in the pre- and post-global financial crisis periods.[28] It seems that the South Korean market was more volatile before the financial crisis.

EXAMPLE 9

The Volatility of Derivatives Expiration Days

Since 2001, the financial markets in the United States have seen the quadruple occurrence of stock option, index option, index futures, and single stock futures expirations on the same day during four months of the year. Such days are known as "quadruple witching days." You are interested in investigating whether quadruple witching days exhibit greater volatility than normal days. Exhibit 10 presents the daily standard deviation of return for normal days and options/futures expiration days during a four-year period. The tabled data refer to options and futures on the 30 stocks that constitute the Dow Jones Industrial Average.

Exhibit 10 Standard Deviation of Return: Normal Trading Days and Derivatives Expiration Days

Type of Day	n	Standard Deviation (%)
Normal trading	138	0.821
Options/futures expiration	16	1.217

1 Formulate null and alternative hypotheses consistent with the belief that quadruple witching days display above-normal volatility.

2 Identify the test statistic for conducting a test of the hypotheses in Part 1.

3 Determine whether to reject the null hypothesis at the 0.05 level of significance. (Use the F-tables in the back of this volume.)

Solution to 1:

We have a "greater than" alternative hypothesis:

$$H_0\colon \sigma^2_{\text{Expirations}} \le \sigma^2_{\text{Normal}} \text{ versus } H_a\colon \sigma^2_{\text{Expirations}} > \sigma^2_{\text{Normal}}$$

28 The critical value decreases as the degrees of freedom increase. Therefore, the critical value for 417 degrees of freedom is even smaller than 1.61, and we can reject the null hypothesis.

Solution to 2:

Let σ_1^2 represent the variance of quadruple witching days, and σ_2^2 represent the variance of normal days, following the convention for the selection of the numerator and the denominator stated earlier. To test the null hypothesis, we use $F = s_1^2/s_2^2$ with 16 – 1 = 15 numerator and 138 – 1 = 137 denominator degrees of freedom.

Solution to 3:

$F = (1.217)^2/(0.821)^2 = 1.481/0.674 = 2.20$. Because this is a one-tailed test at the 0.05 significance level, we use F-tables for the 0.05 level directly. In the tables in the back of the volume, the closest value to 137 degrees of freedom is 120 degrees of freedom. At the 0.05 level, the rejection point is 1.75. Because 2.20 is greater than 1.75, we reject the null hypothesis. It appears that quadruple witching days have above-normal volatility.

4.3 Tests Concerning Correlation

In many contexts in investments, we want to assess the strength of the linear relationship between two variables—the correlation between them. A common approach is to use the correlation coefficient. A significance test of a correlation coefficient allows us to assess whether the relationship between two random variables is the result of chance. If we decide that the relationship does not result from chance, we are inclined to use this information in predictions because a good prediction of one variable will help us predict the other variable.

If the correlation coefficient between two variables is zero, we would conclude that there is no linear relation between the two variables. We use a test of significance to assess whether the correlation is different from zero. After we estimate a correlation coefficient, we need to ask whether the estimated correlation is significantly different from 0. Before we can answer this question, we must know some details about the distribution of the underlying variables themselves. For purposes of simplicity, assume that both of the variables are normally distributed.[29]

We propose two hypotheses: the null hypothesis, H_0, that the correlation in the population is 0 ($\rho = 0$); and the alternative hypothesis, H_a, that the correlation in the population is different from 0 ($\rho \neq 0$). The alternative hypothesis is a test that the correlation is not equal to 0; therefore, a two-tailed test is appropriate. As long as the two variables are distributed normally, we can test to determine whether the null hypothesis should be rejected using the sample correlation, r. The formula for the t-test is

$$t = \frac{r\sqrt{n-2}}{\sqrt{1-r^2}} \qquad (17)$$

This test statistic has a t-distribution with $n - 2$ degrees of freedom if the null hypothesis is true. One practical observation concerning Equation 17 is that the magnitude of r needed to reject the null hypothesis H_0: $\rho = 0$ decreases as sample size n increases, for two reasons. First, as n increases, the number of degrees of freedom increases and the absolute value of the critical value t_c decreases. Second, the absolute value of the numerator increases with larger n, resulting in larger-magnitude t-values. For

29 Actually, we must assume that each observation (x, y) on the two variables (X, Y) is a random observation from a bivariate normal distribution. Informally, in a bivariate or two-variable normal distribution, each individual variable is normally distributed and their joint relationship is completely described by the correlation, ρ, between them. For more details, see, for example, Daniel and Terrell (1995) and Greene (2018).

example, with sample size $n = 12$, $r = 0.58$ results in a t-statistic of 2.252 that is just significant at the 0.05 level ($t_c = 2.228$). With a sample size $n = 32$, a smaller sample correlation $r = 0.35$ yields a t-statistic of 2.046 that is just significant at the 0.05 level ($t_c = 2.042$); the $r = 0.35$ would not be significant with a sample size of 12 even at the 0.10 significance level. Another way to make this point is that sampling from the same population, a false null hypothesis H_0: $\rho = 0$ is more likely to be rejected as we increase sample size, all else equal, because a higher number of observations increases the numerator of the test statistic.

EXAMPLE 10

Testing the Yen–Canadian Dollar Return Correlation

The sample correlation between the GBP monthly returns to Japanese yen and Canadian dollar is 0.5132 for the period from January 2011 through December 2017 (*Source of exchange rate data*: http://fx.sauder.ubc.ca/).

Can we reject a null hypothesis that the underlying or population correlation equals 0 at the 0.05 level of significance?

Solution:

With 84 months from January 2011 through December 2017, we use the following statistic to test the null hypothesis, H_0, that the true correlation in the population is 0, against the alternative hypothesis, H_a, that the correlation in the population is different from 0:

$$t = \frac{0.5132\sqrt{84 - 2}}{\sqrt{1 - 0.5132^2}} = 5.4146$$

In the tables at the back of this volume, at the 0.05 significance level, the critical level for this test statistic is 1.99 ($n = 84$, degrees of freedom = 82). When the test statistic is either larger than 1.99 or smaller than −1.99, we can reject the hypothesis that the correlation in the population is 0. The test statistic is 5.4146, so we can reject the null hypothesis.

OTHER ISSUES: NONPARAMETRIC INFERENCE 5

The hypothesis-testing procedures we have discussed to this point have two characteristics in common. First, they are concerned with parameters, and second, their validity depends on a definite set of assumptions. Mean and variance, for example, are two parameters, or defining quantities, of a normal distribution. The tests also make specific assumptions—in particular, assumptions about the distribution of the population producing the sample. Any test or procedure with either of the above two characteristics is a **parametric test** or procedure. In some cases, however, we are concerned about quantities other than parameters of distributions. In other cases, we may believe that the assumptions of parametric tests do not hold for the particular data we have. In such cases, a nonparametric test or procedure can be useful. A **nonparametric test** is a test that is not concerned with a parameter, or a test that makes minimal assumptions about the population from which the sample comes.[30]

We primarily use nonparametric procedures in three situations: when the data we use do not meet distributional assumptions, when the data are given in ranks, or when the hypothesis we are addressing does not concern a parameter.

The first situation occurs when the data available for analysis suggest that the distributional assumptions of the parametric test are not satisfied. For example, we may want to test a hypothesis concerning the mean of a population but believe that neither a *t*-test nor a *z*-test is appropriate because the sample is small and may come from a markedly non-normally distributed population. In that case, we may use a nonparametric test. The nonparametric test will frequently involve the conversion of observations (or a function of observations) into ranks according to magnitude, and sometimes it will involve working with only "greater than" or "less than" relationships (using the signs + and − to denote those relationships). Characteristically, one must refer to specialized statistical tables to determine the rejection points of the test statistic, at least for small samples.[31] Such tests, then, typically interpret the null hypothesis as a thesis about ranks or signs. In Exhibit 11, we give examples of nonparametric alternatives to the parametric tests concerning means we have discussed in this reading.[32] The reader should consult a comprehensive business statistics textbook for an introduction to such tests, and a specialist textbook for details.[33]

Exhibit 11 Nonparametric Alternatives to Parametric Tests Concerning Means

	Parametric	Nonparametric
Tests concerning a single mean	*t*-test *z*-test	Wilcoxon signed-rank test
Tests concerning differences between means	*t*-test Approximate *t*-test	Mann–Whitney U test
Tests concerning mean differences (paired comparisons tests)	*t*-test	Wilcoxon signed-rank test Sign test

We pointed out that when we use nonparametric tests, we often convert the original data into ranks. In some cases, the original data are already ranked. In those cases, we also use nonparametric tests because parametric tests generally require a stronger measurement scale than ranks. For example, if our data were the rankings of investment managers, hypotheses concerning those rankings would be tested using nonparametric procedures. Ranked data also appear in many other finance contexts. For example, Heaney, Koga, Oliver, and Tran (1999) studied the relationship between the size of Japanese companies (as measured by revenue) and their use of derivatives. The companies studied used derivatives to hedge one or more of five types of risk exposure: interest rate risk, foreign exchange risk, commodity price risk, marketable

30 Some writers make a distinction between "nonparametric" and "distribution-free" tests. They refer to procedures that do not concern the parameters of a distribution as nonparametric and to procedures that make minimal assumptions about the underlying distribution as distribution free. We follow a commonly accepted, inclusive usage of the term nonparametric.

31 For large samples, there is often a transformation of the test statistic that permits the use of tables for the standard normal or *t*-distribution.

32 In some cases, there are several nonparametric alternatives to a parametric test.

33 See, for example, Hettmansperger and McKean (2010) or Siegel and Castellan (1988).

security price risk, and credit risk. The researchers gave a "perceived scope of risk exposure" score to each company that was equal to the number of types of risk exposure that the company reported hedging. Although revenue is measured on a strong scale (a ratio scale), scope of risk exposure is measured on only an ordinal scale.[34] The researchers thus employed nonparametric statistics to explore the relationship between derivatives usage and size.

A third situation in which we use nonparametric procedures occurs when our question does not concern a parameter. For example, if the question concerns whether a sample is random or not, we use the appropriate nonparametric test (a so-called "runs test"). Another type of question nonparametrics can address is whether a sample came from a population following a particular probability distribution (using the Kolmogorov–Smirnov test, for example).

We end this reading by describing in some detail a nonparametric statistic that has often been used in investment research, the Spearman rank correlation.

5.1 Nonparametric Tests Concerning Correlation: The Spearman Rank Correlation Coefficient

Earlier in this reading, we examined the t-test of the hypothesis that two variables are uncorrelated, based on the correlation coefficient. As we pointed out there, this test relies on fairly stringent assumptions. When we believe that the population under consideration meaningfully departs from those assumptions, we can employ a test based on the **Spearman rank correlation coefficient**, r_S. The Spearman rank correlation coefficient is essentially equivalent to the usual correlation coefficient calculated on the *ranks* of the two variables (say X and Y) within their respective samples. Thus it is a number between −1 and +1, where −1 (+1) denotes a perfect inverse (positive) straight-line relationship between the variables and 0 represents the absence of any straight-line relationship (no correlation). The calculation of r_S requires the following steps:

1 Rank the observations on X from largest to smallest. Assign the number 1 to the observation with the largest value, the number 2 to the observation with second-largest value, and so on. In case of ties, we assign to each tied observation the average of the ranks that they jointly occupy. For example, if the third- and fourth-largest values are tied, we assign both observations the rank of 3.5 (the average of 3 and 4). Perform the same procedure for the observations on Y.

2 Calculate the difference, d_i, between the ranks of each pair of observations on X and Y.

3 Then, with n the sample size, the Spearman rank correlation is given by[35]

$$r_s = 1 - \frac{6\sum_{i=1}^{n} d_i^2}{n\left(n^2 - 1\right)} \quad (18)$$

Suppose an investor wants to invest in a diversified emerging markets mutual fund. He has narrowed the field to 10 such funds, which are rated as 5-star funds by Morningstar. In examining the funds, a question arises as to whether the funds' most recent reported Sharpe ratios and expense ratios as of mid-2018 are related. Because the assumptions of the t-test on the correlation coefficient may not be met, it is appropriate to conduct

34 We discussed scales of measurement in the reading on statistical concepts and market returns.

35 Calculating the usual correlation coefficient on the ranks would yield approximately the same result as Equation 18.

a test on the rank correlation coefficient.[36] Exhibit 12 presents the calculation of r_S. The first two rows contain the original data. The row of X ranks converts the Sharpe ratios to ranks; the row of Y ranks converts the expense ratios to ranks. We want to test H_0: ρ = 0 versus H_a: ρ ≠ 0, where ρ is defined in this context as the population correlation of X and Y after ranking. For small samples, the rejection points for the test based on r_S must be looked up in Exhibit 13. For large samples (say $n > 30$), we can conduct a t-test using

$$t = \frac{(n-2)^{1/2} r_S}{\left(1 - r_S^2\right)^{1/2}} \tag{19}$$

based on $n - 2$ degrees of freedom.

Exhibit 12 The Spearman Rank Correlation: An Example

	Mutual Fund									
	1	**2**	**3**	**4**	**5**	**6**	**7**	**8**	**9**	**10**
Sharpe Ratio (X)	0.65	0.80	0.68	0.72	0.64	0.54	0.71	0.76	0.62	0.64
Expense Ratio (Y)	1.04	1.05	1.79	1.26	1.33	1.64	1.01	3.20	6.81	1.07
X Rank	5.5	1	5.5	3	7.5	10	4	2	9	7.5
Y Rank	9	8	3	6	5	4	10	2	1	7
d_i	−3.5	−7	2.5	−3	2.5	6	−6	0	8	0.5
d_i^2	12.25	49	6.25	9	6.25	36	36	0	64	0.25

$$r_s = 1 - \frac{6\sum d_i^2}{10(100-1)} = 1 - \frac{6(219)}{10(100-1)} = -0.3273$$

Source of Sharpe and Expense Ratios: http://markets.on.nytimes.com/research/screener/mutual_funds/mutual_funds.asp accessed 19 August 2018.

In the example at hand, a two-tailed test with a 0.05 significance level, Exhibit 13 gives the upper-tail rejection point for $n = 10$ as 0.6364 (we use the 0.025 column for a two-tailed test at a 0.05 significance level). Accordingly, we reject the null hypothesis if r_S is less than −0.6364 or greater than 0.6364. With r_S equal to−0.3273, we do not reject the null hypothesis.

Exhibit 13 Spearman Rank Correlation Distribution Approximate Upper-Tail Rejection Points

Sample Size: n	α = 0.05	α = 0.025	α = 0.01
5	0.8000	0.9000	0.9000
6	0.7714	0.8286	0.8857

36 The expense ratio (the ratio of a fund's operating expenses to average net assets) is bounded both from below (by zero) and from above. The Sharpe ratio is also observed within a limited range, in practice. Thus, neither variable can be normally distributed, and hence jointly they cannot follow a bivariate normal distribution. In short, the assumptions of a t-test are not met.

Exhibit 13 (Continued)

Sample Size: n	$\alpha = 0.05$	$\alpha = 0.025$	$\alpha = 0.01$
7	0.6786	0.7450	0.8571
8	0.6190	0.7143	0.8095
9	0.5833	0.6833	0.7667
10	0.5515	0.6364	0.7333
11	0.5273	0.6091	0.7000
12	0.4965	0.5804	0.6713
13	0.4780	0.5549	0.6429
14	0.4593	0.5341	0.6220
15	0.4429	0.5179	0.6000
16	0.4265	0.5000	0.5824
17	0.4118	0.4853	0.5637
18	0.3994	0.4716	0.5480
19	0.3895	0.4579	0.5333
20	0.3789	0.4451	0.5203
21	0.3688	0.4351	0.5078
22	0.3597	0.4241	0.4963
23	0.3518	0.4150	0.4852
24	0.3435	0.4061	0.4748
25	0.3362	0.3977	0.4654
26	0.3299	0.3894	0.4564
27	0.3236	0.3822	0.4481
28	0.3175	0.3749	0.4401
29	0.3113	0.3685	0.4320
30	0.3059	0.3620	0.4251

Note: The corresponding lower tail critical value is obtained by changing the sign of the upper-tail critical value.

In the mutual fund example, we converted observations on two variables into ranks. If one or both of the original variables were in the form of ranks, we would need to use r_S to investigate correlation.

5.2 Nonparametric Inference: Summary

Nonparametric statistical procedures extend the reach of inference because they make few assumptions, can be used on ranked data, and may address questions unrelated to parameters. Quite frequently, nonparametric tests are reported alongside parametric tests. The reader can then assess how sensitive the statistical conclusion is to the assumptions underlying the parametric test. However, if the assumptions of the parametric test are met, the parametric test (where available) is generally preferred to the nonparametric test because the parametric test usually permits us to draw sharper conclusions.[37] For complete coverage of all the nonparametric procedures that may be encountered in the finance and investment literature, it is best to consult a specialist textbook.[38]

SUMMARY

In this reading, we have presented the concepts and methods of statistical inference and hypothesis testing.

- A hypothesis is a statement about one or more populations.
- The steps in testing a hypothesis are as follows:
  1. Stating the hypotheses.
  2. Identifying the appropriate test statistic and its probability distribution.
  3. Specifying the significance level.
  4. Stating the decision rule.
  5. Collecting the data and calculating the test statistic.
  6. Making the statistical decision.
  7. Making the economic or investment decision.
- We state two hypotheses: The null hypothesis is the hypothesis to be tested; the alternative hypothesis is the hypothesis accepted when the null hypothesis is rejected.
- There are three ways to formulate hypotheses:
  1. H_0: $\theta = \theta_0$ versus H_a: $\theta \neq \theta_0$
  2. H_0: $\theta \leq \theta_0$ versus H_a: $\theta > \theta_0$
  3. H_0: $\theta \geq \theta_0$ versus H_a: $\theta < \theta_0$

  where θ_0 is a hypothesized value of the population parameter and θ is the true value of the population parameter. In the above, Formulation 1 is a two-sided test and Formulations 2 and 3 are one-sided tests.
- When we have a "suspected" or "hoped for" condition for which we want to find supportive evidence, we frequently set up that condition as the alternative hypothesis and use a one-sided test. To emphasize a neutral attitude, however, the researcher may select a "not equal to" alternative hypothesis and conduct a two-sided test.
- A test statistic is a quantity, calculated on the basis of a sample, whose value is the basis for deciding whether to reject or not reject the null hypothesis. To decide whether to reject, or not to reject, the null hypothesis, we compare the computed value of the test statistic to a critical value (rejection point) for the same test statistic.
- In reaching a statistical decision, we can make two possible errors: We may reject a true null hypothesis (a Type I error), or we may fail to reject a false null hypothesis (a Type II error).

37 To use a concept introduced in an earlier section, the parametric test is often more powerful.
38 See, for example, Hettmansperger and McKean (2010) or Siegel and Castellan (1988).

- The level of significance of a test is the probability of a Type I error that we accept in conducting a hypothesis test. The probability of a Type I error is denoted by the Greek letter alpha, α. The standard approach to hypothesis testing involves specifying a level of significance (probability of Type I error) only.
- The power of a test is the probability of correctly rejecting the null (rejecting the null when it is false).
- A decision rule consists of determining the rejection points (critical values) with which to compare the test statistic to decide whether to reject or not to reject the null hypothesis. When we reject the null hypothesis, the result is said to be statistically significant.
- The $(1 - \alpha)$ confidence interval represents the range of values of the test statistic for which the null hypothesis will not be rejected at an α significance level.
- The statistical decision consists of rejecting or not rejecting the null hypothesis. The economic decision takes into consideration all economic issues pertinent to the decision.
- The *p*-value is the smallest level of significance at which the null hypothesis can be rejected. The smaller the *p*-value, the stronger the evidence against the null hypothesis and in favor of the alternative hypothesis. The *p*-value approach to hypothesis testing does not involve setting a significance level; rather it involves computing a *p*-value for the test statistic and allowing the consumer of the research to interpret its significance.
- For hypothesis tests concerning the population mean of a normally distributed population with unknown (known) variance, the theoretically correct test statistic is the *t*-statistic (*z*-statistic). In the unknown variance case, given large samples (generally, samples of 30 or more observations), the *z*-statistic may be used in place of the *t*-statistic because of the force of the central limit theorem.
- The *t*-distribution is a symmetrical distribution defined by a single parameter: degrees of freedom. Compared to the standard normal distribution, the *t*-distribution has fatter tails.
- When we want to test whether the observed difference between two means is statistically significant, we must first decide whether the samples are independent or dependent (related). If the samples are independent, we conduct tests concerning differences between means. If the samples are dependent, we conduct tests of mean differences (paired comparisons tests).
- When we conduct a test of the difference between two population means from normally distributed populations with unknown variances, if we can assume the variances are equal, we use a *t*-test based on pooling the observations of the two samples to estimate the common (but unknown) variance. This test is based on an assumption of independent samples.
- When we conduct a test of the difference between two population means from normally distributed populations with unknown variances, if we cannot assume that the variances are equal, we use an approximate *t*-test using modified degrees of freedom given by a formula. This test is based on an assumption of independent samples.
- In tests concerning two means based on two samples that are not independent, we often can arrange the data in paired observations and conduct a test of mean differences (a paired comparisons test). When the samples are from normally distributed populations with unknown variances, the appropriate test statistic is a *t*-statistic. The denominator of the *t*-statistic, the standard error of the mean differences, takes account of correlation between the samples.

- In tests concerning the variance of a single, normally distributed population, the test statistic is chi-square (χ^2) with $n - 1$ degrees of freedom, where n is sample size.
- For tests concerning differences between the variances of two normally distributed populations based on two random, independent samples, the appropriate test statistic is based on an F-test (the ratio of the sample variances).
- The F-statistic is defined by the numerator and denominator degrees of freedom. The numerator degrees of freedom (number of observations in the sample minus 1) is the divisor used in calculating the sample variance in the numerator. The denominator degrees of freedom (number of observations in the sample minus 1) is the divisor used in calculating the sample variance in the denominator. In forming an F-test, a convention is to use the larger of the two ratios, s_1^2/s_2^2 or s_2^2/s_1^2, as the actual test statistic.
- In tests concerning correlation, we use a t-statistic to test whether a population correlation coefficient is significantly different from 0. If we have n observations for two variables, this test statistic has a t-distribution with $n - 2$ degrees of freedom.
- A parametric test is a hypothesis test concerning a parameter or a hypothesis test based on specific distributional assumptions. In contrast, a nonparametric test either is not concerned with a parameter or makes minimal assumptions about the population from which the sample comes.
- A nonparametric test is primarily used in three situations: when data do not meet distributional assumptions, when data are given in ranks, or when the hypothesis we are addressing does not concern a parameter.
- The Spearman rank correlation coefficient is calculated on the ranks of two variables within their respective samples.

REFERENCES

Bowerman, Bruce L., Richard T. O'Connell, and Emily S. Murphree. 2016. *Business Statistics in Practice*, 8th edition. New York: McGraw-Hill/Irwin.

Daniel, Wayne W., and James C. Terrell. 1995. *Business Statistics for Management & Economics*, 7th edition. Boston: Houghton-Mifflin.

Davidson, Russell, and James G. MacKinnon. 1993. *Estimation and Inference in Econometrics*. New York: Oxford University Press.

Dimson, Elroy, Paul Marsh, and Mike Staunton. 2018. "Credit Suisse Global Investment Returns Yearbook 2018 (Summary Edition)". Credit Suisse Research Institute.

Freeley, Austin J., and David L. Steinberg. 2013. *Argumentation and Debate: Critical Thinking for Reasoned Decision Making*, 13th edition. Boston, MA: Wadsworth Cengage Learning.

Gupta, Parveen P, and Nandkumar Nayar. 2007. "Information Content of Control Deficiency Disclosures under the Sarbanes-Oxley Act: An Empirical Investigation." *International Journal of Disclosure and Governance*, vol. 4:3–23.

Heaney, Richard, Chitoshi Koga, Barry Oliver, and Alfred Tran. 1999. "The Size Effect and Derivative Usage in Japan." Working paper: The Australian National University.

Hettmansperger, Thomas P., and Joseph W. McKean. 2010. *Robust Nonparametric Statistical Methods*, 2nd edition. Boca Raton, FL: CRC Press.

Jankowitsch, Rainer, Florian Nagler, and Marti G. Subrahmanyam. 2014. "The Determinants of Recovery Rates in the US Corporate Bond Market." *Journal of Financial Economics*, vol. 114, no. 1:155–177.

Moore, David S., George P. McCabe, and Bruce Craig. 2016. *Introduction to the Practice of Statistics*, 9th edition. New York: W.H. Freeman.

Siegel, Sidney, and N. John Castellan. 1988. *Nonparametric Statistics for the Behavioral Sciences*, 2nd edition. New York: McGraw-Hill.

PRACTICE PROBLEMS

1 Which of the following statements about hypothesis testing is correct?

- **A** The null hypothesis is the condition a researcher hopes to support.
- **B** The alternative hypothesis is the proposition considered true without conclusive evidence to the contrary.
- **C** The alternative hypothesis exhausts all potential parameter values not accounted for by the null hypothesis.

2 Identify the appropriate test statistic or statistics for conducting the following hypothesis tests. (Clearly identify the test statistic and, if applicable, the number of degrees of freedom. For example, "We conduct the test using an x-statistic with y degrees of freedom.")

- **A** H_0: $\mu = 0$ versus H_a: $\mu \neq 0$, where μ is the mean of a normally distributed population with unknown variance. The test is based on a sample of 15 observations.
- **B** H_0: $\mu = 0$ versus H_a: $\mu \neq 0$, where μ is the mean of a normally distributed population with unknown variance. The test is based on a sample of 40 observations.
- **C** H_0: $\mu \leq 0$ versus H_a: $\mu > 0$, where μ is the mean of a normally distributed population with known variance σ^2. The sample size is 45.
- **D** H_0: $\sigma^2 = 200$ versus H_a: $\sigma^2 \neq 200$, where σ^2 is the variance of a normally distributed population. The sample size is 50.
- **E** H_0: $\sigma_1^2 = \sigma_2^2$ versus H_a: $\sigma_1^2 \neq \sigma_2^2$, where σ_1^2 is the variance of one normally distributed population and σ_2^2 is the variance of a second normally distributed population. The test is based on two independent random samples.
- **F** H_0: (Population mean 1) – (Population mean 2) = 0 versus H_a: (Population mean 1) – (Population mean 2) $\neq$ 0, where the samples are drawn from normally distributed populations with unknown variances. The observations in the two samples are correlated.
- **G** H_0: (Population mean 1) – (Population mean 2) = 0 versus H_a: (Population mean 1) – (Population mean 2) $\neq$ 0, where the samples are drawn from normally distributed populations with unknown but assumed equal variances. The observations in the two samples (of size 25 and 30, respectively) are independent.

3 For each of the following hypothesis tests concerning the population mean, μ, state the rejection point condition or conditions for the test statistic (e.g., $t > 1.25$); n denotes sample size.

- **A** H_0: $\mu = 10$ versus H_a: $\mu \neq 10$, using a t-test with $n = 26$ and $\alpha = 0.05$
- **B** H_0: $\mu = 10$ versus H_a: $\mu \neq 10$, using a t-test with $n = 40$ and $\alpha = 0.01$
- **C** H_0: $\mu \leq 10$ versus H_a: $\mu > 10$, using a t-test with $n = 40$ and $\alpha = 0.01$
- **D** H_0: $\mu \leq 10$ versus H_a: $\mu > 10$, using a t-test with $n = 21$ and $\alpha = 0.05$
- **E** H_0: $\mu \geq 10$ versus H_a: $\mu < 10$, using a t-test with $n = 19$ and $\alpha = 0.10$
- **F** H_0: $\mu \geq 10$ versus H_a: $\mu < 10$, using a t-test with $n = 50$ and $\alpha = 0.05$

4 For each of the following hypothesis tests concerning the population mean, μ, state the rejection point condition or conditions for the test statistic (e.g., $z > 1.25$); n denotes sample size.

A H_0: $\mu = 10$ versus H_a: $\mu \neq 10$, using a z-test with $n = 50$ and $\alpha = 0.01$

B H_0: $\mu = 10$ versus H_a: $\mu \neq 10$, using a z-test with $n = 50$ and $\alpha = 0.05$

C H_0: $\mu = 10$ versus H_a: $\mu \neq 10$, using a z-test with $n = 50$ and $\alpha = 0.10$

D H_0: $\mu \leq 10$ versus H_a: $\mu > 10$, using a z-test with $n = 50$ and $\alpha = 0.05$

5 Willco is a manufacturer in a mature cyclical industry. During the most recent industry cycle, its net income averaged $30 million per year with a standard deviation of $10 million ($n = 6$ observations). Management claims that Willco's performance during the most recent cycle results from new approaches and that we can dismiss profitability expectations based on its average or normalized earnings of $24 million per year in prior cycles.

A With μ as the population value of mean annual net income, formulate null and alternative hypotheses consistent with testing Willco management's claim.

B Assuming that Willco's net income is at least approximately normally distributed, identify the appropriate test statistic.

C Identify the rejection point or points at the 0.05 level of significance for the hypothesis tested in Part A.

D Determine whether or not to reject the null hypothesis at the 0.05 significance level.

The following information relates to Questions 6–7

Performance in Forecasting Quarterly Earnings per Share

	Number of Forecasts	Mean Forecast Error (Predicted – Actual)	Standard Deviations of Forecast Errors
Analyst A	101	0.05	0.10
Analyst B	121	0.02	0.09

6 Investment analysts often use earnings per share (EPS) forecasts. One test of forecasting quality is the zero-mean test, which states that optimal forecasts should have a mean forecasting error of 0. (Forecasting error = Predicted value of variable – Actual value of variable.)

You have collected data (shown in the table above) for two analysts who cover two different industries: Analyst A covers the telecom industry; Analyst B covers automotive parts and suppliers.

A With μ as the population mean forecasting error, formulate null and alternative hypotheses for a zero-mean test of forecasting quality.

B For Analyst A, using both a t-test and a z-test, determine whether to reject the null at the 0.05 and 0.01 levels of significance.

C For Analyst B, using both a t-test and a z-test, determine whether to reject the null at the 0.05 and 0.01 levels of significance.

7 Reviewing the EPS forecasting performance data for Analysts A and B, you want to investigate whether the larger average forecast errors of Analyst A are due to chance or to a higher underlying mean value for Analyst A. Assume that the forecast errors of both analysts are normally distributed and that the samples are independent.

A Formulate null and alternative hypotheses consistent with determining whether the population mean value of Analyst A's forecast errors (μ_1) are larger than Analyst B's (μ_2).

B Identify the test statistic for conducting a test of the null hypothesis formulated in Part A.

C Identify the rejection point or points for the hypothesis tested in Part A, at the 0.05 level of significance.

D Determine whether or not to reject the null hypothesis at the 0.05 level of significance.

---

8 The table below gives data on the monthly returns on the S&P 500 and small-cap stocks for a forty-year period and provides statistics relating to their mean differences. Furthermore, the entire sample period is split into two subperiods of 20 years each and the returns data for these subperiods is also given in the table.

Measure	S&P 500 Return (%)	Small-Cap Stock Return (%)	Differences (S&P 500– Small-Cap Stock)
Entire sample period, 480 months			
Mean	1.0542	1.3117	−0.258
Standard deviation	4.2185	5.9570	3.752
First subperiod, 240 months			
Mean	0.6345	1.2741	−0.640
Standard deviation	4.0807	6.5829	4.096
Second subperiod, 240 months			
Mean	1.4739	1.3492	0.125
Standard deviation	4.3197	5.2709	3.339

Let μ_d stand for the population mean value of difference between S&P 500 returns and small-cap stock returns. Use a significance level of 0.05 and suppose that mean differences are approximately normally distributed.

A Formulate null and alternative hypotheses consistent with testing whether any difference exists between the mean returns on the S&P 500 and small-cap stocks.

B Determine whether or not to reject the null hypothesis at the 0.05 significance level for the entire sample period.

C Determine whether or not to reject the null hypothesis at the 0.05 significance level for the first subperiod.

D Determine whether or not to reject the null hypothesis at the 0.05 significance level for the second subperiod.

9 During a 10-year period, the standard deviation of annual returns on a portfolio you are analyzing was 15 percent a year. You want to see whether this record is sufficient evidence to support the conclusion that the portfolio's underlying variance of return was less than 400, the return variance of the portfolio's benchmark.

A Formulate null and alternative hypotheses consistent with the verbal description of your objective.

B Identify the test statistic for conducting a test of the hypotheses in Part A.

C Identify the rejection point or points at the 0.05 significance level for the hypothesis tested in Part A.

D Determine whether the null hypothesis is rejected or not rejected at the 0.05 level of significance.

10 You are investigating whether the population variance of returns on the S&P 500/BARRA Growth Index changed subsequent to the October 1987 market crash. You gather the following data for 120 months of returns before October 1987 and for 120 months of returns after October 1987. You have specified a 0.05 level of significance.

Time Period	*n*	Mean Monthly Return (%)	Variance of Returns
Before October 1987	120	1.416	22.367
After October 1987	120	1.436	15.795

A Formulate null and alternative hypotheses consistent with the verbal description of the research goal.

B Identify the test statistic for conducting a test of the hypotheses in Part A.

C Determine whether or not to reject the null hypothesis at the 0.05 level of significance. (Use the *F*-tables in the back of this volume.)

11 The following table shows the sample correlations between the monthly returns for four different mutual funds and the S&P 500. The correlations are based on 36 monthly observations. The funds are as follows:

Fund 1	Large-cap fund
Fund 2	Mid-cap fund
Fund 3	Large-cap value fund
Fund 4	Emerging markets fund
S&P 500	US domestic stock index

	Fund 1	Fund 2	Fund 3	Fund 4	S&P 500
Fund 1	1				
Fund 2	0.9231	1			
Fund 3	0.4771	0.4156	1		
Fund 4	0.7111	0.7238	0.3102	1	
S&P 500	0.8277	0.8223	0.5791	0.7515	1

Test the null hypothesis that each of these correlations, individually, is equal to zero against the alternative hypothesis that it is not equal to zero. Use a 5 percent significance level.

12 In the step "stating a decision rule" in testing a hypothesis, which of the following elements must be specified?

A Critical value

B Power of a test

C Value of a test statistic

13 Which of the following statements is correct with respect to the null hypothesis?

A It is considered to be true unless the sample provides evidence showing it is false.

B It can be stated as "not equal to" provided the alternative hypothesis is stated as "equal to."

C In a two-tailed test, it is rejected when evidence supports equality between the hypothesized value and population parameter.

14 An analyst is examining a large sample with an unknown population variance. To test the hypothesis that the historical average return on an index is less than or equal to 6%, which of the following is the *most* appropriate test?

A One-tailed z-test

B Two-tailed z-test

C One-tailed F-test

15 A hypothesis test for a normally-distributed population at a 0.05 significance level implies a:

A 95% probability of rejecting a true null hypothesis.

B 95% probability of a Type I error for a two-tailed test.

C 5% critical value rejection region in a tail of the distribution for a one-tailed test.

16 Which of the following statements regarding a one-tailed hypothesis test is correct?

A The rejection region increases in size as the level of significance becomes smaller.

B A one-tailed test more strongly reflects the beliefs of the researcher than a two-tailed test.

C The absolute value of the rejection point is larger than that of a two-tailed test at the same level of significance.

17 The value of a test statistic is *best* described as the basis for deciding whether to:

A reject the null hypothesis.

B accept the null hypothesis.

C reject the alternative hypothesis.

18 Which of the following is a Type I error?

A Rejecting a true null hypothesis

B Rejecting a false null hypothesis

C Failing to reject a false null hypothesis

19 A Type II error is *best* described as:

A rejecting a true null hypothesis.

B failing to reject a false null hypothesis.

C failing to reject a false alternative hypothesis.

20 The level of significance of a hypothesis test is *best* used to:

A calculate the test statistic.

B define the test's rejection points.

C specify the probability of a Type II error.

21 You are interested in whether excess risk-adjusted return (alpha) is correlated with mutual fund expense ratios for US large-cap growth funds. The following table presents the sample.

Mutual Fund	1	2	3	4	5	6	7	8	9
Alpha (X)	−0.52	−0.13	−0.60	−1.01	−0.26	−0.89	−0.42	−0.23	−0.60
Expense Ratio (Y)	1.34	0.92	1.02	1.45	1.35	0.50	1.00	1.50	1.45

A Formulate null and alternative hypotheses consistent with the verbal description of the research goal.

B Identify the test statistic for conducting a test of the hypotheses in Part A.

C Justify your selection in Part B.

D Determine whether or not to reject the null hypothesis at the 0.05 level of significance.

22 All else equal, is specifying a smaller significance level in a hypothesis test likely to increase the probability of a:

	Type I error?	Type II error?
A	No	No
B	No	Yes
C	Yes	No

23 The probability of correctly rejecting the null hypothesis is the:

A p-value.

B power of a test.

C level of significance.

24 The power of a hypothesis test is:

A equivalent to the level of significance.

B the probability of not making a Type II error.

C unchanged by increasing a small sample size.

25 When making a decision in investments involving a statistically significant result, the:

A economic result should be presumed meaningful.

B statistical result should take priority over economic considerations.

C economic logic for the future relevance of the result should be further explored.

26 An analyst tests the profitability of a trading strategy with the null hypothesis being that the average abnormal return before trading costs equals zero. The calculated t-statistic is 2.802, with critical values of ± 2.756 at significance level $\alpha = 0.01$. After considering trading costs, the strategy's return is near zero. The results are *most likely*:

A statistically but not economically significant.

B economically but not statistically significant.

C neither statistically nor economically significant.

27 Which of the following statements is correct with respect to the p-value?

A It is a less precise measure of test evidence than rejection points.

B It is the largest level of significance at which the null hypothesis is rejected.

C It can be compared directly with the level of significance in reaching test conclusions.

28 Which of the following represents a correct statement about the *p*-value?

A The *p*-value offers less precise information than does the rejection points approach.

B A larger *p*-value provides stronger evidence in support of the alternative hypothesis.

C A *p*-value less than the specified level of significance leads to rejection of the null hypothesis.

29 Which of the following statements on *p*-value is correct?

A The *p*-value is the smallest level of significance at which H_0 can be rejected.

B The *p*-value indicates the probability of making a Type II error.

C The lower the p-value, the weaker the evidence for rejecting the H_0.

30 The following table shows the significance level (α) and the *p*-value for three hypothesis tests.

	α	*p*-value
Test 1	0.05	0.10
Test 2	0.10	0.08
Test 3	0.10	0.05

The evidence for rejecting H_0 is strongest for:

A Test 1.

B Test 2.

C Test 3.

31 Which of the following tests of a hypothesis concerning the population mean is *most* appropriate?

A A *z*-test if the population variance is unknown and the sample is small

B A *z*-test if the population is normally distributed with a known variance

C A *t*-test if the population is non-normally distributed with unknown variance and a small sample

32 For a small sample with unknown variance, which of the following tests of a hypothesis concerning the population mean is most appropriate?

A A *t*-test if the population is normally distributed

B A *t*-test if the population is non-normally distributed

C A *z*-test regardless of the normality of the population distribution

33 For a small sample from a normally distributed population with unknown variance, the *most* appropriate test statistic for the mean is the:

A *z*-statistic.

B *t*-statistic.

C χ^2 statistic.

34 An investment consultant conducts two independent random samples of 5-year performance data for US and European absolute return hedge funds. Noting a 50 basis point return advantage for US managers, the consultant decides to test whether the two means are statistically different from one another at a 0.05 level of significance. The two populations are assumed to be normally distributed with unknown but equal variances. Results of the hypothesis test are contained in the tables below.

	Sample Size	Mean Return %	Standard Deviation
US Managers	50	4.7	5.4
European Managers	50	4.2	4.8

Null and Alternative Hypotheses	H_0: $\mu_{US} - \mu_E = 0$; H_a: $\mu_{US} - \mu_E \neq 0$
Test Statistic	0.4893
Critical Value Rejection Points	±1.984

μ_{US} is the mean return for US funds and μ_E is the mean return for European funds.

The results of the hypothesis test indicate that the:

A null hypothesis is not rejected.

B alternative hypothesis is statistically confirmed.

C difference in mean returns is statistically different from zero.

35 A pooled estimator is used when testing a hypothesis concerning the:

A equality of the variances of two normally distributed populations.

B difference between the means of two at least approximately normally distributed populations with unknown but assumed equal variances.

C difference between the means of two at least approximately normally distributed populations with unknown and assumed unequal variances.

36 When evaluating mean differences between two dependent samples, the *most* appropriate test is a:

A chi-square test.

B paired comparisons test.

C *z*-test.

37 A fund manager reported a 2% mean quarterly return over the past ten years for its entire base of 250 client accounts that all follow the same investment strategy. A consultant employing the manager for 45 client accounts notes that their mean quarterly returns were 0.25% less over the same period. The consultant tests the hypothesis that the return disparity between the returns of his clients and the reported returns of the fund manager's 250 client accounts are significantly different from zero.

Assuming normally distributed populations with unknown population variances, the *most* appropriate test statistic is:

A a paired comparisons *t*-test.

B a *t*-test of the difference between the two population means.

C an approximate *t*-test of mean differences between the two populations.

38 A chi-square test is *most* appropriate for tests concerning:

A a single variance.

B differences between two population means with variances assumed to be equal.

C differences between two population means with variances assumed to not be equal.

39 Which of the following should be used to test the difference between the variances of two normally distributed populations?

A t-test

B F-test

C Paired comparisons test

40 Jill Batten is analyzing how the returns on the stock of Stellar Energy Corp. are related with the previous month's percent change in the US Consumer Price Index for Energy (CPIENG). Based on 248 observations, she has computed the sample correlation between the Stellar and CPIENG variables to be −0.1452. She also wants to determine whether the sample correlation is statistically significant. The critical value for the test statistic at the 0.05 level of significance is approximately 1.96. Batten should conclude that the statistical relationship between Stellar and CPIENG is:

A significant, because the calculated test statistic has a lower absolute value than the critical value for the test statistic.

B significant, because the calculated test statistic has a higher absolute value than the critical value for the test statistic.

C not significant, because the calculated test statistic has a higher absolute value than the critical value for the test statistic.

41 In which of the following situations would a non-parametric test of a hypothesis *most likely* be used?

A The sample data are ranked according to magnitude.

B The sample data come from a normally distributed population.

C The test validity depends on many assumptions about the nature of the population.

42 An analyst is examining the monthly returns for two funds over one year. Both funds' returns are non-normally distributed. To test whether the mean return of one fund is greater than the mean return of the other fund, the analyst can use:

A a parametric test only.

B a nonparametric test only.

C both parametric and nonparametric tests.

SOLUTIONS

1 C is correct. Together, the null and alternative hypotheses account for all possible values of the parameter. Any possible values of the parameter not covered by the null must be covered by the alternative hypothesis (e.g., H_0: $\theta \leq 5$ versus H_a: $\theta > 5$).

2 **A** The appropriate test statistic is a t-statistic with $n - 1 = 15 - 1 = 14$ degrees of freedom. A t-statistic is theoretically correct when the sample comes from a normally distributed population with unknown variance. When the sample size is also small, there is no practical alternative.

B The appropriate test statistic is a t-statistic with $40 - 1 = 39$ degrees of freedom. A t-statistic is theoretically correct when the sample comes from a normally distributed population with unknown variance. When the sample size is large (generally, 30 or more is a "large" sample), it is also possible to use a z-statistic, whether the population is normally distributed or not. A test based on a t-statistic is more conservative than a z-statistic test.

C The appropriate test statistic is a z-statistic because the sample comes from a normally distributed population with known variance. (The known population standard deviation is used to compute the standard error of the mean using Equation 2 in the text.)

D The appropriate test statistic is chi-square (χ^2) with $50 - 1 = 49$ degrees of freedom.

E The appropriate test statistic is the F-statistic (the ratio of the sample variances).

F The appropriate test statistic is a t-statistic for a paired observations test (a paired comparisons test), because the samples are correlated.

G The appropriate test statistic is a t –statistic using a pooled estimate of the population variance. The t-statistic has $25 + 30 - 2 = 53$ degrees of freedom. This statistic is appropriate because the populations are normally distributed with unknown variances; because the variances are assumed equal, the observations can be pooled to estimate the common variance. The requirement of independent samples for using this statistic has been met.

3 **A** With degrees of freedom (df) $n - 1 = 26 - 1 = 25$, the rejection point conditions for this two-sided test are $t > 2.060$ and $t < -2.060$. Because the significance level is 0.05, $0.05/2 = 0.025$ of the probability is in each tail. The tables give one-sided (one-tailed) probabilities, so we used the 0.025 column. Read across df = 25 to the $\alpha = 0.025$ column to find 2.060, the rejection point for the right tail. By symmetry, −2.060 is the rejection point for the left tail.

B With df = 39, the rejection point conditions for this two-sided test are $t > 2.708$ and $t < -2.708$. This is a two-sided test, so we use the $0.01/2 = 0.005$ column. Read across df = 39 to the $\alpha = 0.005$ column to find 2.708, the rejection point for the right tail. By symmetry, −2.708 is the rejection point for the left tail.

C With df = 39, the rejection point condition for this one-sided test is $t > 2.426$. Read across df = 39 to the $\alpha = 0.01$ column to find 2.426, the rejection point for the right tail. Because we have a "greater than" alternative, we are concerned with only the right tail.

D With df = 20, the rejection point condition for this one-sided test is $t > 1.725$. Read across df = 20 to the $\alpha = 0.05$ column to find 1.725, the rejection point for the right tail. Because we have a "greater than" alternative, we are concerned with only the right tail.

E With df = 18, the rejection point condition for this one-sided test is $t < -1.330$. Read across df = 18 to the $\alpha = 0.10$ column to find 1.330, the rejection point for the right tail. By symmetry, the rejection point for the left tail is −1.330.

F With df = 49, the rejection point condition for this one-sided test is $t < -1.677$. Read across df = 49 to the $\alpha = 0.05$ column to find 1.677, the rejection point for the right tail. By symmetry, the rejection point for the left tail is −1.677.

4 Recall that with a z-test (in contrast to the t-test), we do not employ degrees of freedom. The standard normal distribution is a single distribution applicable to all z-tests. You should refer to "Rejection Points for a z-Test" in Section 3.1 to answer these questions.

A This is a two-sided test at a 0.01 significance level. In Part C of "Rejection Points for a z-Test," we find that the rejection point conditions are $z > 2.575$ and $z < -2.575$.

B This is a two-sided test at a 0.05 significance level. In Part B of "Rejection Points for a z-Test," we find that the rejection point conditions are $z > 1.96$ and $z < -1.96$.

C This is a two-sided test at a 0.10 significance level. In Part A of "Rejection Points for a z-Test," we find that the rejection point conditions are $z > 1.645$ and $z < -1.645$.

D This is a one-sided test at a 0.05 significance level. In Part B of "Rejection Points for a z-Test," we find that the rejection point condition for a test with a "greater than" alternative hypothesis is $z > 1.645$.

5 A As stated in the text, we often set up the "hoped for" or "suspected" condition as the alternative hypothesis. Here, that condition is that the population value of Willco's mean annual net income exceeds \$24 million. Thus we have H_0: $\mu \leq 24$ versus H_a: $\mu > 24$.

B Given that net income is normally distributed with unknown variance, the appropriate test statistic is t with $n - 1 = 6 - 1 = 5$ degrees of freedom.

C In the t-distribution table in the back of the book, in the row for df = 5 under $\alpha = 0.05$, we read the rejection point (critical value) of 2.015. We will reject the null if $t > 2.015$.

D The t-test is given by Equation 4:

$$t_5 = \frac{\overline{X} - \mu_0}{s/\sqrt{n}} = \frac{30 - 24}{10/\sqrt{6}} = \frac{6}{4.082483} = 1.469694$$

or 1.47. Because 1.47 does not exceed 2.015, we do not reject the null hypothesis. The difference between the sample mean of \$30 million and the hypothesized value of \$24 million under the null is not statistically significant.

6 A H_0: $\mu = 0$ versus H_a: $\mu \neq 0$.

B The t-test is based on $t = \dfrac{\overline{X} - \mu_0}{s/\sqrt{n}}$ with $n - 1 = 101 - 1 = 100$ degrees of freedom. At the 0.05 significance level, we reject the null if $t > 1.984$ or if $t < -1.984$. At the 0.01 significance level, we reject the null if $t > 2.626$ or if $t <$

−2.626. For Analyst A, we have $t = (0.05 - 0)/(0.10/\sqrt{101}) = 0.05/0.00995 =$ 5.024938 or 5.025. We clearly reject the null hypothesis at both the 0.05 and 0.01 levels.

The calculation of the z-statistic with unknown variance, as in this case, is the same as the calculation of the t-statistic. The rejection point conditions for a two-tailed test are as follows: $z > 1.96$ and $z < -1.96$ at the 0.05 level; and $z > 2.575$ and $z < -2.575$ at the 0.01 level. Note that the z-test is a less conservative test than the t-test, so when the z-test is used, the null is easier to reject. Because $z = 5.025$ is greater than 2.575, we reject the null at the 0.01 level; we also reject the null at the 0.05 level.

In summary, Analyst A's EPS forecasts appear to be biased upward—they tend to be too high.

C For Analyst B, the t-test is based on t with 121 − 1 = 120 degrees of freedom. At the 0.05 significance level, we reject the null if $t > 1.980$ or if $t < -1.980$. At the 0.01 significance level, we reject the null if $t > 2.617$ or if $t < -2.617$. We calculate $t = (0.02 - 0)/(0.09/\sqrt{121}) = 0.02/0.008182 = 2.444444$ or 2.44. Because 2.44 > 1.98, we reject the null at the 0.05 level. However, 2.44 is not larger than 2.617, so we do not reject the null at the 0.01 level.

For a z-test, the rejection point conditions are the same as given in Part B, and we come to the same conclusions as with the t-test. Because 2.44 > 1.96, we reject the null at the 0.05 significance level; however, because 2.44 is not greater than 2.575, we do not reject the null at the 0.01 level.

The mean forecast error of Analyst B is only \$0.02; but because the test is based on a large number of observations, it is sufficient evidence to reject the null of mean zero forecast errors at the 0.05 level.

7 A Stating the suspected condition as the alternative hypothesis, we have

$$H_0: \mu_1 - \mu_2 \le 0 \text{ versus } H_a: \mu_1 - \mu_2 > 0$$

where

μ_1 = the population mean value of Analyst A's forecast errors
μ_2 = the population mean value of Analyst B's forecast errors

B We have two normally distributed populations with unknown variances. Based on the samples, it is reasonable to assume that the population variances are equal. The samples are assumed to be independent; this assumption is reasonable because the analysts cover quite different industries. The appropriate test statistic is t using a pooled estimate of the common variance. The number of degrees of freedom is

$$n_1 + n_2 - 2 = 101 + 121 - 2 = 222 - 2 = 220.$$

C For df = 200 (the closest value to 220), the rejection point for a one-sided test at the 0.05 significance level is 1.653.

D We first calculate the pooled estimate of variance:

$$s_p^2 = \frac{(n_1 - 1)s_1^2 + (n_2 - 1)s_2^2}{n_1 + n_2 - 2} = \frac{(101 - 1)(0.10)^2 + (121 - 1)(0.09)^2}{101 + 121 - 2}$$

$$= \frac{1.972}{220} = 0.008964$$

Then

$$t = \frac{\left(\bar{X}_1 - \bar{X}_2\right) - \left(\mu_1 - \mu_2\right)}{\left(\dfrac{s_p^2}{n_1} + \dfrac{s_p^2}{n_2}\right)^{1/2}} = \frac{(0.05 - 0.02) - 0}{\left(\dfrac{0.008964}{101} + \dfrac{0.008964}{121}\right)^{1/2}}$$

$$= \frac{0.03}{0.01276} = 2.351018$$

or 2.35. Because 2.35 > 1.653, we reject the null hypothesis in favor of the alternative hypothesis that the population mean forecast error of Analyst A is greater than that of Analyst B.

8 A We test H_0: $\mu_d = 0$ versus H_a: $\mu_d \neq 0$.

B This is a paired comparisons t-test with $n - 1 = 480 - 1 = 479$ degrees of freedom. At the 0.05 significance level, we reject the null hypothesis if either $t > 1.96$ or $t < -1.96$. We use df = ∞ in the t-distribution table under α = 0.025 because we have a very large sample and a two-sided test.

$$t = \frac{\bar{d} - \mu_{d0}}{s_{\bar{d}}} = \frac{-0.258 - 0}{3.752/\sqrt{480}} = \frac{-0.258}{0.171255} = -1.506529 \text{ or } -1.51$$

At the 0.05 significance level, because neither rejection point condition is met, we do not reject the null hypothesis that the mean difference between the returns on the S&P 500 and small-cap stocks during the entire sample period was 0.

C This t-test now has $n - 1 = 240 - 1 = 239$ degrees of freedom. At the 0.05 significance level, we reject the null hypothesis if either $t > 1.972$ or $t < -1.972$, using df = 200 in the t-distribution tables.

$$t = \frac{\bar{d} - \mu_{d0}}{s_{\bar{d}}} = \frac{-0.640 - 0}{4.096/\sqrt{240}} = \frac{-0.640}{0.264396} = -2.420615 \text{ or } -2.42$$

Because $-2.42 < -1.972$, we reject the null hypothesis at the 0.05 significance level. During this subperiod, small-cap stocks significantly outperformed the S&P 500.

D This t-test has $n - 1 = 240 - 1 = 239$ degrees of freedom. At the 0.05 significance level, we reject the null hypothesis if either $t > 1.972$ or $t < -1.972$, using df = 200 in the t-distribution tables.

$$t = \frac{\bar{d} - \mu_{d0}}{s_{\bar{d}}} = \frac{0.125 - 0}{3.339/\sqrt{240}} = \frac{0.125}{0.215532} = 0.579962 \text{ or } 0.58$$

At the 0.05 significance level, because neither rejection point condition is met, we do not reject the null hypothesis that for the second subperiod, the mean difference between the returns on the S&P 500 and small-cap stocks was zero.

9 A We have a "less than" alternative hypothesis, where σ^2 is the variance of return on the portfolio. The hypotheses are H_0: $\sigma^2 \geq 400$ versus H_a: $\sigma^2 < 400$, where 400 is the hypothesized value of variance, σ_0^2.

B The test statistic is chi-square with $10 - 1 = 9$ degrees of freedom.

C The rejection point is found across degrees of freedom of 9, under the 0.95 column (95 percent of probability above the value). It is 3.325. We will reject the null hypothesis if we find that $\chi^2 < 3.325$.

D The test statistic is calculated as

$$\chi^2 = \frac{(n-1)s^2}{\sigma_0^2} = \frac{9 \times 15^2}{400} = \frac{2{,}025}{400} = 5.0625 \text{ or } 5.06$$

Because 5.06 is not less than 3.325, we do not reject the null hypothesis.

10 A We have a "not equal to" alternative hypothesis:

$$H_0\colon \sigma^2_{\text{Before}} = \sigma^2_{\text{After}} \text{ versus } H_a\colon \sigma^2_{\text{Before}} \neq \sigma^2_{\text{After}}$$

B To test a null hypothesis of the equality of two variances, we use an F-test:

$$F = \frac{s_1^2}{s_2^2}$$

C The "before" sample variance is larger, so following a convention for calculating F-statistics, the "before" sample variance goes in the numerator. $F = 22.367/15.795 = 1.416$, with $120 - 1 = 119$ numerator and denominator degrees of freedom. Because this is a two-tailed test, we use F-tables for the 0.025 level (df = 0.05/2). Using the tables in the back of the volume, the closest value to 119 is 120 degrees of freedom. At the 0.05 level, the rejection point is 1.43. (Using the Insert/Function/Statistical feature on a Microsoft Excel spreadsheet, we would find FINV(0.025, 119, 119) = 1.434859 as the critical F-value.) Because 1.416 is not greater than 1.43, we do not reject the null hypothesis that the "before" and "after" variances are equal.

11 The critical t-value for $n - 2 = 34$ df, using a 5 percent significance level and a two-tailed test, is 2.032. First, take the smallest correlation in the table, the correlation between Fund 3 and Fund 4, and see if it is significantly different from zero. Its calculated t-value is

$$t = \frac{r\sqrt{n-2}}{\sqrt{1-r^2}} = \frac{0.3102\sqrt{36-2}}{\sqrt{1-0.3102^2}} = 1.903$$

This correlation is not significantly different from zero. If we take the next lowest correlation, between Fund 2 and Fund 3, this correlation of 0.4156 has a calculated t-value of 2.664. So this correlation is significantly different from zero at the 5 percent level of significance. All of the other correlations in the table (besides the 0.3102) are greater than 0.4156, so they too are significantly different from zero.

12 A is correct. The critical value in a decision rule is the rejection point for the test. It is the point with which the test statistic is compared to determine whether to reject the null hypothesis, which is part of the fourth step in hypothesis testing.

13 A is correct. The null hypothesis is the hypothesis to be tested. The null hypothesis is considered to be true unless the evidence indicates that it is false, in which case the alternative hypothesis is accepted.

14 A is correct. If the population sampled has unknown variance and the sample is large, a z-test may be used. Hypotheses involving "greater than" or "less than" postulations are one-sided (one-tailed). In this situation, the null and alternative hypotheses are stated as H_0: $\mu \leq 6\%$ and H_a: $\mu > 6\%$, respectively. A one-tailed t-test is also acceptable in this case.

15 C is correct. For a one-tailed hypothesis test, there is a 5% critical value rejection region in one tail of the distribution.

16 B is correct. One-tailed tests in which the alternative is "greater than" or "less than" represent the beliefs of the researcher more firmly than a "not equal to" alternative hypothesis.

17 A is correct. Calculated using a sample, a test statistic is a quantity whose value is the basis for deciding whether to reject the null hypothesis.

18 A is correct. The definition of a Type I error is when a true null hypothesis is rejected.

19 B is correct. A Type II error occurs when a false null hypothesis is not rejected.

20 B is correct. The level of significance is used to establish the rejection points of the hypothesis test.

21 **A** We have a "not equal to" alternative hypothesis:

$$H_0\text{: } \rho = 0 \text{ versus } H_a\text{: } \rho \neq 0$$

B We would use the nonparametric Spearman rank correlation coefficient to conduct the test.

C Mutual fund expense ratios are bounded from above and below, and in practice there is at least a lower bound on alpha (as any return cannot be less than −100 percent). These variables are markedly non-normally distributed, and the assumptions of a parametric test are not likely to be fulfilled. Thus a nonparametric test appears to be appropriate.

D The calculation of the Spearman rank correlation coefficient is given in the following table.

Mutual Fund	1	2	3	4	5	6	7	8	9
Alpha (X)	−0.52	−0.13	−0.60	−1.01	−0.26	−0.89	−0.42	−0.23	−0.60
Expense Ratio (Y)	1.34	0.92	1.02	1.45	1.35	0.50	1.00	1.50	1.45
X Rank	5	1	6.5	9	3	8	4	2	6.5
Y Rank	5	8	6	2.5	4	9	7	1	2.5
d_i	0	−7	0.5	6.5	−1	−1	−3	1	4
d_i^2	0	49	0.25	42.25	1	1	9	1	16

$$r_s = 1 - \frac{6\sum d_i^2}{n\left(n^2 - 1\right)} = 1 - \frac{6(119.50)}{9(81 - 1)} = 0.0042$$

We use Table 11 to tabulate the rejection points for a test on the Spearman rank correlation. Given a sample size of 9 in a two-tailed test at a 0.05 significance level, the upper-tail rejection point is 0.6833 (we use the 0.025 column). Thus we reject the null hypothesis if the Spearman rank correlation coefficient is less than −0.6833 or greater than 0.6833. Because r_S is equal to 0.0042, we do not reject the null hypothesis.

22 B is correct. Specifying a smaller significance level decreases the probability of a Type I error (rejecting a true null hypothesis), but increases the probability of a Type II error (not rejecting a false null hypothesis). As the level of significance decreases, the null hypothesis is less frequently rejected.

23 B is correct. The power of a test is the probability of rejecting the null hypothesis when it is false.

24 B is correct. The power of a hypothesis test is the probability of correctly rejecting the null when it is false. Failing to reject the null when it is false is a Type II error. Thus, the power of a hypothesis test is the probability of not committing a Type II error.

25 C is correct. When a statistically significant result is also economically meaningful, one should further explore the logic of why the result might work in the future.

26 A is correct. The hypothesis is a two-tailed formulation. The t-statistic of 2.802 falls outside the critical rejection points of less than −2.756 and greater than 2.756, therefore the null hypothesis is rejected; the result is statistically significant. However, despite the statistical results, trying to profit on the strategy is not likely to be economically meaningful because the return is near zero after transaction costs

27 C is correct. When directly comparing the p-value with the level of significance, it can be used as an alternative to using rejection points to reach conclusions on hypothesis tests. If the p-value is smaller than the specified level of significance, the null hypothesis is rejected. Otherwise, the null hypothesis is not rejected.

28 C is correct. The p-value is the smallest level of significance at which the null hypothesis can be rejected for a given value of the test statistic. The null hypothesis is rejected when the p-value is less than the specified significance level.

29 A is correct. The p-value is the smallest level of significance (α) at which the null hypothesis can be rejected.

30 C is correct. The p-value is the smallest level of significance (α) at which the null hypothesis can be rejected. If the p-value is less than α, the null can be rejected. The smaller the p-value, the stronger the evidence is against the null hypothesis and in favor of the alternative hypothesis. Thus, the evidence for rejecting the null is strongest for Test 3.

31 B is correct. The z-test is theoretically the correct test to use in those limited cases when testing the population mean of a normally distributed population with known variance.

32 A is correct. A t-test is used if the sample is small and drawn from a normally or approximately normally distributed population.

33 B is correct. A t-statistic is the most appropriate for hypothesis tests of the population mean when the variance is unknown and the sample is small but the population is normally distributed.

34 A is correct. The t-statistic value of 0.4893 does not fall into the critical value rejection regions (≤ -1.984 or > 1.984). Instead it falls well within the acceptance region. Thus, H_0 cannot be rejected; the result is not statistically significant at the 0.05 level.

35 B is correct. The assumption that the variances are equal allows for the combining of both samples to obtain a pooled estimate of the common variance.

36 B is correct. A paired comparisons test is appropriate to test the mean differences of two samples believed to be dependent.

37 A is correct. The sample sizes for both the fund manager and the consultant's accounts consists of forty quarterly periods of returns. However, the consultant's client accounts are a subset of the fund manager's entire account base. As such, they are not independent samples. When samples are dependent, a paired comparisons test is appropriate to conduct tests of the differences in dependent items.

38 A is correct. A chi-square test is used for tests concerning the variance of a single normally distributed population.

39 B is correct. An *F*-test is used to conduct tests concerning the difference between the variances of two normally distributed populations with random independent samples.

40 B is correct. The calculated test statistic is

$$t = \frac{r\sqrt{n-2}}{\sqrt{1-r^2}}$$

$$= \frac{-0.1452\sqrt{248-2}}{\sqrt{1-(-0.1452)^2}} = -2.30177$$

Because the absolute value of $t = -2.30177$ is greater than 1.96, the correlation coefficient is statistically significant.

41 A is correct. A non-parametric test is used when the data are given in ranks.

42 B is correct. There are only 12 (monthly) observations over the one year of the sample and thus the samples are small. Additionally, the funds' returns are non-normally distributed. Therefore, the samples do not meet the distributional assumptions for a parametric test. The Mann–Whitney U test (a nonparametric test) could be used to test the differences between population means.

APPENDICES

Appendix A	Cumulative Probabilities for a Standard Normal Distribution
Appendix B	Table of the Student's *t*-Distribution (One-Tailed Probabilities)
Appendix C	Values of X^2 (Degrees of Freedom, Level of Significance)
Appendix D	Table of the *F*-Distribution
Appendix E	Critical Values for the Durbin-Watson Statistic (α = .05)

Appendix A
Cumulative Probabilities for a Standard Normal Distribution
$P(Z \le x) = N(x)$ for $x \ge 0$ or $P(Z \le z) = N(z)$ for $z \ge 0$

x or z	0	0.01	0.02	0.03	0.04	0.05	0.06	0.07	0.08	0.09
0.00	0.5000	0.5040	0.5080	0.5120	0.5160	0.5199	0.5239	0.5279	0.5319	0.5359
0.10	0.5398	0.5438	0.5478	0.5517	0.5557	0.5596	0.5636	0.5675	0.5714	0.5753
0.20	0.5793	0.5832	0.5871	0.5910	0.5948	0.5987	0.6026	0.6064	0.6103	0.6141
0.30	0.6179	0.6217	0.6255	0.6293	0.6331	0.6368	0.6406	0.6443	0.6480	0.6517
0.40	0.6554	0.6591	0.6628	0.6664	0.6700	0.6736	0.6772	0.6808	0.6844	0.6879
0.50	0.6915	0.6950	0.6985	0.7019	0.7054	0.7088	0.7123	0.7157	0.7190	0.7224
0.60	0.7257	0.7291	0.7324	0.7357	0.7389	0.7422	0.7454	0.7486	0.7517	0.7549
0.70	0.7580	0.7611	0.7642	0.7673	0.7704	0.7734	0.7764	0.7794	0.7823	0.7852
0.80	0.7881	0.7910	0.7939	0.7967	0.7995	0.8023	0.8051	0.8078	0.8106	0.8133
0.90	0.8159	0.8186	0.8212	0.8238	0.8264	0.8289	0.8315	0.8340	0.8365	0.8389
1.00	0.8413	0.8438	0.8461	0.8485	0.8508	0.8531	0.8554	0.8577	0.8599	0.8621
1.10	0.8643	0.8665	0.8686	0.8708	0.8729	0.8749	0.8770	0.8790	0.8810	0.8830
1.20	0.8849	0.8869	0.8888	0.8907	0.8925	0.8944	0.8962	0.8980	0.8997	0.9015
1.30	0.9032	0.9049	0.9066	0.9082	0.9099	0.9115	0.9131	0.9147	0.9162	0.9177
1.40	0.9192	0.9207	0.9222	0.9236	0.9251	0.9265	0.9279	0.9292	0.9306	0.9319
1.50	0.9332	0.9345	0.9357	0.9370	0.9382	0.9394	0.9406	0.9418	0.9429	0.9441
1.60	0.9452	0.9463	0.9474	0.9484	0.9495	0.9505	0.9515	0.9525	0.9535	0.9545
1.70	0.9554	0.9564	0.9573	0.9582	0.9591	0.9599	0.9608	0.9616	0.9625	0.9633
1.80	0.9641	0.9649	0.9656	0.9664	0.9671	0.9678	0.9686	0.9693	0.9699	0.9706
1.90	0.9713	0.9719	0.9726	0.9732	0.9738	0.9744	0.9750	0.9756	0.9761	0.9767
2.00	0.9772	0.9778	0.9783	0.9788	0.9793	0.9798	0.9803	0.9808	0.9812	0.9817
2.10	0.9821	0.9826	0.9830	0.9834	0.9838	0.9842	0.9846	0.9850	0.9854	0.9857
2.20	0.9861	0.9864	0.9868	0.9871	0.9875	0.9878	0.9881	0.9884	0.9887	0.9890
2.30	0.9893	0.9896	0.9898	0.9901	0.9904	0.9906	0.9909	0.9911	0.9913	0.9916
2.40	0.9918	0.9920	0.9922	0.9925	0.9927	0.9929	0.9931	0.9932	0.9934	0.9936
2.50	0.9938	0.9940	0.9941	0.9943	0.9945	0.9946	0.9948	0.9949	0.9951	0.9952
2.60	0.9953	0.9955	0.9956	0.9957	0.9959	0.9960	0.9961	0.9962	0.9963	0.9964
2.70	0.9965	0.9966	0.9967	0.9968	0.9969	0.9970	0.9971	0.9972	0.9973	0.9974
2.80	0.9974	0.9975	0.9976	0.9977	0.9977	0.9978	0.9979	0.9979	0.9980	0.9981
2.90	0.9981	0.9982	0.9982	0.9983	0.9984	0.9984	0.9985	0.9985	0.9986	0.9986
3.00	0.9987	0.9987	0.9987	0.9988	0.9988	0.9989	0.9989	0.9989	0.9990	0.9990
3.10	0.9990	0.9991	0.9991	0.9991	0.9992	0.9992	0.9992	0.9992	0.9993	0.9993
3.20	0.9993	0.9993	0.9994	0.9994	0.9994	0.9994	0.9994	0.9995	0.9995	0.9995
3.30	0.9995	0.9995	0.9995	0.9996	0.9996	0.9996	0.9996	0.9996	0.9996	0.9997
3.40	0.9997	0.9997	0.9997	0.9997	0.9997	0.9997	0.9997	0.9997	0.9997	0.9998
3.50	0.9998	0.9998	0.9998	0.9998	0.9998	0.9998	0.9998	0.9998	0.9998	0.9998
3.60	0.9998	0.9998	0.9999	0.9999	0.9999	0.9999	0.9999	0.9999	0.9999	0.9999
3.70	0.9999	0.9999	0.9999	0.9999	0.9999	0.9999	0.9999	0.9999	0.9999	0.9999
3.80	0.9999	0.9999	0.9999	0.9999	0.9999	0.9999	0.9999	0.9999	0.9999	0.9999
3.90	1.0000	1.0000	1.0000	1.0000	1.0000	1.0000	1.0000	1.0000	1.0000	1.0000
4.00	1.0000	1.0000	1.0000	1.0000	1.0000	1.0000	1.0000	1.0000	1.0000	1.0000

For example, to find the z-value leaving 2.5 percent of the area/probability in the upper tail, find the element 0.9750 in the body of the table. Read 1.90 at the left end of the element's row and 0.06 at the top of the element's column, to give 1.90 + 0.06 = 1.96. *Table generated with Excel.*

Appendix A (continued)
Cumulative Probabilities for a Standard Normal Distribution
P(*Z* ≤ x) = *N*(x) for x ≤ 0 or *P*(*Z* ≤ z) = *N*(z) for z ≤ 0

x or z	0	0.01	0.02	0.03	0.04	0.05	0.06	0.07	0.08	0.09
0.0	0.5000	0.4960	0.4920	0.4880	0.4840	0.4801	0.4761	0.4721	0.4681	0.4641
−0.10	0.4602	0.4562	0.4522	0.4483	0.4443	0.4404	0.4364	0.4325	0.4286	0.4247
−0.20	0.4207	0.4168	0.4129	0.4090	0.4052	0.4013	0.3974	0.3936	0.3897	0.3859
−0.30	0.3821	0.3783	0.3745	0.3707	0.3669	0.3632	0.3594	0.3557	0.3520	0.3483
−0.40	0.3446	0.3409	0.3372	0.3336	0.3300	0.3264	0.3228	0.3192	0.3156	0.3121
−0.50	0.3085	0.3050	0.3015	0.2981	0.2946	0.2912	0.2877	0.2843	0.2810	0.2776
−0.60	0.2743	0.2709	0.2676	0.2643	0.2611	0.2578	0.2546	0.2514	0.2483	0.2451
−0.70	0.2420	0.2389	0.2358	0.2327	0.2296	0.2266	0.2236	0.2206	0.2177	0.2148
−0.80	0.2119	0.2090	0.2061	0.2033	0.2005	0.1977	0.1949	0.1922	0.1894	0.1867
−0.90	0.1841	0.1814	0.1788	0.1762	0.1736	0.1711	0.1685	0.1660	0.1635	0.1611
−1.00	0.1587	0.1562	0.1539	0.1515	0.1492	0.1469	0.1446	0.1423	0.1401	0.1379
−1.10	0.1357	0.1335	0.1314	0.1292	0.1271	0.1251	0.1230	0.1210	0.1190	0.1170
−1.20	0.1151	0.1131	0.1112	0.1093	0.1075	0.1056	0.1038	0.1020	0.1003	0.0985
−1.30	0.0968	0.0951	0.0934	0.0918	0.0901	0.0885	0.0869	0.0853	0.0838	0.0823
−1.40	0.0808	0.0793	0.0778	0.0764	0.0749	0.0735	0.0721	0.0708	0.0694	0.0681
−1.50	0.0668	0.0655	0.0643	0.0630	0.0618	0.0606	0.0594	0.0582	0.0571	0.0559
−1.60	0.0548	0.0537	0.0526	0.0516	0.0505	0.0495	0.0485	0.0475	0.0465	0.0455
−1.70	0.0446	0.0436	0.0427	0.0418	0.0409	0.0401	0.0392	0.0384	0.0375	0.0367
−1.80	0.0359	0.0351	0.0344	0.0336	0.0329	0.0322	0.0314	0.0307	0.0301	0.0294
−1.90	0.0287	0.0281	0.0274	0.0268	0.0262	0.0256	0.0250	0.0244	0.0239	0.0233
−2.00	0.0228	0.0222	0.0217	0.0212	0.0207	0.0202	0.0197	0.0192	0.0188	0.0183
−2.10	0.0179	0.0174	0.0170	0.0166	0.0162	0.0158	0.0154	0.0150	0.0146	0.0143
−2.20	0.0139	0.0136	0.0132	0.0129	0.0125	0.0122	0.0119	0.0116	0.0113	0.0110
−2.30	0.0107	0.0104	0.0102	0.0099	0.0096	0.0094	0.0091	0.0089	0.0087	0.0084
−2.40	0.0082	0.0080	0.0078	0.0075	0.0073	0.0071	0.0069	0.0068	0.0066	0.0064
−2.50	0.0062	0.0060	0.0059	0.0057	0.0055	0.0054	0.0052	0.0051	0.0049	0.0048
−2.60	0.0047	0.0045	0.0044	0.0043	0.0041	0.0040	0.0039	0.0038	0.0037	0.0036
−2.70	0.0035	0.0034	0.0033	0.0032	0.0031	0.0030	0.0029	0.0028	0.0027	0.0026
−2.80	0.0026	0.0025	0.0024	0.0023	0.0023	0.0022	0.0021	0.0021	0.0020	0.0019
−2.90	0.0019	0.0018	0.0018	0.0017	0.0016	0.0016	0.0015	0.0015	0.0014	0.0014
−3.00	0.0013	0.0013	0.0013	0.0012	0.0012	0.0011	0.0011	0.0011	0.0010	0.0010
−3.10	0.0010	0.0009	0.0009	0.0009	0.0008	0.0008	0.0008	0.0008	0.0007	0.0007
−3.20	0.0007	0.0007	0.0006	0.0006	0.0006	0.0006	0.0006	0.0005	0.0005	0.0005
−3.30	0.0005	0.0005	0.0005	0.0004	0.0004	0.0004	0.0004	0.0004	0.0004	0.0003
−3.40	0.0003	0.0003	0.0003	0.0003	0.0003	0.0003	0.0003	0.0003	0.0003	0.0002
−3.50	0.0002	0.0002	0.0002	0.0002	0.0002	0.0002	0.0002	0.0002	0.0002	0.0002
−3.60	0.0002	0.0002	0.0001	0.0001	0.0001	0.0001	0.0001	0.0001	0.0001	0.0001
−3.70	0.0001	0.0001	0.0001	0.0001	0.0001	0.0001	0.0001	0.0001	0.0001	0.0001
−3.80	0.0001	0.0001	0.0001	0.0001	0.0001	0.0001	0.0001	0.0001	0.0001	0.0001
−3.90	0.0000	0.0000	0.0000	0.0000	0.0000	0.0000	0.0000	0.0000	0.0000	0.0000
−4.00	0.0000	0.0000	0.0000	0.0000	0.0000	0.0000	0.0000	0.0000	0.0000	0.0000

For example, to find the *z*-value leaving 2.5 percent of the area/probability in the lower tail, find the element 0.0250 in the body of the table. Read −1.90 at the left end of the element's row and 0.06 at the top of the element's column, to give −1.90 − 0.06 = −1.96. *Table generated with Excel.*

Appendix B
Table of the Student's t-Distribution (One-Tailed Probabilities)

df	$p = 0.10$	$p = 0.05$	$p = 0.025$	$p = 0.01$	$p = 0.005$	df	$p = 0.10$	$p = 0.05$	$p = 0.025$	$p = 0.01$	$p = 0.005$
1	3.078	6.314	12.706	31.821	63.657	**31**	1.309	1.696	2.040	2.453	2.744
2	1.886	2.920	4.303	6.965	9.925	**32**	1.309	1.694	2.037	2.449	2.738
3	1.638	2.353	3.182	4.541	5.841	**33**	1.308	1.692	2.035	2.445	2.733
4	1.533	2.132	2.776	3.747	4.604	**34**	1.307	1.691	2.032	2.441	2.728
5	1.476	2.015	2.571	3.365	4.032	**35**	1.306	1.690	2.030	2.438	2.724
6	1.440	1.943	2.447	3.143	3.707	**36**	1.306	1.688	2.028	2.434	2.719
7	1.415	1.895	2.365	2.998	3.499	**37**	1.305	1.687	2.026	2.431	2.715
8	1.397	1.860	2.306	2.896	3.355	**38**	1.304	1.686	2.024	2.429	2.712
9	1.383	1.833	2.262	2.821	3.250	**39**	1.304	1.685	2.023	2.426	2.708
10	1.372	1.812	2.228	2.764	3.169	**40**	1.303	1.684	2.021	2.423	2.704
11	1.363	1.796	2.201	2.718	3.106	**41**	1.303	1.683	2.020	2.421	2.701
12	1.356	1.782	2.179	2.681	3.055	**42**	1.302	1.682	2.018	2.418	2.698
13	1.350	1.771	2.160	2.650	3.012	**43**	1.302	1.681	2.017	2.416	2.695
14	1.345	1.761	2.145	2.624	2.977	**44**	1.301	1.680	2.015	2.414	2.692
15	1.341	1.753	2.131	2.602	2.947	**45**	1.301	1.679	2.014	2.412	2.690
16	1.337	1.746	2.120	2.583	2.921	**46**	1.300	1.679	2.013	2.410	2.687
17	1.333	1.740	2.110	2.567	2.898	**47**	1.300	1.678	2.012	2.408	2.685
18	1.330	1.734	2.101	2.552	2.878	**48**	1.299	1.677	2.011	2.407	2.682
19	1.328	1.729	2.093	2.539	2.861	**49**	1.299	1.677	2.010	2.405	2.680
20	1.325	1.725	2.086	2.528	2.845	**50**	1.299	1.676	2.009	2.403	2.678
21	1.323	1.721	2.080	2.518	2.831	**60**	1.296	1.671	2.000	2.390	2.660
22	1.321	1.717	2.074	2.508	2.819	**70**	1.294	1.667	1.994	2.381	2.648
23	1.319	1.714	2.069	2.500	2.807	**80**	1.292	1.664	1.990	2.374	2.639
24	1.318	1.711	2.064	2.492	2.797	**90**	1.291	1.662	1.987	2.368	2.632
25	1.316	1.708	2.060	2.485	2.787	**100**	1.290	1.660	1.984	2.364	2.626
26	1.315	1.706	2.056	2.479	2.779	**110**	1.289	1.659	1.982	2.361	2.621
27	1.314	1.703	2.052	2.473	2.771	**120**	1.289	1.658	1.980	2.358	2.617
28	1.313	1.701	2.048	2.467	2.763	**200**	1.286	1.653	1.972	2.345	2.601
29	1.311	1.699	2.045	2.462	2.756	∞	1.282	1.645	1.960	2.326	2.576
30	1.310	1.697	2.042	2.457	2.750						

To find a critical t-value, enter the table with df and a specified value for α, the significance level. For example, with 5 df, $\alpha = 0.05$ and a one-tailed test, the desired probability in the tail would be $p = 0.05$ and the critical t-value would be $t(5, 0.05) = 2.015$. With $\alpha = 0.05$ and a two-tailed test, the desired probability in each tail would be $p = 0.025 = \alpha/2$, giving $t(0.025) = 2.571$. *Table generated using Excel.*

Appendix C
Values of χ^2 (Degrees of Freedom, Level of Significance)

Degrees of Freedom	Probability in Right Tail								
	0.99	0.975	0.95	0.9	0.1	0.05	0.025	0.01	0.005
1	0.000157	0.000982	0.003932	0.0158	2.706	3.841	5.024	6.635	7.879
2	0.020100	0.050636	0.102586	0.2107	4.605	5.991	7.378	9.210	10.597
3	0.1148	0.2158	0.3518	0.5844	6.251	7.815	9.348	11.345	12.838
4	0.297	0.484	0.711	1.064	7.779	9.488	11.143	13.277	14.860
5	0.554	0.831	1.145	1.610	9.236	11.070	12.832	15.086	16.750
6	0.872	1.237	1.635	2.204	10.645	12.592	14.449	16.812	18.548
7	1.239	1.690	2.167	2.833	12.017	14.067	16.013	18.475	20.278
8	1.647	2.180	2.733	3.490	13.362	15.507	17.535	20.090	21.955
9	2.088	2.700	3.325	4.168	14.684	16.919	19.023	21.666	23.589
10	2.558	3.247	3.940	4.865	15.987	18.307	20.483	23.209	25.188
11	3.053	3.816	4.575	5.578	17.275	19.675	21.920	24.725	26.757
12	3.571	4.404	5.226	6.304	18.549	21.026	23.337	26.217	28.300
13	4.107	5.009	5.892	7.041	19.812	22.362	24.736	27.688	29.819
14	4.660	5.629	6.571	7.790	21.064	23.685	26.119	29.141	31.319
15	5.229	6.262	7.261	8.547	22.307	24.996	27.488	30.578	32.801
16	5.812	6.908	7.962	9.312	23.542	26.296	28.845	32.000	34.267
17	6.408	7.564	8.672	10.085	24.769	27.587	30.191	33.409	35.718
18	7.015	8.231	9.390	10.865	25.989	28.869	31.526	34.805	37.156
19	7.633	8.907	10.117	11.651	27.204	30.144	32.852	36.191	38.582
20	8.260	9.591	10.851	12.443	28.412	31.410	34.170	37.566	39.997
21	8.897	10.283	11.591	13.240	29.615	32.671	35.479	38.932	41.401
22	9.542	10.982	12.338	14.041	30.813	33.924	36.781	40.289	42.796
23	10.196	11.689	13.091	14.848	32.007	35.172	38.076	41.638	44.181
24	10.856	12.401	13.848	15.659	33.196	36.415	39.364	42.980	45.558
25	11.524	13.120	14.611	16.473	34.382	37.652	40.646	44.314	46.928
26	12.198	13.844	15.379	17.292	35.563	38.885	41.923	45.642	48.290
27	12.878	14.573	16.151	18.114	36.741	40.113	43.195	46.963	49.645
28	13.565	15.308	16.928	18.939	37.916	41.337	44.461	48.278	50.994
29	14.256	16.047	17.708	19.768	39.087	42.557	45.722	49.588	52.335
30	14.953	16.791	18.493	20.599	40.256	43.773	46.979	50.892	53.672
50	29.707	32.357	34.764	37.689	63.167	67.505	71.420	76.154	79.490
60	37.485	40.482	43.188	46.459	74.397	79.082	83.298	88.379	91.952
80	53.540	57.153	60.391	64.278	96.578	101.879	106.629	112.329	116.321
100	70.065	74.222	77.929	82.358	118.498	124.342	129.561	135.807	140.170

To have a probability of 0.05 in the right tail when df = 5, the tabled value is $\chi^2(5, 0.05) = 11.070$.

Quantitative Methods for Investment Analysis, Second Edition, by Richard A. DeFusco, CFA, Dennis W. McLeavey, CFA, Jerald E. Pinto, CFA, and David E. Runkle, CFA.

Appendix D
Table of the *F*-Distribution

Panel A. Critical values for right-hand tail area equal to 0.05 — **Numerator: df_1 and Denominator: df_2**

	df1:1	2	3	4	5	6	7	8	9	10	11	12	15	20	21	22	23	24	25	30	40	60	120	∞
df2: 1	161	200	216	225	230	234	237	239	241	242	243	244	246	248	248	249	249	249	249	250	251	252	253	254
2	18.5	19.0	19.2	19.2	19.3	19.3	19.4	19.4	19.4	19.4	19.4	19.4	19.4	19.4	19.4	19.5	19.5	19.5	19.5	19.5	19.5	19.5	19.5	19.5
3	10.1	9.55	9.28	9.12	9.01	8.94	8.89	8.85	8.81	8.79	8.76	8.74	8.70	8.66	8.65	8.65	8.64	8.64	8.63	8.62	8.59	8.57	8.55	8.53
4	7.71	6.94	6.59	6.39	6.26	6.16	6.09	6.04	6.00	5.96	5.94	5.91	5.86	5.80	5.79	5.79	5.78	5.77	5.77	5.75	5.72	5.69	5.66	5.63
5	6.61	5.79	5.41	5.19	5.05	4.95	4.88	4.82	4.77	4.74	4.70	4.68	4.62	4.56	4.55	4.54	4.53	4.53	4.52	4.50	4.46	4.43	4.40	4.37
6	5.99	5.14	4.76	4.53	4.39	4.28	4.21	4.15	4.10	4.06	4.03	4.00	3.94	3.87	3.86	3.86	3.85	3.84	3.83	3.81	3.77	3.74	3.70	3.67
7	5.59	4.74	4.35	4.12	3.97	3.87	3.79	3.73	3.68	3.64	3.60	3.57	3.51	3.44	3.43	3.43	3.42	3.41	3.40	3.38	3.34	3.30	3.27	3.23
8	5.32	4.46	4.07	3.84	3.69	3.58	3.50	3.44	3.39	3.35	3.31	3.28	3.22	3.15	3.14	3.13	3.12	3.12	3.11	3.08	3.04	3.01	2.97	2.93
9	5.12	4.26	3.86	3.63	3.48	3.37	3.29	3.23	3.18	3.14	3.10	3.07	3.01	2.94	2.93	2.92	2.91	2.90	2.89	2.86	2.83	2.79	2.75	2.71
10	4.96	4.10	3.71	3.48	3.33	3.22	3.14	3.07	3.02	2.98	2.94	2.91	2.85	2.77	2.76	2.75	2.75	2.74	2.73	2.70	2.66	2.62	2.58	2.54
11	4.84	3.98	3.59	3.36	3.20	3.09	3.01	2.95	2.90	2.85	2.82	2.79	2.72	2.65	2.64	2.63	2.62	2.61	2.60	2.57	2.53	2.49	2.45	2.40
12	4.75	3.89	3.49	3.26	3.11	3.00	2.91	2.85	2.80	2.75	2.72	2.69	2.62	2.54	2.53	2.52	2.51	2.51	2.50	2.47	2.43	2.38	2.34	2.30
13	4.67	3.81	3.41	3.18	3.03	2.92	2.83	2.77	2.71	2.67	2.63	2.60	2.53	2.46	2.45	2.44	2.43	2.42	2.41	2.38	2.34	2.30	2.25	2.21
14	4.60	3.74	3.34	3.11	2.96	2.85	2.76	2.70	2.65	2.60	2.57	2.53	2.46	2.39	2.38	2.37	2.36	2.35	2.34	2.31	2.27	2.22	2.18	2.13
15	4.54	3.68	3.29	3.06	2.90	2.79	2.71	2.64	2.59	2.54	2.51	2.48	2.40	2.33	2.32	2.31	2.30	2.29	2.28	2.25	2.20	2.16	2.11	2.07
16	4.49	3.63	3.24	3.01	2.85	2.74	2.66	2.59	2.54	2.49	2.46	2.42	2.35	2.28	2.26	2.25	2.24	2.24	2.23	2.19	2.15	2.11	2.06	2.01
17	4.45	3.59	3.20	2.96	2.81	2.70	2.61	2.55	2.49	2.45	2.41	2.38	2.31	2.23	2.22	2.21	2.20	2.19	2.18	2.15	2.10	2.06	2.01	1.96
18	4.41	3.55	3.16	2.93	2.77	2.66	2.58	2.51	2.46	2.41	2.37	2.34	2.27	2.19	2.18	2.17	2.16	2.15	2.14	2.11	2.06	2.02	1.97	1.92
19	4.38	3.52	3.13	2.90	2.74	2.63	2.54	2.48	2.42	2.38	2.34	2.31	2.23	2.16	2.14	2.13	2.12	2.11	2.11	2.07	2.03	1.98	1.93	1.88
20	4.35	3.49	3.10	2.87	2.71	2.60	2.51	2.45	2.39	2.35	2.31	2.28	2.20	2.12	2.11	2.10	2.09	2.08	2.07	2.04	1.99	1.95	1.90	1.84
21	4.32	3.47	3.07	2.84	2.68	2.57	2.49	2.42	2.37	2.32	2.28	2.25	2.18	2.10	2.08	2.07	2.06	2.05	2.05	2.01	1.96	1.92	1.87	1.81
22	4.30	3.44	3.05	2.82	2.66	2.55	2.46	2.40	2.34	2.30	2.26	2.23	2.15	2.07	2.06	2.05	2.04	2.03	2.02	1.98	1.94	1.89	1.84	1.78
23	4.28	3.42	3.03	2.80	2.64	2.53	2.44	2.37	2.32	2.27	2.24	2.20	2.13	2.05	2.04	2.02	2.01	2.01	2.00	1.96	1.91	1.86	1.81	1.76
24	4.26	3.40	3.01	2.78	2.62	2.51	2.42	2.36	2.30	2.25	2.22	2.18	2.11	2.03	2.01	2.00	1.99	1.98	1.97	1.94	1.89	1.84	1.79	1.73
25	4.24	3.39	2.99	2.76	2.60	2.49	2.40	2.34	2.28	2.24	2.20	2.16	2.09	2.01	2.00	1.98	1.97	1.96	1.96	1.92	1.87	1.82	1.77	1.71
30	4.17	3.32	2.92	2.69	2.53	2.42	2.33	2.27	2.21	2.16	2.13	2.09	2.01	1.93	1.92	1.91	1.90	1.89	1.88	1.84	1.79	1.74	1.68	1.62
40	4.08	3.23	2.84	2.61	2.45	2.34	2.25	2.18	2.12	2.08	2.04	2.00	1.92	1.84	1.83	1.81	1.80	1.79	1.78	1.74	1.69	1.64	1.58	1.51
60	4.00	3.15	2.76	2.53	2.37	2.25	2.17	2.10	2.04	1.99	1.95	1.92	1.84	1.75	1.73	1.72	1.71	1.70	1.69	1.65	1.59	1.53	1.47	1.39
120	3.92	3.07	2.68	2.45	2.29	2.18	2.09	2.02	1.96	1.91	1.87	1.83	1.75	1.66	1.64	1.63	1.62	1.61	1.60	1.55	1.50	1.43	1.35	1.25
Infinity	3.84	3.00	2.60	2.37	2.21	2.10	2.01	1.94	1.88	1.83	1.79	1.75	1.67	1.57	1.56	1.54	1.53	1.52	1.51	1.46	1.39	1.32	1.22	1.00

Appendix D (continued)
Table of the *F*-Distribution

Panel B. Critical values for right-hand tail area equal to 0.025 — Numerator: df_1 and Denominator: df_2

	df1: 1	2	3	4	5	6	7	8	9	10	11	12	15	20	21	22	23	24	25	30	40	60	120	∞
df2: 1	648	799	864	900	922	937	948	957	963	969	973	977	985	993	994	995	996	997	998	1001	1006	1010	1014	1018
2	38.51	39.00	39.17	39.25	39.30	39.33	39.36	39.37	39.39	39.40	39.41	39.41	39.43	39.45	39.45	39.45	39.45	39.46	39.46	39.46	39.47	39.48	39.49	39.50
3	17.44	16.04	15.44	15.10	14.88	14.73	14.62	14.54	14.47	14.42	14.37	14.34	14.25	14.17	14.16	14.14	14.13	14.12	14.12	14.08	14.04	13.99	13.95	13.90
4	12.22	10.65	9.98	9.60	9.36	9.20	9.07	8.98	8.90	8.84	8.79	8.75	8.66	8.56	8.55	8.53	8.52	8.51	8.50	8.46	8.41	8.36	8.31	8.26
5	10.01	8.43	7.76	7.39	7.15	6.98	6.85	6.76	6.68	6.62	6.57	6.52	6.43	6.33	6.31	6.30	6.29	6.28	6.27	6.23	6.18	6.12	6.07	6.02
6	8.81	7.26	6.60	6.23	5.99	5.82	5.70	5.60	5.52	5.46	5.41	5.37	5.27	5.17	5.15	5.14	5.13	5.12	5.11	5.07	5.01	4.96	4.90	4.85
7	8.07	6.54	5.89	5.52	5.29	5.12	4.99	4.90	4.82	4.76	4.71	4.67	4.57	4.47	4.45	4.44	4.43	4.41	4.40	4.36	4.31	4.25	4.20	4.14
8	7.57	6.06	5.42	5.05	4.82	4.65	4.53	4.43	4.36	4.30	4.24	4.20	4.10	4.00	3.98	3.97	3.96	3.95	3.94	3.89	3.84	3.78	3.73	3.67
9	7.21	5.71	5.08	4.72	4.48	4.32	4.20	4.10	4.03	3.96	3.91	3.87	3.77	3.67	3.65	3.64	3.63	3.61	3.60	3.56	3.51	3.45	3.39	3.33
10	6.94	5.46	4.83	4.47	4.24	4.07	3.95	3.85	3.78	3.72	3.66	3.62	3.52	3.42	3.40	3.39	3.38	3.37	3.35	3.31	3.26	3.20	3.14	3.08
11	6.72	5.26	4.63	4.28	4.04	3.88	3.76	3.66	3.59	3.53	3.47	3.43	3.33	3.23	3.21	3.20	3.18	3.17	3.16	3.12	3.06	3.00	2.94	2.88
12	6.55	5.10	4.47	4.12	3.89	3.73	3.61	3.51	3.44	3.37	3.32	3.28	3.18	3.07	3.06	3.04	3.03	3.02	3.01	2.96	2.91	2.85	2.79	2.72
13	6.41	4.97	4.35	4.00	3.77	3.60	3.48	3.39	3.31	3.25	3.20	3.15	3.05	2.95	2.93	2.92	2.91	2.89	2.88	2.84	2.78	2.72	2.66	2.60
14	6.30	4.86	4.24	3.89	3.66	3.50	3.38	3.29	3.21	3.15	3.09	3.05	2.95	2.84	2.83	2.81	2.80	2.79	2.78	2.73	2.67	2.61	2.55	2.49
15	6.20	4.77	4.15	3.80	3.58	3.41	3.29	3.20	3.12	3.06	3.01	2.96	2.86	2.76	2.74	2.73	2.71	2.70	2.69	2.64	2.59	2.52	2.46	2.40
16	6.12	4.69	4.08	3.73	3.50	3.34	3.22	3.12	3.05	2.99	2.93	2.89	2.79	2.68	2.67	2.65	2.64	2.63	2.61	2.57	2.51	2.45	2.38	2.32
17	6.04	4.62	4.01	3.66	3.44	3.28	3.16	3.06	2.98	2.92	2.87	2.82	2.72	2.62	2.60	2.59	2.57	2.56	2.55	2.50	2.44	2.38	2.32	2.25
18	5.98	4.56	3.95	3.61	3.38	3.22	3.10	3.01	2.93	2.87	2.81	2.77	2.67	2.56	2.54	2.53	2.52	2.50	2.49	2.44	2.38	2.32	2.26	2.19
19	5.92	4.51	3.90	3.56	3.33	3.17	3.05	2.96	2.88	2.82	2.76	2.72	2.62	2.51	2.49	2.48	2.46	2.45	2.44	2.39	2.33	2.27	2.20	2.13
20	5.87	4.46	3.86	3.51	3.29	3.13	3.01	2.91	2.84	2.77	2.72	2.68	2.57	2.46	2.45	2.43	2.42	2.41	2.40	2.35	2.29	2.22	2.16	2.09
21	5.83	4.42	3.82	3.48	3.25	3.09	2.97	2.87	2.80	2.73	2.68	2.64	2.53	2.42	2.41	2.39	2.38	2.37	2.36	2.31	2.25	2.18	2.11	2.04
22	5.79	4.38	3.78	3.44	3.22	3.05	2.93	2.84	2.76	2.70	2.65	2.60	2.50	2.39	2.37	2.36	2.34	2.33	2.32	2.27	2.21	2.14	2.08	2.00
23	5.75	4.35	3.75	3.41	3.18	3.02	2.90	2.81	2.73	2.67	2.62	2.57	2.47	2.36	2.34	2.33	2.31	2.30	2.29	2.24	2.18	2.11	2.04	1.97
24	5.72	4.32	3.72	3.38	3.15	2.99	2.87	2.78	2.70	2.64	2.59	2.54	2.44	2.33	2.31	2.30	2.28	2.27	2.26	2.21	2.15	2.08	2.01	1.94
25	5.69	4.29	3.69	3.35	3.13	2.97	2.85	2.75	2.68	2.61	2.56	2.51	2.41	2.30	2.28	2.27	2.26	2.24	2.23	2.18	2.12	2.05	1.98	1.91
30	5.57	4.18	3.59	3.25	3.03	2.87	2.75	2.65	2.57	2.51	2.46	2.41	2.31	2.20	2.18	2.16	2.15	2.14	2.12	2.07	2.01	1.94	1.87	1.79
40	5.42	4.05	3.46	3.13	2.90	2.74	2.62	2.53	2.45	2.39	2.33	2.29	2.18	2.07	2.05	2.03	2.02	2.01	1.99	1.94	1.88	1.80	1.72	1.64
60	5.29	3.93	3.34	3.01	2.79	2.63	2.51	2.41	2.33	2.27	2.22	2.17	2.06	1.94	1.93	1.91	1.90	1.88	1.87	1.82	1.74	1.67	1.58	1.48
120	5.15	3.80	3.23	2.89	2.67	2.52	2.39	2.30	2.22	2.16	2.10	2.05	1.94	1.82	1.81	1.79	1.77	1.76	1.75	1.69	1.61	1.53	1.43	1.31
Infinity	5.02	3.69	3.12	2.79	2.57	2.41	2.29	2.19	2.11	2.05	1.99	1.94	1.83	1.71	1.69	1.67	1.66	1.64	1.63	1.57	1.48	1.39	1.27	1.00

Appendix D (continued)
Table of the *F*-Distribution

Panel C. Critical values for right-hand tail area equal to 0.01 — **Numerator: df_1 and Denominator: df_2**

	df1: 1	2	3	4	5	6	7	8	9	10	11	12	15	20	21	22	23	24	25	30	40	60	120	∞
df2: 1	4052	5000	5403	5625	5764	5859	5928	5982	6023	6056	6083	6106	6157	6209	6216	6223	6229	6235	6240	6261	6287	6313	6339	6366
2	98.5	99.0	99.2	99.2	99.3	99.3	99.4	99.4	99.4	99.4	99.4	99.4	99.4	99.4	99.5	99.5	99.5	99.5	99.5	99.5	99.5	99.5	99.5	99.5
3	34.1	30.8	29.5	28.7	28.2	27.9	27.7	27.5	27.3	27.2	27.1	27.1	26.9	26.7	26.7	26.6	26.6	26.6	26.6	26.5	26.4	26.3	26.2	26.1
4	21.2	18.0	16.7	16.0	15.5	15.2	15.0	14.8	14.7	14.5	14.5	14.4	14.2	14.0	14.0	14.0	13.9	13.9	13.9	13.8	13.7	13.7	13.6	13.5
5	16.3	13.3	12.1	11.4	11.0	10.7	10.5	10.3	10.2	10.1	10.0	9.89	9.72	9.55	9.53	9.51	9.49	9.47	9.45	9.38	9.29	9.20	9.11	9.02
6	13.7	10.9	9.78	9.15	8.75	8.47	8.26	8.10	7.98	7.87	7.79	7.72	7.56	7.40	7.37	7.35	7.33	7.31	7.30	7.23	7.14	7.06	6.97	6.88
7	12.2	9.55	8.45	7.85	7.46	7.19	6.99	6.84	6.72	6.62	6.54	6.47	6.31	6.16	6.13	6.11	6.09	6.07	6.06	5.99	5.91	5.82	5.74	5.65
8	11.3	8.65	7.59	7.01	6.63	6.37	6.18	6.03	5.91	5.81	5.73	5.67	5.52	5.36	5.34	5.32	5.30	5.28	5.26	5.20	5.12	5.03	4.95	4.86
9	10.6	8.02	6.99	6.42	6.06	5.80	5.61	5.47	5.35	5.26	5.18	5.11	4.96	4.81	4.79	4.77	4.75	4.73	4.71	4.65	4.57	4.48	4.40	4.31
10	10.0	7.56	6.55	5.99	5.64	5.39	5.20	5.06	4.94	4.85	4.77	4.71	4.56	4.41	4.38	4.36	4.34	4.33	4.31	4.25	4.17	4.08	4.00	3.91
11	9.65	7.21	6.22	5.67	5.32	5.07	4.89	4.74	4.63	4.54	4.46	4.40	4.25	4.10	4.08	4.06	4.04	4.02	4.01	3.94	3.86	3.78	3.69	3.60
12	9.33	6.93	5.95	5.41	5.06	4.82	4.64	4.50	4.39	4.30	4.22	4.16	4.01	3.86	3.84	3.82	3.80	3.78	3.76	3.70	3.62	3.54	3.45	3.36
13	9.07	6.70	5.74	5.21	4.86	4.62	4.44	4.30	4.19	4.10	4.02	3.96	3.82	3.66	3.64	3.62	3.60	3.59	3.57	3.51	3.43	3.34	3.25	3.17
14	8.86	6.51	5.56	5.04	4.70	4.46	4.28	4.14	4.03	3.94	3.86	3.80	3.66	3.51	3.48	3.46	3.44	3.43	3.41	3.35	3.27	3.18	3.09	3.00
15	8.68	6.36	5.42	4.89	4.56	4.32	4.14	4.00	3.89	3.80	3.73	3.67	3.52	3.37	3.35	3.33	3.31	3.29	3.28	3.21	3.13	3.05	2.96	2.87
16	8.53	6.23	5.29	4.77	4.44	4.20	4.03	3.89	3.78	3.69	3.62	3.55	3.41	3.26	3.24	3.22	3.20	3.18	3.16	3.10	3.02	2.93	2.84	2.75
17	8.40	6.11	5.19	4.67	4.34	4.10	3.93	3.79	3.68	3.59	3.52	3.46	3.31	3.16	3.14	3.12	3.10	3.08	3.07	3.00	2.92	2.83	2.75	2.65
18	8.29	6.01	5.09	4.58	4.25	4.01	3.84	3.71	3.60	3.51	3.43	3.37	3.23	3.08	3.05	3.03	3.02	3.00	2.98	2.92	2.84	2.75	2.66	2.57
19	8.19	5.93	5.01	4.50	4.17	3.94	3.77	3.63	3.52	3.43	3.36	3.30	3.15	3.00	2.98	2.96	2.94	2.92	2.91	2.84	2.76	2.67	2.58	2.49
20	8.10	5.85	4.94	4.43	4.10	3.87	3.70	3.56	3.46	3.37	3.29	3.23	3.09	2.94	2.92	2.90	2.88	2.86	2.84	2.78	2.69	2.61	2.52	2.42
21	8.02	5.78	4.87	4.37	4.04	3.81	3.64	3.51	3.40	3.31	3.24	3.17	3.03	2.88	2.86	2.84	2.82	2.80	2.79	2.72	2.64	2.55	2.46	2.36
22	7.95	5.72	4.82	4.31	3.99	3.76	3.59	3.45	3.35	3.26	3.18	3.12	2.98	2.83	2.81	2.78	2.77	2.75	2.73	2.67	2.58	2.50	2.40	2.31
23	7.88	5.66	4.76	4.26	3.94	3.71	3.54	3.41	3.30	3.21	3.14	3.07	2.93	2.78	2.76	2.74	2.72	2.70	2.69	2.62	2.54	2.45	2.35	2.26
24	7.82	5.61	4.72	4.22	3.90	3.67	3.50	3.36	3.26	3.17	3.09	3.03	2.89	2.74	2.72	2.70	2.68	2.66	2.64	2.58	2.49	2.40	2.31	2.21
25	7.77	5.57	4.68	4.18	3.86	3.63	3.46	3.32	3.22	3.13	3.06	2.99	2.85	2.70	2.68	2.66	2.64	2.62	2.60	2.53	2.45	2.36	2.27	2.17
30	7.56	5.39	4.51	4.02	3.70	3.47	3.30	3.17	3.07	2.98	2.91	2.84	2.70	2.55	2.53	2.51	2.49	2.47	2.45	2.39	2.30	2.21	2.11	2.01
40	7.31	5.18	4.31	3.83	3.51	3.29	3.12	2.99	2.89	2.80	2.73	2.66	2.52	2.37	2.35	2.33	2.31	2.29	2.27	2.20	2.11	2.02	1.92	1.80
60	7.08	4.98	4.13	3.65	3.34	3.12	2.95	2.82	2.72	2.63	2.56	2.50	2.35	2.20	2.17	2.15	2.13	2.12	2.10	2.03	1.94	1.84	1.73	1.60
120	6.85	4.79	3.95	3.48	3.17	2.96	2.79	2.66	2.56	2.47	2.40	2.34	2.19	2.03	2.01	1.99	1.97	1.95	1.93	1.86	1.76	1.66	1.53	1.38
Infinity	6.63	4.61	3.78	3.32	3.02	2.80	2.64	2.51	2.41	2.32	2.25	2.18	2.04	1.88	1.85	1.83	1.81	1.79	1.77	1.70	1.59	1.47	1.32	1.00

Appendix D (continued)
Table of the *F*-Distribution

Panel D. Critical values for right-hand tail area equal to 0.005 — Numerator: df_1 and Denominator: df_2

	df1: 1	2	3	4	5	6	7	8	9	10	11	12	15	20	21	22	23	24	25	30	40	60	120	∞
df2: 1	16211	20000	21615	22500	23056	23437	23715	23925	24091	24222	24334	24426	24630	24836	24863	24892	24915	24940	24959	25044	25146	25253	25359	25464
2	198.5	199.0	199.2	199.2	199.3	199.3	199.4	199.4	199.4	199.4	199.4	199.4	199.4	199.4	199.4	199.4	199.4	199.4	199.4	199.5	199.5	199.5	199.5	200
3	55.55	49.80	47.47	46.20	45.39	44.84	44.43	44.13	43.88	43.68	43.52	43.39	43.08	42.78	42.73	42.69	42.66	42.62	42.59	42.47	42.31	42.15	41.99	41.83
4	31.33	26.28	24.26	23.15	22.46	21.98	21.62	21.35	21.14	20.97	20.82	20.70	20.44	20.17	20.13	20.09	20.06	20.03	20.00	19.89	19.75	19.61	19.47	19.32
5	22.78	18.31	16.53	15.56	14.94	14.51	14.20	13.96	13.77	13.62	13.49	13.38	13.15	12.90	12.87	12.84	12.81	12.78	12.76	12.66	12.53	12.40	12.27	12.14
6	18.63	14.54	12.92	12.03	11.46	11.07	10.79	10.57	10.39	10.25	10.13	10.03	9.81	9.59	9.56	9.53	9.50	9.47	9.45	9.36	9.24	9.12	9.00	8.88
7	16.24	12.40	10.88	10.05	9.52	9.16	8.89	8.68	8.51	8.38	8.27	8.18	7.97	7.75	7.72	7.69	7.67	7.64	7.62	7.53	7.42	7.31	7.19	7.08
8	14.69	11.04	9.60	8.81	8.30	7.95	7.69	7.50	7.34	7.21	7.10	7.01	6.81	6.61	6.58	6.55	6.53	6.50	6.48	6.40	6.29	6.18	6.06	5.95
9	13.61	10.11	8.72	7.96	7.47	7.13	6.88	6.69	6.54	6.42	6.31	6.23	6.03	5.83	5.80	5.78	5.75	5.73	5.71	5.62	5.52	5.41	5.30	5.19
10	12.83	9.43	8.08	7.34	6.87	6.54	6.30	6.12	5.97	5.85	5.75	5.66	5.47	5.27	5.25	5.22	5.20	5.17	5.15	5.07	4.97	4.86	4.75	4.64
11	12.23	8.91	7.60	6.88	6.42	6.10	5.86	5.68	5.54	5.42	5.32	5.24	5.05	4.86	4.83	4.80	4.78	4.76	4.74	4.65	4.55	4.45	4.34	4.23
12	11.75	8.51	7.23	6.52	6.07	5.76	5.52	5.35	5.20	5.09	4.99	4.91	4.72	4.53	4.50	4.48	4.45	4.43	4.41	4.33	4.23	4.12	4.01	3.90
13	11.37	8.19	6.93	6.23	5.79	5.48	5.25	5.08	4.94	4.82	4.72	4.64	4.46	4.27	4.24	4.22	4.19	4.17	4.15	4.07	3.97	3.87	3.76	3.65
14	11.06	7.92	6.68	6.00	5.56	5.26	5.03	4.86	4.72	4.60	4.51	4.43	4.25	4.06	4.03	4.01	3.98	3.96	3.94	3.86	3.76	3.66	3.55	3.44
15	10.80	7.70	6.48	5.80	5.37	5.07	4.85	4.67	4.54	4.42	4.33	4.25	4.07	3.88	3.86	3.83	3.81	3.79	3.77	3.69	3.59	3.48	3.37	3.26
16	10.58	7.51	6.30	5.64	5.21	4.91	4.69	4.52	4.38	4.27	4.18	4.10	3.92	3.73	3.71	3.68	3.66	3.64	3.62	3.54	3.44	3.33	3.22	3.11
17	10.38	7.35	6.16	5.50	5.07	4.78	4.56	4.39	4.25	4.14	4.05	3.97	3.79	3.61	3.58	3.56	3.53	3.51	3.49	3.41	3.31	3.21	3.10	2.98
18	10.22	7.21	6.03	5.37	4.96	4.66	4.44	4.28	4.14	4.03	3.94	3.86	3.68	3.50	3.47	3.45	3.42	3.40	3.38	3.30	3.20	3.10	2.99	2.87
19	10.07	7.09	5.92	5.27	4.85	4.56	4.34	4.18	4.04	3.93	3.84	3.76	3.59	3.40	3.37	3.35	3.33	3.31	3.29	3.21	3.11	3.00	2.89	2.78
20	9.94	6.99	5.82	5.17	4.76	4.47	4.26	4.09	3.96	3.85	3.76	3.68	3.50	3.32	3.29	3.27	3.24	3.22	3.20	3.12	3.02	2.92	2.81	2.69
21	9.83	6.89	5.73	5.09	4.68	4.39	4.18	4.01	3.88	3.77	3.68	3.60	3.43	3.24	3.22	3.19	3.17	3.15	3.13	3.05	2.95	2.84	2.73	2.61
22	9.73	6.81	5.65	5.02	4.61	4.32	4.11	3.94	3.81	3.70	3.61	3.54	3.36	3.18	3.15	3.12	3.10	3.08	3.06	2.98	2.88	2.77	2.66	2.55
23	9.63	6.73	5.58	4.95	4.54	4.26	4.05	3.88	3.75	3.64	3.55	3.47	3.30	3.12	3.09	3.06	3.04	3.02	3.00	2.92	2.82	2.71	2.60	2.48
24	9.55	6.66	5.52	4.89	4.49	4.20	3.99	3.83	3.69	3.59	3.50	3.42	3.25	3.06	3.04	3.01	2.99	2.97	2.95	2.87	2.77	2.66	2.55	2.43
25	9.48	6.60	5.46	4.84	4.43	4.15	3.94	3.78	3.64	3.54	3.45	3.37	3.20	3.01	2.99	2.96	2.94	2.92	2.90	2.82	2.72	2.61	2.50	2.38
30	9.18	6.35	5.24	4.62	4.23	3.95	3.74	3.58	3.45	3.34	3.25	3.18	3.01	2.82	2.80	2.77	2.75	2.73	2.71	2.63	2.52	2.42	2.30	2.18
40	8.83	6.07	4.98	4.37	3.99	3.71	3.51	3.35	3.22	3.12	3.03	2.95	2.78	2.60	2.57	2.55	2.52	2.50	2.48	2.40	2.30	2.18	2.06	1.93
60	8.49	5.79	4.73	4.14	3.76	3.49	3.29	3.13	3.01	2.90	2.82	2.74	2.57	2.39	2.36	2.33	2.31	2.29	2.27	2.19	2.08	1.96	1.83	1.69
120	8.18	5.54	4.50	3.92	3.55	3.28	3.09	2.93	2.81	2.71	2.62	2.54	2.37	2.19	2.16	2.13	2.11	2.09	2.07	1.98	1.87	1.75	1.61	1.43
Infinity	7.88	5.30	4.28	3.72	3.35	3.09	2.90	2.74	2.62	2.52	2.43	2.36	2.19	2.00	1.97	1.95	1.92	1.90	1.88	1.79	1.67	1.53	1.36	1.00

With 1 degree of freedom (df) in the numerator and 3 df in the denominator, the critical *F*-value is 10.1 for a right-hand tail area equal to 0.05.

Appendix E
Critical Values for the Durbin-Watson Statistic (α = .05)

	K = 1		K = 2		K = 3		K = 4		K = 5	
n	d_l	d_u	d_l	d_u	d_l	d_u	d_l	d_u	d_l	d_u
15	1.08	1.36	0.95	1.54	0.82	1.75	0.69	1.97	0.56	2.21
16	1.10	1.37	0.98	1.54	0.86	1.73	0.74	1.93	0.62	2.15
17	1.13	1.38	1.02	1.54	0.90	1.71	0.78	1.90	0.67	2.10
18	1.16	1.39	1.05	1.53	0.93	1.69	0.82	1.87	0.71	2.06
19	1.18	1.40	1.08	1.53	0.97	1.68	0.86	1.85	0.75	2.02
20	1.20	1.41	1.10	1.54	1.00	1.68	0.90	1.83	0.79	1.99
21	1.22	1.42	1.13	1.54	1.03	1.67	0.93	1.81	0.83	1.96
22	1.24	1.43	1.15	1.54	1.05	1.66	0.96	1.80	0.86	1.94
23	1.26	1.44	1.17	1.54	1.08	1.66	0.99	1.79	0.90	1.92
24	1.27	1.45	1.19	1.55	1.10	1.66	1.01	1.78	0.93	1.90
25	1.29	1.45	1.21	1.55	1.12	1.66	1.04	1.77	0.95	1.89
26	1.30	1.46	1.22	1.55	1.14	1.65	1.06	1.76	0.98	1.88
27	1.32	1.47	1.24	1.56	1.16	1.65	1.08	1.76	1.01	1.86
28	1.33	1.48	1.26	1.56	1.18	1.65	1.10	1.75	1.03	1.85
29	1.34	1.48	1.27	1.56	1.20	1.65	1.12	1.74	1.05	1.84
30	1.35	1.49	1.28	1.57	1.21	1.65	1.14	1.74	1.07	1.83
31	1.36	1.50	1.30	1.57	1.23	1.65	1.16	1.74	1.09	1.83
32	1.37	1.50	1.31	1.57	1.24	1.65	1.18	1.73	1.11	1.82
33	1.38	1.51	1.32	1.58	1.26	1.65	1.19	1.73	1.13	1.81
34	1.39	1.51	1.33	1.58	1.27	1.65	1.21	1.73	1.15	1.81
35	1.40	1.52	1.34	1.58	1.28	1.65	1.22	1.73	1.16	1.80
36	1.41	1.52	1.35	1.59	1.29	1.65	1.24	1.73	1.18	1.80
37	1.42	1.53	1.36	1.59	1.31	1.66	1.25	1.72	1.19	1.80
38	1.43	1.54	1.37	1.59	1.32	1.66	1.26	1.72	1.21	1.79
39	1.43	1.54	1.38	1.60	1.33	1.66	1.27	1.72	1.22	1.79
40	1.44	1.54	1.39	1.60	1.34	1.66	1.29	1.72	1.23	1.79
45	1.48	1.57	1.43	1.62	1.38	1.67	1.34	1.72	1.29	1.78
50	1.50	1.59	1.46	1.63	1.42	1.67	1.38	1.72	1.34	1.77
55	1.53	1.60	1.49	1.64	1.45	1.68	1.41	1.72	1.38	1.77
60	1.55	1.62	1.51	1.65	1.48	1.69	1.44	1.73	1.41	1.77
65	1.57	1.63	1.54	1.66	1.50	1.70	1.47	1.73	1.44	1.77
70	1.58	1.64	1.55	1.67	1.52	1.70	1.49	1.74	1.46	1.77
75	1.60	1.65	1.57	1.68	1.54	1.71	1.51	1.74	1.49	1.77
80	1.61	1.66	1.59	1.69	1.56	1.72	1.53	1.74	1.51	1.77
85	1.62	1.67	1.60	1.70	1.57	1.72	1.55	1.75	1.52	1.77
90	1.63	1.68	1.61	1.70	1.59	1.73	1.57	1.75	1.54	1.78
95	1.64	1.69	1.62	1.71	1.60	1.73	1.58	1.75	1.56	1.78
100	1.65	1.69	1.63	1.72	1.61	1.74	1.59	1.76	1.57	1.78

Note: K = the number of slope parameters in the model.

Source: From J. Durbin and G. S. Watson, "Testing for Serial Correlation in Least Squares Regression, II." *Biometrika* 38 (1951): 159–178.

Glossary

A priori probability A probability based on logical analysis rather than on observation or personal judgment.

Abnormal return The amount by which a security's actual return differs from its expected return, given the security's risk and the market's return.

Absolute advantage A country's ability to produce a good or service at a lower absolute cost than its trading partner.

Absolute dispersion The amount of variability present without comparison to any reference point or benchmark.

Absolute frequency The number of observations in a given interval (for grouped data).

Accelerated book build An offering of securities by an investment bank acting as principal that is accomplished in only one or two days.

Accelerated methods Depreciation methods that allocate a relatively large proportion of the cost of an asset to the early years of the asset's useful life.

Accounting costs Monetary value of economic resources used in performing an activity. These can be explicit, out-of-pocket, current payments, or an allocation of historical payments (depreciation) for resources. They do not include implicit opportunity costs.

Accounting profit Income as reported on the income statement, in accordance with prevailing accounting standards, before the provisions for income tax expense. Also called *income before taxes* or *pretax income*.

Accounts payable Amounts that a business owes to its vendors for goods and services that were purchased from them but which have not yet been paid.

Accounts receivable turnover Ratio of sales on credit to the average balance in accounts receivable.

Accrued expenses Liabilities related to expenses that have been incurred but not yet paid as of the end of an accounting period—an example of an accrued expense is rent that has been incurred but not yet paid, resulting in a liability "rent payable." Also called *accrued liabilities*.

Accrued interest Interest earned but not yet paid.

Acid-test ratio A stringent measure of liquidity that indicates a company's ability to satisfy current liabilities with its most liquid assets, calculated as (cash + short-term marketable investments + receivables) divided by current liabilities.

Acquisition method A method of accounting for a business combination where the acquirer is required to measure each identifiable asset and liability at fair value. This method was the result of a joint project of the IASB and FASB aiming at convergence in standards for the accounting of business combinations.

Action lag Delay from policy decisions to implementation.

Active investment An approach to investing in which the investor seeks to outperform a given benchmark.

Active return The return on a portfolio minus the return on the portfolio's benchmark.

Active strategy In reference to short-term cash management, an investment strategy characterized by monitoring and attempting to capitalize on market conditions to optimize the risk and return relationship of short-term investments.

Activity ratios Ratios that measure how efficiently a company performs day-to-day tasks, such as the collection of receivables and management of inventory. Also called *asset utilization ratios* or *operating efficiency ratios*.

Add-on rates Bank certificates of deposit, repos, and indexes such as Libor and Euribor are quoted on an add-on rate basis (bond equivalent yield basis).

Addition rule for probabilities A principle stating that the probability that *A* or *B* occurs (both occur) equals the probability that *A* occurs, plus the probability that *B* occurs, minus the probability that both *A* and *B* occur.

Agency bonds See *quasi-government bond*.

Agency RMBS In the United States, securities backed by residential mortgage loans and guaranteed by a federal agency or guaranteed by either of the two GSEs (Fannie Mae and Freddie Mac).

Aggregate demand The quantity of goods and services that households, businesses, government, and foreign customers want to buy at any given level of prices.

Aggregate demand curve Inverse relationship between the price level and real output.

Aggregate income The value of all the payments earned by the suppliers of factors used in the production of goods and services.

Aggregate output The value of all the goods and services produced in a specified period of time.

Aggregate supply The quantity of goods and services producers are willing to supply at any given level of price.

Aggregate supply curve The level of domestic output that companies will produce at each price level.

Aging schedule A breakdown of accounts into categories of days outstanding.

All-or-nothing (AON) orders An order that includes the instruction to trade only if the trade fills the entire quantity (size) specified.

Allocationally efficient A characteristic of a market, a financial system, or an economy that promotes the allocation of resources to their highest value uses.

Alternative data Non-traditional data types generated by the use of electronic devices, social media, satellite and sensor networks, and company exhaust.

Alternative investment markets Market for investments other than traditional securities investments (i.e., traditional common and preferred shares and traditional fixed income instruments). The term usually encompasses direct and indirect investment in real estate (including timberland and farmland) and commodities (including precious metals); hedge funds, private equity, and other investments requiring specialized due diligence.

Alternative trading systems Trading venues that function like exchanges but that do not exercise regulatory authority over their subscribers except with respect to the conduct of the subscribers' trading in their trading systems. Also called *electronic communications networks* or *multilateral trading facilities*.

American depository receipt A US dollar-denominated security that trades like a common share on US exchanges.

American depositary share The underlying shares on which American depositary receipts are based. They trade in the issuing company's domestic market.

American-style Type of option contract that can be exercised at any time up to the option's expiration date.

Amortisation The process of allocating the cost of intangible long-term assets having a finite useful life to accounting periods; the allocation of the amount of a bond premium or discount to the periods remaining until bond maturity.

Amortised cost The historical cost (initially recognised cost) of an asset, adjusted for amortisation and impairment.

Amortizing bond Bond with a payment schedule that calls for periodic payments of interest and repayments of principal.

Amortizing loan Loan with a payment schedule that calls for periodic payments of interest and repayments of principal.

Annual percentage rate The cost of borrowing expressed as a yearly rate.

Annuity A finite set of level sequential cash flows.

Annuity due An annuity having a first cash flow that is paid immediately.

Anticipation stock Excess inventory that is held in anticipation of increased demand, often because of seasonal patterns of demand.

Antidilutive With reference to a transaction or a security, one that would increase earnings per share (EPS) or result in EPS higher than the company's basic EPS—antidilutive securities are not included in the calculation of diluted EPS.

Arbitrage 1) The simultaneous purchase of an undervalued asset or portfolio and sale of an overvalued but equivalent asset or portfolio, in order to obtain a riskless profit on the price differential. Taking advantage of a market inefficiency in a risk-free manner. 2) The condition in a financial market in which equivalent assets or combinations of assets sell for two different prices, creating an opportunity to profit at no risk with no commitment of money. In a well-functioning financial market, few arbitrage opportunities are possible. 3) A risk-free operation that earns an expected positive net profit but requires no net investment of money.

Arbitrage-free pricing The overall process of pricing derivatives by arbitrage and risk neutrality. Also called the *principle of no arbitrage.*

Arbitrageurs Traders who engage in arbitrage. See *arbitrage*.

Arithmetic mean The sum of the observations divided by the number of observations.

Arms index A flow of funds indicator applied to a broad stock market index to measure the relative extent to which money is moving into or out of rising and declining stocks.

Artificial intelligence Computer systems that exhibit cognitive and decision-making ability comparable (or superior) to that of humans.

Asian call option A European-style option with a value at maturity equal to the difference between the stock price at maturity and the average stock price during the life of the option, or $0, whichever is greater.

Ask The price at which a dealer or trader is willing to sell an asset, typically qualified by a maximum quantity (ask size). See *offer*.

Ask size The maximum quantity of an asset that pertains to a specific ask price from a trader. For example, if the ask for a share issue is $30 for a size of 1,000 shares, the trader is offering to sell at $30 up to 1,000 shares.

Asset allocation The process of determining how investment funds should be distributed among asset classes.

Asset-backed securities A type of bond issued by a legal entity called a *special purpose entity* (SPE) on a collection of assets that the SPE owns. Also, securities backed by receivables and loans other than mortgages.

Asset-based loan A loan that is secured with company assets.

Asset-based valuation models Valuation based on estimates of the market value of a company's assets.

Asset beta The unlevered beta; reflects the business risk of the assets; the asset's systematic risk.

Asset class A group of assets that have similar characteristics, attributes, and risk/return relationships.

Asset swap Converts the periodic fixed coupon of a specific bond to a Libor plus or minus a spread.

Asset utilization ratios Ratios that measure how efficiently a company performs day-to-day tasks, such as the collection of receivables and management of inventory.

Assets Resources controlled by an enterprise as a result of past events and from which future economic benefits to the enterprise are expected to flow.

Assignment of accounts receivable The use of accounts receivable as collateral for a loan.

At the money An option in which the underlying's price equals the exercise price.

Auction A type of bond issuing mechanism often used for sovereign bonds that involves bidding.

Autarkic price The price of a good or service in an autarkic economy.

Autarky A state in which a country does not trade with other countries.

Automated Clearing House (ACH) An electronic payment network available to businesses, individuals, and financial institutions in the United States, US Territories, and Canada.

Automatic stabilizer A countercyclical factor that automatically comes into play as an economy slows and unemployment rises.

Available-for-sale Under US GAAP, debt securities not classified as either held-to-maturity or held-for-trading securities. The investor is willing to sell but not actively planning to sell. In general, available-for-sale debt securities are reported at fair value on the balance sheet, with unrealized gains included as a component of other comprehensive income.

Average accounting rate of return (ARR) Over the life of a project, the AAR can be defined as the average net income divided by the average book value.

Average fixed cost Total fixed cost divided by quantity produced.

Average life See *weighted average life.*

Average product Measures the productivity of inputs on average and is calculated by dividing total product by the total number of units for a given input that is used to generate that output.

Average revenue Total revenue divided by quantity sold.

Average total cost Total cost divided by quantity produced.

Average variable cost Total variable cost divided by quantity produced.

Back simulation Another term for the historical method of estimating VaR. This term is somewhat misleading in that the method involves not a *simulation* of the past but rather what *actually happened* in the past, sometimes adjusted to reflect the fact that a different portfolio may have existed in the past than is planned for the future.

Back-testing With reference to portfolio strategies, the application of a strategy's portfolio selection rules to historical data to assess what would have been the strategy's historical performance.

Backup lines of credit A type of credit enhancement provided by a bank to an issuer of commercial paper to ensure that the issuer will have access to sufficient liquidity to repay maturing commercial paper if issuing new paper is not a viable option.

Balance of payments A double-entry bookkeeping system that summarizes a country's economic transactions with the rest of the world for a particular period of time, typically a calendar quarter or year.

Balance of trade deficit When the domestic economy is spending more on foreign goods and services than foreign economies are spending on domestic goods and services.

Balance sheet The financial statement that presents an entity's current financial position by disclosing resources the entity controls (its assets) and the claims on those resources (its liabilities and equity claims), as of a particular point in time (the date of the balance sheet). Also called *statement of financial position* or *statement of financial condition.*

Balance sheet ratios Financial ratios involving balance sheet items only.

Balanced With respect to a government budget, one in which spending and revenues (taxes) are equal.

Balloon payment Large payment required at maturity to retire a bond's outstanding principal amount.

Bar chart A price chart with four bits of data for each time interval—the high, low, opening, and closing prices. A vertical line connects the high and low. A cross-hatch left indicates the opening price and a cross-hatch right indicates the close.

Barter economy An economy where economic agents as house-holds, corporations, and governments "pay" for goods and services with another good or service.

Base rates The reference rate on which a bank bases lending rates to all other customers.

Basic EPS Net earnings available to common shareholders (i.e., net income minus preferred dividends) divided by the weighted average number of common shares outstanding.

Basis point Used in stating yield spreads, one basis point equals one-hundredth of a percentage point, or 0.01%.

Basket of listed depository receipts An exchange-traded fund (ETF) that represents a portfolio of depository receipts.

Bearer bonds Bonds for which ownership is not recorded; only the clearing system knows who the bond owner is.

Behavioral finance A field of finance that examines the psychological variables that affect and often distort the investment decision making of investors, analysts, and portfolio managers.

Behind the market Said of prices specified in orders that are worse than the best current price; e.g., for a limit buy order, a limit price below the best bid.

Benchmark A comparison portfolio; a point of reference or comparison.

Benchmark issue The latest sovereign bond issue for a given maturity. It serves as a benchmark against which to compare bonds that have the same features but that are issued by another type of issuer.

Benchmark rate Typically the yield-to-maturity on a government bond having the same, or close to the same, time-to-maturity.

Benchmark spread The yield spread over a specific benchmark, usually measured in basis points.

Bernoulli random variable A random variable having the outcomes 0 and 1.

Bernoulli trial An experiment that can produce one of two outcomes.

Best bid The highest bid in the market.

Best effort offering An offering of a security using an investment bank in which the investment bank, as agent for the issuer, promises to use its best efforts to sell the offering but does not guarantee that a specific amount will be sold.

Best-in-class An ESG implementation approach that seeks to identify the most favorable companies in an industry based on ESG considerations.

Best offer The lowest offer (ask price) in the market.

Beta A measure of the sensitivity of a given investment or portfolio to movements in the overall market.

Bid The price at which a dealer or trader is willing to buy an asset, typically qualified by a maximum quantity.

Bid–ask spread The difference between the prices at which dealers will buy from a customer (bid) and sell to a customer (offer or ask). It is often used as an indicator of liquidity.

Bid–offer spread The difference between the prices at which dealers will buy from a customer (bid) and sell to a customer (offer or ask). It is often used as an indicator of liquidity.

Bid size The maximum quantity of an asset that pertains to a specific bid price from a trader.

Big Data The vast amount of data being generated by industry, governments, individuals, and electronic devices that arises from both traditional and non-traditional data sources.

Bilateral loan A loan from a single lender to a single borrower.

Binomial model A model for pricing options in which the underlying price can move to only one of two possible new prices.

Binomial random variable The number of successes in n Bernoulli trials for which the probability of success is constant for all trials and the trials are independent.

Binomial tree The graphical representation of a model of asset price dynamics in which, at each period, the asset moves up with probability p or down with probability $(1 - p)$.

Bitcoin A cryptocurrency using blockchain technology that was created in 2009.

Block brokers A broker (agent) that provides brokerage services for large-size trades.

Blockchain A type of digital ledger in which information is recorded sequentially and then linked together and secured using cryptographic methods.

Blue chip Widely held large market capitalization companies that are considered financially sound and are leaders in their respective industry or local stock market.

Bollinger Bands A price-based technical analysis indicator consisting of a moving average plus a higher line representing the moving average plus a set number of standard deviations from average price (for the same number of periods as used to calculate the moving average) and a lower line that is a moving average minus the same number of standard deviations.

Bond Contractual agreement between the issuer and the bondholders.

Bond equivalent yield A calculation of yield that is annualized using the ratio of 365 to the number of days to maturity. Bond equivalent yield allows for the restatement and comparison of securities with different compounding periods.

Bond indenture The governing legal credit agreement, typically incorporated by reference in the prospectus. Also called *trust deed.*

Bond market vigilantes Bond market participants who might reduce their demand for long-term bonds, thus pushing up their yields.

Bond yield plus risk premium approach An estimate of the cost of common equity that is produced by summing the before-tax cost of debt and a risk premium that captures the additional yield on a company's stock relative to its bonds. The additional yield is often estimated using historical spreads between bond yields and stock yields.

Bonus issue of shares A type of dividend in which a company distributes additional shares of its common stock to shareholders instead of cash.

Book building Investment bankers' process of compiling a "book" or list of indications of interest to buy part of an offering.

Book value The net amount shown for an asset or liability on the balance sheet; book value may also refer to the company's excess of total assets over total liabilities. Also called *carrying value.*

Boom An expansionary phase characterized by economic growth "testing the limits" of the economy.

Bottom-up analysis An investment selection approach that focuses on company-specific circumstances rather than emphasizing economic cycles or industry analysis.

Break point In the context of the weighted average cost of capital (WACC), a break point is the amount of capital at which the cost of one or more of the sources of capital changes, leading to a change in the WACC.

Breakeven point The number of units produced and sold at which the company's net income is zero (Revenues = Total cost); in the case of perfect competition, the quantity at which price, average revenue, and marginal revenue equal average total cost.

Bridge financing Interim financing that provides funds until permanent financing can be arranged.

Broad money Encompasses narrow money plus the entire range of liquid assets that can be used to make purchases.

Broker 1) An agent who executes orders to buy or sell securities on behalf of a client in exchange for a commission. 2) See *futures commission merchants.*

Broker–dealer A financial intermediary (often a company) that may function as a principal (dealer) or as an agent (broker) depending on the type of trade.

Brokered market A market in which brokers arrange trades among their clients.

Budget surplus/deficit The difference between government revenue and expenditure for a stated fixed period of time.

Bullet bond Bond in which the principal repayment is made entirely at maturity.

Business risk The risk associated with operating earnings. Operating earnings are uncertain because total revenues and many of the expenditures contributed to produce those revenues are uncertain.

Buy-side firm An investment management company or other investor that uses the services of brokers or dealers (i.e., the client of the sell side firms).

Buyback A transaction in which a company buys back its own shares. Unlike stock dividends and stock splits, share repurchases use corporate cash.

Call An option that gives the holder the right to buy an underlying asset from another party at a fixed price over a specific period of time.

Call market A market in which trades occur only at a particular time and place (i.e., when the market is called).

Call money rate The interest rate that buyers pay for their margin loan.

Call option An option that gives the holder the right to buy an underlying asset from another party at a fixed price over a specific period of time.

Call protection The time during which the issuer of the bond is not allowed to exercise the call option.

Callable bond A bond containing an embedded call option that gives the issuer the right to buy the bond back from the investor at specified prices on pre-determined dates.

Candlestick chart A price chart with four bits of data for each time interval. A candle indicates the opening and closing price for the interval. The body of the candle is shaded if the opening price was higher than the closing price, and the body is clear if the opening price was lower than the closing price. Vertical lines known as wicks or shadows extend from the top and bottom of the candle to indicate the high and the low prices for the interval.

Cannibalization Cannibalization occurs when an investment takes customers and sales away from another part of the company.

Capacity The ability of the borrower to make its debt payments on time.

Capital account A component of the balance of payments account that measures transfers of capital.

Capital allocation line (CAL) A graph line that describes the combinations of expected return and standard deviation of return available to an investor from combining the optimal portfolio of risky assets with the risk-free asset.

Capital asset pricing model (CAPM) An equation describing the expected return on any asset (or portfolio) as a linear function of its beta relative to the market portfolio.

Capital budgeting The process that companies use for decision making on capital projects—those projects with a life of one year or more.

Capital consumption allowance A measure of the wear and tear (depreciation) of the capital stock that occurs in the production of goods and services.

Capital deepening investment Increases the stock of capital relative to labor.

Capital expenditure Expenditure on physical capital (fixed assets).

Capital lease See *finance lease.*

Capital market expectations An investor's expectations concerning the risk and return prospects of asset classes.

Capital market line (CML) The line with an intercept point equal to the risk-free rate that is tangent to the efficient frontier of risky assets; represents the efficient frontier when a risk-free asset is available for investment.

Capital market securities Securities with maturities at issuance longer than one year.

Capital markets Financial markets that trade securities of longer duration, such as bonds and equities.

Capital rationing A capital rationing environment assumes that the company has a fixed amount of funds to invest.

Capital restrictions Controls placed on foreigners' ability to own domestic assets and/or domestic residents' ability to own foreign assets.

Capital stock The accumulated amount of buildings, machinery, and equipment used to produce goods and services.

Capital structure The mix of debt and equity that a company uses to finance its business; a company's specific mixture of long-term financing.

Captive finance subsidiary A wholly-owned subsidiary of a company that is established to provide financing of the sales of the parent company.

Carry The net of the costs and benefits of holding, storing, or "carrying" an asset.

Carrying amount The amount at which an asset or liability is valued according to accounting principles.

Carrying value The net amount shown for an asset or liability on the balance sheet; book value may also refer to the company's excess of total assets over total liabilities. For a bond, the purchase price plus (or minus) the amortized amount of the discount (or premium).

Cartel Participants in collusive agreements that are made openly and formally.

Cash collateral account Form of external credit enhancement whereby the issuer immediately borrows the credit-enhancement amount and then invests that amount, usually in highly rated short-term commercial paper.

Cash conversion cycle A financial metric that measures the length of time required for a company to convert cash invested in its operations to cash received as a result of its operations; equal to days of inventory on hand + days of sales outstanding – number of days of payables. Also called *net operating cycle.*

Cash flow additivity principle The principle that dollar amounts indexed at the same point in time are additive.

Cash flow from operating activities The net amount of cash provided from operating activities.

Cash flow from operations The net amount of cash provided from operating activities.

Cash flow yield The internal rate of return on a series of cash flows.

Cash market securities Money market securities settled on a "same day" or "cash settlement" basis.

Cash markets See *spot markets.*

Cash prices See *spot prices.*

Cash-settled forwards See *non-deliverable forwards.*

CBOE Volatility Index A measure of near-term market volatility as conveyed by S&P 500 stock index option prices.

Central bank funds market The market in which deposit-taking banks that have an excess reserve with their national central bank can loan money to banks that need funds for maturities ranging from overnight to one year. Called the Federal or Fed funds market in the United States.

Central bank funds rates Interest rates at which central bank funds are bought (borrowed) and sold (lent) for maturities ranging from overnight to one year. Called Federal or Fed funds rates in the United States.

Central banks The dominant bank in a country, usually with official or semi-official governmental status.

Certificate of deposit An instrument that represents a specified amount of funds on deposit with a bank for a specified maturity and interest rate. CDs are issued in various denominations and can be negotiable or non-negotiable.

Change in polarity principle A tenet of technical analysis that once a support level is breached, it becomes a resistance level. The same holds true for resistance levels; once breached, they become support levels.

Change of control put A covenant giving bondholders the right to require the issuer to buy back their debt, often at par or at some small premium to par value, in the event that the borrower is acquired.

Character The quality of a debt issuer's management.

Classified balance sheet A balance sheet organized so as to group together the various assets and liabilities into subcategories (e.g., current and noncurrent).

Clawback A requirement that the general partner return any funds distributed as incentive fees until the limited partners have received back their initial investment and a percentage of the total profit.

Clearing The process by which the exchange verifies the execution of a transaction and records the participants' identities.

Clearing instructions Instructions that indicate how to arrange the final settlement ("clearing") of a trade.

Clearinghouse An entity associated with a futures market that acts as middleman between the contracting parties and guarantees to each party the performance of the other.

Closed economy An economy that does not trade with other countries; an *autarkic economy.*

Closed-end fund A mutual fund in which no new investment money is accepted. New investors invest by buying existing shares, and investors in the fund liquidate by selling their shares to other investors.

Code of ethics An established guide that communicates an organization's values and overall expectations regarding member behavior. A code of ethics serves as a general guide for how community members should act.

Coefficient of variation (CV) The ratio of a set of observations' standard deviation to the observations' mean value.

Coincident economic indicators Turning points that are usually close to those of the overall economy; they are believed to have value for identifying the economy's present state.

Collateral manager Buys and sells debt obligations for and from the CDO's portfolio of assets (i.e., the collateral) to generate sufficient cash flows to meet the obligations to the CDO bondholders.

Collateral trust bonds Bonds secured by securities such as common shares, other bonds, or other financial assets.

Collateralized bond obligations A structured asset-backed security that is collateralized by a pool of bonds.

Collateralized debt obligation Generic term used to describe a security backed by a diversified pool of one or more debt obligations.

Collateralized loan obligations A structured asset-backed security that is collateralized by a pool of loans.

Collateralized mortgage obligation A security created through the securitization of a pool of mortgage-related products (mortgage pass-through securities or pools of loans).

Collaterals Assets or financial guarantees underlying a debt obligation that are above and beyond the issuer's promise to pay.

Combination A listing in which the order of the listed items does not matter.

Commercial paper A short-term, negotiable, unsecured promissory note that represents a debt obligation of the issuer.

Committed capital The amount that the limited partners have agreed to provide to the private equity fund.

Committed lines of credit A bank commitment to extend credit up to a pre-specified amount; the commitment is considered a short-term liability and is usually in effect for 364 days (one day short of a full year).

Commodity swap A swap in which the underlying is a commodity such as oil, gold, or an agricultural product.

Common market Level of economic integration that incorporates all aspects of the customs union and extends it by allowing free movement of factors of production among members.

Common shares A type of security that represent an ownership interest in a company.

Common-size analysis The restatement of financial statement items using a common denominator or reference item that allows one to identify trends and major differences; an example is an income statement in which all items are expressed as a percent of revenue.

Common stock See *common shares.*

Company analysis Analysis of an individual company.

Comparable company A company that has similar business risk; usually in the same industry and preferably with a single line of business.

Comparative advantage A country's ability to produce a good or service at a lower relative cost, or opportunity cost, than its trading partner.

Competitive strategy A company's plans for responding to the threats and opportunities presented by the external environment.

Complements Goods that tend to be used together; technically, two goods whose cross-price elasticity of demand is negative.

Complete markets Informally, markets in which the variety of distinct securities traded is so broad that any desired payoff in a future state-of-the-world is achievable.

Component cost of capital The rate of return required by suppliers of capital for an individual source of a company's funding, such as debt or equity.

Compounding The process of accumulating interest on interest.

Comprehensive income The change in equity of a business enterprise during a period from nonowner sources; includes all changes in equity during a period except those resulting from investments by owners and distributions to owners; comprehensive income equals net income plus other comprehensive income.

Conditional expected value The expected value of a stated event given that another event has occurred.

Conditional probability The probability of an event given (conditioned on) another event.

Conditional variances The variance of one variable, given the outcome of another.

Consistent With reference to estimators, describes an estimator for which the probability of estimates close to the value of the population parameter increases as sample size increases.

Constant-yield price trajectory A graph that illustrates the change in the price of a fixed-income bond over time assuming no change in yield-to-maturity. The trajectory shows the "pull to par" effect on the price of a bond trading at a premium or a discount to par value.

Constituent securities With respect to an index, the individual securities within an index.

Consumer surplus The difference between the value that a consumer places on units purchased and the amount of money that was required to pay for them.

Contingency provision Clause in a legal document that allows for some action if a specific event or circumstance occurs.

Contingent claims Derivatives in which the payoffs occur if a specific event occurs; generally referred to as options.

Contingent convertible bonds Bonds that automatically convert into equity if a specific event or circumstance occurs, such as the issuer's equity capital falling below the minimum requirement set by the regulators. Also called *CoCos.*

Continuation patterns A type of pattern used in technical analysis to predict the resumption of a market trend that was in place prior to the formation of a pattern.

Continuous random variable A random variable for which the range of possible outcomes is the real line (all real numbers between $-\infty$ and $+\infty$ or some subset of the real line).

Continuous time Time thought of as advancing in extremely small increments.

Continuous trading market A market in which trades can be arranged and executed any time the market is open.

Continuously compounded return The natural logarithm of 1 plus the holding period return, or equivalently, the natural logarithm of the ending price over the beginning price.

Contra account An account that offsets another account.

Contract rate See *mortgage rate.*

Contraction The period of a business cycle after the peak and before the trough; often called a *recession* or, if exceptionally severe, called a *depression.*

Contraction risk The risk that when interest rates decline, the security will have a shorter maturity than was anticipated at the time of purchase because borrowers refinance at the new, lower interest rates.

Contractionary Tending to cause the real economy to contract.

Contractionary fiscal policy A fiscal policy that has the objective to make the real economy contract.

Contracts for differences See *non-deliverable forwards.*

Contribution margin The amount available for fixed costs and profit after paying variable costs; revenue minus variable costs.

Controlling shareholders A particular shareholder or block of shareholders holding a percentage of shares that gives them significant voting power.

Convenience yield A non-monetary advantage of holding an asset.

Conventional bond See *plain vanilla bond.*

Conventional cash flow A conventional cash flow pattern is one with an initial outflow followed by a series of inflows.

Convergence The tendency for differences in output per capita across countries to diminish over time; in technical analysis, a term that describes the case when an indicator moves in the same manner as the security being analyzed.

Conversion price For a convertible bond, the price per share at which the bond can be converted into shares.

Conversion ratio For a convertible bond, the number of common shares that each bond can be converted into.

Conversion value For a convertible bond, the current share price multiplied by the conversion ratio.

Convertible bond Bond that gives the bondholder the right to exchange the bond for a specified number of common shares in the issuing company.

Convertible preference shares A type of equity security that entitles shareholders to convert their shares into a specified number of common shares.

Convexity adjustment For a bond, one half of the annual or approximate convexity statistic multiplied by the change in the yield-to-maturity squared.

Core inflation The inflation rate calculated based on a price index of goods and services except food and energy.

Corporate governance The system of internal controls and procedures by which individual companies are managed.

Correlation A number between −1 and +1 that measures the comovement (linear association) between two random variables.

Correlation coefficient A number between −1 and +1 that measures the consistency or tendency for two investments to act in a similar way. It is used to determine the effect on portfolio risk when two assets are combined.

Cost averaging The periodic investment of a fixed amount of money.

Cost of capital The rate of return that suppliers of capital require as compensation for their contribution of capital.

Cost of carry See *carry*.

Cost of debt The cost of debt financing to a company, such as when it issues a bond or takes out a bank loan.

Cost of preferred stock The cost to a company of issuing preferred stock; the dividend yield that a company must commit to pay preferred stockholders.

Cost-push Type of inflation in which rising costs, usually wages, compel businesses to raise prices generally.

Cost structure The mix of a company's variable costs and fixed costs.

Counterparty risk The risk that the other party to a contract will fail to honor the terms of the contract.

Coupon rate The interest rate promised in a contract; this is the rate used to calculate the periodic interest payments.

Cournot assumption Assumption in which each firm determines its profit-maximizing production level assuming that the other firms' output will not change.

Covariance A measure of the co-movement (linear association) between two random variables.

Covariance matrix A matrix or square array whose entries are covariances; also known as a variance–covariance matrix.

Covenants The terms and conditions of lending agreements that the issuer must comply with; they specify the actions that an issuer is obligated to perform (affirmative covenant) or prohibited from performing (negative covenant).

Covered bond Debt obligation secured by a segregated pool of assets called the cover pool. The issuer must maintain the value of the cover pool. In the event of default, bondholders have recourse against both the issuer and the cover pool.

Credit analysis The evaluation of credit risk; the evaluation of the creditworthiness of a borrower or counterparty.

Credit curve A curve showing the relationship between time to maturity and yield spread for an issuer with comparable bonds of various maturities outstanding, usually upward sloping.

Credit default swap (CDS) A type of credit derivative in which one party, the credit protection buyer who is seeking credit protection against a third party, makes a series of regularly scheduled payments to the other party, the credit protection seller. The seller makes no payments until a credit event occurs.

Credit derivatives A contract in which one party has the right to claim a payment from another party in the event that a specific credit event occurs over the life of the contract.

Credit enhancements Provisions that may be used to reduce the credit risk of a bond issue.

Credit-linked coupon bond Bond for which the coupon changes when the bond's credit rating changes.

Credit-linked note (CLN) Fixed-income security in which the holder of the security has the right to withhold payment of the full amount due at maturity if a credit event occurs.

Credit migration risk The risk that a bond issuer's creditworthiness deteriorates, or migrates lower, leading investors to believe the risk of default is higher. Also called *downgrade risk*.

Credit risk The risk of loss caused by a counterparty's or debtor's failure to make a promised payment. Also called *default risk*.

Credit scoring model A statistical model used to classify borrowers according to creditworthiness.

Credit spread option An option on the yield spread on a bond.

Credit tranching A structure used to redistribute the credit risk associated with the collateral; a set of bond classes created to allow investors a choice in the amount of credit risk that they prefer to bear.

Credit-worthiness The perceived ability of the borrower to pay what is owed on the borrowing in a timely manner; it represents the ability of a company to withstand adverse impacts on its cash flows.

Cross-default provisions Provisions whereby events of default such as non-payment of interest on one bond trigger default on all outstanding debt; implies the same default probability for all issues.

Cross-price elasticity of demand The percentage change in quantity demanded for a given percentage change in the price of another good; the responsiveness of the demand for Product A that is associated with the change in price of Product B.

Cross-sectional analysis Analysis that involves comparisons across individuals in a group over a given time period or at a given point in time.

Cross-sectional data Observations over individual units at a point in time, as opposed to time-series data.

Crossing networks Trading systems that match buyers and sellers who are willing to trade at prices obtained from other markets.

Crowding out The thesis that government borrowing may divert private sector investment from taking place.

Cryptocurrency An electronic medium of exchange that lacks physical form.

Cryptography An algorithmic process to encrypt data, making the data unusable if received by unauthorized parties.

Cumulative distribution function A function giving the probability that a random variable is less than or equal to a specified value.

Cumulative preference shares Preference shares for which any dividends that are not paid accrue and must be paid in full before dividends on common shares can be paid.

Cumulative relative frequency For data grouped into intervals, the fraction of total observations that are less than the value of the upper limit of a stated interval.

Cumulative voting A voting process whereby each shareholder can accumulate and vote all his or her shares for a single candidate in an election, as opposed to having to allocate their voting rights evenly among all candidates.

Currencies Monies issued by national monetary authorities.

Currency option bonds Bonds that give the bondholder the right to choose the currency in which he or she wants to receive interest payments and principal repayments.

Currency swap A swap in which each party makes interest payments to the other in different currencies.

Current account A component of the balance of payments account that measures the flow of goods and services.

Current assets Assets that are expected to be consumed or converted into cash in the near future, typically one year or less. *Also called liquid assets.*

Current cost With reference to assets, the amount of cash or cash equivalents that would have to be paid to buy the same or an equivalent asset today; with reference to liabilities, the undiscounted amount of cash or cash equivalents that would be required to settle the obligation today.

Current government spending With respect to government expenditures, spending on goods and services that are provided on a regular, recurring basis including health, education, and defense.

Current liabilities Short-term obligations, such as accounts payable, wages payable, or accrued liabilities, that are expected to be settled in the near future, typically one year or less.

Current ratio A liquidity ratio calculated as current assets divided by current liabilities.

Current yield The sum of the coupon payments received over the year divided by the flat price; also called the *income* or *interest yield* or *running yield.*

Curve duration The sensitivity of the bond price (or the market value of a financial asset or liability) with respect to a benchmark yield curve.

Customs union Extends the free trade area (FTA) by not only allowing free movement of goods and services among members, but also creating a common trade policy against nonmembers.

CVaR Conditional VaR, a tail loss measure. The weighted average of all loss outcomes in the statistical distribution that exceed the VaR loss.

Cyclical See *cyclical companies.*

Cyclical companies Companies with sales and profits that regularly expand and contract with the business cycle or state of economy.

Daily settlement See *mark to market* and *marking to market.*

Dark pools Alternative trading systems that do not display the orders that their clients send to them.

Data mining The practice of determining a model by extensive searching through a dataset for statistically significant patterns. Also called *data snooping.*

Data science An interdisciplinary field that brings computer science, statistics, and other disciplines together to analyze and produce insights from Big Data.

Data snooping See *data mining.*

Day order An order that is good for the day on which it is submitted. If it has not been filled by the close of business, the order expires unfilled.

Day's sales outstanding Estimate of the average number of days it takes to collect on credit accounts.

Days in receivables Estimate of the average number of days it takes to collect on credit accounts.

Days of inventory on hand An activity ratio equal to the number of days in the period divided by inventory turnover over the period.

Dealers A financial intermediary that acts as a principal in trades.

Dealing securities Securities held by banks or other financial intermediaries for trading purposes.

Death cross A technical analysis term that describes a situation where a short-term moving average crosses from above a longer-term moving average to below it; this movement is considered bearish.

Debentures Type of bond that can be secured or unsecured.

Debt incurrence test A financial covenant made in conjunction with existing debt that restricts a company's ability to incur additional debt at the same seniority based on one or more financial tests or conditions.

Debt-rating approach A method for estimating a company's before-tax cost of debt based upon the yield on comparably rated bonds for maturities that closely match that of the company's existing debt.

Debt-to-assets ratio A solvency ratio calculated as total debt divided by total assets.

Debt-to-capital ratio A solvency ratio calculated as total debt divided by total debt plus total shareholders' equity.

Debt-to-equity ratio A solvency ratio calculated as total debt divided by total shareholders' equity.

Declaration date The day that the corporation issues a statement declaring a specific dividend.

Decreasing returns to scale When a production process leads to increases in output that are proportionately smaller than the increase in inputs.

Deductible temporary differences Temporary differences that result in a reduction of or deduction from taxable income in a future period when the balance sheet item is recovered or settled.

Deep learning Machine learning using neural networks with many hidden layers.

Deep learning nets Machine learning using neural networks with many hidden layers.

Default probability The probability that a borrower defaults or fails to meet its obligation to make full and timely payments of principal and interest, according to the terms of the debt security. Also called *default risk.*

Default risk The probability that a borrower defaults or fails to meet its obligation to make full and timely payments of principal and interest, according to the terms of the debt security. Also called *default probability.*

Default risk premium An extra return that compensates investors for the possibility that the borrower will fail to make a promised payment at the contracted time and in the contracted amount.

Defensive companies Companies with sales and profits that have little sensitivity to the business cycle or state of the economy.

Defensive interval ratio A liquidity ratio that estimates the number of days that an entity could meet cash needs from liquid assets; calculated as (cash + short-term marketable investments + receivables) divided by daily cash expenditures.

Deferred coupon bond Bond that pays no coupons for its first few years but then pays a higher coupon than it otherwise normally would for the remainder of its life. Also called *split coupon bond.*

Deferred income A liability account for money that has been collected for goods or services that have not yet been delivered; payment received in advance of providing a good or service.

Deferred revenue A liability account for money that has been collected for goods or services that have not yet been delivered; payment received in advance of providing a good or service.

Deferred tax assets A balance sheet asset that arises when an excess amount is paid for income taxes relative to accounting profit. The taxable income is higher than accounting profit and income tax payable exceeds tax expense. The company expects to recover the difference during the course of future operations when tax expense exceeds income tax payable.

Deferred tax liabilities A balance sheet liability that arises when a deficit amount is paid for income taxes relative to accounting profit. The taxable income is less than the accounting profit and income tax payable is less than tax expense. The company expects to eliminate the liability over the course of future operations when income tax payable exceeds tax expense.

Defined benefit pension plans Plans in which the company promises to pay a certain annual amount (defined benefit) to the employee after retirement. The company bears the investment risk of the plan assets.

Defined contribution pension plans Individual accounts to which an employee and typically the employer makes contributions during their working years and expect to draw on the accumulated funds at retirement. The employee bears the investment and inflation risk of the plan assets.

Deflation Negative inflation.

Degree of confidence The probability that a confidence interval includes the unknown population parameter.

Degree of financial leverage (DFL) The ratio of the percentage change in net income to the percentage change in operating income; the sensitivity of the cash flows available to owners when operating income changes.

Degree of operating leverage (DOL) The ratio of the percentage change in operating income to the percentage change in units sold; the sensitivity of operating income to changes in units sold.

Degree of total leverage The ratio of the percentage change in net income to the percentage change in units sold; the sensitivity of the cash flows to owners to changes in the number of units produced and sold.

Degrees of freedom (df) The number of independent observations used.

Delta The sensitivity of the derivative price to a small change in the value of the underlying asset.

Demand curve Graph of the inverse demand function. A graph showing the demand relation, either the highest quantity willingly purchased at each price or the highest price willingly paid for each quantity.

Demand function A relationship that expresses the quantity demanded of a good or service as a function of own-price and possibly other variables.

Demand-pull Type of inflation in which increasing demand raises prices generally, which then are reflected in a business's costs as workers demand wage hikes to catch up with the rising cost of living.

Demand shock A typically unexpected disturbance to demand, such as an unexpected interruption in trade or transportation.

Dependent With reference to events, the property that the probability of one event occurring depends on (is related to) the occurrence of another event.

Depository bank A bank that raises funds from depositors and other investors and lends it to borrowers.

Depository institutions Commercial banks, savings and loan banks, credit unions, and similar institutions that raise funds from depositors and other investors and lend it to borrowers.

Depository receipt A security that trades like an ordinary share on a local exchange and represents an economic interest in a foreign company.

Depreciation The process of systematically allocating the cost of long-lived (tangible) assets to the periods during which the assets are expected to provide economic benefits.

Depression See *contraction.*

Derivative pricing rule A pricing rule used by crossing networks in which a price is taken (derived) from the price that is current in the asset's primary market.

Derivatives A financial instrument whose value depends on the value of some underlying asset or factor (e.g., a stock price, an interest rate, or exchange rate).

Descriptive statistics The study of how data can be summarized effectively.

Development capital Minority equity investments in more mature companies that are seeking capital to expand or restructure operations, enter new markets, or finance major acquisitions.

Diffuse prior The assumption of equal prior probabilities.

Diffusion index Reflects the proportion of the index's components that are moving in a pattern consistent with the overall index.

Diluted EPS The EPS that would result if all dilutive securities were converted into common shares.

Diluted shares The number of shares that would be outstanding if all potentially dilutive claims on common shares (e.g., convertible debt, convertible preferred stock, and employee stock options) were exercised.

Diminishing balance method An accelerated depreciation method, i.e., one that allocates a relatively large proportion of the cost of an asset to the early years of the asset's useful life.

Diminishing marginal productivity Describes a state in which each additional unit of input produces less output than previously.

Direct debit program An arrangement whereby a customer authorizes a debit to a demand account; typically used by companies to collect routine payments for services.

Direct financing leases Under US GAAP, a type of finance lease, from a lessor perspective, where the present value of the lease payments (lease receivable) equals the carrying value of the leased asset. No selling profit is recognized at lease inception. The revenues earned by the lessor are financing in nature.

Direct format With reference to the cash flow statement, a format for the presentation of the statement in which cash flow from operating activities is shown as operating cash receipts less operating cash disbursements. Also called *direct method.*

Direct method See *direct format.*

Direct taxes Taxes levied directly on income, wealth, and corporate profits.

Direct write-off method An approach to recognizing credit losses on customer receivables in which the company waits until such time as a customer has defaulted and only then recognizes the loss.

Disbursement float The amount of time between check issuance and a check's clearing back against the company's account.

Discount To reduce the value of a future payment in allowance for how far away it is in time; to calculate the present value of some future amount. Also, the amount by which an instrument is priced below its face (par) value.

Discount interest A procedure for determining the interest on a loan or bond in which the interest is deducted from the face value in advance.

Discount margin See *required margin.*

Discount rates In general, the interest rate used to calculate a present value. In the money market, however, discount rate is a specific type of quoted rate.

Discounted cash flow models Valuation models that estimate the intrinsic value of a security as the present value of the future benefits expected to be received from the security.

Discounted payback period the number of years it takes for the cumulative discounted cash flows from a project to equal the original investment.

Discouraged worker A person who has stopped looking for a job or has given up seeking employment.

Discrete random variable A random variable that can take on at most a countable number of possible values.

Discriminatory pricing rule A pricing rule used in continuous markets in which the limit price of the order or quote that first arrived determines the trade price.

Diseconomies of scale Increase in cost per unit resulting from increased production.

Dispersion The variability around the central tendency.

Display size The size of an order displayed to public view.

Distressed investing Investing in securities of companies in financial difficulty. Private equity funds that specialize in distressed investing typically buy the debt of mature companies in financial difficulty.

Distributed ledger A type of database that may be shared among entities in a network.

Distributed ledger technology Technology based on a distributed ledger.

Divergence In technical analysis, a term that describes the case when an indicator moves differently from the security being analyzed.

Diversification ratio The ratio of the standard deviation of an equally weighted portfolio to the standard deviation of a randomly selected security.

Dividend A distribution paid to shareholders based on the number of shares owned.

Dividend discount model (DDM) A present value model that estimates the intrinsic value of an equity share based on the present value of its expected future dividends.

Dividend discount model based approach An approach for estimating a country's equity risk premium. The market rate of return is estimated as the sum of the dividend yield and the growth rate in dividends for a market index. Subtracting the risk-free rate of return from the estimated market return produces an estimate for the equity risk premium.

Dividend payout ratio The ratio of cash dividends paid to earnings for a period.

Divisor A number (denominator) used to determine the value of a price return index. It is initially chosen at the inception of an index and subsequently adjusted by the index provider, as necessary, to avoid changes in the index value that are unrelated to changes in the prices of its constituent securities.

Domestic content provisions Stipulate that some percentage of the value added or components used in production should be of domestic origin.

Double bottoms In technical analysis, a reversal pattern that is formed when the price reaches a low, rebounds, and then sells off back to the first low level; used to predict a change from a downtrend to an uptrend.

Double coincidence of wants A prerequisite to barter trades, in particular that both economic agents in the transaction want what the other is selling.

Double declining balance depreciation An accelerated depreciation method that involves depreciating the asset at double the straight-line rate. This rate is multiplied by the book value of the asset at the beginning of the period (a declining balance) to calculate depreciation expense.

Double top In technical analysis, a reversal pattern that is formed when an uptrend reverses twice at roughly the same high price level; used to predict a change from an uptrend to a downtrend.

Down transition probability The probability that an asset's value moves down in a model of asset price dynamics.

Downgrade risk The risk that a bond issuer's creditworthiness deteriorates, or migrates lower, leading investors to believe the risk of default is higher. Also called *credit migration risk.*

Drag on liquidity When receipts lag, creating pressure from the decreased available funds.

Drawdown A percentage peak-to-trough reduction in net asset value.

Dual-currency bonds Bonds that make coupon payments in one currency and pay the par value at maturity in another currency.

DuPont analysis An approach to decomposing return on investment, e.g., return on equity, as the product of other financial ratios.

Duration A measure of the approximate sensitivity of a security to a change in interest rates (i.e., a measure of interest rate risk).

Duration gap A bond's Macaulay duration minus the investment horizon.

Dutch Book theorem A result in probability theory stating that inconsistent probabilities create profit opportunities.

Early repayment option See *prepayment option.*

Earnings per share The amount of income earned during a period per share of common stock.

Earnings surprise The portion of a company's earnings that is unanticipated by investors and, according to the efficient market hypothesis, merits a price adjustment.

Economic costs All the remuneration needed to keep a productive resource in its current employment or to acquire the resource for productive use; the sum of total accounting costs and implicit opportunity costs.

Economic indicator A variable that provides information on the state of the overall economy.

Economic loss The amount by which accounting profit is less than normal profit.

Economic order quantity–reorder point (EOQ–ROP) An approach to managing inventory based on expected demand and the predictability of demand; the ordering point for new inventory is determined based on the costs of ordering and carrying inventory, such that the total cost associated with inventory is minimized.

Economic profit Equal to accounting profit less the implicit opportunity costs not included in total accounting costs; the difference between total revenue (TR) and total cost (TC). Also called *abnormal profit* or *supernormal profit.*

Economic stabilization Reduction of the magnitude of economic fluctuations.

Economic union Incorporates all aspects of a common market and in addition requires common economic institutions and coordination of economic policies among members.

Economies of scale Reduction in cost per unit resulting from increased production.

Effective annual rate The amount by which a unit of currency will grow in a year with interest on interest included.

Effective convexity A *curve convexity* statistic that measures the secondary effect of a change in a benchmark yield curve on a bond's price.

Effective duration The sensitivity of a bond's price to a change in a benchmark yield curve.

Effective interest rate The borrowing rate or market rate that a company incurs at the time of issuance of a bond.

Efficient market A market in which asset prices reflect new information quickly and rationally.

Elastic Said of a good or service when the magnitude of elasticity is greater than one.

Elasticity The percentage change in one variable for a percentage change in another variable; a general measure of how sensitive one variable is to a change in the value of another variable.

Elasticity of demand A measure of the sensitivity of quantity demanded to a change in a product's own price: $\%\Delta Q^D/\%\Delta P$.

Elasticity of supply A measure of the sensitivity of quantity supplied to a change in price: $\%\Delta Q^S/\%\Delta P$.

Electronic communications networks See *alternative trading systems*.

Electronic funds transfer (EFT) The use of computer networks to conduct financial transactions electronically.

Elliott wave theory A technical analysis theory that claims that the market follows regular, repeated waves or cycles.

Embedded option Contingency provisions that provide the issuer or the bondholders the right, but not the obligation, to take action. These options are not part of the security and cannot be traded separately.

Empirical probability The probability of an event estimated as a relative frequency of occurrence.

Employed The number of people with a job.

Engagement/active ownership An ESG investment style that uses shareholder power to influence corporate behavior through direct corporate engagement (i.e., communicating with senior management and/or boards of companies), filing or co-filing shareholder proposals, and proxy voting that is directed by ESG guidelines.

Enterprise risk management An overall assessment of a company's risk position. A centralized approach to risk management sometimes called firmwide risk management.

Enterprise value A measure of a company's total market value from which the value of cash and short-term investments have been subtracted.

Equal weighting An index weighting method in which an equal weight is assigned to each constituent security at inception.

Equipment trust certificates Bonds secured by specific types of equipment or physical assets.

Equity Assets less liabilities; the residual interest in the assets after subtracting the liabilities.

Equity risk premium The expected return on equities minus the risk-free rate; the premium that investors demand for investing in equities.

Equity swap A swap transaction in which at least one cash flow is tied to the return to an equity portfolio position, often an equity index.

ESG An acronym that encompasses environmental, social and governance.

ESG integration The integration of qualitative and quantitative environmental, social, and governance factors into traditional security and industry analysis; also known as *ESG incorporation.*

ESG investing The consideration of environmental, social, and governance factors in the investment process.

Estimate The particular value calculated from sample observations using an estimator.

Estimation With reference to statistical inference, the subdivision dealing with estimating the value of a population parameter.

Estimator An estimation formula; the formula used to compute the sample mean and other sample statistics are examples of estimators.

Ethical principles Beliefs regarding what is good, acceptable, or obligatory behavior and what is bad, unacceptable, or forbidden behavior.

Ethics The study of moral principles or of making good choices. Ethics encompasses a set of moral principles and rules of conduct that provide guidance for our behavior.

Eurobonds Type of bond issued internationally, outside the jurisdiction of the country in whose currency the bond is denominated.

European option An option that can only be exercised on its expiration date.

European-style Said of an option contract that can only be exercised on the option's expiration date.

Event Any outcome or specified set of outcomes of a random variable.

Ex-dividend date The first date that a share trades without (i.e., "ex") the dividend.

Excess kurtosis Degree of kurtosis (fatness of tails) in excess of the kurtosis of the normal distribution.

Exchanges Places where traders can meet to arrange their trades.

Exclusionary screening An ESG implementation approach that excludes certain sectors or companies that deviate from an investor's accepted standards. Also called *negative screening* or *norms-based screening*.

Execution instructions Instructions that indicate how to fill an order.

Exercise The process of using an option to buy or sell the underlying.

Exercise price The fixed price at which an option holder can buy or sell the underlying. Also called *strike price, striking price,* or *strike.*

Exercise value The value obtained if an option is exercised based on current conditions. Also known as *intrinsic value.*

Exhaustive Covering or containing all possible outcomes.

Expansion The period of a business cycle after its lowest point and before its highest point.

Expansionary Tending to cause the real economy to grow.

Expansionary fiscal policy Fiscal policy aimed at achieving real economic growth.

Expected inflation The level of inflation that economic agents expect in the future.

Expected loss Default probability times Loss severity given default.

Expected value The probability-weighted average of the possible outcomes of a random variable.

Expenses Outflows of economic resources or increases in liabilities that result in decreases in equity (other than decreases because of distributions to owners); reductions in net assets associated with the creation of revenues.

Experience curve A curve that shows the direct cost per unit of good or service produced or delivered as a typically declining function of cumulative output.

Export subsidy Paid by the government to the firm when it exports a unit of a good that is being subsidized.

Exports Goods and services that an economy sells to other countries.

Extension risk The risk that when interest rates rise, fewer prepayments will occur because homeowners are reluctant to give up the benefits of a contractual interest rate that now looks low. As a result, the security becomes longer in maturity than anticipated at the time of purchase.

Externality An effect of a market transaction that is borne by parties other than those who transacted.

Extra dividend A dividend paid by a company that does not pay dividends on a regular schedule, or a dividend that supplements regular cash dividends with an extra payment.

Extreme value theory A branch of statistics that focuses primarily on extreme outcomes.

Face value The amount of cash payable by a company to the bondholders when the bonds mature; the promised payment at maturity separate from any coupon payment.

Factor A common or underlying element with which several variables are correlated.

Fair value The amount at which an asset could be exchanged, or a liability settled, between knowledgeable, willing parties in an arm's-length transaction; the price that would be received to sell an asset or paid to transfer a liability in an orderly transaction between market participants.

Fed funds rate The US interbank lending rate on overnight borrowings of reserves.

Federal funds rate The US interbank lending rate on overnight borrowings of reserves.

Fiat money Money that is not convertible into any other commodity.

Fibonacci sequence A sequence of numbers starting with 0 and 1, and then each subsequent number in the sequence is the sum of the two preceding numbers. In Elliott Wave Theory, it is believed that market waves follow patterns that are the ratios of the numbers in the Fibonacci sequence.

Fiduciary call A combination of a European call and a risk-free bond that matures on the option expiration day and has a face value equal to the exercise price of the call.

FIFO method The first in, first out, method of accounting for inventory, which matches sales against the costs of items of inventory in the order in which they were placed in inventory.

Fill or kill See *immediate or cancel order*.

Finance lease From the lessee perspective, under US GAAP, a type of lease which is more akin to the purchase of an asset by the lessee. From the lessor perspective, under IFRS, a lease which "transfers substantially all the risks and rewards incidental to ownership of an underlying asset."

Financial account A component of the balance of payments account that records investment flows.

Financial flexibility The ability to react and adapt to financial adversity and opportunities.

Financial leverage The extent to which a company can effect, through the use of debt, a proportional change in the return on common equity that is greater than a given proportional change in operating income; also, short for the financial leverage ratio.

Financial leverage ratio A measure of financial leverage calculated as average total assets divided by average total equity.

Financial risk The risk that environmental, social, or governance risk factors will result in significant costs or other losses to a company and its shareholders; the risk arising from a company's obligation to meet required payments under its financing agreements.

Financing activities Activities related to obtaining or repaying capital to be used in the business (e.g., equity and long-term debt).

Fintech Technological innovation in the design and delivery of financial services and products in the financial industry.

Firm commitment offering See *underwritten offering*.

First-degree price discrimination Where a monopolist is able to charge each customer the highest price the customer is willing to pay.

First lien debt Debt secured by a pledge of certain assets that could include buildings, but may also include property and equipment, licenses, patents, brands, etc.

First mortgage debt Debt secured by a pledge of a specific property.

Fiscal multiplier The ratio of a change in national income to a change in government spending.

Fiscal policy The use of taxes and government spending to affect the level of aggregate expenditures.

Fisher effect The thesis that the real rate of interest in an economy is stable over time so that changes in nominal interest rates are the result of changes in expected inflation.

Fisher index The geometric mean of the Laspeyres index.

Fixed charge coverage A solvency ratio measuring the number of times interest and lease payments are covered by operating income, calculated as (EBIT + lease payments) divided by (interest payments + lease payments).

Fixed costs Costs that remain at the same level regardless of a company's level of production and sales.

Fixed-for-floating interest rate swap An interest rate swap in which one party pays a fixed rate and the other pays a floating rate, with both sets of payments in the same currency. Also called *plain vanilla swap* or *vanilla swap*.

Fixed rate perpetual preferred stock Nonconvertible, noncallable preferred stock that has a fixed dividend rate and no maturity date.

Flags A technical analysis continuation pattern formed by parallel trendlines, typically over a short period.

Flat price The full price of a bond minus the accrued interest; also called the *quoted* or *clean* price.

Float In the context of customer receipts, the amount of money that is in transit between payments made by customers and the funds that are usable by the company.

Float-adjusted market-capitalization weighting An index weighting method in which the weight assigned to each constituent security is determined by adjusting its market capitalization for its market float.

Float factor An estimate of the average number of days it takes deposited checks to clear; average daily float divided by average daily deposit.

Floaters See *floating-rate notes.*

Floating-rate notes A note on which interest payments are not fixed, but instead vary from period to period depending on the current level of a reference interest rate.

Flotation cost Fees charged to companies by investment bankers and other costs associated with raising new capital.

Foreclosure Allows the lender to take possession of a mortgaged property if the borrower defaults and then sell it to recover funds.

Foreign currency reserves Holding by the central bank of non-domestic currency deposits and non-domestic bonds.

Foreign direct investment Direct investment by a firm in one country (the source country) in productive assets in a foreign country (the host country).

Foreign exchange gains (or losses) Gains (or losses) that occur when the exchange rate changes between the investor's currency and the currency that foreign securities are denominated in.

Foreign portfolio investment Shorter-term investment by individuals, firms, and institutional investors (e.g., pension funds) in foreign financial instruments such as foreign stocks and foreign government bonds.

Forward commitments Class of derivatives that provides the ability to lock in a price to transact in the future at a previously agreed-upon price.

Forward contract An agreement between two parties in which one party, the buyer, agrees to buy from the other party, the seller, an underlying asset at a later date for a price established at the start of the contract.

Forward curve A series of forward rates, each having the same timeframe.

Forward market For future delivery, beyond the usual settlement time period in the cash market.

Forward price The fixed price or rate at which the transaction scheduled to occur at the expiration of a forward contract will take place. This price is agreed on at the initiation date of the contract.

Forward rate The interest rate on a bond or money market instrument traded in a forward market. A forward rate can be interpreted as an incremental, or marginal, return for extending the time-to-maturity for an additional time period.

Forward rate agreements A forward contract calling for one party to make a fixed interest payment and the other to make an interest payment at a rate to be determined at the contract expiration.

Fractile A value at or below which a stated fraction of the data lies.

Fractional reserve banking Banking in which reserves constitute a fraction of deposits.

Free cash flow The actual cash that would be available to the company's investors after making all investments necessary to maintain the company as an ongoing enterprise (also referred to as free cash flow to the firm); the internally generated funds that can be distributed to the company's investors (e.g., shareholders and bondholders) without impairing the value of the company.

Free cash flow to equity (FCFE) The cash flow available to a company's common shareholders after all operating expenses, interest, and principal payments have been made, and necessary investments in working and fixed capital have been made.

Free-cash-flow-to-equity models Valuation models based on discounting expected future free cash flow to equity.

Free cash flow to the firm (FCFF) The cash flow available to the company's suppliers of capital after all operating expenses have been paid and necessary investments in working capital and fixed capital have been made.

Free float The number of shares that are readily and freely tradable in the secondary market.

Free trade When there are no government restrictions on a country's ability to trade.

Free trade areas One of the most prevalent forms of regional integration, in which all barriers to the flow of goods and services among members have been eliminated.

Frequency distribution A tabular display of data summarized into a relatively small number of intervals.

Frequency polygon A graph of a frequency distribution obtained by drawing straight lines joining successive points representing the class frequencies.

Full integration An ESG investment style that focuses on the explicit inclusion of ESG factors into the traditional financial analysis of individual stocks for the purpose of valuation (e.g., as inputs into cash flow forecasts and/or cost-of-capital estimates).

Full price The price of a security with accrued interest; also called the *invoice* or *dirty* price.

Fundamental analysis The examination of publicly available information and the formulation of forecasts to estimate the intrinsic value of assets.

Fundamental value The underlying or true value of an asset based on an analysis of its qualitative and quantitative characteristics. Also called *intrinsic value.*

Fundamental weighting An index weighting method in which the weight assigned to each constituent security is based on its underlying company's size. It attempts to address the disadvantages of market-capitalization weighting by using measures that are independent of the constituent security's price.

Funds of hedge funds Funds that hold a portfolio of hedge funds, more commonly shortened to *funds of funds.*

Future value (FV) The amount to which a payment or series of payments will grow by a stated future date.

Futures contract A variation of a forward contract that has essentially the same basic definition but with some additional features, such as a clearinghouse guarantee against credit losses, a daily settlement of gains and losses, and an organized electronic or floor trading facility.

Futures price The agreed-upon price of a futures contract.

FX swap The combination of a spot and a forward FX transaction.

G-spread The yield spread in basis points over an actual or interpolated government bond.

Gains Asset inflows not directly related to the ordinary activities of the business.

Game theory The set of tools decision makers use to incorporate responses by rival decision makers into their strategies.

Gamma A numerical measure of how sensitive an option's delta (the sensitivity of the derivative's price) is to a change in the value of the underlying.

GDP deflator A gauge of prices and inflation that measures the aggregate changes in prices across the overall economy.

General partner The partner that runs the business and ultimately bears unlimited liability for the business's debts and obligations.

Geometric mean A measure of central tendency computed by taking the *n*th root of the product of *n* non-negative values.

Giffen goods Goods that are consumed more as the price of the good rises because it is a very inferior good whose income effect overwhelms its substitution effect when price changes.

Gilts Bonds issued by the UK government.

Giro system An electronic payment system used widely in Europe and Japan.

Global depository receipt A depository receipt that is issued outside of the company's home country and outside of the United States.

Global minimum-variance portfolio The portfolio on the minimum-variance frontier with the smallest variance of return.

Global registered share A common share that is traded on different stock exchanges around the world in different currencies.

Gold standard With respect to a currency, if a currency is on the gold standard a given amount can be converted into a prespecified amount of gold.

Golden cross A technical analysis term that describes a situation where a short-term moving average crosses from below a longer-term moving average to above it; this movement is considered bullish.

Good-on-close An execution instruction specifying that an order can only be filled at the close of trading. Also called *market on close.*

Good-on-open An execution instruction specifying that an order can only be filled at the opening of trading.

Good-till-cancelled order An order specifying that it is valid until the entity placing the order has cancelled it (or, commonly, until some specified amount of time such as 60 days has elapsed, whichever comes sooner).

Goodwill An intangible asset that represents the excess of the purchase price of an acquired company over the value of the net assets acquired.

Government equivalent yield A yield that restates a yield-to-maturity based on 30/360 day-count to one based on actual/actual.

Green bonds A bond used in green finance whereby the proceeds are earmarked towards environmental-related products.

Green finance A type of finance that addresses environmental concerns while achieving economic growth.

Grey market The forward market for bonds about to be issued. Also called "when issued" market.

Gross domestic product The market value of all final goods and services produced within the economy in a given period of time (output definition) or, equivalently, the aggregate income earned by all households, all companies, and the government within the economy in a given period of time (income definition).

Gross margin Sales minus the cost of sales (i.e., the cost of goods sold for a manufacturing company).

Gross profit Sales minus the cost of sales (i.e., the cost of goods sold for a manufacturing company).

Gross profit margin The ratio of gross profit to revenues.

Grouping by function With reference to the presentation of expenses in an income statement, the grouping together of expenses serving the same function, e.g. all items that are costs of goods sold.

Grouping by nature With reference to the presentation of expenses in an income statement, the grouping together of expenses by similar nature, e.g., all depreciation expenses.

Growth cyclical A term sometimes used to describe companies that are growing rapidly on a long-term basis but that still experience above-average fluctuation in their revenues and profits over the course of a business cycle.

Growth investors With reference to equity investors, investors who seek to invest in high-earnings-growth companies.

Guarantee certificate A type of structured financial instrument that provides investors capital protection. It combines a zero-coupon bond and a call option on some underlying asset.

Haircut See *repo margin.*

Harmonic mean A type of weighted mean computed by averaging the reciprocals of the observations, then taking the reciprocal of that average.

Head and shoulders pattern In technical analysis, a reversal pattern that is formed in three parts: a left shoulder, head, and right shoulder; used to predict a change from an uptrend to a downtrend.

Headline inflation The inflation rate calculated based on the price index that includes all goods and services in an economy.

Hedge funds Private investment vehicles that typically use leverage, derivatives, and long and short investment strategies.

Hedge portfolio A hypothetical combination of the derivative and its underlying that eliminates risk.

Held-to-maturity Debt (fixed-income) securities that a company intends to hold to maturity; these are presented at their original cost, updated for any amortisation of discounts or premiums.

Herding Clustered trading that may or may not be based on information.

Hidden order An order that is exposed not to the public but only to the brokers or exchanges that receive it.

High-frequency trading A form of algorithmic trading that makes use of vast quantities of data to execute trades on ultra-high-speed networks in fractions of a second.

High-water mark The highest value, net of fees, that a fund has reached in history. It reflects the highest cumulative return used to calculate an incentive fee.

Histogram A bar chart of data that have been grouped into a frequency distribution.

Historical cost In reference to assets, the amount paid to purchase an asset, including any costs of acquisition and/or preparation; with reference to liabilities, the amount of proceeds received in exchange in issuing the liability.

Historical equity risk premium approach An estimate of a country's equity risk premium that is based upon the historical averages of the risk-free rate and the rate of return on the market portfolio.

Historical simulation Another term for the historical method of estimating VaR. This term is somewhat misleading in that the method involves not a *simulation* of the past but rather what *actually happened* in the past, sometimes adjusted to reflect the fact that a different portfolio may have existed in the past than is planned for the future.

Holder-of-record date The date that a shareholder listed on the corporation's books will be deemed to have ownership of the shares for purposes of receiving an upcoming dividend.

Holding period return The return that an investor earns during a specified holding period; a synonym for total return.

Homogeneity of expectations The assumption that all investors have the same economic expectations and thus have the same expectations of prices, cash flows, and other investment characteristics.

Horizon yield The internal rate of return between the total return (the sum of reinvested coupon payments and the sale price or redemption amount) and the purchase price of the bond.

Horizontal analysis Common-size analysis that involves comparing a specific financial statement with that statement in prior or future time periods; also, cross-sectional analysis of one company with another.

Horizontal demand schedule Implies that at a given price, the response in the quantity demanded is infinite.

Hostile takeover An attempt by one entity to acquire a company without the consent of the company's management.

Household A person or a group of people living in the same residence, taken as a basic unit in economic analysis.

Human capital The accumulated knowledge and skill that workers acquire from education, training, or life experience and the corresponding present value of future earnings to be generated by said skilled individual.

Hurdle rate The rate of return that must be met for a project to be accepted.

Hypothesis With reference to statistical inference, a statement about one or more populations.

Hypothesis testing With reference to statistical inference, the subdivision dealing with the testing of hypotheses about one or more populations.

I-spread The yield spread of a specific bond over the standard swap rate in that currency of the same tenor.

Iceberg order An order in which the display size is less than the order's full size.

If-converted method A method for accounting for the effect of convertible securities on earnings per share (EPS) that specifies what EPS would have been if the convertible securities had been converted at the beginning of the period, taking account of the effects of conversion on net income and the weighted average number of shares outstanding.

Immediate or cancel order An order that is valid only upon receipt by the broker or exchange. If such an order cannot be filled in part or in whole upon receipt, it cancels immediately. Also called *fill or kill.*

Impact lag The lag associated with the result of actions affecting the economy with delay.

Implicit price deflator for GDP A gauge of prices and inflation that measures the aggregate changes in prices across the overall economy.

Implied forward rates Calculated from spot rates, an implied forward rate is a break-even reinvestment rate that links the return on an investment in a shorter-term zero-coupon bond to the return on an investment in a longer-term zero-coupon bond.

Implied volatility The volatility that option traders use to price an option, implied by the price of the option and a particular option-pricing model.

Import license Specifies the quantity of a good that can be imported into a country.

Imports Goods and services that a domestic economy (i.e., house-holds, firms, and government) purchases from other countries.

In the money Options that, if exercised, would result in the value received being worth more than the payment required to exercise.

Incentive fee Fees paid to the general partner from the limited partner(s) based on realized net profits.

Income Increases in economic benefits in the form of inflows or enhancements of assets, or decreases of liabilities that result in an increase in equity (other than increases resulting from contributions by owners).

Income elasticity of demand A measure of the responsiveness of demand to changes in income, defined as the percentage change in quantity demanded divided by the percentage change in income.

Income tax paid The actual amount paid for income taxes in the period; not a provision, but the actual cash outflow.

Income tax payable The income tax owed by the company on the basis of taxable income.

Income trust A type of equity ownership vehicle established as a trust issuing ownership shares known as units.

Increasing marginal returns When the marginal product of a resource increases as additional units of that input are employed.

Increasing returns to scale When a production process leads to increases in output that are proportionately larger than the increase in inputs.

Incremental cash flow The cash flow that is realized because of a decision; the changes or increments to cash flows resulting from a decision or action.

Indenture Legal contract that describes the form of a bond, the obligations of the issuer, and the rights of the bondholders. Also called the *trust deed.*

Independent With reference to events, the property that the occurrence of one event does not affect the probability of another event occurring.

Independent projects Independent projects are projects whose cash flows are independent of each other.

Independently and identically distributed (IID) With respect to random variables, the property of random variables that are independent of each other but follow the identical probability distribution.

Index-linked bond Bond for which coupon payments and/or principal repayment are linked to a specified index.

Index of Leading Economic Indicators A composite of economic variables used by analysts to predict future economic conditions.

Indexing An investment strategy in which an investor constructs a portfolio to mirror the performance of a specified index.

Indifference curve A curve representing all the combinations of two goods or attributes such that the consumer is entirely indifferent among them.

Indirect format With reference to cash flow statements, a format for the presentation of the statement which, in the operating cash flow section, begins with net income then shows additions and subtractions to arrive at operating cash flow. Also called *indirect method.*

Indirect method See *indirect format.*

Indirect taxes Taxes such as taxes on spending, as opposed to direct taxes.

Industry A group of companies offering similar products and/or services.

Industry analysis The analysis of a specific branch of manufacturing, service, or trade.

Inelastic Said of a good or service when the magnitude of elasticity is less than one. Insensitive to price changes.

Inferior goods A good whose consumption decreases as income increases.

Inflation The percentage increase in the general price level from one period to the next; a sustained rise in the overall level of prices in an economy.

Inflation-linked bond Type of index-linked bond that offers investors protection against inflation by linking the bond's coupon payments and/or the principal repayment to an index of consumer prices. Also called *linkers.*

Inflation premium An extra return that compensates investors for expected inflation.

Inflation rate The percentage change in a price index—that is, the speed of overall price level movements.

Inflation Reports A type of economic publication put out by many central banks.

Inflation uncertainty The degree to which economic agents view future rates of inflation as difficult to forecast.

Information cascade The transmission of information from those participants who act first and whose decisions influence the decisions of others.

Information-motivated traders Traders that trade to profit from information that they believe allows them to predict future prices.

Informationally efficient market A market in which asset prices reflect new information quickly and rationally.

Initial coin offering An unregulated process whereby companies raise capital by selling crypto tokens to investors in exchange for fiat money or another agreed-upon cryptocurrency.

Initial margin The amount that must be deposited in a clearinghouse account when entering into a futures contract.

Initial margin requirement The margin requirement on the first day of a transaction as well as on any day in which additional margin funds must be deposited.

Initial public offering (IPO) The first issuance of common shares to the public by a formerly private corporation.

Input productivity The amount of output produced by workers in a given period of time—for example, output per hour worked; measures the efficiency of labor.

Intangible assets Assets lacking physical substance, such as patents and trademarks.

Interbank market The market of loans and deposits between banks for maturities ranging from overnight to one year.

Interbank money market The market of loans and deposits between banks for maturities ranging from overnight to one year.

Interest Payment for lending funds.

Interest coverage A solvency ratio calculated as EBIT divided by interest payments.

Interest-only mortgage A loan in which no scheduled principal repayment is specified for a certain number of years.

Interest rate A rate of return that reflects the relationship between differently dated cash flows; a discount rate.

Interest rate swap A swap in which the underlying is an interest rate. Can be viewed as a currency swap in which both currencies are the same and can be created as a combination of currency swaps.

Intergenerational data mining A form of data mining that applies information developed by previous researchers using a dataset to guide current research using the same or a related dataset.

Intermarket analysis A field within technical analysis that combines analysis of major categories of securities—namely, equities, bonds, currencies, and commodities—to identify market trends and possible inflections in a trend.

Internal rate of return (IRR) The discount rate that makes net present value equal 0; the discount rate that makes the present value of an investment's costs (outflows) equal to the present value of the investment's benefits (inflows).

Internet of Things A network arrangement of structures and devices whereby the objects on the network are able to interact and share information.

Interpolated spread The yield spread of a specific bond over the standard swap rate in that currency of the same tenor.

Interquartile range The difference between the third and first quartiles of a dataset.

Interval With reference to grouped data, a set of values within which an observation falls.

Interval scale A measurement scale that not only ranks data but also gives assurance that the differences between scale values are equal.

Intrinsic value See *exercise value.*

Inventory blanket lien The use of inventory as collateral for a loan. Though the lender has claim to some or all of the company's inventory, the company may still sell or use the inventory in the ordinary course of business.

Inventory investment Net change in business inventory.

Inventory turnover An activity ratio calculated as cost of goods sold divided by average inventory.

Inverse demand function A restatement of the demand function in which price is stated as a function of quantity.

Inverse floater A type of leveraged structured financial instrument. The cash flows are adjusted periodically and move in the opposite direction of changes in the reference rate.

Investing activities Activities associated with the acquisition and disposal of property, plant, and equipment; intangible assets; other long-term assets; and both long-term and short-term investments in the equity and debt (bonds and loans) issued by other companies.

Investment banks Financial intermediaries that provide advice to their mostly corporate clients and help them arrange transactions such as initial and seasoned securities offerings.

Investment opportunity schedule A graphical depiction of a company's investment opportunities ordered from highest to lowest expected return. A company's optimal capital budget is found where the investment opportunity schedule intersects with the company's marginal cost of capital.

Investment policy statement (IPS) A written planning document that describes a client's investment objectives and risk tolerance over a relevant time horizon, along with constraints that apply to the client's portfolio.

Investment property Property used to earn rental income or capital appreciation (or both).

January effect Calendar anomaly that stock market returns in January are significantly higher compared to the rest of the months of the year, with most of the abnormal returns reported during the first five trading days in January. Also called *turn-of-the-year effect.*

Joint probability The probability of the joint occurrence of stated events.

Joint probability function A function giving the probability of joint occurrences of values of stated random variables.

Just-in-time (JIT) method Method of managing inventory that minimizes in-process inventory stocks.

Key rate duration A method of measuring the interest rate sensitivities of a fixed-income instrument or portfolio to shifts in key points along the yield curve.

Keynesians Economists who believe that fiscal policy can have powerful effects on aggregate demand, output, and employment when there is substantial spare capacity in an economy.

Kondratieff wave A 54-year long economic cycle postulated by Nikolai Kondratieff.

Kurtosis The statistical measure that indicates the combined weight of the tails of a distribution relative to the rest of the distribution.

Labor force The portion of the working age population (over the age of 16) that is employed or is available for work but not working (unemployed).

Labor productivity The quantity of goods and services (real GDP) that a worker can produce in one hour of work.

Laddering strategy A form of active strategy which entails scheduling maturities on a systematic basis within the investment portfolio such that investments are spread out equally over the term of the ladder.

Lagging economic indicators Turning points that take place later than those of the overall economy; they are believed to have value in identifying the economy's past condition.

Laspeyres index A price index created by holding the composition of the consumption basket constant.

Law of demand The principle that as the price of a good rises, buyers will choose to buy less of it, and as its price falls, they will buy more.

Law of diminishing marginal returns The observation that a variable factor's marginal product must eventually fall as more of it is added to a fixed amount of the other factors.

Law of diminishing returns The smallest output that a firm can produce such that its long run average costs are minimized.

Law of one price The condition in a financial market in which two equivalent financial instruments or combinations of financial instruments can sell for only one price. Equivalent to the principle that no arbitrage opportunities are possible.

Lead underwriter The lead investment bank in a syndicate of investment banks and broker–dealers involved in a securities underwriting.

Leading economic indicators Turning points that usually precede those of the overall economy; they are believed to have value for predicting the economy's future state, usually near-term.

Legal tender Something that must be accepted when offered in exchange for goods and services.

Lender of last resort An entity willing to lend money when no other entity is ready to do so.

Leptokurtic Describes a distribution that has fatter tails than a normal distribution.

Lessee The party obtaining the use of an asset through a lease.

Lessor The owner of an asset that grants the right to use the asset to another party.

Letter of credit Form of external credit enhancement whereby a financial institution provides the issuer with a credit line to reimburse any cash flow shortfalls from the assets backing the issue.

Level of significance The probability of a Type I error in testing a hypothesis.

Leverage In the context of corporate finance, leverage refers to the use of fixed costs within a company's cost structure. Fixed costs that are operating costs (such as depreciation or rent) create operating leverage. Fixed costs that are financial costs (such as interest expense) create financial leverage.

Leveraged buyout A transaction whereby the target company's management team converts the target to a privately held company by using heavy borrowing to finance the purchase of the target company's outstanding shares.

Liabilities Present obligations of an enterprise arising from past events, the settlement of which is expected to result in an outflow of resources embodying economic benefits; creditors' claims on the resources of a company.

Life-cycle stage The stage of the life cycle: embryonic, growth, shakeout, mature, declining.

LIFO layer liquidation With respect to the application of the LIFO inventory method, the liquidation of old, relatively low-priced inventory; happens when the volume of sales rises above the volume of recent purchases so that some sales are made from relatively old, low-priced inventory. Also called *LIFO liquidation*.

LIFO method The last in, first out, method of accounting for inventory, which matches sales against the costs of items of inventory in the reverse order the items were placed in inventory (i.e., inventory produced or acquired last are assumed to be sold first).

LIFO reserve The difference between the reported LIFO inventory carrying amount and the inventory amount that would have been reported if the FIFO method had been used (in other words, the FIFO inventory value less the LIFO inventory value).

Likelihood The probability of an observation, given a particular set of conditions.

Limit down A limit move in the futures market in which the price at which a transaction would be made is at or below the lower limit.

Limit order Instructions to a broker or exchange to obtain the best price immediately available when filling an order, but in no event accept a price higher than a specified (limit) price when buying or accept a price lower than a specified (limit) price when selling.

Limit order book The book or list of limit orders to buy and sell that pertains to a security.

Limit up A limit move in the futures market in which the price at which a transaction would be made is at or above the upper limit.

Limitations on liens Meant to put limits on how much secured debt an issuer can have.

Limited partners Partners with limited liability. Limited partnerships in hedge and private equity funds are typically restricted to investors who are expected to understand and to be able to assume the risks associated with the investments.

Line chart In technical analysis, a plot of price data, typically closing prices, with a line connecting the points.

Linear interpolation The estimation of an unknown value on the basis of two known values that bracket it, using a straight line between the two known values.

Linear scale A scale in which equal distances correspond to equal absolute amounts. Also called *arithmetic scale*.

Linker See *inflation-linked bond*.

Liquid market Said of a market in which traders can buy or sell with low total transaction costs when they want to trade.
Liquidation To sell the assets of a company, division, or subsidiary piecemeal, typically because of bankruptcy; the form of bankruptcy that allows for the orderly satisfaction of creditors' claims after which the company ceases to exist.
Liquidity The ability to purchase or sell an asset quickly and easily at a price close to fair market value. The ability to meet short-term obligations using assets that are the most readily converted into cash.
Liquidity premium An extra return that compensates investors for the risk of loss relative to an investment's fair value if the investment needs to be converted to cash quickly.
Liquidity ratios Financial ratios measuring the company's ability to meet its short-term obligations.
Liquidity risk The risk that a financial instrument cannot be purchased or sold without a significant concession in price due to the size of the market.
Liquidity trap A condition in which the demand for money becomes infinitely elastic (horizontal demand curve) so that injections of money into the economy will not lower interest rates or affect real activity.
Load fund A mutual fund in which, in addition to the annual fee, a percentage fee is charged to invest in the fund and/or for redemptions from the fund.
Loan-to-value ratio The ratio of a property's purchase price to the amount of its mortgage.
Lockbox system A payment system in which customer payments are mailed to a post office box and the banking institution retrieves and deposits these payments several times a day, enabling the company to have use of the fund sooner than in a centralized system in which customer payments are sent to the company.
Locked limit A condition in the futures markets in which a transaction cannot take place because the price would be beyond the limits.
Lockup period The minimum holding period before investors are allowed to make withdrawals or redeem shares from a fund.
Logarithmic scale A scale in which equal distances represent equal proportional changes in the underlying quantity.
London interbank offered rate (Libor) Collective name for multiple rates at which a select set of banks believe they could borrow unsecured funds from other banks in the London interbank market for different currencies and different borrowing periods ranging from overnight to one year.
Long The buyer of a derivative contract. Also refers to the position of owning a derivative.
Long-lived assets Assets that are expected to provide economic benefits over a future period of time, typically greater than one year. Also called *long-term assets.*
Long position A position in an asset or contract in which one owns the asset or has an exercisable right under the contract.
Long-run average total cost The curve describing average total cost when no costs are considered fixed.
Longitudinal data Observations on characteristic(s) of the same observational unit through time.
Look-ahead bias A bias caused by using information that was unavailable on the test date.
Loss aversion The tendency of people to dislike losses more than they like comparable gains.
Loss severity Portion of a bond's value (including unpaid interest) an investor loses in the event of default.
Losses Asset outflows not directly related to the ordinary activities of the business.
Lower bound The lowest possible value of an option.
M^2 A measure of what a portfolio would have returned if it had taken on the same total risk as the market index.
M^2 alpha Difference between the risk-adjusted performance of the portfolio and the performance of the benchmark.
Macaulay duration The approximate amount of time a bond would have to be held for the market discount rate at purchase to be realized if there is a single change in interest rate. It indicates the point in time when the coupon reinvestment and price effects of a change in yield-to- maturity offset each other.
Machine learning Computer based techniques that seek to extract knowledge from large amounts of data by "learning" from known examples and then generating structure or predictions. ML algorithms aim to "find the pattern, apply the pattern."
Macroeconomics The branch of economics that deals with aggregate economic quantities, such as national output and national income.
Maintenance covenants Covenants in bank loan agreements that require the borrower to satisfy certain financial ratio tests while the loan is outstanding.
Maintenance margin The minimum amount that is required by a futures clearinghouse to maintain a margin account and to protect against default. Participants whose margin balances drop below the required maintenance margin must replenish their accounts.
Maintenance margin requirement The margin requirement on any day other than the first day of a transaction.
Management buy-ins Leveraged buyout in which the current management team is being replaced and the acquiring team will be involved in managing the company.
Management buyout A leveraged buyout event in which a group of investors consisting primarily of the company's existing management purchase at least controlling interest in its outstanding shares. At the extreme, they may purchase all shares and take the company private.
Management fee A fee based on assets under management or committed capital, as applicable, also called a *base fee.*
Manufacturing resource planning (MRP) The incorporation of production planning into inventory management. A MRP analysis provides both a materials acquisition schedule and a production schedule.
Margin The amount of money that a trader deposits in a margin account. The term is derived from the stock market practice in which an investor borrows a portion of the money required to purchase a certain amount of stock. In futures markets, there is no borrowing so the margin is more of a down payment or performance bond.
Margin bond A cash deposit required by the clearinghouse from the participants to a contract to provide a credit guarantee. Also called a *performance bond.*
Margin call A request for the short to deposit additional funds to bring their balance up to the initial margin.
Margin loan Money borrowed from a broker to purchase securities.
Marginal cost The cost of producing an additional unit of a good.
Marginal probability The probability of an event *not* conditioned on another event.

Marginal product Measures the productivity of each unit of input and is calculated by taking the difference in total product from adding another unit of input (assuming other resource quantities are held constant).

Marginal propensity to consume The proportion of an additional unit of disposable income that is consumed or spent; the change in consumption for a small change in income.

Marginal propensity to save The proportion of an additional unit of disposable income that is saved (not spent).

Marginal revenue The change in total revenue divided by the change in quantity sold; simply, the additional revenue from selling one more unit.

Marginal value curve A curve describing the highest price consumers are willing to pay for each additional unit of a good.

Mark to market The revaluation of a financial asset or liability to its current market value or fair value.

Market anomaly Change in the price or return of a security that cannot directly be linked to current relevant information known in the market or to the release of new information into the market.

Market bid–ask spread The difference between the best bid and the best offer.

Market-capitalization weighting An index weighting method in which the weight assigned to each constituent security is determined by dividing its market capitalization by the total market capitalization (sum of the market capitalization) of all securities in the index. Also called *value weighting*.

Market discount rate The rate of return required by investors given the risk of the investment in a bond; also called the *required yield* or the *required rate of return*.

Market float The number of shares that are available to the investing public.

Market liquidity risk The risk that the price at which investors can actually transact—buying or selling—may differ from the price indicated in the market.

Market model A regression equation that specifies a linear relationship between the return on a security (or portfolio) and the return on a broad market index.

Market multiple models Valuation models based on share price multiples or enterprise value multiples.

Market-on-close An execution instruction specifying that an order can only be filled at the close of trading.

Market order Instructions to a broker or exchange to obtain the best price immediately available when filling an order.

Market-oriented investors With reference to equity investors, investors whose investment disciplines cannot be clearly categorized as value or growth.

Market rate of interest The rate demanded by purchasers of bonds, given the risks associated with future cash payment obligations of the particular bond issue.

Market risk The risk that arises from movements in interest rates, stock prices, exchange rates, and commodity prices.

Market value The price at which an asset or security can currently be bought or sold in an open market.

Marketable limit order A buy limit order in which the limit price is placed above the best offer, or a sell limit order in which the limit price is placed below the best bid. Such orders generally will partially or completely fill right away.

Markowitz efficient frontier The graph of the set of portfolios offering the maximum expected return for their level of risk (standard deviation of return).

Matching principle The accounting principle that expenses should be recognized in the same period in which the associated revenue is recognized.

Matching strategy An active investment strategy that includes intentional matching of the timing of cash outflows with investment maturities.

Matrix pricing Process of estimating the market discount rate and price of a bond based on the quoted or flat prices of more frequently traded comparable bonds.

Maturity premium An extra return that compensates investors for the increased sensitivity of the market value of debt to a change in market interest rates as maturity is extended.

Maturity structure A factor explaining the differences in yields on similar bonds; also called *term structure*.

Mean absolute deviation With reference to a sample, the mean of the absolute values of deviations from the sample mean.

Mean–variance analysis An approach to portfolio analysis using expected means, variances, and covariances of asset returns.

Measure of central tendency A quantitative measure that specifies where data are centered.

Measure of value A standard for measuring value; a function of money.

Measurement scales A scheme of measuring differences. The four types of measurement scales are nominal, ordinal, interval, and ratio.

Measures of location A quantitative measure that describes the location or distribution of data; includes not only measures of central tendency but also other measures such as percentiles.

Median The value of the middle item of a set of items that has been sorted into ascending or descending order; the 50th percentile.

Medium of exchange Any asset that can be used to purchase goods and services or to repay debts; a function of money.

Medium-term note A corporate bond offered continuously to investors by an agent of the issuer, designed to fill the funding gap between commercial paper and long-term bonds.

Menu costs A cost of inflation in which businesses constantly have to incur the costs of changing the advertised prices of their goods and services.

Mesokurtic Describes a distribution with kurtosis identical to that of the normal distribution.

Mezzanine financing Debt or preferred shares with a relationship to common equity resulting from a feature such as attached warrants or conversion options. Mezzanine financing is subordinate to both senior and high-yield debt but is senior to equity. It is referred to as "mezzanine" because of its location on the balance sheet.

Microeconomics The branch of economics that deals with markets and decision making of individual economic units, including consumers and businesses.

Minimum efficient scale The smallest output that a firm can produce such that its long-run average total cost is minimized.

Minimum-variance portfolio The portfolio with the minimum variance for each given level of expected return.

Minority shareholders A particular shareholder or block of shareholders holding a small proportion of a company's outstanding shares, resulting in a limited ability to exercise control in voting activities.

Minsky moment Named for Hyman Minksy: A point in a business cycle when, after individuals become overextended in borrowing to finance speculative investments, people start realizing that something is likely to go wrong and a panic ensues leading to asset sell-offs.

Mismatching strategy An active investment strategy whereby the timing of cash outflows is not matched with investment maturities.

Modal interval With reference to grouped data, the most frequently occurring interval.

Mode The most frequently occurring value in a set of observations.

Modern portfolio theory (MPT) The analysis of rational portfolio choices based on the efficient use of risk.

Modified duration A measure of the percentage price change of a bond given a change in its yield-to-maturity.

Momentum oscillators A graphical representation of market sentiment that is constructed from price data and calculated so that it oscillates either between a high and a low or around some number.

Monetarists Economists who believe that the rate of growth of the money supply is the primary determinant of the rate of inflation.

Monetary policy Actions taken by a nation's central bank to affect aggregate output and prices through changes in bank reserves, reserve requirements, or its target interest rate.

Monetary transmission mechanism The process whereby a central bank's interest rate gets transmitted through the economy and ultimately affects the rate of increase of prices.

Monetary union An economic union in which the members adopt a common currency.

Money A generally accepted medium of exchange and unit of account.

Money convexity For a bond, the annual or approximate convexity multiplied by the full price.

Money creation The process by which changes in bank reserves translate into changes in the money supply.

Money duration A measure of the price change in units of the currency in which the bond is denominated given a change in its yield-to-maturity.

Money market The market for short-term debt instruments (one-year maturity or less).

Money market securities Fixed-income securities with maturities at issuance of one year or less.

Money market yield A yield on a basis comparable to the quoted yield on an interest-bearing money market instrument that pays interest on a 360-day basis; the annualized holding period yield, assuming a 360-day year.

Money multiplier Describes how a change in reserves is expected to affect the money supply; in its simplest form, 1 divided by the reserve requirement.

Money neutrality The thesis that an increase in the money supply leads in the long-run to an increase in the price level, while leaving real variables like output and employment unaffected.

Money-weighted return The internal rate of return on a portfolio, taking account of all cash flows.

Moneyness The relationship between the price of the underlying and an option's exercise price.

Monopolistic competition Highly competitive form of imperfect competition; the competitive characteristic is a notably large number of firms, while the monopoly aspect is the result of product differentiation.

Monopoly In pure monopoly markets, there are no substitutes for the given product or service. There is a single seller, which exercises considerable power over pricing and output decisions.

Monte Carlo simulation An approach to estimating a probability distribution of outcomes to examine what might happen if particular risks are faced. This method is widely used in the sciences as well as in business to study a variety of problems.

Moral principles Beliefs regarding what is good, acceptable, or obligatory behavior and what is bad, unacceptable, or forbidden behavior.

Mortgage-backed securities Debt obligations that represent claims to the cash flows from pools of mortgage loans, most commonly on residential property.

Mortgage loan A loan secured by the collateral of some specified real estate property that obliges the borrower to make a predetermined series of payments to the lender.

Mortgage pass-through security A security created when one or more holders of mortgages form a pool of mortgages and sell shares or participation certificates in the pool.

Mortgage rate The interest rate on a mortgage loan; also called *contract rate* or *note rate.*

Moving average The average of the closing price of a security over a specified number of periods. With each new period, the average is recalculated.

Moving-average convergence/divergence oscillator (MACD) A momentum oscillator that is constructed based on the difference between short-term and long-term moving averages of a security's price.

Multi-factor model A model that explains a variable in terms of the values of a set of factors.

Multi-market indexes Comprised of indexes from different countries, designed to represent multiple security markets.

Multi-step format With respect to the format of the income statement, a format that presents a subtotal for gross profit (revenue minus cost of goods sold).

Multilateral trading facilities See *alternative trading systems.*

Multinational corporation A company operating in more than one country or having subsidiary firms in more than one country.

Multiplication rule for probabilities The rule that the joint probability of events A and B equals the probability of A given B times the probability of B.

Multiplier models Valuation models based on share price multiples or enterprise value multiples.

Multivariate distribution A probability distribution that specifies the probabilities for a group of related random variables.

Multivariate normal distribution A probability distribution for a group of random variables that is completely defined by the means and variances of the variables plus all the correlations between pairs of the variables.

Municipal bonds A type of non-sovereign bond issued by a state or local government in the United States. It very often (but not always) offers income tax exemptions.

Munis A type of non-sovereign bond issued by a state or local government in the United States. It very often (but not always) offers income tax exemptions.

Mutual fund A comingled investment pool in which investors in the fund each have a pro-rata claim on the income and value of the fund.

Mutually exclusive projects Mutually exclusive projects compete directly with each other. For example, if Projects A and B are mutually exclusive, you can choose A or B, but you cannot choose both.

***n* Factorial** For a positive integer *n*, the product of the first *n* positive integers; 0 factorial equals 1 by definition. *n* factorial is written as *n*!.

Narrow money The notes and coins in circulation in an economy, plus other very highly liquid deposits.

Nash equilibrium When two or more participants in a non-coop-erative game have no incentive to deviate from their respective equilibrium strategies given their opponent's strategies.

National income The income received by all factors of production used in the generation of final output. National income equals gross domestic product (or, in some countries, gross national product) minus the capital consumption allowance and a statistical discrepancy.

Natural language processing Computer programs developed to analyze and interpret human language.

Natural rate of unemployment Effective unemployment rate, below which pressure emerges in labor markets.

Negative screening An ESG investment style that focuses on the exclusion of certain sectors, companies, or practices in a fund or portfolio on the basis of specific ESG criteria.

Neo-Keynesians A group of dynamic general equilibrium models that assume slow-to-adjust prices and wages.

Net book value The remaining (undepreciated) balance of an asset's purchase cost. For liabilities, the face value of a bond minus any unamortized discount, or plus any unamortized premium.

Net exports The difference between the value of a country's exports and the value of its imports (i.e., value of exports minus imports).

Net income The difference between revenue and expenses; what remains after subtracting all expenses (including depreciation, interest, and taxes) from revenue.

Net operating cycle An estimate of the average time that elapses between paying suppliers for materials and collecting cash from the subsequent sale of goods produced.

Net present value (NPV) The present value of an investment's cash inflows (benefits) minus the present value of its cash outflows (costs).

Net profit margin An indicator of profitability, calculated as net income divided by revenue; indicates how much of each dollar of revenues is left after all costs and expenses. Also called *profit margin* or *return on sales*.

Net realisable value Estimated selling price in the ordinary course of business less the estimated costs necessary to make the sale.

Net revenue Revenue after adjustments (e.g., for estimated returns or for amounts unlikely to be collected).

Net tax rate The tax rate net of transfer payments.

Neural networks Computer programs based on how our own brains learn and process information.

Neutral rate of interest The rate of interest that neither spurs on nor slows down the underlying economy.

New classical macroeconomics An approach to macroeconomics that seeks the macroeconomic conclusions of individuals maximizing utility on the basis of rational expectations and companies maximizing profits.

New Keynesians A group of dynamic general equilibrium models that assume slow-to-adjust prices and wages.

No-load fund A mutual fund in which there is no fee for investing in the fund or for redeeming fund shares, although there is an annual fee based on a percentage of the fund's net asset value.

Node Each value on a binomial tree from which successive moves or outcomes branch.

Nominal GDP The value of goods and services measured at current prices.

Nominal rate A rate of interest based on the security's face value.

Nominal risk-free interest rate The sum of the real risk-free interest rate and the inflation premium.

Nominal scale A measurement scale that categorizes data but does not rank them.

Non-accelerating inflation rate of unemployment Effective unemployment rate, below which pressure emerges in labor markets.

Non-agency RMBS In the United States, securities issued by private entities that are not guaranteed by a federal agency or a GSE.

Non-cumulative preference shares Preference shares for which dividends that are not paid in the current or subsequent periods are forfeited permanently (instead of being accrued and paid at a later date).

Non-current assets Assets that are expected to benefit the company over an extended period of time (usually more than one year).

Non-current liabilities Obligations that broadly represent a probable sacrifice of economic benefits in periods generally greater than one year in the future.

Non-cyclical A company whose performance is largely independent of the business cycle.

Non-deliverable forwards Cash-settled forward contracts, used predominately with respect to foreign exchange forwards. Also called *contracts for differences*.

Non-financial risks Risks that arise from sources other than changes in the external financial markets, such as changes in accounting rules, legal environment, or tax rates.

Non-participating preference shares Preference shares that do not entitle shareholders to share in the profits of the company. Instead, shareholders are only entitled to receive a fixed dividend payment and the par value of the shares in the event of liquidation.

Non-recourse loan Loan in which the lender does not have a shortfall claim against the borrower, so the lender can look only to the property to recover the outstanding mortgage balance.

Non-renewable resources Finite resources that are depleted once they are consumed, such as oil and coal.

Non-sovereign bonds A bond issued by a government below the national level, such as a province, region, state, or city.

Non-sovereign government bonds A bond issued by a government below the national level, such as a province, region, state, or city.

Nonconventional cash flow In a nonconventional cash flow pattern, the initial outflow is not followed by inflows only, but the cash flows can flip from positive (inflows) to negative (outflows) again (or even change signs several times).

Nonparametric test A test that is not concerned with a parameter, or that makes minimal assumptions about the population from which a sample comes.

Nonsystematic risk Unique risk that is local or limited to a particular asset or industry that need not affect assets outside of that asset class.

Normal distribution A continuous, symmetric probability distribution that is completely described by its mean and its variance.

Normal goods Goods that are consumed in greater quantities as income increases.

Normal profit The level of accounting profit needed to just cover the implicit opportunity costs ignored in accounting costs.

Notching Ratings adjustment methodology where specific issues from the same borrower may be assigned different credit ratings.

Note rate See *mortgage rate.*

Notice period The length of time (typically 30–90 days) in advance that investors may be required to notify a fund of their intent to redeem some or all of their investment.

Notional principal An imputed principal amount.

Number of days of inventory An activity ratio equal to the number of days in a period divided by the inventory ratio for the period; an indication of the number of days a company ties up funds in inventory.

Number of days of payables An activity ratio equal to the number of days in a period divided by the payables turnover ratio for the period; an estimate of the average number of days it takes a company to pay its suppliers.

Number of days of receivables Estimate of the average number of days it takes to collect on credit accounts.

Objective probabilities Probabilities that generally do not vary from person to person; includes a priori and objective probabilities.

Off-the-run Seasoned government bonds are off-the-run securities; they are not the most recently issued or the most actively traded.

Offer The price at which a dealer or trader is willing to sell an asset, typically qualified by a maximum quantity (ask size).

Official interest rate An interest rate that a central bank sets and announces publicly; normally the rate at which it is willing to lend money to the commercial banks. Also called *official policy rate* or *policy rate.*

Official policy rate An interest rate that a central bank sets and announces publicly; normally the rate at which it is willing to lend money to the commercial banks.

Oligopoly Market structure with a relatively small number of firms supplying the market.

On-the-run The most recently issued and most actively traded sovereign securities.

One-sided hypothesis test A test in which the null hypothesis is rejected only if the evidence indicates that the population parameter is greater than (smaller than) θ_0. The alternative hypothesis also has one side.

One-tailed hypothesis test A test in which the null hypothesis is rejected only if the evidence indicates that the population parameter is greater than (smaller than) θ_0. The alternative hypothesis also has one side.

Open economy An economy that trades with other countries.

Open-end fund A mutual fund that accepts new investment money and issues additional shares at a value equal to the net asset value of the fund at the time of investment.

Open interest The number of outstanding contracts in a clearinghouse at any given time. The open interest figure changes daily as some parties open up new positions, while other parties offset their old positions.

Open market operations The purchase or sale of bonds by the national central bank to implement monetary policy. The bonds traded are usually sovereign bonds issued by the national government.

Operating activities Activities that are part of the day-to-day business functioning of an entity, such as selling inventory and providing services.

Operating breakeven The number of units produced and sold at which the company's operating profit is zero (revenues = operating costs).

Operating cash flow The net amount of cash provided from operating activities.

Operating cycle A measure of the time needed to convert raw materials into cash from a sale; it consists of the number of days of inventory and the number of days of receivables.

Operating efficiency ratios Ratios that measure how efficiently a company performs day-to-day tasks, such as the collection of receivables and management of inventory.

Operating lease An agreement allowing a lessee to use some asset for a period of time; essentially a rental.

Operating leverage The use of fixed costs in operations.

Operating profit A company's profits on its usual business activities before deducting taxes. Also called *operating income.*

Operating profit margin A profitability ratio calculated as operating income (i.e., income before interest and taxes) divided by revenue. Also called *operating margin.*

Operating risk The risk attributed to the operating cost structure, in particular the use of fixed costs in operations; the risk arising from the mix of fixed and variable costs; the risk that a company's operations may be severely affected by environmental, social, and governance risk factors.

Operational independence A bank's ability to execute monetary policy and set interest rates in the way it thought would best meet the inflation target.

Operational risk The risk that arises from inadequate or failed people, systems, and internal policies, procedures, and processes, as well as from external events that are beyond the control of the organization but that affect its operations.

Operationally efficient Said of a market, a financial system, or an economy that has relatively low transaction costs.

Opportunity cost The value that investors forgo by choosing a particular course of action; the value of something in its best alternative use.

Option A financial instrument that gives one party the right, but not the obligation, to buy or sell an underlying asset from or to another party at a fixed price over a specific period of time. Also referred to as *contingent claim* or *option contract.*

Option-adjusted price The value of the embedded option plus the flat price of the bond.

Option-adjusted spread OAS = Z-spread – Option value (in basis points per year).

Option-adjusted yield The required market discount rate whereby the price is adjusted for the value of the embedded option.

Option contract See *option.*

Option premium The amount of money a buyer pays and seller receives to engage in an option transaction.

Order A specification of what instrument to trade, how much to trade, and whether to buy or sell.

Order-driven markets A market (generally an auction market) that uses rules to arrange trades based on the orders that traders submit; in their pure form, such markets do not make use of dealers.

Order precedence hierarchy With respect to the execution of orders to trade, a set of rules that determines which orders execute before other orders.

Ordinal scale A measurement scale that sorts data into categories that are ordered (ranked) with respect to some characteristic.

Ordinary annuity An annuity with a first cash flow that is paid one period from the present.

Ordinary shares Equity shares that are subordinate to all other types of equity (e.g., preferred equity). Also called *common stock* or *common shares*.

Organized exchange A securities marketplace where buyers and seller can meet to arrange their trades.

Other comprehensive income Items of comprehensive income that are not reported on the income statement; comprehensive income minus net income.

Out-of-sample test A test of a strategy or model using a sample outside the time period on which the strategy or model was developed.

Out of the money Options that, if exercised, would require the payment of more money than the value received and therefore would not be currently exercised.

Outcome A possible value of a random variable.

Over-the-counter (OTC) markets A decentralized market where buy and sell orders initiated from various locations are matched through a communications network.

Overbought A market condition in which market sentiment is thought to be unsustainably bullish.

Overcollateralization Form of internal credit enhancement that refers to the process of posting more collateral than needed to obtain or secure financing.

Overfitting An undesirable result from fitting a model so closely to a dataset that it does not perform well on new data.

Overlay/portfolio tilt An ESG investment style that focuses on the use of certain investment strategies or products to change specific aggregate ESG characteristics of a fund or investment portfolio to a desired level (e.g., tilting an investment portfolio toward a desired carbon footprint).

Oversold A market condition in which market sentiment is thought to be unsustainably bearish.

Own price The price of a good or service itself (as opposed to the price of something else).

Own-price elasticity of demand The percentage change in quantity demanded for a percentage change in good's own price, holding all other things constant.

Owners' equity The excess of assets over liabilities; the residual interest of shareholders in the assets of an entity after deducting the entity's liabilities. Also called *shareholders' equity* or *shareholders' funds*.

Paasche index An index formula using the current composition of a basket of products.

Paired comparisons test A statistical test for differences based on paired observations drawn from samples that are dependent on each other.

Paired observations Observations that are dependent on each other.

Pairs arbitrage trade A trade in two closely related stocks involving the short sale of one and the purchase of the other.

Panel data Observations through time on a single characteristic of multiple observational units.

Par curve A sequence of yields-to-maturity such that each bond is priced at par value. The bonds are assumed to have the same currency, credit risk, liquidity, tax status, and annual yields stated for the same periodicity.

Par value The amount of principal on a bond.

Parallel shift A parallel yield curve shift implies that all rates change by the same amount in the same direction.

Parameter A descriptive measure computed from or used to describe a population of data, conventionally represented by Greek letters.

Parametric test Any test (or procedure) concerned with parameters or whose validity depends on assumptions concerning the population generating the sample.

Pari passu On an equal footing.

Partial duration See *key rate duration*.

Participating preference shares Preference shares that entitle shareholders to receive the standard preferred dividend plus the opportunity to receive an additional dividend if the company's profits exceed a pre-specified level.

Pass-through rate The coupon rate of a mortgage pass-through security.

Passive investment A buy and hold approach in which an investor does not make portfolio changes based on short-term expectations of changing market or security performance.

Passive strategy In reference to short-term cash management, it is an investment strategy characterized by simple decision rules for making daily investments.

Payable date The day that the company actually mails out (or electronically transfers) a dividend payment.

Payback period the number of years required to recover the original investment in a project. The payback is based on cash flows.

Payment date The day that the company actually mails out (or electronically transfers) a dividend payment.

Payments system The system for the transfer of money.

Peak The highest point of a business cycle.

Peer group A group of companies engaged in similar business activities whose economics and valuation are influenced by closely related factors.

Pennants A technical analysis continuation pattern formed by trendlines that converge to form a triangle, typically over a short period.

Per capita real GDP Real GDP divided by the size of the population, often used as a measure of the average standard of living in a country.

Per unit contribution margin The amount that each unit sold contributes to covering fixed costs—that is, the difference between the price per unit and the variable cost per unit.

Percentiles Quantiles that divide a distribution into 100 equal parts.

Perfect competition A market structure in which the individual firm has virtually no impact on market price, because it is assumed to be a very small seller among a very large number of firms selling essentially identical products.

Perfectly elastic When the quantity demanded or supplied of a given good is infinitely sensitive to a change in the value of a specified variable (e.g., price).

Perfectly inelastic When the quantity demanded or supplied of a given good is completely insensitive to a change in the value of a specified variable (e.g., price).

Performance bond See *margin bond*.

Performance evaluation The measurement and assessment of the outcomes of investment management decisions.
Performance fee Fees paid to the general partner from the limited partner(s) based on realized net profits.
Period costs Costs (e.g., executives' salaries) that cannot be directly matched with the timing of revenues and which are thus expensed immediately.
Periodicity The assumed number of periods in the year, typically matches the frequency of coupon payments.
Permanent differences Differences between tax and financial reporting of revenue (expenses) that will not be reversed at some future date. These result in a difference between the company's effective tax rate and statutory tax rate and do not result in a deferred tax item.
Permissioned networks Networks that are fully open only to select participants on a DLT network.
Permissionless networks Networks that are fully open to any user on a DLT network.
Permutation An ordered listing.
Perpetual bonds Bonds with no stated maturity date.
Perpetuity A perpetual annuity, or a set of never-ending level sequential cash flows, with the first cash flow occurring one period from now. A bond that does not mature.
Personal consumption expenditures All domestic personal consumption; the basis for a price index for such consumption called the PCE price index.
Personal disposable income Equal to personal income less personal taxes.
Personal income A broad measure of household income that includes all income received by households, whether earned or unearned; measures the ability of consumers to make purchases.
Plain vanilla bond Bond that makes periodic, fixed coupon payments during the bond's life and a lump-sum payment of principal at maturity. Also called *conventional bond.*
Platykurtic Describes a distribution that has relatively less weight in the tails than the normal distribution.
Point and figure chart A technical analysis chart that is constructed with columns of X's alternating with columns of O's such that the horizontal axis represents only the number of changes in price without reference to time or volume.
Point estimate A single numerical estimate of an unknown quantity, such as a population parameter.
Point of sale (POS) Systems that capture transaction data at the physical location in which the sale is made.
Policy rate An interest rate that a central bank sets and announces publicly; normally the rate at which it is willing to lend money to the commercial banks.
Population All members of a specified group.
Population mean The arithmetic mean value of a population; the arithmetic mean of all the observations or values in the population.
Population standard deviation A measure of dispersion relating to a population in the same unit of measurement as the observations, calculated as the positive square root of the population variance.
Population variance A measure of dispersion relating to a population, calculated as the mean of the squared deviations around the population mean.
Portfolio company In private equity, the company in which the private equity fund is investing.
Portfolio demand for money The demand to hold speculative money balances based on the potential opportunities or risks that are inherent in other financial instruments.
Portfolio planning The process of creating a plan for building a portfolio that is expected to satisfy a client's investment objectives.
Position The quantity of an asset that an entity owns or owes.
Positive screening An ESG investment style that focuses on the inclusion of certain sectors, companies, or practices in a fund or portfolio on the basis of specific minimum ESG criteria.
Posterior probability An updated probability that reflects or comes after new information.
Potential GDP The level of real GDP that can be produced at full employment; measures the productive capacity of the economy.
Power of a test The probability of correctly rejecting the null—that is, rejecting the null hypothesis when it is false.
Precautionary money balances Money held to provide a buffer against unforeseen events that might require money.
Precautionary stocks A level of inventory beyond anticipated needs that provides a cushion in the event that it takes longer to replenish inventory than expected or in the case of greater than expected demand.
Preference shares A type of equity interest which ranks above common shares with respect to the payment of dividends and the distribution of the company's net assets upon liquidation. They have characteristics of both debt and equity securities. Also called *preferred stock.*
Preferred stock See *preference shares.*
Premium In the case of bonds, premium refers to the amount by which a bond is priced above its face (par) value. In the case of an option, the amount paid for the option contract.
Prepaid expense A normal operating expense that has been paid in advance of when it is due.
Prepayment option Contractual provision that entitles the borrower to prepay all or part of the outstanding mortgage principal prior to the scheduled due date when the principal must be repaid. Also called *early repayment option.*
Prepayment penalty mortgages Mortgages that stipulate a monetary penalty if a borrower prepays within a certain time period after the mortgage is originated.
Prepayment risk The uncertainty that the timing of the actual cash flows will be different from the scheduled cash flows as set forth in the loan agreement due to the borrowers' ability to alter payments, usually to take advantage of interest rate movements.
Present value (PV) The present discounted value of future cash flows: For assets, the present discounted value of the future net cash inflows that the asset is expected to generate; for liabilities, the present discounted value of the future net cash outflows that are expected to be required to settle the liabilities.
Present value models Valuation models that estimate the intrinsic value of a security as the present value of the future benefits expected to be received from the security. Also called *discounted cash flow models.*
Pretax margin A profitability ratio calculated as earnings before taxes divided by revenue.
Price elasticity of demand Measures the percentage change in the quantity demanded, given a percentage change in the price of a given product.
Price index Represents the average prices of a basket of goods and services.
Price limits Limits imposed by a futures exchange on the price change that can occur from one day to the next.

Price multiple A ratio that compares the share price with some sort of monetary flow or value to allow evaluation of the relative worth of a company's stock.

Price priority The principle that the highest priced buy orders and the lowest priced sell orders execute first.

Price relative A ratio of an ending price over a beginning price; it is equal to 1 plus the holding period return on the asset.

Price return Measures *only* the price appreciation or percentage change in price of the securities in an index or portfolio.

Price return index An index that reflects *only* the price appreciation or percentage change in price of the constituent securities. Also called *price index*.

Price stability In economics, refers to an inflation rate that is low on average and not subject to wide fluctuation.

Price takers Producers that must accept whatever price the market dictates.

Price to book value A valuation ratio calculated as price per share divided by book value per share.

Price to cash flow A valuation ratio calculated as price per share divided by cash flow per share.

Price to earnings ratio (P/E ratio or P/E) The ratio of share price to earnings per share.

Price to sales A valuation ratio calculated as price per share divided by sales per share.

Price value of a basis point A version of money duration, it is an estimate of the change in the full price of a bond given a 1 basis point change in the yield-to-maturity.

Price weighting An index weighting method in which the weight assigned to each constituent security is determined by dividing its price by the sum of all the prices of the constituent securities.

Priced risk Risk for which investors demand compensation for bearing (e.g. equity risk, company-specific factors, macroeconomic factors).

Primary bond markets Markets in which issuers first sell bonds to investors to raise capital.

Primary capital markets (primary markets) The market where securities are first sold and the issuers receive the proceeds.

Primary dealers Financial institutions that are authorized to deal in new issues of sovereign bonds and that serve primarily as trading counterparties of the office responsible for issuing sovereign bonds.

Primary market The market where securities are first sold and the issuers receive the proceeds.

Prime brokers Brokers that provide services that commonly include custody, administration, lending, short borrowing, and trading.

Principal The amount of funds originally invested in a project or instrument; the face value to be paid at maturity.

Principal–agent relationship A relationship in which a principal hires an agent to perform a particular task or service; also known as an *agency relationship*.

Principal amount Amount that an issuer agrees to repay the debt holders on the maturity date.

Principal business activity The business activity from which a company derives a majority of its revenues and/or earnings.

Principal value Amount that an issuer agrees to repay the debt holders on the maturity date.

Principle of no arbitrage See *arbitrage-free pricing*.

Prior probabilities Probabilities reflecting beliefs prior to the arrival of new information.

Priority of claims Priority of payment, with the most senior or highest ranking debt having the first claim on the cash flows and assets of the issuer.

Private equity fund A hedge fund that seeks to buy, optimize, and ultimately sell portfolio companies to generate profits. See *venture capital fund*.

Private equity securities Securities that are not listed on public exchanges and have no active secondary market. They are issued primarily to institutional investors via non-public offerings, such as private placements.

Private investment in public equity (PIPE) An investment in the equity of a publicly traded firm that is made at a discount to the market value of the firm's shares.

Private placement Typically, a non-underwritten, unregistered offering of securities that are sold only to an investor or a small group of investors. It can be accomplished directly between the issuer and the investor(s) or through an investment bank.

Probability A number between 0 and 1 describing the chance that a stated event will occur.

Probability density function A function with non-negative values such that probability can be described by areas under the curve graphing the function.

Probability distribution A distribution that specifies the probabilities of a random variable's possible outcomes.

Probability function A function that specifies the probability that the random variable takes on a specific value.

Producer price index Reflects the price changes experienced by domestic producers in a country.

Production function Provides the quantitative link between the levels of output that the economy can produce and the inputs used in the production process.

Productivity The amount of output produced by workers in a given period of time—for example, output per hour worked; measures the efficiency of labor.

Profession An occupational group that has specific education, expert knowledge, and a framework of practice and behavior that underpins community trust, respect, and recognition.

Profit The return that owners of a company receive for the use of their capital and the assumption of financial risk when making their investments.

Profit and loss (P&L) statement A financial statement that provides information about a company's profitability over a stated period of time. Also called the *income statement*.

Profit margin An indicator of profitability, calculated as net income divided by revenue; indicates how much of each dollar of revenues is left after all costs and expenses.

Profitability index (PI) For a simple project, the PI is the present value of a project's future cash flows divided by the initial investment.

Profitability ratios Ratios that measure a company's ability to generate profitable sales from its resources (assets).

Project sequencing To defer the decision to invest in a future project until the outcome of some or all of a current project is known. Projects are sequenced through time, so that investing in a project creates the option to invest in future projects.

Promissory note A written promise to pay a certain amount of money on demand.

Property, plant, and equipment Tangible assets that are expected to be used for more than one period in either the production or supply of goods or services, or for administrative purposes.

Prospectus The document that describes the terms of a new bond issue and helps investors perform their analysis on the issue.

Protective put An option strategy in which a long position in an asset is combined with a long position in a put.

Proxy contest Corporate takeover mechanism in which shareholders are persuaded to vote for a group seeking a controlling position on a company's board of directors.

Proxy voting A process that enables shareholders who are unable to attend a meeting to authorize another individual to vote on their behalf.

Pseudo-random numbers Numbers produced by random number generators.

Public offer See *public offering.*

Public offering An offering of securities in which any member of the public may buy the securities. Also called *public offer.*

Pull on liquidity When disbursements are paid too quickly or trade credit availability is limited, requiring companies to expend funds before they receive funds from sales that could cover the liability.

Pure discount bonds See *zero-coupon bonds.*

Pure-play method A method for estimating the beta for a company or project; it requires using a comparable company's beta and adjusting it for financial leverage differences.

Put An option that gives the holder the right to sell an underlying asset to another party at a fixed price over a specific period of time.

Put–call–forward parity The relationship among puts, calls, and forward contracts.

Put–call parity An equation expressing the equivalence (parity) of a portfolio of a call and a bond with a portfolio of a put and the underlying, which leads to the relationship between put and call prices.

Put/call ratio A technical analysis indicator that evaluates market sentiment based upon the volume of put options traded divided by the volume of call options traded for a particular financial instrument.

Put option An option that gives the holder the right to sell an underlying asset to another party at a fixed price over a specific period of time.

Putable bonds Bonds that give the bondholder the right to sell the bond back to the issuer at a predetermined price on specified dates.

Quantile A value at or below which a stated fraction of the data lies. Also called *fractile.*

Quantitative easing An expansionary monetary policy based on aggressive open market purchase operations.

Quantity equation of exchange An expression that over a given period, the amount of money used to purchase all goods and services in an economy, $M \times V$, is equal to monetary value of this output, $P \times Y$.

Quantity theory of money Asserts that total spending (in money terms) is proportional to the quantity of money.

Quartiles Quantiles that divide a distribution into four equal parts.

Quasi-fixed cost A cost that stays the same over a range of production but can change to another constant level when production moves outside of that range.

Quasi-government bonds A bond issued by an entity that is either owned or sponsored by a national government. Also called *agency bond.*

Quick assets Assets that can be most readily converted to cash (e.g., cash, short-term marketable investments, receivables).

Quick ratio A stringent measure of liquidity that indicates a company's ability to satisfy current liabilities with its most liquid assets, calculated as (cash + short-term marketable investments + receivables) divided by current liabilities.

Quintiles Quantiles that divide a distribution into five equal parts.

Quota rents Profits that foreign producers can earn by raising the price of their goods higher than they would without a quota.

Quotas Government policies that restrict the quantity of a good that can be imported into a country, generally for a specified period of time.

Quote-driven market A market in which dealers acting as principals facilitate trading.

Quoted interest rate A quoted interest rate that does not account for compounding within the year. Also called *stated annual interest rate.*

Quoted margin The specified yield spread over the reference rate, used to compensate an investor for the difference in the credit risk of the issuer and that implied by the reference rate.

Random number An observation drawn from a uniform distribution.

Random number generator An algorithm that produces uniformly distributed random numbers between 0 and 1.

Random variable A quantity whose future outcomes are uncertain.

Range The difference between the maximum and minimum values in a dataset.

Ratio scales A measurement scale that has all the characteristics of interval measurement scales as well as a true zero point as the origin.

Real GDP The value of goods and services produced, measured at base year prices.

Real income Income adjusted for the effect of inflation on the purchasing power of money. Also known as the *purchasing power of income.* If income remains constant and a good's price falls, real income is said to rise, even though the number of monetary units (e.g., dollars) remains unchanged.

Real interest rate Nominal interest rate minus the expected rate of inflation.

Real risk-free interest rate The single-period interest rate for a completely risk-free security if no inflation were expected.

Realizable (settlement) value With reference to assets, the amount of cash or cash equivalents that could currently be obtained by selling the asset in an orderly disposal; with reference to liabilities, the undiscounted amount of cash or cash equivalents expected to be paid to satisfy the liabilities in the normal course of business.

Rebalancing Adjusting the weights of the constituent securities in an index.

Rebalancing policy The set of rules that guide the process of restoring a portfolio's asset class weights to those specified in the strategic asset allocation.

Recession A period during which real GDP decreases (i.e., negative growth) for at least two successive quarters, or a period of significant decline in total output, income, employment, and sales usually lasting from six months to a year.

Recognition lag The lag in government response to an economic problem resulting from the delay in confirming a change in the state of the economy.

Recourse loan Loan in which the lender has a claim against the borrower for any shortfall between the outstanding mortgage balance and the proceeds received from the sale of the property.

Redemption yield See *yield to maturity.*

Redemptions Withdrawals of funds by investors, as allowed by the notice period and other terms in the partnership agreement.

Refinancing rate A type of central bank policy rate.

Registered bonds Bonds for which ownership is recorded by either name or serial number.

Relative/best-in-class screening An ESG investment style that focuses on sectors, companies, or projects selected for ESG performance relative to industry peers.

Relative dispersion The amount of dispersion relative to a reference value or benchmark.

Relative frequency With reference to an interval of grouped data, the number of observations in the interval divided by the total number of observations in the sample.

Relative price The price of a specific good or service in comparison with those of other goods and services.

Relative strength analysis A comparison of the performance of one asset with the performance of another asset or a benchmark based on changes in the ratio of the securities' respective prices over time.

Relative strength index A technical analysis momentum oscillator that compares a security's gains with its losses over a set period.

Renewable resources Resources that can be replenished, such as a forest.

Rent Payment for the use of property.

Reorganization Agreements made by a company in bankruptcy under which a company's capital structure is altered and/or alternative arrangements are made for debt repayment; US Chapter 11 bankruptcy. The company emerges from bankruptcy as a going concern.

Replication The creation of an asset or portfolio from another asset, portfolio, and/or derivative.

Repo A form of collateralized loan involving the sale of a security with a simultaneous agreement by the seller to buy the same security back from the purchaser at an agreed-on price and future date. The party who sells the security at the inception of the repurchase agreement and buys it back at maturity is borrowing money from the other party, and the security sold and subsequently repurchased represents the collateral.

Repo margin The difference between the market value of the security used as collateral and the value of the loan. Also called *haircut.*

Repo rate The interest rate on a repurchase agreement.

Repurchase agreement A form of collateralized loan involving the sale of a security with a simultaneous agreement by the seller to buy the same security back from the purchaser at an agreed-on price and future date. The party who sells the security at the inception of the repurchase agreement and buys it back at maturity is borrowing money from the other party, and the security sold and subsequently repurchased represents the collateral.

Repurchase date The date when the party who sold the security at the inception of a repurchase agreement buys the security back from the cash lending counterparty.

Repurchase price The price at which the party who sold the security at the inception of the repurchase agreement buys the security back from the cash lending counterparty.

Required margin The yield spread over, or under, the reference rate such that an FRN is priced at par value on a rate reset date.

Required rate of return See *market discount rate.*

Required yield See *market discount rate.*

Required yield spread The difference between the yield-to-maturity on a new bond and the benchmark rate; additional compensation required by investors for the difference in risk and tax status of a bond relative to a government bond. Sometimes called the *spread over the benchmark.*

Reserve accounts Form of internal credit enhancement that relies on creating accounts and depositing in these accounts cash that can be used to absorb losses. Also called *reserve funds.*

Reserve funds See *reserve accounts.*

Reserve requirement The requirement for banks to hold reserves in proportion to the size of deposits.

Resistance In technical analysis, a price range in which selling activity is sufficient to stop the rise in the price of a security.

Responsible investing The practice of identifying companies that can efficiently manage their financial, environmental, and human capital resources to generate attractive long-term profitability; often synonymous with *sustainable investing.*

Restricted payments A bond covenant meant to protect creditors by limiting how much cash can be paid out to shareholders over time.

Retracement In technical analysis, a reversal in the movement of a security's price such that it is counter to the prevailing longerterm price trend.

Return-generating model A model that can provide an estimate of the expected return of a security given certain parameters and estimates of the values of the independent variables in the model.

Return on assets (ROA) A profitability ratio calculated as net income divided by average total assets; indicates a company's net profit generated per dollar invested in total assets.

Return on equity (ROE) A profitability ratio calculated as net income divided by average shareholders' equity.

Return on sales An indicator of profitability, calculated as net income divided by revenue; indicates how much of each dollar of revenues is left after all costs and expenses. Also referred to as *net profit margin.*

Return on total capital A profitability ratio calculated as EBIT divided by the sum of short- and long-term debt and equity.

Revaluation model Under IFRS, the process of valuing long-lived assets at fair value, rather than at cost less accumulated depreciation. Any resulting profit or loss is either reported on the income statement and/or through equity under revaluation surplus.

Revenue The amount charged for the delivery of goods or services in the ordinary activities of a business over a stated period; the inflows of economic resources to a company over a stated period.

Reversal patterns A type of pattern used in technical analysis to predict the end of a trend and a change in direction of the security's price.

Reverse repo A repurchase agreement viewed from the perspective of the cash lending counterparty.

Reverse repurchase agreement A repurchase agreement viewed from the perspective of the cash lending counterparty.

Reverse stock split A reduction in the number of shares outstanding with a corresponding increase in share price, but no change to the company's underlying fundamentals.

Revolving credit agreements The strongest form of short-term bank borrowing facilities; they are in effect for multiple years (e.g., 3–5 years) and may have optional medium-term loan features.

Rho The sensitivity of the option price to the risk-free rate.

Ricardian equivalence An economic theory that implies that it makes no difference whether a government finances a deficit by increasing taxes or issuing debt.

Risk Exposure to uncertainty. The chance of a loss or adverse outcome as a result of an action, inaction, or external event.

Risk averse The assumption that an investor will choose the least risky alternative.

Risk aversion The degree of an investor's inability and unwillingness to take risk.

Risk budgeting The establishment of objectives for individuals, groups, or divisions of an organization that takes into account the allocation of an acceptable level of risk.

Risk exposure The state of being exposed or vulnerable to a risk. The extent to which an organization is sensitive to underlying risks.

Risk factor/risk premium investing An ESG investment style that focuses on the inclusion of ESG information in the analysis of systematic risks as, for example, in smart beta and factor investment strategies (similar to size, value, momentum, and growth strategies).

Risk governance The top-down process and guidance that directs risk management activities to align with and support the overall enterprise.

Risk management The process of identifying the level of risk an organization wants, measuring the level of risk the organization currently has, taking actions that bring the actual level of risk to the desired level of risk, and monitoring the new actual level of risk so that it continues to be aligned with the desired level of risk.

Risk management framework The infrastructure, process, and analytics needed to support effective risk management in an organization.

Risk-neutral pricing Sometimes said of derivatives pricing, uses the fact that arbitrage opportunities guarantee that a risk-free portfolio consisting of the underlying and the derivative must earn the risk-free rate.

Risk-neutral probabilities Weights that are used to compute a binomial option price. They are the probabilities that would apply if a risk-neutral investor valued an option.

Risk premium An extra return expected by investors for bearing some specified risk.

Risk shifting Actions to change the distribution of risk outcomes.

Risk tolerance The amount of risk an investor is willing and able to bear to achieve an investment goal.

Risk transfer Actions to pass on a risk to another party, often, but not always, in the form of an insurance policy.

Robo-adviser A machine-based analytical tool or service that provides technology-driven investment solutions through online platforms.

Robust The quality of being relatively unaffected by a violation of assumptions.

Rule of 72 The principle that the approximate number of years necessary for an investment to double is 72 divided by the stated interest rate.

Running yield See *current yield.*

Safety-first rules Rules for portfolio selection that focus on the risk that portfolio value will fall below some minimum acceptable level over some time horizon.

Safety stock A level of inventory beyond anticipated needs that provides a cushion in the event that it takes longer to replenish inventory than expected or in the case of greater than expected demand.

Sales Generally, a synonym for revenue; "sales" is generally understood to refer to the sale of goods, whereas "revenue" is understood to include the sale of goods or services.

Sales risk Uncertainty with respect to the quantity of goods and services that a company is able to sell and the price it is able to achieve; the risk related to the uncertainty of revenues.

Sales-type leases Under US GAAP, a type of finance lease, from a lessor perspective, where the present value of the lease payments (lease receivable) exceeds the carrying value of the leased asset. The revenues earned by the lessor both a selling profit at inception and financing (interest) revenues.

Sample A subset of a population.

Sample excess kurtosis A sample measure of the degree of a distribution's kurtosis in excess of the normal distribution's kurtosis.

Sample kurtosis A sample measure of the degree of a distribution's peakedness.

Sample mean The sum of the sample observations, divided by the sample size.

Sample selection bias Bias introduced by systematically excluding some members of the population according to a particular attribute—for example, the bias introduced when data availability leads to certain observations being excluded from the analysis.

Sample skewness A sample measure of degree of asymmetry of a distribution.

Sample standard deviation The positive square root of the sample variance.

Sample statistic A quantity computed from or used to describe a sample.

Sample variance A sample measure of the degree of dispersion of a distribution, calculated by dividing the sum of the squared deviations from the sample mean by the sample size minus 1.

Sampling The process of obtaining a sample.

Sampling distribution The distribution of all distinct possible values that a statistic can assume when computed from samples of the same size randomly drawn from the same population.

Sampling error The difference between the observed value of a statistic and the quantity it is intended to estimate.

Sampling plan The set of rules used to select a sample.

Say on pay A process whereby shareholders may vote on executive remuneration (compensation) matters.

Say's law Named for French economist J.B. Say: All that is produced will be sold because supply creates its own demand.

Scatter plot A two-dimensional plot of pairs of observations on two data series.

Scenario analysis Analysis that shows the changes in key financial quantities that result from given (economic) events, such as the loss of customers, the loss of a supply source, or a catastrophic event; a risk management technique involving examination of the performance of a portfolio under specified situations. Closely related to stress testing.

Screening The application of a set of criteria to reduce a set of potential investments to a smaller set having certain desired characteristics.

Seasoned offering An offering in which an issuer sells additional units of a previously issued security.

Second-degree price discrimination When the monopolist charges different per-unit prices using the quantity purchased as an indicator of how highly the customer values the product.

Second lien A secured interest in the pledged assets that ranks below first lien debt in both collateral protection and priority of payment.

Secondary bond markets Markets in which existing bonds are traded among investors.

Secondary market The market where securities are traded among investors.

Secondary precedence rules Rules that determine how to rank orders placed at the same time.

Sector A group of related industries.

Sector indexes Indexes that represent and track different economic sectors—such as consumer goods, energy, finance, health care, and technology—on either a national, regional, or global basis.

Secured bonds Bonds secured by assets or financial guarantees pledged to ensure debt repayment in case of default.

Secured debt Debt in which the debtholder has a direct claim—a pledge from the issuer—on certain assets and their associated cash flows.

Securitization A process that involves moving assets into a special legal entity, which then uses the assets as guarantees to secure a bond issue.

Securitized assets Assets that are typically used to create asset-backed bonds; for example, when a bank securitizes a pool of loans, the loans are said to be securitized.

Security characteristic line A plot of the excess return of a security on the excess return of the market.

Security market index A portfolio of securities representing a given security market, market segment, or asset class.

Security market line (SML) The graph of the capital asset pricing model.

Security selection The process of selecting individual securities; typically, security selection has the objective of generating superior risk-adjusted returns relative to a portfolio's benchmark.

Self-investment limits With respect to investment limitations applying to pension plans, restrictions on the percentage of assets that can be invested in securities issued by the pension plan sponsor.

Sell-side firm A broker/dealer that sells securities and provides independent investment research and recommendations to their clients (i.e., buy-side firms).

Semi-strong-form efficient market A market in which security prices reflect all publicly known and available information.

Semiannual bond basis yield An annual rate having a periodicity of two; also known as a *semiannual bond equivalent yield*.

Semiannual bond equivalent yield See *semiannual bond basis yield*.

Semideviation The positive square root of semivariance (sometimes called *semistandard deviation*).

Semilogarithmic Describes a scale constructed so that equal intervals on the vertical scale represent equal rates of change, and equal intervals on the horizontal scale represent equal amounts of change.

Semivariance The average squared deviation below the mean.

Seniority ranking Priority of payment of various debt obligations.

Sensitivity analysis Analysis that shows the range of possible outcomes as specific assumptions are changed.

Separately managed account (SMA) An investment portfolio managed exclusively for the benefit of an individual or institution.

Serial maturity structure Structure for a bond issue in which the maturity dates are spread out during the bond's life; a stated number of bonds mature and are paid off each year before final maturity.

Settlement The process that occurs after a trade is completed, the securities are passed to the buyer, and payment is received by the seller.

Settlement date Date when the buyer makes cash payment and the seller delivers the security.

Settlement price The official price, designated by the clearinghouse, from which daily gains and losses will be determined and marked to market.

Share repurchase A transaction in which a company buys back its own shares. Unlike stock dividends and stock splits, share repurchases use corporate cash.

Shareholder activism Strategies used by shareholders to attempt to compel a company to act in a desired manner.

Shareholder engagement The process whereby companies engage with their shareholders.

Shareholders' equity Assets less liabilities; the residual interest in the assets after subtracting the liabilities.

Sharpe ratio The average return in excess of the risk-free rate divided by the standard deviation of return; a measure of the average excess return earned per unit of standard deviation of return.

Shelf registration Type of public offering that allows the issuer to file a single, all-encompassing offering circular that covers a series of bond issues.

Short The seller of an asset or derivative contract. Also refers to the position of being short an asset or derivative contract.

Short position A position in an asset or contract in which one has sold an asset one does not own, or in which a right under a contract can be exercised against oneself.

Short-run average total cost The curve describing average total cost when some costs are considered fixed.

Short selling A transaction in which borrowed securities are sold with the intention to repurchase them at a lower price at a later date and return them to the lender.

Shortfall risk The risk that portfolio value will fall below some minimum acceptable level over some time horizon.

Shutdown point The point at which average revenue is equal to the firm's average variable cost.

Simple interest The interest earned each period on the original investment; interest calculated on the principal only.

Simple random sample A subset of a larger population created in such a way that each element of the population has an equal probability of being selected to the subset.

Simple random sampling The procedure of drawing a sample to satisfy the definition of a simple random sample.

Simple yield The sum of the coupon payments plus the straight-line amortized share of the gain or loss, divided by the flat price.

Simulation Computer-generated sensitivity or scenario analysis that is based on probability models for the factors that drive outcomes.

Simulation trial A complete pass through the steps of a simulation.

Single-step format With respect to the format of the income statement, a format that does not subtotal for gross profit (revenue minus cost of goods sold).

Sinking fund arrangement Provision that reduces the credit risk of a bond issue by requiring the issuer to retire a portion of the bond's principal outstanding each year.

Situational influences External factors, such as environmental or cultural elements, that shape our behavior.

Skewed Not symmetrical.

Skewness A quantitative measure of skew (lack of symmetry); a synonym of skew.

Small country A country that is a price taker in the world market for a product and cannot influence the world market price.

Smart beta Involves the use of simple, transparent, rules-based strategies as a basis for investment decisions.

Smart contract A computer program that is designed to self-execute on the basis of pre-specified terms and conditions agreed to by parties to a contract.

Socially responsible investing An investment approach that excludes investments in companies or industries that deviate from an organization's beliefs and sometimes includes investments with favorable environmental or social profiles.

Solvency With respect to financial statement analysis, the ability of a company to fulfill its long-term obligations.

Solvency ratios Ratios that measure a company's ability to meet its long-term obligations.

Solvency risk The risk that an organization does not survive or succeed because it runs out of cash, even though it might otherwise be solvent.

Sovereign A bond issued by a national government.

Sovereign bond A bond issued by a national government.

Sovereign yield spread An estimate of the country spread (country equity premium) for a developing nation that is based on a comparison of bonds yields in country being analyzed and a developed country. The sovereign yield spread is the difference between a government bond yield in the country being analyzed, denominated in the currency of the developed country, and the Treasury bond yield on a similar maturity bond in the developed country.

Spearman rank correlation coefficient A measure of correlation applied to ranked data.

Special dividend A dividend paid by a company that does not pay dividends on a regular schedule, or a dividend that supplements regular cash dividends with an extra payment.

Special purpose entity A non-operating entity created to carry out a specified purpose, such as leasing assets or securitizing receivables; can be a corporation, partnership, trust, limited liability, or partnership formed to facilitate a specific type of business activity. Also called *special purpose vehicle* or *variable interest entity*.

Special purpose vehicle See *special purpose entity*.

Specific identification method An inventory accounting method that identifies which specific inventory items were sold and which remained in inventory to be carried over to later periods.

Speculative demand for money The demand to hold speculative money balances based on the potential opportunities or risks that are inherent in other financial instruments. Also called *portfolio demand for money*.

Speculative money balances Monies held in anticipation that other assets will decline in value.

Split coupon bond See *deferred coupon bond*.

Sponsored A type of depository receipt in which the foreign company whose shares are held by the depository has a direct involvement in the issuance of the receipts.

Spot curve A sequence of yields-to-maturity on zero-coupon bonds. Sometimes called *zero* or *strip curve* because coupon payments are "stripped" off of the bonds.

Spot markets Markets in which assets are traded for immediate delivery.

Spot prices The price of an asset for immediately delivery.

Spot rates A sequence of market discount rates that correspond to the cash flow dates; yields-to-maturity on zero-coupon bonds maturing at the date of each cash flow.

Spread In general, the difference in yield between different fixed income securities. Often used to refer to the difference between the yield-to-maturity and the benchmark.

Spread over the benchmark See *required yield spread*.

Spread risk Bond price risk arising from changes in the yield spread on credit-risky bonds; reflects changes in the market's assessment and/or pricing of credit migration (or downgrade) risk and market liquidity risk.

Spurious correlation A correlation that misleadingly points toward associations between variables.

Stackelberg model A prominent model of strategic decision making in which firms are assumed to make their decisions sequentially.

Stagflation When a high inflation rate is combined with a high level of unemployment and a slowdown of the economy.

Staggered boards Election process whereby directors are typically divided into multiple classes that are elected separately in consecutive years—that is, one class every year.

Stakeholder management The identification, prioritization, and understanding of the interests of stakeholder groups, and managing the company's relationships with these groups.

Stakeholders Individuals or groups of individuals who may be affected either directly or indirectly by a decision and thus have an interest, or stake, in the decision.

Standard deviation The positive square root of the variance; a measure of dispersion in the same units as the original data.

Standard normal distribution The normal density with mean (μ) equal to 0 and standard deviation (σ) equal to 1.

Standardizing A transformation that involves subtracting the mean and dividing the result by the standard deviation.

Standards of conduct Behaviors required by a group; established benchmarks that clarify or enhance a group's code of ethics.

Standing limit orders A limit order at a price below market and which therefore is waiting to trade.

Stated annual interest rate A quoted interest rate that does not account for compounding within the year. Also called *quoted interest rate*.

Statement of changes in equity (statement of owners' equity) A financial statement that reconciles the beginning-of-period and end-of-period balance sheet values of shareholders' equity; provides information about all factors affecting shareholders' equity. Also called *statement of owners' equity*.

Statement of financial condition The financial statement that presents an entity's current financial position by disclosing resources the entity controls (its assets) and the claims on those resources (its liabilities and equity claims), as of a particular point in time (the date of the balance sheet).

Statement of financial position The financial statement that presents an entity's current financial position by disclosing resources the entity controls (its assets) and the claims on those resources (its liabilities and equity claims), as of a particular point in time (the date of the balance sheet).

Statement of operations A financial statement that provides information about a company's profitability over a stated period of time.

Statistic A quantity computed from or used to describe a sample of data.

Statistical inference Making forecasts, estimates, or judgments about a larger group from a smaller group actually observed; using a sample statistic to infer the value of an unknown population parameter.

Statistically significant A result indicating that the null hypothesis can be rejected; with reference to an estimated regression coefficient, frequently understood to mean a result indicating that the corresponding population regression coefficient is different from 0.

Statutory voting A common method of voting where each share represents one vote.

Step-up coupon bond Bond for which the coupon, which may be fixed or floating, increases by specified margins at specified dates.

Stock dividend A type of dividend in which a company distributes additional shares of its common stock to shareholders instead of cash.

Stock-out losses Profits lost from not having sufficient inventory on hand to satisfy demand.

Stock split An increase in the number of shares outstanding with a consequent decrease in share price, but no change to the company's underlying fundamentals.

Stop-loss order See *stop order*.

Stop order An order in which a trader has specified a stop price condition. Also called *stop-loss order*.

Store of value The quality of tending to preserve value.

Store of wealth Goods that depend on the fact that they do not perish physically over time, and on the belief that others would always value the good.

Straight-line method A depreciation method that allocates evenly the cost of a long-lived asset less its estimated residual value over the estimated useful life of the asset.

Straight voting A shareholder voting process in which shareholders receive one vote for each share owned.

Strategic analysis Analysis of the competitive environment with an emphasis on the implications of the environment for corporate strategy.

Strategic asset allocation The set of exposures to IPS-permissible asset classes that is expected to achieve the client's long-term objectives given the client's investment constraints.

Strategic groups Groups sharing distinct business models or catering to specific market segments in an industry.

Street convention Yield measure that neglects weekends and holidays; the internal rate of return on cash flows assuming payments are made on the scheduled dates, even when the scheduled date falls on a weekend or holiday.

Stress testing A specific type of scenario analysis that estimates losses in rare and extremely unfavorable combinations of events or scenarios.

Strong-form efficient market A market in which security prices reflect all public and private information.

Structural (or cyclically adjusted) budget deficit The deficit that would exist if the economy was at full employment (or full potential output).

Structural subordination Arises in a holding company structure when the debt of operating subsidiaries is serviced by the cash flow and assets of the subsidiaries before funds can be passed to the holding company to service debt at the parent level.

Structured financial instruments Financial instruments that share the common attribute of repackaging risks. Structured financial instruments include asset-backed securities, collateralized debt obligations, and other structured financial instruments such as capital protected, yield enhancement, participation and leveraged instruments.

Subjective probability A probability drawing on personal or subjective judgment.

Subordinated debt A class of unsecured debt that ranks below a firm's senior unsecured obligations.

Subordination Form of internal credit enhancement that relies on creating more than one bond tranche and ordering the claim priorities for ownership or interest in an asset between the tranches. The ordering of the claim priorities is called a senior/subordinated structure, where the tranches of highest seniority are called senior followed by subordinated or junior tranches. Also called *credit tranching*.

Substitutes Said of two goods or services such that if the price of one increases the demand for the other tends to increase, holding all other things equal (e.g., butter and margarine).

Sunk cost A cost that has already been incurred.

Supervised learning A machine learning approach that makes use of labeled training data.

Supply shock A typically unexpected disturbance to supply.

Support In technical analysis, a price range in which buying activity is sufficient to stop the decline in the price of a security.

Support tranche A class or tranche in a CMO that protects the PAC tranche from prepayment risk.

Supranational bonds A bond issued by a supranational agency such as the World Bank.

Surety bond Form of external credit enhancement whereby a rated and regulated insurance company guarantees to reimburse bondholders for any losses incurred up to a maximum amount if the issuer defaults.

Survey approach An estimate of the equity risk premium that is based upon estimates provided by a panel of finance experts.

Survivorship bias The bias resulting from a test design that fails to account for companies that have gone bankrupt, merged, or are otherwise no longer reported in a database.

Sustainable growth rate The rate of dividend (and earnings) growth that can be sustained over time for a given level of return on equity, keeping the capital structure constant and without issuing additional common stock.

Sustainable investing The practice of identifying companies that can efficiently manage their financial, environmental, and human capital resources to generate attractive long-term profitability; often synonymous with *responsible investing*.

Sustainable rate of economic growth The rate of increase in the economy's productive capacity or potential GDP.

Swap contract An agreement between two parties to exchange a series of future cash flows.

Syndicated loans Loans from a group of lenders to a single borrower.

Syndicated offering A bond issue that is underwritten by a group of investment banks.

Systematic risk Risk that affects the entire market or economy; it cannot be avoided and is inherent in the overall market. Systematic risk is also known as non-diversifiable or market risk.

Systematic sampling A procedure of selecting every *k*th member until reaching a sample of the desired size. The sample that results from this procedure should be approximately random.

***t*-Test** A hypothesis test using a statistic (*t*-statistic) that follows a *t*-distribution.

Tactical asset allocation The decision to deliberately deviate from the strategic asset allocation in an attempt to add value based on forecasts of the near-term relative performance of asset classes.

Target balance A minimum level of cash to be held available—estimated in advance and adjusted for known funds transfers, seasonality, or other factors.

Target capital structure A company's chosen proportions of debt and equity.

Target independent A bank's ability to determine the definition of inflation that they target, the rate of inflation that they target, and the horizon over which the target is to be achieved.

Target semideviation The positive square root of target semivariance.

Target semivariance The average squared deviation below a target value.

Tariffs Taxes that a government levies on imported goods.

Tax base The amount at which an asset or liability is valued for tax purposes.

Tax expense An aggregate of an entity's income tax payable (or recoverable in the case of a tax benefit) and any changes in deferred tax assets and liabilities. It is essentially the income tax payable or recoverable if these had been determined based on accounting profit rather than taxable income.

Tax loss carry forward A taxable loss in the current period that may be used to reduce future taxable income.

Taxable income The portion of an entity's income that is subject to income taxes under the tax laws of its jurisdiction.

Taxable temporary differences Temporary differences that result in a taxable amount in a future period when determining the taxable profit as the balance sheet item is recovered or settled.

Technical analysis A form of security analysis that uses price and volume data, which is often displayed graphically, in decision making.

Technology The process a company uses to transform inputs into outputs.

Tender offer Corporate takeover mechanism which involves shareholders selling their interests directly to the group seeking to gain control.

Tenor The time-to-maturity for a bond or derivative contract. Also called *term to maturity*.

Term maturity structure Structure for a bond issue in which the bond's notional principal is paid off in a lump sum at maturity.

Term structure See *maturity structure*.

Term structure of credit spreads The relationship between the spreads over the "risk-free" (or benchmark) rates and times-to-maturity.

Term structure of yield volatility The relationship between the volatility of bond yields-to-maturity and times-to-maturity.

Terminal stock value The expected value of a share at the end of the investment horizon—in effect, the expected selling price. Also called *terminal value*.

Terminal value The expected value of a share at the end of the investment horizon—in effect, the expected selling price.

Terms of trade The ratio of the price of exports to the price of imports, representing those prices by export and import price indexes, respectively.

Text analytics The use of computer programs to analyze and derive meaning from typically large, unstructured text- or voice-based datasets.

Thematic investment An ESG investing style that focuses on investing in themes or assets specifically relating to ESG factors, such as clean energy, green technology, or sustainable agriculture.

Third-degree price discrimination When the monopolist segregates customers into groups based on demographic or other characteristics and offers different pricing to each group.

Time-period bias The possibility that when we use a time-series sample, our statistical conclusion may be sensitive to the starting and ending dates of the sample.

Time-series data Observations of a variable over time.

Time tranching The creation of classes or tranches in an ABS/MBS that possess different (expected) maturities.

Time value The difference between the market price of the option and its intrinsic value.

Time value decay Said of an option when, at expiration, no time value remains and the option is worth only its exercise value.

Time value of money The principles governing equivalence relationships between cash flows with different dates.

Time-weighted rate of return The compound rate of growth of one unit of currency invested in a portfolio during a stated measurement period; a measure of investment performance that is not sensitive to the timing and amount of withdrawals or additions to the portfolio.

Tokenization The process of representing ownership rights to physical assets on a blockchain or distributed ledger.

Top-down analysis An investment selection approach that begins with consideration of macroeconomic conditions and then evaluates markets and industries based upon such conditions.

Total comprehensive income The change in equity during a period resulting from transaction and other events, other than those changes resulting from transactions with owners in their capacity as owners.

Total cost The summation of all costs, for which costs are classified as fixed or variable.

Total factor productivity A scale factor that reflects the portion of growth that is not accounted for by explicit factor inputs (e.g. capital and labor).

Total fixed cost The summation of all expenses that do not change as the level of production varies.

Total invested capital The sum of market value of common equity, book value of preferred equity, and face value of debt.

Total probability rule A rule explaining the unconditional probability of an event in terms of probabilities of the event conditional on mutually exclusive and exhaustive scenarios.

Total probability rule for expected value A rule explaining the expected value of a random variable in terms of expected values of the random variable conditional on mutually exclusive and exhaustive scenarios.

Total return Measures the price appreciation, or percentage change in price of the securities in an index or portfolio, plus any income received over the period.

Total return index An index that reflects the price appreciation or percentage change in price of the constituent securities plus any income received since inception.

Total return swap A swap in which one party agrees to pay the total return on a security. Often used as a credit derivative, in which the underlying is a bond.

Total variable cost The summation of all variable expenses.

Tracking error The standard deviation of the differences between a portfolio's returns and its benchmark's returns; a synonym of active risk.

Tracking risk The standard deviation of the differences between a portfolio's returns and its benchmarks returns. Also called *tracking error*.

Trade creation When regional integration results in the replacement of higher cost domestic production by lower cost imports from other members.

Trade credit A spontaneous form of credit in which a purchaser of the goods or service is financing its purchase by delaying the date on which payment is made.

Trade diversion When regional integration results in lower-cost imports from non-member countries being replaced with higher-cost imports from members.

Trade payables Amounts that a business owes to its vendors for goods and services that were purchased from them but which have not yet been paid.

Trade protection Government policies that impose restrictions on trade, such as tariffs and quotas.

Trade surplus (deficit) When the value of exports is greater (less) than the value of imports.

Trading securities Under US GAAP, a category of debt securities held by a company with the intent to trade them. Also called *held-for-trading securities*.

Traditional investment markets Markets for traditional investments, which include all publicly traded debts and equities and shares in pooled investment vehicles that hold publicly traded debts and/or equities.

Transactions money balances Money balances that are held to finance transactions.

Transactions motive In the context of inventory management, the need for inventory as part of the routine production–sales cycle.

Transfer payments Welfare payments made through the social security system that exist to provide a basic minimum level of income for low-income households.

Transparency Said of something (e.g., a market) in which information is fully disclosed to the public and/or regulators.

Treasury Inflation-Protected Securities A bond issued by the United States Treasury Department that is designed to protect the investor from inflation by adjusting the principal of the bond for changes in inflation.

Treasury stock method A method for accounting for the effect of options (and warrants) on earnings per share (EPS) that specifies what EPS would have been if the options and warrants had been exercised and the company had used the proceeds to repurchase common stock.

Tree diagram A diagram with branches emanating from nodes representing either mutually exclusive chance events or mutually exclusive decisions.

Trend A long-term pattern of movement in a particular direction.

Treynor ratio A measure of risk-adjusted performance that relates a portfolio's excess returns to the portfolio's beta.

Triangle patterns In technical analysis, a continuation chart pattern that forms as the range between high and low prices narrows, visually forming a triangle.

Trimmed mean A mean computed after excluding a stated small percentage of the lowest and highest observations.

TRIN A flow of funds indicator applied to a broad stock market index to measure the relative extent to which money is moving into or out of rising and declining stocks.

Triple bottoms In technical analysis, a reversal pattern that is formed when the price forms three troughs at roughly the same price level; used to predict a change from a downtrend to an uptrend.

Triple tops In technical analysis, a reversal pattern that is formed when the price forms three peaks at roughly the same price level; used to predict a change from an uptrend to a downtrend.

Trough The lowest point of a business cycle.

True yield The internal rate of return on cash flows using the actual calendar including weekends and bank holidays.

Trust deed The governing legal credit agreement, typically incorporated by reference in the prospectus. Also called *bond indenture*.

Trust receipt arrangement The use of inventory as collateral for a loan. The inventory is segregated and held in trust, and the proceeds of any sale must be remitted to the lender immediately.

Turn-of-the-year effect Calendar anomaly that stock market returns in January are significantly higher compared to the rest of the months of the year, with most of the abnormal returns reported during the first five trading days in January.

Two-fund separation theorem The theory that all investors regardless of taste, risk preferences, and initial wealth will hold a combination of two portfolios or funds: a risk-free asset and an optimal portfolio of risky assets.

Two-sided hypothesis test A test in which the null hypothesis is rejected in favor of the alternative hypothesis if the evidence indicates that the population parameter is either smaller or larger than a hypothesized value.

Two-tailed hypothesis test A test in which the null hypothesis is rejected in favor of the alternative hypothesis if the evidence indicates that the population parameter is either smaller or larger than a hypothesized value.

Two-week repo rate The interest rate on a two-week repurchase agreement; may be used as a policy rate by a central bank.

Type I error The error of rejecting a true null hypothesis.

Type II error The error of not rejecting a false null hypothesis.

Unanticipated (unexpected) inflation The component of inflation that is a surprise.

Unconditional probability The probability of an event *not* conditioned on another event.

Underemployed A person who has a job but has the qualifications to work a significantly higher-paying job.
Underlying An asset that trades in a market in which buyers and sellers meet, decide on a price, and the seller then delivers the asset to the buyer and receives payment. The underlying is the asset or other derivative on which a particular derivative is based. The market for the underlying is also referred to as the *spot market*.
Underwriter A firm, usually an investment bank, that takes the risk of buying the newly issued securities from the issuer, and then reselling them to investors or to dealers, thus guaranteeing the sale of the securities at the offering price negotiated with the issuer.
Underwritten offering A type of securities issue mechanism in which the investment bank guarantees the sale of the securities at an offering price that is negotiated with the issuer. Also known as *firm commitment offering*.
Unearned revenue A liability account for money that has been collected for goods or services that have not yet been delivered; payment received in advance of providing a good or service. Also called *deferred revenue* or *deferred income*.
Unemployed People who are actively seeking employment but are currently without a job.
Unemployment rate The ratio of unemployed to the labor force.
Unexpected inflation The component of inflation that is a surprise.
Unit elastic An elasticity with a magnitude of negative one. Also called *unitary elastic*.
Unit labor cost The average labor cost to produce one unit of output.
Unit normal distribution The normal density with mean (μ) equal to 0 and standard deviation (σ) equal to 1.
Units-of-production method A depreciation method that allocates the cost of a long-lived asset based on actual usage during the period.
Univariate distribution A distribution that specifies the probabilities for a single random variable.
Universal owners Long-term investors, such as pension funds, that have significant assets invested in globally diversified portfolios.
Unlimited funds An unlimited funds environment assumes that the company can raise the funds it wants for all profitable projects simply by paying the required rate of return.
Unsecured debt Debt which gives the debtholder only a general claim on an issuer's assets and cash flow.
Unsponsored A type of depository receipt in which the foreign company whose shares are held by the depository has no involvement in the issuance of the receipts.
Unsupervised learning A machine learning approach that does not make use of labeled training data.
Up transition probability The probability that an asset's value moves up.
Validity instructions Instructions which indicate when the order may be filled.
Valuation allowance A reserve created against deferred tax assets, based on the likelihood of realizing the deferred tax assets in future accounting periods.
Valuation ratios Ratios that measure the quantity of an asset or flow (e.g., earnings) in relation to the price associated with a specified claim (e.g., a share or ownership of the enterprise).
Value at risk (VaR) A money measure of the minimum value of losses expected during a specified time period at a given level of probability.
Value investors With reference to equity investors, investors who are focused on paying a relatively low share price in relation to earnings or assets per share.
VaR See *value at risk*.
Variable costs Costs that fluctuate with the level of production and sales.
Variance The expected value (the probability-weighted average) of squared deviations from a random variable's expected value.
Variation margin Additional margin that must be deposited in an amount sufficient to bring the balance up to the initial margin requirement.
Veblen goods Goods that increase in desirability with increasing price.
Vega A measure of the sensitivity of an option's price to changes in the underlying's volatility.
Venture capital Investments that provide "seed" or startup capital, early-stage financing, or later-stage financing (including mezzanine-stage financing) to companies that are in early development stages and require additional capital for expansion or preparation for an initial public offering.
Venture capital fund A hedge fund that seeks to buy, optimize, and ultimately sell portfolio companies to generate profits. See *private equity fund*.
Vertical analysis Common-size analysis using only one reporting period or one base financial statement; for example, an income statement in which all items are stated as percentages of sales.
Vertical demand schedule Implies that some fixed quantity is demanded, regardless of price.
Volatility As used in option pricing, the standard deviation of the continuously compounded returns on the underlying asset.
Voluntarily unemployed A person voluntarily outside the labor force, such as a jobless worker refusing an available vacancy.
Voluntary export restraint A trade barrier under which the exporting country agrees to limit its exports of the good to its trading partners to a specific number of units.
Vote by proxy A mechanism that allows a designated party—such as another shareholder, a shareholder representative, or management—to vote on the shareholder's behalf.
Warehouse receipt arrangement The use of inventory as collateral for a loan; similar to a trust receipt arrangement except there is a third party (i.e., a warehouse company) that supervises the inventory.
Warrant Attached option that gives its holder the right to buy the underlying stock of the issuing company at a fixed exercise price until the expiration date.
Weak-form efficient market hypothesis The belief that security prices fully reflect all past market data, which refers to all historical price and volume trading information.
Wealth effect An increase (decrease) in household wealth increases (decreases) consumer spending out of a given level of current income.
Weighted average cost method An inventory accounting method that averages the total cost of available inventory items over the total units available for sale.

Weighted average cost of capital A weighted average of the aftertax required rates of return on a company's common stock, preferred stock, and long-term debt, where the weights are the fraction of each source of financing in the company's target capital structure.

Weighted average coupon rate Weighting the mortgage rate of each mortgage loan in the pool by the percentage of the mortgage outstanding relative to the outstanding amount of all the mortgages in the pool.

Weighted average life A measure that gives investors an indication of how long they can expect to hold the MBS before it is paid off; the convention-based average time to receipt of all principal repayments. Also called *average life*.

Weighted average maturity Weighting the remaining number of months to maturity for each mortgage loan in the pool by the amount of the outstanding mortgage balance.

Weighted mean An average in which each observation is weighted by an index of its relative importance.

Wholesale price index Reflects the price changes experienced by domestic producers in a country.

Winsorized mean A mean computed after assigning a stated percent of the lowest values equal to one specified low value, and a stated percent of the highest values equal to one specified high value.

Working capital The difference between current assets and current liabilities.

Working capital management The management of a company's short-term assets (such as inventory) and short-term liabilities (such as money owed to suppliers).

World price The price prevailing in the world market.

Yield The actual return on a debt security if it is held to maturity.

Yield duration The sensitivity of the bond price with respect to the bond's own yield-to-maturity.

Yield to maturity Annual return that an investor earns on a bond if the investor purchases the bond today and holds it until maturity. It is the discount rate that equates the present value of the bond's expected cash flows until maturity with the bond's price. Also called *yield-to-redemption* or *redemption yield*.

Yield to redemption See *yield to maturity*.

Yield-to-worst The lowest of the sequence of yields-to-call and the yield-to-maturity.

Zero-coupon bonds Bonds that do not pay interest during the bond's life. It is issued at a discount to par value and redeemed at par. Also called *pure discount bonds*.

Zero volatility spread (Z-spread) Calculates a constant yield spread over a government (or interest rate swap) spot curve.